The commentary text in this handbook is written to assist users in understanding and applying the provisions of NFPA 72. The commentary explains the reasoning behind the Code's requirements and provides numerous examples, tables, photographs, and illustrations. The commentary text is printed in red type to distinguish it from the text of NFPA 72. Please note that the commentary is not part of NFPA 72 and therefore is not enforceable.

systems in order to legitimately receive such signals. Some municipalities create regional emergency communications centers to dispatch fire, poli medical services. These centers may have equipment to receive signals f vising station alarm systems.

26.5.1.2 The installation, maintenance, testing, and use of a remote supervis system that serves properties under various ownership from a remote supervising station shall comply with the requirements of Section 26.5.

Some authorities having jurisdiction have interpreted 26.5.1.2 to mean that the requirements of Section 26.5 apply only to those cases where a remote supervising station system serves properties under various ownerships. In so doing, those authorities having jurisdiction have refused to accept the use of hardware and software listed for use in providing a remote station supervising station system at a single facility under one ownership. Instead, those authorities having jurisdiction have required the facility to use hardware and software listed for a proprietary supervising station system.

The intent of 26.5.1.2, however, does not specifically forbid the application of the requirements in Section 26.5 to a remote station supervising station alarm system serving single or multiple facilities under one ownership. At the same time, the requirements in 26.5.1.4 make it clear that alarm, supervisory, and trouble signals must transmit to a location remote from the protected premises.

In analyzing whether a particular type of supervising station system will appropriately serve a facility, the authorities having jurisdiction should carefully examine the protection goals of the owner, as well as the protection goals for the jurisdictions they represent. Obviously, an authority having jurisdiction should not encourage an owner to choose one particular supervising station system simply to avoid having to meet the more stringent requirements of another, more appropriate system.

Exhibit 26.8 illustrates a communications center equipped to receive signals as a remote supervising station in accordance with 26.5.3.1.1.

EXHIBIT 26.8 A Public Emergency Services Communications Center Equipped to Receive Signals as a Remote Station Supervising Station. (Source: James A. Spear, P.E., LeRoy, NY)

Commentary art is set within red lines and labeled "Exhibit." The caption is printed in red ink. The commentary exhibits, including both drawings and photographs, provide detailed views of NFPA 72 concepts and are numbered sequentially throughout each chapter.

3. Notification to the building owner and occupants
4. Notification to the authorities having jurisdiction

3.3.10 Alarm Signal. See 3.3.240, Signal.

3.3.11 Alarm System. See 3.3.95, Fire Alarm System; 3.3.267, Supervising Station Alarm System; 3.3.199, Public Emergency Alarm Reporting System.

3.3.12 Alarm Verification Feature. A feature of automatic fire detection and alarm systems to reduce unwanted alarms wherein smoke detectors report alarm conditions for a minimum period of time, or confirm alarm conditions within a given time period after being reset, in order to be accepted as a valid alarm initiation signal. (SIG-PRO)

Alarm verification is applicable to smoke detectors only. The alarm verification feature can reduce unwanted alarm signals from transient conditions that actuate smoke detectors. The feature may reside within individual smoke detectors, or it may be a feature of the fire alarm control unit to which the smoke detectors are connected. Manufacturers of addressable analog fire alarm systems typically do not recommend the activation of alarm verification during the initial installation. It is not intended as a means of reducing unwanted alarms due to the improper application of smoke detectors, such as installation in a location where they are exposed to unsuitable environmental conditions. Refer to 23.8.5.4.1 for the requirements related to use of alarm verification.

3.3.13 Alert Tone. An attention-getting signal to alert occupants of the pending transmission of a voice message. (SIG-PRO)

Where voice announcements are used for other than complete evacuation, in-building fire voice/alarm communications systems precede the voice announcement with an alert tone to gain occupant attention before broadcast of the voice message. The alert tone is not considered an alarm signal, and the Code does not specify the form of the alert tone. See 24.4.1.8.2 for applicable requirements for the alert tone. Where voice announcements are used for complete evacuation, the announcement must be preceded by the emergency evacuation signal in accordance with 24.4.1.2.1.

3.3.14 Analog Initiating Device (Sensor). See 3.3.122, Initiating Device.

3.3.15 Ancillary Functions. Ancillary functions are those non-emergency activations of the fire alarm or mass notification audible, visual, and textual output circuits allowed. Ancillary

EXHIBIT 3.4 Typical Key-Operated Manual Fire Alarm Box. (Source: Gamewell-FCI, Northford, CT; photo courtesy of Mammoth Fire Alarms, Inc., Lowell, MA)

EXHIBIT 3.5 Master Box. (Source: Gamewell-FCI, Northford, CT; photo courtesy of Mammoth Fire Alarms, Inc., Lowell, MA)

EXHIBIT 3.6 Publicly Accessible Alarm Box. (Source: Gamewell-FCI, Northford, CT; photo courtesy of Mammoth Fire Alarms, Inc., Lowell, MA)

National Fire Alarm and Signaling Code Handbook

National Fire Alarm and Signaling Code Handbook

SIXTH EDITION

Edited by

Lee F. Richardson
Senior Electrical Engineer, NFPA

Richard J. Roux
Senior Electrical Specialist, NFPA

With the complete text of the 2010 edition of *NFPA 72®*, *National Fire Alarm and Signaling Code*

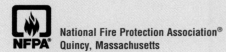
National Fire Protection Association®
Quincy, Massachusetts

Product Manager: Debra Rose
Project Editor: Irene Herlihy
Project Coordinator: Michael S. Barresi, Jr.
Permissions Editor: Josiane Domenici
Copy Editor: Nancy Wirtes

Composition: Modern Graphics, Inc.
Art Coordinator: Cheryl Langway
Cover Designer: Cameron Inc.
Manufacturing Manager: Ellen Glisker
Printer: Quebecor World/Taunton

Copyright © 2010
National Fire Protection Association®
One Batterymarch Park
Quincy, Massachusetts 02169-7471

Important Notices and Disclaimers: Publication of this handbook is for the purpose of circulating information and opinion among those concerned for fire and electrical safety and related subjects. While every effort has been made to achieve a work of high quality, neither the NFPA® nor the contributors to this handbook guarantee the accuracy or completeness of or assume any liability in connection with the information and opinions contained in this handbook. The NFPA and the contributors shall in no event be liable for any personal injury, property, or other damages of any nature whatsoever, whether special, indirect, consequential, or compensatory, directly or indirectly resulting from the publication, use of, or reliance upon this handbook.

This handbook is published with the understanding that the NFPA and the contributors to this handbook are supplying information and opinion but are not attempting to render engineering or other professional services. If such services are required, the assistance of an appropriate professional should be sought.

NFPA codes, standards, recommended practices, and guides ("NFPA Documents"), including the NFPA Document that is the subject of this handbook, are made available for use subject to Important Notices and Legal Disclaimers, which appear at the end of this handbook and can also be viewed at *www.nfpa.org/disclaimers.*

Notice Concerning Code Interpretations: This 2010 edition of the *National Fire Alarm and Signaling Code Handbook* is based on the 2010 edition of *NFPA 72®*. All NFPA codes, standards, recommended practices, and guides ("NFPA Documents") are developed in accordance with the published procedures of the NFPA by technical committees comprised of volunteers drawn from a broad array of relevant interests. The handbook contains the complete text of *NFPA 72* and any applicable Formal Interpretations issued by the NFPA. This NFPA Document is accompanied by explanatory commentary and other supplementary materials.

The commentary and supplementary materials in this handbook are not a part of the NFPA Document and do not constitute Formal Interpretations of the NFPA (which can be obtained only through requests processed by the responsible technical committees in accordance with the published procedures of the NFPA). The commentary and supplementary materials, therefore, solely reflect the personal opinions of the editor or other contributors and do not necessarily represent the official position of the NFPA or its technical committees.

The following are registered trademarks of the National Fire Protection Association®:

National Fire Protection Association®
NFPA®
NFPA 72®
Building Construction and Safety Code® and NFPA 5000®
Fire Protection Handbook®
Life Safety Code® and 101®
National Electrical Code®, NEC®, and NFPA 70®

NFPA No.: 72HB10
ISBN-10: 0-87765-852-8
ISBN-13: 978-0-87765-852-8
Library of Congress Card Control No.: 2009926676

Printed in the United States of America
09   10   11   12   13   5   4   3   2   1

The 2010 *National Fire Alarm and Signaling Code Handbook* is dedicated to Dean K. Wilson and Wayne D. Moore.

Dean is Member Emeritus of the Technical Correlating Committee on Signaling Systems for the Protection of Life and Property and has had a long history of participation and leadership in the codes-and-standards-making process for *NFPA 72*®. Dean's involvement in this process goes back more than 30 years, as a member and subsequent chair of the Technical Committee on Central Station Signaling Systems, responsible for NFPA 71, *Signaling Systems for Central Station Service* (one of the predecessors of the current *NFPA 72*). Dean also played an active role on several other signaling committees and chaired the technical correlating committee from 1993 through mid-1998. Dean has played an important role over the years, providing clear thinking and guidance while never losing perspective on the important mission of fire safety. Even while retired on disability, Dean has recently contributed as a member of the Technical Correlating Committee Task Group on Managed Facility Voice Networks, lending historical insight and perspective as well as sound reasoning in dealing with a controversial subject. In all of this, Dean has been an effective communicator, a skillful presenter of complex issues, and a teacher and mentor to many. The Code and the handbook would not be what they are today without his dedication and devotion.

Wayne is chair of the Technical Committee on Emergency Communications Systems and has served on numerous other NFPA committees since at least 1982 (as member of the Technical Committee on Detection Devices). Wayne has served on the Technical Committee on Protected Premises Fire Alarm Systems since 1993, chairing the committee from 1993 to 1998. He has also served on the Technical Correlating Committee on Signaling Systems for the Protection of Life and Property since 1995, serving as chair from 1998 to 2006. Wayne is editor of the 1993 *National Fire Alarm Code Handbook* and co-editor of the 1996, 1999, 2002, and 2007 editions. Wayne shares many of the qualities and vision of his close friend Dean Wilson. Wayne's ability to lead and manage committees and get things done is largely responsible for the successful development of the recent editions of the Code. In fact, the inclusion of the new chapter on Emergency Communications Systems in the 2010 edition of the Code, and the reorganization of the Code as a whole, would not have been possible without Wayne's vision, perseverance, and leadership.

The contributions that Dean and Wayne have made to the mission of fire detection and protection go far beyond the Code and handbook, and it is with deep appreciation that this handbook is dedicated to them.

Contents

Preface

The 2010 edition of *NFPA 72®*, *National Fire Alarm and Signaling Code*, represents the culmination of over a century of signaling standards, and this edition is the most significant edition since it was established as the *National Fire Alarm Code* in 1993. The first signaling standard, NFPA 71-D, *General Rules for the Installation of Wiring and Apparatus for Automatic Fire Alarms, Hatch Closers, Sprinkler Alarms, and Other Automatic Alarm Systems and Their Auxiliaries,* was written in 1899. That document was only fifteen pages in length, including the committee report! We are certain the original framers of that document would be astonished to see what their work looks like today.

Fire alarm signaling has come a long way since NFPA published that first signaling standard over one hundred years ago. Many technologies related to fire alarm systems have evolved, while others have changed little since the middle part of the nineteenth century. For example, conventional fixed-temperature heat detectors and McCulloh loops have not changed significantly since they were invented in the late 1800s. Many technologies emerged in just the past thirty or forty years. More recent technologies, such as electronic addressable analog smoke detectors and analog heat detectors, continue to develop and improve. Additionally, the computer age has ushered in an era of major changes in fire alarm system control units. Software-driven system designs have resulted in fire alarm systems that are more flexible, richer in features, and easier to test and maintain.

As computer systems are becoming more sophisticated, fire alarm system designers are integrating these systems more with other building systems such as HVAC systems, security and access control systems, energy management systems, and mass notification systems. Requirements have been incorporated in the Code in an effort to keep pace with this ongoing evolution in integrated system designs and to preserve the integrity, reliability, and performance that are essential for fire alarm systems. Integration of these systems requires technicians from both the fire alarm and non–fire alarm system fields to possess a more detailed and functional knowledge of these Code requirements. Systems integration also requires a more complete understanding of the application and operation of the various building systems technologies and how they interact with fire alarm systems. Education will continue to play a critical role in the understanding and application of fire alarm systems and their integration with other building systems. This edition of the *National Fire Alarm and Signaling Code* has continued to retain requirements for performance-based designs as they continue to play a more prominent part within the building process. The acceptance of performance-based designs on an equal footing with traditional prescriptive designs establishes an environment and incentive to perform much needed research. The fire alarm industry has and will continue to research and develop a better understanding of the metrics needed to model fire scenarios and predict detection system responses to those scenarios. More and more commonly, fire protection needs are served more effectively and precisely by performance-based approaches than by those based on the more traditional prescriptive rules. Performance-based approaches are not limited to fire detection and are becoming more widely used in the areas of audible and visible signaling and in the design of mass notification systems. This continued growth has been reflected within the Code both in terms of new requirements and in terms of information provided in the annexes and supplements in this handbook.

The 2010 edition of *NFPA 72* reflects an expanded scope and reorganization of the Code. Changes made for the 2007 edition introduced requirements and guidance for mass notification systems and included provisions allowing these systems to work with and take precedence over fire alarm systems. The 2010 edition has built on these changes and has added a new chapter on emergency communications systems, which not only includes new requirements for the various forms of mass notification systems but also includes requirements for emergency voice/alarm communications systems (relocated from the protected premises chapter), requirements for two-way telephone communications service (relocated from the protected premises chapter), new requirements for two-way radio communications enhancement systems, and new requirements for area of refuge emergency communications systems. The new chapter recognizes that the design of mass notification systems needs to reflect the range of potentially complex applications for these systems and includes requirements for the design of these systems (including the establishment of signal priorities) based on a risk analysis.

Along with the new chapter on emergency communications systems the Code has been updated as a whole so that, where applicable, requirements apply to emergency communications systems in addition to fire alarm systems. In fact, requirements relating to circuits and pathways have been relocated to a new chapter providing a common location for requirements that can be used by any type of system. Similarly, the requirements for fire safety functions have been relocated to a new chapter on emergency control functions and interfaces. With the addition of three new chapters the opportunity to reorganize the Code into a more logical order of chapters was realized and accomplished with the inclusion of reserved chapters to minimize the potential need for chapter renumbering in the future. Exhibit P.1 shows the new Code organization with its chapters arranged within four basic groupings: front chapters, support chapters, system chapters, and usability chapters. In addition, the expanded scope of the Code is reflected in its new title: *National Fire Alarm and Signaling Code.*

The 2010 edition of the Code has also benefited in significant ways from recent research. Recent research has led to new provisions for the use of low frequency audible signaling in sleeping rooms for those with mild to severe hearing loss and for the use of tactile (vibration) appliances in addition to high intensity strobes for signaling in sleeping rooms to those with profound hearing loss. New research has been responsible for revised and new prescriptive requirements to address troublesome joist and beam ceiling applications for smoke detection. These include requirements to specifically address "waffle" ceilings, corridors, and small rooms. Provisions have also been included to address joist and beam applications for sloping ceilings in addition to level ceilings. New research on the intelligibility of fire alarm and emergency communications systems has also been responsible for the revision of the requirements for voice intelligibility and a new annex providing guidance for planning, design, installation, and testing of intelligible voice communications systems.

All of these changes have resulted from the work of over 200 technical committee members who have volunteered countless hours in the preparation and review of hundreds of proposals and comments — all evaluated through the NFPA consensus-based standards-making processes. The development of the proposals and comments processed by the technical committees represents even further countless hours contributed by members of the public and the fire protection community. The preparation of both the Code and the handbook has also been the beneficiary of very significant time and care from dedicated NFPA staff members. All of these collective efforts, along with NFPA's rigorous public review process, have continued to make the *National Fire Alarm and Signaling Code Handbook* one of the best documents available in the world to detail the installation requirements for fire alarm and emergency communications systems.

The editors wish to thank John M. Cholin, P.E., of J. M. Cholin Consultants, Inc. (commentary author for Chapter 17 and Annex B, and author of Supplement 1); Daniel T. Gottuk, Ph.D., P.E., of Hughes Associates, Inc. (commentary author for Chapter 29); Shane M. Clary, Bay Alarm Company (commentary author for Chapters 1 and 10); Leonard Belliveau, Jr.,

FRONT CHAPTERS	1	Administration
	2	Referenced Publications
	3	Definitions
	4	Reserved
	5	Reserved
	6	Reserved
	7	Reserved
	8	Reserved
	9	Reserved
SUPPORT CHAPTERS	10	Fundamentals
	11	Reserved
	12	Circuits and Pathways
	13	Reserved
	14	Inspection, Testing, and Maintenance
	15	Reserved
	16	Reserved
	17	Initiating Devices
	18	Notification Appliances
	19	Reserved
SYSTEM CHAPTERS	20	Reserved
	21	Emergency Control Functions and Interfaces
	22	Reserved
	23	Protected Premises Fire Alarm Systems
	24	Emergency Communications Systems (ECS)
	25	Reserved
	26	Supervising Station Alarm Systems
	27	Public Emergency Alarm Reporting Systems
	28	Reserved
	29	Single- and Multiple-Station Alarms and Household Fire Alarm Systems
USABILITY	Annex	
	A	Explanatory Material
	B	Engineering Guide for Automatic Fire Detector Spacing
	C	System Performance and Design Guide
	D	Speech Intelligibility
	E	NEMA SB 30, *Fire Service Annunciator and Interface*
	F	Sample Ordinance Adopting *NFPA 72*
	G	Wiring Diagrams and Guide for Testing Fire Alarm Circuits
	H	Informational References
	I	Cross-Reference Table
		Index

EXHIBIT P.1 *Chapter Arrangement for NFPA 72, 2010 Edition. (Source: R. P. Schifiliti Associates, Inc., Reading MA)*

P.E., CET, of Hughes Associates, Inc. (commentary author for Chapter 14); Jeffrey Moore, P.E., of Hughes Associates, Inc. (commentary author for Chapters 12, 21, and 23); Wayne D. Moore, P.E., FSFPE, CFPS, SET, of Hughes Associates, Inc. (commentary author for Chapter 24 and author of Supplement 2); Robert P. Schifiliti, P.E., of R. P. Schifiliti Associates, Inc. (commentary author for Chapter 18 and author of Supplement 3); Dean K. Wilson, P.E., formerly of Hughes Associates, Inc. (commentary author for Chapters 26 and 27); and Paul Choiniere, NFPA Senior Electrical Specialist (contributor to Supplement 4). Their contributions have made this handbook truly exceptional. The editors wish to thank the many manufacturers whose expertise, generosity, and patience helped us to provide many new photographs for this edition. We also thank Pam Nolan, ROP/ROC Editor, Kim Cervantes, NFPA Senior Project Editor, David March, NFPA Proofreader, and Lynn Lupo, NFPA Composition Supervisor, for their diligence and attention to detail in preparing and proofing the

Code texts; Josiane Domenici, NFPA Permissions Editor, for her efforts in cataloging the handbook artwork and obtaining copyright permissions; and Debra Rose, NFPA Product Manager, Michael Barresi, Jr., NFPA Project Coordinator, Irene Herlihy, NFPA Senior Project Editor, Cheryl Langway, NFPA Art Coordinator, and Nancy Wirtes, NFPA Senior Project Editor, for their project management and editing contributions and for keeping the project on schedule.

We also wish to thank our wives, Lynn and Robbie, for their patience, love, and understanding. Their encouragement and support made the development of this handbook much easier for both of us.

Richard J. Roux
Lee F. Richardson

About the Contributors

Leonard Belliveau (Chapter 14)

Leonard Belliveau, Jr., P.E., CET, is the office manager and senior fire protection engineer for the Warwick, Rhode Island, office of Hughes Associates, Inc. Mr. Belliveau currently serves on the NFPA Technical Committee on Testing and Maintenance of Fire Alarm Systems, the NFPA Technical Committee on Telecommunications, and the NFPA Technical Committee on Commissioning Fire Protection Systems. He is a registered professional engineer (FPE) in seven states and is NICET Level III certified in the field of fire alarms.

John M. Cholin (Chapter 17, Annex B, and Supplement 1)

John M. Cholin, P.E., FSFPE, M.E., is an independent fire protection consultant and engineer with J. M. Cholin Consultants, Inc., Oakland, New Jersey. He is a licensed professional engineer in the discipline of fire protection engineering and a Fellow of the Society of Fire Protection Engineers. He has served on the Technical Committee on Initiating Devices for Fire Alarm Systems since 1985 and serves as one of several faculty for the NFPA Fire Alarm Workshop as well as an instructor for the SFPE.

Paul Choiniere (Supplement 4)

Paul Choiniere is a Senior Electrical Specialist at NFPA with 28 years' experience as a construction electrician. Mr. Choiniere is a licensed journeyman electrician, having spent 18 years as an electrical inspector for the towns of Amherst, Belchertown, and Hadley, Massachusetts. He is past president of the International Association of Electrical Inspectors, Western Massachusetts chapter, and past president of the Municipal Inspectors Association of Massachusetts and Rhode Island. A certified instructor and teacher in the Massachusetts 15-hour continuing education courses, and member of IBEW local 7, Mr. Choiniere has also taught the IBEW fifth year apprentice classes. He is a graduate of their National Instructor Training Institute and the newest member of the electrical division at NFPA. He assists staff liaisons with assigning tasks and answering code interpretation requests for *NFPA 70*®, *NFPA 70E*®, and *NFPA 72*®.

Shane M. Clary (Chapters 1 and 10)

Shane M. Clary, Ph.D., is vice-president for codes and standards compliance at Bay Alarm Company in Pacheco, California. He is chair of the Technical Committee on Fundamentals of Fire Alarms, is the Chair Elect for the Automatic Fire Alarm Association, is a member of the NFPA Standards Council, serves on several NFPA technical committees, and is the author of the *NFPA Pocket Guide to Electronic Security System Installation*.

Daniel T. Gottuk (Chapter 29)

Daniel T. Gottuk, Ph.D., is a senior engineer at Hughes Associates, Inc., and is a project manager for a variety of fire-related forensic, research, testing, and development programs. He is chair of the NFPA Technical Committee on Single- and Multiple-Station Alarms and Household Fire Alarm Systems and serves on NFPA 720 and 921 technical committees. Dr. Gottuk's work has focused on fire dynamics, fuel spill fires, and fire and carbon monoxide detection.

J. Jeffrey Moore (Chapters 12, 21, 23, and Annex C)

J. Jeffrey Moore, P.E., is a senior fire protection engineer with Hughes Associates, Inc., at the firm's Cincinnati, Ohio, office, and chair of the Technical Committee on Protected Premises Fire Alarm Systems. Mr. Moore has also served as a fire instructor, an EMS instructor, and a training officer in the municipal fire service. He has taught courses at the OSHA Training Institute and the Air Force Institute of Technology. He is also an instructor for several NFPA seminars, including the NFPA Fire Alarm Workshop, NFPA Sprinkler Systems Seminars, and the NFPA Facility Fire Safety Seminar.

Wayne D. Moore (Chapter 24 and Supplement 2)

Wayne D. Moore, P.E., CFPS, SET, FSFPE, F.NSPE, is a licensed professional fire protection engineer and a principal with the fire protection engineering and code-consulting firm, Hughes Associates, Inc., at the firm's Warwick, Rhode Island, office. He is past chair of the NFPA Technical Correlating Committee on Signaling Systems for the Protection of Life and Property, is chair of the NFPA Technical Committee on Emergency Communications Systems (ECS), and is an active member of a number of other NFPA technical committees. Mr. Moore is chair of the Fire Protection Research Foundation's Detection and Alarm Research Council, is a past-president of the Society of Fire Protection Engineers, and has served as member of the NFPA Standards Council. He was also a member and past chairman of the NICET Board of Governors. Mr. Moore is a contributor for the NFPA *Fire Protection Handbook* and editor and co-editor, respectively, for the 1993 edition and the 1996 through 2007 editions of the *National Fire Alarm Code Handbook*. Mr. Moore serves as one of several faculty for the NFPA Fire Alarm Workshop and is the 2009 recipient of the NFPA Standard Medal.

Robert P. Schifiliti (Chapter 18 and Supplement 3)

Robert P. Schifiliti, P.E., FSFPE, founder and President of R. P. Schifiliti Associates, Inc., is the current chair of the NFPA Technical Correlating Committee on Signaling Systems for the Protection of Life and Property and is a member and past chair of the Technical Committee on Notification Appliances for Fire Alarm Systems. Mr. Schifiliti is co-chair of the Fire Protection Research Foundation's Detection and Alarm Research Council. He has authored the fire alarm supplement in the *Life Safety Code® Handbook,* the Notification Appliances chapter in the NFPA *Fire Protection Handbook®*, and the Design of Detection Systems chapter in the *SFPE Handbook of Fire Protection Engineering*. Mr. Schifiliti serves as one of several faculty for the NFPA Fire Alarm Workshop, is a licensed fire protection engineer, and a Fellow in the Society of Fire Protection Engineers. He received his Master of Science degree in Fire Protection Engineering from Worcester Polytechnic Institute.

Dean K. Wilson (Chapters 26 and 27)

Dean K. Wilson, P.E., FSFPE, CFPS, now retired on disability, formerly worked as a senior engineer with Hughes Associates, Inc. He is a member emeritus and former chair of the Technical Correlating Committee on Signaling Systems for the Protection of Life and Property. In 2006, he received the NFPA Standards Medal in recognition of his more than 30 years of service to the NFPA standards-making process.

About the Editors

Lee F. Richardson is a Senior Electrical Engineer at NFPA, where he is responsible for *NFPA 72®, National Fire Alarm and Signaling Code*, and NFPA 720, *Standard for the Installation of Carbon Monoxide (CO) Detection and Warning Equipment*. His responsibilities have also included NFPA 85, *Boiler and Combustion Systems Hazards Code*; NFPA 86, *Standard for Ovens and Furnaces*; NFPA 86C, *Standard for Industrial Furnaces Using a Special Processing Atmosphere*; and NFPA 86D, *Standard for Industrial Furnaces Using Vacuum as an Atmosphere*. Mr. Richardson has also played an active role in the staffing duties for the code-making panel processing of proposals and comments for recent editions of *NFPA 70®, National Electrical Code®*. He is also a member of the ASME A17.1, *Elevator and Escalator Safety Code,* Emergency Operations Committee.

Mr. Richardson holds a Bachelor of Science degree in Electrical Engineering from Lowell Technological Institute (now part of the University of Massachusetts). Prior to his work at NFPA, he worked for more than 20 years as an instrumentation and controls engineer in the engineering and design of commercial power plants, particularly nuclear power plants.

Mr. Richardson has written articles for the *NFPA Journal,* and he is the author of the Fire Alarm Systems chapter of the *Fire and Life Safety Inspection Manual* and the co-editor of the 2002 and 2007 editions of the *National Fire Alarm Code Handbook*.

Richard J. Roux, SET, FAI, FAM, is Senior Electrical Specialist at NFPA. He serves as staff liaison to several NFPA technical committees, including NFPA 780, 79, 790, and 791. He provides advisory service and field service, as well as other technical support for these documents in addition to *NFPA 72®, National Fire Alarm and Signaling Code*. He joined NFPA after 25 years in the fire detection systems field.

Mr. Roux is licensed in Massachusetts and is NICET Level IV certified, IMSA Level II certified in both Municipal Fire Alarm and Interior Fire Alarm. He is a member of SFPE, IMSA, and AFAA. He serves as one of several faculty for the NFPA Fire Alarm Workshop, moderator for several IMSA Fire Alarm Certification Programs, and technical editor for NFPA's video *Inspection and Testing of Fire Alarm Systems*. He is co-author of NFPA's reference book *NFPA Pocket Guide to Fire Alarm System Installation* and has been editor and reviewer for many book projects. He has written numerous articles on fire alarm systems and is author of several fire alarm feature columns.

PART ONE

NFPA 72®, National Fire Alarm and Signaling Code, 2010 Edition, with Commentary

Part One of this handbook includes the complete text and illustrations of the 2010 edition of *NFPA 72®, National Fire Alarm and Signaling Code*. The text and illustrations from the Code are printed in black, as are the official requirements of *NFPA 72*. Line drawings from the Code are labeled "Figures."

Paragraphs that begin with the letter *A* are extracted from Annex A of the Code. Although printed in black ink, this nonmandatory material is purely explanatory in nature. For ease of use, this handbook places Annex A material after the Code paragraph to which it refers.

In addition to Code text and annexes, Part One includes commentary, which provides the history and other background information for specific paragraphs in the Code. This insightful commentary takes the reader behind the scenes, into some of the thought processes underlying the requirements.

To readily identify commentary material, commentary text, illustration captions, and tables are printed in red. So that the reader may easily distinguish between figures in the Code, the line drawings and photographs in the commentary are labeled "Exhibits."

This edition of the *Handbook* includes a Frequently Asked Questions feature. The marginal FAQs are based on commonly asked questions of the *NFPA 72* staff.

Administration

Chapter 1 contains the administrative rules that apply to every chapter of *NFPA 72*®, *National Fire Alarm and Signaling Code*. In addition, the first section of each chapter of the Code contains an "Application" section that outlines the scope of the chapter and its relationship with other chapters.

1.1 Scope

1.1.1 *NFPA 72* covers the application, installation, location, performance, inspection, testing, and maintenance of fire alarm systems, supervising station alarm systems, public emergency alarm reporting systems, fire warning equipment and emergency communications systems (ECS), and their components.

NFPA 72 provides the minimum installation, inspection, testing, maintenance, and performance requirements for fire alarm systems used in any application. Included in the Code are requirements for the application, location, and limitations of fire alarm system components, such as manual fire alarm boxes, automatic fire detectors, and notification appliances. The Code also provides the minimum requirements for fire warning equipment, which includes single- and multiple-station alarms and household fire alarm systems addressed in Chapter 29.

The 2010 edition of the Code reflects a change in the landscape of the systems addressed, including a substantial reorganization of the chapters. The 2010 edition addresses not only fire alarm systems but also the broader scope of fire/alarm/emergency signaling systems. Systems formerly identified as fire alarm systems, such as supervising station fire alarm systems, now called supervising station alarm systems, are included, as are emergency communications systems such as those identified in 1.3.2 and addressed in the new Chapter 24, Emergency Communications Systems (ECS).

The requirements of Chapter 24 apply to communications systems used for any emergency purpose, including fires. Some of the communications system requirements of this new chapter were relocated from the chapter on protected premises fire alarm systems, and these requirements are still applicable to fire alarm systems. Many other provisions of the Code apply to both fire and emergency communications systems. Numerous requirements, terms, and definitions have been modified throughout the Code to reflect their broader application. This has been accomplished in part by removal of the word *fire* in many places and by the selective use of the word *emergency* in other places.

Organizational changes have been included in this edition to facilitate the application of requirements common to both fire systems and emergency systems. Although these changes are needed to correlate with the changing landscape, the Code has not lost focus on its need to clearly present requirements for fire alarm systems.

The organization of the Code includes a chapter renumbering and the addition of "reserved" chapters. This reorganization conceptually places Code content into four common groupings:

1. "Administrative chapters," which include Administration; Referenced Publications; and Definitions

2. "Support chapters," which include Fundamentals; Circuits and Pathways; Inspection, Testing, and Maintenance; Initiating Devices; and Notification Appliances

3. "System chapters," which include Emergency Control Functions and Interfaces; Protected Premises Fire Alarm Systems; Emergency Communications Systems (ECS); Supervising Station Alarm Systems; Public Emergency Alarm Reporting Systems; and Single- and Multiple-Station Alarms and Household Fire Alarm Systems

4. "Usability annexes," which include Annex A, Explanatory Material; Annex B, Engineering Guide for Automatic Fire Detector Spacing; Annex C, System Performance and Design Guide; Annex D, Speech Intelligibility; Annex E, NEMA SB 30, *Fire Service Annunciator and Interface*; Annex F, Sample Ordinance Adopting *NFPA 72*; Annex G, Wiring Diagrams and Guide for Testing Fire Alarm Circuits; Annex H, Informational References; and Annex I, Cross-Reference Table (2007 edition to 2010 edition)

The "reserved" chapters have been added to avoid continual renumbering of the existing chapters in the Code to ultimately improve its usability.

NFPA 72 does not mandate the installation of a fire alarm system, fire warning equipment, or emergency communications systems. The need for the installation of these systems or equipment is established through a framework of higher level mandates established through the requirements of NFPA *101*®, *Life Safety Code*®; *NFPA 5000*®, *Building Construction and Safety Code*®; and NFPA 1, *Fire Code*; as well as other building codes; federal, state, or local ordinances; insurance company requirements; military design criteria; corporate policies; other organizational policies (both private and public); and the individual needs of the property owner or occupant. *NFPA 72* provides the requirements for how to install this equipment regardless of the reason it is installed.

FAQ ▶
Does *NFPA 72* require the installation of a fire alarm system or other emergency system?

1.1.2 The provisions of this chapter apply throughout the Code unless otherwise noted.

Chapter 1 provides a foundation from which to apply the rules of the Code. These administrative rules apply throughout the Code but can be modified by the special requirements set forth in the subsequent chapters. As an example, Section 1.4 indicates that the requirements of the Code are not intended to be retroactively applied except for the requirements of inspection, testing, and maintenance of systems as noted in 14.1.4.

In order to provide a consistent framework for users, all NFPA documents follow a standardized format, which is specified in the *Manual of Style for NFPA Technical Committee Documents*. This format is particularly specific for the administrative rules in Chapter 1.

1.2* Purpose

A.1.2 Fire alarm systems intended for life safety should be designed, installed, and maintained to provide indication and warning of abnormal fire conditions. The system should alert building occupants and summon appropriate aid in adequate time to allow for occupants to travel to a safe place and for rescue operations to occur. The fire alarm system should be part of a life safety plan that also includes a combination of prevention, protection, egress, and other features particular to that occupancy.

1.2.1 The purpose of this Code is to define the means of signal initiation, transmission, notification, and annunciation; the levels of performance; and the reliability of the various types of fire alarm systems, supervising station alarm systems, public emergency alarm reporting systems, fire warning equipment, emergency communications systems, and their components.

The Code describes the various types of alarm and supervisory initiating devices as well as alarm, supervisory, and trouble audible and visible notification appliances for fire alarm and other emergency systems. Requirements for how these devices and appliances must be installed and used and how they must perform are provided in the Code. The Code also describes the types of systems, the methods of signal transmission, and the features that determine system reliability and performance. However, the Code is not an installation specification, an approval guide, or a training manual.

1.2.2 This Code defines the features associated with these systems and also provides information necessary to modify or upgrade an existing system to meet the requirements of a particular system classification.

Whenever a system is modified or updated, it is vital that the system designer have a thorough understanding of the existing equipment, including its capabilities and the system's wiring (i.e., circuit class, type, and configuration). Where applicable, the software and firmware of existing systems need to be examined to verify compatibility with the new equipment. Often, the existing equipment is too old to interface easily with the newer technology used in the planned additional equipment. The existing equipment may or may not be able to be modified to conform to current Code requirements.

1.2.3 This Code establishes minimum required levels of performance, extent of redundancy, and quality of installation but does not establish the only methods by which these requirements are to be achieved.

NFPA 72 provides a minimum set of requirements. A designer may choose to exceed the requirements of the Code, based upon a risk assessment of the premises in which the system is to be installed. The requirements of the Code apply to voluntary installations as well as mandated installations.

1.2.4* This Code shall not be interpreted to require a level of protection that is greater than that which would otherwise be required by the applicable building or fire code.

A.1.2.4 The intent of this paragraph is to make it clear that the protection requirements are derived from the applicable building or fire code, not from *NFPA 72*.

As noted in the commentary following 1.1.1, the need for a fire alarm system, fire warning equipment, or an emergency communications system is established outside the requirements of *NFPA 72* through a framework that includes other codes, standards, and jurisdictional documents. The level of protection required by this framework varies depending on the type of occupancy. Variations can include the type of detection (manual, automatic, or both), the extent of detection coverage (complete, partial, or selected), the need for occupant notification (audible, visible, or both), the need for a particular type of emergency communications system, the need for emergency forces notification (including automatic transmission of alarm signals to an off-site location), and other protection features. A requirement for the installation to comply with *NFPA 72* will normally be included with these specified features. Supplement 4 provides a summary of the higher level requirements for fire alarm systems for various occupancies based on the 2009 edition of NFPA *101*.

Once the need for a fire alarm system, other fire warning equipment, or an emergency communications system has been established, the protection features have been specified, and *NFPA 72* has been referenced, the system and equipment must conform to all the applicable requirements of the Code. For instance, *NFPA 72* includes numerous minimum requirements common to all systems to ensure the reliability and performance of the system, such as requirements for monitoring the integrity of circuits and power supplies. In other cases, minimum requirements are included for specific features such as survivability of audible and visible notification appliance circuits when systems are used for partial evacuation or relocation of occupants or other emergency communications purposes. Although these items may not be discussed within the framework of other codes, standards, and jurisdictional documents, once *NFPA 72* is referenced, the minimum installation requirements of *NFPA 72* must be followed for a Code-compliant installation.

Additionally, many of the requirements of *NFPA 72* are stated in conditional terms such as "Where required. . . ." The needs and features of the system as determined by the framework noted in the commentary following 1.1.1 provide the basis for the application of these requirements. Where the needs and features of the system are not specified by other codes, standards, or jurisdictional documents, they still need to be determined. The system designer in conjunction with the authority having jurisdiction and the system owner must establish these needs and features as a part of the basis of the system design. This collaboration is especially true for systems that are installed voluntarily (nonrequired systems). The requirements of the *NFPA 72* apply to the installation of nonrequired systems.

FAQ ▶
Where the required system features are not specified through a framework of higher level mandates, who must determine the needs and features?

1.3 Application

1.3.1 Alarm systems shall be classified as follows:

Section 1.3.1 was revised and reorganized to reflect the more general category of "alarm systems." As noted in the commentary following 1.1.1, some systems formerly identified as "fire alarm" systems are now identified as "alarm" systems since they can also serve other purposes.

(1) Fire alarm systems

(a) Household fire alarm systems

Fire warning equipment in residential-type occupancies is installed to warn the occupants of a fire emergency so they can immediately evacuate the building. *Fire warning equipment*, defined in 3.3.100, can comprise a *household fire alarm system*, defined in 3.3.95.2, or *single-station* or *multiple-station alarms*, defined in 3.3.245 and 3.3.149. The requirements for fire warning equipment are detailed in Chapter 29. These requirements typically apply to certain occupancies such as one- and two-family dwellings or portions of certain occupancies such as sleeping rooms or guest suites of hotels.

(b) Protected premises (local) fire alarm systems

The primary purpose of most fire alarm systems within protected premises is to warn building occupants to evacuate the premises. Other purposes of these fire alarm systems include actuating the building fire protection features, providing property protection, ensuring mission continuity, providing heritage preservation, and providing environmental protection. The term *protected premises (local) fire alarm system* applies to any fire alarm system located at the protected premises, including *building fire alarm systems, dedicated function fire alarm systems,* and *releasing fire alarm systems*. Definitions for these systems can be found in 3.3.95.4. Chapter 23 describes the requirements for fire alarm systems within protected premises.

(2) Supervising station alarm systems

Supervising station alarm systems, described in Chapter 26, provide the means of communication between the protected premises and a location called a supervising station. The types of supervising station alarm systems are addressed in 1.3.1(2)(a) through 1.3.1(2)(c).

(a) Central station (service) alarm systems

Central station service alarm systems typically involve fire alarm systems of those protected premises where signals are supervised by a listed central station providing central station service. [As noted in the commentary following 1.3.1(2)(b), a listed central station can also provide remote supervising station service.] *Central station service,* defined in 3.3.268.1, includes installation and maintenance of the supervised system as well as monitoring, alarm retransmission to the fire department, runner service, and record keeping. The elements of central station service must be provided by a listed central station or a listed central station in combination with a listed alarm service local company, controlled and operated by a person, firm, or corporation whose business is the furnishing of such service. As the *prime contractor,* defined in 3.3.186, such companies will have obtained specific listing from a third-party listing agency acceptable to the authority having jurisdiction as a provider of central station service. Central station service may be used where a facility has either a high risk of loss or a high value. For example, a facility that has a large number of nonambulatory people may benefit from central station service. Similarly, a high-hazard or high-value manufacturing facility may benefit from central station service. Central station service may also be used for the supervision of sprinkler systems in which monitoring at a constantly attended location is required. See Chapter 26 for requirements pertaining to alarm systems for central station service.

(b) Remote supervising station alarm systems

If a building owner does not want to use a central station service alarm system, if a proprietary supervising station alarm system is not appropriate, or if a public emergency alarm reporting system is not available, then the owner can choose to use a remote supervising station alarm system. These systems provide a means for transmitting alarm, supervisory, and trouble signals from the protected premises to a remote location. The remote location will be the communications center (see 3.3.49), a fire station or responsible governmental agency, or, if permitted by the authority having jurisdiction, an alternative approved location. Because the communications center does not always respond to supervisory and trouble signals, the use of a privately operated remote supervising station may be needed. Note that a listed central supervising station can also be used to provide remote supervising station service and in doing so needs to comply only with the requirements for remote supervising station alarm systems. See Chapter 26 for requirements pertaining to remote supervising station alarm systems.

(c) Proprietary supervising station alarm systems

Proprietary supervising station alarm systems typically involve the fire alarm systems of those protected premises where the signals are monitored by a supervising station under the same ownership as the protected premises. The supervising station can be located at the protected property or at one of multiple protected properties. The property may consist of a single building, such as a high-rise building, or several buildings, such as a college campus, where the dormitories and other buildings report to a single proprietary supervising station at the campus police department or campus fire department. The property may be contiguous or noncontiguous. If noncontiguous, it may consist of protected properties at remote locations, such as across town or across the country. An example of a proprietary supervising station with contiguous property is a college campus. A proprietary supervising station with noncontiguous property would be a retail store chain with properties across the country that are monitored from a single location owned by the retail store chain. See Chapter 26 for requirements pertaining to proprietary supervising stations.

(3) Public emergency alarm reporting systems

Public emergency alarm reporting systems, formerly called public fire alarm reporting systems or municipal fire alarm systems, involve systems of alarm initiating devices, receiving equipment, and connecting circuits used to transmit alarms from street locations to the communications center. Public emergency alarm reporting systems provide publicly accessible

◀ **FAQ**
What is a public emergency alarm reporting system?

alarm boxes at strategic locations throughout a municipality. A *publicly accessible alarm box,* defined in 3.3.8.5, is an enclosure accessible to the public that houses a manually operated transmitter. Citizens initiate an emergency alarm signal by actuating one of these alarm boxes.

Auxiliary systems provide a direct means of communication between the protected premises and the communications center using public emergency alarm reporting systems. An auxiliary system provides a connection from the system at the protected premises to a public emergency alarm reporting system auxiliary box or master box. An *auxiliary box,* defined in 3.3.8.1, is an alarm box that can only be operated remotely. A *master box*, defined in 3.3.8.4, is a publicly accessible alarm box that is equipped for remote actuation. If a municipality does not have a public emergency alarm reporting system, then an auxiliary alarm system cannot be provided. See Chapter 27 for requirements pertaining to public emergency alarm reporting systems and auxiliary alarm systems.

(a) Auxiliary alarm systems — local energy type

Typically, when a fire alarm signal at the protected premises is actuated, contacts in the fire alarm system control unit at the protected premises actuate a circuit that, in turn, causes a public emergency alarm reporting system auxiliary or master box to transmit a fire alarm signal to the communications center.

Power to operate the local energy interface circuit comes from the fire alarm system control unit at the protected premises. In addition, the fire alarm system control unit at the protected premises monitors the interface circuit for integrity and monitors the set or unset condition of the public emergency alarm reporting system auxiliary or master box. A wired public emergency alarm reporting system, a series telephone public emergency alarm reporting system, and a wireless public emergency alarm reporting system all use a local energy interface circuit (provided in the fire alarm control unit at the protected premises) to allow a fire alarm system control unit at the protected premises to actuate the auxiliary or master box. See 27.6.3.2 for requirements pertaining to local energy type auxiliary systems.

(b) Auxiliary alarm systems — shunt type

As an alternative to a local energy interface, some wired public emergency alarm reporting system boxes offer a shunt connection. A closed contact at the protected premises is electrically connected to a circuit that is derived from the public emergency alarm reporting telegraph circuit. When the closed contact opens the circuit and removes the shunt, the box trips and initiates a signal to the communications center.

A ground fault on the shunt circuit also becomes a ground fault on the public emergency alarm reporting circuit. If an open fault occurs on the public emergency alarm reporting circuit, a subsequent actuation of the shunt circuit will not cause the public emergency alarm reporting box to initiate an alarm signal. Unfortunately, unless the fire department somehow notifies all the building owners that the public emergency alarm reporting circuit has an impairment, the owners will not know that their connection to the public circuit is also impaired.

The Code limits the devices connected to a shunt circuit to manual fire alarm boxes and automatic sprinkler waterflow switches. Automatic fire detectors are not permitted to be connected to a shunt circuit. A shunt-type system has very specific requirements and is not allowed to be interconnected to a protected premises system unless the city circuits entering the protected premises are installed in rigid metal conduit or electrical metallic tubing. These wiring methods help to prevent faults in one premises from disabling the city circuit. Faults in the circuit can prevent transmission from other protected premises, leaving them unprotected. Because the wiring necessary to actuate shunt-type master boxes must enter the protected premises, and damage or tampering to these circuits is out of the control of the fire department, many jurisdictions do not allow shunt-type master boxes to be installed on their municipal loop. See 27.6.3.2 for requirements pertaining to shunt-type auxiliary systems.

1.3.2 Emergency communications systems shall be classified as follows:

As noted in the commentary following 1.1.1, the scope of the Code has expanded to include a number of emergency communications systems. An emergency communications system, in accordance with 3.3.79, is "a system for the protection of life by indicating the existence of an emergency situation and communicating information necessary to facilitate an appropriate response and action." Referring to 24.2.3, "an emergency communications system is intended to communicate information about emergencies including, but not limited to, fire, human-caused events (accidental and intentional), other dangerous situations, accidents, and natural disasters." Some of these systems may be used as part of a stand-alone fire alarm system, while others may be used as part of a combination (fire alarm) system or as part of another emergency system.

(1) One-way emergency communications systems

One-way emergency communications systems are defined in 3.3.79.1. These systems are intended to broadcast emergency messages using audible, visible, or textual means. Refer to Section 24.4.

(a) Distributed recipient mass notification systems

Distributed recipient mass notification systems are intended to communicate directly with targeted individuals and groups that might not be in a contiguous area. Refer to 3.3.79.1.1 and 24.4.4. Distributed recipient mass notification systems include net-centric alerting systems (NCASs) that are based on internet protocol (IP) technologies. NCASs leverage the IP network infrastructure to instantly reach those personnel who have access to nearly any IP-connected devices [such as pop-up alerts on personal computers (PCs), text messages to personal data assistants (PDAs) and cellular telephones, electronic mail to IP-capable cellular telephones, and recorded voice messages to voice over-IP (VoIP) telephones and PCs]. Additionally, NCASs can be used to actuate, through a single interface, non-IP alerting systems, such as in-building mass notification systems, wide-area alerting systems, and traditional dial-up telephone alerting systems.

(b) In-building fire emergency voice/alarm communications systems

In-building fire emergency voice/alarm communications systems are the traditional emergency voice/alarm communications systems used for fire alarm systems. As the name implies, these systems are intended for fire alarm system applications within buildings. The requirements for these systems have been relocated from the protected premises fire alarm system chapter to the emergency communications systems chapter because they fall under the scope of an emergency communications system. Refer to 3.3.79.1.2 and 24.4.1.

(c) In-building mass notification systems

In-building mass notification systems, defined in 3.3.79.1.3, are somewhat similar in concept to an in-building fire emergency voice/alarm communications system, but their potential application is much broader. The requirements for these systems are more extensive and reflect the level of sophistication needed for systems that may involve a variety of complex scenarios (including fire scenarios). Refer to 24.4.2.

(d) Wide area mass notification systems

Wide area mass notification systems are intended to serve outdoor areas, such as a campus. These systems may also communicate with other notification systems provided for other campus areas, military bases, municipalities, or other similar areas. Refer to 3.3.79.1.4 and 24.4.3. Wide area mass notification systems can also be integrated with in-building mass notification systems.

(2) Two-way emergency communications systems

Two-way emergency communications systems, defined in 3.3.79.2, are used to facilitate the exchange of information and the communication of instructions in buildings. Some systems are intended primarily for emergency services personnel or building fire wardens, while others are intended for occupants such as those in an area of refuge.

(a) In-building emergency communications systems

In-building emergency communications systems include two-way in-building wired emergency services communications systems (two-way telephone communications systems), two-way radio communications enhancement systems (bi-directional antenna and signal booster systems), area of refuge emergency communications systems, and elevator emergency communications systems. Refer to Section 24.5.

1.3.3 Any reference or implied reference to a particular type of hardware shall be for the purpose of clarity and shall not be interpreted as an endorsement.

NFPA does not manufacture, test, distribute, endorse, approve, certify, or list services, products, or components. See Section 3.2 and the associated annex material for definitions of *approved* and *listed*.

1.3.4 The intent and meaning of the terms used in this Code shall be, unless otherwise defined herein, the same as those of *NFPA 70, National Electrical Code®*.

For the installation of the systems addressed by *NFPA 72, NFPA 70®, National Electrical Code® (NEC®)*, must also be used. To avoid confusion, the definitions and use of terms that are found in *NFPA 72* are the same as those found in the *NEC*, unless a separate definition is provided in this Code.

1.4 Retroactivity

1.4.1 Unless otherwise noted, it is not intended that the provisions of this document be applied to facilities, equipment, structures, or installations that were existing or approved for construction or installation prior to the effective date of the document.

FAQ ▶
Are the requirements of *NFPA 72* retroactive?

With the exception of Chapter 14, the Code does not apply retroactively to existing installations. See the commentary following 14.1.4, which clearly indicates the retroactive application of Chapter 14 requirements.

It should be noted that the requirements of Chapter 29 have been rewritten (beginning with the 2007 edition of the Code) to exclude any reference to "new" or "existing" construction. The retroactive application of the requirements of Chapter 29 is not intended to automatically occur as a result of these changes. However, as changes are made to existing installations of fire warning equipment, it is expected that the full requirements of Chapter 29 would apply unless exempted by governing codes or statutes.

1.4.2 In those cases where it is determined by the authority having jurisdiction that the existing situation involves a distinct hazard to life or property, retroactive application of the provisions of this document shall be permitted.

From time to time, the authority having jurisdiction may feel that while the system still meets the minimum requirements of the version of the Code that was in effect at the time of installation, the system may no longer meet the minimum requirements for the premises' current use. A change of occupancy use, tenant improvements to the building, or system upgrades may be the reason.

1.5 Equivalency

1.5.1 Nothing in this Code shall prevent the use of systems, methods, devices, or appliances of equivalent or superior quality, strength, fire resistance, effectiveness, durability, and safety over those prescribed by this Code.

1.5.2 Technical documentation shall be submitted to the authority having jurisdiction to demonstrate equivalency.

1.5.3 The systems, methods, devices, or appliances that are found equivalent shall be approved.

Devices or systems that do not meet the specific requirements of the Code can be presented to the authority having jurisdiction as equivalent to the Code. Technical documentation to substantiate the request for equivalency must be submitted with the request. Examples of technical documentation include testing laboratory reports, engineering calculations, experiential data, and documented engineering judgments. The authority having jurisdiction determines whether a product, method, or device is suitable. Also refer to the definition of *approved* in 3.2.1, the related annex material, and related commentary.

1.6 Units and Formulas

1.6.1 The units of measure in this Code are presented in U.S. customary units (inch-pound units).

1.6.2 Where presented, the International System (SI) of units follow the inch-pound units in parentheses.

1.6.3 Where both systems of units are presented, either system shall be acceptable for satisfying the requirements in this Code.

1.6.4 Where both systems of units are presented, users of this Code shall apply one set of units consistently and shall not alternate between units.

1.6.5* The values presented for measurements in this Code are expressed with a degree of precision appropriate for practical application and enforcement. It is not intended that the application or enforcement of these values be more precise than the precision expressed.

A.1.6.5 Where dimensions are expressed in inches, it is intended that the precision of the measurement be 1 in., thus plus or minus $\frac{1}{2}$ in. The conversion and presentation of dimensions in millimeters would then have a precision of 25 mm, thus plus or minus 13 mm.

Section 1.6 includes requirements for the application and enforcement of the units of measure provided in the Code. Where measurements are presented in the Code in terms of inches (and millimeters), the precision assumed for enforcement is 1 inch (25 millimeters). Values presented in the Code are not intended to be enforced to a higher level of precision.

1.6.6 Where extracted text contains values expressed in only one system of units, the values in the extracted text have been retained without conversion to preserve the values established by the responsible technical committee in the source document.

1.7 Code Adoption Requirements

This Code shall be administered and enforced by the authority having jurisdiction designated by the governing authority. *(See Annex F for sample wording for enabling legislation.)*

REFERENCES CITED IN COMMENTARY

Manual of Style for NFPA Technical Committee Documents, 2004 edition, National Fire Protection Association, Quincy, MA.

NFPA 1, *Fire Code,* 2009 edition, National Fire Protection Association, Quincy, MA.

NFPA 70®, National Electrical Code®, 2008 edition, National Fire Protection Association, Quincy, MA.

NFPA *101®, Life Safety Code®,* 2009 edition, National Fire Protection Association, Quincy, MA.

NFPA 5000®, Building Construction and Safety Code®, 2009 edition, National Fire Protection Association, Quincy, MA.

Referenced Publications

CHAPTER 2

This chapter lists the publications that are referenced in the mandatory chapters of *NFPA 72*®. These mandatory referenced publications are needed for the effective use of and compliance with *NFPA 72*. The requirements contained in these references constitute part of the requirements of *NFPA 72*. Annex H lists nonmandatory publications that are referenced in the nonmandatory annexes of *NFPA 72*.

2.1 General

The documents or portions thereof listed in this chapter are referenced within this Code and shall be considered part of the requirements of this document.

2.2 NFPA Publications

National Fire Protection Association, 1 Batterymarch Park, Quincy, MA 02169-7471.

NFPA 10, *Standard for Portable Fire Extinguishers,* 2007 edition.

NFPA 11, *Standard for Low-, Medium-, and High-Expansion Foam,* 2005 edition.

NFPA 13, *Standard for the Installation of Sprinkler Systems,* 2010 edition.

NFPA 25, *Standard for the Inspection, Testing, and Maintenance of Water-Based Fire Protection Systems,* 2008 edition.

NFPA 37, *Standard for the Installation and Use of Stationary Combustion Engines and Gas Turbines,* 2006 edition.

NFPA 70®, *National Electrical Code*®, 2008 edition.

NFPA 75, *Standard for the Protection of Information Technology Equipment,* 2009 edition.

NFPA 90A, *Standard for the Installation of Air-Conditioning and Ventilating Systems,* 2009 edition.

NFPA 110, *Standard for Emergency and Standby Power Systems,* 2010 edition.

NFPA 111, *Standard on Stored Electrical Energy Emergency and Standby Power Systems,* 2010 edition.

NFPA 601, *Standard for Security Services in Fire Loss Prevention,* 2005 edition.

NFPA 720, *Standard for the Installation of Carbon Monoxide (CO) Detection and Warning Equipment,* 2009 edition.

NFPA 780, *Standard for the Installation of Lightning Protection Systems,* 2008 edition.

NFPA 1221, *Standard for the Installation, Maintenance, and Use of Emergency Services Communications Systems,* 2010 edition.

NFPA 1600®, *Standard on Disaster/Emergency Management and Business Continuity Programs,* 2007 edition.

NFPA 1620, *Recommended Practice for Pre-Incident Planning,* 2003 edition.

2.3 Other Publications

2.3.1 ANSI Publications.

American National Standards Institute, Inc., 25 West 43rd Street, 4th Floor, New York, NY 10036.

ANSI A-58.1, *Building Code Requirements for Minimum Design Loads in Buildings and Other Structures.*

ANSI S1.4a, *Specifications for Sound Level Meters*, 1985, reaffirmed 2006.

ANSI S3.2, *Method for Measuring the Intelligibility of Speech Over Communications Systems*, 1989, revised 1999.

ANSI S3.41, *American National Standard Audible Emergency Evacuation Signal*, 1990, reaffirmed 2008.

ANSI/ASME A17.1a/CSA B44a, *Safety Code for Elevators and Escalators*, 2008.

ANSI/IEEE C2, *National Electrical Safety Code*, 2007.

ANSI/UL 217, *Standard for Single and Multiple Station Smoke Alarms*, 2006, revised 2008.

ANSI/UL 268, *Standard for Smoke Detectors for Fire Alarm Systems*, 2006.

ANSI/UL 827, *Standard for Central-Station Alarm Services*, 2008.

ANSI/UL 864, *Standard for Control Units and Accessories for Fire Alarm Systems*, 2003, revised 2006.

ANSI/UL 985, *Standard for Household Fire Warning System Units*, 2000, revised 2003.

ANSI/UL 1730, *Standard for Smoke Detector Monitors and Accessories for Individual Living Units of Multifamily Residences and Hotel/Motel Rooms*, 2006, revised 2007.

ANSI/UL 1971, *Standard for Signaling Devices for the Hearing Impaired*, 2002, revised 2008.

UL 2017, *Standard for General-Purpose Signaling Devices and Systems*, 2000, revised 2004.

2.3.2 EIA Publications.

Electronic Industries Alliance, 2500 Wilson Boulevard, Arlington, VA 22201-3834.

EIA Tr 41.3, *Telephones.*

2.3.3 IEC Publications.

International Electrotechnical Commission, 3 rue de Varembé, P.O. Box 131, CH-1211 Geneva 20, Switzerland. IEC documents are available through ANSI.

IEC 61260, *Electroacoustics — Octave-Band and Fractional-Octave-Band Filters*, 1995.

2.3.4 ISO Publications.

Standards Secretariat, Acoustical Society of America, 335 East 45th Street, New York, NY 10017–3483.

ISO 7240-19, *Fire Detection and Alarm Systems — Part 19: Design, Installation, Commissioning and Service of Sound Systems for Emergency Purposes,* 8/15/07.

ISO 7731, *Danger signals for work places — Auditory danger signals.*

2.3.5 Telcordia Publications.

One Telcordia Drive, Piscataway, NJ 08854.

GR-506-CORE, LATA Switching Systems Generic Requirements: Signaling for Analog Interface, 2006.

GR-909-CORE, Fiber in the Loop Systems Generic Requirements, 2004.

2.3.6 Other Publications.

Merriam-Webster's Collegiate Dictionary, 11th edition, Merriam-Webster, Inc., Springfield, MA, 2003.

2.4 References for Extracts in Mandatory Sections

NFPA 70®, *National Electrical Code®*, 2008 edition.

NFPA 96, *Standard for Ventilation Control and Fire Protection of Commercial Cooking Operations,* 2008 edition.

NFPA *101®*, *Life Safety Code®*, 2009 edition.

NFPA 654, *Standard for the Prevention of Fire and Dust Explosions from the Manufacturing, Processing, and Handling of Combustible Particulate Solids,* 2006 edition.

NFPA 720, *Standard for the Installation of Carbon Monoxide (CO) Detection and Warning Equipment,* 2009 edition.

NFPA 1221, *Standard for the Installation, Maintenance, and Use of Emergency Services Communications Systems,* 2010 edition.

NFPA 5000®, *Building Construction and Safety Code®*, 2009 edition.

Definitions

All definitions that apply to subjects covered throughout the Code are located in Chapter 3. In addition, where a particular term is not defined in Chapter 3 but is defined in *NFPA 70®*, *National Electrical Code®* (*NEC®*), the definition contained in the *NEC* applies, in accordance with 1.3.4. Otherwise, where terms are not defined, the ordinary meanings as given in *Merriam-Webster's Collegiate Dictionary,* 11th edition, apply (see 2.3.6).

3.1 General

The definitions contained in this chapter shall apply to the terms used in this Code. Where terms are not defined in this chapter or within another chapter, they shall be defined using their ordinarily accepted meanings within the context in which they are used. *Merriam-Webster's Collegiate Dictionary*, 11th edition, shall be the source for the ordinarily accepted meaning.

3.2 NFPA Official Definitions

The definitions in Section 3.2 come from the NFPA Regulations Governing Committee Projects. These terms are commonly found in NFPA technical committee documents, and the definitions cannot be altered without the approval of the NFPA Standards Council.

3.2.1* Approved. Acceptable to the authority having jurisdiction.

A.3.2.1 Approved. The National Fire Protection Association does not approve, inspect, or certify any installations, procedures, equipment, or materials; nor does it approve or evaluate testing laboratories. In determining the acceptability of installations, procedures, equipment, or materials, the authority having jurisdiction may base acceptance on compliance with NFPA or other appropriate standards. In the absence of such standards, said authority may require evidence of proper installation, procedure, or use. The authority having jurisdiction may also refer to the listings or labeling practices of an organization that is concerned with product evaluations and is thus in a position to determine compliance with appropriate standards for the current production of listed items.

The term *approved* has a specific meaning in the Code, as defined in 3.2.1, which is "acceptable to the authority having jurisdiction." Only the authority having jurisdiction can approve equipment and installations. The authority having jurisdiction may choose to grant approval on the basis of whether or not a product has received a listing and has been labeled by a qualified testing laboratory. However, listing or labeling alone does not constitute approval. (See 3.2.4 for the definition of *labeled* and 3.2.5 for the definition of *listed*.)

◄ FAQ
Who approves equipment and installations?

Whereas 10.3.1 requires that all installed fire alarm equipment be listed, Section 1.5 allows the use of equivalent methods and equipment where equivalency has been demonstrated to the authority having jurisdiction. The authority having jurisdiction may also grant approval on this basis. Refer to Section 10.18 for approval and documentation requirements.

3.2.2* Authority Having Jurisdiction (AHJ). An organization, office, or individual responsible for enforcing the requirements of a code or standard, or for approving equipment, materials, an installation, or a procedure.

A.3.2.2 Authority Having Jurisdiction (AHJ). The phrase "authority having jurisdiction," or its acronym AHJ, is used in NFPA documents in a broad manner, since jurisdictions and approval agencies vary, as do their responsibilities. Where public safety is primary, the authority having jurisdiction may be a federal, state, local, or other regional department or individual such as a fire chief; fire marshal; chief of a fire prevention bureau, labor department, or health department; building official; electrical inspector; or others having statutory authority. For insurance purposes, an insurance inspection department, rating bureau, or other insurance company representative may be the authority having jurisdiction. In many circumstances, the property owner or his or her designated agent assumes the role of the authority having jurisdiction; at government installations, the commanding officer or departmental official may be the authority having jurisdiction.

Any given physical property may have multiple authorities having jurisdiction, who may be concerned with life safety, property protection, mission continuity, heritage preservation, and environmental protection. Some authorities having jurisdiction may impose additional requirements beyond those of the Code. If requirements for the installation of a specific fire alarm system conflict, the installer must follow the most stringent requirements.

3.2.3* Code. A standard that is an extensive compilation of provisions covering broad subject matter or that is suitable for adoption into law independently of other codes and standards.

A.3.2.3 Code. The decision to designate a standard as a "code" is based on such factors as the size and scope of the document, its intended use and form of adoption, and whether it contains substantial enforcement and administrative provisions.

3.2.4 Labeled. Equipment or materials to which has been attached a label, symbol, or other identifying mark of an organization that is acceptable to the authority having jurisdiction and concerned with product evaluation, that maintains periodic inspection of production of labeled equipment or materials, and by whose labeling the manufacturer indicates compliance with appropriate standards or performance in a specified manner.

3.2.5* Listed. Equipment, materials, or services included in a list published by an organization that is acceptable to the authority having jurisdiction and concerned with evaluation of products or services, that maintains periodic inspection of production of listed equipment or materials or periodic evaluation of services, and whose listing states that either the equipment, material, or service meets appropriate designated standards or has been tested and found suitable for a specified purpose.

A.3.2.5 Listed. The means for identifying listed equipment may vary for each organization concerned with product evaluation; some organizations do not recognize equipment as listed unless it is also labeled. The authority having jurisdiction should utilize the system employed by the listing organization to identify a listed product.

3.2.6 Shall. Indicates a mandatory requirement.

3.2.7 Should. Indicates a recommendation or that which is advised but not required.

3.3 General Definitions

Each of the definitions in Section 3.3 has been assigned to a specific technical committee of the *National Fire Alarm and Signaling Code* by the Technical Correlating Committee on Signaling Systems for the Protection of Life and Property. The committee assignment is indicated by a designation in parenthesis at the end of each definition. These designations correlate with the committee roster for each technical committee found at the beginning of *NFPA 72®, National Fire Alarm and Signaling Code*. These designations, shown in sequence as provided in the Code, correlate as follows:

SIG-FUN	Technical Committee on Fundamentals of Fire Alarm Systems
SIG-TMS	Technical Committee on Testing and Maintenance of Fire Alarm Systems
SIG-IDS	Technical Committee on Initiating Devices for Fire Alarm Systems
SIG-NAS	Technical Committee on Notification Appliances for Fire Alarm Systems
SIG-PRO	Technical Committee on Protected Premises Fire Alarm Systems
SIG-ECS	Technical Committee on Emergency Communications Systems
SIG-SSS	Technical Committee on Supervising Station Fire Alarm Systems
SIG-PRS	Technical Committee on Public Fire Reporting Systems
SIG-HOU	Technical Committee on Single- and Multiple-Station Alarms and Household Fire Alarm Systems

3.3.1 Acknowledge. To confirm that a message or signal has been received, such as by the pressing of a button or the selection of a software command. (SIG-SSS)

3.3.2* Acoustically Distinguishable Space (ADS). An emergency communications system notification zone, or subdivision thereof, that might be an enclosed or otherwise physically defined space, or that might be distinguished from other spaces because of different acoustical, environmental, or use characteristics, such as reverberation time and ambient sound pressure level. (SIG-NAS)

As a part of the requirements for voice intelligibility in 18.4.10, a new term, *acoustically distinguishable space (ADS)*, has been established. As part of the research conducted by the Fire Protection Research Foundation on how to design and test intelligible voice systems, it became evident that there was a need to identify spaces with common acoustical characteristics. Identifying these spaces would help system designers better assess the needs for design and testing of each space. It also allowed for the identification of areas that may not require voice intelligibility, depending on how the system is to be used. Also refer to the definition of *intelligible* in 3.3.126, related annex explanation in A.3.3.126, Annex D, and Supplement 3.

A.3.3.2 Acoustically Distinguishable Space (ADS). All parts of a building or area intended to have occupant notification are subdivided into ADSs as defined. Some ADSs might be designated to have voice communication capability and require that those communications be intelligible. Other spaces might not require voice intelligibility or might not be capable of reliable voice intelligibility. An ADS might have acoustical design features that are conducive for voice intelligibility, or it might be a space where voice intelligibility could be difficult or impossible to achieve. Each is still referred to as an ADS.

In smaller areas, such as those under 400 ft^2 (40 m^2), walls alone will define the ADS. In larger areas, other factors might have to be considered. In spaces that might be subdivided by temporary or movable partitions, such as ballrooms and meeting rooms, each individual configuration should be considered a separate ADS. Physical characteristics, such as a change in ceiling height of more than 20 percent, or a change in acoustical finish, such as carpet in one area and tile in another, would require those areas to be treated as separate ADSs. In larger areas, there might be noise sources that require a section to be treated as a separate ADS. Any significant change in ambient noise level or frequency might necessitate an area be considered a separate ADS.

In areas of 85 dBA or greater ambient sound pressure level, meeting the pass/fail criteria for intelligibility might not be possible, and other means of communication might be necessary. So, for example, the space immediately surrounding a printing press or other high-noise machine might be designated as a separate ADS, and the design might call for some form of effective notification but not necessarily require the ability to have intelligible voice communication. The aisles or operator's control stations might be separate ADSs where intelligible voice communication might be desired.

Significant differences in furnishings, for example, an area with tables, desks, or low dividers, adjacent to an area with high shelving, would require separate consideration. The entire desk area could be a single acoustic zone, whereas each area between shelving could be a unique zone. Essentially, any noteworthy change in the acoustical environment within an area will mandate consideration of that portion of the area to be treated as an acoustic zone. Hallways and stairwells will typically be considered as individual acoustic zones.

Spaces confined by walls with carpeting and acoustical ceilings can be deemed to be one ADS. An ADS should be an area of consistent size and material. A change of materials from carpet to hard tile, the existence of sound sources, such as decorative waterfalls, large expanses of glass, and changes in ceiling height, are all factors that might separate one ADS from another.

Each ADS might require different components and design features to achieve intelligible voice communication. For example, two ADSs with similar acoustical treatments and noise levels might have different ceiling heights. The ADS with the lower ceiling height might require more ceiling-mounted speakers to ensure that all listeners are in a direct sound field *(see Figure A.3.3.2)*. Other ADSs might benefit from the use of alternate speaker technologies, such as line arrays, to achieve intelligibility.

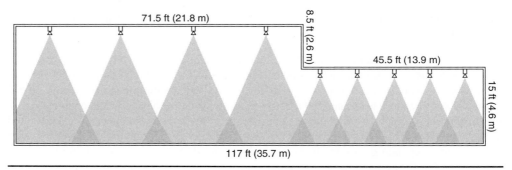

FIGURE A.3.3.2 *Illustration Demonstrating the Effect of Ceiling Height. (Source: R. P. Schifiliti Associates, Inc.)*

An ADS that differs from another because of the frequency and level of ambient noise might require the use of speakers and system components that have a wider frequency bandwidth than conventional emergency communications equipment. However, designers should not use higher bandwidth speakers in all locations, unless needed to overcome certain acoustic and ambient conditions. This is because the higher bandwidth appliance will require more energy to perform properly. This increases amplifier and wire size and power supply requirements.

In some spaces, it might be impractical to achieve intelligibility, and, in such a case, alternatives to voice evacuation might be required within such areas.

There might be some areas of a facility where there are several spaces of the same approximate size and the same acoustic properties. For example, there might be an office space with multiple individual offices, each with one speaker. If one or two are satisfactorily tested, there is no need to test all of them for speech intelligibility.

The intent is that all parts of a building or space be divided into definable ADSs. See 18.4.10.

3.3.3 Active Multiplex System. A multiplexing system in which signaling devices such as transponders are employed to transmit status signals of each initiating device or initiating device circuit within a prescribed time interval so that the lack of receipt of such a signal can be interpreted as a trouble signal. (SIG-SSS)

Circuits of *active multiplex systems*, defined in 3.3.3, use an interrogation and response routine to determine the status of a device or connected system control unit. Failure to receive a response signal from a device initiates a trouble signal. This interrogation routine serves to monitor the interconnecting path for integrity. See 10.17.1 for requirements pertaining to monitoring for integrity.

3.3.4 Addressable Device. A fire alarm system component with discrete identification that can have its status individually identified or that is used to individually control other functions. (SIG-IDS)

Addressable devices, defined in 3.3.4, can be either initiating devices or control/notification appliances. The circuit between the addressable devices or appliances and the fire alarm control unit is essentially a time-domain multiplex circuit and is called a *signaling line circuit* in the Code. Each device or appliance has an address that consists of a binary string of 1s and 0s. The fire alarm control unit communicates with devices and appliances on the circuit with a series of voltage pulses corresponding to logical 1s and 0s and superimposed on the dc power supply. When the fire alarm control unit polls or addresses an initiating device, the initiating device responds with its status. Similarly, the fire alarm control unit can also address a control module(s) or appliance(s) and issue a command such as a transfer of a relay contact to appliances connected to the circuit. Digital addresses for each device or appliance can be assigned by the system hardware or software. Examples of addressable devices are shown in Exhibits 3.1 and 3.2.

3.3.5 Adverse Condition. Any condition occurring in a communications or transmission channel that interferes with the proper transmission or interpretation, or both, of status change signals at the supervising station. *(See also 3.3.240.7, Trouble Signal.)* (SIG-SSS)

Adverse conditions, defined in 3.3.5, include circuits or communications paths with open circuit faults or ground faults, electrical or radio frequency interference with communications paths, and circuit wiring with short-circuit faults.

3.3.6 Air Sampling–Type Detector. See 3.3.59, Detector.

3.3.7 Alarm. A warning of danger. (SIG-FUN)

The term *alarm*, defined in 3.3.7, indicates a danger condition. This fundamental change was introduced in the 2007 edition. Prior editions defined *alarm* as a warning of fire danger. With the inclusion of emergency communications systems and the recognition of many different alarm system purposes, the technical committee made the definition of *alarm* generic. Where a particular code requirement is intended to apply to a specific type of alarm, such as fire, the text will clearly state so. Otherwise, where the text says only "alarm," the requirement is intended to apply to all types of danger warnings. The phrases *supervisory alarm* and *trouble alarm* are not appropriate terms to indicate supervisory or trouble conditions. The actions required for alarm are very specific and are different from those of a trouble or supervisory condition. In order not to confuse those trying to communicate the condition and therefore the required response, the appropriate terms are *supervisory signal* and *trouble signal*. See the definitions of *supervisory signal* and *trouble signal* in 3.3.240.

> **3.3.7.1 Nuisance Alarm.** Any alarm caused by mechanical failure, malfunction, improper installation, or lack of proper maintenance, or any alarm activated by a cause than cannot be determined. (SIG-FUN)

Fire officials often use the term *nuisance alarm* in place of the term *false alarm* to describe fire alarm signals initiated when an otherwise properly functioning fire alarm system detects

EXHIBIT 3.1 *Device Programming Unit and Smoke Detector. (Source: Seimens Building Technologies, Fire Safety Division, Florham Park, NJ)*

EXHIBIT 3.2 *Addressable Smoke Detector Showing Programming Switches. (Source: System Sensor Corp., St. Charles, IL)*

◀ **FAQ**
Is the term *alarm* intended to indicate only a warning of fire danger?

conditions that it interprets as a fire signature. Nuisance alarms can be caused by faulty equipment, improper application of detection devices, and poor installation of equipment. Although an alarm when fire is not present is still a false alarm and nuisance alarms are, in fact, false alarms, the term *false alarm* is often reserved for a malicious act whereby a person falsely initiates a fire alarm. Such acts are also called *malicious false alarms*. Regardless of what they are called, alarms transmitted under non-fire conditions can put occupants and first responders at risk during the response. Adherence to the requirements of the Code and workmanlike installations reduce nuisance alarms.

3.3.8 Alarm Box.

3.3.8.1 Auxiliary Box. An alarm box that can only be operated from one or more remote initiating devices or an auxiliary alarm system used to send an alarm to the communications center. (SIG-PRS)

FAQ ▶
What is the difference between an auxiliary alarm box and a master alarm box?

An auxiliary alarm box is used to transmit alarm signals from remote initiating devices or from auxiliary alarm systems to the communications center utilizing the emergency alarm reporting system when manual initiation of an alarm signal is not required. By contrast, a master box includes the features of an auxiliary box as well as a feature allowing manual operation. Refer to the definition of *publicly accessible alarm box*. A protected premises fire alarm system connected to either an auxiliary alarm box or a master alarm box will automatically actuate the box when an alarm occurs. Upon actuation, the box transmits a coded signal to the communications center. Also see the commentary following 1.3.1(3).

3.3.8.2 Combination Fire Alarm and Guard's Tour Box. A manually operated box for separately transmitting a fire alarm signal and a distinctive guard patrol tour supervisory signal. (SIG-IDS)

3.3.8.3 Manual Fire Alarm Box. A manually operated device used to initiate a fire alarm signal. (SIG-IDS)

Operation of a manual fire alarm box, shown in Exhibit 3.3, may require one action, such as pulling a lever, or two actions, such as lifting a cover and then pulling a lever. In some institutional occupancies, building codes, NFPA *101*®, *Life Safety Code*®, and local ordinances permit the use of key-operated manual fire alarm boxes, such as the one shown in Exhibit 3.4.

EXHIBIT 3.3 *Typical Single-Action Manual Fire Alarm Box. (Source: The Protectowire Co., Plymouth, MA)*

3.3.8.4 Master Box. A publicly accessible alarm box that can also be operated by one or more remote initiating devices or an auxiliary alarm system used to send an alarm to the communications center. (SIG-PRS)

Public emergency alarm reporting system master boxes, as shown in Exhibit 3.5, have an interface circuit that allows a protected premises fire alarm system control unit to actuate the master box whenever the system initiates a fire alarm signal.

3.3.8.5 Publicly Accessible Alarm Box. An enclosure, accessible to the public, housing a manually operated transmitter used to send an alarm to the communications center. (SIG-PRS)

Exhibit 3.6 shows a publicly accessible alarm box, also known as a municipal fire alarm box or street box. See 3.3.153.

3.3.9 Alarm Service. The service required following the receipt of an alarm signal. (SIG-SSS)

The action taken when an alarm signal is received is called the *alarm service*. The alarm service can include any or all of the following:

1. Response by a private fire brigade or public fire department
2. Dispatch of an alarm service provider's runner

3. Notification to the building owner and occupants

4. Notification to the authorities having jurisdiction

3.3.10 Alarm Signal. See 3.3.240, Signal.

3.3.11 Alarm System. See 3.3.95, Fire Alarm System; 3.3.267, Supervising Station Alarm System; 3.3.199, Public Emergency Alarm Reporting System.

3.3.12 Alarm Verification Feature. A feature of automatic fire detection and alarm systems to reduce unwanted alarms wherein smoke detectors report alarm conditions for a minimum period of time, or confirm alarm conditions within a given time period after being reset, in order to be accepted as a valid alarm initiation signal. (SIG-PRO)

Alarm verification is applicable to smoke detectors only. The alarm verification feature can reduce unwanted alarm signals from transient conditions that actuate smoke detectors. The feature may reside within individual smoke detectors, or it may be a feature of the fire alarm control unit to which the smoke detectors are connected. Manufacturers of addressable analog fire alarm systems typically do not recommend the activation of alarm verification during the initial installation. It is not intended as a means of reducing unwanted alarms due to the improper application of smoke detectors, such as installation in a location where they are exposed to unsuitable environmental conditions. Refer to 23.8.5.4.1 for the requirements related to use of alarm verification.

3.3.13 Alert Tone. An attention-getting signal to alert occupants of the pending transmission of a voice message. (SIG-PRO)

Where voice announcements are used for other than complete evacuation, in-building fire voice/alarm communications systems precede the voice announcement with an alert tone to gain occupant attention before broadcast of the voice message. The alert tone is not considered an alarm signal, and the Code does not specify the form of the alert tone. See 24.4.1.8.2 for applicable requirements for the alert tone. Where voice announcements are used for complete evacuation, the announcement must be preceded by the emergency evacuation signal in accordance with 24.4.1.2.1.

3.3.14 Analog Initiating Device (Sensor). See 3.3.122, Initiating Device.

3.3.15 Ancillary Functions. Ancillary functions are those non-emergency activations of the fire alarm or mass notification audible, visual, and textual output circuits allowed. Ancillary

EXHIBIT 3.4 *Typical Key-Operated Manual Fire Alarm Box. (Source: Gamewell-FCI, Northford, CT; photo courtesy of Mammoth Fire Alarms, Inc., Lowell, MA)*

EXHIBIT 3.5 *Master Box. (Source: Gamewell-FCI, Northford, CT; photo courtesy of Mammoth Fire Alarms, Inc., Lowell, MA)*

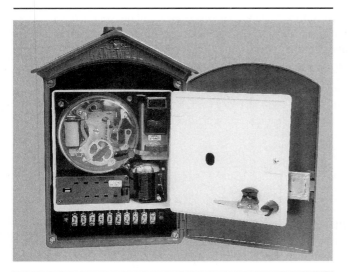

EXHIBIT 3.6 *Publicly Accessible Alarm Box. (Source: Gamewell-FCI, Northford, CT; photo courtesy of Mammoth Fire Alarms, Inc., Lowell, MA)*

functions can include general paging, background music, or other non-emergency signals. (SIG-ECS)

3.3.16 Annunciator. A unit containing one or more indicator lamps, alphanumeric displays, or other equivalent means in which each indication provides status information about a circuit, condition, or location. (SIG-FUN)

An annunciator is used to provide an on-site point of information as to where the alarm, supervisory, or trouble signal is reported within the protected premises. The annunciator may be a simple lamp display with a labeled description of the zone, an alphanumeric display providing either a static or running information stream of the event, or a graphic representation of the protected premises and the location of the event. With the everyday use of computer-aided drafting (CAD), some annunciators use CAD images to display the events in real time. Requirements that relate to annunciation and annunciation zoning can be found in Section 10.16. In addition, requirements for a standard emergency service interface can be found in Section 18.11 along with guidance in A.18.11 and in Annex E, NEMA Standard SB 30, *Standard Fire Service Annunciator and Interface.*

3.3.17 Apartment Building. A building or portion thereof containing three or more dwelling units with independent cooking and bathroom facilities. (SIG-HOU) [*5000*, 2009]

3.3.18 Audible Notification Appliance. See 3.3.160, Notification Appliance.

3.3.19 Automatic Extinguishing System Supervisory Device. See 3.3.122, Initiating Device.

3.3.20 Automatic Fire Detector. See 3.3.59, Detector.

3.3.21 Automatic Fire Extinguishing or Suppression System Operation Detector. See 3.3.59, Detector.

3.3.22 Autonomous Control Unit (ACU). See 3.3.53, Control Unit.

3.3.23 Auxiliary Alarm System. See 3.3.199, Public Emergency Alarm Reporting System.

3.3.24 Auxiliary Box. See 3.3.8, Alarm Box.

3.3.25* Average Ambient Sound Level. The root mean square, A-weighted, sound pressure level measured over the period of time that any person is present, or a 24-hour period, whichever time period is the lesser. (SIG-NAS)

A.3.3.25 Average Ambient Sound Level. The term *average ambient sound level* is also called the equivalent A-weighted sound level measured over t hours, where t is the time period over which the measurement is made. The standard industry symbol is $L_{A.eq.t}$. Where a measurement is taken over a 24-hour time period, the designation would be $L_{A.eq.24}$.

The definition of *average ambient sound level* was modified in the 2002 edition. The previous definition was a 24-hour average. Now, the average ambient sound level is the greater of a 24-hour average or an average taken over the period of time that any person is present. Exhibit 3.7 shows a sample 24-hour noise survey. The 24-hour average is 56 dBA versus 65 dBA for the occupied period (6:00 a.m. until 6:00 p.m.).

3.3.26 Beam Construction. See 3.3.33, Ceiling Surfaces.

3.3.27 Building Fire Alarm System. See 3.3.95, Fire Alarm System.

3.3.28 Building Fire Safety Plan. Documentation that provides information on the use of alarms, transmission of alarms, response to alarms, evacuation of immediate area, evacuation of smoke compartment, preparation of floors and building for evacuation and extinguishment of fire. [SIG-ECS]

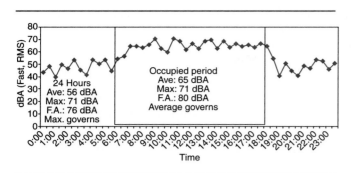

EXHIBIT 3.7 *Sample Noise Survey. (Source: R. P. Schifiliti Associates, Inc., Reading, MA)*

3.3.29 Carrier. High-frequency energy that can be modulated by voice or signaling impulses. (SIG-SSS)

3.3.30 Carrier System. A means of conveying a number of channels over a single path by modulating each channel on a different carrier frequency and demodulating at the receiving point to restore the signals to their original form. (SIG-SSS)

3.3.31 Ceiling. The upper surface of a space, regardless of height. Areas with a suspended ceiling have two ceilings, one visible from the floor and one above the suspended ceiling. (SIG-IDS)

> **3.3.31.1 Level Ceilings.** Ceilings that are level or have a slope of less than or equal to 1 in 8. (SIG-IDS)

> **3.3.31.2 Sloping Ceiling.** A ceiling that has a slope of more than 1 in 8. (SIG-IDS)

> **3.3.31.3* Sloping Peaked-Type Ceiling.** A ceiling in which the ceiling slopes in two directions from the highest point. Curved or domed ceilings can be considered peaked with the slope figured as the slope of the chord from highest to lowest point. (SIG-IDS)

> **A.3.3.31.3 Sloping Peaked-Type Ceiling.** Refer to Figure A.17.6.3.4(a) for an illustration of smoke or heat detector spacing on peaked-type sloped ceilings.

> **3.3.31.4* Sloping Shed-Type Ceiling.** A ceiling in which the high point is at one side with the slope extending toward the opposite side. (SIG-IDS)

> **A.3.3.31.4 Sloping Shed-Type Ceiling.** Refer to Figure A.17.6.3.4(b) for an illustration of smoke or heat detector spacing on shed-type sloped ceilings.

3.3.32 Ceiling Height. The height from the continuous floor of a room to the continuous ceiling of a room or space. (SIG-IDS)

Where a ceiling is supported by beams, joists, or open web beams (bar-joists), the ceiling height is measured from the floor deck to the bottom surface of the ceiling supported by the beams or joists.

◀ **FAQ**
How is ceiling height measured?

3.3.33 Ceiling Surfaces.

The ceiling design can have a profound effect on the flow of smoke and hot combustion product gases from the fire to the location of a heat or smoke detector. The ceiling design affects the speed of response of spot-type smoke and heat detectors. Anything that retards the response of a smoke or heat detector allows the fire to become larger before the occupants are notified. Consequently, categorizing ceiling surfaces is necessary because different detector location and spacing criteria apply, depending upon the size and spacing of downward-projection beams or joists.

> **3.3.33.1 Beam Construction.** Ceilings that have solid structural or solid nonstructural members projecting down from the ceiling surface more than 4 in. (100 mm) and spaced more than 36 in (910 mm), center to center. (SIG-IDS)

3.3.33.2 Girder. A support for beams or joists that runs at right angles to the beams or joists. If the top of the girder is within 4 in. (100 mm) of the ceiling, the girder is a factor in determining the number of detectors and is to be considered a beam. If the top of the girder is more than 4 in. (100 mm) from the ceiling, the girder is not a factor in detector location. (SIG-IDS)

3.3.33.3* Smooth Ceiling. A ceiling surface uninterrupted by continuous projections, such as solid joists, beams, or ducts, extending more than 4 in. (100 mm) below the ceiling surface. (SIG-IDS)

A.3.3.33.3 Smooth Ceiling. Open truss constructions are not considered to impede the flow of fire products unless the upper member, in continuous contact with the ceiling, projects below the ceiling more than 4 in. (100 mm).

3.3.33.4 Solid Joist Construction. Ceilings that have solid structural or solid nonstructural members projecting down from the ceiling surface for a distance of more than 4 in. (100 mm) and spaced at intervals of 36 in (910 mm) or less, center to center. (SIG-IDS)

Solid joists, whether structural or nonstructural, impede the flow of products of combustion. Web or bar joists are not considered to be solid joists unless the top chord is over 4 in. (100 mm) deep, in which case, only the top chord is considered a ceiling obstruction.

3.3.34 Central Control Station. See 3.3.80, Emergency Communications System — Central Control Station.

3.3.35 Central Station. See 3.3.266.1, Central Supervising Station.

3.3.36 Central Station Alarm System. See 3.3.267.1, Central Station Service Alarm System.

3.3.37 Central Station Service. See 3.3.268, Supervising Station Service.

3.3.38 Central Station Service Alarm System. See 3.3.267, Supervising Station Alarm System.

3.3.39 Central Supervising Station. See 3.3.266, Supervising Station.

3.3.40 Channel. A path for voice or signal transmission that uses modulation of light or alternating current within a frequency band. (SIG-SSS)

3.3.40.1 Communications Channel. A circuit or path connecting a subsidiary station(s) to a supervising station(s) over which signals are carried. (SIG-SSS)

3.3.40.2 Derived Channel. A signaling line circuit that uses the local leg of the public switched network as an active multiplex channel while simultaneously allowing that leg's use for normal telephone communications. (SIG-SSS)

3.3.40.3* Radio Channel. A band of frequencies of a width sufficient to allow its use for radio communications. (SIG-SSS)

A.3.3.40.3 Radio Channel. The width of the channel depends on the type of transmissions and the tolerance for the frequency of emission. Channels normally are allocated for radio transmission in a specified type for service by a specified transmitter.

3.3.40.4 Transmission Channel. A circuit or path connecting transmitters to supervising stations or subsidiary stations on which signals are carried. (SIG-SSS)

3.3.41 Circuit Interface. See 3.3.127, Interface.

3.3.42 Cloud Chamber Smoke Detection. See 3.3.252, Smoke Detection.

3.3.43* Coded. An audible or visible signal that conveys several discrete bits or units of information. (SIG-NAS)

Table A.10.9.3 provides recommended assignments for simple zone-coded signals. In addition to the designations in Table A.10.9.3, textual signals may use words that are familiar only to those concerned with response to the signal. This practice avoids general alarm notification and disruption of the occupants. Hospitals often use this type of signal. To hospital occupants who do not know the code words, a typical message might sound like a normal paging announcement: "Paging Dr. Firestone, Dr. Firestone, Building 4 West Wing." In other words, a fire is in the west wing of Building 4.

A.3.3.43 Coded. Notification signal examples are numbered strokes of an impact-type appliance and numbered flashes of a visible appliance.

3.3.44 Combination Detector. See 3.3.59, Detector.

3.3.45 Combination Emergency Communications Systems. See 3.3.81, Emergency Communications Systems — Combination.

3.3.46 Combination Fire Alarm and Guard's Tour Box. See 3.3.8, Alarm Box.

3.3.47 Combination System. See 3.3.95, Fire Alarm System.

3.3.48 Common Talk Mode. See 3.3.277, Talk Mode.

3.3.49* Communications Center. A building or portion of a building that is specifically configured for the primary purpose of providing emergency communications services or public safety answering point (PSAP) services to one or more public safety agencies under the authority or authorities having jurisdiction. [**1221,** 2007] (SIG-PRS)

In a large municipality, the municipal government may choose to locate the communications center at the main fire department station, at the public safety complex, at a specially designed communications building, or at some other suitably designed location. The communications center may or may not include the public safety answering point (PSAP) for the community's 9-1-1 emergency telephone system. NFPA 1221, *Standard for the Installation, Maintenance, and Use of Emergency Services Communications Systems*, provides requirements for the installation, performance, operation, and maintenance of communications systems and facilities. In previous editions, *NFPA 72* used the term *public fire service communications center*, while NFPA 1221 referred to this facility as just *communications center*. In the 2010 edition, *NFPA 72* also refers to the facility simply as *communications center*.

Public emergency alarm reporting systems (see Chapter 27) terminate at the communications center.

◀ **FAQ**
Where do public emergency alarm reporting systems terminate?

A.3.3.49 Communications Center. Examples of functions of a communications center are as follows:

(1) Communications between the public and the communications center
(2) Communications between the communications centers, the emergency response agency (ERA), and emergency response facilities (ERFs)
(3) Communications within the ERA and between different ERAs
(4) Communications with the public emergency alarm reporting system

The central operating part of the public emergency alarm reporting system is usually located at the communications center.

3.3.50 Communications Channel. See 3.3.40, Channel.

3.3.51 Communications Circuit. Any signaling path of an emergency communications system that carries voice, audio, data or other signals. [SIG-ECS]

3.3.52 Contiguous Property. See 3.3.191, Property.

3.3.53 Control Unit. A system component that monitors inputs and controls outputs through various types of circuits. (SIG-PRO)

The definition of *control unit* in 3.3.53 is not limited to fire alarm systems applications. Applications can include systems such as those used for mass notification or emergency communication. A control unit used in a fire alarm system falls under the definition of a *fire alarm control unit*, defined in 3.3.92. Note that the term *control unit* is used throughout the Code instead of the term *control panel*.

> **3.3.53.1* Autonomous Control Unit (ACU).** The primary control unit for an in-building mass notification system. (SIG-ECS)

> **A.3.3.53.1 Autonomous Control Unit (ACU).** Although an ACU might incorporate provisions for messages or signals from external sources, the ACU is fully capable of building controls without the need for sources outside the building. An ACU is allowed to be located within a primary building and supply circuits to immediately adjacent support buildings such as detached storage buildings. Larger buildings will generally have their own ACUs to allow individual control within each building.

An autonomous control unit (ACU) for an in-building mass notification system is analogous to a fire alarm control unit for a protected premises fire alarm system. Requirements for ACUs can be found in 24.4.2.14.

> **3.3.53.2 Emergency Communications Control Unit (ECCU).** A system capable of sending mass notification messages to individual buildings, zones of buildings, individual outdoor speaker arrays, zones of outdoor speaker arrays or; a building, multiple buildings, outside areas, or a combination of these. (SIG-ECS)

An emergency communications control unit (ECCU) is a control unit that serves the central control station and assigns priorities to all transmitted signals between the central control station and selectable locations, including individual buildings, portions of buildings, multiple buildings, outdoor areas, portions of outdoor areas, other ECCUs, or any combination of these. Emergency communications control units are addressed in 24.6.2. Also refer to the definition of *central control station* in 3.3.80.

> **3.3.53.3 Fire Alarm Control Unit.** See 3.3.92, Fire Alarm Control Unit.

> **3.3.53.4 Wireless Control Unit.** A component that transmits/receives and processes wireless signals. (SIG-PRO)

3.3.54 Day-Care Home. A building or portion of a building in which more than 3 but not more than 12 clients receive care, maintenance, and supervision, by other than their relative(s) or legal guardian(s), for less than 24 hours per day. [*101*, 2009] (SIG-HOU)

3.3.55 Dedicated Function Fire Alarm Control Unit. See 3.3.92, Fire Alarm Control Unit.

3.3.56 Dedicated Function Fire Alarm System. See 3.3.95, Fire Alarm System.

3.3.57 Delinquency Signal. See 3.3.240, Signal.

3.3.58 Derived Channel. See 3.3.40, Channel.

3.3.59 Detector. A device suitable for connection to a circuit that has a sensor that responds to a physical stimulus such as heat or smoke. (SIG-IDS)

> **3.3.59.1 Air Sampling–Type Detector.** A detector that consists of a piping or tubing distribution network that runs from the detector to the area(s) to be protected. An aspiration fan in the detector housing draws air from the protected area back to the detector through air sampling ports, piping, or tubing. At the detector, the air is analyzed for fire products. (SIG-IDS)

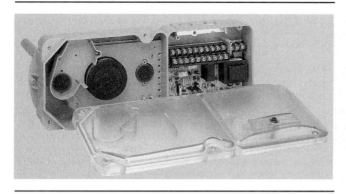

EXHIBIT 3.8 *Duct Smoke Detector (Passive). (Source: System Sensor Corp., St. Charles, IL)*

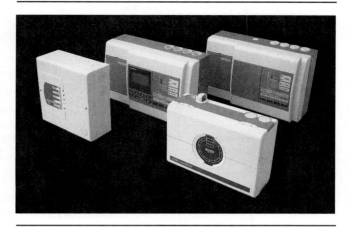

EXHIBIT 3.9 *Air-Sampling Smoke Detectors (Active). (Source: Xtralis, Inc., Norwell, MA)*

Air sampling–type detectors are either passive or active. Duct smoke detectors, as shown in Exhibit 3.8, are typically considered passive detection devices. Active sampling requires the creation of a negative pressure within a sampling tube to draw products of combustion from the protected area or protected space into the sampling network. Vacuum pumps or blower assemblies normally create this negative pressure. An active air-sampling smoke detector is illustrated in Exhibit 3.9.

◀ **FAQ**
What is the difference between passive and active air sampling?

> **3.3.59.2 Automatic Fire Detector.** A device designed to detect the presence of a fire signature and to initiate action. For the purpose of this Code, automatic fire detectors are classified as follows: Automatic Fire Extinguishing or Suppression System Operation Detector, Fire–Gas Detector, Heat Detector, Other Fire Detectors, Radiant Energy–Sensing Fire Detector, Smoke Detector. (SIG-IDS)

> **3.3.59.3 Automatic Fire Extinguishing or Suppression System Operation Detector.** A device that automatically detects the operation of a fire extinguishing or suppression system by means appropriate to the system employed. (SIG-IDS)

Examples of automatic fire extinguishing or suppression system operation alarm initiating devices are agent discharge flow switches and agent discharge pressure switches.

> **3.3.59.4* Combination Detector.** A device that either responds to more than one of the fire phenomena or employs more than one operating principle to sense one of these phenomena. Typical examples are a combination of a heat detector with a smoke detector or a combination rate-of-rise and fixed-temperature heat detector. This device has listings for each sensing method employed. (SIG-IDS)

> **A.3.3.59.4 Combination Detector.** These detectors do not utilize a mathematical evaluation principle of signal processing more than a simple "or" function. Normally, these detectors provide a single response resulting from either sensing method, each of which operates independent of the other. These detectors can provide a separate and distinct response resulting from either sensing method, each of which is processed independent of the other.

Exhibits 3.10 and 3.11 illustrate two common types of combination detectors.

> **3.3.59.5 Electrical Conductivity Heat Detector.** A line-type or spot-type sensing element in which resistance varies as a function of temperature. (SIG-IDS)

> **3.3.59.6 Fire–Gas Detector.** A device that detects gases produced by a fire. (SIG-IDS)

EXHIBIT 3.10 *Combination Rate-of-Rise and Fixed-Temperature Heat Detector (Mechanical). (Source: Kidde-Fenwal, Ashland, MA; photo courtesy of Mammoth Fire Alarms, Inc., Lowell, MA)*

EXHIBIT 3.11 *Combination Rate-of-Rise and Fixed-Temperature Heat Detector (Electronic). (Source: System Sensor Corp., St. Charles, IL)*

EXHIBIT 3.12 *Typical Fixed-Temperature (Nonrestorable) Heat Detector. (Source: Kidde-Fenwal, Ashland, MA; photo courtesy of Mammoth Fire Alarms, Inc., Lowell, MA)*

EXHIBIT 3.13 *Typical Flame Detector. (Source: Det-Tronics Corp., Minneapolis, MN)*

Examples of fire gases include hydrogen chloride (HCl) and carbon monoxide (CO). Users should not confuse fire-gas detectors designed for CO detection with CO warning equipment designed to prevent CO poisoning by alerting occupants to the presence of CO gas in the home.

3.3.59.7* Fixed-Temperature Detector. A device that responds when its operating element becomes heated to a predetermined level. (SIG-IDS)

A.3.3.59.7 Fixed-Temperature Detector. The difference between the operating temperature of a fixed-temperature device and the surrounding air temperature is proportional to the rate at which the temperature is rising. The rate is commonly referred to as *thermal lag*. The air temperature is always higher than the operating temperature of the device.

Typical examples of fixed-temperature sensing elements are as follows:

(1) *Bimetallic.* A sensing element comprised of two metals that have different coefficients of thermal expansion arranged so that the effect is deflection in one direction when heated and in the opposite direction when cooled.

(2) *Electrical Conductivity.* A line-type or spot-type sensing element in which resistance varies as a function of temperature.

(3) *Fusible Alloy.* A sensing element of a special composition metal (eutectic) that melts rapidly at the rated temperature.

(4) *Heat-Sensitive Cable.* A line-type device in which the sensing element comprises, in one type, two current-carrying wires separated by heat-sensitive insulation that softens at the rated temperature, thus allowing the wires to make electrical contact. In another type, a single wire is centered in a metallic tube, and the intervening space is filled with a substance that becomes conductive at a critical temperature, thus establishing electrical contact between the tube and the wire.

(5) *Liquid Expansion.* A sensing element comprising a liquid that is capable of marked expansion in volume in response to an increase in temperature.

Exhibit 3.12 illustrates a typical fixed-temperature heat detector.

3.3.59.8* Flame Detector. A radiant energy–sensing fire detector that detects the radiant energy emitted by a flame. *(Refer to A.17.8.2.)* (SIG-IDS)

A.3.3.59.8 Flame Detector. Flame detectors are categorized as ultraviolet, single wavelength infrared, ultraviolet infrared, or multiple wavelength infrared.

Exhibit 3.13 illustrates a typical flame detector.

3.3.59.9 Heat Detector. A fire detector that detects either abnormally high temperature or rate of temperature rise, or both. (SIG-IDS)

Many types of heat detectors are available. A typical spot-type heat detector is shown in Exhibit 3.14. For descriptions of other types of heat detectors, see definitions of *electrical conductivity heat detector, fixed-temperature detector* (see Exhibit 3.12), *line-type detector, rate compensation detector,* and *rate-of-rise detector* in 3.3.59. Also refer to the definition of *nonrestorable initiating device* in 3.3.122.3.

3.3.59.10 Line-Type Detector. A device in which detection is continuous along a path. Typical examples are rate-of-rise pneumatic tubing detectors, projected beam smoke detectors, and heat-sensitive cable. (SIG-IDS)

3.3.59.11* Multi-Criteria Detector. A device that contains multiple sensors that separately respond to physical stimulus such as heat, smoke, or fire gases, or employs more than one sensor to sense the same stimulus. This sensor is capable of generating only one alarm signal from the sensors employed in the design either independently or in combination. The sensor output signal is mathematically evaluated to determine when an alarm signal is warranted. The evaluation can be performed either at the detector or at the con-

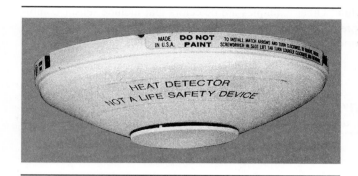

EXHIBIT 3.14 *Typical Heat Detector. (Source: GE Security, Bradenton, FL)*

trol unit. This detector has a single listing that establishes the primary function of the detector. (SIG-IDS)

A.3.3.59.11 Multi-Criteria Detector. A multi-criteria detector is a detector that contains multiple sensing methods that respond to fire signature phenomena and utilizes mathematical evaluation principles to determine the collective status of the device and generates a single output. Typical examples of multi-criteria detectors are a combination of a heat detector with a smoke detector, or a combination rate-of-rise and fixed-temperature heat detector that evaluates both signals using an algorithm to generate an output such as pre-alarm or alarm. The evaluation can be performed either at the detector or at the control unit. Other examples are detectors that include sensor combinations that respond in a predictable manner to any combination of heat, smoke, carbon monoxide, or carbon dioxide.

According to one manufacturer, "Multi-criteria detectors process inputs from two sensors using software algorithms that equate signals into pre-determined responses, which are based on a 'decision tree' programmed to react to defined scenarios."

Typically, the signals from a photoelectric smoke detector are combined with a temperature sensor using microprocessor-based logic to process signals from both detectors. Through the use of a combination of inputs, the device is more likely to reject false or nuisance alarms while increasing the likelihood of a quick response to a real fire condition. According to some manufacturers' literature, new software has been developed to allow the detector to continuously monitor its environment and "learn" the ambient conditions, further reducing the chances for a nuisance alarm.

Exhibit 3.15 illustrates a multi-criteria detector. This device contains multiple sensing technologies that independently collect fire signatures and environmental conditions and are not limited to heat, rate of heat rise, smoke, carbon monoxide, or carbon dioxide. The detector collects these signatures and environmental conditions and evaluates the signals using an algorithm to provide a single output. The signals are examined by an algorithm and are not available as individual outputs.

3.3.59.12* Multi-Sensor Detector. A device that contains multiple sensors that separately respond to physical stimulus such as heat, smoke, or fire gases, or employs more than one sensor to sense the same stimulus. A device capable of generating multiple alarm signals from any one of the sensors employed in the design, independently or in combination. The sensor output signals are mathematically evaluated to determine when an alarm signal is warranted. The evaluation can be performed either at the detector or at the control unit. This device has listings for each sensing method employed. (SIG-IDS)

A.3.3.59.12 Multi-Sensor Detector. Typical examples of multi-sensor detectors are a combination of a heat detector with a smoke detector, or a combination rate-of-rise and fixed-temperature heat detector that evaluates both signals using an algorithm to generate an output such as pre-alarm or alarm. The evaluation can be performed either at the

EXHIBIT 3.15 *Multi-Criteria Detector. (Source: Bosch Security Systems, Fairport, NY)*

detector or at the control unit. Other examples are detectors that include sensor combinations that respond in a predictable manner to any combination of heat, smoke, carbon monoxide, or carbon dioxide.

See Commentary Table 3.1 for a comparison of combination, multi-criteria, and multi-sensor detectors.

COMMENTARY TABLE 3.1 *Comparison of Combination, Multi-Criteria, and Multi-Sensor Detectors*

Detector Type	Features
Combination	• Multiple sensors • Does not utilize a mathematical evaluation principle, just a simple "or" function • Multiple listings
Multi-criteria	• Multiple sensors • Mathematically evaluated • Only one alarm signal • Single listing
Multi-sensor	• Multiple sensors • Mathematically evaluated • Capable of generating multiple alarm signals • Multiple listings

FAQ ▶
What is the difference between a multi-criteria detector and a multi-sensor detector?

The major difference between the definitions of *multi-criteria detector* and *multi-sensor detector* is that a multi-sensor detector is "a device capable of generating multiple alarm signals from any one of the sensors employed in the design, independently or in combination." A multi-sensor detector can be a photoelectric smoke detector with an additional carbon monoxide (CO) sensor; it can also be a combination of ionization and photoelectric smoke detectors and a heat detector all within one multi-sensor unit. Multi-sensor devices collect data on several different environmental parameters at the same time and then, based on the results of an on-board microprocessor, determine whether an alarm should be sent to the control panel. This process allows the detector to effectively distinguish between a legitimate change of state and adverse ambient conditions that may cause a nuisance alarm. Analog information from each sensor can also be digitally communicated to the control panel, where it is analyzed.

3.3.59.13 Other Fire Detectors. Devices that detect a phenomenon other than heat, smoke, flame, or gases produced by a fire. (SIG-IDS)

3.3.59.14 Pneumatic Rate-of-Rise Tubing Heat Detector. A line-type detector comprising small-diameter tubing, usually copper, that is installed on the ceiling or high on the walls throughout the protected area. The tubing is terminated in a detector unit containing diaphragms and associated contacts set to actuate at a predetermined pressure. The system is sealed except for calibrated vents that compensate for normal changes in temperature. (SIG-IDS)

3.3.59.15 Projected Beam–Type Detector. A type of photoelectric light obscuration smoke detector wherein the beam spans the protected area. (SIG-IDS)

Projected beam–type detection is often used in large open areas such as atria, convention halls, auditoriums, and gymnasiums and where a building or portion of a building has a high ceiling. Exhibit 3.16 illustrates a typical projected beam–type smoke detector, and Exhibit 3.17 shows a projected beam–type smoke detector with a reflector. Beam detectors used in an environment such as a gymnasium where the devices can be harmed by normal activities must be protected to prevent mechanical damage.

EXHIBIT 3.16 *Typical Projected Beam–Type Smoke Detector. (Source: Hochiki America Corp., Buena Park, CA)*

EXHIBIT 3.17 *Projected Beam–Type Smoke Detector with Reflector. (Source: Hochiki America Corp., Buena Park, CA)*

3.3.59.16 Radiant Energy–Sensing Fire Detector. A device that detects radiant energy, such as ultraviolet, visible, or infrared, that is emitted as a product of combustion reaction and obeys the laws of optics. (SIG-IDS)

3.3.59.17* Rate Compensation Detector. A device that responds when the temperature of the air surrounding the device reaches a predetermined level, regardless of the rate of temperature rise. (SIG-IDS)

A.3.3.59.17 Rate Compensation Detector. A typical example of a rate compensation detector is a spot-type detector with a tubular casing of a metal that tends to expand lengthwise as it is heated and an associated contact mechanism that closes at a certain point in the elongation. A second metallic element inside the tube exerts an opposing force on the contacts, tending to hold them open. The forces are balanced in such a way that, on a slow rate-of-temperature rise, there is more time for heat to penetrate to the inner element, which inhibits contact closure until the total device has been heated to its rated temperature level. However, on a fast rate-of-temperature rise, there is not as much time for heat to penetrate to the inner element, which exerts less of an inhibiting effect so that contact closure is achieved when the total device has been heated to a lower temperature. This, in effect, compensates for thermal lag.

Exhibit 3.18 illustrates a typical rate compensation heat detector.

3.3.59.18* Rate-of-Rise Detector. A device that responds when the temperature rises at a rate exceeding a predetermined value. (SIG-IDS)

A.3.3.59.18 Rate-of-Rise Detector. Typical examples of rate-of-rise detectors are as follows:

(1) *Pneumatic Rate-of-Rise Tubing.* A line-type detector comprising small-diameter tubing, usually copper, that is installed on the ceiling or high on the walls throughout the protected area. The tubing is terminated in a detector unit that contains diaphragms and associated contacts set to actuate at a predetermined pressure. The system is sealed except for calibrated vents that compensate for normal changes in temperature.

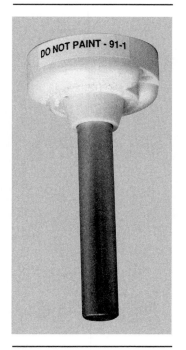

EXHIBIT 3.18 *Typical Rate Compensation Heat Detector. (Source: Thermotech Inc., Ogden, UT; photo courtesy of Mammoth Fire Alarms, Inc., Lowell, MA)*

EXHIBIT 3.19 *Typical Spot-Type Smoke Detector. (Source: System Sensor Corp., St. Charles, IL)*

(2) *Spot-Type Pneumatic Rate-of-Rise Detector.* A device consisting of an air chamber, a diaphragm, contacts, and a compensating vent in a single enclosure. The principle of operation is the same as that described for pneumatic rate-of-rise tubing.

(3) *Electrical Conductivity–Type Rate-of-Rise Detector.* A line-type or spot-type sensing element in which resistance changes due to a change in temperature. The rate of change of resistance is monitored by associated control equipment, and an alarm is initiated when the rate of temperature increase exceeds a preset value.

3.3.59.19 Smoke Detector. A device that detects visible or invisible particles of combustion. (SIG-IDS)

The definition of *smoke detector* uses the phrase "particles of combustion" to distinguish the effluent matter consisting of soot particles, gas molecules, vapor molecules, and ash particles from the heat and radiant energy liberated by the combustion reaction that is deemed energy. All matter flowing from the fire in the effluent plume is encompassed within the term *smoke*. The many types of smoke detectors are distinguished by the technology used to detect the matter in the smoke plume. For examples, see the definitions of *ionization smoke detection* and *photoelectric smoke detection* in 3.3.252 and *air sampling–type detector* and *spot-type smoke detector* (shown in Exhibit 3.19) in 3.3.59.

3.3.59.20 Spark/Ember Detector. A radiant energy–sensing fire detector that is designed to detect sparks or embers, or both. These devices are normally intended to operate in dark environments and in the infrared part of the spectrum. (SIG-IDS)

3.3.59.21 Spot-Type Detector. A device in which the detecting element is concentrated at a particular location. Typical examples are bimetallic detectors, fusible alloy detectors, certain pneumatic rate-of-rise detectors, certain smoke detectors, and thermoelectric detectors. (SIG-IDS)

3.3.60 Digital Alarm Communicator Receiver (DACR). A system component that accepts and displays signals from digital alarm communicator transmitters (DACTs) sent over the public switched telephone network. (SIG-SSS)

Exhibit 3.20 illustrates a typical DACR.

EXHIBIT 3.20 *Digital Alarm Communicator Receiver (DACR). (Source: Keltron Corp., Waltham, MA)*

3.3.61 Digital Alarm Communicator System (DACS). A system in which signals are transmitted from a digital alarm communicator transmitter (DACT) located at the protected premises through the public switched telephone network to a digital alarm communicator receiver (DACR). (SIG-SSS)

3.3.62 Digital Alarm Communicator Transmitter (DACT). A system component at the protected premises to which initiating devices or groups of devices are connected. The DACT seizes the connected telephone line, dials a preselected number to connect to a DACR, and transmits signals indicating a status change of the initiating device. (SIG-SSS)

The communications portion of a DACT functions very much like a modem that allows a personal computer to connect to an internet service provider. When a fire alarm system initiates a fire alarm, supervisory, or trouble signal, the DACT dials one of two preprogrammed telephone numbers. Once a digital alarm communicator receiver (DACR) answers the incoming call, it provides a handshake signal to the DACT. The DACT then transmits digital information. Upon receipt of the information, the DACR transmits a "kiss off" signal to the DACT, which causes the DACT to disconnect and end the transmission. The DACR then interprets and displays the digital information as a fire alarm, supervisory, or trouble signal. The DACT, as shown in Exhibit 3.21, provides the most commonly used means for transmitting fire alarm, supervisory, and trouble signals to a supervising station.

◀ **FAQ**
What are the basic functional steps performed by a DACT?

EXHIBIT 3.21 *Digital Alarm Communicator Transmitter (DACT). (Source: Silent Knight by Honeywell, Maple Grove, MN)*

3.3.63 Digital Alarm Radio Receiver (DARR). A system component composed of two subcomponents: one that receives and decodes radio signals, the other that annunciates the decoded data. These two subcomponents can be coresident at the central station or separated by means of a data transmission channel. (SIG-SSS)

3.3.64 Digital Alarm Radio System (DARS). A system in which signals are transmitted from a digital alarm radio transmitter (DART) located at a protected premises through a radio channel to a digital alarm radio receiver (DARR). (SIG-SSS)

Exhibit 3.22 illustrates a typical digital alarm radio system (DARS) arrangement.

3.3.65 Digital Alarm Radio Transmitter (DART). A system component that is connected to or an integral part of a digital alarm communicator transmitter (DACT) that is used to provide an alternate radio transmission channel. (SIG-SSS)

Exhibit 3.23 illustrates a typical digital alarm radio transmitter (DART).

3.3.66 Display. The visual representation of output data, other than printed copy. (SIG-NAS)

3.3.67 Distributed Recipient Mass Notification System (DRMNS). See 3.3.79, Emergency Communications System.

3.3.68 Donor Antenna. The outside antenna on the building where a public safety radio enhancement system operates. (SIG-ECS)

EXHIBIT 3.22 *Digital Alarm Radio System (DARS). (Source: Honeywell Security and Custom Electronics, Syosset, NY; courtesy of AFA Protective Systems, Inc.)*

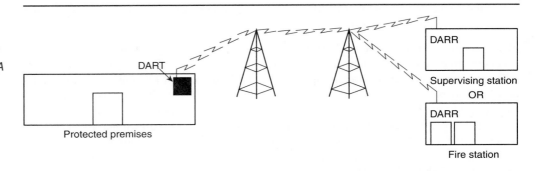

EXHIBIT 3.23 *Digital Alarm Radio Transmitter (DART). (Source: Honeywell Security and Custom Electronics, Syosset, NY; photo courtesy of AFA Protective Systems, Inc.)*

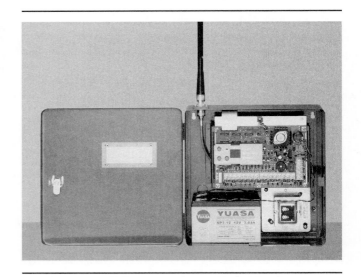

3.3.69 Donor Site. The repeater or base station site with which the public safety radio enhancement system communicates. (SIG-ECS)

3.3.70 Dormitory. A building or a space in a building in which group sleeping accommodations are provided for more than 16 persons who are not members of the same family in one room, or a series of closely associated rooms, under joint occupancy and single management, with or without meals, but without individual cooking facilities. [*101,* 2009] (SIG-HOU)

3.3.71* Double Doorway. A single opening that has no intervening wall space or door trim separating the two doors. (SIG-IDS)

A.3.3.71 Double Doorway. Refer to Figure 17.7.5.6.5.3(A) for an illustration of detector location requirements for double doors.

3.3.72 Downlink. The radio signal from the base station transmitter to the portable public safety subscriber receiver. (SIG-ECS)

3.3.73 Dual Control. The use of two primary trunk facilities over separate routes or different methods to control one communications channel. (SIG-SSS)

3.3.74 Dwelling Unit. One or more rooms arranged for complete, independent housekeeping purposes with space for eating, living, and sleeping; facilities for cooking; and provisions for sanitation. [*5000,* 2009] (SIG-HOU)

3.3.74.1 Multiple Dwelling Unit. A building containing three or more dwelling units. (SIG-HOU)

3.3.74.2 Single Dwelling Unit. A building consisting solely of one dwelling unit. (SIG-HOU)

3.3.75 Effective Masked Threshold. The minimum sound level at which the tone signal is audible in ambient noise. (SIG-NAS)

Requirements in 18.4.6 allow designers to use an alternative method to the A-weighted signaling requirements in the Code for audible signaling. This method involves an evaluation of the background noise levels at each octave (or one-third octave) of the frequency spectrum to provide an audible alarm signal tailored for the specific signaling application. Refer to 18.4.6 and related annex material and commentary, as well as the definitions for *octave* and *one-third octave* in 3.3.163.

3.3.76 Electrical Conductivity Heat Detector. See 3.3.59, Detector.

3.3.77* Ember. A particle of solid material that emits radiant energy due either to its temperature or the process of combustion on its surface. *(See also 3.3.258, Spark.)* (SIG-IDS)

A.3.3.77 Ember. Class A and Class D combustibles burn as embers under conditions where the flame typically associated with fire does not necessarily exist. This glowing combustion yields radiant emissions in parts of the radiant energy spectrum that are radically different from those parts affected by flaming combustion. Specialized detectors that are specifically designed to detect those emissions should be used in applications where this type of combustion is expected. In general, flame detectors are not intended for the detection of embers.

3.3.78 Emergency Communications Control Unit (ECCU). See 3.3.53, Control Unit.

3.3.79 Emergency Communications System. A system for the protection of life by indicating the existence of an emergency situation and communicating information necessary to facilitate an appropriate response and action. (SIG-ECS)

3.3.79.1 One-Way Emergency Communications System. One-way emergency communications systems are intended to broadcast information, in an emergency, to people in one or more specified indoor or outdoor areas. It is intended that emergency messages be conveyed either by audible, visible, or textual means, or any combination thereof. (SIG-ECS)

3.3.79.1.1 Distributed Recipient Mass Notification System (DRMNS). A distributed recipient mass notification system is a system meant to communicate directly to targeted individuals and groups that might not be in a contiguous area. (SIG-ECS)

Distributed recipient mass notification systems (DRMNSs) are (normally) one-way emergency communications systems that are intended to communicate with a wide range of targeted individuals and groups. (Some DRMNSs may have features that allow for confirmation that the message has been received by the recipient.) Methods of communication include a variety of means such as reverse 9-1-1 and email. Requirements for these systems are contained in 24.4.4. See A.24.4.4 for a detailed overview of these systems.

3.3.79.1.2 In-Building Fire Emergency Voice/Alarm Communications System. Dedicated manual or automatic equipment for originating and distributing voice instructions, as well as alert and evacuation signals pertaining to a fire emergency, to the occupants of a building. (SIG-ECS)

A building code or an authority having jurisdiction may require an in-building fire emergency voice/alarm communications system (also called simply "emergency voice/alarm communications system") in which the fire safety plan for a building calls for partial evacuation of the building or relocation of the occupants to areas of refuge instead of total evacuation.

High-rise buildings and large area industrial, commercial, or institutional facilities are typical applications for in-building fire emergency voice/alarm communications systems. *NFPA 72* does not require the use of such systems but provides the requirements for the systems if they are required by other codes, standards, owners, or authorities having jurisdiction.

> **3.3.79.1.3 In-Building Mass Notification System.** A system used to provide information and instructions to people in a building(s) or other space using intelligible voice communications and including visible signals, text, graphics, tactile, or other communication methods. (SIG-ECS)

An in-building mass notification system is somewhat similar in concept to a fire alarm system that includes an in-building fire emergency voice/alarm communications system. In an in-building fire emergency voice/alarm communications system, the only purpose of the system is for fire emergencies, while the in-building mass notification system has a much broader set of potential applications and is likely to be subject to a much more complex set of potential design conditions and operation scenarios, which could also include fire emergencies.

> **3.3.79.1.4 Wide-Area Mass Notification System.** Wide-area mass notification systems are generally installed to provide real-time information to outdoor areas and could have the capability to communicate with other notification systems provided for a campus, military base, municipality, or similar single or multiple contiguous areas. (SIG-ECS)

Wide-area mass notification systems are one-way emergency communications systems that are intended to communicate to outdoor areas such as those in college or military campuses. The primary means of communications is high power speaker arrays. Requirements for these systems are contained in 24.4.3. See A.24.4.3 for additional explanation.

> **3.3.79.2 Two-Way Emergency Communications System.** Two-way emergency communications systems are divided into two categories, those systems that are anticipated to be used by building occupants and those systems that are to be used by fire fighters, police, and other emergency services personnel. Two-way emergency communications systems are used to both exchange information and to communicate information such as, but not limited to, instructions, acknowledgement of receipt of messages, condition of local environment, and condition of persons, and to give assurance that help is on the way. (SIG-ECS)

3.3.80 Emergency Communications System — Central Control Station. A mass notification system facility(s) with communications and control equipment serving one or more buildings where responsible authorities receive information from premises sources or systems or from (higher level) regional or national sources or systems and then disseminate appropriate information to a building, multiple buildings, outside campus areas, or a combination of these in accordance with the emergency response plan established for the premises. (SIG-ECS)

Central control stations for emergency communications systems are centralized facilities to enable the receipt and control of emergency information. These facilities are served by an emergency communications control unit (ECCU) to facilitate the automatic or manual distribution of signals and messages to selectable locations based on information from responsible authorities. Requirements for these systems are contained in 24.6.1. Also refer to the definition of *emergency communications control unit* in 3.3.53.2 and associated commentary.

3.3.81 Emergency Communications Systems — Combination. Various emergency communication systems such as fire alarm, mass notification, fire fighter communications, area of refuge communications, elevator communications, or others and which may be served through a single control system or through an interconnection of several control systems. (SIG-ECS)

3.3.82 Emergency Control Function Device. The fire alarm or signaling system component that directly interfaces with the system that controls the emergency function. (SIG-PRO)

An emergency control function device, formerly called a fire safety function control device, is used to control safety functions that enhance life safety and property protection during a fire or other emergency. The control unit may operate emergency (fire safety) control functions manually or automatically. Those functions might include unlocking doors, starting fans, recalling elevators, or actuating a fire suppression system.

3.3.83 Emergency Control Functions. Building, fire, and emergency control functions that are intended to increase the level of life safety for occupants or to control the spread of the harmful effects of fire. (SIG-PRO)

Emergency control functions are referred to as "fire safety functions" in Chapter 23 in the context of a protected premises fire alarm system. Due to the broader scope of *NFPA 72* in the 2010 edition, the more general term *emergency control function* is now used in other locations of the Code to reflect the broader range of potential life-safety control applications. The provisions for these functions have been relocated from the chapter on protected premises fire alarm systems to a separate chapter.

Emergency control functions include shutdown of air-handling systems, elevator recall, closure of HVAC dampers, actuation of fire suppression systems, and release of doors to enhance life safety and property protection during a fire. Specific functions are described in more detail in Section 23.17 and Chapter 21.

3.3.84 Emergency Response Plan. A documented set of actions to address response to natural, technological, and man-made disasters and other emergencies prepared by the stakeholders from information obtained during the risk analysis. (SIG-ECS)

3.3.85* Evacuation. The withdrawal of occupants from a building. (SIG-PRO)

A.3.3.85 Evacuation. Evacuation does not include the relocation of occupants within a building.

3.3.86 Evacuation Signal. See 3.3.240, Signal.

3.3.87 Evacuation Signaling Zone. See 3.3.300, Zone.

3.3.88 Executive Software. See 3.3.255, Software.

3.3.89 Exit Marking Audible Notification Appliance. See 3.3.160, Notification Appliance.

3.3.90 Field of View. The solid cone that extends out from the detector within which the effective sensitivity of the detector is at least 50 percent of its on-axis, listed, or approved sensitivity. (SIG-IDS)

Field of view applies to radiant energy fire detectors. Designers who use these detectors need to understand that the field of view defines the line-of-sight area of coverage in which the detector can view a spark, ember, or flaming fire. Unintended sources within a field of view, such as welding arcs or sunlight, can cause nuisance alarms.

3.3.91 Fire Alarm Control Interface (FACI). See 3.3.127, Interface.

3.3.92* Fire Alarm Control Unit. (FACU) A component of the fire alarm system, provided with primary and secondary power sources, which receives signals from initiating devices or other fire alarm control units, and processes these signals to determine part or all of the required fire alarm system output function(s). (SIG-PRO)

A.3.3.92 Fire Alarm Control Unit. (FACU) In addition to the functions identified in the definition, a fire alarm control unit might have an integral operator interface, supply power to

EXHIBIT 3.24 *Fire Alarm Control Unit. (Source: Gamewell-FCI, Northford, CT)*

detection devices, notification appliances, transponder(s), or off-premises transmitter(s) or any combination of these. The control unit might also provide transfer of condition to relay or devices connected to the control unit. There can be multiple fire alarm control units in a fire alarm system.

A fire alarm control unit is a control unit (see 3.3.53) that is used within a fire alarm system. A fire alarm control unit can be more than just the main (master) fire alarm control unit for a building. Depending on the design of the system, an application may use multiple fire alarm control units with different functions. Such system components are also called *subpanels* or *satellite control units*. These control units may receive signals from initiating devices or other fire alarm control units and process the signals to determine all or part of the required output for the fire alarm system. Exhibit 3.24 illustrates a typical fire alarm control unit, and Exhibit 3.25 shows a fire alarm control unit with an integral communications system.

> **3.3.92.1** *Master Fire Alarm Control Unit.* A fire alarm control unit that serves the protected premises or portion of the protected premises as a local fire alarm control unit and accepts inputs from other fire alarm control units. (SIG-PRO)

Where more than one fire alarm control unit is installed in a facility, one of the control units may be designated as the master control unit to monitor alarm, supervisory, and trouble signals from other control units installed as part of the overall fire alarm system.

> **3.3.92.2** *Protected Premises (Local) Control Unit.* A fire alarm control unit that serves the protected premises or a portion of the protected premises. (SIG-PRO)

> **3.3.92.2.1*** *Dedicated Function Fire Alarm Control Unit.* A protected premises fire alarm control unit which is intended to provide operation of a specifically identified fire safety function. (SIG-PRO)

The term *dedicated function fire alarm control unit* was introduced in the 2007 edition of the Code. Many functions within a building that are required by other codes, standards, or authorities having jurisdiction need to be controlled or monitored by a fire alarm system. For example, controlling and monitoring the operation of a fire suppression system usually requires the use of a fire alarm control unit to accomplish those functions. When this is the case, and a building fire alarm system (see 3.3.95.4.1) is not otherwise required or installed, the installation of a fire alarm control unit will be needed. However, the Code does not require and does not intend to require the installation of fire alarm system components, devices, and functions beyond those required to accomplish the intended tasks. Fire alarm control units installed for a specific purpose, such as elevator recall and control, supervision of sprinkler systems, control of special extinguishing systems, or other similar functions, are designated as dedicated function fire alarm control units. The installation of a dedicated function fire alarm control unit does not trigger a requirement to provide any features beyond those necessary to accomplish the tasks assigned to the control unit.

EXHIBIT 3.25 *Fire Alarm Control Unit with Integral Communications System. (Source: Gamewell-FCI, Northford, CT)*

> **A.3.3.92.2.1** *Dedicated Function Fire Alarm Control Unit.* Examples of a dedicated function fire alarm control unit include an automatic sprinkler alarm and supervisory control unit or an elevator recall control and supervisory control unit.

> **3.3.92.2.2** *Releasing Service Fire Alarm Control Unit.* A protected premises fire alarm control unit specifically listed for releasing service that is part of a fire suppression system and which provides control outputs to release a fire suppression agent based on either automatic or manual input. (SIG-PRO)

FAQ ▶
What is a releasing service fire alarm control unit?

A releasing service fire alarm control unit is specifically listed to be used for control of a fire suppression system or other fire protection system and is an example of a type of dedicated function fire alarm control unit. Requirements specific to control units and releasing systems can be found in 23.8.2, 23.8.5.10, Section 23.13, and Chapter 21.

3.3.93 Fire Alarm/Evacuation Signal Tone Generator. A device that produces a fire alarm/evacuation tone upon command. (SIG-PRO)

3.3.94 Fire Alarm Signal. See 3.3.240, Signal.

3.3.95 Fire Alarm System. A system or portion of a combination system that consists of components and circuits arranged to monitor and annunciate the status of fire alarm or supervisory signal-initiating devices and to initiate the appropriate response to those signals. (SIG-FUN)

The definition of *fire alarm system* includes fire alarm systems whose sole purpose is to provide a specific function or functions, such as sprinkler supervisory service. These systems fall under the definition of *dedicated function fire alarm system*.

> **3.3.95.1* Combination System.** A fire alarm system in which components are used, in whole or in part, in common with a non-fire signaling system. (SIG-PRO)

> **A.3.3.95.1 Combination System.** Examples of non-fire systems are security, card access control, closed circuit television, sound reinforcement, background music, paging, sound masking, building automation, time, and attendance.

Subsection 23.8.4 addresses combination systems. Exhibit 3.26 illustrates a typical combination system.

EXHIBIT 3.26 *Combination Burglary and Fire Alarm System Control Unit and Associated System Components. (Source: Honeywell Security and Custom Electronics, Syosset, NY)*

> **3.3.95.2 Household Fire Alarm System.** A system of devices that uses a fire alarm control unit to produce an alarm signal in the household for the purpose of notifying the occupants of the presence of a fire so that they will evacuate the premises. (SIG-HOU)

> **3.3.95.3 Municipal Fire Alarm System.** A public emergency alarm reporting system. (SIG-PRS)

> **3.3.95.4* Protected Premises (Local) Fire Alarm System.** A fire alarm system located at the protected premises. (SIG-PRO)

> **A.3.3.95.4 Protected Premises (Local) Fire Alarm System.** A protected premises fire alarm system is any fire alarm system located at the protected premises. It can include any of the functions identified in Section 23.3. Where signals are transmitted to a communication center or supervising station, the protected premises fire alarm system also falls under the definition of one of the following systems: central station service alarm system, remote supervising station alarm system, proprietary supervising station alarm

system, or auxiliary alarm system. The requirements that pertain to these systems apply in addition to the requirements for the protected premises fire alarm systems.

3.3.95.4.1 Building Fire Alarm System. A protected premises fire alarm system that includes any of the features identified in 23.3.3.1 and that serves the general fire alarm needs of a building or buildings and that provides fire department or occupant notification or both. (SIG-PRO)

3.3.95.4.2 Dedicated Function Fire Alarm System. A protected premises fire alarm system installed specifically to perform fire safety function(s) where a building fire alarm system is not required. (SIG-PRO)

3.3.95.4.3 Releasing Fire Alarm System. A protected premises fire alarm system that is part of a fire suppression system and/or which provides control inputs to a fire suppression system related to the fire suppression system's sequence of operations and outputs for other signaling and notification. (SIG-PRO)

The definition of *protected premises (local) fire alarm system* was modified for the 2007 edition of the Code to simplify the main term and create three new sub-definitions to better relate to the requirements intended for these systems. Similar changes were made to the definition of *protected premises control unit.* Under the revised definition, a protected premises (local) fire alarm system includes any fire alarm system located at the protected premises, whether or not it sounds a local alarm. A more precise version of the previous definition of *protected premises (local) fire alarm system* is now used to define a *building fire alarm system* that serves the general fire alarm needs of a building. Two additional terms, *dedicated function fire alarm system* and *releasing fire alarm system,* have also been added. A premises can have any or all of these systems. Requirements that relate to these systems can be found in 23.3.3, 23.8.5, Section 23.13, and Section 21.3.

3.3.96 Fire Command Center. The principal attended or unattended location where the status of the detection, alarm communications, and control systems is displayed and from which the system(s) can be manually controlled. (SIG-PRO)

Where an in-building fire emergency voice/alarm communications system is provided, the applicable building code generally requires a fire command center. The fire command center houses the fire alarm system controls and may include controls for other building systems such as security, HVAC, and elevator and lighting systems. During an emergency, the fire command center serves as the central point for the command of emergency operations and communications. The fire command center is generally located in a separate room or other area approved by the authority having jurisdiction. The location must allow for the incident commander to assess the changing conditions during an emergency and communicate with the building occupants and emergency responders. The applicable building code usually provides details on construction of the fire command center.

In the application of an in-building fire emergency voice/alarm communications system, the requirements in 24.4.1.5 apply even though the term *fire command center* is not used. [In the application of two-way in-building wired emergency services communications systems (two-way telephone communications service) the requirements in 24.5.1 use the terms *control equipment, control location,* and *control center* in place of *fire command center.*] These terms should not be confused with the term *central control station for emergency communications systems,* defined in 3.3.80. Also refer to the term *emergency communications control unit (ECCU)* and the associated commentary.

3.3.97 Fire Extinguisher Electronic Monitoring Device. A device connected to a control unit that monitors the fire extinguisher in accordance with the requirements of NFPA 10, *Standard for Portable Fire Extinguishers.* (SIG-IDS)

3.3.98 Fire Safety Functions. See 3.3.83, Emergency Control Functions.

3.3.99 Fire Warden. A building staff member or a tenant trained to perform assigned duties in the event of a fire emergency. (SIG-PRO)

Depending on the design of the fire alarm system and the site-specific fire safety plan for a facility, fire wardens may be used to initiate or facilitate evacuation or relocation during a fire. Fire wardens are typically found in large area buildings with high occupant loads where direction may be required to prompt building occupants to follow the established emergency procedures. Fire wardens may also be used to sweep through their assigned areas to ensure that all occupants heard and responded properly to an alarm.

3.3.100 Fire Warning Equipment. Any detector, alarm, device, or material related to single- and multiple-station alarms or household fire alarm systems. (SIG-HOU)

The Technical Committee on Single- and Multiple-Station Alarms and Household Fire Alarm Systems added the definition of *fire warning equipment* in the 2007 edition to correlate with the use of this and other equipment terms used in Chapter 29. Fire warning equipment includes all the equipment addressed in Chapter 29, whereas single- and multiple-station alarms and household fire alarm systems are three subcategories of fire warning equipment. The requirements in Chapter 29 are specific to these different terms. Refer to the related definitions in 3.3.95, 3.3.245, and 3.3.149.

3.3.101 Fire–Gas Detector. See 3.3.59, Detector.

3.3.102 Fixed-Temperature Detector. See 3.3.59, Detector.

3.3.103 Flame. A body or stream of gaseous material involved in the combustion process and emitting radiant energy at specific wavelength bands determined by the combustion chemistry of the fuel. In most cases, some portion of the emitted radiant energy is visible to the human eye. (SIG-IDS)

3.3.104 Flame Detector. See 3.3.59, Detector.

3.3.105 Flame Detector Sensitivity. The distance along the optical axis of the detector at which the detector can detect a fire of specified size and fuel within a given time frame. (SIG-IDS)

3.3.106 Frequency. Minimum and maximum time between events (SIG-TMS).

> **3.3.106.1 Weekly Frequency.** Fifty-two times per year, once per calendar week.

> **3.3.106.2 Monthly Frequency.** Twelve times per year, once per calendar month.

> **3.3.106.3 Quarterly Frequency.** Four times per year with a minimum of 2 months, maximum of 4 months.

> **3.3.106.4 Semiannual Frequency.** Twice per year with a minimum of 4 months, maximum of 8 months.

> **3.3.106.5 Annual Frequency.** Once per year with a minimum of 9 months, maximum 15 months.

3.3.107 Gateway. A device that is used in the transmission of serial data (digital or analog) from the fire alarm control unit to other building system control units, equipment, or networks and/or from other building system control units to the fire alarm control unit. (SIG-PRO)

3.3.108 Girder. See 3.3.33, Ceiling Surfaces.

3.3.109 Guard's Tour Reporting Station. A device that is manually or automatically initiated to indicate the route being followed and the timing of a guard's tour. (SIG-IDS)

3.3.110 Guard's Tour Supervisory Signal. See 3.3.240, Signal.

3.3.111 Guest Room. An accommodation combining living, sleeping, sanitary, and storage facilities within a compartment. [*101*, 2009] (SIG-HOU)

3.3.112 Guest Suite. An accommodation with two or more contiguous rooms comprising a compartment, with or without doors between such rooms, that provides living, sleeping, sanitary, and storage facilities. [*101*, 2009] (SIG-HOU)

3.3.113* Hearing Loss. A full or partial decrease in the ability to detect or comprehend sounds. (SIG-NAS)

A.3.3.113 Hearing Loss. The severity of hearing loss is measured by the degree of loudness, as measured in decibels, a sound must attain before being detected by an individual. Hearing loss can be ranked as mild, moderate, severe, or profound. It is quite common for someone to have more than one degree of hearing loss (e.g., mild sloping to severe). The following list shows the rankings and their corresponding decibel ranges:

(1) Mild:
  (a) For adults: between 25 and 40 dB
  (b) For children: between 15 and 40 dB
(2) Moderate: between 41 and 55 dB
(3) Moderately severe: between 56 and 70 dB
(4) Severe: between 71 and 90 dB
(5) Profound: 90 dB or greater

NIOSH defines material hearing impairment as an average of the hearing threshold levels for both ears that exceeds 25 dB at 1000, 2000, 3000, and 4000 Hz.

The American Medical Association indicates that a person has suffered material impairment when testing reveals a 25 dB average hearing loss from audiometric zero at 500, 1000, 2000, and 3000 Hz. OSHA has recognized that this is the lowest level of hearing loss that constitutes any material hearing impairment.

The term *hearing loss* is used in 29.3.8, and the provisions of 29.3.8.1 and 29.3.8.2 are specified in terms of "mild to severe" hearing loss and "profound" hearing loss. Those terms are explained in A.3.3.113.

> **3.3.113.1 Profound Hearing Loss.** A hearing threshold of greater than 90 dB.

3.3.114 Heat Alarm. A single or multiple station alarm responsive to heat. (SIG-IDS)

3.3.115 Heat Detector. See 3.3.59, Detector.

3.3.116 High Power Speaker Array (HPSA). High power speaker arrays provide capability for voice and tone communications to large outdoor areas. (SIG-ECS)

3.3.117 Hotel. A building or groups of buildings under the same management in which there are sleeping accommodations for more than 16 persons and primarily used by transients for lodging with or without meals. [*101*, 2009] (SIG-HOU)

3.3.118 Household Fire Alarm System. See 3.3.95, Fire Alarm System.

3.3.119 Hunt Group. A group of associated telephone lines within which an incoming call is automatically routed to an idle (not busy) telephone line for completion. (SIG-SSS)

3.3.120* Identified (as Applied to Equipment). Recognizable as suitable for the specific purpose, function, use, environment, application, and so forth, where described in a particular *Code* requirement. (SIG-PRS) [*70*, 2008]

A.3.3.120 Identified (as Applied to Equipment). Some examples of ways to determine suitability of equipment for a specific purpose, environment, or application include investigations by a qualified testing laboratory (listing and labeling), an inspection agency, or other organizations concerned with product evaluation. [*70*:100, FPN]

3.3.121 In-Building Mass Notification System. See 3.3.79, Emergency Communications System.

3.3.122 Initiating Device. A system component that originates transmission of a change-of-state condition, such as in a smoke detector, manual fire alarm box, or supervisory switch. (SIG-IDS)

>   ***3.3.122.1 Analog Initiating Device (Sensor).*** An initiating device that transmits a signal indicating varying degrees of condition as contrasted with a conventional initiating device, which can only indicate an on–off condition. (SIG-IDS)

Analog initiating devices measure and transmit a range of values of smoke density, temperature variation, water level, water pressure changes, and other variables to a fire alarm system control unit. Typically, the control unit software determines the set points for initiation of an alarm, supervisory, or trouble signal. By storing reported values over time, some smoke detector technology uses the analog feature to provide a warning signal to the owner when the detector is dirty or when the detector drifts outside its listed sensitivity range. Some analog technology can be used for smoke detector sensitivity testing per 14.4.5.3.

◄ FAQ
What do analog initiating devices measure and transmit?

>   ***3.3.122.2 Automatic Extinguishing System Supervisory Device.*** A device that responds to abnormal conditions that could affect the proper operation of an automatic sprinkler system or other fire extinguishing system(s) or suppression system(s), including, but not limited to, control valves, pressure levels, liquid agent levels and temperatures, pump power and running, engine temperature and overspeed, and room temperature. (SIG-IDS)

When an abnormal condition is detected, a supervisory signal is activated to warn the owner or attendant that the extinguishing system requires attention. Supervisory signals are distinct from alarm signals or trouble signals.

>   ***3.3.122.3 Nonrestorable Initiating Device.*** A device in which the sensing element is designed to be destroyed in the process of operation. (SIG-IDS)

One example of a nonrestorable initiating device is the fixed-temperature heat detector (see Exhibit 3.12), which uses a fusible element that melts when subjected to heat. When the element melts, the electrical contacts are shorted together and the alarm signal is activated.

>   ***3.3.122.4 Restorable Initiating Device.*** A device in which the sensing element is not ordinarily destroyed in the process of operation, whose restoration can be manual or automatic. (SIG-IDS)

>   ***3.3.122.5 Supervisory Signal-Initiating Device.*** An initiating device such as a valve supervisory switch, water level indicator, or low air pressure switch on a dry-pipe sprinkler system in which the change of state signals an off-normal condition and its restoration to normal of a fire protection or life safety system; or a need for action in connection with guard tours, fire suppression systems or equipment, or maintenance features of related systems. (SIG-IDS)

3.3.123 Initiating Device Circuit. A circuit to which automatic or manual initiating devices are connected where the signal received does not identify the individual device operated. (SIG-PRO)

Conventional (nonanalog) initiating devices are typically detectors that use a switch contact or a solid-state switch to short the positive and negative sides of the circuit together. By doing so, the initiating device causes a step-function increase in current flowing through the circuit. The fire alarm control unit interprets the increase in current as an "alarm" signal from one of the initiating devices. Since any one of the initiating devices can cause the incremental current flow, and no other initiating devices can subsequently be recognized because the power supply has been shorted by the first responding device, only one signal can be obtained. Sometimes initiating device circuits are called *zones,* and the device puts the whole zone into the alarm state.

3.3.124 Inspection Personnel. See 3.3.177, Personnel.

3.3.125 Intelligibility. The quality or condition of being intelligible. (SIG-NAS)

The term *intelligibility* relates to voice communications used in emergency communications systems. If voice messages to occupants in buildings and other locations cannot be understood, the message system will have little, if any, benefit. Requirements for voice messages to be intelligible are not new to the Code; however, with the expansion of requirements for emergency communications systems, intelligible voice communications have become even more important. Requirements for voice intelligibility, contained in 18.4.10, have been updated in this edition of the Code and are referenced from Chapter 24. New Annex D, Speech Intelligibility, provides guidance on system design with emphasis on testing.

3.3.126* Intelligible. Capable of being understood; comprehensible; clear. (SIG-NAS)

A.3.3.126 Intelligible. The term *intelligible* is intended to address only the communications channel and the acoustic environment as shown in Figure A.3.3.126. Intelligibility assumes that the talker or recorded voice message is in a language and using words known to the listener. It also assumes that the listener has normal hearing.

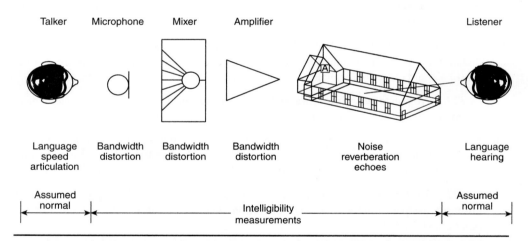

FIGURE A.3.3.126 *Voice Signal Path. (Source: K. Jacob, Bose® Professional Systems)*

3.3.127 Interface.

> **3.3.127.1 Circuit Interface.** A circuit component that interfaces initiating devices or control circuits, or both; notification appliances or circuits, or both; system control outputs; and other signaling line circuits to a signaling line circuit. (SIG-PRO)

> **3.3.127.1.1 Signaling Line Circuit Interface.** A system component that connects a signaling line circuit to any combination of initiating devices, initiating device circuits, notification appliances, notification appliance circuits, system control outputs, and other signaling line circuits. (SIG-PRO)

A signaling line circuit interface (SLCI) (see Exhibit 3.27) is a means of interconnecting signaling line circuits (addressable circuits) with nonaddressable or conventional initiating de-

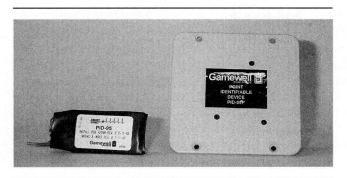

EXHIBIT 3.27 *Typical Signaling Line Circuit Interface (SLCI) and Enclosure Cover. (Source: Gamewell-FCI, Northford, CT)*

vice circuits or control devices. An SLCI is also referred to as a *monitor module*, a *zone addressable module*, a *transponder*, and other terms used by various manufacturers of the products. An SLCI provides a means of translating the signal from a conventional circuit to one that can be understood by an addressable system. In essence, the SLCI provides an "address" for a nonaddressable circuit, device, or appliance.

3.3.127.2* Fire Alarm Control Interface. The fire alarm control interface coordinates signals to and from the fire alarm system and other systems. (SIG-ECS)

A.3.3.127.2 Fire Alarm Control Interface. Some mass notification systems' autonomous control units (ACUs) might not be listed to UL 864 for fire alarm service. Any component that is connected to the fire alarm system must be connected through a listed interface that will protect the functions of other systems should one system experience a failure. This can be through isolation modules, control relays, or other approved means that are listed for the intended use. As an example, failure of a stand-alone ACU should not affect any function of the FACU.

3.3.128 Ionization Smoke Detection. See 3.3.252, Smoke Detection.

3.3.129 Leg Facility. The portion of a communications channel that connects not more than one protected premises to a primary or secondary trunk facility. The leg facility includes the portion of the signal transmission circuit from its point of connection with a trunk facility to the point where it is terminated within the protected premises at one or more transponders. (SIG-SSS)

3.3.130 Level Ceilings. See 3.3.31, Ceiling.

3.3.131 Life Safety Network. A type of combination system that transmits fire safety control data through gateways to other building system control units. (SIG-PRO)

3.3.132 Line-Type Detector. See 3.3.59, Detector.

3.3.133 Living Area. Any normally occupiable space in a residential occupancy, other than sleeping rooms or rooms that are intended for combination sleeping/living, bathrooms, toilet compartments, kitchens, closets, halls, storage or utility spaces, and similar areas. [*101*, 2009] (SIG-HOU)

3.3.134 Loading Capacity. The maximum number of discrete elements of fire alarm systems permitted to be used in a particular configuration. (SIG-SSS)

Loading capacity applies to various transmission technologies used by supervising station alarm systems. The loading capacity of a system depends on the performance characteristic of the particular transmission technology employed. Chapter 26 provides the loading capacities for various types of supervising station transmission technologies.

3.3.135 Local Energy Type Auxiliary Alarm System. See 3.3.199, Public Emergency Alarm Reporting System.

3.3.136* Local Operating Console (LOC). A station used by authorized personnel and emergency responders to activate and operate an in-building mass notification system. (SIG-ECS)

A.3.3.136 Local Operating Console (LOC). An LOC allows users within a building to activate prerecorded messages, deliver live voice messages, observe current status of the main autonomous control unit (ACU), or have similar such ACU operator functions at various locations within the building. An LOC serves a similar function as a remote fire alarm annunciator. However, there can be multiple LOC locations within a building, such as on each floor, at each main entry point, at the switchboard or receptionist's console, or as determined by a risk analysis.

3.3.137 Lodging or Rooming House. A building or portion thereof that does not qualify as a one- or two-family dwelling, that provides sleeping accommodations for a total of 16 or fewer people on a transient or permanent basis, without personal care services, with or without meals, but without separate cooking facilities for individual occupants. [*101*, 2009] (SIG-HOU)

3.3.138 Loss of Power. The reduction of available voltage at the load below the point at which equipment can function as designed. (SIG-FUN)

3.3.139 Low-Power Radio Transmitter. Any device that communicates with associated control/receiving equipment by low-power radio signals. (SIG-PRO)

3.3.140 Maintenance. Work, including, but not limited to, repair, replacement, and service, performed to ensure that equipment operates properly. (SIG-TMS)

3.3.141* Managed Facilities-Based Voice Network (MFVN). A physical facilities-based network capable of transmitting real time signals with formats unchanged that is managed, operated, and maintained by the service provider to ensure service quality and reliability from the subscriber location to public switched telephone network (PSTN) interconnection points or other MFVN peer networks. (SIG-SSS)

Subsection 3.3.141 was revised by a tentative interim amendment (TIA).

A.3.3.141 Managed Facilities-Based Voice Network (MFVN). Managed facilities-based voice network service is functionally equivalent to traditional PSTN-based services provided by authorized common carriers (public utility telephone companies) with respect to dialing, dial plan, call completion, carriage of signals and protocols, and loop voltage treatment and provides all of the following features:

(1) A loop start telephone circuit service interface.
(2) Pathway reliability that is assured by proactive management, operation, and maintenance by the MFVN provider.
(3) 8 hours of standby power supply capacity for MFVN communications equipment either located at the protected premises or field deployed. Industry standards followed by the authorized common carriers (public utility telephone companies), and the other communications service providers that operate MFVNs, specifically engineer the selection of the size of the batteries, or other permanently located standby power source, in order to provide 8 hours of standby power with a reasonable degree of accuracy. Of course, over time, abnormal ambient conditions and battery aging can always have a potentially adverse effect on battery capacity. The MFVN field-deployed equipment typically monitors the condition of the standby battery and signals potential battery failure to permit the communications service provider to take appropriate action.
(4) 24 hours of standby power supply capacity for MFVN communications equipment located at the communication service provider's central office.
(5) Installation of network equipment at the protected premises with safeguards to prevent unauthorized access to the equipment and its connections.

When providing telephone service to a new customer, MFVN providers give notice to the telephone service subscriber of the need to have any connected alarm system tested by authorized fire alarm service personnel in accordance with Chapter 14 to make certain that all signal transmission features have remained operational. These features include the proper functioning of line seizure and the successful transmission of signals to the supervising station. In this way, the MFVN providers assist their new customers in complying with a testing procedure similar to that outlined in 26.2.3 for changes to providers of supervising station service.

The evolution of the deployment of telephone service has moved beyond the sole use of metallic conductors connecting a telephone subscriber's premises with the nearest telephone service provider's control and routing point (wire center). In the last 25 years, telephone service providers have introduced a variety of technologies to transport multiple, simultaneous telephone calls over shared communication's pathways. In order to facilitate the further development of the modernization of the telephone network, the authorized common carriers (public utility telephone companies) have transitioned their equipment into a managed facilities-based voice network (MFVN) capable of providing a variety of communications services in addition to the provision of traditional telephone service.

Similarly, the evolution of digital communications technology has permitted entities other than the authorized common carriers (public utility telephone companies) to deploy robust communications networks and offer a variety of communications services, including telephone service.

These alternate service providers fall into two broad categories. The first category includes those entities that have emulated the MFVN provided by the authorized common carriers. The second category includes those entities that offer telephone service using means that do not offer the rigorous quality assurance, operational stability, and consistent features provided by an MFVN.

The Code intends to only recognize the use of the telephone network transmission of alarm, supervisory, trouble, and other emergency signals by means of MFVNs.

For example, the Code intends to permit an MFVN to provide facilities-based telephone (voice) service that interfaces with the premises fire alarm or emergency signal control unit through a digital alarm communicator transmitter (DACT) using a loop start telephone circuit and signaling protocols fully compatible with and equivalent to those used in public switched telephone networks. The loop start telephone circuit and associated signaling can be provided through traditional copper wire telephone service (POTS — "plain old telephone service") or by means of equipment that emulates the loop start telephone circuit and associated signaling and then transmits the signals over a pathway using packet switched (IP) networks or other communications methods that are part of an MFVN.

Providers of MFVNs have disaster recovery plans to address both individual customer outages and widespread events such as tornados, ice storms, or other natural disasters, which include specific network power restoration procedures equivalent to those of traditional landline telephone services.

Subsection A.3.3.141 was added by a tentative interim amendment (TIA).

The definition of *managed facilities-based voice network (MFVN)* has been introduced in the 2010 edition to correlate with the revised definition of *public switched telephone network* (PSTN) in 3.3.273.2, which is used within the requirements for digital alarm communicator transmitters (DACTs) in 26.6.3.2.1. A DACT is part of a digital alarm communicator system, one of the types of transmission methods that the Code recognizes for transmission of signals from a protected premises to a supervising station. The provisions of 26.6.3.2.1.1 require a DACT to be connected to a PSTN upstream of any private telephone system at the protected premises. The provisions of 26.6.3.2.1.1 also require the connection to be made to a loop start telephone circuit, which has also been defined for this edition of the Code in 3.3.273.1.

A PSTN has traditionally been viewed as being comprised of the copper telephone lines and connected system of the local telephone company (sometimes referred to as the "plain old telephone system (POTS)." In recent years, telephone (voice) service has been provided not only by the traditional telephone company but also by other service providers, including those offering other services such as television and/or internet access. As a consequence questions have arisen as to whether the Code permits the connection of a DACT to equipment and systems of these more recent providers. The revised and new definitions and related explanatory annex material clarify and answer that question. In accordance with the revised definition of PSTN, if the telephone service is provided through the use a MFVN, the answer is yes. The annex material in A.3.3.141 provides insight into what constitutes a MFVN. Telephone service that is not provided using a MFVN would not be permitted for connection to a DACT.

3.3.142 Manual Fire Alarm Box. See 3.3.8, Alarm Box.

3.3.143* Mass Notification Priority Mode. The mode of operation whereby all fire alarm occupant notification is superseded by emergency mass notification action. (SIG-ECS)

A.3.3.143 Mass Notification Priority Mode. Non-emergency mass notification activations are not intended to initiate this mode of operation.

3.3.144* Mass Notification System. See 3.3.79.1.3, In-Building Mass Notification System. (SIG-PRO)

A.3.3.144 Mass Notification System. A mass notification system can use intelligible voice communications, visible signals, text, graphics, tactile, or other communications methods. The system can be used to initiate evacuation or relocation or to provide information to occupants. The system can be intended for fire emergencies, weather emergencies, terrorist events, biological, chemical or nuclear emergencies, or any combination of these. The system can be automatic, manual, or both. Access to and control of the system can be from a single, on-site location or can include multiple command locations, including some remote from the area served. Systems can be wired, wireless, or some combination of the two.

3.3.145 Master Box. See 3.3.8, Alarm Box.

3.3.146 Master Fire Alarm Control Unit. See 3.3.92, Fire Alarm Control Unit.

3.3.147 Multi-Criteria Detector. See 3.3.59, Detector.

3.3.148 Multiple Dwelling Unit. See 3.3.74, Dwelling Unit.

3.3.149 Multiple Station Alarm. A single station alarm capable of being interconnected to one or more additional alarms so that the actuation of one causes the appropriate alarm signal to operate in all interconnected alarms. (SIG-HOU)

The definition of *multiple-station alarm* helps differentiate between automatic fire detectors connected to and powered by a fire alarm system control unit and single- and multiple-station smoke alarms that may be powered by a battery, an alternating current (ac) power source, or both (ac with battery back-up). This definition corresponds with the terminology used internationally.

3.3.150 Multiple Station Alarm Device. Two or more single station alarm devices that can be interconnected so that actuation of one causes all integral or separate audible alarms to operate; or one single station alarm device having connections to other detectors or to a manual fire alarm box. (SIG-HOU)

3.3.151 Multiplexing. A signaling method characterized by simultaneous or sequential transmission, or both, and reception of multiple signals on a signaling line circuit, a transmission channel, or a communications channel, including means for positively identifying each signal. (SIG-SSS)

Within a protected premises, a fire alarm system may use multiplexing between the fire alarm system control unit and the fire alarm initiating devices and notification appliances or between the fire alarm system control unit and multiplex interfaces to which the initiating devices or notification appliances connect. A fire alarm system may also use multiplexing between the protected premises and a supervising station as a means of signal transmission.

Multiplexing for fire alarm system signal transmission includes two technologies: active and passive. An active multiplex system establishes two-way communication on a signaling line circuit.

In the case of a protected premises application, the multiplex fire alarm system control unit transmits an interrogation signal to the devices, appliances, or their multiplex interfaces connected to the protected premises signaling line circuit. The devices, appliances, or multiplex interfaces then transmit a response signal to the fire alarm system control unit. This response signal gives the status of the interrogated unit.

In the case of a supervising station application, the supervising station multiplex receiver transmits an interrogation signal to the protected premises fire alarm system control unit or transmitter connected to the supervising station signaling line circuit. The control unit or transmitter then transmits a response signal to the supervising station receiver that gives the status of the interrogated unit.

In addition to conveying status information, this interrogation and response signaling provides a means to monitor the integrity of the signaling line circuit.

Devices connected to a passive multiplex system transmit multiple signals over the same signaling line circuit. However, the circuit must have some other means to monitor its integrity, which may include a voltage, current, or subcarrier continuously present on the circuit, or other similar means.

3.3.152 Multi-Sensor Detector. See 3.3.59, Detector.

3.3.153 Municipal Fire Alarm Box (Street Box). A publicly accessible alarm box. See 3.3.8, Alarm Box.

3.3.154 Municipal Fire Alarm System. See 3.3.95, Fire Alarm System.

3.3.155 Net-Centric Alerting System (NCAS). A net-centric alerting system incorporates web-based management and alert activation application through which all operators and administrators could gain access to the system's capabilities based on the users' permissions and the defined access policy. (SIG-ECS)

3.3.156 Network Architecture. The physical and logical design of a network, and the inherent ability of the design to carry data from one point to another. [SIG-ECS]

3.3.157 Noncontiguous Property. See 3.3.191, Property.

3.3.158* Nonrequired. A fire alarm system component or group of components that is installed at the option of the owner, and is not installed due to a building or fire code requirement. (SIG-FUN)

A.3.3.158 Nonrequired. There are situations where the applicable building or fire code does not require the installation of a fire alarm system or specific fire alarm system components, but the building owner wants to install a fire alarm system or component to meet site-specific needs or objectives. A building owner always has the option of installing protection that is above the minimum requirements of the Code. It is the intent of the Code that any fire alarm system, or fire alarm system components installed voluntarily by a building owner, meet the requirements of the applicable portions of the Code. However, it is not the intent of the Code that the installation of a nonrequired fire alarm system, or fire alarm system components, trigger requirements for the installation of additional fire alarm system components or features. For example, the installation of a fire alarm control unit and fire detectors to service a specific area, such as a computer room or flammable liquid storage room, does not

◄ **FAQ**
How is multiplexing used within a protected premises?

EXHIBIT 3.28 *Typical Audible Notification Appliance. (Source: Gentex Corp., Zeeland, MI)*

EXHIBIT 3.29 *Typical Visible Notification Appliance. (Source: Cooper Notification, Long Branch, NJ)*

EXHIBIT 3.30 *Amber and Blue Strobes. (Source: Gentex Corp., Zeeland, MI)*

trigger a requirement for audible or visible notification appliances, manual fire alarm boxes, or other fire alarm system features in other parts of the building.

The term *nonrequired* should not be confused with the term *supplementary*, defined in 3.3.272. A nonrequired system is one that is not required by a building code or by any statutory authority but is installed voluntarily at the request of the owner. Nonrequired systems must fully comply with all the applicable requirements of the Code and be designed and installed to satisfy the goals intended for the system. The goals and the design intent also must be documented.

3.3.159 Nonrestorable Initiating Device. See 3.3.122, Initiating Device.

3.3.160 Notification Appliance. A fire alarm system component such as a bell, horn, speaker, light, or text display that provides audible, tactile, or visible outputs, or any combination thereof. (SIG-NAS)

Many types of notification appliances are available. The most common are audible and visible appliances. Exhibits 3.28 and 3.29 illustrate these two types of notification appliances. Exhibit 3.30 shows amber and blue strobes that might be used in non-fire applications such as for mass notification systems. In addition, other types of notification appliances are sometimes used, including tactile notification appliances in the form of bed shakers or vibrating pocket pagers. Olfactory notification appliances are often used in mines and other hazardous locations.

3.3.160.1 Audible Notification Appliance. A notification appliance that alerts by the sense of hearing. (SIG-NAS)

3.3.160.1.1 Exit Marking Audible Notification Appliance. An audible notification appliance that marks building exits and areas of refuge by the sense of hearing for the purpose of evacuation or relocation. (SIG-NAS)

3.3.160.1.2* Textual Audible Notification Appliance. A notification appliance that conveys a stream of audible information. (SIG-NAS)

A.3.3.160.1.2 Textual Audible Notification Appliance. An example of a textual audible notification appliance is a speaker that reproduces a voice message.

3.3.160.2 Tactile Notification Appliance. A notification appliance that alerts by the sense of touch or vibration. (SIG-NAS)

Tactile notification appliances include vibrating pagers and bed shakers used to notify persons with disabilities who are not able to respond to an audible or visual fire alarm notification appliance. These appliances must be listed for their intended purpose.

3.3.160.3 Visible Notification Appliance. A notification appliance that alerts by the sense of sight. (SIG-NAS)

3.3.160.3.1 Textual Visible Notification Appliance. A notification appliance that conveys a stream of visible information that displays an alphanumeric or pictorial message. Textual visible notification appliances provide temporary text, permanent text, or symbols. Textual visible notification appliances include, but are not limited to, annunciators, monitors, CRTs, displays, and printers. (SIG-NAS)

3.3.161 Notification Appliance Circuit. A circuit or path directly connected to a notification appliance(s). (SIG-PRO)

3.3.162 Notification Zone. See 3.3.300, Zone.

3.3.163* Octave Band. The bandwidth of a filter that comprises a frequency range of a factor of 2. (SIG-NAS)

A.3.3.163 Octave Band. Frequencies are generally reported based on a standard, preferred center frequency, f_c. The bandwidth of a particular octave band has a lower frequency, f_n, and an upper frequency, f_{n+1}. The relationships are as follows:

$$\frac{f_{n+1}}{f_n} = 2^k$$

where:

$k = 1$ for octave bands

$k = \frac{1}{3}$ for one-third octave bands

and

$f_c = f_n\, 2^{\frac{1}{2}}$

For example, the 500 Hz octave band (center frequency) has a lower limit of 354 and an upper limit of 707 Hz. The octave band with a center frequency of 1000 Hz has a lower frequency of 707 Hz and an upper frequency of 1414 Hz.

> **3.3.163.1 One-Third Octave Band.** The bandwidth of a filter that comprises a frequency range of a factor of $2^{\frac{1}{3}}$. (SIG-NAS)

3.3.164 Off-Hook. To make connection with the public-switched telephone network in preparation for dialing a telephone number. (SIG-SSS)

When someone lifts a telephone handset from its normal resting position, the telephone instrument is said to be "off-hook." Digital alarm communicator transmitters use equipment to access the public switched network and automatically provide an off-hook condition prior to beginning a transmission sequence.

3.3.165 One-Third Octave Band. See 3.3.163, Octave Band.

3.3.166 One-Way Emergency Communications System. See 3.3.79, Emergency Communications System.

3.3.167 On-Hook. To disconnect from the public-switched telephone network. (SIG-SSS)

When someone returns a telephone handset to its normal resting position, the telephone instrument is said to be "on-hook." When a digital alarm communicator transmitter completes its transmission, the associated digital alarm communicator receiver transmits a "kiss off" signal that completes the transmission sequence and initiates the equipment within the transmitter and receiver to go on-hook and end the communications connection.

3.3.168 Open Area Detection (Protection). Protection of an area such as a room or space with detectors to provide early warning of fire. (SIG-IDS)

3.3.169 Operating Mode.

> **3.3.169.1 Private Operating Mode.** Audible or visible signaling only to those persons directly concerned with the implementation and direction of emergency action initiation and procedure in the area protected by the fire alarm system. (SIG-NAS)

◄ **FAQ**
Which individuals are private operating mode signals intended to alert?

At some locations, the fire alarm system uses the private operating mode to alert individuals who have responsibility to take prescribed action during a fire emergency. Such individuals may include operators in a supervising station, telephone switchboard operators, building receptionists, nurses at a nursing station, building engineers, plant managers, boiler room operators, emergency response team members, or other specially trained personnel. Some building codes, the *Life Safety Code*, and local ordinances may permit private operating mode notification to precede public operating mode notification of the general occupants. The term *private operating mode* does not refer to applications in private versus public buildings.

3.3.169.2 Public Operating Mode. Audible or visible signaling to occupants or inhabitants of the area protected by the fire alarm system. (SIG-NAS)

The fire alarm system uses the public operating mode to notify the general occupants of a building to take specified action during a fire. This action may include complete evacuation of the building or selective, partial evacuation or relocation to areas of refuge within the building. The term *public operating mode* does not refer to applications in public versus private buildings.

3.3.170 Other Fire Detectors. See 3.3.59, Detector.

3.3.171* Ownership. Any property or building or its contents under legal control by the occupant, by contract, or by holding of a title or deed. (SIG-SSS)

A.3.3.171 Ownership. Inspection, testing, and maintenance is the responsibility of the property or building owner, or it can be transferred by contract. Systems installed, owned, or leased by a tenant are the responsibility of the tenant. The installing company should provide written notice of these responsibilities to the system user.

Paragraph 14.2.2.1 requires the property or building or system owner or the owner's designated representative to be responsible for inspection, testing, and maintenance of fire alarm systems.

3.3.172 Paging System. A system intended to page one or more persons by such means as voice over loudspeaker, coded audible signals or visible signals, or lamp annunciators. (SIG-PRO)

Exhibits 3.31 and 3.32 illustrate examples and usage of paging systems. Also refer to the definition of *public address system* in 3.3.198 and associated commentary.

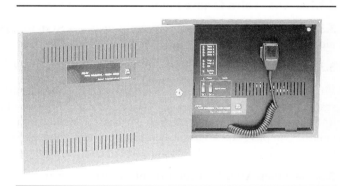

EXHIBIT 3.32 *Typical Single-Channel Paging System. (Source: Signal Communications Corp., Woburn, MA)*

EXHIBIT 3.31 *Fire Official Using Paging System. (Source: SimplexGrinnell, Westminster, MA)*

3.3.173 Parallel Telephone System. A telephone system in which an individually wired circuit is used for each fire alarm box. (SIG-SSS)

3.3.174 Path (Pathways). Any circuit, conductor, optic fiber, radio carrier, or other means connecting two or more locations. (SIG-PRO)

In the 2010 edition of the Code, the definition of *path (pathways)* was expanded to include circuits. Requirements for pathways are addressed primarily in Chapter 12.

3.3.175 Pathway Survivability. The ability of any conductor, optic fiber, radio carrier, or other means for transmitting system information to remain operational during fire conditions. [SIG-ECS]

3.3.176 Permanent Visual Record (Recording). An immediately readable, not easily alterable, print, slash, or punch record of all occurrences of status change. (SIG-SSS)

3.3.177 Personnel.

3.3.177.1 Inspection Personnel. Individuals who conduct a visual examination of a system or portion thereof to verify that it appears to be in operating condition, in proper location, and is free of physical damage or conditions that impair operation. (SIG-TMS)

3.3.177.2 Service Personnel. Individuals who perform those procedures, adjustments, replacement of components, system programming, and maintenance as described in the manufacturer's service instructions that can affect any aspect of the performance of the system. (SIG-TMS)

3.3.177.3 Testing Personnel. Individuals who perform procedures used to determine the status of a system as intended by conducting acceptance, reacceptance, or periodic physical checks on systems. (SIG-TMS)

3.3.178 Photoelectric Light Obscuration Smoke Detection. See 3.3.252, Smoke Detection.

3.3.179 Photoelectric Light-Scattering Smoke Detection. See 3.3.252, Smoke Detection.

3.3.180 Plant. One or more buildings under the same ownership or control on a single property. (SIG-SSS)

3.3.181 Pneumatic Rate-of-Rise Tubing Heat Detector. See 3.3.59, Detector.

3.3.182 Positive Alarm Sequence. An automatic sequence that results in an alarm signal, even when manually delayed for investigation, unless the system is reset. (SIG-PRO)

3.3.183 Power Supply. A source of electrical operating power, including the circuits and terminations connecting it to the dependent system components. (SIG-FUN)

The power supply can be either internal or external to the control unit. Power supplies also include notification appliance circuit (NAC) power extenders.

3.3.184 Primary Battery (Dry Cell). A nonrechargeable battery requiring periodic replacement. (SIG-FUN)

3.3.185 Primary Trunk Facility. That part of a transmission channel connecting all leg facilities to a supervising or subsidiary station. (SIG-SSS)

3.3.186 Prime Contractor. The one company contractually responsible for providing central station services to a subscriber as required by this Code. The prime contractor can be either a listed central station or a listed alarm service–local company. (SIG-SSS)

The term *prime contractor* may refer to a person, firm, or corporation listed by an organization acceptable to the authority having jurisdiction to install, maintain, test, and monitor a central station service alarm system. See the definition of *listed* in 3.2.5 and Chapter 26 for further requirements on central station service alarm systems.

3.3.187 Private Operating Mode. See 3.3.169, Operating Mode.

3.3.188 Private Radio Signaling. A radio system under control of the proprietary supervising station. (SIG-SSS)

3.3.189 Profound Hearing Loss. See 3.3.113, Hearing Loss.

3.3.190 Projected Beam–Type Detector. See 3.3.59, Detector.

3.3.191 Property.

3.3.191.1 Contiguous Property. A single-owner or single-user protected premises on a continuous plot of ground, including any buildings thereon, that is not separated by a public thoroughfare, transportation right-of-way, property owned or used by others, or body of water not under the same ownership. (SIG-SSS)

3.3.191.2 Noncontiguous Property. An owner- or user-protected premises where two or more protected premises, controlled by the same owner or user, are separated by a public thoroughfare, body of water, transportation right-of-way, or property owned or used by others. (SIG-SSS)

3.3.192 Proprietary Supervising Station. See 3.3.266, Supervising Station.

3.3.193 Proprietary Supervising Station Alarm System. See 3.3.267, Supervising Station Alarm System.

3.3.194 Proprietary Supervising Station Service. See 3.3.268, Supervising Station Service.

3.3.195 Protected Premises. The physical location protected by a fire alarm system. (SIG-PRO)

3.3.196 Protected Premises (Local) Control Unit. See 3.3.92, Fire Alarm Control Unit.

3.3.197 Protected Premises (Local) Fire Alarm System. See 3.3.95, Fire Alarm System.

3.3.198 Public Address System. An electronic amplification system with a mixer, amplifier, and loudspeakers, used to reinforce a given sound and distributing the "sound" to the general public around a building. [SIG-ECS]

The means for emergency voice communications to building occupants is normally through the use of an in-building fire emergency voice/alarm communications systems or in-building mass notification system. (These systems may also serve as public address systems.) In situations where a public address system is used for emergency voice communications, the requirements of 24.4.2.27 or 24.4.2.28 apply.

3.3.199 Public Emergency Alarm Reporting System. A system of alarm-initiating devices, transmitting and receiving equipment, and communication infrastructure (other than a public telephone network) used to communicate with the communications center to provide any combination of manual or auxiliary alarm service. (SIG-PRS)

The word *fire* has been removed from the term *public fire alarm reporting system* as well as from other terms associated with these systems. This change has been made to reflect the broader application now permitted for *public emergency alarm reporting systems*. See Section 27.8.

3.3.199.1* Auxiliary Alarm System. A protected premises fire alarm system or other emergency system at the protected premises and the system used to connect the protected premises system to a public emergency alarm reporting system for transmitting an alarm to the communications center. (SIG-PRS)

A.3.3.199.1 Auxiliary Alarm System. Alarms from an auxiliary alarm system are received at the communications center on the same equipment and by the same methods as alarms transmitted from public alarm boxes.

3.3.199.1.1 Local Energy Type Auxiliary Alarm System. An auxiliary system that employs a locally complete arrangement of parts, initiating devices, relays, power supply, and associated components to automatically activate a master box or auxiliary box over circuits that are electrically isolated from the public emergency alarm reporting system circuits. (SIG-PRS)

3.3.199.1.2 Shunt-Type Auxiliary Alarm System. An auxiliary system electrically connected to the public emergency alarm reporting system extending a public emergency alarm reporting circuit to interconnect initiating devices within a protected premises, which, when operated, opens the public emergency alarm reporting circuit shunted around the trip coil of the master box or auxiliary box. The master box or auxiliary box is thereupon energized to start transmission without any assistance from a local source of power. (SIG-PRS)

3.3.199.2 Type A Public Emergency Alarm Reporting System. A system in which an alarm from an alarm box is received and is retransmitted to fire stations either manually or automatically. (SIG-PRS)

3.3.199.3 Type B Public Emergency Alarm Reporting System. A system in which an alarm from an alarm box is automatically transmitted to fire stations and, if used, is transmitted to supplementary alerting devices. (SIG-PRS)

3.3.200 Public Operating Mode. See 3.3.169, Operating Mode.

3.3.201 Public Safety Agency. A fire, emergency medical services, or law enforcement agency. (SIG-ECS)

3.3.202 Public Safety Radio Enhancement System. A system installed to assure the effective operation of radio communication systems used by fire, emergency medical services, or law enforcement agencies. (SIG-ECS)

Public safety radio enhancement systems, addressed as two-way radio communication enhancement systems in 24.5.2, are systems used to ensure the performance of public safety radio systems within buildings. Often problems occur in buildings due to radio signal attenuation caused by the building structure itself. These enhancement systems are intended to ensure that radio coverage is adequately provided throughout the building for the first responders. Extensive commissioning and testing requirements are provided in 14.4.12.

3.3.203 Public Safety Radio System. A radio communication system used by fire, emergency medical services, or law enforcement agencies. (SIG-ECS)

3.3.204 Public Switched Telephone Network. See 3.3.273, Switched Telephone Network.

3.3.205 Publicly Accessible Fire Alarm Box. See 3.3.8, Fire Alarm Box.

3.3.206* Qualified. A competent and capable person or company that has met the requirements and training for a given field acceptable to the authority having jurisdiction. [**96,** 2008] (SIG-TMS)

A.3.3.206 Qualified. *Qualified* might also mean that the person has knowledge of the installation, construction, or operation of apparatus and the hazards involved.

3.3.207 Radiant Energy–Sensing Fire Detector. See 3.3.59, Detector.

3.3.208 Radio Alarm Repeater Station Receiver (RARSR). A system component that receives radio signals and resides at a repeater station that is located at a remote receiving location. (SIG-SSS)

3.3.209 Radio Alarm Supervising Station Receiver (RASSR). A system component that receives data and annunciates that data at the supervising station. (SIG-SSS)

3.3.210 Radio Alarm System (RAS). A system in which signals are transmitted from a radio alarm transmitter (RAT) located at a protected premises through a radio channel to two or more radio alarm repeater station receivers (RARSR) and that are annunciated by a radio alarm supervising station receiver (RASSR) located at the central station. (SIG-SSS)

Exhibit 3.33 illustrates a typical radio alarm system.

3.3.211 Radio Alarm Transmitter (RAT). A system component at the protected premises to which initiating devices or groups of devices are connected that transmits signals indicating a status change of the initiating devices. (SIG-SSS)

EXHIBIT 3.33 *Radio Alarm System. (Source: Keltron Corp., Waltham, MA)*

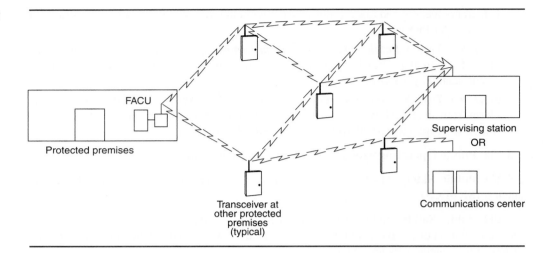

FACU

Protected premises

Transceiver at other protected premises (typical)

Supervising station

OR

Communications center

3.3.212 Radio Channel. See 3.3.40, Channel.

3.3.213 Rate Compensation Detector. See 3.3.59, Detector.

3.3.214 Rate-of-Rise Detector. See 3.3.59, Detector.

3.3.215 Record Drawings. Drawings (as-built) that document the location of all devices, appliances, wiring sequences, wiring methods, and connections of the components of the fire alarm system as installed. (SIG-FUN)

Record drawings (also called *as-built drawings* or *record set drawings*) provide information that is essential to those who test and maintain the fire alarm system. These drawings must be developed during the installation by the installer and consist of original fire alarm system shop drawings that have been annotated during the installation of the system to show exactly where the fire alarm system components (including remote power supplies or extenders and control units or modules) have been installed, how the cable and conduit have been routed, and the locations of all terminal and junction boxes.

Record drawings show details of how each conductor of each fire alarm system circuit was installed, the color codes used, the actual location of each device and appliance, terminal cabinets, terminal identifications, and dates of software and system revisions. They also document all field changes that were made during the installation. Any changes made throughout the life of the fire alarm system must be noted on the record drawings.

The system owner is responsible for retention of all record drawings. Record drawings, based on the shop drawings, must reflect the actual system installation. The record drawings, once completed by the contractor, should be transmitted to the designer for review and acceptance before being delivered to the owner or authority having jurisdiction. For requirements and information related to the original fire alarm system shop drawings, refer to 3.3.238, 10.18.1.2, and A.10.18.1.2.

3.3.216 Record of Completion. A document that acknowledges the features of installation, operation (performance), service, and equipment with representation by the property owner, system installer, system supplier, service organization, and the authority having jurisdiction. (SIG-FUN)

Requirements for the record of completion are contained in 10.18.2.1.1. Refer to the commentary following A.10.18.2.1.1. The record of completion is used to verify that the system has been installed as per the specifications and drawings and that the system has been fully tested before the authority having jurisdiction is called for the final inspection.

3.3.217 Regional Operations Center (ROC). A network control center that covers multiple geographically separated facilities and installations. (SIG-ECS)

3.3.218 Releasing Fire Alarm System. See 3.3.95, Fire Alarm System.

3.3.219 Releasing Service Fire Alarm Control Unit. See 3.3.92, Fire Alarm Control Unit.

3.3.220 Relocation. The movement of occupants from a fire zone to a safe area within the same building. (SIG-PRO)

In hospitals, high-rise buildings, and large area facilities, where evacuation of all occupants on every alarm signal is impractical and often undesirable, occupants in the fire zone may be directed to move to a specific area where they will be safer. Also refer to the definition of *evacuation signaling zone* in 3.3.300.1.

3.3.221 Remote Supervising Station. See 3.3.266, Supervising Station.

3.3.222 Remote Supervising Station Alarm System. See 3.3.267, Supervising Station Alarm System.

3.3.223 Remote Supervising Station Service. See 3.3.268, Supervising Station Service.

3.3.224 Repeater Station. The location of the equipment needed to relay signals between supervising stations, subsidiary stations, and protected premises. (SIG-SSS)

3.3.225 Reset. A control function that attempts to return a system or device to its normal, nonalarm state. (SIG-FUN)

Reset should not be confused with alarm signal deactivation, which only deactivates the alarm signal and does not return the fire alarm system to its normal standby quiescent condition.

3.3.226 Residential Board and Care Occupancy. A building or portion thereof that is used for lodging and boarding of four or more residents, not related by blood or marriage to the owners or operators, for the purpose of providing personal care services. [*101,* 2009] (SIG-HOU)

The definitions for several occupancy terms are included in Chapter 3 to correlate with their use in Chapter 29. *NFPA 72,* including Chapter 29, is not an occupancy-based code. However, some of the installation and performance rules that are provided in Chapter 29 are specified differently for the different types of occupancies. These terms have been extracted from NFPA *101* as indicated by the reference in brackets at the end of the definition.

3.3.227 Residential Occupancy. An occupancy that provides sleeping accommodations for purposes other than health care or detention and correctional. [*101,* 2009] (SIG-HOU)

3.3.228 Restorable Initiating Device. See 3.3.122, Initiating Device.

3.3.229 Risk Analysis. A process to characterize the likelihood, vulnerability, and magnitude of incidents associated with natural, technological, and manmade disasters and other emergencies that address scenarios of concern, their probability, and their potential consequences. [SIG-ECS]

Requirements for performing a risk analysis are contained in 24.4.2.2 and 24.7.7. Many of the requirements in Chapter 24 are predicated on the performance of a risk analysis to form a basis for the system design and signal priorities.

3.3.230 Runner. A person other than the required number of operators on duty at central, supervising, or runner stations (or otherwise in contact with these stations) available for prompt dispatching, when necessary, to the protected premises. (SIG-SSS)

FAQ ▶
What are some of the duties that a runner may be called to perform?

The Code intends that the runner have the qualifications to perform the required duties at the protected premises. These duties may include resetting equipment; investigating alarm, supervisory, or trouble signals; and taking corrective action when necessary. Runners must receive training so that they have an in-depth knowledge of the fire alarm systems and equipment within the protected premises; they may or may not have the knowledge or training to actually service or repair equipment. In some cases, upon receipt of a trouble signal from equipment at the protected premises, a supervising station may first dispatch a runner to attempt to determine whether the fire alarm system needs the attention of a qualified service technician. See 10.4.3.1 for requirements pertaining to qualifications of service personnel.

3.3.231 Runner Service. The service provided by a runner at the protected premises, including restoration, resetting, and silencing of all equipment transmitting fire alarm or supervisory or trouble signals to an off-premises location. (SIG-SSS)

Runner service is generally provided as part of either central station service or a proprietary supervising station alarm system. A runner is sent to the protected premises from which the signal was received and takes appropriate action, as outlined in the commentary following the definition of *runner* in 3.3.230.

3.3.232 Scanner. Equipment located at the telephone company wire center that monitors each local leg and relays status changes to the alarm center. Processors and associated equipment might also be included. (SIG-SSS)

3.3.233 Secondary Trunk Facility. That part of a transmission channel connecting two or more, but fewer than all, leg facilities to a primary trunk facility. (SIG-SSS)

3.3.234 Selective Talk Mode. See 3.3.277, Talk Mode.

3.3.235 Separate Sleeping Area. The area of a dwelling unit where the bedrooms or sleeping rooms are located. [**720,** 2009] (SIG-HOU)

3.3.236 Service Personnel. See 3.3.177, Personnel.

3.3.237 Shapes of Ceilings. The shapes of ceilings can be classified as sloping or smooth. (SIG-IDS)

3.3.238 Shop Drawings. Documents that provide information pertaining to the system, such as property location, scaled floor plans, equipment wiring details, typical equipment installation details, riser details, conduit/conductor size and routing information, and other information necessary for the installer to complete the fire alarm installation. (SIG-FUN)

Shop drawings are a method of conveying information to the authority having jurisdiction and others on the system that is to be installed at a location. See 10.18.1.2 for the requirements pertaining to shop drawings and A.10.18.1.2 for information that should be included on shop drawings. The term *record drawings* is used in other locations in the Code. Record drawings, defined in 3.3.215, are the as-built version of the shop drawings. Refer to the commentary following 3.3.215.

3.3.239 Shunt-Type Auxiliary Alarm System. See 3.3.199, Public Emergency Alarm Reporting System.

3.3.240 Signal. A status indication communicated by electrical or other means. (SIG-FUN)

    3.3.240.1 Alarm Signal. A signal indicating an emergency condition or an alert that requires action. (SIG-FUN)

    3.3.240.2 Delinquency Signal. A signal indicating the need for action in connection with the supervision of guards or system attendants. (SIG-PRO)

A delinquency signal applies only to guard's tour systems. Some fire alarm systems are arranged as combination systems that contain specific guard patrol stations at which a touring guard inserts a key that registers a signal to show the date and time a location was visited. If the guard fails to initiate a signal within a prescribed amount of time, the fire alarm system initiates a supervisory signal. This feature was once common in fire alarm systems in large industrial facilities but is rarely used today.

> ***3.3.240.3 Evacuation Signal.*** A distinctive signal intended to be recognized by the occupants as requiring evacuation of the building. (SIG-PRO)

The Code requires fire alarm systems to use a three-pulse temporal pattern evacuation signal. This signal is described in 18.4.2.1. The only exception is where the authority having jurisdiction approves the continued use of a previously established evacuation signal.

> ***3.3.240.4 Fire Alarm Signal.*** A signal initiated by a fire alarm-initiating device such as a manual fire alarm box, automatic fire detector, waterflow switch, or other device in which activation is indicative of the presence of a fire or fire signature. (SIG-FUN)

Fire alarm signals are not permitted to indicate supervisory or trouble conditions. See Section 10.7 for requirements pertaining to distinctive signals. However, it should be noted that in some cases a device alarm condition is permitted to be indicated by a supervisory signal. For example, 21.7.4 allows smoke detectors installed in an air duct to initiate an alarm or supervisory signal.

> ***3.3.240.5 Guard's Tour Supervisory Signal.*** A supervisory signal monitoring the performance of guard patrols. (SIG-PRO)

> ***3.3.240.6 Supervisory Signal.*** A signal indicating the need for action in connection with the supervision of guard tours, the fire suppression systems or equipment, or the maintenance features of related systems. (SIG-FUN)

> ***3.3.240.7 Trouble Signal.*** A signal initiated by a system or device indicative of a fault in a monitored circuit, system, or component. (SIG-FUN)

3.3.241 Signal Transmission Sequence. A DACT that obtains dial tone, dials the number(s) of the DACR, obtains verification that the DACR is ready to receive signals, transmits the signals, and receives acknowledgment that the DACR has accepted that signal before disconnecting (going on-hook). (SIG-SSS)

3.3.242 Signaling Line Circuit. A circuit path between any combination of addressable appliances or devices, circuit interfaces, control units, or transmitters over which multiple system input signals or output signals or both are carried. (SIG-PRO)

3.3.243 Signaling Line Circuit Interface. See 3.3.127, Interface.

3.3.244 Single Dwelling Unit. See 3.3.74, Dwelling Unit.

3.3.245 Single Station Alarm. A detector comprising an assembly that incorporates a sensor, control components, and an alarm notification appliance in one unit operated from a power source either located in the unit or obtained at the point of installation. (SIG-HOU)

See the commentary following the definition of *multiple-station alarm* in 3.3.149.

3.3.246 Single Station Alarm Device. An assembly that incorporates the detector, the control equipment, and the alarm-sounding device in one unit operated from a power supply either in the unit or obtained at the point of installation. (SIG-HOU)

3.3.247 Site-Specific Software. See 3.3.255, Software.

3.3.248 Sloping Ceiling. See 3.3.31, Ceiling.

3.3.249 Sloping Peaked-Type Ceiling. See 3.3.31, Ceiling.

3.3.250 Sloping Shed-Type Ceiling. See 3.3.31, Ceiling.

3.3.251 Smoke Alarm. A single or multiple station alarm responsive to smoke. (SIG-HOU)

Exhibit 3.34 illustrates a typical single-station smoke alarm.

3.3.252 Smoke Detection.

3.3.252.1 Cloud Chamber Smoke Detection. The principle of using an air sample drawn from the protected area into a high-humidity chamber combined with a lowering of chamber pressure to create an environment in which the resultant moisture in the air condenses on any smoke particles present, forming a cloud. The cloud density is measured by a photoelectric principle. The density signal is processed and used to convey an alarm condition when it meets preset criteria. (SIG-IDS)

FAQ ▶
What is cloud chamber smoke detection?

Cloud chamber smoke detection is a form of active air sampling–type smoke detection. Cloud chamber smoke detectors are extremely sensitive to low levels of combustion products and are frequently used to detect very small fires in vital equipment. Also see the definition of *air sampling–type detector* in 3.3.59.1.

EXHIBIT 3.34 *Typical Single-Station Smoke Alarm. (Source: Gentex Corp., Zeeland, MI)*

3.3.252.2* Ionization Smoke Detection. The principle of using a small amount of radioactive material to ionize the air between two differentially charged electrodes to sense the presence of smoke particles. Smoke particles entering the ionization volume decrease the conductance of the air by reducing ion mobility. The reduced conductance signal is processed and used to convey an alarm condition when it meets preset criteria. (SIG-IDS)

A.3.3.252.2 Ionization Smoke Detection. Ionization smoke detection is more responsive to invisible particles (smaller than 1 micron in size) produced by most flaming fires. It is somewhat less responsive to the larger particles typical of most smoldering fires. Smoke detectors that use the ionization principle are usually of the spot type.

Although all listed smoke detectors must pass the same series of tests at listing agencies, system designers typically use ionization-type smoke detectors in locations in which they expect a greater risk of a flaming rather than a smoldering fire scenario. Generally, fire scientists consider ionization detectors to be slightly more sensitive to the smaller particles of smoke produced by a flaming fire. In locations where smoldering fires are more likely to occur, photoelectric-type smoke detectors, rather than ionization-type smoke detectors, may offer better protection. Additionally, light-scattering, photoelectric-type smoke detectors respond better to light-colored smoke than to black particles because black particles absorb light. Exhibit 3.35 provides details of operation for ionization-type smoke detectors. Measured current flow decreases as smoke particles enter the sensing chamber and attach themselves to ionized air molecules.

EXHIBIT 3.35 *Operation of an Ionization Smoke Detector.*

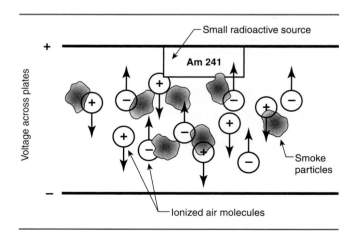

3.3.252.3* Photoelectric Light Obscuration Smoke Detection. The principle of using a light source and a photosensitive sensor onto which the principal portion of the source emissions is focused. When smoke particles enter the light path, some of the light is scattered and some is absorbed, thereby reducing the light reaching the receiving sensor. The light reduction signal is processed and used to convey an alarm condition when it meets preset criteria. (SIG-IDS)

A.3.3.252.3 Photoelectric Light Obscuration Smoke Detection. The response of photoelectric light obscuration smoke detectors is usually not affected by the color of smoke.

Smoke detectors that use the light obscuration principle are usually of the line type. These detectors are commonly referred to as "projected beam smoke detectors."

Exhibit 3.36 illustrates the principle of operation of a photoelectric-type light obscuration smoke detector.

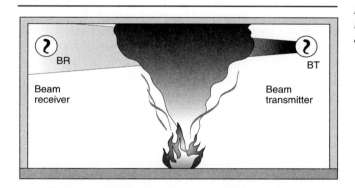

EXHIBIT 3.36 *Operation of a Photoelectric Light Obscuration Smoke Detector.*

3.3.252.4* Photoelectric Light-Scattering Smoke Detection. The principle of using a light source and a photosensitive sensor arranged so that the rays from the light source do not normally fall onto the photosensitive sensor. When smoke particles enter the light path, some of the light is scattered by reflection and refraction onto the sensor. The light signal is processed and used to convey an alarm condition when it meets preset criteria. (SIG-IDS)

A.3.3.252.4 Photoelectric Light-Scattering Smoke Detection. Photoelectric light-scattering smoke detection is more responsive to the visible particles (larger than 1 micron in size) produced by most smoldering fires. It is somewhat less responsive to the smaller particles typical of most flaming fires. It is also less responsive to black smoke than to lighter colored smoke. Smoke detectors that use the light-scattering principle are usually of the spot type.

Although all listed smoke detectors must pass the same series of tests at listing agencies, system designers typically use photoelectric-type smoke detectors where they expect a fire to produce larger smoke particles, such as with a smoldering fire or an aged smoke scenario. A photoelectric-type smoke detector is better at detecting the larger or lighter-colored particles produced by smoldering fires or smoke particles that have agglomerated or "aged" as the particles move away from the thermal energy source at the fire. In locations where flaming fires are more likely to occur, ionization-type smoke detectors, rather than photoelectric-type smoke detectors, may offer better protection.

Exhibit 3.37 illustrates the principle of operation for a photoelectric light-scattering smoke detector.

3.3.252.5* Video Image Smoke Detection (VISD). The principle of using automatic analysis of real-time video images to detect the presence of smoke. (SIG-IDS)

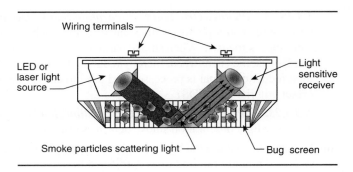

EXHIBIT 3.37 *Operation of a Photoelectric Light-Scattering Smoke Detector.*

A.3.3.252.5 Video Image Smoke Detection (VISD). Video image smoke detection (VISD) is a software-based method of smoke detection that has become practical with the advent of digital video systems. Listing agencies have begun testing VISD components for several manufacturers. VISD systems can analyze images for changes in features such as brightness, contrast, edge content, loss of detail, and motion. The detection equipment can consist of cameras producing digital or analog (converted to digital) video signals and processing unit(s) that maintain the software and interfaces to the fire alarm control unit.

3.3.253 Smoke Detector. See 3.3.59, Detector.

3.3.254 Smooth Ceiling. See 3.3.33, Ceiling Surfaces.

3.3.255 Software. Programs, instruments, procedures, data, and the like that are executed by a central processing unit of a product and that influences the functional performance of that product. For the purpose of this Code, software is one of two types: executive software and site-specific software. (SIG-TMS)

> *3.3.255.1 Executive Software.* Control and supervisory program which manages the execution of all other programs and directly or indirectly causes the required functions of the product to be performed. Executive software is sometimes referred to as firmware, BIOS, or executive program. (SIG-TMS)

Fire alarm control unit executive software is similar to the main operating system software used in computers. This software is listed for use with the specific fire alarm system control unit and is generally not accessible to the end user.

> *3.3.255.2 Site-Specific Software.* Program that is separate from, but controlled by, the executive software which allows inputs, outputs, and system configuration to be selectively defined to meet the needs of a specific installation. Typically it defines the type and quantity of hardware, customized labels and the specific operating features of a system. (SIG-TMS)

Site-specific software is a program that runs at a level under the executive software and is specific to the particular fire alarm system installation. Testing in accordance with 14.4.1.2.1.4 must be performed after any changes to the site-specific software.

3.3.256 Solid Joist Construction. See 3.3.33, Ceiling Surfaces.

3.3.257 Spacing. A horizontally measured dimension related to the allowable coverage of fire detectors. (SIG-IDS)

Spacing refers to the maximum linear horizontal distance permitted by the Code between automatic fire detection initiating devices. Spacing is based on the listing of the device for heat detectors and on the manufacturer's guidelines for smoke detectors in accordance with the rules in Chapter 17.

3.3.258* Spark. A moving particle of solid material that emits radiant energy due either to its temperature or the process of combustion on its surface. [**654,** 2006] (SIG-IDS)

A.3.3.258 Spark. The overwhelming majority of applications involving the detection of Class A and Class D combustibles with radiant energy–sensing detectors involve the transport of particulate solid materials through pneumatic conveyor ducts or mechanical conveyors. It is common in the industries that include such hazards to refer to a moving piece of burning material as a *spark* and to systems for the detection of such fires as *spark detection systems.*

3.3.259 Spark/Ember Detector. See 3.3.59, Detector.

3.3.260 Spark/Ember Detector Sensitivity. The number of watts (or the fraction of a watt) of radiant power from a point source radiator, applied as a unit step signal at the wavelength of maximum detector sensitivity, necessary to produce an alarm signal from the detector within the specified response time. (SIG-IDS)

3.3.261 Spot-Type Detector. See 3.3.59, Detector.

3.3.262 Stakeholder. Any individual, group, or organization that might affect, be affected by, or perceive itself to be affected by the risk. (SIG-ECS)

3.3.263 Stratification. The phenomenon where the upward movement of smoke and gases ceases due to the loss of buoyancy. (SIG-IDS)

The combustion of the fuel in a fire liberates heat. That heat causes the gaseous component of the smoke to expand, making it less dense than the surrounding air. Thus, the smoke is buoyant and flows upward in a plume. As the smoke gases flow upward, they lose heat through two processes. The first process is expansion: As gases expand, they lose heat and cool. The second is cool air entrainment: As the smoke plume rises, cool ambient air is entrained (drawn) into the flow, cooling the plume. Eventually, these processes cool the smoke to the point where it is at the same temperature and density as the surrounding air. At that point buoyancy is gone, and the smoke stops rising. The plume then spreads out horizontally, regardless of whether or not it has reached the ceiling of the space. If the fire detection devices such as smoke detectors are installed on the ceiling, the fire will not be detected. As the fire continues to grow, the height of the smoke layer slowly rises. However, in rooms or compartments with high ceilings, it is conceivable that the smoke would not arrive at ceiling-mounted detectors before the fire has exceeded the design objective. Care must be exercised in the installation of detection devices in areas subject to this phenomenon, such as an atrium, any other high ceiling space, or an area with unusually high upper level airflow. Also see 17.7.1.10, A.17.7.1.10, and related commentary for more details on this phenomenon and detector placement.

Exhibit 3.38 illustrates stratification. The various levels of stratification shown depend on the fire scenario(s) determined for the space under consideration.

◀ **FAQ**
What causes stratification?

3.3.264 Subscriber. The recipient of a contractual supervising station signal service(s). In case of multiple, noncontiguous properties having single ownership, the term refers to each protected premises or its local management. (SIG-SSS)

3.3.265 Subsidiary Station. A subsidiary station is a normally unattended location that is remote from the supervising station and is linked by a communications channel(s) to the supervising station. Interconnection of signals on one or more transmission channels from protected premises with a communications channel(s) to the supervising station is performed at this location. (SIG-SSS)

3.3.266 Supervising Station. A facility that receives signals from protected premises fire alarm systems and at which personnel are in attendance at all times to respond to these signals. (SIG-SSS)

EXHIBIT 3.38 Stratification.

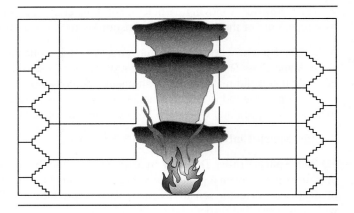

3.3.266.1 Central Supervising Station. A supervising station that is listed for central station service and that also commonly provides less stringent supervising station services such as remote supervising services. (SIG-SSS)

The listed central station serves as the constantly attended location that receives signals from the central station service alarm system located at the protected premises. Central station operators take action on signals, including initiating a retransmission of the signals, and provide runner service. See Chapter 26 for requirements pertaining to central station systems and central station service.

3.3.266.2 Proprietary Supervising Station. A supervising station under the same ownership as the protected premises fire alarm system(s) that it supervises (monitors) and to which alarm, supervisory, or trouble signals are received and where personnel are in attendance at all times to supervise operation and investigate signals. (SIG-SSS)

3.3.266.3 Remote Supervising Station. A supervising station to which alarm, supervisory, or trouble signals or any combination of those signals emanating from protected premises fire alarm systems are received and where personnel are in attendance at all times to respond. (SIG-SSS)

3.3.267 Supervising Station Alarm Systems.

3.3.267.1 Central Station Service Alarm System. A system or group of systems in which the operations of circuits and devices are transmitted automatically to, recorded in, maintained by, and supervised from a listed central station that has competent and experienced servers and operators who, upon receipt of a signal, take such action as required by this Code. Such service is to be controlled and operated by a person, firm, or corporation whose business is the furnishing, maintaining, or monitoring of supervised alarm systems. (SIG-SSS)

A central station service alarm system is illustrated in Exhibit 3.39.

3.3.267.2 Proprietary Supervising Station Alarm System. An installation of an alarm system that serves contiguous and noncontiguous properties, under one ownership, from a proprietary supervising station located at the protected premises, or at one of multiple non-contiguous protected premises, at which trained, competent personnel are in constant attendance. This includes the protected premises fire alarm system(s): proprietary supervising station; power supplies; signal-initiating devices; initiating device circuits; signal notification appliances; equipment for the automatic, permanent visual recording of signals; and equipment for initiating the operation of emergency building control services. (SIG-SSS)

EXHIBIT 3.39 Central Station Service Alarm System. (Source: Simplex-Grinnell, Westminster, MA)

Many large industrial plants, college campuses, large hospital complexes, department store chains, and detention and correctional facilities use a proprietary supervising station, as shown in Exhibit 3.40, to monitor all portions of the contiguous or noncontiguous protected premises.

EXHIBIT 3.40 Proprietary Supervising Station. (Source: SimplexGrinnell, Westminster, MA)

3.3.267.3 *Remote Supervising Station Alarm System.* A protected premises fire alarm system (exclusive of any connected to a public emergency reporting system) in which alarm, supervisory, or trouble signals are transmitted automatically to, recorded in, and supervised from a remote supervising station that has competent and experienced servers and operators who, upon receipt of a signal, take such action as required by this Code. (SIG-SSS)

A remote supervising station alarm system provides a supervising station connection for an alarm system at the protected premises when the building owner does not want or is not required to provide a central station service alarm system or a proprietary supervising station alarm system. Section 26.5 permits alarm, supervisory, and trouble signals to be transmitted to three possible locations: the communications center, the fire station or other governmental agency, or an alternative location. The permitted alternative locations can include a telephone

◀ **FAQ**
When is a remote supervising station alarm system used?

answering service, an alarm monitoring center, a listed central station, or any other constantly attended location acceptable to the authority having jurisdiction. See 26.5.3 for specific allowances and conditions.

3.3.268 Supervising Station Service.

> **3.3.268.1 Central Station Service.** The use of a system or a group of systems including the protected premises fire alarm system(s) in which the operations of circuits and devices are signaled to, recorded in, and supervised from a listed central station that has competent and experienced operators who, upon receipt of a signal, take such action as required by this Code. Related activities at the protected premises, such as equipment installation, inspection, testing, maintenance, and runner service, are the responsibility of the central station or a listed alarm service local company. Central station service is controlled and operated by a person, firm, or corporation whose business is the furnishing of such contracted services or whose properties are the protected premises. (SIG-SSS)

Central station service, defined in 3.3.268.1, involves six elements identified by the Code: installation, testing and maintenance, and runner service at the protected premises; and monitoring, retransmission, and record keeping at the central station. Under contract, the prime contractor must provide all six elements of this service to the subscriber. The prime contractor must provide this service either alone or in conjunction with subcontractors working with the prime contractor. See Chapter 26 for requirements pertaining to central station service.

> **3.3.268.2 Proprietary Supervising Station Service.** The use of a system or a group of systems including the protected premises fire alarm system(s) in which the operations of circuits and devices are signaled to, recorded in, and supervised from a supervising station under the same ownership as the protected premises that has competent and experienced operators who, upon receipt of a signal, take such action as required by this Code. Related activities at the protected premises, such as equipment installation, inspection, testing, maintenance, and runner service, are the responsibility of the owner. Proprietary supervising station service is controlled and operated by the entity whose properties are the protected premises. (SIG-SSS)

> **3.3.268.3 Remote Supervising Station Service.** The use of a system including the protected premises fire alarm system(s) in which the operations of circuits and devices are signaled to, recorded in, and supervised from a supervising station that has competent and experienced operators who, upon receipt of a signal, take such action as required by this Code. Related activities at the protected premises, such as equipment installation, inspection, testing, and maintenance, are the responsibility of the owner. (SIG-SSS)

3.3.269 Supervisory Service. The service required to monitor performance of guard tours and the operative condition of fixed suppression systems or other systems for the protection of life and property. (SIG-PRO)

3.3.270 Supervisory Signal. See 3.3.240, Signal.

3.3.271 Supervisory Signal-Initiating Device. See 3.3.122, Initiating Device.

3.3.272 Supplementary. As used in this Code, *supplementary* refers to equipment or operations not required by this Code and designated as such by the authority having jurisdiction. (SIG-FUN)

For equipment to be designated as *supplementary*, it must meet two specific conditions. First, the equipment must not be required by the Code. Second, the authority having jurisdiction must specifically declare in writing that the equipment is supplementary. This two-fold test helps limit the use of supplementary equipment. Use of supplementary equipment must be limited because such equipment enjoys somewhat relaxed requirements regarding the monitoring of the integrity of system interconnections and power supplies.

Supplementary equipment must not be confused with *nonrequired* components or systems, defined in 3.3.158. While supplementary equipment may be installed at the owner's option, it is not generally considered essential in the intended mission or goals of the fire alarm system. The same cannot be said for nonrequired components and systems. In the latter instance, the components or systems are not required by a building or fire code, but they are needed to fulfill the fire protection goals intended for the system.

◀ **FAQ**
How is supplementary equipment distinguished from nonrequired equipment?

3.3.273 Switched Telephone Network.

3.3.273.1 Loop Start Telephone Circuit. A loop start telephone circuit is an analog telephone circuit that supports loop start signaling as specified in either Telcordia *GR-506-CORE, LATA Switching Systems Generic Requirements: Signaling for Analog Interface,* or Telcordia *GR-909-CORE, Fiber in the Loop Systems Generic Requirements.* (SIG-SSS)

3.3.273.2 Public Switched Telephone Network. An assembly of communications equipment and telephone service providers that utilize managed facilities-based voice networks (MFVN) to provide the general public with the ability to establish communications channels via discrete dialing codes. (SIG-SSS)

Subsection 3.3.273 was revised by a tentative interim amendment (TIA).

The definition of *public switched telephone network (PSTN)* has been revised to include the communications equipment and systems of telephone service providers that use a managed facility-based voice network (MFVN), defined in 3.3.141. These definitions are integral to the requirements for digital alarm communicator systems used to transmit signals from a protected premises to a supervising station in 26.6.3.2.1. These requirements also include use of the term *loop start telephone circuit,* which is defined in 3.3.273.1 to provide a specific reference to the industry standards used to establish the performance for these circuits. Refer to the definition of MFVN in 3.3.141 and the related annex material and commentary.

3.3.274 System Operator. An individual trained to operate and or initiate a mass notification system. (SIG-ECS)

3.3.275 System Unit. The active subassemblies at the supervising station used for signal receiving, processing, display, or recording of status change signals; a failure of one of these subassemblies causes the loss of a number of alarm signals by that unit. (SIG-SSS)

3.3.276 Tactile Notification Appliance. See 3.3.160, Notification Appliance.

3.3.277 Talk Mode. A means of communications within a building normally dedicated to emergency functions. Commonly referred to as fire fighters' phones, but can also be used for communications with fire fighters and/or fire wardens, including occupants, during an emergency, such as between a fire command center and a designated location, such as a stair, stairwell, or location of emergency equipment. (SIG-ECS)

3.3.277.1 Common Talk Mode. The ability to conference multiple telephones in a single conversation. This is similar to what was referred to as a party line. (SIG-ECS)

3.3.277.2 Selective Talk Mode. The ability for personnel at the fire command center to receive indication of incoming calls and choose which call to answer. This includes the ability to transfer between incoming calls and conference multiple phone locations. Selective calling may include the ability to initiate calls to emergency phone locations. (SIG-ECS)

3.3.278 Testing Personnel. See 3.3.177, Personnel.

3.3.279 Textual Audible Notification Appliance. See 3.3.160, Notification Appliance.

3.3.280 Textual Visible Notification Appliance. See 3.3.160, Notification Appliance.

3.3.281 Transmission Channel. See 3.3.40, Channel.

3.3.282 Transmitter. A system component that provides an interface between signaling line circuits, initiating device circuits, or control units and the transmission channel. (SIG-SSS)

3.3.283 Transponder. A multiplex alarm transmission system functional assembly located at the protected premises. (SIG-SSS)

3.3.284 Trouble Signal. See 3.3.240, Signal.

3.3.285 Two-Way Emergency Communications System. See 3.3.79, Emergency Communications System.

3.3.286 Type A Public Emergency Alarm Reporting System. See 3.3.199, Public Emergency Alarm Reporting System.

3.3.287 Type B Public Emergency Alarm Reporting System. See 3.3.199, Public Emergency Alarm Reporting System.

3.3.288 Uplink. The radio signal from the portable public safety subscriber transmitter to the base station receiver. (SIG-ECS)

3.3.289* Video Image Flame Detection (VIFD). The principle of using automatic analysis of real-time video images to detect the presence of flame. (SIG-IDS)

A.3.3.289 Video Image Flame Detection (VIFD). Video image flame detection (VIFD) is a software-based method of flame detection that can be implemented by a range of video image analysis techniques. VIFD systems can analyze images for changes in features such as brightness, contrast, edge content, loss of detail, and motion. The detection equipment can consist of cameras producing digital or analog (converted to digital) video signals and processing unit(s) that maintain the software and interfaces to the fire alarm control unit.

3.3.290 Video Image Smoke Detection (VISD). See 3.3.252, Smoke Detection.

3.3.291 Visible Notification Appliance. See 3.3.160, Notification Appliance.

3.3.292 Voice Message Priority. A scheme for prioritizing mass notification messages. (SIG-ECS)

3.3.293 WATS (Wide Area Telephone Service). Telephone company service allowing reduced costs for certain telephone call arrangements. In-WATS or 800-number service calls can be placed from anywhere in the continental United States to the called party at no cost to the calling party. Out-WATS is a service whereby, for a flat-rate charge, dependent on the total duration of all such calls, a subscriber can make an unlimited number of calls within a prescribed area from a particular telephone terminal without the registration of individual call charges. (SIG-SSS)

3.3.294* Wavelength. The distance between the peaks of a sinusoidal wave. All radiant energy can be described as a wave having a wavelength. Wavelength serves as the unit of measure for distinguishing between different parts of the spectrum. Wavelengths are measured in microns (μm), nanometers (nm), or angstroms (Å). (SIG-IDS)

A.3.3.294 Wavelength. The concept of wavelength is extremely important in selecting the proper detector for a particular application. There is a precise interrelation between the wavelength of light being emitted from a flame and the combustion chemistry producing the flame. Specific subatomic, atomic, and molecular events yield radiant energy of specific wavelengths. For example, ultraviolet photons are emitted as the result of the complete loss of electrons or very large changes in electron energy levels. During combustion, molecules are violently torn apart by the chemical reactivity of oxygen, and electrons are released in the process, recombining at drastically lower energy levels, thus giving rise to ultraviolet radiation. Visible radiation is generally the result of smaller changes in electron energy levels within the molecules of fuel, flame intermediates, and products of combustion. Infrared radiation comes from the vibration of molecules or parts of molecules when they are in the superheated state associated with combustion. Each chemical compound exhibits a group of wavelengths at which it is resonant. These wavelengths constitute the chemical's infrared spectrum, which is usually unique to that chemical.

This interrelationship between wavelength and combustion chemistry affects the relative performance of various types of detectors with respect to various fires.

3.3.295 Wide-Area Mass Notification System. See 3.3.79, Emergency Communications System.

3.3.296 Wide Area Signaling. Signaling intended to provide alerting or information to exterior open spaces, such as campuses, neighborhood streets, a city, a town, or a community. (SIG-NAS)

3.3.297 Wireless Control Unit. See 3.3.53, Control Unit.

3.3.298 Wireless Protection System. A system or a part of a system that can transmit and receive signals without the aid of interconnection wiring. It can consist of either a wireless control unit or a wireless repeater. (SIG-PRO)

3.3.299 Wireless Repeater. A component used to relay signals among wireless devices, appliances, and control units. (SIG-PRO)

The terms *wireless control unit* (see 3.3.53.4), *wireless protection system* (see 3.3.298), and *wireless repeater* apply to systems covered by Section 23.18.

3.3.300 Zone. A defined area within the protected premises. A zone can define an area from which a signal can be received, an area to which a signal can be sent, or an area in which a form of control can be executed. (SIG-FUN)

> **3.3.300.1* Evacuation Signaling Zone.** A discrete area of a building, bounded by smoke or fire barriers, from which occupants are intended to relocate or evacuate. (SIG-PRO)
>
> **A.3.3.300.1 Evacuation Signaling Zone.** Evacuation signaling zones can be as small as a single room, or as large as an entire building, but more commonly are an entire floor or portions of floors divided by smoke or fire barriers.

The term *evacuation signaling zone* is used in the requirements for in-building fire emergency voice/alarm communications systems in 23.10.2 and 24.4.1. See the commentary for *notification zone* following 3.3.300.2.

> **3.3.300.2 Notification Zone.** An area covered by notification appliances that are activated simultaneously. (SIG-PRO)

◄ **FAQ**
What is a notification zone?

A notification zone is the smallest discrete area that is signaled by a system. For a general evacuation system, the notification zone is the entire building. In that case, the evacuation signaling zone and the notification zone are the same. Note that this definition is not defining a zone based on the area served by a notification appliance circuit; rather, it is based on the area that receives the signal simultaneously. In a high-rise building, as well as other occupancies, the system may be designed for partial or selective evacuation or relocation. In that case, most building codes, including *NFPA 5000®, Building Construction and Safety Code®*; NFPA 1, *Fire Code*; and NFPA *101*, would require each fire or smoke zone to be a notification zone — typically each floor is a notification zone. If the automatic response to a fire is to signal the fire floor as well as one floor above and one floor below of the need to evacuate or relocate, the evacuation signaling zone comprises three notification zones. Note that each notification zone is determined by the design of the system. Evacuation signaling zones may be dynamic.

An evacuation signaling zone can have more than one notification zone but can never be smaller than a single notification zone.

REFERENCES CITED IN COMMENTARY

Merriam-Webster's Collegiate Dictionary, 11th edition, Merriam-Webster, Inc., Springfield, MA, 2003.

NEMA SB 30-2005, *Fire Service Annunciator and Interface,* 2005 edition, National Electrical Manufacturers Association, Rosslyn, VA.

NFPA 1, *Fire Code*, 2009 edition, National Fire Protection Association, Quincy, MA.

NFPA 70®, National Electrical Code®, 2008 edition, National Fire Protection Association, Quincy, MA.

NFPA *101®, Life Safety Code®*, 2009 edition, National Fire Protection Association, Quincy, MA.

NFPA 1221, *Standard for the Installation, Maintenance, and Use of Emergency Services Communications Systems*, 2007 edition, National Fire Protection Association, Quincy, MA.

NFPA 5000®, Building Construction and Safety Code®, 2009 edition, National Fire Protection Association, Quincy, MA.

Reserved

CHAPTER 4

In this 2010 edition of *NFPA 72®, National Fire Alarm and Signaling Code*, Chapter 4 is reserved for future use.

Reserved

CHAPTER 5

In this 2010 edition of *NFPA 72®, National Fire Alarm and Signaling Code*, Chapter 5 is reserved for future use.

Reserved

CHAPTER 6

In this 2010 edition of *NFPA 72®, National Fire Alarm and Signaling Code*, Chapter 6 is reserved for future use.

Reserved   CHAPTER 7

In this 2010 edition of *NFPA 72®, National Fire Alarm and Signaling Code*, Chapter 7 is reserved for future use.

Reserved   CHAPTER 8

In this 2010 edition of *NFPA 72®, National Fire Alarm and Signaling Code*, Chapter 8 is reserved for future use.

Reserved   CHAPTER 9

In this 2010 edition of *NFPA 72®, National Fire Alarm and Signaling Code*, Chapter 9 is reserved for future use.

Fundamentals

CHAPTER 10

Chapter 10 (Chapter 4 in previous editions of the Code) includes requirements that are common to all fire alarm systems except household fire alarm systems. Many of the requirements of this chapter also apply to the broader scope of fire/alarm/emergency signaling systems, as reflected in the revised title of the chapter (which was Fundamentals of Fire Alarm Systems in the 2007 edition). The requirements of Chapter 10 apply to protected premises (local) fire alarm systems, supervising station alarm systems, public emergency alarm reporting systems, and emergency communications systems. The scope of this chapter includes requirements for equipment suitability and compatibility, personnel qualification, power supplies, signal distinction and priority, signal indication, fundamental equipment performance, protection of fire alarm systems, annunciation and annunciation zoning, monitoring integrity of circuits/pathways and power supplies, documentation and approvals, and impairments.

In addition to the qualifications for the system designer and installer, the qualifications for those who test, inspect, maintain, and monitor fire alarm and emergency communication systems (ECSs) have been added to this chapter.

The following list is a summary of significant changes to the chapter on fundamentals in the 2010 edition:

- Revisions throughout to reflect the broader application of fire/alarm/emergency systems
- New 10.4.3 relocating service personnel qualification requirements from the inspection, testing, and maintenance chapter
- New 10.4.4 requiring qualification for supervising station operators
- New 10.5.4 allowing an uninterruptible power supply rather than two independent (primary and secondary) power supplies
- New 10.5.6.1.2 requiring protection against physical damage to secondary power circuits
- New 10.5.6.3.1(1) requiring a 20 percent safety factor for all battery calculations
- New Section 10.6 establishing signal priority for different signals and allowing ECS priority signals to have priority over a fire alarm signal
- Revised Section 10.7 (formerly 4.4.3.6) clarifying requirements for distinction of different signals
- New Section 10.8 requiring ECS priority signals to be indicated within 10 seconds
- New 10.17.1.19 requiring that the conductors interconnecting two or more systems be monitored for integrity.
- Revised Figure 10.18.2.1.1 (Record of Completion) providing an extensive update, including mass notification systems
- New 10.18.2.1.2.7 requiring the alternative storage location of the record of completion to be identified at the main fire alarm control unit
- New 10.18.2.1.2.8 requiring the alternative location of the record of completion to be labeled "FIRE ALARM DOCUMENTS"

10.1 Application

10.1.1 The basic functions of a complete fire alarm or signaling system shall comply with the requirements of this chapter.

As noted in the commentary following 1.1.1, the 2010 edition of the Code has been expanded to address the broader scope of fire/alarm/emergency signaling systems, including emergency communications systems, which are covered in Chapter 24. Since the Code now addresses more than just fire alarm systems, the addition of the word "signaling" in 10.1.1 reflects the broader scope of the Code.

10.1.2 The requirements of this chapter shall apply to systems, equipment, and components addressed in Chapters 12, 14, 17, 18, 21, 23, 24, 26 and 27.

The basic requirements for all fire alarm systems, except household fire alarm systems, and for emergency communications systems are contained in Chapter 10. The requirements for household fire alarm systems are addressed in Chapter 29, and, unless noted otherwise, the requirements of Chapter 10 do not apply.

   The requirements of Chapter 1, the references in Chapter 2, and the definitions in Chapter 3 apply throughout the Code, including Chapter 10.

   NFPA 72®, *National Fire Alarm and Signaling Code*, does not address carbon monoxide detection systems, which are covered by NFPA 720, *Standard for the Installation of Carbon Monoxide (CO) Detection and Warning Equipment*. *NFPA 72* also does not address electronic intrusion detection systems, which are covered by NFPA 731, *Standard for the Installation of Electronic Premises Security Systems*.

10.2 Purpose

The purpose of fire alarm and signaling systems shall be primarily to provide notification of alarm, supervisory, and trouble conditions; to alert the occupants; to summon aid; and to control emergency control functions.

10.3 Equipment

10.3.1 Equipment constructed and installed in conformity with this Code shall be listed for the purpose for which it is used.

In accordance with the requirements of 10.3.1, equipment must be listed for the purpose for which it is used. The listing of equipment involves evaluation of the equipment to determine its suitability for a specific purpose. The evaluation is usually accomplished through the use of product testing standards developed to demonstrate that specific performance requirements have been met. Many of these performance requirements are based on specific requirements in the Code and go far beyond requirements used only to demonstrate electrical safety.

FAQ ▶
What type of information does the equipment listing contain?

   Equipment listings generally contain information pertaining to the permitted use, required ambient conditions in the installed location, mounting orientation, voltage tolerances, compatibility, and so on. Equipment must be installed, tested, and maintained in conformance with the listing and the manufacturer's published instructions to meet the requirements of the Code. Conformance with the listing and the manufacturer's instructions has been a longstanding requirement, originating in the rules of *NFPA 70®*, *National Electrical Code® (NEC®)*, and now reinforced in 10.3.1.

10.3.2 System components shall be installed, tested, and maintained in accordance with the manufacturer's published instructions and this Code.

10.3.3* All devices and appliances that receive their power from the initiating device circuit or signaling line circuit of a control unit shall be listed for use with the control unit.

A.10.3.3 This requirement does not apply to notification appliance circuits.

Subsection 10.3.3 has been revised to include appliances in the requirement for compatibility. It is the intent of the Code that devices and appliances that receive their power directly from either an initiating device circuit (IDC) or a signaling line circuit (SLC) have those devices or appliances listed for that particular control unit. This listing is not required for notification appliance circuits (NACs).

This requirement applies generically to all detection devices and notification appliances that receive their power from initiating device or signaling line circuits. The most common applications where this is a concern are two-wire and addressable (addressable/analog) smoke detectors. A two-wire smoke detector obtains its power from the control unit initiating device circuit. Analog addressable devices and appliances on signaling line circuits communicate with the control unit using manufacturer-specific protocols. Therefore, 10.3.3 requires that these devices and appliances be listed for use with the control unit and its associated initiating device or signaling line circuit. The listing organizations have developed specific requirements for this listing process and should be consulted if necessary to confirm the detector's or appliance's compatibility with a specific control unit.

10.4 Personnel Qualifications

10.4.1 System Designer.

10.4.1.1 Fire alarm system and emergency communications system plans and specifications shall be developed in accordance with this Code by persons who are experienced in the proper design, application, installation, and testing of the systems.

The Code requires that fire alarm and emergency communications system designers be qualified to perform this type of work through training, education, and experience. Typically a state-licensed professional engineer regularly engaged in the design of these systems meets this requirement. Most state engineering license laws require that only licensed engineers be allowed to perform design work and only in their field of expertise.

10.4.1.2 State or local licensure regulations shall be followed to determine qualified personnel. Depending on state or local licensure regulations, qualified personnel shall include, but not be limited to, one or more of the following:

This paragraph was added to make it clear that state or local licensure requirements must be followed. Depending on the state or local jurisdiction, the designer may be required to be a registered professional engineer, or the designer may be allowed to be a contractor who is installing the system. In either case, the designer needs to be competent with either fire alarm systems or emergency communications systems, depending on which system is being designed.

(1) Personnel who are registered, licensed, or certified by a state or local authority

This category involves state or local programs that provide assurance of designer qualification.

(2) Personnel who are certified by a nationally recognized certification organization acceptable to the authority having jurisdiction

For this category, there are a number of independent organizations that provide third-party certification for designers of these systems. The authority having jurisdiction is responsible for independently assessing these programs and certifications to determine if the designer's certification provides the competency required for the system being submitted.

(3) Personnel who are factory trained and certified for fire alarm system design and emergency communications system design of the specific type and brand of system and who are acceptable to the authority having jurisdiction

This category demonstrates that the designer has a basic understanding of the system to be installed in addition to the broader knowledge needed for a system designer. The authority having jurisdiction is responsible for assessing the acceptability of designer's qualifications.

10.4.1.3 The system designer shall provide evidence of their qualifications and/or certifications when requested by the authority having jurisdiction.

10.4.1.4 The system designer shall be identified on the system design documents.

Requiring that the system designer be identified on the system design documents encourages the designer to feel a sense of ownership toward the design. This identification, in turn, provides an additional incentive for the designer to meet the requirements of the Code and provides the authority having jurisdiction with the name of the person responsible for the design who can respond to questions or comments from the authority having jurisdiction.

10.4.2 System Installer.

10.4.2.1 Fire alarm systems and emergency communications systems installation personnel shall be qualified or shall be supervised by persons who are qualified in the installation, inspection, and testing of the systems.

The qualifications required under 10.4.2 for installation personnel or the personnel supervising the installation of these systems correlate with similar requirements in 10.4.1, except the requirements under 10.4.2 focus on installation, inspection, and testing qualifications.

10.4.2.2 State or local licensure regulations shall be followed to determine qualified personnel. Depending on state or local licensure regulations, qualified personnel shall include, but not be limited to, one or more of the following:

(1) Personnel who are registered, licensed, or certified by a state or local authority
(2) Personnel who are certified by a nationally recognized certification organization acceptable to the authority having jurisdiction
(3) Personnel who are factory trained and certified for fire alarm system installation and emergency communications system installation of the specific type and brand of system and who are acceptable to the authority having jurisdiction

10.4.2.3 The system installer shall provide evidence of their qualifications and/or certifications when requested by the authority having jurisdiction.

10.4.3 Inspection, Testing, and Maintenance Personnel. (SIG-TMS)

The Code recognizes four methods, in 10.4.3.1(1) through 10.4.3.1(4), to demonstrate that service personnel are qualified. Refer to A.14.2.2.5 for a list of the basic skills that service personnel should be able to perform.

10.4.3.1* Service personnel shall be qualified and experienced in the inspection, testing, and maintenance of systems addressed within the scope of this Code. Qualified personnel shall include, but not be limited to, one or more of the following:

(1)* Personnel who are factory trained and certified for the specific type and brand of system being serviced
(2)* Personnel who are certified by a nationally recognized certification organization acceptable to the authority having jurisdiction
(3)* Personnel who are registered, licensed, or certified by a state or local authority to perform service on systems addressed within the scope of this Code

(4) Personnel who are employed and qualified by an organization listed by a nationally recognized testing laboratory for the servicing of systems within the scope of this Code

A.10.4.3.1 It is not the intent to require personnel performing simple inspections or operational tests of initiating devices to require factory training or special certification provided such personnel can demonstrate knowledge in these areas.

A.10.4.3.1(1) Factory training and certification is intended to allow an individual to service equipment only for which he or she has specific brand and model training.

One of the methods permitted to demonstrate a technician's qualifications is factory training. Often, service personnel are factory trained to perform or assist in the performance of system testing. This is especially true when system maintenance (servicing) is needed. Because each manufacturer's control equipment is different, the servicing of control equipment, including things such as the replacement of circuit boards or system programming, should be done only by technicians trained to service the specific equipment (manufacturer and model) that they will be working on. Without proper training from a system manufacturer on critical system components, properly maintaining a system will prove to be difficult.

A.10.4.3.1(2) Nationally recognized fire alarm certification programs might include those programs offered by the International Municipal Signal Association (IMSA) and National Institute for Certification in Engineering Technologies (NICET). NOTE: These organizations and the products or services offered by them have not been independently verified by the NFPA, nor have the products or services been endorsed or certified by the NFPA or any of its technical committees.

The International Municipal Signal Association (IMSA) is the professional association of those individuals who oversee public fire communications systems and traffic signaling systems. This organization offers educational programs for technicians and authorities having jurisdiction. IMSA also offers interior fire alarm certification programs for fire alarm technicians and publishes cable requirements for public (fire) reporting systems. Interior Fire Alarm Level IIB certification is the minimum level that should be considered to meet this requirement. IMSA can be reached at P.O. Box 539, 165 East Union Street, Newark, NY 14513-0539 or at *www.imsasafety.org*.

The National Institute for Certification in Engineering Technologies (NICET) offers a program of certification for fire alarm technicians. NICET Level II certification is the minimum level that should be considered to meet this qualification. NICET can be reached at 1420 King Street, Alexandria, VA 22314-2794 or at *www.nicet.org*.

A.10.4.3.1(3) Licenses and certifications offered at a state or local level are intended to recognize those individuals who have demonstrated a minimum level of technical competency in the area of fire alarm servicing.

The category identified in 10.4.3.1(3) recognizes that the state or local authority having jurisdiction may have specific certification or licensing tests or other requirements that must be met.

The category identified in 10.4.3.1(4) recognizes service personnel employed by a listed central station or listed alarm service–local company may be used for servicing of fire alarm systems in accordance with 26.3.3.

10.4.3.2 Evidence of qualifications shall be provided to the authority having jurisdiction upon request.

10.4.4 Supervising Station Operators. (SIG-SSS)

Requirements for supervising station operators are new for the 2010 edition. While the methods of demonstrating qualification are somewhat similar to those of persons who design, install, and service fire alarm and emergency communications systems, the subject matter is quite different. Supervising station operators play a vital role in the response to emergencies and must be well versed in the procedures and equipment they use in performing their duties.

10.4.4.1 All operators in the supervising station shall demonstrate competence in all tasks required of them in Chapter 26 by one or more of the following:

(1) Certified by the manufacturer of the receiving system or equipment or the alarm-monitoring automation system
(2)* Certified by an organization acceptable to the authority having jurisdiction

A.10.4.4.1(2) An example of an organization providing alarm monitoring operator training is the Central Station Alarm Association (CSAA). Note that this reference is for information purposes only, information concerning the product or service has been provided by the manufacturer or other outside sources, and the information concerning the product or service has not been independently verified nor has the product or service been endorsed or certified by the NFPA or any of its technical committees.

(3) Licensed or certified by a state or local authority
(4) Other training or certification approved by the authority having jurisdiction

10.4.4.2 Evidence of qualifications and/or certification shall be provided when requested by the authority having jurisdiction. A license or qualification listing shall be current in accordance with the requirements of the issuing authority or organization.

10.4.4.3 Operator trainees shall be under the direct supervision of a qualified operator until qualified as required by 10.4.4.1.

10.5 Power Supplies

10.5.1 Scope. The provisions of this section shall apply to power supplies used for protected premises fire alarm systems, supervising station alarm systems, public emergency alarm reporting systems, and emergency communications systems and equipment.

The requirements of Section 10.5 generally apply to all systems addressed by the Code, except household fire alarm systems addressed in Chapter 29. These requirements apply unless they conflict with the requirements specified in other chapters. As an example, the chapter on Protected Premises Fire Alarm Systems includes special provisions for low-power wireless systems in 23.18.2.

10.5.2 Code Conformance. All power supplies shall be installed in conformity with the requirements of *NFPA 70, National Electrical Code*, for such equipment and with the requirements indicated in this subsection.

10.5.3 Power Supply Sources.

10.5.3.1 Power shall be supplied in compliance with either 10.5.3.2 or 10.5.4.

10.5.3.2 Unless configured in compliance with 10.5.4, at least two independent and reliable power supplies shall be provided, one primary and one secondary.

Prior to the 1993 edition, *NFPA 72* required three sources of power: primary, secondary (standby), and trouble. The requirement for a trouble signal power supply had an exception that permitted the secondary power supply to provide power to the trouble signal. Because the majority of fire alarm system control unit designs applied this exception, subsequent editions of the Code deleted the requirement for a separate trouble power source.

Editions of the Code prior to 2002 included exceptions that permitted fire alarm systems to be supplied by only a primary power source, eliminating the secondary source if the primary source was from a dedicated branch circuit of an emergency, legally required standby, or optional standby power system. In the 2002 edition, these exceptions were eliminated, and a primary power source and a secondary power source were always required.

Paragraph 10.5.3.1 was added in the 2010 edition to provide an option to use an uninterruptible power supply in accordance with 10.5.4, instead of having both a primary and a secondary power supply.

10.5.3.3 Each power supply shall be of adequate capacity for the application.

10.5.3.4 Monitoring the integrity of power supplies shall be in accordance with 10.5.9.6.

10.5.4 Uninterruptible Power Supplies (UPS).

The requirements for an uninterruptible power supply (UPS) were added to provide details as to the type of system required if the UPS option is used

The Type, Class, and Level designations specified in 10.5.4.1 refer to the classifications specified in Chapter 4 of NFPA 111, *Standard on Stored Electrical Energy Emergency and Standby Power Systems*. The Type O designation requires that the UPS have no interruptions — it must be able to carry the load in 0 seconds. The Class 24 designation requires the UPS to be able to operate at its rated load without being refueled or recharged for 24 hours. The Level 1 designation requires the system to be permanently installed and have equipment performance requirements for the most stringent applications where failure of the equipment to perform could result in loss of human life or serious injuries. The equipment, design, inspection, and testing requirements for Level 1 systems go beyond those for Level 2 systems.

The UPS must be supplied by a dedicated branch circuit from a source, as described in 10.5.5.1. Careful consideration must be given in determining the proper capacity for the UPS to ensure that its rated load is adequate for the fire/alarm/emergency system that it serves.

10.5.4.1 The UPS device shall be configured in compliance with NFPA 111, *Standard on Stored Electrical Energy Emergency and Standby Power Systems*, for a Type 0, Class 24, Level 1 system.

10.5.4.2 The UPS device shall be supplied by a dedicated branch circuit as described in 10.5.5.1.

10.5.4.3 Failure of the UPS shall result in the initiation of a trouble signal in accordance with Section 10.12.

10.5.5 Primary Power Supply.

10.5.5.1 Dedicated Branch Circuit. A dedicated branch circuit of one of the following shall supply primary power:

(1) Commercial light and power
(2) An engine-driven generator or equivalent in accordance with 10.5.10.2, where a person specifically trained in its operation is on duty at all times
(3) An engine-driven generator or equivalent arranged for cogeneration with commercial light and power in accordance with 10.5.10.2, where a person specifically trained in its operation is on duty at all times

The Code requires that the primary power for the system be supplied from a power distribution branch circuit dedicated to the fire/alarm/emergency system. The dedicated circuit may be used to power other control units and power supplies that are part of the system, but this power circuit cannot be used to power other equipment, such as phone switches, music-on-hold, fax machines, computer stations, and so forth. Also refer to the commentary following 10.5.5.4.

An engine-driven generator is permitted as a primary power supply because commercial light and power service may not be available at all locations. Paragraph 10.5.5.1 also recognizes the use of engine-driven generators arranged for cogeneration with commercial light and power. Where an engine-driven generator is used as the primary power supply, it must comply with 10.5.10.2 but is not required to be part of an emergency power system.

10.5.5.2 Circuit Identification and Accessibility.

10.5.5.2.1 The location of the dedicated branch circuit disconnecting means shall be permanently identified at the control unit.

10.5.5.2.2 For fire alarm systems the circuit disconnecting means shall be identified as "FIRE ALARM CIRCUIT."

10.5.5.2.3 For fire alarm systems the circuit disconnecting means shall have a red marking.

10.5.5.2.4 The circuit disconnecting means shall be accessible only to authorized personnel.

10.5.5.3 Mechanical Protection. The dedicated branch circuit(s) and connections shall be protected against physical damage.

In the 2010 edition the requirements for circuit identification and accessibility have been grouped separately from mechanical protection and are now addressed under 10.5.5.2. It should be noted that the requirements in 10.5.5.2.1 and 10.5.5.2.4 apply to any system, while the requirements in 10.5.5.2.2 and 10.5.5.2.3 apply only to fire alarm systems.

FAQ ▶
What is the purpose of mechanical protection and identification of the power supply circuit?

The requirements of 10.5.5.2 and 10.5.5.3 are intended to protect the power supply from tampering, to aid in troubleshooting, and to help ensure the safety of those who service the equipment. They are also intended to help ensure reliability. By limiting access, there is a decreased chance that the power to the fire alarm system is turned off. Because the circuit disconnecting means can include the use of a circuit breaker, the requirements of 10.5.5.2.4 limiting access to authorized personnel can usually be accomplished by using a circuit breaker lock that is listed for use with the circuit breaker. Circuit breaker locks allow the breaker to trip but inhibit tampering and inadvertent operations. The requirement of 10.5.5.3 for mechanical protection is to ensure that the circuit supplying primary power to the system is protected against physical damage. This protection can usually be provided through the use of an appropriate wiring method installed in accordance with the requirements of the *NEC*. A similar requirement has been added in 10.5.6.1.2 for circuits that supply secondary power.

10.5.5.4 Overcurrent Protection. An overcurrent protective device of suitable current-carrying capacity that is capable of interrupting the maximum short-circuit current to which it can be subject shall be provided in each ungrounded conductor.

All wiring and equipment, including the circuits that supply power to the fire/alarm/emergency system, must be installed in accordance with *NFPA 70*. The *NEC* also includes requirements for overcurrent protection. Primary power must be supplied through a dedicated branch circuit in accordance with 10.5.5.1 of *NFPA 72*. The term *branch circuit* is specifically defined in the *NEC,* and requirements are included in Article 210. A branch circuit includes "the circuit conductors between the final overcurrent device protecting the circuit and the outlet(s)." (In this case, the outlet would be the point where the connections are made to the fire/alarm/emergency system equipment.) The branch circuit overcurrent protective device should not be confused with service equipment that is used to connect the (power) service conductors at their entrance to the building. A branch circuit overcurrent protective device is always located after a service-disconnect and service overcurrent device.

In some cases, the branch circuit supplying the fire/alarm/emergency system is served by a remote electrical subpanel. When this arrangement occurs, the information as to which feeder circuit or main electrical panel circuit is connected to the electrical subpanel should be marked in the subpanel. Access to the main panel or circuit supplying the subpanel should be restricted and marked in a similar manner as the subpanel.

10.5.6 Secondary Power Supply.

The requirements for secondary power supplies are organized into separate sections for fire alarm systems located at the protected premises and emergency communications systems (see 10.5.6.1) and for the facilities of the supervising station (see 10.5.6.2).

10.5.6.1* Secondary Power Supply for Protected Premises Fire Alarm Systems and Emergency Communications Systems.

A.10.5.6.1 The secondary power supply is not required to supply power to the fire alarm system through parallel distribution paths. Automatic transfer switches are commonly used to allow secondary power to be supplied over the same distribution system as the primary power.
  The generator does not need to be dedicated to the fire alarm system.

10.5.6.1.1 The secondary power supply shall consist of one of the following:

(1) A storage battery dedicated to the system arranged in accordance with 10.5.9
(2) An automatic-starting, engine-driven generator serving the dedicated branch circuit specified in 10.5.5.1 and arranged in accordance with 10.5.10.3.1, and storage batteries dedicated to the system with 4 hours of capacity arranged in accordance with 10.5.9

Paragraph 10.5.6.1.1(2) recognizes that power from the automatic-starting, engine-driven generator is typically supplied upstream of the dedicated circuit supplying primary power and that a separate dedicated branch circuit is not required.
  Where an automatic-starting, engine-driven generator is used as the secondary power supply, it must comply with 10.5.10.3.1 and be part of an emergency power system in accordance with Article 700 of the *NEC*. Four hours of battery capacity is required by 10.5.6.1.1(2) to power the fire/emergency system in case the engine-driven generator fails to start, allowing time for the generator to be serviced or repaired.

10.5.6.1.2 Secondary circuits that provide power to the control unit and are not integral to the unit shall be protected against physical damage.

Paragraph 10.5.6.1.2 was added to the 2010 edition of the Code. The requirement for mechanical protection found in 10.5.5.3 for the dedicated branch circuit of the primary power supply is now extended to external circuits that supply secondary power. All supply circuits that are not part of the control unit must be protected against physical damage. Also refer to the commentary following 10.5.5.3.

10.5.6.2 Secondary Power Supply for Supervising Station Facilities.

10.5.6.2.1 The secondary power supply shall consist of one of the following:

(1) Storage batteries dedicated to the supervising station equipment arranged in accordance with 10.5.9
(2) A dedicated branch circuit of an automatic-starting, engine-driven generator arranged in accordance with 10.5.10.3.2.1 and 10.5.10.3.2.2, and storage batteries dedicated to the supervising station equipment with 4 hours of capacity arranged in accordance with 10.5.9
(3) A dedicated branch circuit of multiple engine-driven generators, at least one of which is arranged for automatic starting in accordance with 10.5.10.3.2.1 and 10.5.10.3.2.2

The requirements for supervising station facilities in 10.5.6.2.1(1) and 10.5.6.2.1(2) are similar to those for protected premises. By reference to 10.5.10.3.2 as compared to 10.5.10.3.1, an automatic-starting, engine-driven generator used as the secondary power supply does not need to be part of an emergency power system, but it must be part of a legally required standby power system in accordance with Article 701 of the *NEC*. In addition, the reference to NFPA 110, *Standard for Emergency and Standby Power Systems*, and specification of Type 60 versus Type 10 require a 60-second start instead of a 10-second start.

The use of multiple engine-driven generators, where one generator is automatic starting and the other(s) can be arranged for a manual start, has been maintained as an option for secondary power at supervising station facilities. This provision recognizes the continual nature of these operations, 24 hours a day, 7 days a week. Additional requirements are imposed in 10.5.6.2.2, and compliance with NFPA 110 is required.

10.5.6.2.2 Where 10.5.6.2.1(3) is used, the following shall apply:

(1) Each generator shall be capable of supplying the energy required.
(2) Generators that are started manually shall be arranged in accordance with 10.5.10.3.2.3 and 10.5.10.3.2.4.
(3) When manual-start generators are employed, a person trained in the procedure of starting the generator shall be on duty at all times.

10.5.6.3* Capacity.

Although the requirement for 60 hours of secondary supply for auxiliary (fire) alarm systems and remote supervising station (fire) alarm systems was changed in the 2002 edition of the Code to 24 hours to be consistent with the other systems, in some applications it might be prudent to include a capacity sufficient for periods longer than 24 hours. Additional consideration of this point is provided in A.10.5.6.3.

A.10.5.6.3 When a fire alarm system is used to alert occupants, the associated premises are generally evacuated during prolonged power outages. When this is not the case, as in emergency shelters or certain government facilities, additional secondary power should be required to address a more prolonged outage. These outages might be expected to result from weather or earthquake in locations subject to these events. Reasonable judgment should be employed when requiring additional secondary capacity.

When a fire alarm system is used to protect property, the associated premises might be vacant for prolonged periods (weekend, long holiday) or in very remote locations. When this is the case, and when the risk of loss is significant, additional secondary power should be required to address a more prolonged outage. These outages might be expected to result from weather or earthquake in locations subject to these events. Reasonable judgment should be employed when requiring additional secondary capacity.

10.5.6.3.1 The secondary power supply shall have sufficient capacity to operate the system under quiescent load (system operating in a nonalarm condition) for a minimum of 24 hours and, at the end of that period, shall be capable of operating all alarm notification appliances used for evacuation or to direct aid to the location of an emergency for 5 minutes, unless otherwise permitted or required by the following:

(1) Battery calculations shall include a 20 percent safety margin to the calculated amp-hour rating.
(2) The secondary power supply for in-building fire emergency voice/alarm communications service shall be capable of operating the system under quiescent load for a minimum of 24 hours and then shall be capable of operating the system during a fire or other emergency condition for a period of 15 minutes at maximum connected load.
(3) The secondary power supply capacity for supervising station facilities and equipment shall be capable of supporting operations for a minimum of 24 hours.
(4) The secondary power supply for high-power speaker arrays used for wide-area mass notification systems shall be in accordance with 24.4.3.4.2.2.
(5) The secondary power supply for textual visible appliances shall be in accordance with 24.4.3.4.7.1.

(6) The secondary power supply capacity for central control stations of a wide-area mass notification systems shall be capable of supporting operations for a minimum of 24 hours.

(7) The secondary power supply for in-building mass notification systems shall be capable of operating the system under quiescent load for a minimum of 24 hours and then shall be capable of operating the system during emergency condition for a period of 15 minutes at maximum connected load.

10.5.6.3.2 The secondary power supply capacity required shall include all power supply loads that are not automatically disconnected upon the transfer to secondary power supply.

The proper amount of battery standby capacity can be calculated. The calculation should include the normal standby supervisory quiescent load for a specified period of time (24 hours) as well as the load during the specified period of alarm. In general, this rule applies to all systems except as noted otherwise in 10.5.6.3.1(1) through 10.5.6.3.1(7).

◄ **FAQ**
What should the battery calculation include?

The Code now includes a requirement in 10.5.6.3.1(1) for a 20 percent safety factor to be added to all battery calculations. This provision recognizes that battery output will decrease over the life of the battery.

Paragraph 10.5.6.3.1(2) requires that in-building fire emergency voice/alarm communications system be capable of operating under fire or other emergency conditions for 15 minutes at maximum connected load. Although the Code specifies a minimum capacity of 15 minutes at maximum connected load, the system is still intended to remain operational for a period of 2 hours in accordance with the survivability rules in Section 12.4 and 24.3.5. The expected load during actual operation of the system would be distributed over the 2-hour period.

Provisions were added in the 2010 edition of the Code for emergency communications systems. Paragraphs 10.5.6.3.1(4) through 10.5.6.3.1(6) involve requirements for wide-area mass notification systems. The secondary power supply for high-power speaker arrays must have a minimum of 7-day standby capacity followed by 60 minutes of full load capacity. The secondary power supply capacity for textual visible appliances must have the capacity to support a minimum of 2 hours of continuous display time. The secondary power supply for central control stations must have a capacity to support operation for at least 24 hours. Paragraph 10.5.6.3.1(7) was added for in-building mass notification systems and requires a capacity similar to that specified in 10.5.6.3.1(2) for in-building fire emergency voice alarm communications systems.

If combination systems are used, the secondary supply must be able to power the entire system for the required 24-hour period. Other loads, such as security or building management systems, must be figured into the secondary power calculations unless those loads are automatically disconnected upon transfer to secondary power in accordance with 10.5.6.3.2.

A sample battery calculation is shown in Exhibit 10.1 for a modestly sized local fire alarm system.

10.5.6.4 Secondary Power Operation.

10.5.6.4.1 Operation on secondary power shall not affect the required performance of a system or supervising station facility, including alarm, supervisory, and trouble signals and indications.

10.5.6.4.2 Systems operating on secondary power shall comply with Section 10.17.

10.5.6.4.3 While operating on secondary power, audio amplifier monitoring shall comply with 10.17.2.1.2.

Manufacturers have supplied systems in the past that, in order to save battery power, eliminated annunciation of additional trouble conditions and eliminated some supplementary functions when in the standby power mode. The Code in 10.5.6.4.1 and 10.5.6.4.2 prevents this practice by requiring the system to operate with all the same features as when it is pow-

EXHIBIT 10.1 Sample Battery Calculation.

ITEM	DESCRIPTION	STANDBY CURRENT PER UNIT (AMPS)		QTY		TOTAL STANDBY CURRENT PER UNIT (AMPS)	TOTAL ALARM CURRENT PER UNIT (AMPS)		QTY		TOTAL SYSTEM ALARM CURRENT (AMPS)
A	FACU	0.1200	X	1	=	0.1200	1.5000	X	1	=	1.5000
B	Smoke Det	0.0005	X	42	=	0.0210	0.0010	X	42	=	0.0420
C	Duct Det	0.0005	X	16	=	0.0080	0.0010	X	16	=	0.0160
D	Horn/Strobe	none	X	14	=	none	0.0950	X	14	=	1.33
E	Strobe	none	X	6	=	none	0.0720	X	6	=	0.4320
F	Relay	0.0070	X	4	=	0.0280	none	X	4	=	none
			X		=			X		=	
			X		=			X		=	
			X		=			X		=	
			X		=			X		=	
			X		=			X		=	
		TOTAL SYSTEM STANDBY CURRENT (AMPS)				0.1770	**TOTAL SYSTEM ALARM CURRENT (AMPS)**				3.32

REQUIRED OPERATING TIME OF SECONDARY POWER SOURCE FROM NFPA 72 10.5.6.3.

STANDBY: ___24___ HOURS   ALARM: ___5___ MINUTES × 1/60 ___0.0833___ HOURS

REQUIRED STANDBY TIME (HOURS)		TOTAL SYSTEM STANDBY CURRENT (AMPS)		REQUIRED STANDBY CAPACITY (AMP-HOURS)	REQUIRED ALARM TIME (HOURS)		TOTAL SYSTEM ALARM CURRENT (AMPS)		REQUIRED ALARM CURRENT (AMP-HOURS)
24	X	0.1770	=	4.2480	0.0833	X	3.32	=	.2766

REQUIRED STANDBY CAPACITY (AMP-HOURS)		REQUIRED ALARM CAPACITY (AMP-HOURS)		TOTAL REQUIRED CAPACITY (AMP-HOURS)	FACTOR OF SAFETY		REQUIRED BATTERY CAPACITY (AMP-HOURS)
4.2480	+	.2766	=	4.5246	X	1.2	5.43

ered by the primary power source. An allowance for audio amplifiers is provided in 10.5.6.4.3 by reference to 10.17.2.1.2. Paragraph 10.17.2.1.2 recognizes that systems are typically arranged to disconnect power to amplifiers that are operating under secondary power in order to conserve power. Paragraph 10.17.2.1 provides more specific requirements for monitoring the integrity of audio amplifiers and when trouble signals are required to be transmitted.

10.5.7* Continuity of Power Supplies.

A.10.5.7 Where a computer system of any kind is used to receive and process alarm or supervisory signals, an uninterruptible power supply (UPS) with sufficient capacity to operate the system until the secondary supply is capable of operating the fire alarm system might be required in order to prevent signal loss or a greater than 10-second signal delay.

UPS equipment often contains an internal bypass arrangement to supply the load directly from the line. These internal bypass arrangements are a potential source of failure. UPS equipment also requires periodic maintenance. It is, therefore, necessary to provide a means of promptly and safely bypassing and isolating the UPS equipment from all power sources while maintaining continuity of power supply to the equipment normally supplied by the UPS.

10.5.7.1 The secondary power supply shall automatically provide power to the protected premises system within 10 seconds whenever the primary power supply fails to provide the minimum voltage required for proper operation.

Paragraph 10.5.7.1 requires the secondary power supply to provide power to the protected premises system within 10 seconds of the primary power supply failure. This requirement correlates with the Type 10 requirement in 10.5.10.3.1.1. Editions of *NFPA 72* prior to 2002 allowed 30 seconds.

10.5.7.2 The secondary power supply shall automatically provide power to the supervising station facility and equipment within 60 seconds whenever the primary power supply fails to provide the minimum voltage required for proper operation.

Paragraph 10.5.7.2 requires the secondary power supply to provide power to the supervising station facility and equipment within 60 seconds of the primary power supply failure. This requirement correlates with the Type 60 requirement in 10.5.10.3.2.1. The Code recognizes the potential increased complexity of transferring to secondary power at a supervising station facility.

10.5.7.3 Required signals shall not be lost, interrupted, or delayed by more than 10 seconds as a result of the primary power failure.

10.5.7.3.1 Storage batteries dedicated to the system or UPS arranged in accordance with the provisions of NFPA 111, *Standard on Stored Electrical Energy Emergency and Standby Power Systems*, shall be permitted to supplement the secondary power supply to ensure required operation during the transfer period.

10.5.7.3.2 Where a UPS is employed in 10.5.7.3.1, a positive means for disconnecting the input and output of the UPS system while maintaining continuity of power supply to the load shall be provided.

Paragraph 10.5.7.3 of *NFPA 72* was rewritten in the 2002 edition to provide more performance-oriented requirements. Reference to computer systems was removed. However, the Code recognizes the potential need for an uninterruptible power supply (UPS), and, when one is used, the requirements in this paragraph that are applicable to UPS systems must be met.

The requirement in 10.5.7.3.2 for disconnection of the UPS is to ensure that power is provided to the system during maintenance and testing of the UPS.

10.5.8 Power Supply for Remotely Located Control Equipment.

10.5.8.1 Additional power supplies, where provided for control units, circuit interfaces, or other equipment essential to system operation, and located remotely from the main control unit, shall be comprised of a primary and secondary power supply that shall meet the same requirements as those of 10.5.1 through 10.5.7 and 10.17.3.

10.5.8.2 The location of any remotely located power supply shall be identified at the master control unit.

10.5.8.3 The master control unit display shall be permitted to satisfy the requirement of 10.5.8.2.

10.5.8.4 The location of any remotely located power supply shall be identified on the record drawings.

Paragraph 10.5.8.1 requires that the power supply for remotely located control units and other essential equipment meet the same requirements as that of the main (master) control unit. Paragraphs 10.5.8.2 and 10.5.8.4 require that the location of all remotely located power supplies be identified at the master control unit and on the record drawings. In accordance with 10.5.8.3, identification at the master control unit can be accomplished on the master control unit display itself.

10.5.9* Storage Batteries.

A.10.5.9 The following newer types of rechargeable batteries are normally used in protected premises applications:

(1) *Vented Lead-Acid, Gelled, or Starved Electrolyte Battery.* This rechargeable-type battery is generally used in place of primary batteries in applications that have a relatively high current drain or that require the extended standby capability of much lower currents. The nominal voltage of a single cell is 2 volts, and the battery is available in multiples of 2 volts (e.g., 2, 4, 6, 12). Batteries should be stored according to the manufacturer's published instructions.

(2) *Nickel-Cadmium Battery.* The sealed-type nickel-cadmium battery generally used in applications where the battery current drain during a power outage is low to moderate (typically up to a few hundred milliamperes) and is fairly constant. Nickel-cadmium batteries are also available in much larger capacities for other applications. The nominal voltage per cell is 1.42 volts, with batteries available in multiples of 1.42 (e.g., 12.78, 25.56). Batteries in storage can be stored in any state of charge for indefinite periods. However, a battery in storage will lose capacity (will self-discharge), depending on storage time and temperature. Typically, batteries stored for more than 1 month require an 8-hour to 14-hour charge period to restore capacity. In service, the battery should receive a continuous, constant-charging current that is sufficient to keep it fully charged. (Typically, the charge rate equals $\frac{1}{10}$ to $\frac{1}{20}$ of the ampere-hour rating of the battery.) Because batteries are made up of individual cells connected in series, the possibility exists that, during deep discharge, one or more cells that are low in capacity will reach complete discharge prior to other cells. The cells with remaining life tend to charge the depleted cells, causing a polarity reversal resulting in permanent battery damage. This condition can be determined by measuring the open cell voltage of a fully charged battery (voltage should be a minimum of 1.28 volts per cell multiplied by the number of cells). Voltage depression effect is a minor change in discharge voltage level caused by constant current charging below the system discharge rate. In some applications of nickel-cadmium batteries (e.g., battery-powered shavers), a memory characteristic also exists. Specifically, if the battery is discharged daily for 1 minute, followed by a recharge, operation for 5 minutes will not result in the rated ampere-hour output because the battery has developed a 1-minute discharge memory.

(3) *Sealed Lead-Acid Battery.* In a sealed lead-acid battery, the electrolyte is totally absorbed by the separators, and no venting normally occurs. Gas evolved during recharge is internally recombined, resulting in minimal loss of capacity life. A high-pressure vent, however, is provided to avoid damage under abnormal conditions.

10.5.9.1 Marking.

10.5.9.1.1 Batteries shall be marked with the month and year of manufacture using the month/year format.

10.5.9.1.2 Where the battery is not marked with the month/year by the manufacturer, the installer shall obtain the date-code and mark the battery with the month/year of battery manufacture.

FAQ ▶
What format must be used to mark the date of manufacture on the battery?

Paragraph 10.5.9.1.1 requires that batteries be marked with the month and year of manufacture, using the month/year format. Thus, a battery that is manufactured in February of 2010 must be marked 02/2010. This paragraph does not require that the maker of the battery mark the battery in this format. The maker may choose to use a date code. If this is the case, 10.5.9.1.2 requires that the installer then translate the date code into the format required by 10.5.9.1.1 and mark the battery accordingly.

10.5.9.2 Location. Storage batteries shall be located so that the equipment, including overcurrent devices, are not adversely affected by battery gases and shall conform to the requirements of *NFPA 70, National Electrical Code,* Article 480.

Battery gases can cause severe corrosion of terminals and contacts in equipment enclosures. Sealed lead-acid batteries are generally permitted inside control units; however, vented lead-acid batteries are not permitted inside control units. See Exhibit 10.2 for an example of a sealed lead-acid battery. If large batteries are necessary, a separate battery cabinet, as shown in Exhibit 10.3, may be required to adequately house the batteries. If batteries are located remotely from the control unit, the location must be identified at the control unit.

10.5.9.2.1 Cells shall be suitably insulated against grounds.

10.5.9.2.2 Cells shall be suitably insulated against crosses.

10.5.9.2.3 Cells shall be mounted in such a manner so as to be protected from physical damage.

10.5.9.2.4 Racks shall be suitably protected against deterioration.

10.5.9.2.5 If not located in or adjacent to the control unit, the batteries and their charger location shall be permanently identified at the control unit.

The requirement in 10.5.9.2.5 for identification of the location of remotely located batteries or chargers, or both, is intended to simplify system inspections and tests. Long runs of conductors to remote batteries can create unacceptable voltage drops that can affect system performance. Voltage-drop calculations must be conducted to ensure that the system has adequate voltage under full load.

EXHIBIT 10.2 *Typical Sealed Lead-Acid Battery. (Source: Power-Sonic Corp., San Diego, CA)*

10.5.9.3 Battery Charging.

10.5.9.3.1 Adequate facilities shall be provided to automatically maintain the battery fully charged under all conditions of normal operation.

10.5.9.3.2 Adequate facilities shall be provided to recharge batteries within 48 hours after fully charged batteries have been subject to a single discharge cycle as specified in 10.5.6.3.

Unless the capacity of the battery charger has been carefully calculated, systems with large batteries may have difficulty meeting the requirement in 10.5.9.3.2. The manufacturer's data sheets should provide maximum charging capabilities.

10.5.9.3.3 Upon attaining a fully charged condition, the charge rate shall not be so excessive as to result in battery damage.

10.5.9.3.4* Batteries shall be either trickle- or float-charged.

A.10.5.9.3.4 Batteries are trickle-charged if they are off-line and waiting to be put under load in the event of a loss of power.

Float-charged batteries are fully charged and connected across the output of the rectifiers to smooth the output and to serve as a standby source of power in the event of a loss of line power.

EXHIBIT 10.3 *Separate Battery Cabinet. (Source: Space Age Electronics, Inc., Hudson, MA)*

10.5.9.3.5 Supervising stations shall maintain spare parts or units available, which shall be used to restore failed charging capacity prior to the consumption of one-half of the capacity of the batteries for the supervising station equipment.

This paragraph is intended for the batteries that are located at the supervising station.

10.5.9.4 Overcurrent Protection.

10.5.9.4.1 The batteries shall be protected against excessive load current by overcurrent devices.

10.5.9.4.2 The batteries shall be protected from excessive charging current by overcurrent devices or by automatic current-limiting design of the charging source.

10.5.9.5 Metering. The charging equipment shall provide either integral meters or readily accessible terminal facilities for the connection of portable meters by which the battery voltage and charging current can be determined.

10.5.9.6 Monitoring Integrity of Battery Charger.

10.5.9.6.1 Means for monitoring integrity appropriate for the batteries and charger employed shall be provided to detect a battery charger failure.

10.5.9.6.2 Failure of the battery charger shall result in the initiation of a trouble signal in accordance with Section 10.12.

The requirements in 10.5.9.6.1 and 10.5.9.6.2 were part of the metering requirement of the 1989 edition of NFPA 71, *Standard for the Installation, Maintenance, and Use of Signaling Systems for Central Station Service*. The battery-charging circuits of all systems are now required to be monitored and to produce a trouble signal upon failure. Requirements for monitoring the integrity of power supplies are contained in 10.17.3.

10.5.10 Engine-Driven Generators.

Subsection 10.5.10 applies when the power for the system is supplied from an engine-driven generator. The requirements for secondary power supplies in 10.5.10.3 relate back to the requirements for secondary power supplies in 10.5.6 and are also organized into separate sections to reflect different provisions for the fire alarm systems at the protected premises and emergency communications systems (see 10.5.6.1) and for supervising station facilities (see 10.5.6.2). NFPA 110 applies when engine-driven generators are used for the secondary power supply. The requirements within NFPA 110 are specified in terms of specific system types, classes, and levels. *NFPA 72* specifies the appropriate classifications in 10.5.10.3 to correlate with the designations in NFPA 110. These classifications are defined in Chapter 4 of NFPA 110. The requirements in NFPA 110 address the performance, installation, maintenance, operation, and testing requirements for the emergency power supply system. The requirements in *NFPA 70* address the complete electrical installation, including these (and other) sources of power, as well as the equipment used to distribute and control power from these systems when the normal supply is interrupted.

10.5.10.1 Application and Installation. The application and installation of engine-driven generators shall be as specified in 10.5.10.2 through 10.5.10.7.

10.5.10.2 Primary Power Supply.

10.5.10.2.1 Engine-driven generators arranged as the primary supply shall be designed in an approved manner.

10.5.10.2.2 Engine-driven generators arranged as the primary supply shall be installed in an approved manner.

10.5.10.3 Secondary Power Supplies.

10.5.10.3.1 Protected Premises.

10.5.10.3.1.1 Engine-driven generators used to provide secondary power for a protected premises fire alarm system or an emergency communications system shall comply with NFPA 110, *Standard for Emergency and Standby Power Systems*, Chapter 4, requirements for a Type 10, Class 24, Level 1 system.

10.5.10.3.1.2 Installation of engine-driven generators used to provide secondary power for a protected premises fire alarm system or an emergency communications system shall be in accordance with *NFPA 70, National Electrical Code*, Article 700.

10.5.10.3.1.3 Where survivability of circuits is required by another section of the Code, equal protection shall be provided for power supply circuits.

10.5.10.3.2 Supervising Station.

10.5.10.3.2.1 Automatic-starting, engine-driven generators used to provide secondary power for a supervising station shall comply with NFPA 110, *Standard for Emergency and Standby Power Systems*, Chapter 4, requirements for a Type 60, Class 24, Level 2 system.

10.5.10.3.2.2 Installation of automatic-starting, engine-driven generators used to provide secondary power for a supervising station shall be in accordance with *NFPA 70, National Electrical Code*, Article 701.

10.5.10.3.2.3 Manual-starting, engine-driven generators used to provide secondary power for a supervising station shall comply with NFPA 110, *Standard for Emergency and Standby Power Systems*, Chapter 10, requirements for a Type M, Class 24, Level 2 system.

10.5.10.3.2.4 Installation of manual-starting, engine-driven generators used to provide secondary power for a supervising station shall be in accordance with *NFPA 70, National Electrical Code*, Article 702.

10.5.10.4 Performance, Operation, Testing, and Maintenance. The requirements for performance, operation, testing, and maintenance of engine-driven generators shall conform to the applicable provisions of NFPA 110, *Standard for Emergency and Standby Power Systems*.

NFPA 110 provides requirements for testing of engine-driven generators. The manufacturer's equipment data sheets should provide fuel consumption rates for the engine-driven generator.

◄ **FAQ**
What document provides testing requirements for engine-driven generators?

10.5.10.5 Capacity. The unit shall be of a capacity that is sufficient to operate the system under the maximum normal load conditions in addition to all other demands placed upon the unit.

10.5.10.6 Fuel. Unless otherwise required or permitted in 10.5.10.6.1 through 10.5.10.6.3, fuel shall be available in storage sufficient for 6 months of testing plus the capacity specified in 10.5.6.

10.5.10.6.1 For public emergency alarm reporting systems, the requirements of Chapter 27 shall apply.

10.5.10.6.2 If a reliable source of supply is available at any time on a 2-hour notice, it shall be permitted to have fuel in storage sufficient for 12 hours of operation at full load.

10.5.10.6.3 Fuel systems using natural or manufactured gas supplied through reliable utility mains shall not be required to have fuel storage tanks unless located in seismic risk zone 3 or greater as defined in ANSI A-58.1, *Building Code Requirements for Minimum Design Loads in Buildings and Other Structures*.

10.5.10.7 Battery and Charger. A separate storage battery and separate automatic charger shall be provided for starting the engine-driven generator and shall not be used for any other purpose.

10.6 Signal Priority

The priority of signals shall be in accordance with Section 10.6.

This new section on signal priority was added in the 2010 edition. Signal distinction is addressed separately in Section 10.7.

The term *signal* is defined in 3.3.240 as "a status indication communicated by electrical or other means." Definitions for the terms *alarm signal, fire alarm signal, supervisory signal*, and *trouble signal*, among others, are included as subdefinitions. Each signal has a specific purpose, each elicits a different response, and with few exceptions each type of signal must be treated separately. This includes the maintenance of separate circuits for each type of signal, or the ability to process information transmitted over circuits so that signal priority and distinction can be maintained in accordance with Sections 10.6 and 10.7.

New emergency communications systems signaling terms are being used in this edition of the Code. These terms include *ECS priority signals, emergency mass notification signals*, and *priority alarms*. These terms are not specifically defined in the Code. The meaning of these terms must be taken from the context of their usage.

10.6.1 ECS priority signals when evaluated by stakeholders through a risk analysis in accordance with 14.4.2.2 shall be permitted to take precedence over all other signals.

10.6.2 Fire alarm signals shall take precedence over all other signals, except as permitted by 10.6.1 or 10.6.3.

10.6.3* Emergency mass notification signals and messages shall be permitted to have priority over fire alarm notification signals in accordance with the requirements of Chapter 24.

A.10.6.3 Mass notification signals might, at times, be more important to the building or area occupants than the fire alarm signal. Stakeholders should perform a risk analysis in accordance with 24.4.2.2 to determine which, if any, messages should receive priority.

10.6.4 Emergency mass notification signals and messages shall have priority over supervisory and trouble signals in accordance with the requirements of Chapter 24.

10.6.5 Supervisory signals shall take precedence over trouble signals.

10.6.6 Hold-up alarms or other life-threatening signals shall be permitted to take precedence over supervisory and trouble signals where acceptable to the authority having jurisdiction.

10.6.7* Where separate systems are installed, they shall be permitted to achieve the priority of signals in accordance with Section 10.6.

Revisions were made in the Protected Premises Fire Alarm Systems chapter of the 2007 edition of the Code to allow mass notification input to take priority over fire alarm signals. With the addition of emergency communications systems to the Code in the 2010 edition, signal priority requirements needed to be further refined and added to the Fundamentals chapter. Subsection 10.6.1 allows for an ECS priority signal to take priority over a fire alarm signal if the stakeholders of the system have determined after a risk analysis, detailed in 24.4.2.2, that the ECS priority signal for the protected premises must have priority over the fire alarm signal. The ECS priority signal may be for an emergency event that is determined to be more critical than a fire alarm signal, such as an attack on the building and its occupants by terrorist shooters. It should be noted that not all ECS signals are necessarily ECS priority signals.

This distinction should be addressed as a part of the risk assessment required in Chapter 24. Subsections 10.6.2 through 10.6.5 further establish the relative priority of fire alarm signals, emergency mass notification signals, supervisory signals, and trouble signals.

Subsection 10.6.6 allows for a hold-up alarm or other life-threatening signals with the approval of the authority having jurisdiction to have priority over supervisory and trouble signals.

Subsection 10.6.7 permits separate systems installed at the same premises to achieve the same priority scheme as allowed by Section 10.6 for a single system.

Signal priority requirements are also addressed for combination fire alarm systems in 23.8.4.5 and for various types of emergency communications systems throughout Chapter 24.

A.10.6.7 In addition, the override of circuits should be indicated at the control panel of each system to ensure signals are restored to normal.

10.7 Distinctive Signals

With the addition of emergency communications systems to the Code, revision of the requirements for distinctive signals was needed. Priority alarms or ECS priority signals from mass notification systems add to the list of different signals that can be present at a protected premises in addition to the traditional signals from a fire alarm system.

10.7.1 Priority alarms, fire alarms, supervisory signals, and trouble signals shall be distinctively and descriptively annunciated.

All alarm, supervisory, and trouble signals must be distinctively annunciated. The typical means of accomplishing this is through the display at the control unit. It could also be accomplished through the use of a separate annunciator panel. It is important that signal descriptions be sufficiently detailed to provide a clear indication of the condition being annunciated. This feature is especially important when both mass notification systems signals and fire alarm system signals are included in the system design. Refer to 10.7.3 and A.10.7.3 for additional requirements for and explanation of control unit signals.

10.7.2 Audible alarm notification appliances for a fire alarm system shall produce signals that are distinctive from other similar appliances used for other purposes in the same area that are not part of the fire alarm or emergency communications system.

Notification appliances used for the fire alarm system or emergency communications system must produce signals that are distinctive from the signals produced by notification appliances of other systems that might be in the same area.

10.7.3* Audible signals on a control unit, or on multiple control units that are interconnected to form a system, or at a remote location, shall be permitted to have the same audible characteristics for all alerting functions including, but not limited to, alarm, trouble, and supervisory, provided that the distinction between signals shall be by other appropriate means, such as visible annunciation.

A.10.7.3 Control unit signals can be audible, visible, or both for any particular function. Some older systems used only audible indicators that had to be coded in order for users to know what the signal meant. Where a control unit uses both audible and visible indicators, the purpose of the audible signal is to get someone's attention. In large system configurations, there might be multiple control units with audible signals. Also, there might be several different functions requiring an audible alert as a part of the whole signal. Thus, there could be several different audible signals. It is not the intent of the code to have separate and distinct audible signals where there is clear visual distinction that provides the user with the needed information. Visible signals, whether a lamp with a text label, an LCD screen, or a computer monitor, are a better form of human interface.

The requirements in 10.7.3 have been revised to make it clear that alarm, supervisory, and trouble signals on a control unit or on multiple control units of the same system are permitted to have the same audible characteristics as long as the different signals are distinctively indicated by other appropriate means, such as an LED or LCD message.

10.7.4* Supervisory signals shall be distinctive in sound from other signals, and their sound shall not be used for any other purpose except as permitted in 10.7.3.

A.10.7.4 A valve supervisory, a low-pressure switch, or another device intended to cause a supervisory signal when actuated should not be connected in series with the end-of-line supervisory device of initiating device circuits, unless a distinctive signal, different from a trouble signal, is indicated.

10.7.5 Trouble signals required to indicate at the protected premises shall be indicated by distinctive audible signals, which shall be distinctive from alarm signals except as permitted in 10.7.3.

Distinctive audible signals are required for supervisory and trouble signals in accordance with 10.7.4 and 10.7.5, respectively. However, both subsections refer back to 10.7.3, which permits a common audible signal as long as signal distinction is indicated by other appropriate means, such as an LED or LCD message.

10.7.6 Fire alarm evacuation signals shall be distinctive in sound from other signals, shall comply with the requirements of 18.4.2.1, and their sound shall not be used for any other purpose.

Fire alarm signals used to notify occupants of the need to evacuate must produce the distinctive emergency evacuation signal required by 18.4.2.1.

10.8* ECS Priority Signals

Visible indication of priority signals shall be automatically indicated within 10 seconds at the fire alarm control unit or other designated location. (SIG-ECS)

A.10.8 Other locations could include the following:

(1) Building fire command center for in-building fire emergency voice/alarm communications systems
(2) Fire alarm control unit for network fire alarm systems
(3) Supervising station locations for systems installed in compliance with Chapter 26

Section 10.8 was added to the 2010 edition of the Code. This section requires that priority signals from an emergency communications system be automatically indicated within 10 seconds. This time period is required in various places in the Code to limit the signal processing time.

10.9 Fire Alarm Signals

10.9.1 Fire alarm signals shall be distinctive in sound from other signals, shall comply with the requirements of 18.4.2.1, and their sound shall not be used for any other purpose.

10.9.2 Actuation of alarm notification appliances or emergency voice communications, emergency control functions, and annunciation at the protected premises shall occur within 10 seconds after the activation of an initiating device.

10.9.3* A coded alarm signal shall consist of not less than three complete rounds of the number transmitted.

A.10.9.3 The recommended coded signal designations for buildings that have four floors and multiple basements are provided in Table A.10.9.3.

10.9.4 Each round of a coded alarm signal shall consist of not less than three impulses.

Subsection 10.9.3 refers to a coded signal. The term *coded* is defined in 3.3.43 as "an audible or visible signal that conveys discrete bits or units of information." A coded signal is meant to notify personnel of the nature or origin of the signal. Table A.10.9.3 provides recommended assignments for simple zone-coded signals. In addition to the examples described in Table A.10.9.3, textual audible signals may use words that are familiar only to those concerned with response to the signal. This practice avoids general alarm notification and disruption of the occupants. Hospitals often use this type of signal. For example, to hospital occupants who do not know the code words, the message "Paging Dr. Firestone, Dr. Firestone, Building 4 West Wing" might sound like a normal paging announcement, but the coded message is that there is a fire in the West Wing of Building 4.

Subsection 10.9.4 requires that upon activation, the code will sound at least three times, alerting the users of the location of the alarm. A coded system should not be confused with 18.4.2.1 and the requirements of ANSI S3.41, *American National Standard Audible Emergency Evacuation Signal.*

TABLE A.10.9.3
Recommended Coded Signal Designations

Location	Coded Signal
Fourth floor	2–4
Third floor	2–3
Second floor	2–2
First floor	2–1
Basement	3–1
Sub-basement	3–2

10.10* Fire Alarm Signal Deactivation

A.10.10 It is the intent that both visual and audible appliances are shut off when the signal silence feature is activated on the fire alarm control unit.

Per the ADA, it is important not to provide conflicting signals for the hearing impaired.

10.10.1 A means for turning off activated alarm notification appliance(s) shall be permitted only if it complies with 10.10.3 through 10.10.7.

10.10.2 When an alarm signal deactivation means is actuated, both audible and visible notification appliances shall be simultaneously deactivated.

10.10.3 The means shall be key-operated or located within a locked cabinet, or arranged to provide equivalent protection against unauthorized use.

10.10.4 The means shall provide a visible zone alarm indication or the equivalent as specified in 10.16.1.

10.10.5 Subsequent actuation of initiating devices on other initiating device circuits or subsequent actuation of addressable initiating devices on signaling line circuits shall cause the notification appliances to reactivate.

Exception: Subsequent actuation of another addressable initiating device of the same type in the same room or space shall not be required to cause the notification appliance(s) to reactivate.

10.10.6 A means that is left in the "off" position when there is no alarm shall operate an audible trouble signal until the means is restored to normal.

10.10.7* Resetting of alarm signals shall comply with the requirements of 23.8.2.2.

The requirements of Section 10.10 address the means to manually deactivate fire alarm system notification appliances from the fire alarm system. It should be recognized that in some situations mass notification systems are permitted to override fire alarm signals and prevent notification appliances from producing fire alarm signals or messages until released manually by the mass notification system. Refer to 24.4.1.7 for in-building fire emergency voice/alarm communications systems. Refer to 24.4.2.1.7 through 24.4.2.1.10, 24.4.2.16, and 24.4.2.25.1, among others, for signal deactivation criteria for in-building mass notification systems.

Section 10.10 permits activated fire alarm notification appliances to be deactivated under specified conditions. Both audible and visible notification appliances must be deactivated simultaneously. Protection must be provided to prevent unauthorized use of the deactivation means. Visible alarm zone indication must be provided to indicate the location of an operated initiating device. The notification appliances must reactivate upon subsequent actuation of initiating devices (discussed in more detail in following paragraphs). An audible trouble indication must operate if the means to deactivate is left in the "off" position when no alarm signal is present.

Deactivation of the notification appliances can assist the fire service in responding to alarm conditions and making assessments in the management of the fire scene. In using the deactivation feature, the responding personnel must assess the conditions at the scene and work in concert with the evacuation plan for the building. Prior to deactivation of notification appliances, access to the facility needs to be secured so that unauthorized persons do not inadvertently enter the building.

Simultaneous deactivation of both audible and visible appliances was introduced in the 2007 edition as a new condition required for alarm signal deactivation. The reason for this change was concern over the mixed message that would be sent to the hearing impaired if the visible appliances are left activated while the audible appliances are silenced.

Subsection 10.10.5 requires the reactivation of the alarm notification appliances when a subsequent alarm signal from another initiating device circuit or a subsequent alarm signal from an addressable initiating device on any signaling line circuit is received. The exception allows the system to be arranged so that subsequent alarms from other addressable initiating devices of the same type in the same area as the device that initiated the first alarm need not reactivate the alarm notification appliances. Note that the exception was changed in the 2010 edition of the Code so that approval of the authority having jurisdiction is no longer required as a condition of the exception.

Use of the deactivation feature during testing of the fire alarm system is not addressed by the Code. However, the requirements of Section 10.19 for system impairment must be considered whenever the system is taken out of service.

A.10.10.7 Resetting of alarm signals should not require the simultaneous operation of multiple reset switches or the disconnection of any wiring or equipment to reset the alarm condition.

10.11 Supervisory Signals

10.11.1 Coded Supervisory Signal.

10.11.1.1 A coded supervisory signal shall be permitted to consist of two rounds of the number transmitted to indicate a supervisory off-normal condition.

10.11.1.2 A coded supervisory signal shall be permitted to consist of one round of the number transmitted to indicate the restoration of the supervisory condition to normal.

10.11.2 Combined Coded Alarm and Supervisory Signal Circuits. Where both coded sprinkler supervisory signals and coded fire or waterflow alarm signals are transmitted over the same signaling line circuit, provision shall be made to obtain either alarm signal precedence or sufficient repetition of the alarm signal to prevent the loss of an alarm signal.

10.11.3 Self-Restoring Supervisory Signal Indication. Visible and audible indication of self-restoring supervisory signals and visible indication of their restoration to normal shall be automatically indicated within 90 seconds at the following locations:

(1) Fire alarm control unit for local fire alarm systems
(2) Building fire command center for in-building fire emergency voice/alarm communications systems
(3) Supervising station location for systems installed in compliance with Chapter 26

10.11.4 Latching Supervisory Signal Indication.

The requirements in 10.11.3 and 10.11.4 provide reporting requirements for self-restoring and latching supervisory signals. The 90-second requirement is considered adequate because supervisory signals do not represent immediate life-threatening conditions. Separate requirements for self-restoring and latching supervisory signals were developed in *NFPA 72* to recognize the use of both types in the Code. Refer to 23.8.5.8.2 and the associated commentary for additional information on latching supervisory signals.

10.11.4.1 Visible and audible indication of latching supervisory signals shall be indicated within 90 seconds at the locations specified in 10.11.3.

10.11.4.2 Restoration of latching supervisory signals shall be indicated within 90 seconds at the locations specified in 10.11.3.

10.11.5 Supervisory Signal Silencing.

10.11.5.1 A means for silencing a supervisory signal notification appliance(s) shall be permitted only if it complies with 10.11.5.2 through 10.11.5.5.

10.11.5.2 The means shall be key-operated or located within a locked cabinet, or arranged to provide equivalent protection against unauthorized use.

10.11.5.3 The means shall transfer the supervisory indication to a lamp or other visible indicator, and subsequent supervisory signals in other zones shall cause the supervisory notification appliance(s) to re-sound.

10.11.5.4 A means that is left in the "silence" position where there is no supervisory off-normal signal shall operate a visible signal silence indicator.

10.11.5.5 A means that is left in the "silence" position shall cause the trouble signal to sound until the silencing means is restored to normal position.

The requirements in 10.11.5 for silencing of an audible supervisory signal are somewhat similar to the provisions for alarm signal deactivation. Exhibit 10.4 illustrates the display and controls for alarm, supervisory, and trouble signals on a fire alarm control unit.

10.12 Trouble Signals

10.12.1 Trouble signals and their restoration to normal shall be indicated within 200 seconds at the locations identified in 10.12.6 or 10.12.7.

10.12.2 Indication of primary power failure trouble signals transmitted to a supervising station shall be delayed in accordance with 10.17.3.3.

Subsection 10.12.2 correlates with 10.17.3.3 to reflect that the Code requires delaying the transmission of primary power supply failure trouble signals to supervising stations unless the delay is prohibited by the authority having jurisdiction. The requirement in 10.17.3.3 applies to all methods used to transmit signals to the supervising station.

EXHIBIT 10.4 *Fire Alarm Control Unit Showing Display Area and Controls for Alarm, Supervisory, and Trouble Signals. (Source: SimplexGrinnell, Westminster, MA)*

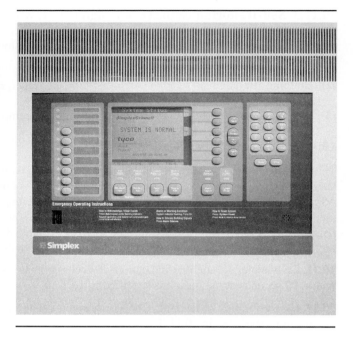

10.12.3 If an intermittent signal is used, it shall sound at least once every 10 seconds, with a minimum duration of $\frac{1}{2}$ second.

10.12.4 A single audible trouble signal shall be permitted to annunciate multiple fault conditions.

10.12.5 The trouble signal(s) shall be located in an area where it is likely to be heard.

FAQ ▶
Where must trouble signal notification appliances be located?

Subsection 10.12.5 requires that the local trouble signal be located in an area within the protected premises that ensures that it will be heard. A sounding appliance installed separate from the control unit may be required.

10.12.6 Visible and audible trouble signals and visible indication of their restoration to normal shall be indicated at the following locations:

(1) Fire alarm control unit for protected premises alarm systems
(2) Building fire command center for in-building fire emergency voice/alarm communications systems
(3) Central station or remote station location for systems installed in compliance with Chapter 26

10.12.7 Trouble signals and their restoration to normal shall be visibly and audibly indicated at the proprietary supervising station for systems installed in compliance with Chapter 26.

10.12.8 Audible Trouble Signal Silencing Means.

10.12.8.1 A means for silencing the trouble notification appliance(s) shall be permitted only if it complies with the following:

(1) The means shall be key-operated or located within a locked cabinet, or arranged to provide equivalent protection against unauthorized use.
(2) The means shall transfer the trouble indication to a suitably identified lamp or other acceptable visible indicator.

(3) The visible indication specified in 10.12.8.1(2) shall persist until the trouble condition has been corrected.
(4) The audible trouble signal shall sound when the silencing means is in its silence position and no trouble exists.

The word *means* in 10.12.8.1 recognizes that this function can be performed with alphanumeric keypads, switches, or touch screens.

10.12.8.2 If an audible trouble notification appliance is also used to indicate a supervisory condition, as permitted by 10.7.3, a trouble signal silencing switch shall not prevent subsequent sounding of supervisory signals.

10.12.8.3* An audible trouble signal that has been silenced at the protected premises shall comply with the following:

(1) The audible trouble signal shall automatically re-sound every 24 hours or less until fault conditions are restored to normal.
(2) The audible trouble signal shall sound until it is manually silenced or acknowledged.
(3) The re-sounded trouble signal shall also be automatically retransmitted to any supervising station to which the original trouble signal was transmitted.

A.10.12.8.3 The purpose of automatic trouble re-sound is to remind owners, or those responsible for the system, that the system remains in a fault condition. A secondary benefit is to possibly alert occupants of the building that the fire alarm system is in a fault condition.

Trouble signals indicate a fault that may impair system operation. Paragraph 10.12.8.3 requires that a silenced trouble signal re-sound at least once every 24 hours until the source of the trouble signal has been identified and corrected by the system operator. This requirement helps ensure that trouble signals are not ignored. Additionally, if a supervising station alarm system is provided, the re-sound of the trouble signal must also be transmitted *daily* to the supervising station.

10.12.8.4* If permitted by the authority having jurisdiction, the requirement for a 24-hour re-sound of an audible trouble signal shall be permitted to occur only at a supervising station that meets the requirements of Chapter 26 and not at the protected premises.

A.10.12.8.4 In large, campus-style arrangements with proprietary supervising stations monitoring protected premises systems, and in other situations where off-premises monitoring achieves the desired result, the authority having jurisdiction is permitted to allow the re-sound to occur only at the supervising station. Approval by the authority having jurisdiction is required so it can consider all fire safety issues and make a determination that there are procedures in place to ensure that the intent is met; in other words, someone is available to take action to correct the problem.

10.13 Emergency Control Function Status Indicators

Section 10.13, formerly Fire Safety Function Status Indicators, has been retitled Emergency Control Function Status Indicators to reflect that the Code now addresses more than just fire alarm systems.

10.13.1 All controls provided specifically for the purpose of manually overriding any automatic emergency control function shall provide visible indication of the status of the associated control circuits.

The visible status indication required by 10.13.1 can be achieved by a labeled annunciator (or equivalent means) or by the labeled position of a toggle or rotary switch.

10.13.2* Where status indicators are provided for emergency equipment or control functions, they shall be arranged to reflect the actual status of the associated equipment or function.

A.10.13.2 The operability of controlled mechanical equipment (e.g., smoke and fire dampers, elevator recall arrangements, and door holders) should be verified by periodic testing. Failure to test and properly maintain controlled mechanical equipment can result in operational failure during an emergency, with potential consequences up to and including loss of life.

10.14 Performance and Limitations

10.14.1 Voltage, Temperature, and Humidity Variation. Equipment shall be designed so that it is capable of performing its intended functions under the following conditions:

(1)*At 85 percent and at 110 percent of the nameplate primary (main) and secondary (standby) input voltage(s)
(2) At ambient temperatures of 0°C (32°F) and 49°C (120°F)
(3) At a relative humidity of 85 percent and an ambient temperature of 30°C (86°F)

A.10.14.1(1) The requirement of 10.14.1(1) does not preclude transfer to secondary supply at less than 85 percent of nominal primary voltage, provided the requirements of 10.5.6 are met.

Equipment not listed for use outside the limits specified in 10.14.1(1) through 10.14.1(3) must be relocated or the space must be conditioned to meet these parameters. If the space must be artificially conditioned, standby power to operate that artificial conditioning should be considered to ensure that the artificial conditioning continues during a power outage for at least as long as the standby power required for the alarm system.

10.14.2 Installation and Design.

10.14.2.1* All systems shall be installed in accordance with the specifications and standards approved by the authority having jurisdiction.

A.10.14.2.1 Fire alarm specifications can include some or all of the following:

(1) Address of the protected premises
(2) Owner of the protected premises
(3) Authority having jurisdiction
(4) Applicable codes, standards, and other design criteria to which the system is required to comply
(5) Type of building construction and occupancy
(6) Fire department response point(s) and annunciator location(s)
(7) Type of fire alarm system to be provided
(8) Calculations (e.g., secondary supply and voltage drop calculations)
(9) Type(s) of fire alarm–initiating devices, supervisory alarm–initiating devices, and evacuation notification appliances to be provided
(10) Intended area(s) of coverage
(11) Complete list of detection, evacuation signaling, and annunciator zones
(12) Complete list of emergency control functions
(13) Complete sequence of operations detailing all inputs and outputs

What information should be considered for the specification package?

FAQ ▶

Prior to the installation of the system, the designer's plans and specifications must first receive the approval of the authority having jurisdiction. Annex paragraph A.10.14.2.1 identifies some of the information to be considered for inclusion in the specification package. Section 10.18 identifies documentation that must be submitted to the authority having jurisdiction if requested. A prudent designer will contact the authority having jurisdiction prior to beginning the detailed design to make sure the submittal requirements are clearly understood. Refer to Section 10.18 and related commentary for additional documentation and approval requirements and recommendations.

10.14.2.2 Devices and appliances shall be located and mounted so that accidental operation or failure is not caused by vibration or jarring.

10.14.2.3 All apparatus requiring rewinding or resetting to maintain normal operation shall be restored to normal as promptly as possible after each alarm and kept in normal condition for operation.

10.14.2.4 Equipment shall be installed in locations where conditions do not exceed the voltage, temperature, and humidity limits specified in the manufacturer's published instructions.

10.14.3 Initiating Devices.

10.14.3.1 Initiating devices of the manual or automatic type shall be selected and installed so as to minimize nuisance alarms.

10.14.3.2 Manual fire alarm boxes shall comply with Section 17.14 and 23.8.5.2.1.

10.15* Protection of Fire Alarm System

In areas that are not continuously occupied, automatic smoke detection shall be provided at the location of each fire alarm control unit(s), notification appliance circuit power extenders, and supervising station transmitting equipment to provide notification of fire at that location.

Exception: Where ambient conditions prohibit installation of automatic smoke detection, automatic heat detection shall be permitted.

The requirements of Section 10.15 indicate a clear need for protection of fire alarm system equipment beyond what is normally thought of as a fire alarm control unit as specified in the Code prior to the 2007 edition. The Code specifically includes notification appliance circuit power extenders and supervising station transmitting equipment in the requirement for protection. Also refer to A.10.15, the definition of fire alarm control unit in 3.3.92, the related explanatory material in A.3.3.92, and associated commentary for further explanation of what constitutes a fire alarm control unit.

Smoke detection is required in the areas where this equipment is located anytime these areas are not continuously occupied. The term *continuously occupied* means that a person is *always* at the location (24 hours per day, 7 days per week, 365 days per year).

The exception allows the use of heat detectors where conditions are not suitable for smoke detectors. However, areas that are not suitable for smoke detectors most often are not suitable for control equipment. The listing of the control equipment should always be checked to determine suitable locations. Additional cautionary material is provided in A.4.4.5.

In the 2007 edition, an additional exception was provided to exempt the need for protection in fully sprinklered buildings. This allowance has been removed from the 2010 edition of the Code. The protection of the fire alarm system is now required in all buildings and does not depend on the building being covered by an automatic sprinkler system.

A.10.15 The fire alarm control unit(s) that are to be protected are those that provide notification of a fire to the occupants and responders. The term *fire alarm control unit* does not include equipment such as annunciators and addressable devices. Requiring smoke detection at the transmitting equipment is intended to increase the probability that an alarm signal will be transmitted to a supervising station prior to that transmitting equipment being disabled due to the fire condition.

> CAUTION: The exception to 10.15 permits the use of a heat detector if ambient conditions are not suitable for smoke detection. It is important to also evaluate whether the area is suitable for the control unit.

Where the area or room containing the control unit is provided with total smoke-detection coverage, additional smoke detection is not required to protect the control unit. Where total smoke-detection coverage is not provided, the Code intends that only one smoke detector is required at the control unit even when the area of the room would require more than one detector if installed according to the spacing rules in Chapter 17. The intent of selective coverage is to address the specific location of the equipment.

Location of the required detection should be in accordance with one of the following:

(1) Where the ceiling is 15 ft (4.6 m) in height or less, the smoke detector should be located on the ceiling or the wall within 21 ft (6.4 m) of the centerline of the fire alarm control unit being protected by the detector in accordance with 17.7.3.2.1.

(2) Where the ceiling exceeds 15 ft (4.6 m) in height, the automatic smoke detector should be installed on the wall above and within 6 ft (1.8 m) from the top of the control unit.

Where selective coverage is needed, finding a suitable location for a smoke detector(s) for protection of control equipment can prove to be a difficult challenge in some situations, such as where control equipment is located in a high bay area. Guidance for smoke detector location is provided in A.10.15. In addition a new provision has been included in 17.7.3.1.4 to address the need to locate a detector in close proximity to the equipment it protects. Refer to A.17.7.3.1.4 for further explanation of this provision.

10.16 Annunciation and Annunciation Zoning

Section 10.16 was rewritten in the 2007 edition to more clearly present the requirement, provide a more consistent use of terminology, and address annunciation of supervisory and trouble signals.

10.16.1 Alarm Annunciation.

10.16.1.1 Where required by other governing laws, codes, or standards, the location of an operated initiating device shall be annunciated by visible means.

10.16.1.1.1 Visible annunciation of the location of an operated initiating device shall be by an indicator lamp, alphanumeric display, printout, or other approved means.

10.16.1.1.2 The visible annunciation of the location of operated initiating devices shall not be canceled by the means used to deactivate alarm notification appliances.

FAQ ▶
What is the purpose of alarm annunciation?

Annunciation, not to be confused with building occupant notification, provides a display for arriving emergency personnel to use so they can assess alarm and other conditions upon arrival. The need for annunciation is established outside the requirements of *NFPA 72* through the framework of higher level mandates discussed in the commentary following 1.1.1. Annunciation can be accomplished through the use of a separately located annunciator (remote display panel) or through the display associated with the master fire alarm control unit. Exhibits 10.5 to 10.7 illustrate typical annunciators used to provide the zone information required by 10.16.6.

Subsection 10.16.1 makes it clear that the means used to deactivate alarm notification appliances, addressed in Section 10.10, must not cancel the visible annunciation of the alarm locations.

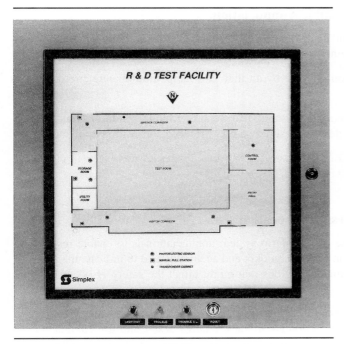

EXHIBIT 10.6 *Typical Back-Lit Labeled Annunciator. (Source: Space Age Electronics, Inc., Hudson, MA)*

EXHIBIT 10.5 *Typical Graphic Fire Alarm Annunciator. (Source: SimplexGrinnell, Westminster, MA)*

EXHIBIT 10.7 *Fire Alarm Control Unit with Liquid Crystal Display Screen. (Source: Mircom Technologies Ltd., Cheektowaga, NY)*

10.16.2 Supervisory and Trouble Annunciation.

10.16.2.1 Where required by other governing laws, codes, or standards, supervisory and/or trouble conditions shall be annunciated by visible means.

10.16.2.1.1 Visible annunciation shall be by an indicator lamp, an alphanumeric display, a printout, or other means.

10.16.2.1.2 The visible annunciation of supervisory and/or trouble conditions shall not be canceled by the means used to deactivate supervisory or trouble notification appliances.

Requirements for annunciation of supervisory and trouble conditions were added in the 2007 edition of the Code. The requirements in 10.16.2 parallel those in 10.16.1 for alarm annunciation.

10.16.3* Annunciator Access and Location.

A.10.16.3 The primary purpose of fire alarm system annunciation is to enable responding personnel to identify the location of a fire quickly and accurately and to indicate the status of emergency equipment or fire safety functions that might affect the safety of occupants in a fire situation.

The authority having jurisdiction determines the type and location of any required annunciation. Common locations for annunciation are lobbies, guard's desks, and fire command centers. *NFPA 72* does not prescribe requirements for the location of the fire alarm control unit. However, if annunciation is required and the fire alarm control unit is being used as the means for annunciation, it must be located in accordance with 10.16.3. Further, if NFPA *101®, Life Safety Code®*, 2009 edition, is being used, NFPA *101* requires controls to be located in accordance with the following excerpt:

> **9.6.6 Location of Controls.** Operator controls, alarm indicators, and manual communications capability shall be installed at a convenient location acceptable to the authority having jurisdiction. [*101:*9.6.6]

For applications involving an emergency communications system, the requirements of Chapter 24 should be reviewed when locations for control equipment are being considered. For example, Section 24.6, Information, Command, and Control, includes requirements for central control stations of emergency communications systems and for emergency communications control units. Other locations in Chapter 24 that may impact decisions on the location of controls include 24.4.1.5 for in-building fire emergency voice/alarm communications systems; 24.4.2.4, 24.4.2.14, and 24.4.2.15 for in-building mass notification systems; 24.5.1 and 24.5.2.6.2 for two-way in-building communications systems; and 24.5.3 for area of refuge emergency communications systems.

10.16.3.1 All required annunciation means shall be readily accessible to responding personnel.

10.16.3.2 All required annunciation means shall be located as required by the authority having jurisdiction to facilitate an efficient response to the fire situation.

10.16.4 Alarm Annunciation Display. Visible annunciators shall be capable of displaying all zones in alarm.

10.16.4.1 If all zones in alarm are not displayed simultaneously, the zone of origin shall be displayed.

10.16.4.2 If all zones in alarm are not displayed simultaneously, there shall be an indication that other zones are in alarm.

The requirement in 10.16.4 ensures that where systems require scrolling to view all the zones in alarm, the system will display the zone of origin and provide an indication that more alarms can be viewed than are currently displayed. The intent is to aid emergency responders in quickly obtaining complete information from the system. The zone of origin must always be displayed.

Although the arrangement of the display is not prescribed in 10.16.4, users of the Code should be aware of the standard emergency service interface requirements of Section 18.11, the guidance in related A.18.11, and the information contained in Annex E.

10.16.5 Fire Command Center. Annunciation at the fire command center shall be by means of audible and visible indicators.

10.16.6* Annunciation Zoning.

A.10.16.6 Fire alarm system annunciation should, as a minimum, be sufficiently specific to identify a fire alarm signal in accordance with the following:

(1) If a floor exceeds 22,500 ft^2 (2090 m^2) in area, the floor should be subdivided into detection zones of 22,500 ft^2 (2090 m^2) or less, consistent with the existing smoke and fire barriers on the floor.
(2) If a floor exceeds 22,500 ft^2 (2090 m^2) in area and is undivided by smoke or fire barriers, detection zoning should be determined on a case-by-case basis in consultation with the authority having jurisdiction.
(3) Waterflow switches on sprinkler systems that serve multiple floors, areas exceeding 22,500 ft^2 (2090 m^2), or areas inconsistent with the established detection system zoning should be annunciated individually.
(4) In-duct smoke detectors on air-handling systems that serve multiple floors, areas exceeding 22,500 ft^2 (2090 m^2), or areas inconsistent with the established detection system zoning should be annunciated individually.
(5) If a floor area exceeds 22,500 ft^2 (2090 m^2), additional zoning should be provided. The length of any zone should not exceed 300 ft (91 m) in any direction. If the building is provided with automatic sprinklers throughout, the area of the alarm zone should be permitted to coincide with the allowable area of the sprinkler zone.

The provisions of 10.16.6 specify the minimum zoning required by *NFPA 72*. Fire alarm system notification zones, which are addressed by these provisions, should correlate with building smoke and fire zones. This correlation is especially important if an in-building fire emergency voice/alarm communications system is used to selectively or partially evacuate occupants or to relocate occupants to areas of refuge during a fire. Definitions for *zone*, *evacuation signaling zone*, and *notification zone* can be found in 3.3.300. In addition, refer to the requirements in 23.8.6.3 for notification zones and the requirements in 24.4.1.9 for evacuation signaling zones.

Additional zoning requirements may exist in the governing building codes; NFPA *101*; *NFPA 5000*®, *Building Construction and Safety Code*®; and local ordinances. These higher level documents often require each floor of a building to be zoned separately for smoke detectors, waterflow switches, manual fire alarm boxes, and other initiating devices. The zoning recommendations found in A.10.16.6 parallel the annunciation zoning requirements found in NFPA *101* and the model building codes.

10.16.6.1 For the purpose of alarm annunciation, each floor of the building shall be considered as a separate zone.

10.16.6.2 For the purposes of alarm annunciation, if a floor of the building is subdivided into multiple zones by fire or smoke barriers and the fire plan for the protected premises allows relocation of occupants from the zone of origin to another zone on the same floor, each zone on the floor shall be annunciated separately.

10.16.6.3 Where the system serves more than one building, each building shall be annunciated separately.

10.17 Monitoring Integrity

10.17.1* Monitoring Integrity of Installation Conductors and Other Signaling Channels.

A.10.17.1 The provision of a double loop or other multiple path conductor or circuit to avoid electrical monitoring is not acceptable.

Subsection 10.17.1 requires connections to devices and appliances to be made so that the opening of any installer's connection to the device or appliance causes a trouble signal. Many installers loop the conductor around the terminal without cutting the conductor and making the necessary two connections. If the wire is disconnected from the terminal, trouble may not be indicated. This practice is in violation of the Code. If a listed device installed on an initiating device circuit is furnished with pigtail connections, the installer must use separate in/out wires for each circuit passing into or through the device in order to prevent T-tapping of the device connections.

However, addressable devices on signaling line circuits typically use an interrogation/response routine to monitor for integrity. Some types of signaling line circuits can be wired without duplicate terminals; they are often T-tapped. The control unit interrogates each device on a regular basis and "knows" when a device has become disconnected.

FAQ ▶
Where is T-tapping allowed and not allowed?

T-tapping is an acceptable practice for Class B signaling line circuits, when allowed by the designer. T-tapping is never allowed on an initiating device circuit, a notification appliance circuit, or a Class A signaling line circuit. Note that pathway class designations are now addressed in Section 12.3.

Exhibit 10.8 shows a schematic example of how a device on an initiating device circuit should and should not be connected. Exhibits 10.9 and Exhibit 10.10 illustrate typical field-wired equipment with duplicate terminals. Exhibit 10.11 shows an example of where T-tapping is permitted.

10.17.1.1 Unless otherwise permitted or required by 10.17.1.3 through 10.17.1.14, all means of interconnecting equipment, devices, and appliances and wiring connections shall be monitored for the integrity of the interconnecting conductors or equivalent path so that the occurrence of a single open or a single ground-fault condition in the installation conductors or other signaling channels is automatically indicated within 200 seconds.

EXHIBIT 10.8 *Acceptable and Unacceptable Connection of a Device on an Initiating Device Circuit.*

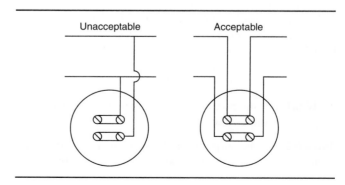

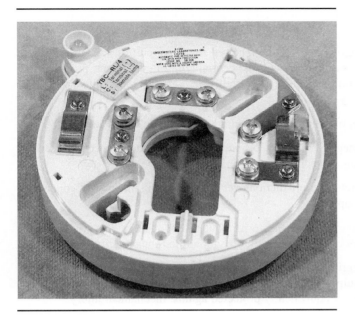

EXHIBIT 10.9 *Initiating Device Base Showing Duplicate Terminals. (Source: Bosch Security, Fairport, NY)*

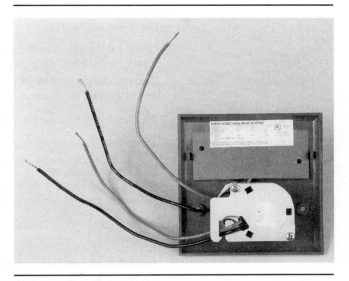

EXHIBIT 10.10 *Notification Appliance Showing Duplicate Leads. (Source: Gentex Corp., Zeeland, MI; photo courtesy of R. P. Schifiliti Associates Inc., Reading, MA)*

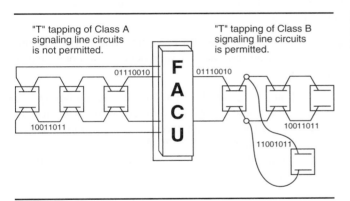

EXHIBIT 10.11 *T-Tapping in Class B Signaling Line Circuits.*

10.17.1.2 Unless otherwise permitted or required by 10.17.1.3 through 10.17.1.14, all means of interconnecting equipment, devices, and appliances and wiring connections shall be monitored for the integrity of the interconnecting conductors or equivalent path so that the restoration to normal of a single open or a single ground-fault condition in the installation conductors or other signaling channels is automatically indicated within 200 seconds.

10.17.1.3 Shorts between conductors shall not be required to be monitored for integrity, unless required by 10.17.1.18, 10.17.1.19 and 10.17.2.2.

10.17.1.4 Monitoring for integrity shall not be required for a noninterfering shunt circuit, provided that a fault circuit condition on the shunt circuit wiring results only in the loss of the noninterfering feature of operation.

10.17.1.5 Monitoring for integrity shall not be required for connections to and between supplementary system components, provided that single open, ground, or short-circuit conditions of the supplementary equipment or interconnecting means, or both, do not affect the required operation of the fire alarm system.

See the commentary following the definition of *supplementary* (see 3.3.272) for further explanation of the term.

10.17.1.6 Monitoring for integrity shall not be required for the circuit of an alarm notification appliance installed in the same room with the central control equipment, provided that the notification appliance circuit conductors are installed in conduit or are equivalently protected against mechanical injury.

10.17.1.7 Monitoring for integrity shall not be required for a trouble signal circuit.

10.17.1.8* Monitoring for integrity shall not be required for the interconnection between listed equipment within a common enclosure.

A.10.17.1.8 This Code does not have jurisdiction over the monitoring integrity of conductors within equipment, devices, or appliances.

The requirement for monitoring applies only to installation conductors. The wiring within equipment, devices, or appliances is not required to be monitored for integrity.

10.17.1.9 Monitoring for integrity shall not be required for the interconnection between enclosures containing control equipment located within 20 ft (6 m) of each other where the conductors are installed in conduit or equivalently protected against mechanical injury.

10.17.1.10 Monitoring for integrity shall not be required for the conductors for ground detection where a single ground does not prevent the required normal operation of the system.

10.17.1.11 Monitoring for integrity shall not be required for central station circuits serving notification appliances within a central station.

10.17.1.12 Monitoring for integrity shall not be required for pneumatic rate-of-rise systems of the continuous line type in which the wiring terminals of such devices are connected in multiple across electrically supervised circuits.

10.17.1.13 Monitoring for integrity shall not be required for the interconnecting wiring of a stationary computer and the computer's keyboard, video monitor, mouse-type device, or touch screen, as long as the interconnecting wiring does not exceed 8 ft (2.4 m) in length; is a listed computer/data processing cable as permitted by *NFPA 70, National Electrical Code*; and failure of cable does not cause the failure of the required system functions not initiated from the keyboard, mouse, or touch screen.

Paragraph 10.17.1.13 recognizes that the interconnecting wiring of certain listed equipment does not have to be monitored for integrity if a stated length of a particular type of cable is used and if a cable failure does not prevent the fire alarm system from performing a required system function.

10.17.1.14 Monitoring for integrity of the installation conductors for a ground-fault condition shall not be required for the communications and transmission channels extending from a supervising station to a subsidiary station(s) or protected premises, or both, that comply with the requirements of Chapter 26 and are electrically isolated from the fire alarm system (or circuits) by a transmitter(s), provided that a single ground condition does not affect the required operation of the fire alarm system.

10.17.1.15 Interconnection means shall be arranged so that a single break or single ground fault does not cause an alarm signal.

10.17.1.16 Unacknowledged alarm signals shall not be interrupted if a fault on an initiating device circuit or a signaling line circuit occurs while there is an alarm condition on that circuit.

Exception: Circuits used to interconnect fire alarm control units.

10.17.1.17 An open, ground, or short-circuit fault on the installation conductors of one alarm notification appliance circuit shall not affect the operation of any other alarm notification circuit.

10.17.1.17.1* Notification alarm circuits that do not have notification appliances tied directly to the circuit shall be considered control circuits.

A.10.17.1.17.1 Initially this requirement was meant to apply to notification appliance circuits (NACs) emanating from a single fire alarm control unit and did not contemplate the use of NAC extender panels. Acknowledging the control circuit concept allows NAC extender panels and relays to be connected to a control circuit.

10.17.1.17.2 Control circuits shall not be required to comply with 10.17.1.17, provided that the circuit is monitored for integrity in accordance with 10.17.1 and a fault in the installation conductors shall result in a trouble signal in accordance with Section 10.12.

Paragraphs 10.17.1.17.1 and 10.17.1.17.2 were added in the 2010 edition to recognize that some notification appliance circuits are not connected directly to notification appliances but instead are connected to a notification appliance extender. In such cases, the circuit is considered to be a control circuit and is not required to comply with 10.17.1.17, provided the conditions in 10.17.1.17.2 are met. Note that circuits from a power extender to notification appliances are still notification appliance circuits and must comply with 10.17.1.17.

10.17.1.18 A wire-to-wire short-circuit fault on any alarm notification appliance circuit shall result in a trouble signal in accordance with Section 10.12, except as permitted by 10.17.1.5, 10.17.1.6, or 10.17.1.11.

Paragraph 10.17.1.18 was revised in the 2007 edition of the Code to eliminate redundancy and to clarify that trouble signals must follow the requirements of Section 10.12.

10.17.1.19 Where two or more systems are interconnected, the interconnecting circuit conductors shall be monitored for integrity so that open, short, or ground-fault conditions that affect the required normal operation of either system are indicated as a trouble condition.

Paragraph 10.17.1.19 was added to the 2010 edition of the Code. This paragraph requires that when two or more systems are interconnected, the interconnecting circuit conductors must be monitored for integrity. The systems may be interconnected fire alarm systems or a fire alarm system and an emergency communications system that are being interconnected and integrated.

10.17.2 Monitoring Integrity of In-Building Fire Emergency Voice/Alarm Communications Systems.

10.17.2.1* Speaker Amplifier and Tone-Generating Equipment. If speakers are used to produce audible fire alarm signals, the required trouble signal for 10.17.2.1.1 through 10.17.2.1.3 shall be in accordance with Section 10.12.

A.10.17.2.1 Amplifiers generally require significant power regardless of load. To reduce the secondary power demand, there is no requirement to monitor the integrity of amplifiers during non-alarm operation on secondary power. This allows the amplifiers to be shut down while the system is operating on secondary power until an alarm occurs. When an alarm occurs, monitoring of integrity must resume so that an operator is aware of current conditions and so that any backup amplifiers can be engaged.

Backup amplifying and evacuation signal–generating equipment is recommended with automatic transfer upon primary equipment failure to ensure prompt restoration of service in the event of equipment failure.

10.17.2.1.1 When primary power is available, failure of any audio amplifier shall result in a trouble signal.

10.17.2.1.2 When an alarm is present and primary power is not available (i.e., system is operating from the secondary power source), failure of any audio amplifier shall result in a trouble signal.

10.17.2.1.3 Failure of any tone-generating equipment shall result in a trouble signal, unless the tone-generating and amplifying equipment are enclosed as integral parts and serve only a single, listed loudspeaker.

10.17.2.2 Two-Way Telephone Communications Circuits.

10.17.2.2.1 Two-way telephone communications circuit installation conductors shall be monitored for open circuit fault conditions that would cause the telephone communications circuit to become fully or partially inoperative.

10.17.2.2.2 Two-way telephone communications circuit installation conductors shall be monitored for short circuit fault conditions that would cause the telephone communications circuit to become fully or partially inoperative.

10.17.2.2.3 Two-way telephone communications circuit fault conditions shall result in a trouble signal in accordance with Section 10.12.

The paragraphs under 10.17.2.2 require that the installation conductors of a two-way telephone circuit be monitored for both open and short circuit fault conditions. These fault conditions will result in a trouble signal in accordance with Section 10.12.

10.17.3 Monitoring Integrity of Power Supplies.

10.17.3.1 Unless otherwise permitted or required by 10.17.3.1.3 and 10.17.3.1.6, all primary and secondary power supplies shall be monitored for the presence of voltage at the point of connection to the system.

10.17.3.1.1 Failure of either supply shall result in a trouble signal in accordance with Section 10.12.

The requirement in 10.17.3.1.1 means that the failure of either the primary or the secondary power supply initiates a trouble signal.

10.17.3.1.2 Where the digital alarm communicator transmitter (DACT) is powered from a protected premises fire alarm system control unit, power failure indication shall be in accordance with 10.17.3.1.

10.17.3.1.3 Monitoring shall not be required for a power supply for supplementary equipment.

10.17.3.1.4 Monitoring shall not be required for the neutral of a three-, four-, or five-wire alternating current (ac) or direct current (dc) supply source.

10.17.3.1.5 Monitoring shall not be required for the main power supply in a central station, provided that the fault condition is otherwise indicated so as to be obvious to the operator on duty.

10.17.3.1.6 Monitoring shall not be required for the output of an engine-driven generator that is part of the secondary power supply, provided that the generator is tested weekly in accordance with Chapter 14.

When an engine-driven generator is not running, voltage will not be present on the output terminals. Therefore, monitoring for integrity is impossible.

10.17.3.2* Power supply sources and electrical supervision for digital alarm communications systems shall be in accordance with Sections 10.5 and 10.17.

A.10.17.3.2 Because digital alarm communicator systems establish communications channels between the protected premises and the central station via the public switched telephone network, the requirement to supervise circuits between the protected premises and the central station *(see 10.17.1.1 and 10.17.1.2)* is considered to be met if the communications channel is periodically tested in accordance with 26.6.3.2.1.5.

10.17.3.3* Unless prohibited by the authority having jurisdiction, supervising station alarm systems shall be arranged to delay transmission of primary power failure signals for a period ranging from 60 minutes to 180 minutes.

A.10.17.3.3 This requirement is intended to prevent all of the supervising station alarm systems in a given geographic area from transmitting simultaneous trouble signals (and overwhelming the associated supervising stations) in the event of a widespread power failure. A trouble signal is not intended to be transmitted if primary power is restored within the time delay.

All supervising station alarm systems are required to transmit primary power failure signals no sooner than 60 minutes from initial power failure and no longer than 180 minutes from initial power failure. This rule previously applied only to digital alarm communicator transmitters (DACTs) but now applies to any communications method. This requirement prevents jamming of telephone lines or other transmission channels at the supervising station during the first hour of a widespread power outage.

10.17.3.4 Power supervisory devices shall be arranged so as not to impair the receipt of fire alarm or supervisory signals.

10.18 Documentation

10.18.1 Approval and Acceptance.

10.18.1.1 The authority having jurisdiction shall be notified prior to installation or alteration of equipment or wiring.

10.18.1.2* At the authority having jurisdiction's request, complete information regarding the system or system alterations, including specifications, type of system or service, shop drawings, input/output matrix, battery calculations, and notification appliance circuit voltage drop calculations, shall be submitted for approval.

Many authorities having jurisdiction require a permit for the installation or modification of a system. Paragraph 10.18.1.2 identifies the information that must be provided to the authority having jurisdiction for approval when requested. Participation in the system design process as early as possible by the authority having jurisdiction is strongly recommended. This practice often saves a building owner a great deal of money and allows the authority having jurisdiction to provide guidance throughout the design process rather than simply provide a list of additional requirements after reviewing the plans.

System specifications, type of system or service, shop drawings, input/output matrix, battery calculations, and notification appliance circuit voltage-drop calculations are required to be furnished if requested by the authority having jurisdiction. Refer to A.10.18.1.2 for information on shop drawings, to Figure A.14.6.2.4(9) for typical input/output matrix, and to the commentary following 10.5.6.3.2 for information on battery calculations. Additional information on voltage-drop calculations can be found in the commentary following 18.3.2.3.

A.10.18.1.2 Shop Drawings.

General. Shop drawings for fire alarm systems should provide basic information and should provide the basis for the record drawings required elsewhere in this Code.

Content. Shop drawings should include, to an extent commensurate with the extent of the work being performed, floor plan drawings, riser diagrams, control panel wiring diagrams, point-to-point wiring diagrams, conduit, conductor routing, typical wiring diagrams, and other information as described herein.

All shop drawings should be drawn on sheets of uniform size and should include the following information:

(1) Name of protected premises, owner, and occupant (where applicable)
(2) Name of installer or contractor
(3) Location of protected premises
(4) Device legend in accordance with NFPA 170, *Standard for Fire Safety and Emergency Symbols*
(5) Date of issue and any revisions

Floor plan drawings should be drawn to an indicated scale and should include the following information:

(1) Floor identification
(2) Point of compass (indication of north)
(3) Graphic scale
(4) All walls and doors
(5) All partitions extending to within 10 percent of the ceiling height (where applicable)
(6) Room descriptions
(7) Fire alarm device/component locations
(8) Locations of fire alarm primary power connection(s)
(9) Locations of monitor/control interfaces to other systems
(10) Riser locations
(11) Type and number of fire alarm system components/devices on each circuit, on each floor or level
(12) Type and quantity of conductors and conduit (if used) used for each circuit
(13) Location of all supply and return air diffusers (where automatic detection is used)

Fire alarm system riser diagrams should include the following information:

(1) General arrangement of the system in building cross-section
(2) Number of risers
(3) Type and number of circuits in each riser
(4) Type and number of fire alarm system components/devices on each circuit, on each floor or level
(5) Type and quantity of conductors and conduit (if used) for each circuit

Control unit wiring diagrams should be provided for all control equipment (i.e., equipment listed as either a control unit or control unit accessory), power supplies, battery chargers, and annunciators and should include the following information:

(1) Identification of the control equipment depicted
(2) Location(s)
(3) All field wiring terminals and terminal identifications
(4) All circuits connected to field wiring terminals and circuit identifications
(5) All indicators and manual controls, including the full text of all labels

(6) All field connections to supervising station signaling equipment, releasing equipment, and fire safety control interfaces

Typical wiring diagrams should be provided for all initiating devices, notification appliances, remote indicators, annunciators, remote test stations, and end-of-line and power supervisory devices.

10.18.1.3 Before requesting final approval of the installation, if required by the authority having jurisdiction, the installing contractor shall furnish a written statement stating that the system has been installed in accordance with approved plans and tested in accordance with the manufacturer's published instructions and the appropriate NFPA requirements.

Prior to requesting final approval from the authority having jurisdiction, the installing contractor may need to furnish a written statement that the system has been installed in accordance with approved plans and tested in accordance with the manufacturer's published instructions as well as other appropriate NFPA requirements, including those in this Code. In accordance with 10.18.1.4, the system record of completion form is permitted to be used as a part of the written statement. A completed inspection and testing form would also be of value as a part of this statement.

10.18.1.4* The record of completion form, Figure 10.18.2.1.1, shall be permitted to be a part of the written statement required in 10.18.1.3. When more than one contractor has been responsible for the installation, each contractor shall complete the portions of the form for which that contractor had responsibility.

A.10.18.1.4 Protected premises fire alarm systems are often installed under construction or remodeling contracts and subsequently connected to a supervising station alarm system under a separate contract. All contractors should complete the portions of the record of completion form for the portions of the connected systems for which they are responsible. Several partially completed forms might be accepted by the authority having jurisdiction provided that all portions of the connected systems are covered in the set of forms.

10.18.1.5 The record of completion form, Figure 10.18.2.1.1, shall be permitted to be a part of the documents that support the requirements of 10.18.2.4.

10.18.2 Completion Documents.

10.18.2.1 Preparation.

10.18.2.1.1* The preparation of a record of completion, Figure 10.18.2.1.1, shall be the responsibility of the qualified and experienced person described in 10.4.2.

A.10.18.2.1.1 The requirements of Chapter 14 should be used to perform the installation wiring and operational acceptance tests required when completing the record of completion.

The record of completion form shall be permitted to be used to record decisions reached prior to installation regarding intended system type(s), circuit designations, device types, notification appliance type, power sources, and the means of transmission to the supervising station.

An example of a completed record of completion form is shown in Figure A.10.18.2.1.1.

The record of completion form has been completely revised for this edition of the Code to make it easier to fill out and to more clearly document the system installation. In addition, it has been substantially expanded and now includes entries to document mass notification systems and two-way emergency communications systems. An example of a completed form has been provided as a part of the related annex material. The information contained in the example has been correlated with a similar example of a completed inspection and testing form included in A.14.6.2.4. For an interactive version of the form, visit *www.nfpa.org/72forms*.

FIRE ALARM AND EMERGENCY COMMUNICATION SYSTEM RECORD OF COMPLETION

To be completed by the system installation contractor at the time of system acceptance and approval.
It shall be permitted to modify this form as needed to provide a more complete and/or clear record.
Insert N/A in all unused lines.
Attach additional sheets, data, or calculations as necessary to provide a complete record.

1. PROPERTY INFORMATION

Name of property: _____

Address: _____

Description of property: _____

Occupancy type: _____

Name of property representative: _____

Address: _____

Phone: _____ Fax: _____ E-mail: _____

Authority having jurisdiction over this property: _____

Phone: _____ Fax: _____ E-mail: _____

2. INSTALLATION, SERVICE, AND TESTING CONTRACTOR INFORMATION

Installation contractor for this equipment: _____

Address: _____

License or certification number: _____

Phone: _____ Fax: _____ E-mail: _____

Service organization for this equipment: _____

Address: _____

License or certification number: _____

Phone: _____ Fax: _____ E-mail: _____

A contract for test and inspection in accordance with NFPA standards is in effect as of: _____

Contracted testing company: _____

Address: _____

Phone: _____ Fax: _____ E-mail: _____

Contract expires: _____ Contract number: _____ Frequency of routine inspections: _____

3. DESCRIPTION OF SYSTEM OR SERVICE

❑ Fire alarm system (nonvoice)

❑ Fire alarm with in-building fire emergency voice alarm communication system (EVACS)

❑ Mass notification system (MNS)

❑ Combination system, with the following components:

   ❑ Fire alarm   ❑ EVACS   ❑ MNS   ❑ Two-way, in-building, emergency communication system

❑ Other (specify): _____

© 2009 National Fire Protection Association   NFPA 72 (p. 1 of 12)

FIGURE 10.18.2.1.1 *Record of Completion.*

3. DESCRIPTION OF SYSTEM OR SERVICE *(continued)*

NFPA 72 edition: _____   Additional description of system(s): _____

_____

3.1 Control Unit

Manufacturer: _____   Model number: _____

3.2 Mass Notification System   ❏ This system does not incorporate an MNS.

3.2.1 System Type:

❏ In-building MNS — combination

❏ In-building MNS — stand-alone   ❏ Wide-area MNS   ❏ Distributed recipient MNS

❏ Other (specify): _____

3.2.2 System Features:

❏ Combination fire alarm/MNS   ❏ MNS autonomous control unit   ❏ Wide-area MNS to regional national alerting interface

❏ Local operating console (LOC)   ❏ Distributed recipient MNS (DRMNS)   ❏ Wide-area MNS to DRMNS interface

❏ Wide-area MNS to high-power speaker array (HPSA) interface   ❏ In-building MNS to wide-area MNS interface

❏ Other (specify): _____

3.3 System Documentation

❏ An owner's manual, a copy of the manufacturer's instructions, a written sequence of operation, and a copy of
the numbered record drawings are stored on site.   Location: _____

3.4 System Software   ❏ This system does not have alterable site-specific software.

Operating system (executive) software revision level: _____

Site-specific software revision date: _____   Revision completed by: _____

❏ A copy of the site-specific software is stored on site.   Location: _____

3.5 Off-Premises Signal Transmission   ❏ This system does not have off-premises transmission.

Name of organization receiving alarm signals with phone numbers:

Alarm: _____   Phone: _____

Supervisory: _____   Phone: _____

Trouble: _____   Phone: _____

Entity to which alarms are retransmitted: _____   Phone: _____

Method of retransmission: _____

If Chapter 26, specify the means of transmission from the protected premises to the supervising station:

_____

If Chapter 27, specify the type of auxiliary alarm system: ❏ Local energy   ❏ Shunt   ❏ Wired   ❏ Wireless

NFPA 72 (p. 2 of 12)

(continues)

4. CIRCUITS AND PATHWAYS

4.1 Signaling Line Pathways

4.1.1 Pathways Class Designations and Survivability

Pathways class: _____   Survivability level: _____   Quantity: _____

(See NFPA 72, Sections 12.3 and 12.4)

4.1.2 Pathways Utilizing Two or More Media

Quantity: _____   Description: _____

_____

4.1.3 Device Power Pathways

❑ No separate power pathways from the signaling line pathway
❑ Power pathways are separate but of the same pathway classification as the signaling line pathway
❑ Power pathways are separate and different classification from the signaling line pathway

4.1.4 Isolation Modules

Quantity: _____

4.2 Alarm Initiating Device Pathways

4.2.1 Pathways Class Designations and Survivability

Pathways class: _____   Survivability level: _____   Quantity: _____

(See NFPA 72, Sections 12.3 and 12.4)

4.2.2 Pathways Utilizing Two or More Media

Quantity: _____   Description: _____

_____

4.2.3 Device Power Pathways

❑ No separate power pathways from the initiating device pathway
❑ Power pathways are separate but of the same pathway classification as the initiating device pathway
❑ Power pathways are separate and different classification from the initiating device pathway

4.3 Non-Voice Audible System Pathways

4.3.1 Pathways Class Designations and Survivability

Pathways class: _____   Survivability level: _____   Quantity: _____

(See NFPA 72, Sections 12.3 and 12.4)

4.3.2 Pathways Utilizing Two or More Media

Quantity: _____   Description: _____

_____

4.3.3 Appliance Power Pathways

❑ No separate power pathways from the notification appliance pathway
❑ Power pathways are separate but of the same pathway classification as the notification appliance pathway
❑ Power pathways are separate and different classification from the notification appliance pathway

NFPA 72 (p. 3 of 12)

FIGURE 10.18.2.1.1 *Continued*

5. ALARM INITIATING DEVICES

5.1 Manual Initiating Devices

5.1.1 Manual Fire Alarm Boxes   ❏ This system does not have manual fire alarm boxes.

Type and number of devices: Addressable: _____ Conventional: _____ Coded: _____ Transmitter: _____

Other (specify): _____

5.1.2 Other Alarm Boxes   ❏ This system does not have other alarm boxes.

Description: _____

Type and number of devices: Addressable: _____ Conventional: _____ Coded: _____ Transmitter: _____

Other (specify): _____

5.2 Automatic Initiating Devices

5.2.1 Smoke Detectors   ❏ This system does not have smoke detectors.

Type and number of devices: Addressable: _____ Conventional: _____

Other (specify): _____

Type of coverage: ❏ Complete area   ❏ Partial area   ❏ Nonrequired partial area

Other (specify): _____

Type of smoke detector sensing technology: ❏ Ionization ❏ Photoelectric ❏ Multicriteria ❏ Aspirating ❏ Beam

Other (specify): _____

5.2.2 Duct Smoke Detectors   ❏ This system does not have alarm-causing duct smoke detectors.

Type and number of devices: Addressable: _____ Conventional: _____

Other (specify): _____

Type of coverage: _____

Type of smoke detector sensing technology: ❏ Ionization ❏ Photoelectric ❏ Aspirating ❏ Beam

5.2.3 Radiant Energy (Flame) Detectors   ❏ This system does not have radiant energy detectors.

Type and number of devices: Addressable: _____ Conventional: _____

Other (specify): _____

Type of coverage: _____

5.2.4 Gas Detectors   ❏ This system does not have gas detectors.

Type of detector(s): _____

_____

Number of devices: Addressable: _____ Conventional: _____

Type of coverage: _____

5.2.5 Heat Detectors   ❏ This system does not have heat detectors.

Type and number of devices: Addressable: _____ Conventional: _____

Type of coverage: ❏ Complete area ❏ Partial area ❏ Nonrequired partial area ❏ Linear ❏ Spot

Type of heat detector sensing technology: ❏ Fixed temperature ❏ Rate-of-rise ❏ Rate compensated

NFPA 72 (p. 4 of 12)

(continues)

5. ALARM INITIATING DEVICES *(continued)*

5.2.6 Addressable Monitoring Modules
❑ This system does not have monitoring modules.

Number of devices:_____

5.2.7 Waterflow Alarm Devices
❑ This system does not have waterflow alarm devices.

Type and number of devices: Addressable:_____   Conventional:_____   Coded:_____   Transmitter:_____

5.2.8 Alarm Verification
❑ This system does not incorporate alarm verification.

Number of devices subject to alarm verification:_____   Alarm verification set for _____ seconds

5.2.9 Presignal
❑ This system does not incorporate pre-signal.

Number of devices subject to presignal: _____

Describe presignal functions:_____

5.2.10 Positive Alarm Sequence (PAS)
❑ This system does not incorporate PAS.

Describe PAS:_____

5.2.11 Other Initiating Devices
❑ This system does have other initiating devices.

Describe:_____

6. SUPERVISORY SIGNAL–INITIATING DEVICES

6.1 Sprinkler System Supervisory Devices
❑ This system does not have sprinkler supervisory devices.

Type and number of devices: Addressable:_____   Conventional:_____   Coded:_____   Transmitter:_____

Other (specify):_____

6.2 Fire Pump Description and Supervisory Devices
❑ This system does not have a fire pump.

Type fire pump: ❑ Electric   ❑ Engine

Type and number of devices: Addressable:_____   Conventional:_____   Coded:_____   Transmitter:_____

Other (specify):_____

6.2.1 Fire Pump Functions Supervised

❑ Power   ❑ Running   ❑ Phase reversal   ❑ Selector switch not in auto   ❑ Engine or control panel trouble   ❑ Low fuel

Other (specify):_____

6.3 Duct Smoke Detectors (DSDs)
❑ This system does not have DSDs causing supervisory signals.

Type and number of devices: Addressable:_____   Conventional:_____

Other (specify):_____

Type of coverage:_____

Type of smoke detector sensing technology: ❑ Ionization   ❑ Photoelectric   ❑ Aspirating   ❑ Beam

6.4 Other Supervisory Devices
❑ This system does not have other supervisory devices.

Describe:_____

FIGURE 10.18.2.1.1 *Continued*

7. MONITORED SYSTEMS

7.1 Engine-Driven Generator   ❏ This system does not have a generator.

7.1.1 Generator Functions Supervised

❏ Engine or control panel trouble   ❏ Generator running   ❏ Selector switch not in auto   ❏ Low fuel
❏ Other (specify): _____

7.2 Special Hazard Suppression Systems   ❏ This system does not monitor special hazard systems.

Description of special hazard system(s): _____
_____

7.3 Other Monitoring Systems   ❏ This system does not monitor other systems.

Description of other system(s): _____
_____

8. ANNUNCIATORS   ❏ This system does not have annunciators.

8.1 Location and Description of Annunciators

Location 1: _____
Location 2: _____
Location 3: _____

9. ALARM NOTIFICATION APPLIANCES

9.1 In-Building Fire Emergency Voice Alarm Communication System   ❏ This system does not have an EVACS.

Number of single voice alarm channels: _____   Number of multiple voice alarm channels: _____
Number of speakers: _____   Number of speaker circuits: _____
Location of amplification and sound-processing equipment: _____
_____

Location of paging microphone stations:
Location 1: _____
Location 2: _____
Location 3: _____

9.2 Nonvoice Notification Appliances   ❏ This system does not have nonvoice notification appliances.

Horns: _____   With visible: _____   Bells: _____   With visible: _____
Chimes: _____   With visible: _____
Visible only: _____   Other (describe): _____

9.3 Notification Appliance Power Extender Panels   ❏ This system does not have power extender panels.

Quantity: _____
Locations: _____
_____

NFPA 72 (p. 6 of 12)

(continues)

10. MASS NOTIFICATION CONTROLS, APPLIANCES, AND CIRCUITS ❏ This system does not have an MNS.

10.1 MNS Local Operating Consoles

Location 1: _____

Location 2: _____

Location 3: _____

10.2 High-Power Speaker Arrays

Number of HPSA speaker initiation zones: _____

Location 1: _____

Location 2: _____

Location 3: _____

10.3 Mass Notification Devices

Combination fire alarm/MNS visible appliances: _____   MNS-only visible appliances: _____

Textual signs: _____   Other (describe): _____

Supervision class: _____

10.3.1 Special Hazard Notification

❏ This system does not have special suppression predischarge notification.

❏ MNS systems DO NOT override notification appliances required to provide special suppression predischarge notification.

11. TWO-WAY EMERGENCY COMMUNICATION SYSTEMS

11.1 Telephone System   ❏ This system does not have a two-way telephone system.

Number of telephone jacks installed: _____   Number of warden stations installed: _____

Number of telephone handsets stored on site: _____

Type of telephone system installed: ❏ Electrically powered   ❏ Sound powered

11.2 Two-Way Radio Communications Enhancement System

❏ This system does not have a two-way radio communications enhancement system.

Percentage of area covered by two-way radio service: Critical areas: _____ %   General building areas: _____ %

Amplification component locations: _____

_____

Inbound signal strength: _____ dBm   Outbound signal strength: _____ dBm

Donor antenna isolation is _____ dB above the signal booster gain

Radio frequencies covered: _____

Radio system monitor panel location: _____

FIGURE 10.18.2.1.1 *Record of Completion.*

11. TWO-WAY EMERGENCY COMMUNICATION SYSTEMS *(continued)*

11.3 Area of Refuge (Area of Rescue Assistance) Emergency Communications Systems

❑ This system does not have an area of refuge (area of rescue assistance) emergency communications system.

Number of stations: _____ Location of central control point: _____

Days and hours when central control point is attended: _____

Location of alternate control point: _____

Days and hours when alternate control point is attended: _____

11.4 Elevator Emergency Communications Systems

❑ This system does not have an elevator emergency communications system.

Number of elevators with stations: _____ Location of central control point: _____

Days and hours when central control point is attended: _____

Location of alternate control point: _____

Days and hours when alternate control point is attended: _____

11.5 Other Two-Way Communication Systems

Describe: _____

12. CONTROL FUNCTIONS

This system activates the following control functions:

❑ Hold-open door releasing devices ❑ Smoke management ❑ HVAC shutdown ❑ F/S dampers

❑ Door unlocking ❑ Elevator recall ❑ Fuel source shutdown ❑ Extinguishing agent release

❑ Elevator shunt trip ❑ Mass notification system override of fire alarm notification appliances

Other (specify): _____

12.1 Addressable Control Modules   ❑ This system does not have control modules.

Number of devices: _____

Other (specify): _____

13. SYSTEM POWER

13.1 Control Unit

13.1.1 Primary Power

Input voltage of control panel: _____ Control panel amps: _____

Overcurrent protection: Type: _____ Amps: _____

Location (of primary supply panel board): _____

Disconnecting means location: _____

13.1.2 Engine-Driven Generator   ❑ This system does not have a generator.

Location of generator: _____

Location of fuel storage: _____ Type of fuel: _____

NFPA 72 (p. 8 of 12)

(continues)

13. SYSTEM POWER *(continued)*

13.1.3 Uninterruptible Power System

❏ This system does not have a UPS.

Equipment powered by a UPS system: _____

Location of UPS system: _____

Calculated capacity of UPS batteries to drive the system components connected to it:

In standby mode (hours): _____ In alarm mode (minutes): _____

13.1.4 Batteries

Location: _____ Type: _____ Nominal voltage: _____ Amp/hour rating: _____

Calculated capacity of batteries to drive the system:

In standby mode (hours): _____ In alarm mode (minutes): _____

❏ Batteries are marked with date of manufacture   ❏ Battery calculations are attached

13.2 In-Building Fire Emergency Voice Alarm Communication System or Mass Notification System

❏ This system does not have an EVACS or MNS system.

13.2.1 Primary Power

Input voltage of EVACS or MNS panel: _____ EVACS or MNS panel amps: _____

Overcurrent protection: Type: _____ Amps: _____

Location (of primary supply panel board): _____

Disconnecting means location: _____

13.2.2 Engine-Driven Generator

❏ This system does not have a generator.

Location of generator: _____

Location of fuel storage: _____ Type of fuel: _____

13.2.3 Uninterruptible Power System

❏ This system does not have a UPS.

Equipment powered by a UPS system: _____

Location of UPS system: _____

Calculated capacity of UPS batteries to drive the system components connected to it:

In standby mode (hours): _____ In alarm mode (minutes): _____

13.2.4 Batteries

Location: _____ Type: _____ Nominal voltage: _____ Amp/hour rating: _____

Calculated capacity of batteries to drive the system:

In standby mode (hours): _____ In alarm mode (minutes): _____

❏ Batteries are marked with date of manufacture   ❏ Battery calculations are attached

FIGURE 10.18.2.1.1 *Continued*

13. SYSTEM POWER *(continued)*

13.3 Notification Appliance Power Extender Panels   ❏ This system does not have power extender panels.

13.3.1 Primary Power

Input voltage of power extender panel(s): _____   Power extender panel amps: _____

Overcurrent protection: Type: _____   Amps: _____

Location (of primary supply panel board): _____

Disconnecting means location: _____

13.3.2 Engine-Driven Generator   ❏ This system does not have a generator.

Location of generator: _____

Location of fuel storage: _____   Type of fuel: _____

13.3.3 Uninterruptible Power System   ❏ This system does not have a UPS.

Equipment powered by a UPS system: _____

Location of UPS system: _____

Calculated capacity of UPS batteries to drive the system components connected to it:

In standby mode (hours): _____   In alarm mode (minutes): _____

13.3.4 Batteries

Location: _____   Type: _____   Nominal voltage: _____   Amp/hour rating: _____

Calculated capacity of batteries to drive the system:

In standby mode (hours): _____   In alarm mode (minutes): _____

❏ Batteries are marked with date of manufacture   ❏ Battery calculations are attached

14. RECORD OF SYSTEM INSTALLATION

Fill out after all installation is complete and wiring has been checked for opens, shorts, ground faults, and improper branching, but before conducting operational acceptance tests.

This is a: ❏ New system   ❏ Modification to an existing system   Permit number: _____

The system has been installed in accordance with the following requirements: (Note any or all that apply.)

❏ *NFPA 72,* Edition: _____

❏ *NFPA 70, National Electrical Code,* Article 760, Edition: _____

❏ Manufacturer's published instructions

Other (specify): _____

_____

System deviations from referenced NFPA standards: _____

_____

Signed: _____   Printed name: _____   Date: _____

Organization: _____   Title: _____   Phone: _____

(continues)

15. RECORD OF SYSTEM OPERATONAL ACCEPTANCE TEST

❏ New system

All operational features and functions of this system were tested by, or in the presence of, the signer shown below, on the date shown below, and were found to be operating properly in accordance with the requirements for the following:

❏ Modifications to an existing system

All newly modified operational features and functions of the system were tested by, or in the presence of, the signer shown below, on the date shown below, and were found to be operating properly in accordance with the requirements of the following:

❏ *NFPA 72,* Edition: _____

❏ *NFPA 70, National Electrical Code,* Article 760, Edition: _____

❏ Manufacturer's published instructions

Other (specify): _____

_____

❏ Individual device testing documentation [Inspection and Testing Form (Figure 14.6.2.4) is attached]

Signed: _____   Printed name: _____   Date: _____

Organization: _____   Title: _____   Phone: _____

16. CERTIFICATIONS AND APPROVALS

16.1 System Installation Contractor:

This system, as specified herein, has been installed and tested according to all NFPA standards cited herein.

Signed: _____   Printed name: _____   Date: _____

Organization: _____   Title: _____   Phone: _____

16.2 System Service Contractor:

The undersigned has a service contract for this system in effect as of the date shown below.

Signed: _____   Printed name: _____   Date: _____

Organization: _____   Title: _____   Phone: _____

16.3 Supervising Station:

This system, as specified herein, will be monitored according to all NFPA standards cited herein.

Signed: _____   Printed name: _____   Date: _____

Organization: _____   Title: _____   Phone: _____

© 2009 National Fire Protection Association   *NFPA 72* (p. 11 of 12)

FIGURE 10.18.2.1.1 *Continued.*

16. CERTIFICATIONS AND APPROVALS *(continued)*

16.4 Property or Owner Representative:

I accept this system as having been installed and tested to its specifications and all NFPA standards cited herein.

Signed: _____   Printed name: _____   Date: _____

Organization: _____   Title: _____   Phone: _____

16.5 Authority Having Jurisdiction:

I have witnessed a satisfactory acceptance test of this system and find it to be installed and operating properly in accordance with its approved plans and specifications, with its approved sequence of operations, and with all NFPA standards cited herein.

Signed: _____   Printed name: _____   Date: _____

Organization: _____   Title: _____   Phone: _____

NFPA 72 (p. 12 of 12)

FIRE ALARM AND EMERGENCY COMMUNICATION SYSTEM RECORD OF COMPLETION

To be completed by the system installation contractor at the time of system acceptance and approval.
It shall be permitted to modify this form as needed to provide a more complete and/or clear record.
Insert N/A in all unused lines.
Attach additional sheets, data, or calculations as necessary to provide a complete record.

1. PROPERTY INFORMATION

Name of property: __Main Street Towers__

Address: __12345 Main Street, Pleasantville, NY O1111__

Description of property: __40-story high-rise building with an adjacent 1-story parking structure__

Occupancy type: __B__

Name of property representative: __Mary Morris, Property Manager, Mary's Management Company__

Address: __12345 Main Street, Pleasantville, NY O1111__

Phone: __222/222-2222__   Fax: __333/333-3333__   E-mail: __mm@mmc.com__

Authority having jurisdiction over this property: __Inspector Jack Jones, Pleasantville Fire Department__

Phone: __444/444-4444__   Fax: __555/555-5555__   E-mail: __jackjones@pfd.org__

2. INSTALLATION, SERVICE, AND TESTING CONTRACTOR INFORMATION

Installation contractor for this equipment: __Fred's Fine Fire Alarm Systems__

Address: __789 Broad Street, Pleasantville, NY O1113__

License or certification number: __NY-1634__

Phone: __888/888-8888__   Fax: __999/999-9999__   E-mail: __fredfriendly@fffas.com__

Service organization for this equipment: __Fred's Fine Fire Alarm Systems__

Address: __Same__

License or certification number: _____

Phone: _____   Fax: _____   E-mail: _____

A contract for test and inspection in accordance with NFPA standards is in effect as of: __June 11, 2010__

Contracted testing company: __Fred's Fine Fire Alarm Systems__

Address: __Same__

Phone: _____   Fax: _____   E-mail: _____

Contract expires: __June 11, 2011__   Contract number: __45678__   Frequency of routine inspections: __Quarterly__

3. DESCRIPTION OF SYSTEM OR SERVICE

❑ Fire alarm system (nonvoice)

❑ Fire alarm with in-building fire emergency voice alarm communication system (EVACS)

❑ Mass notification system (MNS)

☑ Combination system, with the following components:

☑ Fire alarm   ☑ EVACS   ☑ MNS   ☑ Two-way, in-building, emergency communication system

❑ Other (specify): __N/A__

NFPA 72 (p. 1 of 12)

FIGURE A.10.18.2.1.1 Example of a Filled Out Record of Completion for a Fire Alarm System.

3. DESCRIPTION OF SYSTEM OR SERVICE *(continued)*

NFPA 72 edition: ___2010___   Additional description of system(s): ___N/A___

3.1 Control Unit

Manufacturer: ___Megasystems___   Model number: ___AZ–1230___

3.2 Mass Notification System

❏ This system does not incorporate an MNS.

3.2.1 System Type:

☑ In-building MNS — combination

❏ In-building MNS — stand-alone   ❏ Wide-area MNS   ❏ Distributed recipient MNS

❏ Other (specify): ___N/A___

3.2.2 System Features:

☑ Combination fire alarm/MNS   ❏ MNS autonomous control unit   ❏ Wide-area MNS to regional national alerting interface

❏ Local operating console (LOC)   ❏ Distributed recipient MNS (DRMNS)   ❏ Wide-area MNS to DRMNS interface

❏ Wide-area MNS to high-power speaker array (HPSA) interface   ❏ In-building MNS to wide-area MNS interface

❏ Other (specify): ___N/A___

3.3 System Documentation

☑ An owner's manual, a copy of the manufacturer's instructions, a written sequence of operation, and a copy of the numbered record drawings are stored on site. Location: ___Building management office, Suite 2222___

3.4 System Software

❏ This system does not have alterable site-specific software.

Operating system (executive) software revision level: ___4.567___

Site-specific software revision date: ___June 26, 2010___   Revision completed by: ___Fred Friendly___

☑ A copy of the site-specific software is stored on site. Location: ___Building management office, Suite 2222___

3.5 Off-Premises Signal Transmission

❏ This system does not have off-premises transmission.

Name of organization receiving alarm signals with phone numbers:

Alarm: ___Manny's Monitoring___   Phone: ___777/777-7777___

Supervisory: ___Manny's Monitoring___   Phone: ___777/777-7777___

Trouble: ___Manny's Monitoring___   Phone: ___777/777-7777___

Entity to which alarms are retransmitted: ___Pleasantville Fire Department___   Phone: ___444/444-4444___

Method of retransmission: ___Central station operator calls 444/444-4444 after receiving a signal___

If Chapter 26, specify the means of transmission from the protected premises to the supervising station:
___DACT___

If Chapter 27, specify the type of auxiliary alarm system: ❏ Local energy   ❏ Shunt   ❏ Wired   ❏ Wireless

NFPA 72 (p. 2 of 12)

(continues)

4. CIRCUITS AND PATHWAYS

4.1 Signaling Line Pathways

4.1.1 Pathways Class Designations and Survivability

Pathways class: _____A_____ Survivability level: _____2_____ Quantity: _____12_____

(See NFPA 72, Sections 12.3 and 12.4)

4.1.2 Pathways Utilizing Two or More Media

Quantity: _____O_____ Description: _____N/A_____

4.1.3 Device Power Pathways

☑ No separate power pathways from the signaling line pathway

❏ Power pathways are separate but of the same pathway classification as the signaling line pathway

❏ Power pathways are separate and different classification from the signaling line pathway

4.1.4 Isolation Modules

Quantity: _____4_____

4.2 Alarm Initiating Device Pathways

4.2.1 Pathways Class Designations and Survivability

Pathways class: _____N/A_____ Survivability level: _____N/A_____ Quantity: _____O_____

(See NFPA 72, Sections 12.3 and 12.4)

4.2.2 Pathways Utilizing Two or More Media

Quantity: _____O_____ Description: _____N/A_____

4.2.3 Device Power Pathways

❏ No separate power pathways from the initiating device pathway

❏ Power pathways are separate but of the same pathway classification as the initiating device pathway

❏ Power pathways are separate and different classification from the initiating device pathway

4.3 Non-Voice Audible System Pathways

4.3.1 Pathways Class Designations and Survivability

Pathways class: _____B_____ Survivability level: _____N/A_____ Quantity: _____24_____

(See NFPA 72, Sections 12.3 and 12.4)

4.3.2 Pathways Utilizing Two or More Media

Quantity: _____O_____ Description: _____N/A_____

4.3.3 Appliance Power Pathways

☑ No separate power pathways from the notification appliance pathway

❏ Power pathways are separate but of the same pathway classification as the notification appliance pathway

❏ Power pathways are separate and different classification from the notification appliance pathway

© 2009 National Fire Protection Association   NFPA 72 (p. 3 of 12)

FIGURE A.10.18.2.1.1 *Continued*

5. ALARM INITIATING DEVICES

5.1 Manual Initiating Devices

5.1.1 Manual Fire Alarm Boxes
❏ This system does not have manual fire alarm boxes.

Type and number of devices: Addressable: _74_   Conventional: _O_   Coded: _O_   Transmitter: _O_

Other (specify): _____N/A_____

5.1.2 Other Alarm Boxes
❏ This system does not have other alarm boxes.

Description: _____

Type and number of devices: Addressable: _10_   Conventional: _O_   Coded: _O_   Transmitter: _O_

Other (specify): _____N/A_____

5.2 Automatic Initiating Devices

5.2.1 Smoke Detectors
❏ This system does not have smoke detectors.

Type and number of devices: Addressable: _96_   Conventional: _O_

Other (specify): _____N/A_____

Type of coverage: ❏ Complete area   ☑ Partial area   ❏ Nonrequired partial area

Other (specify): _____Located in all electrical and equipment rooms, in elevator lobbies, and at fire doors_____

Type of smoke detector sensing technology: ❏ Ionization ☑ Photoelectric ❏ Multicriteria ❏ Aspirating ❏ Beam

Other (specify): _____N/A_____

5.2.2 Duct Smoke Detectors
❏ This system does not have alarm-causing duct smoke detectors.

Type and number of devices: Addressable: _33_   Conventional: _O_

Other (specify): _____N/A_____

Type of coverage: _____Located at the supply and return of all air handling units_____

Type of smoke detector sensing technology: ❏ Ionization ☑ Photoelectric ❏ Aspirating ❏ Beam

5.2.3 Radiant Energy (Flame) Detectors
☑ This system does not have radiant energy detectors.

Type and number of devices: Addressable: _____   Conventional: _____

Other (specify): _____N/A_____

Type of coverage: _____N/A_____

5.2.4 Gas Detectors
☑ This system does not have gas detectors.

Type of detector(s): _____N/A_____

Number of devices: Addressable: _____   Conventional: _____

Type of coverage: _____N/A_____

5.2.5 Heat Detectors
❏ This system does not have heat detectors.

Type and number of devices: Addressable: _12_   Conventional: _O_

Type of coverage: ❏ Complete area   ☑ Partial area   ❏ Nonrequired partial area   ❏ Linear   ☑ Spot

Type of heat detector sensing technology: ☑ Fixed temperature   ☑ Rate-of-rise   ❏ Rate compensated

(continues)

5. ALARM INITIATING DEVICES *(continued)*

5.2.6 Addressable Monitoring Modules

Number of devices: _____67_____

❏ This system does not have monitoring modules.

5.2.7 Waterflow Alarm Devices

☑ This system does not have waterflow alarm devices.

Type and number of devices: Addressable: ___42___ Conventional:___0___ Coded: ___0___ Transmitter: ___0___

5.2.8 Alarm Verification

☑ This system does not incorporate alarm verification.

Number of devices subject to alarm verification:_____ Alarm verification set for _____ seconds

5.2.9 Presignal

❏ This system does not incorporate pre-signal.

Number of devices subject to presignal: ___N/A___

Describe presignal functions: ___N/A___

5.2.10 Positive Alarm Sequence (PAS)

☑ This system does not incorporate PAS.

Describe PAS: ___N/A___

5.2.11 Other Initiating Devices

☑ This system does have other initiating devices.

Describe: ___N/A___

6. SUPERVISORY SIGNAL–INITIATING DEVICES

6.1 Sprinkler System Supervisory Devices

❏ This system does not have sprinkler supervisory devices.

Type and number of devices: Addressable: ___49___ Conventional:___0___ Coded: ___0___ Transmitter: ___0___

Other (specify): ___N/A___

6.2 Fire Pump Description and Supervisory Devices

❏ This system does not have a fire pump.

Type fire pump: ☑ Electric ❏ Engine

Type and number of devices: Addressable: ___3___ Conventional:___0___ Coded: ___0___ Transmitter: ___0___

Other (specify): ___N/A___

6.2.1 Fire Pump Functions Supervised

☑ Power ☑ Running ☑ Phase reversal ❏ Selector switch not in auto ❏ Engine or control panel trouble ❏ Low fuel

Other (specify): ___N/A___

6.3 Duct Smoke Detectors (DSDs)

☑ This system does not have DSDs causing supervisory signals.

Type and number of devices: Addressable:_____ Conventional:_____

Other (specify): ___N/A___

Type of coverage: ___N/A___

Type of smoke detector sensing technology: ❏ Ionization ❏ Photoelectric ❏ Aspirating ❏ Beam

6.4 Other Supervisory Devices

☑ This system does not have other supervisory devices.

Describe: _____

FIGURE A.10.18.2.1.1 *Continued*

7. MONITORED SYSTEMS

7.1 Engine-Driven Generator
❑ This system does not have a generator.

7.1.1 Generator Functions Supervised

☑ Engine or control panel trouble   ☑ Generator running   ☑ Selector switch not in auto   ☑ Low fuel

❑ Other (specify): _____N/A_____

7.2 Special Hazard Suppression Systems
❑ This system does not monitor special hazard systems.

Description of special hazard system(s): _____Sprinkler preaction system in 24th floor computer room_____

7.3 Other Monitoring Systems
☑ This system does not monitor other systems.

Description of other system(s): _____

8. ANNUNCIATORS
❑ This system does not have annunciators.

8.1 Location and Description of Annunciators

Location 1: _____Fire command center_____

Location 2: _____Front lobby at east entrance doors_____

Location 3: _____Engineering office on P1 level_____

9. ALARM NOTIFICATION APPLIANCES

9.1 In-Building Fire Emergency Voice Alarm Communication System
❑ This system does not have an EVACS.

Number of single voice alarm channels: _____58_____   Number of multiple voice alarm channels: _____0_____

Number of speakers: _____490_____   Number of speaker circuits: _____58_____

Location of amplification and sound-processing equipment: _____Fire command center_____

Location of paging microphone stations:

Location 1: _____Fire command center_____

Location 2: _____N/A_____

Location 3: _____N/A_____

9.2 Nonvoice Notification Appliances
❑ This system does not have nonvoice notification appliances.

Horns: _____0_____   With visible: _____0_____   Bells: _____0_____   With visible: _____0_____

Chimes: _____0_____   With visible: _____0_____

Visible only: _____566_____   Other (describe): _____0_____

9.3 Notification Appliance Power Extender Panels
❑ This system does not have power extender panels.

Quantity: _____42_____

Locations: _____2 in the fire command center and 1 in the electrical equipment room on each floor_____

(continues)

10. MASS NOTIFICATION CONTROLS, APPLIANCES, AND CIRCUITS   ❑ This system does not have an MNS.

10.1 MNS Local Operating Consoles

Location 1: _____Fire command center_____

Location 2: _____N/A_____

Location 3: _____N/A_____

10.2 High-Power Speaker Arrays

Number of HPSA speaker initiation zones: _____None_____

Location 1: _____

Location 2: _____

Location 3: _____

10.3 Mass Notification Devices

Combination fire alarm/MNS visible appliances: _____0_____   MNS-only visible appliances: _____216_____

Textual signs: _____0_____   Other (describe): _____N/A_____

Supervision class: _____B_____

10.3.1 Special Hazard Notification

☑ This system does not have special suppression predischarge notification.

❑ MNS systems DO NOT override notification appliances required to provide special suppression
predischarge notification.

11. TWO-WAY EMERGENCY COMMUNICATION SYSTEMS

11.1 Telephone System   ❑ This system does not have a two-way telephone system.

Number of telephone jacks installed: _____138_____   Number of warden stations installed: _____0_____

Number of telephone handsets stored on site: _____8_____

Type of telephone system installed: ☑ Electrically powered   ❑ Sound powered

11.2 Two-Way Radio Communications Enhancement System

☑ This system does not have a two-way radio communications enhancement system.

Percentage of area covered by two-way radio service: Critical areas: _____%   General building areas: _____%

Amplification component locations: _____N/A_____

Inbound signal strength: _____ dBm   Outbound signal strength: _____ dBm

Donor antenna isolation is _____ dB above the signal booster gain

Radio frequencies covered: _____

Radio system monitor panel location: _____

© 2009 National Fire Protection Association   *NFPA 72* (p. 7 of 12)

FIGURE A.10.18.2.1.1 Continued

11. TWO-WAY EMERGENCY COMMUNICATION SYSTEMS *(continued)*

11.3 Area of Refuge (Area of Rescue Assistance) Emergency Communications Systems

❏ This system does not have an area of refuge (area of rescue assistance) emergency communications system.

Number of stations: _____43_____   Location of central control point: _____Fire command center_____

Days and hours when central control point is attended: _____During incident_____

Location of alternate control point: _____Building management office_____

Days and hours when alternate control point is attended: _____8 to 5 on weekdays_____

11.4 Elevator Emergency Communications Systems

❏ This system does not have an elevator emergency communications system.

Number of elevators with stations: _____12_____   Location of central control point: _____Fire command center_____

Days and hours when central control point is attended: _____During incident_____

Location of alternate control point: _____Building management office_____

Days and hours when alternate control point is attended: _____8 to 5 on weekdays_____

11.5 Other Two-Way Communication Systems

Describe: _____N/A_____

12. CONTROL FUNCTIONS

This system activates the following control functions:

☑ Hold-open door releasing devices   ☑ Smoke management   ❏ HVAC shutdown   ☑ F/S dampers

☑ Door unlocking   ☑ Elevator recall   ☑ Fuel source shutdown   ❏ Extinguishing agent release

☑ Elevator shunt trip   ☑ Mass notification system override of fire alarm notification appliances

Other (specify): _____N/A_____

12.1 Addressable Control Modules   ❏ This system does not have control modules.

Number of devices: _____122_____

Other (specify): _____N/A_____

13. SYSTEM POWER

13.1 Control Unit

13.1.1 Primary Power

Input voltage of control panel: _____120 VAC_____   Control panel amps: _____6.2_____

Overcurrent protection: Type: _____Circuit breaker_____   Amps: _____15_____

Location (of primary supply panel board): _____First floor electrical room_____

Disconnecting means location: _____First floor electrical room_____

13.1.2 Engine-Driven Generator   ❏ This system does not have a generator.

Location of generator: _____Lower level generator room_____

Location of fuel storage: _____Sub basement fuel storage room_____   Type of fuel: _____Diesel_____

NFPA 72 (p. 8 of 12)

(continues)

13. SYSTEM POWER *(continued)*

13.1.3 Uninterruptible Power System

☑ This system does not have a UPS.

Equipment powered by a UPS system: _____

Location of UPS system: _____

Calculated capacity of UPS batteries to drive the system components connected to it:

In standby mode (hours): _____   In alarm mode (minutes): _____

13.1.4 Batteries

Location: _Fire command center_   Type: _Gel cell_   Nominal voltage: _24 VDC_   Amp/hour rating: _30_

Calculated capacity of batteries to drive the system:

In standby mode (hours): _38_____   In alarm mode (minutes): _11_____

☑ Batteries are marked with date of manufacture   ☑ Battery calculations are attached

13.2 In-Building Fire Emergency Voice Alarm Communication System or Mass Notification System

❏ This system does not have an EVACS or MNS system.

13.2.1 Primary Power

Input voltage of EVACS or MNS panel: _120 VAC_____   EVACS or MNS panel amps: _11.9_____

Overcurrent protection: Type: _Circuit breaker_____   Amps: _15_____

Location (of primary supply panel board): _First floor electrical room_____

Disconnecting means location: _First floor electrical room_____

13.2.2 Engine-Driven Generator

❏ This system does not have a generator.

Location of generator: _Lower level generator room_____

Location of fuel storage: _Sub basement fuel storage room_   Type of fuel: _Diesel_____

13.2.3 Uninterruptible Power System

☑ This system does not have a UPS.

Equipment powered by a UPS system: _____

Location of UPS system: _____

Calculated capacity of UPS batteries to drive the system components connected to it:

In standby mode (hours): _____   In alarm mode (minutes): _____

13.2.4 Batteries

Location: _Fire command center_   Type: _Gel cell_   Nominal voltage: _24 VDC_   Amp/hour rating: _120_

Calculated capacity of batteries to drive the system:

In standby mode (hours): _30_____   In alarm mode (minutes): _8_____

☑ Batteries are marked with date of manufacture   ☑ Battery calculations are attached

FIGURE A.10.18.2.1.1 *Continued*

13. SYSTEM POWER *(continued)*

13.3 Notification Appliance Power Extender Panels   ❑ This system does not have power extender panels.

13.3.1 Primary Power

Input voltage of power extender panel(s): ___120 VAC___   Power extender panel amps: ___2___

Overcurrent protection: Type: ___Circuit breaker___   Amps: ___15___

Location (of primary supply panel board): ___E Power panels located every three floors in the electrical rooms___

Disconnecting means location: ___E Power panels___

13.3.2 Engine-Driven Generator   ❑ This system does not have a generator.

Location of generator: ___Lower level generator room___

Location of fuel storage: ___Sub basement fuel storage room___   Type of fuel: ___Diesel___

13.3.3 Uninterruptible Power System   ☑ This system does not have a UPS.

Equipment powered by a UPS system: _____

Location of UPS system: _____

Calculated capacity of UPS batteries to drive the system components connected to it:

In standby mode (hours): _____   In alarm mode (minutes): _____

13.3.4 Batteries

Location: ___Inside each panel___   Type: ___Gel cell___   Nominal voltage: ___24 VDC___   Amp/hour rating: ___14___

Calculated capacity of batteries to drive the system:

In standby mode (hours): _____   In alarm mode (minutes): ___See attached calculations___

☑ Batteries are marked with date of manufacture   ☑ Battery calculations are attached

14. RECORD OF SYSTEM INSTALLATION

Fill out after all installation is complete and wiring has been checked for opens, shorts, ground faults, and improper branching, but before conducting operational acceptance tests.

This is a: ☑ New system   ❑ Modification to an existing system   Permit number: ___4567___

The system has been installed in accordance with the following requirements: (Note any or all that apply.)

☑ *NFPA 72*, Edition: ___2010___

☑ *NFPA 70, National Electrical Code*, Article 760, Edition: ___2008___

☑ Manufacturer's published instructions

Other (specify): ___Pleasantville local codes, revised 2008___

System deviations from referenced NFPA standards: ___None known___

Signed: ___Fred Friendly___   Printed name: ___Fred Friendly___   Date: ___8/21/2010___

Organization: ___Fred's Fine Fire Alarm Syst.___   Title: ___President___   Phone: ___444/444-4444___

NFPA 72 (p. 10 of 12)

(continues)

15. RECORD OF SYSTEM OPERATONAL ACCEPTANCE TEST

☑ New system

All operational features and functions of this system were tested by, or in the presence of, the signer shown below, on the date shown below, and were found to be operating properly in accordance with the requirements for the following:

❑ Modifications to an existing system

All newly modified operational features and functions of the system were tested by, or in the presence of, the signer shown below, on the date shown below, and were found to be operating properly in accordance with the requirements of the following:

☑ *NFPA 72*, Edition: ___2010___

☑ *NFPA 70, National Electrical Code*, Article 760, Edition: ___2008___

☑ Manufacturer's published instructions

Other (specify): ___Pleasantville local codes, revised 2008___

☑ Individual device testing documentation [Inspection and Testing Form (Figure 14.6.2.4) is attached]

Signed: ___Fred Friendly___   Printed name: ___Fred Friendly___   Date: ___8/21/2010___

Organization: ___Fred's Fine Fire Alarm Syst.___   Title: ___President___   Phone: ___444/444-4444___

16. CERTIFICATIONS AND APPROVALS

16.1 System Installation Contractor:

This system, as specified herein, has been installed and tested according to all NFPA standards cited herein.

Signed: ___Fred Friendly___   Printed name: ___Fred Friendly___   Date: ___8/21/2010___

Organization: ___Fred's Fine Fire Alarm Syst.___   Title: ___President___   Phone: ___888/888-8888___

16.2 System Service Contractor:

The undersigned has a service contract for this system in effect as of the date shown below.

Signed: ___Fred Friendly___   Printed name: ___Fred Friendly___   Date: ___8/21/2010___

Organization: ___Fred's Fine Fire Alarm Syst.___   Title: ___President___   Phone: ___888/888-8888___

16.3 Supervising Station:

This system, as specified herein, will be monitored according to all NFPA standards cited herein.

Signed: ___Manny Monitor___   Printed name: ___Manny Monitor___   Date: ___8/30/2010___

Organization: ___Manny's Monitoring___   Title: ___President___   Phone: ___777/777-7777___

© 2009 National Fire Protection Association   *NFPA 72* (p. 11 of 12)

FIGURE A.10.18.2.1.1 *Continued*

16. CERTIFICATIONS AND APPROVALS *(continued)*

16.4 Property or Owner Representative:

I accept this system as having been installed and tested to its specifications and all NFPA standards cited herein.

Signed: *Mary Morris*   Printed name: Mary Morris   Date: 8/30/2010

Organization: Mary's Management   Title: Property Manager   Phone: 222/222-2222

16.5 Authority Having Jurisdiction:

I have witnessed a satisfactory acceptance test of this system and find it to be installed and operating properly in accordance with its approved plans and specifications, with its approved sequence of operations, and with all NFPA standards cited herein.

Signed: *Jack Jones*   Printed name: Jack Jones   Date: 9/10/2010

Organization: Pleasantville Fire Dept.   Title: Inspector   Phone: 444/444-4444

NFPA 72 (p. 12 of 12)

FAQ ▶
Who is responsible for completing the record of completion form?

The system installer is responsible for the preparation of the record of completion form. It documents the type of system; the names of installers; and the location of record drawings, owners' manuals, and test reports. The form also provides a confirming record of the acceptance test and gives details of the components and wiring of the system. A record of completion is required for all installed fire alarm and emergency communications systems.

10.18.2.1.2 The preparation of a record of completion, Figure 10.18.2.1.1 shall be in accordance with 10.18.2.1.2.1 through 10.18.2.1.2.8.

10.18.2.1.2.1 Parts 1 through 14 of the record of completion shall be completed after the system is installed and the installation wiring has been checked.

10.18.2.1.2.2 Parts 15 and 16 of the record of completion shall be completed after the operational acceptance tests have been completed.

10.18.2.1.2.3 A preliminary copy of the record of completion shall be given to the system owner and, if requested, to other authorities having jurisdiction after completion of the installation wiring tests.

10.18.2.1.2.4 A final copy of the record of completion shall be provided after completion of the operational acceptance tests.

10.18.2.1.2.5 One copy of the record of completion shall be stored at the fire alarm control unit or other approved location.

10.18.2.1.2.6 This copy shall be updated to reflect all system additions or modifications and maintained in a current condition at all times.

10.18.2.1.2.7 Where not stored at the main fire alarm control unit, the location of these documents shall be identified at the main fire alarm control unit.

10.18.2.1.2.8 If the documents are located in a separate enclosure or cabinet, the separate enclosure or cabinet shall be prominently labeled FIRE ALARM DOCUMENTS.

Paragraphs 10.18.2.1.2.5 through 10.18.2.1.2.8 address the storage requirements for the record of completion. These requirements are specific to fire alarm systems. Storage of the record of completion for some emergency communications systems may need to be at a more secure location.

An up-to-date copy of the record of completion form must be stored at the fire alarm control unit or other approved location to make sure persons servicing the system have the latest information about the system. Also refer to the requirements for record keeping in Section 14.6. Exhibit 14.19 shows an example of an as-built drawing cabinet.

Paragraphs 10.18.2.1.2.7 and 10.18.2.1.2.8 were added to the 2010 edition of the Code. If the record of completion is not located next to the main fire alarm control unit, its location must be identified at the main fire alarm control unit to allow retrieval of the document.

If the record of completion is located away from the main fire alarm control unit, it must be in a separate enclosure or cabinet that is prominently labeled "FIRE ALARM DOCUMENTS." The Code does not specify a color for this enclosure or cabinet.

10.18.2.2 Revision. All fire alarm system modifications made after the initial installation shall be recorded on a revised version of the original record of completion.

Documentation of revisions made to a system after the original installation has been completed is just as important as documentation of the original installation. Every change to the system must be documented so that designers, service personnel, and others will know exactly what is on the system and how the system is to function.

10.18.2.2.1 All changes from the original information shall be shown.

10.18.2.2.2 The revised record of completion shall include a revision date.

10.18.2.3 Documentation Required. Every system shall include the following documentation, which shall be delivered to the owner or the owner's representative upon final acceptance of the system:

(1)*An owner's manual and manufacturer's published instructions covering all system equipment
(2) Record drawings
(3) For software-based systems, record copy of the site-specific software

The Code requires in 10.18.2.3(3) that a record copy of the site-specific software be delivered to the owner or the owner's representative upon final acceptance of the system. Having a backup copy of the software will help facilitate reconfiguring the system in situations where catastrophic failure has occurred due to lightning or other causes. Refer to the definition of *site-specific software* in 3.3.255.2. The site-specific software is the programming of the system for its specific application. It is not the executive software or the source code used to develop the site-specific software.

(4) A written sequence of operation

The requirement for a copy of the written sequence of operation of the system was added to the 2010 edition of the Code. By having copy of the sequence of operation on-site, anyone who works on or provides further designs to the existing system will be able to have a full understanding of how the system is intended to work. As these systems become more complex and have greater interactions with other building systems, this information is critical.

A.10.18.2.3(1) The owner's manual should include the following:

(1) A detailed narrative description of the system inputs, evacuation signaling, ancillary functions, annunciation, intended sequence of operations, expansion capability, application considerations, and limitations
(2) Operator instructions for basic system operations, including alarm acknowledgment, system reset, interpretation of system output (LEDs, CRT display, and printout), operation of manual evacuation signaling and ancillary function controls, and change of printer paper
(3) A detailed description of routine maintenance and testing as required and recommended and as would be provided under a maintenance contract, including testing and maintenance instructions for each type of device installed. This information should include the following:

    (a) Listing of the individual system components that require periodic testing and maintenance
    (b) Step-by-step instructions detailing the requisite testing and maintenance procedures, and the intervals at which these procedures shall be performed, for each type of device installed
    (c) A schedule that correlates the testing and maintenance procedures that are recommended by A.10.18.2.3(1)(3)(b) with the listing recommended by A.10.18.2.3(1)(3)(a)

(4) Detailed troubleshooting instructions for each trouble condition generated from the monitored field wiring, including opens, grounds, and loop failures [These instructions should include a list of all trouble signals annunciated by the system, a description of the condition(s) that causes such trouble signals, and step-by-step instructions describing how to isolate such problems and correct them (or how to call for service, as appropriate).]
(5) A service directory, including a list of names and telephone numbers of those who provide service for the system

10.18.2.4* Verification of Compliant Installation. Where required, compliance of the completed installation with the requirements of this Code, as implemented via the referring code(s), specifications, and/or other criteria applicable to the specific installation, shall be certified by a qualified and impartial third-party organization acceptable to the authority having jurisdiction.

A.10.18.2.4 This section is intended to provide a basis for the authority having jurisdiction to require third-party verification and certification that the authority having jurisdiction and the system owner can rely on to reasonably assure that the fire alarm system installation complies with the applicable requirements.

10.18.2.4.1 Verification shall ensure that the installed system includes all components and functions, that those components and functions are installed and operate as required, that the system has been 100 percent acceptance tested in accordance with Chapter 14, and that all required documentation has been provided to the system owner.

Exception: Where the installation is an extension, modification, or reconfiguration of an existing system, the verification shall be required for the new work only, and reacceptance testing in accordance with Chapter 14 shall be acceptable.

10.18.2.4.2 For supervising station systems, the verification shall also ascertain proper arrangement, transmission, and receipt of all signals required to be transmitted off-premises.

Exception: Where the installation is an extension, modification, or reconfiguration of an existing system, the verification shall be required for the new work only, and reacceptance testing in accordance with Chapter 14 shall be acceptable.

10.18.2.4.3 Verification shall include written confirmation that any required corrective actions have been completed.

The requirement in 10.18.2.4 allows the authority having jurisdiction to mandate a third party to review and certify an installation for compliance with *NFPA 72*. This requirement applies to all systems and is not the same as the documentation required for central station alarm systems in 26.3.4.

10.18.3 Records.

10.18.3.1 A complete record of the tests and operations of each system shall be kept until the next test and for 1 year thereafter.

10.18.3.2 The record shall be available for examination and, if required, reported to the authority having jurisdiction. Archiving of records by any means shall be permitted if hard copies of the records can be provided promptly when requested.

10.18.3.3 If off-premises monitoring is provided, records of all signals, tests, and operations recorded at the supervising station shall be maintained for not less than 1 year.

Keeping good records on the system is very important. The records must include not only the installation, programming, and sequence of operation, but the testing of the system as well. The Code requires that records of any test be maintained for each system until the time of the next test, and then for one year after that test. In addition, if the system transmits signals to off-site monitoring as described in Chapter 26 of the Code, the records of all signals, tests, and operations must be maintained there for not less than one year.

10.19* Impairments

A.10.19 The term *impairments* encompasses a broad range of circumstances wherein a fire alarm system or portion thereof is taken out of service for a variety of reasons. Fire alarm systems are routinely impaired in order to perform hot work (e.g., open flame operations) in areas with automatic detection, construction, painting, etc., as well as to conduct normal fire alarm system maintenance and testing. Impairments can be limited to specific initiating devices and/or functions (e.g., disconnecting the supervising station connection during system testing), or they can involve taking entire systems or portions of systems out of service. This section is intended to help building owners control impairments of the fire alarm system(s) in their building(s) and to ensure that systems are restored to full operation and/or returned to service afterward.

Additional requirements for impairments and out-of-service conditions exist in 14.2.1.2.

Requirements addressing impairments to fire alarm systems have been added in this chapter to provide a program to manage these occurrences. Impairments can be caused by system defects or by out-of-service events. System defects and malfunctions have been and still are addressed in the testing and maintenance chapter. Refer to 14.2.1.2 and related commentary.

10.19.1 The system owner or their designated representative shall be notified when a fire alarm system or part thereof is impaired. Impairments to systems shall include out-of-service events.

10.19.2 A record shall be maintained by the system owner or designated representative for a period of 1 year from the date the impairment is corrected.

10.19.3* Where required, mitigating measures acceptable to the authority having jurisdiction shall be implemented for the period that the system is impaired.

A.10.19.3 The need for mitigating measures is typically determined on a case-by-case basis. This considers the building, occupancy type, nature and duration of impairment, building occupancy level during impairment period, active work being conducted on the fire alarm system during the impairment, condition of other fire protection systems and features (i.e., sprinklers, structural compartmentation, etc.), and hazards and assets at risk.

Appropriate mitigating measures range from simple occupant notification to full-time fire watch. Determining factors vary from testing-related impairments and maintenance activities during normal business through extensive impairments to high-value, high-hazard situations.

10.19.4 The system owner or owner's designated representative shall be notified when an impairment period is completed or discontinued.

REFERENCES CITED IN COMMENTARY

ANSI S3.41, *American National Standard Audible Emergency Evacuation Signal*, 1996 edition, American National Standards Institute, Inc., New York, NY.

NFPA 70®, National Electrical Code®, 2008 edition, National Fire Protection Association, Quincy, MA.

NFPA 71, *Standard for the Installation, Maintenance, and Use of Signaling Systems for Central Station Service*, 1989 edition, National Fire Protection Association, Quincy, MA.

NFPA *101®, Life Safety Code®*, 2009 edition, National Fire Protection Association, Quincy, MA.

NFPA 110, *Standard for Emergency and Standby Power Systems*, 2010 edition, National Fire Protection Association, Quincy, MA.

NFPA 111, *Standard on Stored Electrical Energy Emergency and Standby Power Systems*, 2010 edition, National Fire Protection Association, Quincy, MA.

NFPA 720, *Standard for the Installation of Carbon Monoxide (CO) Detection and Warning Equipment*, 2009 edition, National Fire Protection Association, Quincy, MA.

NFPA 731, *Standard for the Installation of Electronic Premises Security Systems*, 2008 edition, National Fire Protection Association, Quincy, MA.

NFPA 5000®, Building Construction and Safety Code®, 2009 edition, National Fire Protection Association, Quincy, MA.

Reserved

In this 2010 edition of *NFPA 72®*, *National Fire Alarm and Signaling Code*, Chapter 11 is reserved for future use.

Circuits and Pathways

CHAPTER 12

Chapter 12, Circuits and Pathways, is a new chapter in the 2010 edition of the Code. The information that forms the basis for this new chapter was originally found in the chapter on the fundamentals of fire alarm systems and in the chapter on protected premises fire alarm systems. In previous editions of the Code, the requirements for circuit performance were essentially limited to initiating device circuits, signaling line circuits, and notification appliance circuits. There were no specific performance requirements for other types of fire alarm circuits, such as those that control fire suppression systems or various emergency control functions. Additionally, with the advent of mass notification systems, which are now addressed under emergency communications systems in Chapter 24, a more precise means of identifying circuit performance was needed. It would be confusing to have two sets of differing performance criteria for fire alarm systems and for emergency communications systems. It could also be confusing to have the requirements of emergency communications systems referencing fire alarm–specific requirements.

The solution was to create a new chapter to generally cover wiring requirements and circuit and pathway performance designations. The terms *circuits* and *pathways* are somewhat redundant. However, in the transition to the new chapter, the term *circuit* was retained even though the term *pathway* includes any type of circuit. By placing the wiring requirements and the performance designations into a single chapter that is not designated for any specific type of application, the requirements and designations can be referenced by any other chapter. In some cases, additional requirements are included in chapters that cover specific applications.

In the 2010 edition, the means of designating the performance requirements of circuits was changed significantly. Pathways are still designated by class, although the classes now include Classes A, B, C, D, E, and X, depending on their performance. Pathways are also designated by a level of survivability ranging from Level 0 to Level 3. The methods of designating pathway performance and survivability were chosen with the idea that the designations can be used for any type of fire alarm circuit and still retain flexibility in the Code to accommodate pathway designations and levels of survivability for other applications.

12.1 Application

12.1.1 Pathways (interconnections) shall be designated based on the performance characteristics defined in this chapter.

The Code requires that pathways be designated by performance class and survivability level, but Chapter 12 does not require any specific class or level for a particular application. Unless another chapter designates specific performance requirements, it is up to the enabling code, standard, or authority having jurisdiction to designate the required performance class and survivability level; otherwise, it is the responsibility of the system designer to conduct an analysis to determine the class and level to be provided. See 23.4.3.2 for the items to be considered as part of this analysis for fire alarm systems.

12.1.2 The requirements of Chapter 14 shall apply.

Chapter 14 details the requirements for inspection, testing, and maintenance of all parts of a system, including circuits and pathways.

12.2 General

12.2.1* Performance and survivability characteristics of signaling pathways (interconnections) shall comply with the defined designations of this chapter.

The designation of circuit class is dependent on the performance of the circuit under various conditions. These conditions, as described in 12.3.1 through 12.3.6, include requirements for operation under fault conditions, as well as whether the circuit contains a redundant pathway. In addition to the pathway performance designations detailed in Chapter 12, other chapters may specify additional requirements for pathways in specific types of systems. See 23.4.2.2 for specific requirements on the separation of conductors in a fire alarm system.

A.12.2.1 In the 2007 edition of *NFPA 72*, initiating device circuit, signaling line circuit, and notification appliance circuit performance class/style tables were rooted in "copper" wiring methods. Fire alarm control units use new communication technologies, such as Ethernet, fiber optics, and wireless, which do not fit in the "copper" wiring methods.

12.2.2 A pathway (interconnection) class designation shall be dependent on the pathway (interconnection) capability to continue to operate during abnormal conditions.

12.2.3 The designation of the pathways shall be permitted to also include the performance of the pathway (interconnection) to survivability from attack by fire.

In addition to having a class designation, the pathway may also be assigned a survivability level. While the means of providing survivability for a pathway can offer some level of mechanical protection that may be useful for situations other than a fire, currently the levels of survivability described in the Code are for protection against fire damage to the pathway.

12.2.4* The installation of all pathway wiring, cable, and equipment shall be in accordance with *NFPA 70, National Electrical Code*, and the applicable requirements of 12.2.4.1 through 12.2.4.5. (SIG-FUN)

The installation of wiring, circuits, and pathways is required to comply with the minimum requirements of *NFPA 70®, National Electrical Code®* (*NEC®*). It is important to understand that the primary concern of *NFPA 70* is to ensure that the installation does not pose an electrocution or fire hazard. In addition to the safety requirements of *NFPA 70*, the installation must also comply with the installation requirements provided by the fire alarm equipment manufacturer.

A.12.2.4 The installation of all system wiring should take into account the system manufacturer's published installation instructions, the limitations of the applicable product listings or approvals, and communications circuit protection as required by 12.2.4.2.

12.2.4.1 Optical fiber cables installed as part of the fire alarm system shall meet the requirements of *NFPA 70, National Electrical Code*, Article 770, and be protected against physical damage in accordance with *NFPA 70, National Electrical Code*, Article 760. (SIG-FUN)

12.2.4.2* Where fire alarm circuits enter or exit buildings, the circuits and equipment shall be installed in accordance with the requirements of Article 760 of *NFPA 70, National Electrical Code*. (SIG-FUN)

Subsection 12.2.4.2 was revised by a tentative interim amendment (TIA).

Where fire alarm circuits extend beyond one building and run outdoors, they must meet the requirements of Section 760.32 of the *NEC*, which reads as follows:

**760.32 FIRE ALARM CIRCUITS EXTENDING
BEYOND ONE BUILDING.**

Power-limited fire alarm circuits that extend beyond one building and run outdoors either shall meet the installation requirements of Parts II, III, and IV of Article 800 or shall meet the installation requirements of Part I of Article 300. Non–power-limited fire alarm circuits that extend beyond one building and run outdoors shall meet the installation requirements of Part I of Article 300 and the applicable sections of Part I of Article 225. [**70**:760.32]

These requirements include separate provisions for power-limited fire alarm circuits and for non–power-limited circuits. Power-limited circuits must meet either Parts II, III, and IV of Article 800 or Part I of Article 300. Non–power-limited circuits must meet both Part I of Article 225 (as applicable) and Part I of Article 300.

Part II of *NEC* Article 800 addresses communications wires and cables entering buildings and includes requirements for clearances of overhead wires and cables, and separation from light or power conductors. Part III of *NEC* Article 800 addresses requirements for the use of listed primary protector devices under certain conditions of exposure to light or power conductors or lightning. (Listed primary protectors include both fuse and fuseless types. They are intended to protect equipment, wiring, and personnel against the effects of excessive potentials and currents caused by lightning. Refer to UL 497B, *Standard for Protectors for Data Communications and Fire Alarm Circuits.*) FPN No. 2 of Section 800.90, extracted as part of A.12.2.4.2, provides guidance as to when lightning exposure may exist. Part IV of *NEC* Article 800 addresses requirements for grounding of the primary protector and for grounding of the metal sheath of cables.

Part I of *NEC* Article 300 includes a number of requirements that wiring installations must meet, including requirements for underground installations.

Part I of *NEC* Article 225 includes a number of requirements addressing support and clearance for overhead conductors.

A.12.2.4.2 Interbuilding circuits are considered to have a lightning exposure unless one or more of the following conditions exist:

(1) Circuits in large metropolitan areas where buildings are close together and sufficiently high to intercept lightning.
(2) Interbuilding cable runs of 140 ft (42 m) or less, directly buried or in underground conduit, where a continuous metallic cable shield or a continuous metallic conduit containing the cable is connected to each building grounding electrode system.
(3) Areas having an average of five or fewer thunderstorm days per year and earth resistivity of less than 100 ohm-meters. Such areas are found along the Pacific coast. [**70**:800.90(A), FPN No. 2]

It is important to protect the fire alarm system from lightning. One of the key requirements related to transient protection is NFPA 70, *National Electrical Code,* Section 760.32, which covers installation requirements. Part of those installation requirements are the grounding and bonding rules contained in Part IV of Article 800. Connections to the building grounding electrode system should be made where the circuits enter and exit a building. To minimize potential damage from induced transients, the circuits entering and exiting a building should connect to the grounding electrode system and transient protection equipment nearest the point of entry, before being intermingled with other circuits.

NEC Section 760.32 provides references for fire alarm circuits extending beyond one building. The requirements for the installation of power-limited circuits and communications circuits are covered by Parts II, III, and IV of Article 800, Communications Circuits. The methods and equipment used for providing transient protection of circuits addressed by Article 800 are not necessarily suitable for voltages expected on all fire alarm circuits.

The requirements for the installation of non–power-limited underground outdoor circuits are found in Part I of Article 300 and the applicable sections in Part I of Article 225,

Underground Branch Circuits and Feeders. It should be noted that Article 225 does not specifically require transient protection of circuits, but consideration should be given to protecting underground circuits.

In both power-limited and non–power-limited circuits, surge protective devices may be installed to protect against electrical surges. When installing surge protective devices, the requirements of NEC Article 285 should be followed.

Subsections A.12.2.4 and A.12.2.4.2 were revised by a tentative interim amendment (TIA).

In addition to compliance with the requirements of the *NEC*, designers and installers should consult with the fire alarm or signaling system manufacturer and manufacturers of transient voltage surge suppressors for proper selection and installation of primary protectors. The selection of protection for circuits should consider how the whole fire alarm or signaling system is being used. For example, protectors are available that can be installed in series or in parallel.

A series protector might dissipate small transients to ground and allow the protected circuit to continue to operate. But when subjected to a large transient, a series protector will fail open. The circuit will no longer be operational, but the equipment will have been protected and will not be subjected to any secondary transients. Most fire alarm circuits that open will result in a trouble condition. Some emergency control functions that are wired as Class D per 12.3.4 will cause the control function to operate when the circuit is opened. In the case of a primary power supply circuit, the open circuit will result in a trouble condition and the system will transfer to secondary power.

A parallel protector dissipates the energy of transients to ground but leaves the protected circuit operational. In the event of a large transient, the protection device might protect the circuit and be destroyed in the process. The circuit remains operational, but it no longer has any protection against subsequent transients.

Most protection devices have a visual means to indicate failure. Others also have a set of contacts that can be monitored to signal failure. The choice of a series or a parallel protection device should consider the mission of the system, the use of the particular circuit, the impact of circuit failure, the likelihood and the impact of secondary transients, and the response and repair capabilities or the owner or service company.

12.2.4.3* Fire alarm system wiring and equipment, including all circuits controlled and powered by the fire alarm system, shall be installed in accordance with the requirements of this Code and of *NFPA 70, National Electrical Code*, Article 760. (SIG-FUN)

All fire alarm system wiring installations must conform to the requirements of *NFPA 70*. The *NEC* provides general wiring methods and requirements in Chapter 1 through Chapter 4. Article 760, Fire Alarm Systems, contained in Chapter 7, supplements and modifies the requirements of Chapter 1 through Chapter 4 specifically for fire alarm systems. The wiring methods permitted in Article 760 include the use of Chapter 3 wiring methods as well as the use of specific types of non–power-limited and power-limited cables. The wiring method used must be installed in accordance with the manufacturer's instructions, any listing limitations, and the requirements of Article 760.

One of the general requirements of *NEC* Article 760 that applies to all fire alarm system wiring is the requirement in 760.30, which reads as follows:

760.30 FIRE ALARM CIRCUIT IDENTIFICATION

Fire alarm circuits shall be identified at terminal and junction locations in a manner that helps to prevent unintentional signals on fire alarm system circuit(s) during testing and servicing of other systems. [**70**:760.30]

One possible way to facilitate circuit identification is to use a terminal cabinet, such as the one shown in Exhibit 12.1.

A.12.2.4.3 Fire alarm systems include fire detection and alarm notification, guard's tour, sprinkler waterflow, and sprinkler supervisory systems. Circuits controlled and powered by the fire alarm system include circuits for the control of building systems safety functions, elevator capture, elevator shutdown, door release, smoke doors and damper control, fire doors and damper control, and fan shutdown, but only where these circuits are powered by and controlled by the fire alarm system. [**70:**760.1 FPN No.1] (SIG-FUN)

Class 1, 2, and 3 circuits are defined in Article 725 (of *NFPA 70, National Electrical Code*). [**70:**760.1 FPN No. 2]

12.2.4.4 All fire alarm systems shall test free of grounds.

Exception: Parts of circuits or equipment that are intentionally and permanently grounded to provide ground-fault detection, noise suppression, emergency ground signaling, and circuit protection grounding shall be permitted. (SIG-FUN)

12.2.4.5* Wiring methods permitted by other sections of this Code to resist attack by fire shall be installed in accordance with manufacturer's published instructions and the requirements of *NFPA 70*, Article 760. (SIG-FUN)

A.12.2.4.5 It is important for the intended functionality of circuit integrity cable or electrical circuit protective systems to follow manufacturer's installation instructions. An electrical circuit protective system has detailed installation requirements, and additional requirements can be found in the manufacturer's installation instructions, *NFPA 70, National Electrical Code*, or the listing organizations' guide information.

12.3* Pathway Class Designations

Pathways shall be designated as Class A, Class B, Class C, Class D, Class E, or Class X, depending on their performance.

Although the pathway class designations are in alphabetical order, the Code simply describes the performance requirements of each class. The Code does not imply a preference of one class of circuit over another for a particular application. It is up to the enabling codes, standards, authority having jurisdiction, or system designer to determine the class of pathway that best meets the site-specific conditions and design objectives for a particular application. The circuit designations were also set up with the intention of accommodating additional types of circuits in the future.

A.12.3 The intent of the circuit designations is not to create a hierarchal ranking; rather it is to provide guidance on the levels of performance.

The initiating device circuit, signal line circuit, and notification appliance circuit performance class/style tables from previous editions of the Code have been included as Table A.12.3(a), Table A.12.3(b), and Table A.12.3(c) but have been modified to include the enhanced class references. These tables reflect the classifications as applied to fire alarm systems. Some of the operations are a combination of the requirements of Chapter 12 in conjunction with the requirements of Chapters 10 and 23. Singular ground-fault conditions that do not affect operation of the pathway are not specifically covered in Chapter 12, but are covered by the requirements of other chapters. Users of the Chapter 12 designations should review whether there are other abnormal conditions not specified in Chapter 12 that the pathways need to annunciate and operate through for their application.

TABLE A.12.3(a) *Performance of Initiating Device Circuits (IDCs)*

NFPA 72-2007 Class	B			A		
NFPA 72-2010 Class	**B**			**A**		
	Alm	*Trbl*	*ARC*	*Alm*	*Trbl*	*ARC*
Abnormal Condition	1	2	3	4	5	6
Single open	—	X	—	—	X	R
Single ground	—	X	R	—	X	R

Alm: Alarm. Trbl: Trouble. ARC: Alarm receipt capability during abnormal condition. R: Required capability. X: Indication required at protected premises and as required by Chapter 26.

TABLE A.12.3(b) *Performance of Signal Line Circuits (SLCs)*

NFPA 72-2007 Class	B			A			A		
Style	**4**			**6**			**7**		
NFPA 72-2010 Class	**B**			**A**			**X**		
	Alarm	*Trouble*	*ARC*	*Alarm*	*Trouble*	*ARC*	*Alarm*	*Trouble*	*ARC*
Abnormal Condition	*1*	*2*	*3*	*4*	*5*	*6*	*7*	*8*	*9*
Single open	—	X	—	—	X	R	—	X	R
Single ground	—	X	R	—	X	R	—	X	R
Wire-to-wire short	—	X	—	—	X	—	—	X	R
Wire-to-wire short & open	—	X	—	—	X	—	—	X	—
Wire-to-wire short & ground	—	X	—	—	X	—	—	X	—
Open and ground	—	X	—	—	X	R	—	X	R
Loss of carrier (if used) / channel interface	—	X	—	—	X	—	—	X	—

ARC: Alarm receipt capability during abnormal condition. R: Required capability. X: Indication required at protected premises and as required by Chapter 26.

TABLE A.12.3(c) *Notification Appliance Circuits (NACs)*

NFPA 72-2007 Class	B		A	
NFPA 72-2010 Class	B		A	
	Trouble Indications at Protective Premise	Alarm Capability During Abnormal Condition	Trouble Indications at Protective Premise	Alarm Capability During Abnormal Condition
Abnormal Condition	1	2	3	4
Single open	X	—	X	R
Single ground	X	R	X	R
Wire-to-wire short	X	—	X	—

X: Indication required at protected premises and as required by Chapter 26. R: Required capability.

12.3.1* Class A. A pathway shall be designated as Class A when it performs as follows:

(1) It includes a redundant path.
(2) Operational capability continues past a single open.
(3) Conditions that affect the intended operation of the path are annunciated.

A Class A pathway most closely resembles the performance requirements of a Class A circuit as described in the 2007 edition of the Code.

A.12.3.1 The Class A references for initiating device circuit and notification appliance circuit performance have been changed to eliminate the need for alarm receipt capability during a single ground or annunciation of a single ground fault. The signal line circuit performance has changed to provide a clear separation between the Class A Style 6 and Class A Style 7 performance. The Class A Style 7 performance is now defined as Class X.

Fiber optic or wireless pathways are examples of Class A circuitry not impaired by earth ground connection, and short-circuits, and therefore do not annunciate those conditions as a fault. Users of the code are advised that fire alarm circuits still require alarm receipt capability during a single ground. See Chapter 23.

12.3.2* Class B. A pathway shall be designated as Class B when it performs as follows:

(1) It does not include a redundant path.
(2) Operational capability stops at a single open.
(3) Conditions that affect the intended operation of the path are annunciated.

A Class B pathway most closely resembles the performance requirements of a Class B circuit as described in the 2007 edition of the Code.

A.12.3.2 The Class B references for initiating device circuit, signal line circuit, and notification appliance circuit performance have been changed to eliminate the need for alarm receipt capability during a single ground or annunciation of a single ground fault. Users of the code are advised that fire alarm circuits still require alarm receipt capability during a single ground. *(See Chapter 23.)*

12.3.3* Class C. A pathway shall be designated as Class C when it performs as follows:

(1) It includes one or more pathways where operational capability is verified via end-to-end communication, but the integrity of individual paths is not monitored.
(2) A loss of end-to-end communication is annunciated.

A.12.3.3 The Class C reference is new and is intended to describe technologies that supervise the communication pathway by polling or continuous communication "handshaking" such as the following:

(1) Fire control unit or supervisory station connections to a wired LAN, WAN, or Internet
(2) Fire control unit or supervisory station connections to a wireless LAN, WAN, and Internet
(3) Fire control unit or supervisory station connections to a wireless (proprietary communications)
(4) Fire control unit digital alarm communication transmitter or supervisory station digital alarm communication receiver connections to the public switched telephone network

12.3.4* Class D. A pathway shall be designated as Class D when it has fail-safe operation, where no fault is annunciated, but the intended operation is performed in the event of a pathway failure.

A.12.3.4 The Class D reference is intended to describe pathways that are not supervised but have a fail-safe operation that performs the intended function when the connection is lost. Examples of such pathways include the following:

(1) Power to door holders where interruption of the power results in the door closing
(2) Power to locking hardware that release upon an open circuit or fire alarm operation

12.3.5* Class E. A pathway shall be designated as Class E when it is not monitored for integrity.

A.12.3.5 The Class E reference is new and is intended to describe pathways, which do not require supervision as described in 10.17.

12.3.6* Class X. A pathway shall be designated as Class X when it performs as follows:

(1) It includes a redundant path.
(2) Operational capability continues past a single open or short-circuit.
(3) Conditions that affect the intended operation of the path are annunciated.

A.12.3.6 The Class X reference is new and is intended to describe pathways as described as Class A Style 7 of the signal line circuit performance of Table A.12.3(b). *(Also see A.12.3.)*

12.4 Pathway Survivability

All pathways shall comply with *NFPA 70, National Electrical Code.*

Chapter 12 does not require any specific level of survivability, but it provides various options when other chapters, codes, standards, or authorities having jurisdiction require survivability. While the Code lists the levels of survivability in ascending numerical order, it is not intended to imply that one level of survivability is preferred over another for a specific application.

12.4.1 Pathway Survivability Level 0. Level 0 pathways shall not be required to have any provisions for pathway survivability.

12.4.2 Pathway Survivability Level 1. Pathway survivability Level 1 shall consist of pathways in buildings that are fully protected by an automatic sprinkler system in accordance with NFPA 13, *Standard for the Installation of Sprinkler Systems*, with any interconnecting conductors, cables, or other physical pathways installed in metal raceways.

12.4.3 Pathway Survivability Level 2. Pathway survivability Level 2 shall consist of one or more of the following:

(1) 2-hour fire-rated circuit integrity (CI) cable
(2) 2-hour fire-rated cable system [electrical circuit protective system(s)]
(3) 2-hour fire-rated enclosure or protected area
(4) 2-hour performance alternatives approved by the authority having jurisdiction

12.4.4 Pathway Survivability Level 3. Pathway survivability Level 3 shall consist of pathways in buildings that are fully protected by an automatic sprinkler system in accordance with NFPA 13, *Standard for the Installation of Sprinkler Systems*, and one or more of the following:

(1) 2-hour fire rated circuit integrity (CI) cable
(2) 2-hour fire rated cable system (electrical circuit protective system(s))
(3) 2-hour fire rated enclosure or protected area
(4) 2-hour performance alternatives approved by the authority having jurisdiction

Subsections 12.4.3 and 12.4.4 each includes a list of four methods used for ensuring pathway survivability.

Fire alarm circuit integrity (CI) cables are addressed among the specific types of non–power-limited and power-limited cables that are permitted in Article 760. A "CI" suffix is added to the specific cable types to identify cables that meet the circuit integrity requirements. For example, Type NPLF-CI is a general purpose (excluding riser, ducts, plenums, and other space used for environmental air) non–power-limited circuit integrity cable. Also refer to the test methods used to evaluate the fire resistive performance of cables in UL 2196, *Standard for Tests of Fire Resistive Cable.*

An electrical circuit protective system is a system of cables and other materials designed and evaluated to ensure electrical circuit integrity upon exposure to a fire. The installation of these systems requires compliance with specific procedures using specific materials evaluated as a part of the listing of these systems. Some of these systems include the use of mineral insulated cable as a part of the system. The requirements in *NEC* Article 332, Mineral-Insulated, Metal-Sheathed Cable: Type MI, also apply to the installation of mineral insulated cable. Also refer to UL 1724, *Outline of Investigation for Fire Tests for Electrical Circuit Protective Systems.*

Exhibits 12.2 and 12.3 show examples of circuit integrity cable and mineral insulated cable.

The UL *Fire Resistance Directory,* Volume 2, identifies many types of construction that provide a 2-hour fire resistance rating. The enclosure can be constructed of masonry, concrete, or an assembly of classified products, such as metal studs and gypsum wallboard. To attain the desired fire rating, the enclosure must be constructed exactly as required by the list-

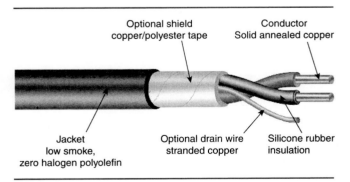

EXHIBIT 12.2 *Circuit Integrity (CI) Cable. (Source: Tyco Thermal Controls, Menlo Park, CA)*

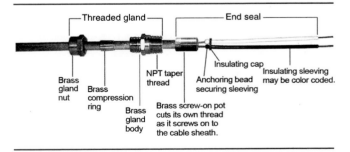

EXHIBIT 12.3 *Mineral Insulated (MI) Cable — Part of an Electrical Circuit Protective System. (Source: Tyco Thermal Controls, Menlo Park, CA)*

ing. Any penetrations in the enclosure must be sealed in a manner that provides a fire resistance rating equivalent to the enclosure. Two-hour rated enclosures include 2-hour rated exit stairwells, where building codes permit their use.

The authority having jurisdiction may approve other methods of providing protection. This might be a combination of installation methods and protection by the building structure. Technical justification must be provided by the designer to support the survivability design.

12.5 Nomenclature

To identify the properties of the system(s) interconnections and survivability requirements, the following identification nomenclature shall be used:

(1) System(s) interconnections
(2) Survivability levels (not required if Level 0)

This section explains the nomenclature for describing the pathway class and survivability level. The nomenclature "system(s) interconnections" in 12.5(1) is intended to refer to the pathway class designation. A Class B pathway installed to provide survivability Level 3 by using 2-hour rated circuit integrity cable in a building fully protected by automatic sprinklers designed and installed in accordance with NFPA 13, *Standard for the Installation of Sprinkler Systems*, would be designated as B3. If no level of survivability is designated, it is taken to be Level 0.

REFERENCES CITED IN COMMENTARY

NFPA 13, *Standard for the Installation of Sprinkler Systems*, 2010 edition, National Fire Protection Association, Quincy, MA.

NFPA 70®, *National Electrical Code®*, 2008 edition, National Fire Protection Association, Quincy, MA.

UL 497B, *Standard for Protectors for Data Communications and Fire Alarm Circuits*, Underwriters Laboratories Inc., Northbrook, IL, 2008.

UL 1724, *Outline of Investigation for Fire Tests for Electrical Circuit Protective Systems*, Underwriters Laboratories Inc., Northbrook, IL, 2006.

UL 2196, *Standard for Tests of Fire Resistive Cable*, Underwriters Laboratories Inc., Northbrook, IL, 2006.

UL *Fire Resistance Directory*, Volume 2, Underwriters Laboratories Inc., Northbrook, IL, 2009.

Reserved

CHAPTER 13

In this 2010 edition of *NFPA 72®*, *National Fire Alarm and Signaling Code*, Chapter 13 is reserved for future use.

Inspection, Testing, and Maintenance

CHAPTER 14

Chapter 14 (Chapter 10 in previous editions of the Code) covers minimum requirements for inspection, testing, and maintenance of fire alarm systems; supervising station alarm systems; public emergency alarm reporting systems; emergency communications systems (ECSs); single- and multiple-station smoke and heat alarms; and household fire alarm systems. Chapter 14 includes requirements for visual inspection and inspection frequencies, testing and test methods, testing frequencies, maintenance requirements, and record keeping.

An important note is that the provisions of Chapter 1 apply in addition to those of Chapter 14. The use of equivalent test methods or test devices is permitted by the Code, provided their use complies with the equivalency rules in Section 1.5. Equivalent methods or devices must meet the intent of the requirements of Chapter 14, and evidence demonstrating equivalence must be provided to the authority having jurisdiction.

The following list is a summary of significant changes to the chapter on inspection, testing, and maintenance in the 2010 edition:

- Revised throughout to reflect the broader application of fire/alarm/emergency systems
- Revised Table 14.4.2.2, item 15(b), and 14.4.13 providing updated requirements for the verification of intelligible voice communications
- Revised Tables 14.3.1, 14.4.2.2, and 14.4.5 adding new requirements for the inspection and testing of mass notification systems (MNSs)
- New 14.2.4.1 and 14.2.4.2 requiring documentation of current revisions and compatibility of fire alarm software
- New 14.2.7 providing an allowance for automated testing
- New 14.2.8 providing an allowance for performance-based inspection and testing
- New 14.4.4 requiring the inspection, testing, and maintenance of gas detectors
- Revised 14.4.5.6 adding new requirements for circuit and pathway testing
- New 14.4.8.2 requiring replacement of combination smoke/carbon monoxide alarms after 10 years or when the end-of-life signal activates
- Revised Figure 14.6.2.4 (Inspection and Testing Form) providing an extensive update, including MNSs
- New 14.4.12 providing extensive requirements for the system commissioning testing, acceptance test, and annual tests of in-building emergency radio communications systems

14.1 Application

14.1.1 The inspection, testing, and maintenance of systems, their initiating devices, and notification appliances shall comply with the requirements of this chapter.

In 14.1.1 and other specific locations within Chapter 14, the term *fire alarm system(s)* was replaced with just *system(s)*. This change allows the Code to address the inspection, testing, and maintenance requirements of systems in addition to fire alarm systems when appropriate. These systems include, but are not limited to, supervising station alarm systems, public emergency alarm reporting systems, emergency communications systems (ECSs), and other systems discussed herein (see 1.3.1 and 1.3.2).

Chapter 14 addresses inspection, testing, and maintenance requirements for systems and the initiating devices and notification appliances connected to them. The installation of these systems is covered by the requirements in other chapters of the Code. Listed smoke detection devices not connected to a fire alarm system (often called stand-alone detectors) are sometimes found in HVAC systems, door-releasing applications, and special hazard releasing devices. The requirements in Chapter 14, including sensitivity testing, apply to these types of detectors. (Note: Smoke alarms are not tested or listed to operate door-releasing devices, HVAC controls, or special hazard systems and are not considered in this context to be stand-alone devices.)

14.1.2 The inspection, testing, and maintenance of single- and multiple-station smoke and heat alarms and household fire alarm systems shall comply with the requirements of this chapter.

As stated in 14.1.2, Chapter 14 also includes the testing and maintenance requirements for all single- and multiple-station smoke alarms and heat alarms; household fire alarm systems, including those in one- and two-family dwelling units; and in other residential occupancies, such as apartments, hotel and motel rooms, and dormitory living units. The installation of this fire-warning equipment is covered by the requirements in Chapter 29. Refer to the definition of *fire warning equipment* in 3.3.100.

The requirements in Chapter 14, including sensitivity testing, apply to single- and multiple-station smoke alarms in other than one- or two-family dwelling units. Sensitivity testing is not required for smoke alarms in one- or two-family dwelling units. Smoke alarms installed in one- and two-family dwelling units are not permitted to remain in service for longer than 10 years from the date of manufacture (see 14.4.8).

In the context of these requirements, it is important to understand that the terms *smoke alarm* and *smoke detector* are not interchangeable. A smoke alarm is a device that includes detection and notification components, whereas a smoke detector may contain detection and control components and requires connection to additional equipment to perform notification functions. Refer to the definitions of *smoke alarm, single station alarm, detector,* and *smoke detector* in Chapter 3.

14.1.3 Procedures that are required by other parties and that exceed the requirements of this chapter shall be permitted.

14.1.4 The requirements of this chapter shall apply to both new and existing systems.

FAQ ▶
Are the requirements of Chapter 14 retroactive?

Because the requirements of Chapter 14 apply to both new and existing systems, as stated in 14.1.4, they are retroactive. The committee intends that the most current edition of the Code be used for inspection, testing, and maintenance of both new and existing fire alarm systems and fire-warning equipment. The requirements of the other chapters are generally not retroactive and apply only to new installations. Refer to Section 1.4 regarding retroactivity as applied in general to the Code.

14.2 General

14.2.1 Performance.

14.2.1.1 Performance Verification. To ensure operational integrity, the system shall have an inspection, testing, and maintenance program.

14.2.1.1.1 Inspection, testing, and maintenance programs shall satisfy the requirements of this Code and conform to the equipment manufacturer's published instructions.

14.2.1.1.2 Inspection, testing, and maintenance programs shall verify correct operation of the system.

Paragraph 14.2.1.1 reinforces the requirements of building and occupancy codes for testing of systems. Paragraph 14.2.1.1.1 incorporates the "manufacturer's published instructions" into the requirements of the Code. System manufacturers are required to submit manufacturer's published instructions to the organization conducting the product evaluations for the listing of their system or component. Therefore, these instructions should be enforced as code in accordance with 10.3.2 and 14.2.1.1.1. Verifying the correct operation of the system includes conformance with the Code and also with the owner's fire protection or other goals and the designer's specifications. These goals and specifications should be included with the system design documentation. Refer to 10.18.1.2, 14.2.4, Section 17.3, 17.6.1.1, 17.7.1.1, 23.3.1, 23.3.2, and 24.4.2.2. The fire alarm system designer should be retained to ensure that the system goals and the owner's fire protection goals are met.

14.2.1.2 Impairments.

14.2.1.2.1 The requirements of Section 10.19 shall be applicable when a system is impaired.

14.2.1.2.2 System defects and malfunctions shall be corrected.

14.2.1.2.3 If a defect or malfunction is not corrected at the conclusion of system inspection, testing, or maintenance, the system owner or the owner's designated representative shall be informed of the impairment in writing within 24 hours.

The purpose of the requirement in 14.2.1.2.3 to notify the owner or the owner's designated representative (usually the building manager) in writing is to ensure that they are aware of the defects and malfunctions so that they can take steps to have the defects or malfunctions corrected. Section 10.19 also covers administrative requirements for all impairments, including out-of-service events.

14.2.2 Responsibilities.

14.2.2.1* The property or building or system owner or the owner's designated representative shall be responsible for inspection, testing, and maintenance of the system and for alterations or additions to this system.

A.14.2.2.1 See definition of *Ownership* in 3.3.171.

Usually the property or building owner is responsible for the inspection, testing, and maintenance of the system. The requirements of 14.2.2.1 have been revised to clarify that in some cases the system owner is the responsible party. The owner can designate a representative to assume this responsibility. The owner relationships are further explained in the context of system inspection, testing, and maintenance in A.3.3.171.

14.2.2.2 The delegation of responsibility shall be in writing, with a copy of such delegation provided to the authority having jurisdiction upon request.

In accordance with 14.2.2.1, the property, building, or system owner is responsible for testing and maintaining the system. If the owner chooses to appoint a representative to assume this responsibility, the delegation must be confirmed in writing. The delegated representative is often the building manager.

This requirement does not necessarily mean that the owner or the designated representative can legally perform any of the testing or maintenance of the system, which depends on the licensing laws of the applicable state or local jurisdiction. This requirement simply means that the owner or designated representative is responsible for ensuring that the system is properly tested and maintained in accordance with the requirements of this chapter.

14.2.2.3 Inspection, testing, or maintenance shall be permitted to be done by the building or system owner or a person or organization other than the building or system owner if conducted under a written contract.

If the owner or designated representative does not choose to perform the inspection, testing, and maintenance or is not allowed to due to licensing laws, 14.2.2.3 permits the owner to contract with a qualified contractor to perform these services. This written delegation can take the form of a testing and maintenance contract.

14.2.2.4 Testing and maintenance of central station service systems shall be performed under the contractual arrangements specified in 26.3.3.

Paragraph 14.2.2.4 clarifies that a contractual agreement per 26.3.3 is required to provide the services for testing of central station alarm systems. Only a listed central station or listed alarm service–local company can be contracted to perform the testing and maintenance requirements for central station alarm systems.

14.2.2.5* Service Personnel Qualifications and Experience.   Service personnel shall be qualified and experienced in accordance with the requirements of 10.4.3.

A.14.2.2.5 Service personnel should be able to do the following:

(1) Understand the requirements contained in *NFPA 72*, *National Fire Alarm and Signaling Code* and the fire alarm requirements contained in *NFPA 70*, *National Electrical Code*
(2) Understand basic job site safety laws and requirements
(3) Apply troubleshooting techniques, and determine the cause of fire alarm system trouble conditions
(4) Understand equipment specific requirements, such as programming, application, and compatibility
(5) Read and interpret fire alarm system design documentation and manufacturer's inspection, testing, and maintenance guidelines
(6) Properly use tools and test equipment required for testing and maintenance of fire alarm systems and their components
(7) Properly apply the test methods required by *NFPA 72*, *National Fire Alarm and Signaling Code*

FAQ ▶
What is the purpose of the requirements in 14.2.2.5?

The qualification requirements previously in 14.2.2.5 have been relocated to Chapter 10 so that all personnel qualification requirements (except those for public emergency alarm reporting systems) are in a common Code location. The requirements in 10.4.3 are intended to ensure that the persons testing and maintaining fire alarm systems have an appropriate level of knowledge, skill, and understanding of the systems and equipment. As a minimum, the Code recognizes four methods in 10.4.3.1(1) through 10.4.3.1(4) to demonstrate that service personnel are qualified. Service personnel should be able to perform the basic skills identified in A.14.2.2.5.

Exhibit 14.1 is a photograph of a technician performing a test.

14.2.3* Notification.

A.14.2.3 Prior to any scheduled inspection or testing, the service company should consult with the building or system owner or the owner's designated representative. Issues of advance notification in certain occupancies, including advance notification time, building posting, systems interruption and restoration, evacuation procedures, accommodation for evacuees, and other related issues, should be agreed upon by all parties prior to any inspection or testing.

14.2.3.1 Before proceeding with any testing, all persons and facilities receiving alarm, supervisory, or trouble signals and all building occupants shall be notified of the testing to prevent unnecessary response.

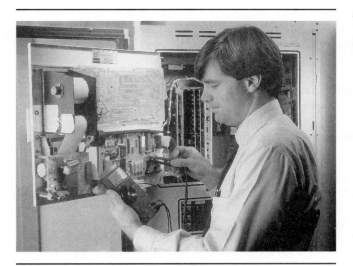

EXHIBIT 14.1 *Technician Testing Fire Alarm System. (Source: SimplexGrinnell, Westminster, MA)*

Paragraph 14.2.3.1 requires notification of those affected that system testing is about to take place. In many cases, the building owner or the owner's designated representative (e.g., a property management company) best knows the location of all the building occupants, the building employees, or the tenant occupants and the best means of communication with such occupants. Typically, the building owner or the owner's designated representative has the resources and authority to use broadcast email, to use the building's public address system, and to display signage. Notification of building occupants should be the responsibility of the owner or the owner's designated representative in addition to the system technician who will be performing the system testing.

Everyone who might be affected by the testing of a fire alarm system installed at a protected premises must be notified that the testing will take place. In addition to building occupants in general, those notified should include, but not be limited to, the building owner, the building manager, switchboard operators, the building engineer, building or floor fire wardens, and building maintenance personnel. Methods of notification include bulletin board postings, email, public address announcements, and lobby signs.

In addition, notification of personnel at the supervising station or communication center prior to testing is also required. Paragraphs 26.3.7.5.5 and 26.3.7.5.6 require the prime contractor (or designated representative) to provide a unique identification code to the central station before placing the central station alarm system into test status. The requirements of 26.3.7.5.6 and 14.2.3.1 are intended to prevent unauthorized tampering with the fire alarm system and unnecessary response by the fire department and by others who may be affected by the test.

A fire emergency plan (or other appropriate emergency plan) should be established for the protected premises that provides for notifying occupants, the communications center, and the supervising station in case a fire (or other emergency) occurs during testing.

Note that fire alarm drills are not part of fire alarm system testing and are not addressed by the Code. Requirements for fire alarm drills are usually specified as a part of building or fire code requirements and may be occupancy dependent.

◄ FAQ
Who should be notified prior to the testing of a fire alarm system?

14.2.3.2 At the conclusion of testing, those previously notified (and others, as necessary) shall be notified that testing has been concluded.

14.2.3.3 The owner or the owner's designated representative and service personnel shall coordinate system testing to prevent interruption of critical building systems or equipment.

As addressed in 14.2.3.3, if the system is interconnected with other building systems, such as elevators and HVAC systems, the system testing must be managed so it does not disrupt those building systems or equipment that may be critical to the continuity of building operations. Requirements for the testing of interfaced equipment and emergency control functions are contained in 14.2.6 as well as Table 14.3.1, Table 14.4.2.2, and Table 14.4.5. The testing must be coordinated with the specialists maintaining these interfaced systems.

14.2.4 System Documentation. Prior to system maintenance or testing, the record of completion and any information required by Section 10.18 regarding the system and system alterations, including specifications, wiring diagrams, and floor plans, shall be provided by the owner or a designated representative to the service personnel upon request.

At the time of an acceptance test, the authority having jurisdiction and the system contractor must ensure that all documentation for the system installation has been completed and is presented to the owner or the owner's designated representative in a usable format. The required documentation includes all documents outlined in both Chapter 10 (see Section 10.18) and Chapter 14. Maintenance of a system directly impacts the mission effectiveness of the system. Service personnel cannot effectively maintain or test a system without full access to all of the required system documentation. Also refer to the commentary following 14.2.1.1.2.

Exhibit 14.2 is a suggested checklist of documents needed to test and maintain a system. All items on this checklist should be provided prior to testing or maintaining the system.

EXHIBIT 14.2 *Checklist for Required System Testing Documentation.*

Documentation Checklist:
- ❏ Fire Alarm System Record of Completion
- ❏ Point-to-Point Wiring Diagrams
- ❏ Individual Device Interconnection Drawings
- ❏ As-Built (Record) Drawings
- ❏ Copy of Original Equipment Submittals
- ❏ Operational Manuals
- ❏ Manufacturer's Proper Testing and Maintenance Requirements
- ❏ Device Address List/Conventional Device Location List

14.2.4.1 The provided documentation shall include the current revisions of all fire alarm software and the revisions of software of any systems with which the fire alarm software interfaces.

14.2.4.2 The revisions of fire alarm software, and the revisions of the software in the systems with which the fire alarm software interfaces, shall be verified for compatibility in accordance with the requirements of 23.2.2.1.1.

Paragraphs 14.2.4.1 and 14.2.4.2 were added in the 2010 edition to correlate with a new requirement in 23.2.2.1.1 that fire alarm system software be compatible with the software used in other systems that interface with the fire alarm systems. The system documentation required by 14.2.4 must include the current software revision of all systems involved, and software compatibility must be verified. Paragraph A.23.2.2.1.1 includes a detailed discussion of some of the compatibility issues involved. See 3.3.255 for the definition of *software* and 23.2.2 for additional requirements on software and firmware documentation.

14.2.5 Releasing Systems. Requirements pertinent to testing the fire alarm systems initiating fire suppression system releasing functions shall be covered by 14.2.5.1 through 14.2.5.6.

Subsection 14.2.5 addresses the special requirements and precautions that apply to fire alarm systems that are also used for suppression system actuation. Testing the suppression system itself is covered by separate standards that address the specific suppression system or special hazard system. Testing of special hazard fire protection systems that are equipped with their own fire alarm control unit should be conducted as a separate series of tests from those of the building fire alarm system. Only the interface functions between the separate control unit and the building fire alarm system should be tested as part of the building fire alarm system testing. If the building fire alarm system is listed for releasing service and also controls the special hazard fire protection system, the special hazard system operation (without the discharge of suppression agent) must be tested as part of the building fire alarm system testing procedures. Care must be taken to ensure that the special hazard system is not inadvertently actuated. Also refer to the requirements of 23.3.3, 23.8.2, 23.8.5.10, and Section 23.13.

14.2.5.1 Testing personnel shall be qualified and experienced in the specific arrangement and operation of a suppression system(s) and a releasing function(s) and shall be cognizant of the hazards associated with inadvertent system discharge.

If the technician testing the fire alarm system is not qualified to test the special hazard system, then additional technicians trained and qualified to work on the special hazard system should be present to assist in conducting the tests. Having trained and qualified personnel present during testing of special hazard systems is necessary to prevent unwanted discharge of the fire suppression agent, which can cause significant property damage or cause accidental injury or death to the building occupants. Also refer to 14.2.2.5 and 10.4.3 for service personnel qualification requirements.

14.2.5.2 Occupant notification shall be required whenever a fire alarm system configured for releasing service is being serviced or tested.

The notification required by 14.2.5.2 allows the occupants to either evacuate the area being tested or prepare for the possible interruption of their work caused by the test. Also see 14.2.3.

14.2.5.3 Discharge testing of suppression systems shall not be required by this Code.

14.2.5.4 Suppression systems shall be secured from inadvertent actuation, including disconnection of releasing solenoids or electric actuators, closing of valves, other actions, or combinations thereof, for the specific system, for the duration of the fire alarm system testing.

It is recommended that fire alarm systems used for releasing service be identified as such. A typical suppression release panel identification label could include information such as the following:

"SUPPRESSION RELEASE PANEL.

CAUTION: This Control Unit has been arranged for releasing service. Disable all releasing device circuits prior to servicing."

One way to "secure" or "disable" a suppression system from inadvertent actuation during fire alarm system testing is by actuating a keyed service disconnect switch, which physically disconnects the suppression releasing mechanism (i.e., solenoid or electronic actuator) from the suppression releasing circuit. The Code does not permit the use of a software interlock. See 23.13.5.2.

Disconnection of releasing solenoids or electronic actuators, closing of valves, or other actions taken to secure or disable a suppression system from inadvertent actuation during fire alarm system testing is required to initiate an "off-normal" or supervisory signal on the fire alarm system control unit. The off-normal or supervisory signal is required to remain active on the fire alarm system control unit until the device that has been secured or disabled is placed back in service — that is, returned to its normal operating condition. See 23.13.5.1.

14.2.5.5 Testing shall include verification that the releasing circuits and components energized or actuated by the fire alarm system are electrically monitored for integrity and operate as intended on alarm.

14.2.5.6 Suppression systems and releasing components shall be returned to their functional operating condition upon completion of system testing.

14.2.6 Interface Equipment and Emergency Control Functions.

FAQ ▶
What is the purpose of
subsection 14.2.6?

This subsection, along with the requirements in Table 14.4.2.2, items 22 and 23, and Table 14.4.5, item 18, is intended to emphasize that testing of interfaced equipment and emergency safety functions should not be overlooked as a part of the system testing.

Proper testing of interfaced systems and emergency control functions may require the involvement of additional personnel not typically associated with testing of fire alarm systems. For example, testing the operation of elevator recall through actuation of the fire alarm system will likely require the involvement of building management, qualified elevator service personnel, and inspection authorities.

14.2.6.1* Testing personnel shall be qualified and experienced in the arrangement and operation of interface equipment and emergency control functions.

A.14.2.6.1 As an example, testing of the elevator fire service and shutdown functions will usually require a coordinated multi-discipline effort with presence of qualified service personnel for the fire alarm system, the elevator system, and other building systems. The presence of inspection authorities might also be needed in some jurisdictions. The development of a test plan should be considered to ensure that the testing of these features is accomplished in a coordinated and timely manner. This plan should also ensure that all appropriate parties and personnel are present when needed, and that the testing requirements for both the fire alarm system and the elevator system are fulfilled. See Section 21.3 and Section 21.4 for specific elevator emergency control functions.

14.2.6.2 Testing shall be accomplished in accordance with Table 14.4.2.2.

14.2.7 Automated Testing.

Automated testing of sprinkler system components, such as waterflow switches, is becoming more prevalent in buildings. The Code now permits the use of automated testing where the arrangement provides a means "equivalent" to the method specified in Table 14.4.2.2 with the frequency specified in Table 14.4.5. These system components should be controlled or monitored by the fire alarm system, which should provide notification of any detected failures, as required in 14.2.7.2.

14.2.7.1 Automated testing arrangements that provide equivalent means of testing devices to those specified in Table 14.4.2.2 at a frequency at least equivalent to those specified in Table 14.4.5 shall be permitted to be used to comply with the requirements of this chapter.

14.2.7.2 Failure of a device on an automated test shall result in an audible and visual trouble signal.

14.2.8* Performance-Based Inspection and Testing.
As an alternate means of compliance, subject to the authority having jurisdiction, components and systems shall be permitted to be inspected and tested under a performance-based program.

A.14.2.8 This section provides the option to adopt a performance-based inspection and testing method as an alternate means of compliance for Sections 14.3 and 14.4. The prescriptive test and requirements contained in this Code are essentially qualitative. Equivalent or superior levels of performance can be demonstrated through quantitative performance-based analyses. This section provides a basis for implementing and monitoring a performance-based program acceptable under this option (provided that approval is obtained by the authority having jurisdiction). The concept of a performance-based inspection and testing program is to establish the requirements and frequencies at which inspection and testing must be performed to demonstrate an acceptable level of operational reliability. The goal is to balance the inspection and testing frequency with proven reliability of the system or component. The goal of a performance-based inspection program is also to adjust inspection and testing frequencies commensurate with historical documented equipment performance and desired reliability. Frequencies of inspection and testing under a performance-based program may be extended or reduced from the prescriptive inspection and testing requirements contained in this Code when continued inspection and testing has been documented indicating a higher or lower degree of reliability as compared to the authority having jurisdiction's expectations of performance. Additional program attributes should be considered when adjusting inspection and testing.

A fundamental requirement of a performance-based program is the continual monitoring of fire system/component failure rates and determining if they exceed the maximum allowable failure rates as agreed upon with the authority having jurisdiction. The process used to complete this review should be documented and be repeatable. Coupled with this ongoing review is a requirement for a formalized method of increasing or decreasing the frequency of inspection and testing when systems exhibit either a higher than expected failure rate or an increase in reliability as a result of a decrease in failures. A formal process for reviewing the failure rates and increasing or decreasing the frequency of inspection and testing must be well documented. Concurrence from the authority having jurisdiction on the process used to determine test frequencies should be obtained in advance of any alterations to the inspection and testing program. The frequency required for future inspections and tests may be reduced to the next inspection frequency and maintained there for a period equaling the initial data review or until the ongoing review indicates that the failure rate is no longer being exceeded — for example, going from an annual to a semiannual testing when the failure rate exceeds the authority having jurisdiction's expectations, or from annual to every 18 months when the failure trend indicates an increase in reliability.

See also NFPA 551, *Guide for the Evaluation of Fire Risk Assessments*, for additional guidance.

The provisions of 14.2.8 permit alternatives to the prescriptive methods and frequencies for testing system components, if approved by the authority having jurisdiction. Under such a program, adjustment of the inspection and testing frequencies may be possible using a qualitative performance-based analysis that demonstrates an acceptable level of reliability is provided. This program would require the continual monitoring of system/component failure rates. The guidance in NFPA 551, *Guide for the Evaluation of Fire Risk Assessments*, may be helpful in assessing the adequacy of these programs.

14.3 Inspection

14.3.1* Unless otherwise permitted by 14.3.2 visual inspections shall be performed in accordance with the schedules in Table 14.3.1 or more often if required by the authority having jurisdiction.

Table 14.3.1 specifies the minimum frequencies required for visual inspections on various components and subsystems of the system. Where the authority having jurisdiction suspects building conditions are changing more rapidly than normal and that these changes are likely to affect the performance of the system, the authority having jurisdiction may require more frequent visual inspections.

A visual inspection should always be conducted prior to any testing. Copies of the as-built shop drawings (record drawings) and system documentation provide quantities and locations of devices. Improperly located, damaged, or nonfunctional equipment should be identified and corrected before tests begin.

A.14.3.1 Equipment performance can be affected by building modifications, occupancy changes, changes in environmental conditions, device location, physical obstructions, device orientation, physical damage, improper installation, degree of cleanliness, or other obvious problems that might not be indicated through electrical supervision.

The intent of 14.3.1 is to prevent an inspection being made at intervals exceeding those allowed by Table 14.3.1. Annual inspections should be made every 12 months; monthly inspections should be made every 30 days, and so forth. For example, it is not acceptable to conduct an annual inspection in January of year one, and December of year two (23 month frequency) just because Table 14.3.1 requires an inspection once each year.

14.3.2 Devices or equipment that is inaccessible for safety considerations (e.g., continuous process operations, energized electrical equipment, radiation, and excessive height) shall be permitted to be inspected during scheduled shutdowns if approved by the authority having jurisdiction.

The provision in 14.3.2 is an exception to the requirement for visual inspection frequencies in 14.3.1. Subsection 14.3.2 clearly defines the intended safety considerations where special conditions are encountered that would require or permit the visual inspection frequency to be different from that identified in Table 14.3.1.

14.3.3 Extended intervals shall not exceed 18 months.

14.3.4 The visual inspection shall be made to ensure that there are no changes that affect equipment performance.

TABLE 14.3.1 *Visual Inspection Frequencies*

Component	Initial/ Reacceptance	Monthly	Quarterly	Semiannually	Annually
1. Control equipment: fire alarm systems monitored for alarm, supervisory, and trouble signals					
(a) Fuses	X	—	—	—	X
(b) Interfaced equipment	X	—	—	—	X
(c) Lamps and LEDs	X	—	—	—	X
(d) Primary (main) power supply	X	—	—	—	X

The term *monitored* in the component description refers to systems connected to a supervising station that receives all three signals — alarm, trouble, and supervisory. In unmonitored systems, signals are not transmitted to a supervising station for appropriate action to be taken. Therefore, weekly inspection of fuses, lamps, LEDs, interfaced equipment, and power supplies to ensure reliability is necessary. See Table 14.3.1, item 2, for weekly inspection for unmonitored systems.

Fuses should be visually inspected for appearance and condition and to verify that they are properly installed. In some instances, it will be apparent from visual inspection whether a fuse is blown — that is, whether the internal element is still intact or the fuse has actual signs of damage or scorch marks. If the fuse shows any signs of damage or it appears that it is not installed properly, that should be documented and the fuse replaced. In addition, fuse sizes should be noted and checked against the manufacturer's documentation.

Equipment that is interfaced to the fire alarm system for monitoring or control purposes should be visually inspected for status (i.e., if the equipment is in its "normal" operating status or if it has been disabled due to maintenance reasons). The actual connection between the equipment and the fire alarm system should be checked — for example: Are junction box cov-

TABLE 14.3.1 *Continued*

Component	Initial/ Reacceptance	Monthly	Quarterly	Semiannually	Annually

ers open? Are wiring connections not completed (removed from terminal blocks, disconnected/removed from wire nuts, etc.)? Is wiring or raceway leading to such connections damaged or broken?

Primary (main) power supplies should be visually inspected for physical condition. It should be noted whether the power supply is producing an unusually loud noise, is giving off an unusually high amount of heat, or has any appearance of physical damage, such as corrosion, scorch marks, or dents. Wiring terminals should be checked for corrosion and other damage, and it should be noted whether circuits are properly installed at terminals. Additionally, it should be noted whether the green LED on the control equipment is lit and operational.

Component	Initial/ Reacceptance	Monthly	Quarterly	Semiannually	Annually
2. Control equipment: fire alarm systems unmonitored for alarm, supervisory, and trouble signals					
(a) Fuses	X (weekly)	—	—	—	—
(b) Interfaced equipment	X (weekly)	—	—	—	—
(c) Lamps and LEDs	X (weekly)	—	—	—	—
(d) Primary (main) power supply	X (weekly)	—	—	—	—
3. Batteries					
(a) Lead-acid	X	X	—	—	—
(b) Nickel-cadmium	X	—	—	X	—
(c) Primary (dry cell)	X	X	—	—	—
(d) Sealed lead-acid	X	—	—	X	—
4. Transient suppressors	X	—	—	X	—
5. Fire alarm control unit trouble signals	X (weekly)	—	—	X	—
6. Fiber-optic cable connections	X	—	—	—	X
7. In-building fire emergency voice/alarm communications equipment	X	—	—	X	—
8. Remote annunciators	X	—	—	X	—

A visual inspection of the remote annunciators ensures that obstructions such as plants, file cabinets, or other large objects are not placed in front of the annunciators, thus interfering with fire fighter operations during an emergency condition. If such conditions are found, corrective action should be taken to remove the obstruction. See Exhibit 14.3 following Table 14.3.1 for an example of an obstructed remote annunciator.

Component	Initial/ Reacceptance	Monthly	Quarterly	Semiannually	Annually
9. Initiating devices					
(a) Air sampling	X	—	—	X	—
(b) Duct detectors	X	—	—	X	—

Duct detectors, including their sampling tubes, should be inspected to ensure that smoke entry into the detection chamber will not be inhibited by a buildup of dust and dirt.

Component	Initial/ Reacceptance	Monthly	Quarterly	Semiannually	Annually
(c) Electromechanical releasing devices	X	—	—	X	—
(d) Fire extinguishing system(s) or suppression system(s) switches	X	—	—	X	—
(e) Manual fire alarm boxes	X	—	—	X	—

(continues)

TABLE 14.3.1 *Continued*

Component	Initial/ Reacceptance	Monthly	Quarterly	Semiannually	Annually
Often, after a system has been installed, an owner or occupant will place large plants, file cabinets, or other obstructions in front of manual fire alarm boxes. A visual inspection ensures that these conditions are found and corrective measures can be taken. See Exhibit 14.4 following Table 14.3.1 for an example of a concealed manual fire alarm box.					
(f) Heat detectors	X	—	—	X	—
Heat detectors should be inspected to ensure that they do not have mechanical or water damage, that they have not been painted, that they are properly located, and that building conditions (such as the installation of a new wall) have not changed, possibly reducing the effectiveness of the devices.					
(g) Radiant energy fire detectors	X	—	X	—	—
Radiant energy fire detectors should be inspected to ensure that no obstructions are between the detector and the protected area, that the lenses are clear and free of contaminants, that they do not have mechanical damage, and that the unit is directed toward the intended hazard.					
(h) Smoke detectors (excluding one- and two-family dwellings)	X	—	—	X	—
Some smoke detectors may be monitored for contamination by the fire alarm control unit. Such monitoring, however, will not detect obstructions (e.g., covered detectors). During construction or special cleaning or renovation projects, smoke detectors are often covered to avoid contamination or possible nuisance alarms. After the project is complete, the covers may be forgotten and inadvertently left in place. A visual inspection will ensure that covers, bags, and tape have been removed. See Exhibit 14.5 following Table 14.3.1 for an example of a cover for smoke detectors. Refer to 17.7.1.11 for requirements related to the protection of smoke detectors during construction.					
(i) Supervisory signal devices	X	—	X	—	—
Supervisory signal devices located outdoors should be visually inspected to ensure that the covers and watertight seals are in place and that control valves are not inhibited by branches or other obstructions. See Exhibit 14.6 following Table 14.3.1 for an example of an obstructed sprinkler water supply control valve and supervisory signal device.					
(j) Waterflow devices	X	—	X	—	—
10. Guard's tour equipment	X	—	—	X	—
11. Combination systems					
(a) Fire extinguisher electronic monitoring device/ systems	X	—	—	X	—
(b) Carbon monoxide detectors/systems	X	—	—	X	—
Combination systems are systems that include a fire alarm system, and the fire alarm system is required to be inspected. Although in general the non–fire alarm components of the combination system are not required to be visually inspected, such inspections are always recommended. Refer to the definition of *combination system* in 3.3.95.1 and to the requirements in 23.8.4.					

Specific requirements for the inspection, testing, and maintenance of carbon monoxide detection systems and equipment are provided in NFPA 720, *Standard for the Installation of Carbon Monoxide (CO) Detection and Warning Equipment*.

TABLE 14.3.1 *Continued*

Component	Initial/ Reacceptance	Monthly	Quarterly	Semiannually	Annually
12. Interface equipment	X	—	—	X	—
13. Alarm notification appliances — supervised	X	—	—	X	—

Both audible and visual notification appliances should be inspected to ensure that no obstructions impair their effectiveness, that they do not have physical damage, and that changing building conditions have not rendered the appliance ineffective. Where walls have been added to a space, or floor or wall coverings have changed, additional sound pressure level measurements need to be performed for audible appliances, and the effectiveness of visual appliances should be assessed. The term *supervised* refers to "monitored for integrity," as covered by Section 10.17.

Component	Initial/ Reacceptance	Monthly	Quarterly	Semiannually	Annually
14. Exit marking audible notification appliances	X	—	—	X	—
15. Supervising station alarm systems — transmitters					
(a) DACT	X	—	—	X	—
(b) DART	X	—	—	X	—
(c) McCulloh	X	—	—	X	—
(d) RAT	X	—	—	X	—
16. Special procedures	X	—	—	X	—

A situation might occur in which a fire alarm system is involved with a special procedure that is required to take place upon actuation of the system. For example, a written response procedure might require the security officer on duty at a college to report to the fire department point of entry at the building that has the active alarm with a set of master keys that will provide access for the fire department. This type of special procedure should be reviewed for accuracy and applicability at initial acceptance or reacceptance and then semiannually to ensure that changes have not been made in personnel, procedures, building construction, or other factors that would require an alteration of the procedure.

Questions that should be asked as the procedure in the college example is reviewed include the following:

- Has the college decided to no longer employ a full-time security force?
- Has the college installed key-access boxes with a building master key at the entrance to the building?
- Has significant construction occurred so that the main entrance is no longer the main entrance, or is the point of fire department access different from where it was when the procedure was written?

Component	Initial/ Reacceptance	Monthly	Quarterly	Semiannually	Annually
17. Supervising station alarm systems — receivers*	X	—	—	X	—
18. Public emergency alarm reporting system transmission equipment					
(a) Publicly accessible alarm box	X	—	—	X	—
(b) Auxiliary box	X	—	—	—	X
(c) Master box					
(1) Manual operation	X	—	—	X	—
(2) Auxiliary operation	X	—	—	—	X

(continues)

TABLE 14.3.1 *Continued*

Component	Initial/ Reacceptance	Monthly	Quarterly	Semiannually	Annually
19. Mass notification system, supervised					
(a) Control equipment					

The visual inspection frequencies identified in Table 14.3.1, item 19, for mass notification systems (MNSs) are for stand-alone systems monitored by a supervising station. In case an integrated fire alarm system and an MNS are installed in the building, or in case the fire alarm system is also serving as the MNS for the building, the intent of the Code is to require the visual inspection frequencies identified for fire alarm systems — that is, the requirements of Table 14.3.1(1), 14.3.1(2), 14.3.1(3), etc. — to be used in lieu of those frequencies identified for MNSs.

Component	Initial/ Reacceptance	Monthly	Quarterly	Semiannually	Annually
(1) Fuses	X	—	—	—	X
(2) Interfaces	X	—	—	—	X
(3) Lamps/LED	X	—	—	—	X
(4) Primary (main) power supply	X	—	—	—	X
(b) Secondary power batteries					
(1) Lead-acid	X	—	—	—	X
(2) Nickel-cadmium	X	—	—	—	X
(3) Primary (dry-cell)	X	—	—	—	X
(4) Sealed lead-acid	X	—	—	—	X
(c) Initiating devices	X	—	—	—	X
(d) Notification appliances	X	—	—	—	X
20. Mass notification system, non-supervised systems installed prior to adoption of this edition					

Table 14.3.1, item 20, applies to stand-alone MNSs that are not monitored by a supervising station and that were installed prior to adoption of the 2010 edition of the Code. Where an MNS is integrated with a fire alarm system, visual inspections must comply with the requirements for fire alarm systems as explained in the commentary for item 19 of the table.

Component	Initial/ Reacceptance	Monthly	Quarterly	Semiannually	Annually
(a) Control equipment					
(1) Fuses	X	—	X	—	
(2) Interfaces	X	—	X	—	
(3) Lamps/LED	X	—	X	—	
(4) Primary (main) power supply	X	—	X	—	
(b) Secondary power batteries					
(1) Lead-acid	X	—	X	—	
(2) Nickel-cadmium	X	—	X	—	
(3) Primary (dry cell)	X	—	X	—	
(4) Sealed lead-acid	X	—	X	—	
(c) Initiating devices	X	—	X	—	
(d) Notification appliances	X	—	X	—	
21. Mass notification system Antenna	X	—	—	—	X
22. Mass notification system Transceivers	X	—	—	—	X

*Reports of automatic signal receipt shall be verified daily.

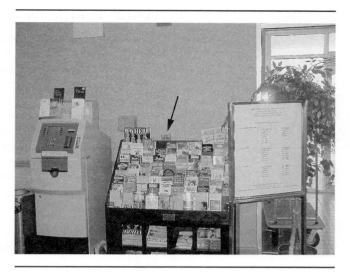

EXHIBIT 14.4 *Concealed Manual Fire Alarm Box. (Source: Automatic Fire Alarm Association, Inc., Lake Mary, FL)*

EXHIBIT 14.3 *Obstructed Remote Annunciator. (Source: Hughes Associates, Inc., Warwick, RI)*

EXHIBIT 14.6 *Obstructed Sprinkler Water Supply Control Valve and Supervisory Signal Device. (Source: Automatic Fire Alarm Association, Inc., Lake Mary, FL)*

EXHIBIT 14.5 *Smoke Detector Cover. (Source: Mammoth Fire Alarms, Inc., Lowell, MA)*

14.4 Testing

14.4.1 System Testing.

14.4.1.1 Initial Acceptance Testing.

14.4.1.1.1 Initial acceptance testing shall be performed as required in 14.4.1.1.1.1 through 14.4.1.1.1.2.

14.4.1.1.1.1 All new systems shall be inspected and tested in accordance with the requirements of Chapter 14.

14.4.1.1.1.2 The authority having jurisdiction shall be notified prior to the initial acceptance test.

14.4.1.2* Reacceptance Testing.

A.14.4.1.2 Reacceptance testing is performed to verify the proper operation of added or replaced devices, appliances, emergency control function devices, control equipment, and so forth. It is not the intent of the committee to unduly burden the system owner with increased costs for repeated testing of devices not directly affected by the replacement of devices with like devices.

For example, if a 2 amp fuse is replaced with another 2 amp fuse in the fire alarm control unit, verification of the circuit(s) served by the fused supply is required, but it would not be necessary to test 10 percent of initiating devices not directly affected by replacing the fuse. Likewise, it is not necessary to test all these initiating devices whenever a smoke detector is replaced with a like smoke detector.

When wiring changes are made to correct improperly supervised circuits, a test of the affected device or appliance is required, but not a test of 10 percent of initiating devices not directly affected.

14.4.1.2.1 Reacceptance testing shall be performed as required in 14.4.1.2.1.1 through 14.4.1.2.1.4.

14.4.1.2.1.1 When an initiating device, notification appliance, or control relay is added, it shall be functionally tested.

14.4.1.2.1.2 When an initiating device, notification appliance, or control relay is deleted, another device, appliance, or control relay on the circuit shall be operated.

14.4.1.2.1.3 When modifications or repairs to control equipment hardware are made, the control equipment shall be tested in accordance with Table 14.4.2.2, items 1(a) and 1(d).

The requirements for reacceptance testing addressed in 14.4.1.2 were revised in the 2002 edition to specify more directed reacceptance testing following additions, modifications, or repairs to system hardware. Complete retesting of the entire system is not required when only a single device or circuit has been modified.

14.4.1.2.1.4 When changes are made to site-specific software, the following shall apply:

(1) All functions known to be affected by the change, or identified by a means that indicates changes, shall be 100 percent tested.
(2) In addition, 10 percent of initiating devices that are not directly affected by the change, up to a maximum of 50 devices, also shall be tested and correct system operation shall be verified.
(3) A revised record of completion in accordance with 10.18.2.1 shall be prepared to reflect these changes.

FAQ ▶
What testing is required following modifications to site-specific software?

The requirements for reacceptance testing following changes to site-specific software remain substantially as they were in the 1999 edition. Seemingly harmless changes in software have caused tremendous changes in operation and have sometimes resulted in disastrous events. Systems have been found to have large portions inoperable due to faulty reprogramming during a repair or test. The requirements of 14.4.1.2.1.4 ensure that the affected portion of the system will be completely tested. The paragraph also requires further testing to ensure that other portions of the system have not been adversely affected by the modification. The 10 percent sample should be randomly selected, and it should include at least one device per initiating device circuit or signaling line circuit to ensure correct operation. If all the devices are installed on one signaling line circuit, multiple devices (a 10 percent sample) should be tested at different sections of the circuit. Use of software comparison algorithms can also help determine where changes may have occurred. See 3.3.255 for the definition of *site-specific software*.

14.4.1.2.2 Changes to all control units connected or controlled by the system executive software shall require a 10 percent functional test of the system, including a test of at least one device on each input and output circuit to verify critical system functions such as notification appliances, control functions, and off-premises reporting.

Changes to software are frequently made in the field using laptop computers and manufacturer's software. See Exhibit 14.7 for a photograph of a technician programming a fire alarm control unit.

EXHIBIT 14.7 *Technician Using a Laptop Computer to Modify Software. (Source: Mammoth Fire Alarms, Inc., Lowell, MA)*

14.4.2* Test Methods.

Prior to any testing, a visual inspection should be conducted. Refer to the commentary following 14.3.1.

A.14.4.2 Fire alarm system testing can be conducted using silent testing and the bypassing of emergency control functions. All input signals should be verified according to the system matrix of operation to ensure they create the appropriate outputs. Tests of audible notification appliances and emergency control functions should be conducted at the conclusion of satisfactory tests of all inputs.

The intent is to reduce the amount of time spent causing audible and visible occupant notification during tests in an occupied building. This reduction will help reduce the negative (cry wolf) impact on occupants caused by excessive operation of notification appliances. System printouts or history logs are an effective way of verifying the correct receipt of signals. However, many outputs such as occupant notification and emergency control functions are tested for correct operation, because logs do not necessarily verify operation of the system output. Operation of audible and visible notification appliances could be accomplished in a lump sum fashion after all inputs are proven correct by silent testing. All inputs tested in this manner must be proved to cause the appropriate signal by verifying alarm receipt at the controls as each device is actuated. Manufacturer-specific protocols such as "walk test" or "alarm bypass" are an acceptable means of testing under this section. Other methods of mitigating the negative impact include off-hours tests when the building is not occupied.

The Code currently permits silent tests, but clarification was needed to avoid confusion. Therefore the explanation in A.14.4.2 is intended to allow a minimization of the "cry wolf" syndrome by allowing a reduction in the amount of time that occupant notification is operated. Also see the article "Cry Wolf," *NEMA Magazine*, Fall 2003.

14.4.2.1* At the request of the authority having jurisdiction, the central station facility installation shall be inspected for complete information regarding the central station system, including specifications, wiring diagrams, and floor plans that have been submitted for approval prior to installation of equipment and wiring.

A.14.4.2.1 If the authority having jurisdiction strongly suspects significant deterioration or otherwise improper operation by a central station, a surprise inspection to test the operation of the central station should be made, but extreme caution should be exercised. This test is to be conducted without advising the central station. However, the communications center must be contacted when manual alarms, waterflow alarms, or automatic fire detection systems are tested so that the fire department will not respond. In addition, persons normally receiving calls for supervisory alarms should be notified when items such as gate valves and functions such as pump power are tested. Confirmation of the authenticity of the test procedure should be obtained and should be a matter for resolution between plant management and the central station.

14.4.2.2* Systems and associated equipment shall be tested according to Table 14.4.2.2.

A.14.4.2.2 Table 14.4.2.2, Item 3. Refer to Table 14.4.2.2, Item 18(a) for the testing of transmission equipment.

Table 14.4.2.2, Item 18(a). Some transmission equipment (such as but not limited to cable modems, fiber optic interface nodes, and VoIP interfaces) are typically powered by the building electrical system using a standby power supply that does not meet the requirements of this Code. This is intended to ensure that the testing authority verifies full standby power as required by Chapter 10. Additionally, refer to Table 14.4.2.2, Items 3 through 6 for secondary power supply testing.

Table 14.4.2.2, Item 23. Initiating devices configured to operate an emergency control function are required to be tested per the test methods listed in Table 14.4.2.2, Item 14 and the test frequencies listed in Table 14.4.5, Item 15. Whenever an emergency control function is observed to not operate properly during a test of an emergency control function initiating device, the problem should be reported to the building owner or designated representative. The failure of the emergency control function should be reported as a possible failure of the fire safety feature and not necessarily of the fire alarm system.

TABLE 14.4.2.2 Test Methods

Device	Method
1. Control equipment	
(a) Functions	At a minimum, control equipment shall be tested to verify correct receipt of alarm, supervisory, and trouble signals (inputs); operation of evacuation signals and auxiliary functions (outputs); circuit supervision, including detection of open circuits and ground faults; and power supply supervision for detection of loss of ac power and disconnection of secondary batteries.

TABLE 14.4.2.2 *Continued*

Device	*Method*
	The input/output control equipment functions must be tested to ensure proper operation. The checking of functions internal to the equipment, such as software algorithms and communications protocols (sometimes called *firmware*), is not intended. An example of a functional test is verifying that Class A circuits transmit an alarm in either direction under a single-fault condition.
(b) Fuses	The rating and supervision shall be verified.
	Verifying the rating and supervision of fuses is important because incorrect fuse rating can lead to equipment damage or unnecessary loss of power. It is not always possible to tell by visual inspection whether a fuse is open. The most reliable method to check whether a fuse is still intact is to remove it from its receptacle and connect both sides of the fuse to a continuity tester (e.g., an electrical multi-meter). This test should not be performed while the fuse is plugged in, because it is possible to detect continuity through a path other than the fuse.
(c) Interfaced equipment	Integrity of single or multiple circuits providing interface between two or more control units shall be verified. Interfaced equipment connections shall be tested by operating or simulating operation of the equipment being supervised. Signals required to be transmitted shall be verified at the control unit.
	The wiring connections must be tested by simulating a single open and a single ground to verify proper indications for the monitoring of the interfaced equipment wiring integrity. In addition, the interfaced equipment must be placed in a simulated trouble condition to test for proper supervisory signal receipt and reaction at the main control unit. See Exhibit 14.8 following Table 14.4.2.2 for a photograph of one method of checking electrical supervision. Also see 14.4.5.6 for new requirements for circuit and pathway testing during initial acceptance and reacceptance testing.
(d) Lamps and LEDs	Lamps and LEDs shall be illuminated.
(e) Primary (main) power supply	All secondary (standby) power shall be disconnected and tested under maximum load, including all alarm appliances requiring simultaneous operation. All secondary (standby) power shall be reconnected at end of test. For redundant power supplies, each shall be tested separately.
2. Engine-driven generator	If an engine-driven generator dedicated to the system is used as a required power source, operation of the generator shall be verified in accordance with NFPA 110, *Standard for Emergency and Standby Power Systems*, by the building owner.
3. Secondary (standby) power supply[a]	All primary (main) power supplies shall be disconnected, and the occurrence of required trouble indication for loss of primary power shall be verified. The system's standby and alarm current demand shall be measured or verified, and, using manufacturer's data, the ability of batteries to meet standby and alarm requirements shall be verified. General alarm systems shall be operated for a minimum of 5 minutes, and emergency voice communications systems for a minimum of 15 minutes. Primary (main) power supply shall be reconnected at end of test.
	Determining the correct amount of battery capacity needed is usually accomplished by calculating the standby and alarm loads on the system. Several revisions to capacity requirements have been made in 10.5.6.3.1 for the 2010 edition, including a requirement to include a 20 percent safety margin in the calculated amp-hour rating

(continues)

TABLE 14.4.2.2 *Continued*

Device	*Method*
	for the battery. This will help ensure correct operation as the batteries age or are subjected to extreme ambient conditions.
4. Uninterrupted power supply (UPS)	If a UPS system dedicated to the system is used as a required power source, operation of the UPS system shall be verified by the building owner in accordance with NFPA 111, *Standard on Stored Electrical Energy Emergency and Standby Power Systems.*
5. Batteries — general tests	Prior to conducting any battery testing, the person conducting the test shall ensure that all system software stored in volatile memory is protected from loss.
(a) Visual inspection	Batteries shall be inspected for corrosion or leakage. Tightness of connections shall be checked and ensured. If necessary, battery terminals or connections shall be cleaned and coated. Electrolyte level in lead-acid batteries shall be visually inspected.
	Batteries are now required to be marked with the month and year of manufacture. The batteries should be checked to verify that they are still within the acceptable date range. See 10.5.9.1.
(b) Battery replacement	Batteries shall be replaced in accordance with the recommendations of the alarm equipment manufacturer or when the recharged battery voltage or current falls below the manufacturer's recommendations.
	Sealed lead-acid batteries are required to be replaced within 5 years of date of manufacture. See Table 14.4.5, item 6(d)(1).
(c) Charger test	Operation of battery charger shall be checked in accordance with charger test for the specific type of battery.
(d) Discharge test	With the battery charger disconnected, the batteries shall be load tested following the manufacturer's recommendations. The voltage level shall not fall below the levels specified. *Exception: An artificial load equal to the full fire alarm load connected to the battery shall be permitted to be used in conducting this test.*
	Battery load simulation testers that meet the intent of this requirement are commonly available.
	Completely draining a battery during the discharge test is not desirable because, in the event of a power failure shortly after the test, the system could be left without a power supply. A typical test places the battery under load for a shorter period (1 to 2 hours). However, the battery should be tested to ensure that it can deliver the required current at rated voltage under maximum expected load. Battery calculations must be relied on to ensure capacity. See Table 14.4.2.2, item 3, and 10.5.6.
	Batteries can be discharged over a longer period of time at lower current than at higher current. As the load applied to a battery increases, the amount of discharge time decreases due to internal battery energy losses. Battery manufacturers have developed battery discharge curves expressing this concept of discharge time as a function of cell voltage and applied current value leading toward an "end-of-discharge cut-off" value (volts per cell).
	Battery discharge curves demonstrate that the power available from a battery is dependent on time as well as the amount of current drawn from it and that most of those relationships are not linear.
	In all cases, the battery manufacturer's testing documentation should be used when the battery discharge test is performed.

TABLE 14.4.2.2 Continued

Device	Method
(e) Load voltage test	With the battery charger disconnected, the terminal voltage shall be measured while supplying the maximum load required by its application. The voltage level shall not fall below the levels specified for the specific type of battery. If the voltage falls below the level specified, corrective action shall be taken and the batteries shall be retested. *Exception: An artificial load equal to the full fire alarm load connected to the battery shall be permitted to be used in conducting this test.*

Load testing a battery is done to verify that the battery is able to deliver the specified power when such power is needed — that is, loss of ac power at the control unit while an alarm signal is active in the system. The load on the battery that is used is a load that would be representative of the conditions present when switchover from ac power to battery could be present.

In all cases, the battery manufacturer's testing documentation should be used for the battery load test.

The battery charger is disconnected from the batteries, a voltmeter is connected to the batteries across the terminals, and ac power is disconnected from the control unit. Once the control unit has switched over to standby battery power, the system is actuated by introduction of an alarm condition (e.g., actuating a manual fire alarm box). All notification appliances and control functions must not be bypassed at time of this test, because the intent of the test is to verify that the batteries can handle the load applied to them during an active alarm sequence.

If the voltage level measured on the voltmeter drops below the level specified by the battery manufacturer's specification literature under full load, corrective action must take place and the test redone. Replacing the batteries with new, fully charged batteries is one method of corrective action that should be considered.

Device	Method
6. Battery tests (specific types) 　(a) Primary battery load voltage test	The maximum load for a No. 6 primary battery shall not be more than 2 amperes per cell. An individual (1.5 volt) cell shall be replaced when a load of 1 ohm reduces the voltage below 1 volt. A 6–volt assembly shall be replaced when a test load of 4 ohms reduces the voltage below 4 volts.
(b) Lead-acid type 　　(1) Charger test	With the batteries fully charged and connected to the charger, the voltage across the batteries shall be measured with a voltmeter. The voltage shall be 2.30 volts per cell ±0.02 volts at 77°F (25°C) or as specified by the equipment manufacturer.
(2) Load voltage test	Under load, the battery shall not fall below 2.05 volts per cell.
(3) Specific gravity	The specific gravity of the liquid in the pilot cell or all of the cells shall be measured as required. The specific gravity shall be within the range specified by the manufacturer. Although the specified specific gravity varies from manufacturer to manufacturer, a range of 1.205–1.220 is typical for regular lead-acid batteries, while 1.240–1.260 is typical for high-performance batteries. A hydrometer that shows only a pass or fail condition of the battery and does not indicate the specific gravity shall not be used, because such a reading does not give a true indication of the battery condition.

CAUTION: Adding acid to a lead-acid type battery cell may destroy the plates, affecting battery capacity.

(continues)

TABLE 14.4.2.2 *Continued*

Device	Method
6. Battery tests (specific types) *(continued)*	
(c) Nickel-cadmium type	
(1) Charger test[b]	With the batteries fully charged and connected to the charger, an ampere meter shall be placed in series with the battery under charge. The charging current shall be in accordance with the manufacturer's recommendations for the type of battery used. In the absence of specific information, $\frac{1}{30}$ to $\frac{1}{25}$ of the battery rating shall be used.
(2) Load voltage test	Under load, the float voltage for the entire battery shall be 1.42 volts per cell, nominal. If possible, cells shall be measured individually.
(d) Sealed lead-acid type	
(1) Charger test	With the batteries fully charged and connected to the charger, the voltage across the batteries shall be measured with a voltmeter. The voltage shall be 2.30 volts per cell ±0.02 volts at 77°C (25°C) or as specified by the equipment manufacturer.
(2) Load voltage test	Under load, the battery shall perform in accordance with the battery manufacturer's specifications.
7. Public emergency alarm reporting system power supply	
(a) Lead-acid type	Perform the battery tests in accordance with item 6(b)
(b) Nickel-cadmium type	Perform the battery tests in accordance with item 6(c)
(c) Sealed lead-acid type	Perform the battery tests in accordance with item 6(d)
(d) Wired system	Manual tests of the power supply for public reporting circuits shall be made and recorded at least once during each 24-hour period. Such tests shall include the following: (1) Current strength of each circuit. Changes in current of any circuit exceeding 10 percent shall be investigated immediately. (2) Voltage across terminals of each circuit inside of terminals of protective devices. Changes in voltage of any circuit exceeding 10 percent shall be investigated immediately. (3)[c] Voltage between ground and circuits. If this test shows a reading in excess of 50 percent of that shown in the test specified in (2), the trouble shall be immediately located and cleared. Readings in excess of 25 percent shall be given early attention. These readings shall be taken with a calibrated voltmeter of not more than 100 ohms resistance per volt. Systems in which each circuit is supplied by an independent current source (Forms 3 and 4) require tests between ground and each side of each circuit. Common current source systems (Form 2) require voltage tests between ground and each terminal of each battery and other current source. (4) Ground current reading shall be permitted in lieu of (3). If this method of testing is used, all grounds showing a current reading in excess of 5 percent of the supplied line current shall be given immediate attention. (5) Voltage across terminals of common battery, on switchboard side of fuses. (6) Voltage between common battery terminals and ground. Abnormal ground readings shall be investigated immediately. Tests specified in (5) and (6) shall apply only to those systems using a common battery. If more than one common battery is used, each common battery shall be tested.
8. Public emergency alarm reporting system transmission equipment	
(a) Publicly accessible alarm box	Publicly accessible initiating device(s) shall be actuated. Receipt of not less than three complete rounds of signal impulses shall be verified. This test shall be per-

TABLE 14.4.2.2 *Continued*

Device	Method
	formed under normal circuit conditions. If the device is equipped for open circuit operation (ground return), it shall be tested in this condition as one of the semiannual tests.
(b) Auxiliary box	Each initiating circuit of the auxiliary box shall be tested by actuation of a protected premises initiating device connected to that circuit. Receipt of not less than three complete rounds of signal impulses shall be verified.
(c) Master box	
(1) Manual operation	Perform the tests prescribed for 8(a).
(2) Auxiliary operation	Perform the tests prescribed for 8(b).
9. Transient suppressors	Lightning protection equipment shall be inspected and maintained per the manufacturer's published instructions. Additional inspections shall be required after any lightning strikes. Equipment located in moderate to severe areas outlined in NFPA 780, *Standard for the Installation of Lightning Protection Systems*, Annex L, shall be inspected semiannually and after any lightning strikes.
	In areas prone to lightning storms, the owner should be advised to notify the fire alarm service company when a storm has occurred so that all installed lightning protection can be checked.
10. Fire alarm control unit trouble signals	
(a) Audible and visual	Operation of control unit trouble signals shall be verified, as well as ring-back feature for systems using a trouble-silencing switch that requires resetting.
(b) Disconnect switches	If control unit has disconnect or isolating switches, performance of intended function of each switch shall be verified and receipt of trouble signal when a supervised function is disconnected shall also be verified.
(c) Ground-fault monitoring circuit	If the system has a ground detection feature, the occurrence of ground-fault indication shall be verified whenever any installation conductor is grounded.
	It is important to test for a ground fault by using a jumper from a wired terminal (not a power terminal) on the control unit to ground and to verify that the ground-fault light illuminates. The results of these tests should be recorded on the acceptance test report for future troubleshooting information. Note that the control equipment may take up to 200 seconds to indicate a trouble/ground condition. See 10.17.1. Testing for ground-fault trouble signals at each installed device is not necessary.
(d) Transmission of signals to off-premises location	An initiating device shall be actuated and receipt of alarm signal at the off-premises location shall be verified. A trouble condition shall be created and receipt of a trouble signal at the off-premises location shall be verified. A supervisory device shall be actuated and receipt of a supervisory signal at the off-premises location shall be verified. If a transmission carrier is capable of operation under a single- or multiple-fault condition, an initiating device shall be activated during such fault condition and receipt of a trouble signal at the off-premises location shall be verified, in addition to the alarm signal.
11. Remote annunciators	The correct operation and identification of annunciators shall be verified. If provided, the correct operation of annunciator under a fault condition shall be verified.
	Remote annunciation is very important to the fire department personnel responding to the alarm. The intent of remote annunciation is to reduce the time spent find-

(continues)

TABLE 14.4.2.2 *Continued*

Device	*Method*
11. Remote annunciators *(continued)*	ing the source of the alarm by providing clear and accurate information to the responding fire service. For that reason, remote annunciation information should be given to the fire department that is assigned to respond to the protected premises for review and input. Too much detail is as harmful as too little information, so a balance must be found to help locate the fire as quickly as possible. The responding fire department should be asked to review the information provided by the remote annunciator to ensure it will be helpful to the first responders.
	Legends and/or room labels (room description and room number) identified on graphic maps mounted adjacent to the control equipment or as-built (record) drawings must be accurate and represent the current use of the space. It is imperative that the descriptors identified on the maps or record drawings match the description of the device location identified on the annunciator(s). Upon arrival on scene, the fire department personnel should be able see the information displayed on the annunciator screen and be able to cross-reference that location with the map or record drawings in order to know where to dispatch fire fighters and what is in the area or what the area is used for prior to proceeding with fire-fighting operations.
12. Conductors — metallic	
(a) Stray voltage	All installation conductors shall be tested with a volt/ohmmeter to verify that there are no stray (unwanted) voltages between installation conductors or between installation conductors and ground. Unless a different threshold is specified in the published manufacturer's instructions for the installed equipment, the maximum allowable stray voltage shall not exceed 1 volt ac/dc.
(b) Ground faults	All installation conductors, other than those intentionally and permanently grounded, shall be tested for isolation from ground per the installed equipment manufacturer's published instructions.
(c) Short-circuit faults	All installation conductors, other than those intentionally connected together, shall be tested for conductor-to-conductor isolation per the published manufacturer's instructions for the installed equipment. These same circuits also shall be tested conductor-to-ground.
(d) Loop resistance	With each initiating and indicating circuit installation conductor pair short-circuited at the far end, the resistance of each circuit shall be measured and recorded. It shall be verified that the loop resistance does not exceed the limits specified in the published manufacturer's instructions for the installed equipment.
	If the loop resistance exceeds the installed equipment manufacturer's specified limits, the wiring must be changed. In such an instance, the fire alarm control equipment manufacturer, rather than the cable manufacturer, would be consulted because the equipment manufacturer generally has more stringent operational requirements. Loop resistance can also play an important role in the performance of notification appliance circuits due to voltage drop concerns. Refer to the commentary following 18.3.2.3.
(e) Supervision	Introduction of a fault in any circuit monitored for integrity shall result in a trouble indication at the fire alarm control unit. One connection shall be opened at not less than 10 percent of the initiating devices, notification appliances and controlled devices on every initiating device circuit, notification appliance circuit, and signaling line circuit.
	The term *supervision* as used in Table 14.4.2.2, item 12(e), means the monitoring of the circuit conductor integrity. Verifying the monitoring for integrity require-

TABLE 14.4.2.2 *Continued*

Device	Method
	ments for fire alarm circuits is required at the time of acceptance, and although not required by the Code, annual verification of a sample percentage is prudent to verify that the wiring has not been tampered with by unqualified individuals.
13. Conductors — nonmetallic	
(a) Circuit integrity	Each initiating device, notification appliance, and signaling line circuit shall be tested to confirm that the installation conductors are monitored for integrity in accordance with the requirements of Chapters 10 and 23.
(b) Fiber optics	The fiber-optic transmission line shall be tested in accordance with the manufacturer's published instructions by the use of an optical power meter or by an optical time domain reflectometer used to measure the relative power loss of the line. This relative figure for each fiber-optic line shall be recorded in the fire alarm control unit. If the power level drops 2 percent or more from the value recorded during the initial acceptance test, the transmission line, section thereof, or connectors shall be repaired or replaced by a qualified technician to bring the line back into compliance with the accepted transmission level per the manufacturer's published instructions.
(c) Supervision	Introduction of a fault in any supervised circuit shall result in a trouble indication at the control unit. One connection shall be opened at not less than 10 percent of the initiating device, notification appliance, and signaling line circuit.
	Each initiating device, notification appliance, and signaling line circuit shall be tested for correct indication at the control unit. All circuits shall perform as indicated in 23.5.2, 23.5.3, 23.6.2 through 23.6.5, 23.7.2 and 23.7.3.
	The term *supervision* as used in Table 14.4.2.2, item 13(c), means the monitoring of the circuit conductor integrity.
14. Initiating devices	
(a) Electromechanical releasing device	
(1) Nonrestorable-type link	Correct operation shall be verified by removal of the fusible link and operation of the associated device. Any moving parts shall be lubricated as necessary.
(2) Restorable-type link[d]	Correct operation shall be verified by removal of the fusible link and operation of the associated device. Any moving parts shall be lubricated as necessary.
(b) Fire extinguishing system(s) or suppression system(s) alarm switch	The switch shall be mechanically or electrically operated and receipt of signal by the fire alarm control unit shall be verified.
(c) Fire–gas and other detectors	Fire–gas detectors and other fire detectors shall be tested as prescribed by the manufacturer and as necessary for the application.
(d) Heat detectors	
(1) Fixed-temperature, rate-of-rise, rate of compensation, restorable line, spot type (excluding pneumatic tube type)	Heat test shall be performed with a heat source per the manufacturer's published instructions. A test method shall be used that is specified in the manufacturer's published instructions for the installed equipment, or other method shall be used that will not damage the nonrestorable fixed-temperature element of a combination rate-of-rise/fixed-temperature element detector.
	In previous editions of the Code, the heat source was required to be applied for "response within 1 minute." It is assumed that the 1-minute time requirement was introduced as an added level of protection to ensure that the test did not damage the thermal element or the detector housing. The requirement for response within 1 minute was removed from the 2010 edition, because it was found that in some instances the 1-minute time frame was being incorrectly interpreted as a sensitivity test of the heat detectors.

(continues)

TABLE 14.4.2.2 *Continued*

Device	*Method*
14. Initiating devices *(continued)* 　(d) Heat detectors *(continued)*	The ability of a heat detector to respond within 1 minute clearly depends on a variety of factors, including, but not limited to, the amount of heat applied to the detector, the distance of the heat source from the detector, and the rate at which the heat causes a rise in temperature. There is no standardized, repeatable test method or test apparatus for all brands and all types of heat detectors. It is important that the heat source and the test method specified in the manufacturer's published instructions be used and that caution be exercised to avoid damaging the detector or its components. Extreme caution must be used in hazardous locations (those containing explosive vapors or dusts) during heat testing of these types of detectors. Heat detectors must not be tested with live flame — a bucket of hot water or hot towels are recommended.
(2) Fixed-temperature, 　　nonrestorable line type	Heat test shall not be performed. Functionality shall be tested mechanically and electrically. Loop resistance shall be measured and recorded. Changes from acceptance test shall be investigated. The test should be performed by shorting across the conductors at the end of the line to simulate actuation of the circuit or by using some other approved method identified in the manufacturer's published instructions for the device. Do not heat test.
(3) Fixed-temperature, 　　nonrestorable spot type	After 15 years from initial installation, all devices shall be replaced or 2 detectors per 100 shall be laboratory tested. The 2 detectors shall be replaced with new devices. If a failure occurs on any of the detectors removed, additional detectors shall be removed and tested to determine either a general problem involving faulty detectors or a localized problem involving 1 or 2 defective detectors. If detectors are tested instead of replaced, tests shall be repeated at intervals of 5 years. The laboratory test referred to in item 14(d)(3) is conducted by an independent testing laboratory engaged in the listing or approval of heat detectors.
(4) Nonrestorable (general)	Heat tests shall not be performed. Functionality shall be tested mechanically and electrically. Contacts can be operated by hand or electrically shorted, or some other approved method identified in the manufacturer's published instructions can be used to ensure alarm response.
(5) Restorable line type, 　　pneumatic tube only	Heat tests shall be performed (where test chambers are in circuit), or a test with pressure pump shall be conducted.
(6) Single- and multiple-station 　　heat alarms	Functional tests shall be conducted according to manufacturer's published instructions. Nonrestorable heat detectors shall not be tested with heat.
(e) Manual fire alarm boxes	Manual fire alarm boxes shall be operated per the manufacturer's published instructions. Key-operated presignal and general alarm manual fire alarm boxes shall both be tested. Functionally testing the manual fire alarm box should include physically actuating the station, as it is intended to be operated in a real emergency situation. If the station is a double-action station with a push-in and pull-down feature, the intent is that personnel physically push in on the device and pull down on the lever to actuate the station. The intent of this test is to not use the manufacturer's key to open the box and actuate the station in order to cause the alarm. The key should be used only to reset the station after it has been physically operated.

TABLE 14.4.2.2 *Continued*

Device	Method
(f) Radiant energy fire detectors	Flame detectors and spark/ember detectors shall be tested in accordance with the manufacturer's published instructions to determine that each detector is operative. Flame detector and spark/ember detector sensitivity shall be determined using any of the following:
	(1) Calibrated test method
	(2) Manufacturer's calibrated sensitivity test instrument
	(3) Listed control unit arranged for the purpose
	(4) Other approved calibrated sensitivity test method that is directly proportional to the input signal from a fire, consistent with the detector listing or approval
	If designed to be field adjustable, detectors found to be outside of the approved range of sensitivity shall be replaced or adjusted to bring them into the approved range.
	Flame detector and spark/ember detector sensitivity shall not be determined using a light source that administers an unmeasured quantity of radiation at an undefined distance from the detector.
(g) Smoke detectors	
(1) In other than one- and two-family dwellings, system detectors and single- or multiple-station smoke alarms	[e]Smoke detectors/smoke alarms shall be tested in place to ensure smoke entry into the sensing chamber and an alarm response. Testing with smoke or listed aerosol, acceptable to the manufacturer of the aerosol or the manufacturer of the smoke detector/smoke alarm and identified in their published instructions, shall be permitted as acceptable test methods. Other methods listed in the manufacturer's published instructions that ensure smoke entry from the protected area, through the vents, into the sensing chamber shall be permitted.
	Any of the following tests shall be performed to ensure that each smoke detector is within its listed and marked sensitivity range:
	(1) Calibrated test method
	(2) Manufacturer's calibrated sensitivity test instrument
	(3) Listed control equipment arranged for the purpose
	(4) Smoke detector/control unit arrangement whereby the detector causes a signal at the control unit when its sensitivity is outside its listed sensitivity range
	(5) Other calibrated sensitivity test method approved by the authority having jurisdiction

The test method described in the first paragraph of Table 14.4.2.2, item 14(g)(1), is a "go, no-go" functional test to ensure smoke entry into the chamber and alarm response. The test does not test the detector's sensitivity. See Exhibit 14.9 and Exhibit 14.10 following the table for examples of equipment used in a functional test of smoke detectors and smoke alarms. Because verification of smoke entry must be part of the test, use of a test button or a magnet does not meet the functional test requirement of item 14(g)(1). Be sure to use only a smoke source acceptable to the manufacturer of the aerosol or the manufacturer of the smoke detector/smoke alarm and identified in the published instructions.

The test methods outlined in item 14(g)(1), including sensitivity testing as well as functional testing, apply to all smoke detectors and smoke alarms except those used in one- and two-family dwelling units. Single-station smoke alarms are often found in other residential occupancies, such as apartments, hotel and motel rooms, and dormitory living units. See 14.4.5.3 for related requirements. Also refer to the commentary following 14.1.2.

Other listed smoke detection devices not connected to a fire alarm system (often called stand-alone detectors) are sometimes found in HVAC systems, door-releasing applications, and special hazards releasing devices. The requirements in

(continues)

TABLE 14.4.2.2 *Continued*

Device	*Method*
14. Initiating devices *(continued)* (g) Smoke detectors *(continued)*	Chapter 14, including sensitivity testing, apply to these types of detectors. Note that in the context of item 14(g)(1), the term *system detector* applies generally to smoke detection devices other than smoke alarms.
(2) Smoke/carbon monoxide alarms in other than one- and two-family dwellings.	The smoke alarms shall be tested in place to ensure smoke entry into the sensing chamber and an alarm response. Testing with real smoke or listed simulated aerosol or listed smoke particulate approved by the manufacturer shall be permitted as acceptable test methods. Other methods listed in the manufacturer's published instructions that ensure smoke entry from the protected area, through the vents, into the sensing chamber shall be permitted. Any of the following tests shall be performed to ensure that each smoke alarm is within its listed and marked sensitivity range: (1) Calibrated test method (2) Manufacturer's calibrated sensitivity test instrument (3) Other calibrated sensitivity test method approved by the authority having jurisdiction The carbon monoxide alarm shall be tested in accordance with NFPA 720.
	The test methods specified for combination smoke and carbon monoxide alarms are similar to those specified in Table 14.4.2.2, item (14)(g)(1), for the smoke detection portion. Testing for the carbon monoxide detection portion must conform to that required by NFPA 720.
(3) Single-and multiple-station smoke alarms connected to protected premises systems	A functional test shall be performed on all single-and-multiple station smoke alarms connected to a protected premises fire alarm system by putting the smoke alarm into an alarm condition and verifying that the protected premises system receives a supervisory signal and does not cause a fire alarm signal.
	Paragraph 23.8.3.2 permits the connection of dwelling unit smoke alarms to a protected premises fire alarm system. Paragraph 23.8.3.5 prohibits the operation of any test switch or an automatic alarm condition from causing an alarm condition on the protected premises fire alarm system. Where these smoke alarms are connected to the protected premises system, and a specific provision is made that the signal be monitored and annunciate as a supervisory signal, a functional test must be performed to demonstrate that the correct signal is received.
(4) Single- and multiple-station smoke alarms and system smoke detectors used in one- and two-family dwellings	Functional tests shall be conducted according to manufacturer's published instructions.
	Smoke alarms and smoke detectors used in one- and two-family dwellings are required to be functionally tested per the manufacturer's instructions but are not required by the Code to include a smoke entry test or to be sensitivity tested, unless required by the manufacturer.
(5) Air sampling	Per test methods documented in the manufacturer's published instructions, detector alarm response shall be verified through the end sampling port on each pipe run; airflow through all other ports shall be verified as well.
(6) Duct type	In addition to the testing required in Table 14.4.2.2(g)(1), duct smoke detectors utilizing sampling tubes shall be tested by verifying the correct pressure differential (within the manufacturer's published ranges) between the inlet and exhaust tubes using a method acceptable to the manufacturer to ensure that the device will properly sample the airstream. These tests shall be made in accordance with the manufacturer's published instructions for the device installed.

TABLE 14.4.2.2 *Continued*

Device	Method
	As noted previously, visual inspection should always be performed before or with testing. Visual inspection of duct detectors should include an inspection to ensure that the inlet sampling tube is installed properly (i.e., the holes are not installed backwards), that there are no obstructions to the sampling tube, and that the end cap is not missing on the tube. Often, duct-type smoke detectors are installed by a mechanical contractor and connected to the fire alarm system by the alarm system contractor. The final responsibility for ensuring that the sampling tubes and the smoke detector have been installed correctly rests with the alarm system contractor.
	Previous editions of the Code stated that duct detectors were required to be "tested or inspected to ensure that the device will sample the airstream" but provided no further guidance regarding what that meant. Language has been added specifying that the detector is required to be tested for smoke entry and sensitivity in accordance with Table 14.4.2.2, item 14(g)(1) and is also required to be tested for airflow by verification of the required pressure differential between the sampling tubes. This verification needs to be done in a manner acceptable to the manufacturer in accordance with manufacturer's published instructions. One method that might be acceptable is to use a manometer, which is shown in Exhibit 14.11 following the table.
(7) Projected beam type	The detector shall be tested by introducing smoke, other aerosol, or an optical filter into the beam path.
(8) Smoke detector with built-in thermal element	Both portions of the detector shall be operated independently as described for the respective devices.
	Table 14.4.2.2, item 14(g)(8), requires a test of both portions of a combination unit if possible. The Code does not explicitly address the issue of the failure of one feature. However, it is assumed that if one feature of a combination smoke/heat detector fails a test, the entire unit should be removed and replaced. Also refer to Table 14.4.2.2, item 14(k), for additional testing methods required for multi-sensor, multi-criteria, and combination detectors.
(9) Smoke detectors with control output functions	It shall be verified that the control capability shall remain operable even if all of the initiating devices connected to the same initiating device circuit or signaling line circuit are in an alarm state.
	The test method in Table 14.4.2.2, item 14(g)(9), verifies that when smoke detectors are installed on an initiating device circuit and are used for controlling operations (e.g., fan shutdown or elevator recall) with other devices installed on the same circuit, the control function must perform correctly, even with all other devices on the circuit in an alarm condition. If, for instance, a two-wire smoke detector tries to actuate after a manual fire alarm box has been actuated, the smoke detector may not actuate. Smoke detectors should be powered separately in these situations. See 21.3.4 and related commentary for more detailed information.
(h) Carbon monoxide detectors/ carbon monoxide alarms for the purposes of fire detection	The devices shall be tested in place to ensure CO entry to the sensing chamber by introduction of CO gas from the protected area, through the vents, to the sensing chamber.
	Carbon monoxide detectors/alarms described in Table 14.4.2.2, item 14(h), are detectors/alarms that provide fire detection using the principle of detecting carbon

(continues)

TABLE 14.4.2.2 *Continued*

Device	*Method*
14. Initiating devices *(continued)* (h) Carbon monoxide detectors/ carbon monoxide alarms for the purposes of fire detection *(continued)*	monoxide emissions. Such detectors are required to be functionally tested for carbon monoxide entry into the device. These are not the same alarms described in item 14(g)(2), which are used to detect carbon monoxide for toxicity/life safety; those alarms are required to be tested in accordance with NFPA 720.
(i) Initiating devices, supervisory (1) Control valve switch	Valve shall be operated and signal receipt shall be verified to be within the first two revolutions of the handwheel or within one-fifth of the travel distance, or per the manufacturer's published instructions.
(2) High- or low-air pressure switch	Switch shall be operated. Receipt of signal obtained where the required pressure is increased or decreased a maximum 10 psi (70 kPa) from the required pressure level shall be verified.
(3) Room temperature switch	Switch shall be operated. Receipt of signal to indicate the decrease in room temperature to 40°F (4.4°C) and its restoration to above 40°F (4.4°C) shall be verified.
(4) Water level switch	Switch shall be operated. Receipt of signal indicating the water level raised or lowered a maximum 3 in. (70 mm) from the required level within a pressure tank, or a maximum 12 in. (300 mm) from the required level of a nonpressure tank, shall be verified, as shall its restoral to required level.
(5) Water temperature switch	Switch shall be operated. Receipt of signal to indicate the decrease in water temperature to 40°F (4.4°C) and its restoration to above 40°F (4.4°C) shall be verified.
(j) Mechanical, electrosonic, or pressure-type waterflow device	Water shall be flowed through an inspector's test connection indicating the flow of water equal to that from a single sprinkler of the smallest orifice size installed in the system for wet-pipe systems, or an alarm test bypass connection for dry-pipe, pre-action, or deluge systems in accordance with NFPA 25, *Standard for the Inspection, Testing, and Maintenance of Water-Based Fire Protection Systems.* It is unacceptable to electrically or mechanically (without waterflow) operate the waterflow switch. The flow test ensures that when the automatic sprinkler system is operated, an alarm signal is generated on the fire alarm system. One of the leading causes of failure to alarm by existing waterflow paddle switches installed on horizontal sprinkler piping is the paddle getting stuck in the sludge at the bottom of the piping.
(k) Multi-sensor fire detector or multi-criteria fire detector or combination fire detector	(1) Each of the detection principles present within the detector (e.g. smoke/heat/CO, etc.) shall be tested independently for the specific detection principle, regardless of the configuration status at the time of testing. Each detector shall also be tested in accordance with the published manufacturer's instructions. (2) Individual sensors shall be tested together if the technology allows individual sensor responses to be verified. (3) Tests shall be performed as described for the respective devices by introduction of the physical phenomena to the sensing chamber of element, and an electronic check (magnets, analogue values, etc.) is not sufficient to comply with this requirement. (4) The result of each sensor test shall be confirmed. This shall be through indication at the detector or control unit. (5) Where individual sensors cannot be tested individually, the primary sensor shall be tested[f] (6) All tests and results shall be recorded. The methods in Table 14.4.2.2, item 14(k) expand on those contained in item 14(g)(8). Refer to the definitions for *combination, multi-criteria,* and *multi-sensor*

TABLE 14.4.2.2 *Continued*

Device	*Method*
	detectors in 3.3.59.4, 3.3.59.11, 3.3.59.12. These test methods apply to all three types of detectors. The intent of these requirements is to independently verify the performance of each sensor employed in the detector by introducing the physical phenomena for detection by each sensor into the sensing chamber.
15. Alarm notification appliances (a) Audible	(1) Initial and reacceptance testing shall comply with the following: Sound pressure levels for signals shall be measured with a sound level meter meeting ANSI S1.4a, *Specifications for Sound Level Meters,* Type 2 requirements. Sound pressure levels throughout the protected area shall be measured to confirm that they are in compliance with Chapter 18. The sound level meter shall be set in accordance with ANSI S3.41, *American National Standard Audible Evacuation Signal,* using the time-weighted characteristic F (FAST). (2) Periodic testing shall comply with the following: Sound pressure levels for signals shall be measured with a sound level meter meeting ANSI S1.4a, *Specifications for Sound Level Meters,* Type 2 requirements. Sound pressure levels shall be measured for conformity to Chapter 18 where building, system, or occupancy changes have occurred. The sound level meter shall be set in accordance with ANSI S3.41, *American National Standard Audible Evacuation Signal,* using the time-weighted characteristic F (FAST).
	During initial and reacceptance testing, sound pressure level measurements are required throughout the protected area. However, with careful planning, the number of test locations can be minimized by selection of "worst-case" locations. With the approval of the authority having jurisdiction, areas that are physically remote from the audible notification appliances are selected as worst-case locations to measure and record sound pressure levels. If these areas comply with Code requirements, then the authority having jurisdiction may deem further measurements unnecessary. However, areas that fail to meet the requirements of Section 18.4 will require additional appliances. When a sound level meter is used, it should be set to the "FAST" response time on the "A" weighted scale (i.e., dbA). Audible notification appliances used for evacuation employ the ANSI Emergency Evacuation Signal (three-pulse temporal pattern). Testing on the "SLOW" response would give readings that are too low, because the "SLOW" response reads the average signal, not the peak signal.
Ω FAQ ▶ Are measurements of sound pressure level required throughout the building for periodic testing?	For periodic testing, sound pressure level measurements are required only for areas that have been affected by building, system, or occupancy changes. These areas should become evident during the visual inspection required throughout the building. As specified in 14.3.4, the visual inspections are intended to ensure that no changes have been made that will adversely affect equipment performance. Building modifications that include areas that have been significantly remodeled can impact sound pressure levels. Where significant changes have been made, retesting is required.
(b) Audible textual notification appliances (speakers and other appliances to convey voice messages)	(1) Initial and reacceptance testing shall comply with the following: Sound pressure levels for signals shall be measured with a sound level meter meeting ANSI S1.4a, *Specifications for Sound Level Meters,* Type 2 requirements. Sound pressure levels throughout the protected area shall be measured to confirm that they are in compliance with Chapter 18. The sound level meter shall be set in accordance with ANSI S3.41, *American National Standard Audible Evacuation Signal,* using the time-weighted characteristic F (FAST).

(continues)

TABLE 14.4.2.2 Continued

Device	*Method*
15. Alarm notification appliances *(continued)* (b) Audible textual notification appliances (speakers and other appliances to convey voice messages) *(continued)*	Audible information shall be verified to be distinguishable and understandable and shall comply with 14.4.13. (2) Periodic testing shall comply with the following: Sound pressure levels for signals shall be measured with a sound level meter meeting ANSI S1.4a, *Specifications for Sound Level Meters,* Type 2 requirements. Sound pressure levels shall be measured for conformity to Chapter 18 where building, system, or occupancy changes have occurred. The sound level meter shall be set in accordance with ANSI S3.41, *American National Standard Audible Evacuation Signal,* using the time-weighted characteristic F (FAST). Audible information shall be verified to be distinguishable and understandable and shall comply with 14.4.13 where building, system, or occupancy changes have occurred.

The test methods in Table 14.4.2.2, item (15)(b), address both the signals produced by audible textual notification appliances (speakers) and the intelligibility of voice messages produced by these appliances. Requirements for the measurement of sound pressure levels for "signals" are similar to those in item (15)(a). The requirements for the verification of voice message intelligibility have changed from the 2007 edition. The 2007 edition of the Code specified that where voice intelligibility was required, intelligibility was required to be verified via test methods identified in ANSI S3.2, *Method for Measuring the Intelligibility of Speech over Communications Systems*; IEC 60849, *Sound Systems for Emergency Purposes*; and other methods acceptable to the authority having jurisdiction. Since issuance of the 2007 edition of the Code, extensive research has been conducted under the auspices of the Fire Protection Research Foundation (see the findings in the final report, *Intelligibility of Fire Alarm and Emergency Communication Systems*). Since the research was performed, the intelligibility testing requirements outlined in the Code have been refined and a new chapter on Emergency Communications Systems (Chapter 24) and a new Annex on Speech Intelligibility (Annex D) have been included in the Code.

Table 14.4.2.2, item (15)(b) states that audible information is required to be verified to be distinguishable and understandable and in compliance with 14.4.13 and 18.4.10 (by reference). Voice intelligibility requirements in 18.4.10 are specified using the term *acoustically distinguishable space (ADS)*, defined in 3.3.2. Only those spaces requiring voice intelligibility need to be verified as distinguishable and understandable. It important to recognize that the sound pressure level measurements required in item (15)(b) apply to "signals" (evacuations signals and alert tones). The measurement of sound pressure levels for voice messages is not specifically required (see 18.4.1.5), although it may be done in conjunction with measurements for intelligibility. Item (15)(b) requires verification that intelligibility is provided but does not require that the verification be specifically by testing (intelligibility measurements). Subjective verification (listening) may be sufficient in some situations. Designers, owners, and authorities having jurisdiction have to decide when and where testing is desirable, if at all. Annex D provides detailed guidance on the testing of the intelligibility of voice communications systems.

For periodic testing, Table 14.4.2.2, item (15)(b) requires measurements of "signals" to be performed only where there are changes in occupancy, the building, or the system — all factors that can affect intelligibility. Similar considerations would also apply to intelligibility verification.

TABLE 14.4.2.2 *Continued*

Device	Method
	Compliance with the requirement for voice intelligibility (and verification of it) begins with the system design. To comply with requirements for audibility and intelligibility, many installers attempt to tap speakers at a higher wattage rather than increase the number of speakers in an area. This incorrect approach to sound level compliance leads to distortion of voice messages through the speakers. The 2010 edition of the Code provides new requirements and guidance for the proper design of intelligible voice systems. Refer to 18.4.10, 24.4.1.2, the related Annex A material, and commentary for these paragraphs and to Annex D. Also refer to Supplements 2 and 3 in this handbook. Exhibit 14.12 following the table is an example of a meter that can be used to measure the total integrated sound pressure level in dBA or the voice intelligibility score.
(c) Visible	Test shall be performed in accordance with the manufacturer's published instructions. Appliance locations shall be verified to be per approved layout, and it shall be confirmed that no floor plan changes affect the approved layout. It shall be verified that the candela rating marking agrees with the approved drawing. It shall be confirmed that each appliance flashes. The tests must ensure that visible notification appliances operate and that the marked candela rating agrees with the approved drawings. Visible inspection, required by 14.3.1, should include verification that the strobe is not blocked by shelving, furniture, ceiling-mounted light fixtures, or movable partitions. The owner also should be advised to keep all viewing paths to visible notification appliances clear.
16. Exit marking audible notification appliance	Tests shall be performed in accordance with manufacturer's published instructions.
17. Special hazard equipment	
(a) Abort switch (dead-man type)	Abort switch shall be operated. Correct sequence and operation shall be verified.
(b) Abort switch (recycle type)	Abort switch shall be operated. Development of correct matrix with each sensor operated shall be verified.
(c) Abort switch (special type)	Abort switch shall be operated. Correct sequence and operation in accordance with authority having jurisdiction shall be verified. Sequencing on as-built drawings or in system owner's manual shall be observed.
(d) Cross-zone detection circuit	One sensor or detector on each zone shall be operated. Occurrence of correct sequence with operation of first zone and then with operation of second zone shall be verified.
(e) Matrix-type circuit	All sensors in system shall be operated. Development of correct matrix with each sensor operated shall be verified.
(f) Release solenoid circuit	Solenoid shall be used with equal current requirements. Operation of solenoid shall be verified.
(g) Squibb release circuit	AGI flashbulb or other test light approved by the manufacturer shall be used. Operation of flashbulb or light shall be verified.
(h) Verified, sequential, or counting zone circuit	Required sensors at a minimum of four locations in circuit shall be operated. Correct sequence with both the first and second detector in alarm shall be verified.
(i) All above devices or circuits or combinations thereof	Supervision of circuits shall be verified by creating an open circuit. Use caution when testing the interfaced special hazard equipment to avoid unnecessary actuation — never assume that the previous tests were conducted properly. The manufacturer's test procedures should always be reviewed prior to conducting

(continues)

TABLE 14.4.2.2 Continued

Device	Method
17. Special hazard equipment *(continued)*	
(i) All above devices or circuits or combinations thereof *(continued)*	these tests. After all equipment has been tested independently, all connections or test switches must be returned to their normal positions. Also refer to the requirements in 14.2.5 and to the related commentary.
18. Supervising station alarm systems — transmission equipment[g]	
(a) All equipment	Test shall be performed on all system functions and features in accordance with the equipment manufacturer's published instructions for correct operation in conformance with the applicable sections of Chapter 26.
	Initiating device shall be actuated. Receipt of the correct initiating device signal at the supervising station within 90 seconds shall be verified. Upon completion of the test, the system shall be restored to its functional operating condition.
	If test jacks are used, the first and last tests shall be made without the use of the test jack.
(b) Digital alarm communicator transmitter (DACT)	Connection of the DACT to two separate means of transmission shall be ensured.
	Exception: DACTs that are connected to a telephone line (number) that is also supervised for adverse conditions by a derived local channel.
	DACT shall be tested for line seizure capability by initiating a signal while using the primary line for a telephone call. Receipt of the correct signal at the supervising station shall be verified. Completion of the transmission attempt within 90 seconds from going off-hook to on-hook shall be verified.
	The primary line from the DACT shall be disconnected. Indication of the DACT trouble signal at the premises shall be verified, as well as transmission to the supervising station within 4 minutes of detection of the fault.
	The secondary means of transmission from the DACT shall be disconnected. Indication of the DACT trouble signal at the premises shall be verified as well as transmission to the supervising station within 4 minutes of detection of the fault.
	The DACT shall be caused to transmit a signal to the DACR while a fault in the primary telephone number is simulated. Utilization of the secondary telephone number by the DACT to complete the transmission to the DACR shall be verified.
	The primary line from the digital alarm communicator transmitter (DACT) must be a loop start telephone line (number). Where two telephone lines are used, both lines must be loop start lines. See 26.6.3.2.1.1 and 26.6.3.2.1.4 for more information on this requirement. When testing for trouble signals, it is assumed that the primary line has been reconnected prior to disconnecting the secondary means of transmission from the DACT.
(c) Digital alarm radio transmitter (DART)	The primary telephone line shall be disconnected. Transmission of a trouble signal to the supervising station by the DART within 4 minutes shall be verified.
(d) McCulloh transmitter	Initiating device shall be actuated. Production of not less than three complete rounds of not less than three signal impulses each by the McCulloh transmitter shall be verified.
	If end-to-end metallic continuity is present and with a balanced circuit, each of the following four transmission channel fault conditions shall be caused in turn, and receipt of correct signals at the supervising station shall be verified:
	(1) Open
	(2) Ground
	(3) Wire-to-wire short
	(4) Open and ground

TABLE 14.4.2.2 *Continued*

Device	Method
(e) Radio alarm transmitter (RAT)	If end-to-end metallic continuity is not present and with a properly balanced circuit, each of the following three transmission channel fault conditions shall be caused in turn, and receipt of correct signals at the supervising station shall be verified: (1) Open (2) Ground (3) Wire-to-wire short A fault between elements of the transmitting equipment shall be caused. Indication of the fault at the protected premises shall be verified, or it shall be verified that a trouble signal is transmitted to the supervising station.

The tests required in Table 14.4.2.2, items 18 and 19, provide comprehensive methods for testing supervising station transmission and receiving equipment. The transmission and receipt of fire alarm signals are no less important than the detection of the fire. The goal of fire alarm systems with off-premises transmission is to ensure that the fire department response is not delayed in any way.

Device	Method
19. Supervising station alarm systems — receiving equipment	
(a) All equipment	Tests shall be performed on all system functions and features in accordance with the equipment manufacturer's published instructions for correct operation in conformance with the applicable sections of Chapter 26. Initiating device shall be actuated. Receipt of the correct initiating device signal at the supervising station within 90 seconds shall be verified. Upon completion of the test, the system shall be restored to its functional operating condition. If test jacks are used, the first and last tests shall be made without the use of the test jack.
(b) Digital alarm communicator receiver (DACR)	Each telephone line (number) shall be disconnected in turn from the DACR, and audible and visual annunciation of a trouble signal in the supervising station shall be verified. A signal shall be caused to be transmitted on each individual incoming DACR line at least once every 24 hours. Receipt of these signals shall be verified.
(c) Digital alarm radio receiver (DARR)	The following conditions of all DARRs on all subsidiary and repeater station receiving equipment shall be caused. Receipt at the supervising station of correct signals for each of the following conditions shall be verified: (1) AC power failure of the radio equipment (2) Receiver malfunction (3) Antenna and interconnecting cable failure (4) Indication of automatic switchover of the DARR (5) Data transmission line failure between the DARR and the supervising or subsidiary station
(d) McCulloh systems	The current on each circuit at each supervising and subsidiary station under the following conditions shall be tested and recorded: (1) During functional operation (2) On each side of the circuit with the receiving equipment conditioned for an open circuit A single break or ground condition shall be caused on each transmission channel. If such a fault prevents the functioning of the circuit, receipt of a trouble signal shall be verified. Each of the following conditions at each of the supervising or subsidiary stations and all repeater station radio transmitting and receiving equipment shall be caused; receipt of correct signals at the supervising station shall be verified:

(continues)

TABLE 14.4.2.2 *Continued*

Device	*Method*
19. Supervising station alarm systems — receiving equipment *(continued)*	
(d) McCulloh systems *(continued)*	(1) RF transmitter in use (radiating) (2) AC power failure supplying the radio equipment (3) RF receiver malfunction (4) Indication of automatic switchover
(e) Radio alarm supervising station receiver (RASSR) and radio alarm repeater station receiver (RARSR)	Each of the following conditions at each of the supervising or subsidiary stations and all repeater station radio transmitting and receiving equipment shall be caused; receipt of correct signals at the supervising station shall be verified: (1) AC power failure supplying the radio equipment (2) RF receiver malfunction (3) Indication of automatic switchover, if applicable
(f) Private microwave radio systems	Each of the following conditions at each of the supervising or subsidiary stations and all repeater station radio transmitting and receiving equipment shall be caused; receipt of correct signals at the supervising station shall be verified: (1) RF transmitter in use (radiating) (2) AC power failure supplying the radio equipment (3) RF receiver malfunction (4) Indication of automatic switchover
20. Emergency communications equipment	
(a) Amplifier/tone generators	Correct switching and operation of backup equipment shall be verified.
(b) Call-in signal silence	Function shall be operated and receipt of correct visual and audible signals at control unit shall be verified.
(c) Off-hook indicator (ring down)	Phone set shall be installed or phone shall be removed from hook and receipt of signal at control unit shall be verified.
(d) Phone jacks	Phone jack shall be visually inspected and communications path through jack shall be initiated. During an acceptance test and at the testing frequencies listed in Table 14.4.5, all phone jacks on each floor or zone must be checked for proper operation.
(e) Phone set	Each phone set shall be activated and correct operation shall be verified.
(f) System performance	System shall be operated with a minimum of any five handsets simultaneously. Voice quality and clarity shall be verified.
21. Combination systems	
(a) Fire extinguisher electronic monitoring device/system	Communication between the device connecting the fire extinguisher electronic monitoring device/system and the fire alarm control unit shall be tested to ensure proper signals are received at the fire alarm control unit and remote annunciator(s) if applicable. The Code addresses specific subcategories of combination systems and specifies the required methods for testing. Also refer to the commentary following Table 14.3.1, item 11.
22. Interface equipment	Interface equipment connections shall be tested by operating or simulating the equipment being supervised. Signals required to be transmitted shall be verified at the control unit. Test frequency for interface equipment shall be the same as the frequency required by the applicable NFPA standard(s) for the equipment being supervised.

TABLE 14.4.2.2 *Continued*

Device	Method
23. Emergency control functions[h]	The signals being verified include the status (i.e., alarm, trouble, and supervisory conditions) of the interfaced equipment. Examples of interfaced equipment could include a special hazards fire suppression control unit or a pre-action sprinkler system control unit. Emergency control functions (i.e., fan control, smoke damper operation, elevator recall, elevator power shutdown, door holder release, shutter release, door unlocking, etc.) shall be tested by operating or simulating alarm signals. Testing frequency for emergency control functions shall be the same as the frequency required for the initiating device that activates the emergency control function. The Code now generally uses the term *emergency control functions* to refer to fire safety functions as well as other non-fire-related control functions that may be applicable in other emergency applications. The term *fire safety function* is still used in Chapter 23, Protected Premises Fire Alarm Systems, and the provisions in Table 14.4.2.2, item 23, specified in terms of "emergency control functions" apply. Refer to the definition of *emergency control function* in 3.3.83.
24. Guard's tour equipment	The device shall be tested in accordance with the manufacturer's published instructions.
25. Special procedures (a) Alarm verification	Time delay and alarm response for smoke detector circuits identified as having alarm verification shall be verified. Alarm verification may be disconnected during a system test and then reconnected after the initial test. If this happens, all circuits with devices to be verified must be tested again to ensure that the alarm verification feature is operable.
(b) Multiplex systems	Communications between sending and receiving units under both primary and secondary power shall be verified. Communications between sending and receiving units under open circuit and short circuit trouble conditions shall be verified. Communications between sending and receiving units in all directions where multiple communications pathways are provided shall be verified. If redundant central control equipment is provided, switchover and all required functions and operations of secondary control equipment shall be verified. All system functions and features shall be verified in accordance with manufacturer's published instructions. System functions and features should be verified in accordance with the circuit designations (classes) as designed, as well as the manufacturer's specifications. The authority having jurisdiction requires testing to meet the minimum requirements of the Code; however, it is possible that the system design exceeds minimum requirements. All system devices and functions installed should be verified for proper operation. For various reasons, the authority having jurisdiction might not witness testing of all installed devices and functions. The contractor is responsible for testing the entire system for its operation as described in the design documents.
26. Low-power radio (wireless systems)	The following procedures describe additional acceptance and reacceptance test methods to verify wireless protection system operation: (1) The manufacturer's published instructions and the as-built drawings provided by the system supplier shall be used to verify correct operation after the initial testing phase has been performed by the supplier or by the supplier's designated representative.

(continues)

TABLE 14.4.2.2 *Continued*

Device	*Method*
26. Low-power radio (wireless systems) *(continued)*	(2) Starting from the functional operating condition, the system shall be initialized in accordance with the manufacturer's published instructions. A test shall be conducted to verify the alternative path, or paths, by turning off or disconnecting the primary wireless repeater. The alternative communications path shall exist between the wireless control unit and peripheral devices used to establish initiation, indication, control, and annunciation. The system shall be tested for both alarm and trouble conditions. (3) Batteries for all components in the system shall be checked monthly. If the control unit checks all batteries and all components daily, the system shall not require monthly testing of the batteries.
	The requirement of Table 14.4.2.2, item 26, applies to low-power wireless systems covered by Section 23.18, not radio-type public emergency reporting systems.
27. Mass notification systems (a) Functions	At a minimum, control equipment shall be tested to verify correct receipt of alarm, supervisory, and trouble signals (inputs); operation of evacuation signals and auxiliary functions (outputs); circuit supervision, including detection of open circuits and ground faults; and power supply supervision for detection of loss of ac power and disconnection of secondary batteries.
(b) Fuses	The rating and supervision shall be verified.
(c) Interfaced equipment	Integrity of single or multiple circuits providing interface between two or more control units shall be verified. Interfaced equipment connections shall be tested by operating or simulating operation of the equipment being supervised. Signals required to be transmitted shall be verified at the control unit.
(d) Lamps and LEDs	Lamps and LEDs shall be illuminated.
(e) Primary (main) power supply	All secondary (standby) power shall be disconnected and tested under maximum load, including all alarm appliances requiring simultaneous operation. All secondary (standby) power shall be reconnected at end of test. For redundant power supplies, each shall be tested separately.
(f) Audible textual notification appliances (speakers and other appliances to convey voice messages)	Sound pressure level shall be measured with a sound level meter meeting ANSI S1.2a, *Specifications for Sound Level Meters,* Type 2 requirements. Levels throughout protected area shall be measured and recorded. The sound level meter shall be set in accordance with ANSI S3.41, *American National Standard Audible Evacuation Signal,* using the time-weighted characteristic F (FAST). The maximum output shall be recorded when the audible emergency evacuation signal is on. Audible information shall be verified to be distinguishable and understandable.
	Note that the method in Table 14.4.2.2, item 27(f), for textual audible notification appliances (speakers) that are part of a mass notification system differs from that in item 15(b), which more clearly addresses the test methods for acceptance testing versus periodic testing. Refer to Table 14.4.2.2, item 15(b) and the related commentary for clarity on the intended testing of textual audible notification appliances.
(g) Visible	Test shall be performed in accordance with manufacturer's published instructions. Appliance locations shall be verified to be per approved layout, and it shall be confirmed that no floor plan changes affect the approved layout. It shall be verified that the candela rating marking agrees with the approved drawing. It shall be confirmed that each appliance flashes.
(h) Control unit functions and no diagnostic failures are indicated	Review event log file, verify that the correct events were logged. Review system diagnostic log file; correct deficiencies noted in file. Delete unneeded log files. Delete unneeded error files. Verify that sufficient free disk space is available. Verify unobstructed flow of cooling air is available. Change/clean filters, cooling fans, and intake vents.

TABLE 14.4.2.2 *Continued*

Device	Method
(i) Control unit reset	Power down the central control unit computer and restart it.
(j) Control unit security	If remote control software is loaded onto the system, verify that it is disabled to prevent unauthorized system access.
(k) Audible/visible functional test	Send out an alert to a diverse set of predesignated receiving devices and confirm receipt. Include at least one of each type of receiving device.
(l) Software backup	Make full system software backup. Rotate backups based on accepted practice at site.
(m) Secondary power test	Disconnect ac power. Verify the ac power failure alarm status on central control equipment. With ac power disconnected, verify battery voltage under load.
(n) Wireless signals	Check forward/reflected radio power is within specifications.
(o) Antenna	Check forward/reflected radio power is within specifications. Verify solid electrical connections with no observable corrosion.
(p) Transceivers	Verify proper operation and mounting is not compromised.

^aSee A.14.4.2.2.

^bExample: 4000 mAh × $\frac{1}{25}$ = 160 mA charging current at 77°F (25°C).

^cThe voltmeter sensitivity has been changed from 1000 ohms per volt to 100 ohms per volt so that false ground readings (caused by induced voltages) are minimized.

^dFusible thermal link detectors are commonly used to close fire doors and fire dampers. They are actuated by the presence of external heat, which causes a solder element in the link to fuse, or by an electric thermal device, which, when energized, generates heat within the body of the link, causing the link to fuse and separate.

^eNote, it is customary for the manufacturer of the smoke detector/smoke alarm to test a particular product from an aerosol provider to determine acceptability for use in smoke entry testing of their smoke detector/smoke alarm.

^fFor example, it might not be possible to individually test the heat sensor in a thermally enhanced smoke detector.

^gSee A.14.4.2.2.

^hSee A.14.4.2.2.

EXHIBIT 14.8 *Technician Removing Wire from Device to Check Electrical Supervision. (Source: Simplex-Grinnell, Westminster, MA)*

EXHIBIT 14.9 *Functional Test of a Smoke Detector. (Source: No Climb Products Ltd., Hertfordshire, UK)*

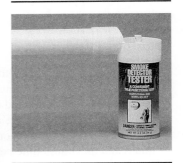

EXHIBIT 14.10 *Aerosol Smoke Product for Functional Test of a Smoke Detector. (Source: Home Safeguard Industries, Inc., Rolling Meadows, IL; photo courtesy of R. P. Schifiliti & Associates)*

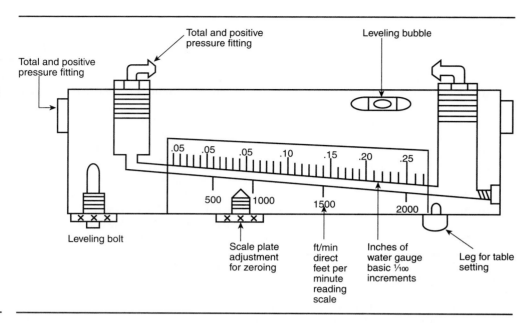

EXHIBIT 14.11 *Inclined Manometer for Velocity Pressure Readings in Low Velocity Ducts, 400 ft/min to 2000 ft/min (2.0 m/sec to 14.2 m/sec). (Source: System Sensor, St. Charles, IL)*

EXHIBIT 14.12 *Speech Intelligibility Meter. (Source: Gold Line, West Reading, CT)*

14.4.3 Video Image Smoke and Flame Detectors. Video image smoke and flame detectors shall be inspected, tested, and maintained in accordance with the manufacturer's published instructions.

14.4.4 Gas Detectors. Gas detectors shall be inspected, tested, and maintained in accordance with the manufacturers' published instructions.

Requirements were added in the 2007 edition of the Code for video image smoke and flame detection in 17.7.7 and 17.8.5. Requirements for gas detection have now been added in Section 17.10 in the 2010 edition. Subsections 14.4.3 and 14.4.4 include provisions for the testing of this equipment to comply with the manufacturer's published instructions.

14.4.5* Testing Frequency. Unless otherwise permitted by other sections of this Code, testing shall be performed in accordance with the schedules in Table 14.4.5, or more often if required by the authority having jurisdiction.

Table 14.4.5 indicates the frequencies for tests on the various components and subsystems of the fire alarm system.

A.14.4.5 It is suggested that the annual test be conducted in segments so that all devices are tested annually.

The intent of 14.4.5 is to prevent a test from being made at intervals exceeding those allowed by Table 14.4.5. Annual tests should be made every 12 months; monthly tests should be made every 30 days, and so forth. For example, it is not acceptable to conduct an annual test in January of year one, and December of year two (23-month frequency), just because Table 14.4.5 requires a test once each year. See the definition of *frequency* in 3.3.106 for minimum and maximum time between testing events.

Table 14.4.5, Item 15. Initiating devices such as smoke detectors used for elevator recall, closing dampers, or releasing doors held in the open position that are permitted by the Code *(see NFPA 101, 9.6.3)* to initiate supervisory signals at the fire alarm control unit (FACU) should be tested at the same frequency (annual) as those devices when they are generating an alarm signal. They are not "supervisory devices," but they initiate a supervisory signal at the FACU.

TABLE 14.4.5 *Testing Frequencies*

Initial/ Component	Reacceptance	Monthly	Quarterly	Semiannually	Annually	Table 14.4.2.2 Reference
1. Control equipment — building systems connected to supervising station						1, 7, 18, 19
(a) Functions	X	—	—	—	X	—
(b) Fuses	X	—	—	—	X	—
(c) Interfaced equipment	X	—	—	—	X	—
(d) Lamps and LEDs	X	—	—	—	X	—
(e) Primary (main) power supply	X	—	—	—	X	—
(f) Transponders	X	—	—	—	X	—

Item 1 in Table 14.4.5 refers to systems connected to a supervising station that receives all three signals: alarm, trouble, and supervisory. In unmonitored systems, signals are not transmitted to a supervising station for appropriate action to be taken. Therefore, quarterly testing of these items to ensure reliability is necessary. See Table 14.4.5, item 2, for quarterly testing for unmonitored systems.

Initial/ Component	Reacceptance	Monthly	Quarterly	Semiannually	Annually	Table 14.4.2.2 Reference
2. Control equipment — building systems not connected to a supervising station						1
(a) Functions	X	—	X	—	—	—
(b) Fuses	X	—	X	—	—	—
(c) Interfaced equipment	X	—	X	—	—	—
(d) Lamps and LEDs	X	—	X	—	—	—
(e) Primary (main) power supply	X	—	X	—	—	—
(f) Transponders	X	—	X	—	—	—
3. Engine-driven generator — central station facilities and fire alarm systems	X	X	—	—	—	—
4. Engine-driven generator — public emergency alarm reporting systems	X (weekly)	—	—	—	—	—
5. Batteries — central station facilities						
(a) Lead-acid type						6b
(1) Charger test (Replace battery as needed.)	X	—	—	—	X	—
(2) Discharge test (30 minutes)	X	X	—	—	—	—
(3) Load voltage test	X	X	—	—	—	—
(4) Specific gravity	X	—	—	X	—	—
(b) Nickel-cadmium type						6c
(1) Charger test (Replace battery as needed.)	X	—	X	—	—	—
(2) Discharge test (30 minutes)	X	—	—	—	X	—
(3) Load voltage test	X	—	—	—	X	—
(c) Sealed lead-acid type						6d
(1) Charger test (Replace battery within 5 years after manufacture or more frequently as needed.)	X	X	X	—	—	—
(2) Discharge test (30 minutes)	X	X	—	—	—	—
(3) Load voltage test	X	X	—	—	—	—

(continues)

TABLE 14.4.5 *Continued*

Initial/ Component	Reacceptance	Monthly	Quarterly	Semiannually	Annually	Table 14.4.2.2 Reference

Table 14.4.5, item 5(c), was modified in the 2002 edition to require that sealed lead-acid batteries be replaced within 5 years of the date of manufacture or more frequently as needed. In the past, sealed lead-acid batteries were required to be replaced after 4 years with no mention of whether this was 4 years after the date of manufacture or 4 years after the date of installation. [Also see Table 14.4.5, items 6(d)1 and 7(c)1.]

Initial/ Component	Reacceptance	Monthly	Quarterly	Semiannually	Annually	Table 14.4.2.2 Reference
6. Batteries — fire alarm systems						
(a) Lead-acid type						6b
(1) Charger test (Replace battery as needed.)	X	—	—	—	X	—
(2) Discharge test (30 minutes)	X	—	—	X	—	—
(3) Load voltage test	X	—	—	X	—	—
(4) Specific gravity	X	—	—	X	—	—
(b) Nickel-cadmium type						6c
(1) Charger test (Replace battery as needed.)	X	—	—	—	X	—
(2) Discharge test (30 minutes)	X	—	—	—	X	—
(3) Load voltage test	X	—	—	X	—	—
(c) Primary type (dry cell)						6a
(1) Age test	X	X	—	—	—	—
(d) Sealed lead-acid type						6d
(1) Charger test (Replace battery within 5 years after manufacture or more frequently as needed.)	X	—	—	—	X	—
(2) Discharge test (30 minutes)	X	—	—	—	X	—
(3) Load voltage test	X	—	—	X	—	—
7. Power supply — public emergency alarm reporting systems						
(a) Lead-acid type batteries						6b
(1) Charger test (Replace battery as needed.)	X	—	—	—	X	—
(2) Discharge test (2 hours)	X	—	X	—	—	—
(3) Load voltage test	X	—	X	—	—	—
(4) Specific gravity	X	—	—	X	—	—
(b) Nickel-cadmium type batteries						6c
(1) Charger test (Replace battery as needed.)	X	—	—	—	X	—
(2) Discharge test (2 hours)	X	—	—	—	X	—
(3) Load voltage test	X	—	X	—	—	—
(c) Sealed lead-acid type batteries						6d
(1) Charger test (Replace battery within 5 years after manufacture or more frequently if needed	X	—	—	—	X	—
(2) Discharge test (2 hours)	X	—	—	—	X	—
(3) Load voltage test	X	—	X	—	—	—
(d) Wired system — voltage tests	X (daily)	—	—	—	—	7d
8. Fiber-optic cable power	X	—	—	—	X	13b
9. Control unit trouble signals	X	—	—	—	X	10

TABLE 14.4.5 Continued

Initial/ Component	Reacceptance	Monthly	Quarterly	Semiannually	Annually	Table 14.4.2.2 Reference
10. Conductors — metallic	X	—	—	—	—	12
11. Conductors — nonmetallic	X	—	—	—	—	13
12. In-building fire emergency voice/ alarm communications equipment	X	—	—	—	X	20
13. Retransmission Equipment (The requirements of 14.4.10 shall apply.)	X	—	—	—	—	—
14. Remote Annunciators	X	—	—	—	X	11
15. Initiating Devices[*]						14
(a) Duct detectors	X	—	—	—	X	—
(b) Electromechanical releasing device	X	—	—	—	X	—
(c) Fire extinguishing system(s) or suppression system(s) switches	X	—	—	—	X	—
(d) Fire–gas and other detectors	X	—	—	—	X	—
(e) Heat detectors (The requirements of 14.4.5.5 shall apply.)	X	—	—	—	X	—
(f) Manual fire alarm boxes	X	—	—	—	X	—
(g) Radiant energy fire detectors	X	—	—	X	—	—
(h) System smoke detectors — functional test	X	—	—	—	X	—
(i) Smoke detectors — sensitivity testing in other than one- and two- family dwellings (The requirements of 14.4.5.3 shall apply.)	—	—	—	—	—	—
(j) Single- and multiple-station smoke alarms (The requirements for monthly testing in accordance with 14.4.6 shall also apply.)	X	—	—	—	X	—
(k) Single- and multiple-station heat alarms	X	—	—	—	X	—
(l) Supervisory signal devices						
(1) Valve supervisory switches	X	—	—	X	—	—
(2) Pressure supervisory indicating devices	X	—	X	—	—	—
(3) Water level supervisory indicating devices	X	—	X	—	—	—
(4) Water temperature supervisory indicating devices	X	—	X	—	—	—
(5) Room temperature supervisory indicating devices	X	—	X	—	—	—
(6) Other suppression system supervisory initiating devices	X	—	X	—	—	—
(7) Other supervisory initiating devices	X	—	—	—	X	—
(m) Waterflow devices	X	—	—	X	—	—
16. Guard's tour equipment	X	—	—	—	X	24

(continues)

TABLE 14.4.5 *Continued*

Component	Initial/ Reacceptance	Monthly	Quarterly	Semiannually	Annually	Table 14.4.2.2 Reference
17. Combination systems						21a
(a) Fire extinguisher electronic monitoring device/systems	X	—	—	—	X	21a
(b) Carbon monoxide detectors/systems	X	—	—	—	X	

The Code addresses two specific subcategories of combination systems and specifies the required methods for testing them. Also refer to the commentary following Table 14.3.1, item 11.

Specific requirements for the inspection, testing, and maintenance of carbon monoxide detection systems and equipment are provided in NFPA 720. These requirements include functional testing and sensitivity testing. Carbon monoxide detectors are required to be tested in accordance with the manufacturer's published testing instructions.

Component	Initial/ Reacceptance	Monthly	Quarterly	Semiannually	Annually	Table 14.4.2.2 Reference
18. Interface equipment and emergency control functions	X	—	—	—	X	22, 23
19. Special hazard equipment	X	—	—	—	X	17
20. Alarm notification appliances						15
(a) Audible devices	X	—	—	—	X	—
(b) Audible textual notification appliances	X	—	—	—	X	—
(c) Visible devices	X	—	—	—	X	—
21. Exit marking notification appliances	X	—	—	—	X	16
22. Supervising station alarm systems — transmitters	X	—	—	—	X	18
23. Special procedures	X	—	—	—	X	25
24. Supervising station alarm systems — receivers						19
(a) DACR	X	X	—	—	—	—
(b) DARR	X	X	—	—	—	—
(c) McCulloh systems	X	X	—	—	—	—
(d) Two-way RF multiplex	X	X	—	—	—	—
(e) RASSR	X	X	—	—	—	—
(f) RARSR	X	X	—	—	—	—
(g) Private microwave	X	X	—	—	—	—
25. Public emergency alarm reporting system transmission equipment						—
(a) Publicly accessible alarm box	X	—	—	X	—	8a
(b) Auxiliary box	X	—	—	—	X	8b
(c) Master box	—	—	—	—	—	8c
(1) Manual operation	X	—	—	X	—	—
(2) Auxiliary operation	X	—	—	—	X	—
26. Mass notification system — protected premise, supervised						27

The testing frequencies identified in Table 14.4.5, item 26, for mass notification systems are for stand-alone systems monitored by a supervising station. In case an integrated fire alarm

TABLE 14.4.5 *Continued*

Component	Initial/ Reacceptance	Monthly	Quarterly	Semiannually	Annually	Table 14.4.2.2 Reference

system and mass notification system are installed in the building, or in case the fire alarm system is also serving as the mass notification system for the building, the intent of the Code is to require the testing frequencies identified for fire alarm systems (e.g., items 1 and 2 in Table 14.4.5) in lieu of those frequencies identified for mass notification systems (i.e., item 26 in Table 14.4.5).

Component	Initial/ Reacceptance	Monthly	Quarterly	Semiannually	Annually	Table 14.4.2.2 Reference
(a) Control unit functions and no diagnostic failures are indicated	X	—	—	—	X	27
(b) Audible/visible functional test	X	—	—	—	X	27
(c) Secondary Power	X	—	—	—	X	27
(d) Verify content of prerecorded messages	X	—	—	—	X	27
(e) Verify activation of correct prerecorded messages	X	—	—	—	X	27
(f) Verify activation of correct prerecorded message based on a targeted area	X	—	—	—	X	27
(g) Verify control unit security mechanism is functional	X	—	—	—	X	27
27. Mass notification system — protected premise, nonsupervised systems installed prior to adoption of this Code						27

Item 27 in Table 14.4.5 applies to stand-alone mass notification systems that are not monitored by a supervising station and that were installed prior to adoption of the 2010 edition of the Code. Where a mass notification system is integrated with a fire alarm system, test frequencies must comply with the requirements for fire alarm systems as explained in the commentary for item 26 in Table 14.4.5.

Component	Initial/ Reacceptance	Monthly	Quarterly	Semiannually	Annually	Table 14.4.2.2 Reference
(a) Control unit functions and no diagnostic failures are indicated	X	—	X	—		27
(b) Audible/visible functional test	X	—	X	—		27
(c) Secondary power	X	—	X	—		27
(d) Verify content of prerecorded messages	X	—	X	—		27
(e) Verify activation of correct prerecorded message based on a selected event	X	—	X	—		27
(f) Verify activation of correct prerecorded message based on a targeted area	X	—	X	—		27
(g) Verify control unit security mechanism is functional	X	—	X	—		27
28. Mass notification system — wide-area (UFC 4-021-01)						27
(a) Control unit functions and no diagnostic failures are indicated	X	—	—	—	X	27
(b) Control unit reset	X	—	—	—	X	27
(c) Control unit security	X	—	—	—	X	27

(continues)

TABLE 14.4.5 *Continued*

Component	Initial/ Reacceptance	Monthly	Quarterly	Semiannually	Annually	Table 14.4.2.2 Reference
(d) Audible/visible functional test	X	—	—	—	X	27
(e) Software backup	X	—	—	—	X	27
(f) Secondary power test	X	—	—	—	X	27
(g) Antenna	X	—	—	—	X	27
(h) Transceivers	X	—	—	—	X	27
(i) Verify content of prerecorded messages	X	—	—	—	X	27
(j) Verify activation of correct prerecorded message based on a selected event	X	—	—	—	X	27
(k) Verify activation of correct prerecorded message base on a targeted area	X	—	—	—	X	27
(l) Verify control unit security mechanism is functional	X	—	—	—	X	27

*See A.14.4.5.

14.4.5.1 Devices or equipment that are inaccessible for safety considerations (e.g., continuous process operations, energized electrical equipment, radiation, and excessive height) shall be permitted to be tested during scheduled shutdowns if approved by the authority having jurisdiction. Extended intervals shall not exceed 18 months.

The provisions in 14.4.5.1 are an exception to the requirement for testing frequencies in 14.4.5. Paragraph 14.4.5.1 clearly defines the intended safety considerations where special conditions are encountered that would require or permit the testing frequency to be different from that identified in Table 14.4.5.

14.4.5.2 If automatic testing is performed at least weekly by a remotely monitored fire alarm control unit specifically listed for the application, the manual testing frequency shall be permitted to be extended to annually. Table 14.4.5 shall apply.

Paragraph 14.4.5.2 is intended to allow development of new technologies that will be able to test equipment remotely. However, this equipment must be specifically listed to perform remote testing. The testing frequency would then be allowed to be extended to annual testing.

14.4.5.3* In other than one- and two-family dwellings, sensitivity of smoke detectors and single- and multiple-station smoke alarms shall be tested in accordance with 14.4.5.3.1 through 14.4.5.3.7.

The term *smoke detector* generally refers to system-type detectors. In editions of the Code prior to 2002, the term *single-station smoke detector* was used to refer to smoke alarms. Refer to the commentary following 14.1.2.

The intent to include sensitivity testing for all single- and multiple-station smoke alarms in other than one- or two-family dwellings, as well as for all smoke detectors, was made clear in the 2002 edition of the Code. Revisions in the 2007 edition clarify that sensitivity testing for system smoke detectors is required only in other than one- or two-family dwellings.

A.14.4.5.3 Detectors that cause unwanted alarms should be tested at their lower listed range (or at 0.5 percent obscuration if unmarked or unknown). Detectors that activate at less than this level should be replaced.

14.4.5.3.1 Sensitivity shall be checked within 1 year after installation.

14.4.5.3.2 Sensitivity shall be checked every alternate year thereafter unless otherwise permitted by compliance with 14.4.5.3.3.

14.4.5.3.3 After the second required calibration test, if sensitivity tests indicate that the device has remained within its listed and marked sensitivity range (or 4 percent obscuration light gray smoke, if not marked), the length of time between calibration tests shall be permitted to be extended to a maximum of 5 years.

Older detectors manufactured prior to current standards did not require a sensitivity range to be marked on the product. These detectors should have a sensitivity of between 0.5 and 4 percent per foot obscuration (light gray smoke) depending on the type of the detector. Sensitivities less than 0.5 percent obscuration per foot may lead to unwanted alarms, and sensitivities over 4 percent per foot may cause delays in or failure of detection.

◄ **FAQ**
What sensitivity should be used for older smoke detectors without sensitivity markings?

14.4.5.3.3.1 If the frequency is extended, records of nuisance alarms and subsequent trends of these alarms shall be maintained.

14.4.5.3.3.2 In zones or in areas where nuisance alarms show any increase over the previous year, calibration tests shall be performed.

14.4.5.3.4 To ensure that each smoke detector or smoke alarm is within its listed and marked sensitivity range, it shall be tested using any of the following methods:

(1) Calibrated test method
(2) Manufacturer's calibrated sensitivity test instrument
(3) Listed control equipment arranged for the purpose
(4) Smoke detector/fire alarm control unit arrangement whereby the detector causes a signal at the fire alarm control unit where its sensitivity is outside its listed sensitivity range
(5) Other calibrated sensitivity test methods approved by the authority having jurisdiction

The requirements of 14.4.5.3.4 give the options for testing the sensitivity of smoke detectors. It is important to note that each of the five options provides a measured means of ensuring sensitivity. Furthermore, after two successful tests in which sensitivity has remained stable, sensitivity testing extends to 5-year intervals, in recognition of the apparent stability of the environment in which the detector is installed, as well as the apparent stability of the detector itself. When the frequency of sensitivity testing is extended, the required records of detector operation help to warn of possible changes in the environment or changes in the stability of the detector. Such changes may warrant more frequent testing. See Exhibits 14.13, 14.14, and 14.15 for illustrations of calibrated test instruments for testing sensitivity of smoke detectors.

Detectors that are outside their marked sensitivity range must be recalibrated and then retested or replaced in accordance with 14.4.5.3.5. Removal tools can assist maintenance personnel in removal of smoke detectors. See Exhibit 14.16 for an example of a removal tool.

14.4.5.3.5 Unless otherwise permitted by 14.4.5.3.6, smoke detectors or smoke alarms found to have a sensitivity outside the listed and marked sensitivity range shall be cleaned and recalibrated or be replaced.

EXHIBIT 14.13 *Calibrated Test Instrument. (Source: Gemini Scientific, Sunnyvale, CA)*

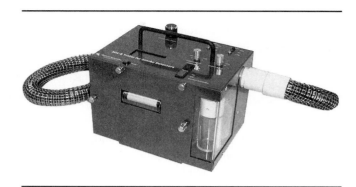

EXHIBIT 14.15 *Manufacturer's Calibrated Test Instruments. (Source: Top: Kidde-Fenwal, Ashland, MA; Bottom: System Sensor, St. Charles, IL; top photo courtesy of Mammoth Fire Alarms, Inc., Lowell, MA)*

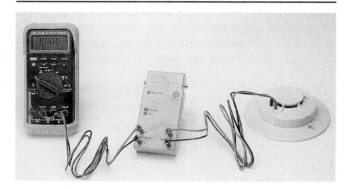

EXHIBIT 14.14 *Technician Using Calibrated Test Instrument. (Source: Gemini Scientific, Sunnyvale, CA)*

14.4.5.3.6 Smoke detectors or smoke alarms listed as field adjustable shall be permitted to either be adjusted within the listed and marked sensitivity range, cleaned, and recalibrated, or be replaced.

14.4.5.3.7 The detector or smoke alarm sensitivity shall not be tested or measured using any device that administers an unmeasured concentration of smoke or other aerosol into the detector or smoke alarm.

14.4.5.4 Test frequency of interfaced equipment shall be the same as specified by the applicable NFPA standards for the equipment being supervised.

In reference to 14.4.5.4, the test frequency for a carbon dioxide special hazard fire extinguishing system, for example, is specified in NFPA 12, *Standard on Carbon Dioxide Extinguishing Systems.*

14.4.5.5 Restorable fixed-temperature, spot-type heat detectors shall be tested in accordance with 14.4.5.5.1 through 14.4.5.5.4.

Keeping accurate records is imperative so that the same detectors are not tested each year. Paragraph 14.4.5.5 and its subparagraphs apply only to restorable fixed-temperature-type detectors. All other heat detectors still require annual tests. See Exhibit 14.17.

14.4.5.5.1 Two or more detectors shall be tested on each initiating circuit annually.

14.4.5.5.2 Different detectors shall be tested each year.

14.4.5.5.3 Records shall be kept by the building owner specifying which detectors have been tested.

14.4.5.5.4 Within 5 years, each detector shall have been tested.

14.4.5.6* Circuit and pathway testing of each monitored circuit or pathway shall be conducted with initial acceptance or re-acceptance testing to verify signals are indicated at the control unit for each of the abnormal conditions specified in 23.5.2, 23.5.3, 23.6.2 through 23.6.5, 23.7.2 and 23.7.3.

A.14.4.5.6 It is not intended to require testing the pathways at every device or circuit junctions.

Circuits are required to be tested to ensure that the proper signal is received at the control unit as the abnormal condition is introduced. The abnormal conditions to be introduced refer to those specified in Sections 23.5, 23.6, and 23.7 as applicable to the circuit designation for each circuit.

14.4.6 Single- and Multiple-Station Smoke Alarms. In one- and two-family dwellings, smoke alarms and all connected appliances shall be inspected and tested in accordance with the manufacturer's published instructions at least monthly.

Subsection 14.4.6 requires smoke alarms to be tested in accordance with the manufacturer's published instructions at least monthly. It is important that homeowners keep the manufacturer's instructions that were supplied with the smoke alarm. These instructions may require testing more frequently than once per month. The instructions also include important information about maintenance of the smoke alarm, including periodic cleaning and battery replacement information. Also refer to 14.4.8 and 14.4.9.

14.4.7 Household Fire Alarm Systems.

14.4.7.1 Testing. Household fire alarm systems shall be tested by a qualified service technician at least annually according to the methods of Table 14.4.2.2.

14.4.7.2 Maintenance. Maintenance of household fire alarm systems shall be conducted according to the manufacturer's published instructions.

14.4.8 Replacement of Smoke Alarms in One- and Two-Family Dwellings.

14.4.8.1 Unless otherwise recommended by the manufacturer's published instructions, single- and multiple-station smoke alarms installed in one- and two-family dwellings shall be

EXHIBIT 14.16 *Removal Tool Used to Remove Detectors on High Ceilings. (Source: No Climb Products, Ltd., Hertfordshire, UK)*

EXHIBIT 14.17 *Technician Using a Heat Detector Tester. (Source: Home Safeguard Industries, Inc., Rolling Meadows, IL)*

replaced when they fail to respond to operability tests but shall not remain in service longer than 10 years from the date of manufacture.

14.4.8.2 Combination smoke/carbon monoxide alarms shall be replaced when the end-of-life signal activates or 10 years from the date of manufacture, whichever comes first.

FAQ ▶
Does the requirement to replace smoke alarms every 10 years apply to system smoke detectors?

The 10-year maximum replacement period addressed in 14.4.8 is based on information that smoke alarms installed in one- or two-family dwellings are not maintained to the extent that system detectors are maintained. Therefore, replacement is required at intervals not exceeding 10 years. This requirement applies only to smoke alarms (not smoke detectors) located in one- and two-family dwelling units.

Combination smoke/carbon monoxide alarms include carbon monoxide sensing elements that may have a shorter life span than 10 years. These alarms include an end-of-life signal for the carbon monoxide sensor. Therefore, these alarms must be replaced when the end-of-life signal activates or at the 10-year limit, whichever occurs first.

14.4.9 Battery Replacement. Where batteries are used as a source of energy, they shall be replaced in accordance with the alarm equipment manufacturer's published instructions.

14.4.10 Circuits from Central Station. Tests of all circuits extending from the central station shall be made at intervals of not more than 24 hours.

Operators at the central station initiate these tests to verify that all circuits are operational.

14.4.11 Public Emergency Alarm Reporting Systems.

14.4.11.1 Emergency power sources other than batteries shall be tested at least weekly in accordance with 14.4.11.1.1 and 14.4.11.1.2.

14.4.11.1.1 Testing shall include operation of the power source to supply the system for a continuous period of 1 hour.

14.4.11.1.2 Testing shall require simulated failure of the normal power source.

14.4.11.2 Unless otherwise permitted by 14.4.11.3, testing facilities shall be installed at the communications center and each subsidiary communications center, if used.

14.4.11.3 Testing facilities for systems leased from a nonmunicipal organization shall be permitted to be installed at locations other than the communications center if approved by the authority having jurisdiction.

14.4.12* In-Building Emergency Radio Communication Systems. In-building emergency radio communication systems shall be inspected and operationally tested in accordance with the manufacturer's published requirements by the local fire department, the building owner, or a designated representative.

In accordance with 24.5.2, two-way in-building radio communications enhancement systems are permitted by the Code. Where installed, inspection and testing of these systems must be accomplished in accordance with the manufacturer's published instructions and the requirements outlined in 14.4.12.1.

An extensive set of new testing requirements has been added in 14.4.12.1 for two-way radio communications enhancement systems. These requirements correlate with the system installation requirements added in 24.5.2 and include requirements for signal level testing and commissioning testing, as well as acceptance testing and periodic testing.

A.14.4.12 In-building emergency radio communication systems where the ac power source is monitored for integrity should be tested annually. Systems where the ac power source is not monitored for integrity should be tested quarterly.

14.4.12.1 Testing.

14.4.12.1.1 Signal Level Testing. Signal level testing shall be conducted to verify the signal strengths as required in 24.5.2.3 at the following times:

(1) Initial assessment of radio coverage in accordance with 24.5.2.2.1 and 24.5.2.2.2 for new or existing buildings
(2) After installation or modification of public safety radio enhancement system needed to ensure compliance with 24.5.2.2.3
(3) On an annual basis or other interval as specified by the authority having jurisdiction

14.4.12.1.2 System Commissioning Testing. System commissioning tests shall comply with the following:

(1) The building owner shall be responsible for ensuring that a commissioning test of the public safety radio enhancement system occurs prior to final acceptance testing with the authority having jurisdiction.
(2) The commissioning test shall ensure that two-way coverage on each floor of the building meets the minimum coverage requirements of 24.5.2.2.1 and 24.5.2.2.2.
(3) Tests shall be made using the frequencies assigned to the jurisdiction.
(4) Testing shall be coordinated with the authority having jurisdiction to ensure no undue interference to any public safety operations.
(5) All testing shall be done on frequencies authorized by the FCC.

14.4.12.1.3* Test Procedures. The test plan shall ensure testing throughout the building. Test procedures shall be as directed by the authority having jurisdiction.

A.14.4.12.1.3 Testing procedures typically are done on a grid system. A grid is overlaid onto a floor area to provide 20 grid cells. Grid cells are provided with definite minimum and maximum dimensions. For most buildings, using a minimum grid dimension of 20 ft (6.1 m) and a maximum grid dimension of 80 ft (24.4 m) will suffice to encompass the entire floor area. Where a floor exceeds 128,000 ft^2 (11,890 m^2), which is the floor area that can be covered by the maximum grid dimension of 80 ft (24.4 m), it is recommended that the floor be subdivided into sectors, each having an area of less than or equal to 128,000 ft^2 (11,890 m^2), and that each sector be tested individually with 20 grid cells in each sector. Signal strength measurements should be taken at the center of each grid and should be performed using standardized parameters as specified in A.14.4.12.1.4. Signal strength typically is recorded on the delivered audio quality (DAQ) scale. This scale is a universal standard often cited in system designs and specifications, using the following measures:

(1) DAQ 1: Unusable speech present but unreadable.
(2) DAQ 2: Understandable with considerable effort. Frequent repetition due to noise/distortion.
(3) DAQ 3: Speech understandable with slight effort. Occasional repetition required due to noise/distortion.
(4) DAQ 3.5: Speech understandable with repetition only rarely required. Some noise/distortion.
(5) DAQ 4: Speech easily understood. Occasional noise/distortion.
(6) DAQ 4.5: Speech easily understood. Infrequent noise/distortion.
(7) DAQ 5: Speech easily understood.

The minimum allowable DAQ for each grid cell typically is DAQ 3. Not more than two nonadjacent grid cells should be allowed to fail the test. In the event that three of the areas fail the test, or if two adjacent areas fail the test, in order to be more statistically accurate, the testing grid resolution should be doubled. This would require decreasing the size to one-half the dimension used in the failed test to a minimum of 10 ft (3.0 m) and a maximum of 40 ft (12.2 m). Further, to cover the same floor area, the number of grids is quadrupled to 80. Not more than eight nonadjacent or five adjacent grid cells should then be allowed to fail the test. In the event that nine or more nonadjacent and/or six or more adjacent grid cells fail the test, consideration should be given to redesigning and reinstalling the public safety radio enhancement system to meet the minimum system design requirements. Failures should not be allowed in critical areas. Measurements should be made with the antenna held in a vertical position at (3 ft to 4 ft) [0.91 m to 1.22 m] above the floor. The DAQ readings should be recorded on small-scale drawings that are used for testing with the authority having jurisdiction. In addition, the gain values of all amplifiers should be measured, and the test measurement results should be kept on file with the building owner so that the measurements can be verified each year during annual tests.

14.4.12.1.4* Measurement Parameters. Signal levels shall be measured to ensure the system meets the criteria of 24.5.2.3 according to parameters as directed by the authority having jurisdiction.

A.14.4.12.1.4 Downlink measurements should be made with the following standardized parameters:

(1) A calibrated spectrum analyzer, or a calibrated automatic signal level measurement recording system
(2) Receiving antennas of equal gain to the agency's standard portable radio antenna, oriented vertically, with a centerline between 3 ft and 4 ft above floor
(3) A resolution bandwidth nearest the bandwidth of the channel under test
(4) Levels recorded while walking an "X" pattern, with the center of the pattern located approximately in the center of each grid area
(5) The linear distance of each side of the "X" equal to at least 10 percent of the length of the grid's side, and a minimum length of 10 ft (3.0 m)
(6) Measurement sampled in averaging mode to include a minimum of one sample per each 5 ft (1.52 m) traveled, recorded with not less than five samples per measurement recorded per side of the "X"

14.4.12.1.5* Acceptance Test. An acceptance test of the public safety radio enhancement system shall be scheduled with the authority having jurisdiction. Acceptance test procedures and requirements shall be as directed by the authority having jurisdiction.

A.14.4.12.1.5 Typically, acceptance tests are required by the authority having jurisdiction prior to building occupancy. As-built drawings should be provided along with other information required from the signal level and commissioning tests, including a full report with grid locations, DAQ measurements, and amplifier gain values should be provided at the acceptance test. The acceptance test typically entails a random test by the authority having jurisdiction of radio communication in various portions of the building, especially including the critical areas. The authority having jurisdiction can review any test documentation and ensure that the findings of the commissioning test with respect to DAQ levels and gain values are supported by the acceptance test.

If amplification systems are utilized in the public safety radio enhancement system, a spectrum analyzer should be utilized to ensure spurious oscillations are not being generated or unauthorized carriers are being repeated in violation of FCC regulations. This testing should be conducted at time of installation and during subsequent inspections. Downlink and uplink spectrum should be recorded with a maximum-hold screen capture at the active system air interfaces, with the system under normal load and at least one uplink carrier active on the indoor portion of the system. Measurements should be analyzed for correct gains on both unlink and downlink paths, noise floor elevation from active components, intermodulation, and other parameters determined necessary by the authority having jurisdiction.

Gain values of all amplifiers should be measured and the results kept on file with the building owner and the authority having jurisdiction. In the event that the measurement results become lost, the building owner will need to repeat the acceptance test to reestablish the gain values.

14.4.12.1.6* Annual Tests. Where a public safety radio enhancement system is required, it shall be the building owner's responsibility to have all live components of the system, such as signal boosters, newer supplies, and backup batteries tested at a minimum of once every 12 months. The authority having jurisdiction shall be notified in advance and shall direct annual test procedures and requirements.

A.14.4.12.1.6 Typically, annual tests require several items to be checked. Annual tests should include all procedures encompassed in 14.4.12.1.1 through 14.4.12.1.4. Signal boosters should be tested to ensure that the gain is the same as it was upon initial installation and acceptance. Backup batteries and power supplies should be tested under load for a period of 1 hour to verify that they will properly operate during an actual power outage. Other active components are typically checked to determine that they are operating within the manufacturer's specifications for the intended purpose.

14.4.13* Voice Intelligibility. Voice communication using prerecorded messages and manual voice announcements shall be verified as being intelligible in accordance with the requirements of 18.4.10.

A.14.4.13 See Annex D, Speech Intelligibility.

Annex D, Speech Intelligibility, provides guidance on the planning, design, installation, and especially the testing of voice communication systems. Refer to the commentary following Table 14.4.2.2, item 15(b), method (2).

14.5 Maintenance

See 3.3.140 for the definition of *maintenance*.

14.5.1 System equipment shall be maintained in accordance with the manufacturer's published instructions.

14.5.2 The frequency of maintenance of system equipment shall depend on the type of equipment and the local ambient conditions.

14.5.3 The frequency of cleaning of system equipment shall depend on the type of equipment and the local ambient conditions.

Subsections 14.5.1 through 14.5.3 require that periodic maintenance be performed. The emphasis is on cleaning, which should be done in strict accordance with the manufacturer's published instructions and as frequently as the ambient conditions of the placement area necessitate.

Examples of areas subject to accumulations of dust and dirt are elevator hoistways and machine rooms, HVAC ducts, and boiler rooms. Exhibit 14.18 shows an example of a product used to clean smoke detectors.

14.5.4 All apparatus requiring rewinding or resetting to maintain normal operation shall be rewound or reset as promptly as possible after each test and alarm.

14.5.5 Unless otherwise permitted by 14.5.6, the retransmission means as defined in Section 26.3 shall be tested at intervals of not more than 12 hours.

Subsection 14.5.5 defines the testing frequency of retransmission means between the supervising station and the communications center.

14.5.6 When the retransmission means is the public switched telephone network, testing shall be permitted at weekly intervals to confirm its operation to each communications center.

14.5.7 As a part of the testing required in 14.5.5, the retransmission signal and the time and date of the retransmission shall be recorded in the central station.

14.6 Records

14.6.1* Permanent Records. After successful completion of acceptance tests approved by the authority having jurisdiction, the requirements in 14.6.1.1 through 14.6.1.3 shall apply.

A.14.6.1 For final determination of record retention, see 14.4.5.3 for sensitivity options.

14.6.1.1 A set of reproducible as-built installation drawings, operation and maintenance manuals, and a written sequence of operation shall be provided to the building owner or the owner's designated representative.

14.6.1.2* Site-Specific Software.

A.14.6.1.2 With many software-based fire systems, a copy of the site-specific software is required to restore system operation if a catastrophic system failure should occur. Without a back-up copy readily available on site, recovery of system operation by authorized service personnel can be substantially delayed.

The intent of this requirement is to provide authorized service personnel with an on-site copy of the site-specific software. The on-site copy should provide a means to recover the last installed and tested version of the site-specific operation of the system. This typically would be an electronic copy of the source files required to load an external programming device with the site-specific data. This requirement does not extend to the system executive software, nor does it require that the external programmer software if required be stored on site.

It is intended that this copy of the software be an electronic version stored on a nonrewritable media containing all of the file(s) or data necessary to restore the system and not just a printed version of the operation stored on electronic media. One example of a nonrewritable media is a CD-R.

14.6.1.2.1 For software-based systems, a copy of the site-specific software shall be provided to the system owner or owner's designated representative.

14.6.1.2.2 A copy of the site-specific software shall be stored on-site in non-volatile, nonerasable, non-rewritable memory.

14.6.1.3 The system owner shall be responsible for maintaining these records for the life of the system for examination by any authority having jurisdiction. Paper or electronic media shall be permitted.

A historical record of the system installation that includes the information required by 14.6.1 gives the technician valuable assistance in promptly diagnosing and repairing system faults. Paragraph 14.6.1.2 requires that a copy of the site-specific software, such as programmed detector locations, be provided to the system owner. This helps verify proper identification of installed addressable devices.

Paragraph 14.6.1.3 indicates that the system owner is responsible for maintaining records for the life of the system. Exhibit 14.19 shows an example of a cabinet that can be used to help meet this need.

◄ **FAQ**
Who is responsible for maintaining the fire alarm system records?

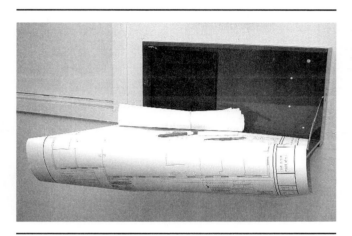

EXHIBIT 14.19 *Documentation Cabinet. (Source: Space Age Electronics, Inc., Hudson, MA)*

14.6.2 Maintenance, Inspection, and Testing Records.

For an interactive version of the form in this section, visit *www.nfpa.org/72forms*.

14.6.2.1 Records shall be retained until the next test and for 1 year thereafter.

14.6.2.2 For systems with restorable fixed-temperature, spot-type heat detectors tested over multiple years, records shall be retained for the 5 years of testing and for 1 year thereafter.

14.6.2.3 The records shall be on a medium that will survive the retention period. Paper or electronic media shall be permitted.

FIRE ALARM AND EMERGENCY COMMUNICATION SYSTEM INSPECTION AND TESTING FORM

To be completed by the system inspector or tester at the time of the inspection or test.
It shall be permitted to modify this form as needed to provide a more complete and/or clear record.
Insert N/A in all unused lines.
Attach additional sheets, data, or calculations as necessary to provide a complete record.

Date of this inspection or test: _____ Time of inspection or test: _____

1. PROPERTY INFORMATION

Name of property: _____

Address: _____

Description of property: _____

Occupancy type: _____

Name of property representative: _____

Address: _____

Phone: _____ Fax: _____ E-mail: _____

Authority having jurisdiction over this property: _____

Phone: _____ Fax: _____ E-mail: _____

2. INSTALLATION, SERVICE, AND TESTING CONTRACTOR INFORMATION

Service and/or testing organization for this equipment: _____

Address: _____

Phone: _____ Fax: _____ E-mail: _____

Service technician or tester: _____

Qualifications of technician or tester: _____

A contract for test and inspection in accordance with NFPA standards is in effect as of: _____

The contract expires: _____ Contract number: _____ Frequency of tests and inspections: _____

Monitoring organization for this equipment: _____

Address: _____

Phone: _____ Fax: _____ E-mail: _____

Entity to which alarms are retransmitted: _____ Phone: _____

3. TYPE OF SYSTEM OR SERVICE

❑ Fire alarm system (nonvoice)

❑ Fire alarm with in-building fire emergency voice alarm communication system (EVACS)

❑ Mass notification system (MNS)

❑ Combination system, with the following components:

    ❑ Fire alarm   ❑ EVACS   ❑ MNS   ❑ Two-way, in-building, emergency communication system

❑ Other (specify): _____

     NFPA 72 (p. 1 of 11)

FIGURE 14.6.2.4 *Example of an Inspection and Testing Form.*

3. TYPE OF SYSTEM OR SERVICE *(continued)*

NFPA 72 edition: _____   Additional description of system(s):_____

_____

3.1 Control Unit

Manufacturer: _____   Model number: _____

3.2 Mass Notification System   ❏ This system does not incorporate an MNS.

3.2.1 System Type:

❏ In-building MNS — combination

❏ In-building MNS — stand-alone   ❏ Wide-area MNS   ❏ Distributed recipient MNS

❏ Other (specify): _____

3.2.2 System Features:

❏ Combination fire alarm/MNS   ❏ MNS ACU only   ❏ Wide-area MNS to regional national alerting interface

❏ Local operating console (LOC)   ❏ Direct recipient MNS (DRMNS)   ❏ Wide-area MNS to DRMNS interface

❏ Wide-area MNS to high-power speaker array (HPSA) interface   ❏ In-building MNS to wide-area MNS interface

❏ Other (specify): _____

3.3 System Documentation

❏ An owner's manual, a copy of the manufacturer's instructions, a written sequence of operation, and a copy of the record drawings are stored on site. Location:_____

3.4 System Software   ❏ This system does not have alterable site-specific software.

Software revision number: _____   Software last updated on: _____

❏ A copy of the site-specific software is stored on site. Location: _____

4. SYSTEM POWER

4.1 Control Unit

4.1.1 Primary Power

Input voltage of control panel: _____   Control panel amps: _____

4.1.2 Engine-Driven Generator   ❏ This system does not have a generator.

Location of generator: _____

Location of fuel storage: _____   Type of fuel: _____

4.1.3 Uninterruptible Power System   ❏ This system does not have a UPS.

Equipment powered by a UPS system: _____

Location of UPS system: _____

Calculated capacity of UPS batteries to drive the system components connected to it:

In standby mode (hours): _____   In alarm mode (minutes): _____

(continues)

4. SYSTEM POWER *(continued)*

4.1.4 Batteries

Location: _____ Type: _____ Nominal voltage: _____ Amp/hour rating: _____

Calculated capacity of batteries to drive the system:

In standby mode (hours): _____ In alarm mode (minutes): _____

❏ Batteries are marked with date of manufacture.

4.2 In-Building Fire Emergency Voice Alarm Communication System or Mass Notification System

❏ This system does not have an EVACS or MNS.

4.2.1 Primary Power

Input voltage of EVACS or MNS panel: _____ EVACS or MNS panel amps: _____

4.2.2 Engine-Driven Generator   ❏ This system does not have a generator.

Location of generator: _____

Location of fuel storage: _____ Type of fuel: _____

4.2.3 Uninterruptible Power System   ❏ This system does not have a UPS.

Equipment powered by a UPS system: _____

Location of UPS system: _____

Calculated capacity of UPS batteries to drive the system components connected to it:

In standby mode (hours): _____ In alarm mode (minutes): _____

4.2.4 Batteries

Location: _____ Type: _____ Nominal voltage: _____ Amp/hour rating: _____

Calculated capacity of batteries to drive the system:

In standby mode (hours): _____ In alarm mode (minutes): _____

❏ Batteries are marked with date of manufacture.

4.3 Notification Appliance Power Extender Panels   ❏ This system does not have power extender panels.

4.3.1 Primary Power

Input voltage of power extender panel(s): _____ Power extender panel amps: _____

4.3.2 Engine-Driven Generator   ❏ This system does not have a generator.

Location of generator: _____

Location of fuel storage: _____ Type of fuel: _____

4.3.3 Uninterruptible Power System   ❏ This system does not have a UPS.

Equipment powered by a UPS system: _____

Location of UPS system: _____

Calculated capacity of UPS batteries to drive the system components connected to it:

In standby mode (hours): _____ In alarm mode (minutes): _____

NFPA 72 (p. 3 of 11)

FIGURE 14.6.2.4 Continued

4. SYSTEM POWER *(continued)*

4.3.4 Batteries

Location: _____   Type: _____   Nominal voltage: _____   Amp/hour rating: _____

Calculated capacity of batteries to drive the system:

In standby mode (hours): _____   In alarm mode (minutes): _____

❏ Batteries are marked with date of manufacture.

5. ANNUNCIATORS   ❏ This system does not have annunciators.

5.1 Location and Description of Annunciators

Annunciator 1: _____

Annunciator 2: _____

Annunciator 3: _____

6. NOTIFICATIONS MADE PRIOR TO TESTING

Monitoring organization	Contact: _____	Time: _____
Building management	Contact: _____	Time: _____
Building occupants	Contact: _____	Time: _____
Authority having jurisdiction	Contact: _____	Time: _____
Other, if required	Contact: _____	Time: _____

7. TESTING RESULTS

7.1 Control Unit and Related Equipment

Description	Visual Inspection	Functional Test	Comments
Control unit	❏	❏	
Lamps/LEDs/LCDs	❏	❏	
Fuses	❏	❏	
Trouble signals	❏	❏	
Disconnect switches	❏	❏	
Ground-fault monitoring	❏	❏	
Supervision	❏	❏	
Local annunciator	❏	❏	
Remote annunciators	❏	❏	
Power extender panels	❏	❏	
Isolation modules	❏	❏	
Other (specify)	❏	❏	

NFPA 72 (p. 4 of 11)

(continues)

7. TESTING RESULTS *(continued)*

7.2 Control Unit Power Supplies

Description	Visual Inspection	Functional Test	Comments
120-volt power	❏	❏	
Generator or UPS	❏	❏	
Battery condition	❏	❏	
Load voltage	❏	❏	
Discharge test	❏	❏	
Charger test	❏	❏	
Other (specify)	❏	❏	

7.3 In-Building Fire Emergency Voice Alarm Communications Equipment

Description	Visual Inspection	Functional Test	Comments
Control unit	❏	❏	
Lamps/LEDs/LCDs	❏	❏	
Fuses	❏	❏	
Primary power supply	❏	❏	
Secondary power supply	❏	❏	
Trouble signals	❏	❏	
Disconnect switches	❏	❏	
Ground-fault monitoring	❏	❏	
Panel supervision	❏	❏	
System performance	❏	❏	

Sound pressure levels
 	
Occupied ❏ Yes ❏ No
  Ambient _____ dBA
  Alarm _____ dBA
(attach report with locations, values, and weather conditions)
	❏	❏	

System intelligibility ❏ CSI ❏ STI (attach report with locations, values, and weather conditions)	❏	❏	
Other (specify)	❏	❏	

FIGURE 14.6.2.4 *Continued*

7. TESTING RESULTS *(continued)*

7.4 Notification Appliance Power Extender Panels

Description	Visual Inspection	Functional Test	Comments
Lamps/LEDs/LCDs	❏	❏	
Fuses	❏	❏	
Primary power supply	❏	❏	
Secondary power supply	❏	❏	
Trouble signals	❏	❏	
Ground-fault monitoring	❏	❏	
Panel supervision	❏	❏	
Other (specify)	❏	❏	

7.5 Mass Notification Equipment

Description	Visual Inspection	Functional Test	Comments
Functional test	❏	❏	
Reset/power down test	❏	❏	
Fuses	❏	❏	
Primary power supply	❏	❏	
UPS power test	❏	❏	
Trouble signals	❏	❏	
Disconnect switches	❏	❏	
Ground-fault monitoring	❏	❏	
CCU security mechanism	❏	❏	
Prerecorded message content	❏	❏	
Prerecorded message activation	❏	❏	
Software backup performed	❏	❏	
Test backup software	❏	❏	
Fire alarm to MNS interface	❏	❏	
MNS to fire alarm interface	❏	❏	
In-building MNS to wide-area MNS	❏	❏	

NFPA 72 (p. 6 of 11)

(continues))

7. TESTING RESULTS *(continued)*

7.5 Mass Notification Equipment *(continued)*

Description	Visual Inspection	Functional Test	Comments
MNS to direct recipient MNS	❏	❏	

Sound pressure levels
Occupied   ❏ Yes   ❏ No
   Ambient _____ dBA
   Alarm _____ dBA
(attach report with locations, values, and weather conditions)
	❏	❏	

System intelligibility ❏ CSI ❏ STI (attach report with locations, values, and weather conditions)	❏	❏	
Other (specify)	❏	❏	

7.6 Two-Way Communications Equipment

Description	Visual Inspection	Functional Test	Comments
Phone handsets	❏	❏	
Phone jacks	❏	❏	
Off-hook indicator	❏	❏	
Call-in signal	❏	❏	
System performance	❏	❏	
System audibility	❏	❏	
System intelligibility	❏	❏	
Radio communications enhancement system	❏	❏	
Area of refuge communication system	❏	❏	
Elevator emergency communications system	❏	❏	
Other (specify)	❏	❏	

NFPA 72 (p. 7 of 11)

FIGURE 14.6.2.4 Continued

7. TESTING RESULTS *(continued)*

7.7 Combination Systems

Description	Visual Inspection	Functional Test	Comments
Fire extinguishing monitoring devices/system	❏	❏	
Carbon monoxide detector/system	❏	❏	
Combination fire/ security system	❏	❏	
Other (specify)	❏	❏	

7.8 Special Hazard Systems

Description (specify)	Visual Inspection	Functional Test	Comments
	❏	❏	
	❏	❏	
	❏	❏	

7.9 Emergency Communications System

❏ Visual

❏ Functional

❏ Simulated operation

❏ Ensure predischarge notification appliances of special hazard systems are not overridden by the MNS. See *NFPA 72*, 24.4.1.7.1.

7.10 Monitored Systems

Description (specify)	Visual Inspection	Functional Test	Comments
Engine-driven generator	❏	❏	
Fire pump	❏	❏	
Special suppression systems	❏	❏	
Other (specify)	❏	❏	

NFPA 72 (p. 8 of 11)

(continues))

7. TESTING RESULTS *(continued)*

7.11 Auxiliary Functions

Description	Visual Inspection	Functional Test	Comments
Door-releasing devices	❏	❏	
Fan shutdown	❏	❏	
Smoke management/ Smoke control	❏	❏	
Smoke damper operation	❏	❏	
Smoke shutter release	❏	❏	
Door unlocking	❏	❏	
Elevator recall	❏	❏	
Elevator shunt trip	❏	❏	
MNS override of FA signals	❏	❏	
Other (specify)	❏	❏	

7.12 Alarm Initiating Device

❏ Device test results sheet attached listing all devices tested and the results of the testing

7.13 Supervisory Alarm Initiating Device

❏ Device test results sheet attached listing all devices tested and the results of the testing

7.14 Alarm Notification Appliances

❏ Appliance test results sheet attached listing all appliances tested and the results of the testing

7.15 Supervisory Station Monitoring

Description	Yes	No	Time	Comments
Alarm signal	❏	❏		
Alarm restoration	❏	❏		
Trouble signal	❏	❏		
Trouble restoration	❏	❏		
Supervisory signal	❏	❏		
Supervisory restoration	❏	❏		

FIGURE 14.6.2.4 *Continued*

8. NOTIFICATIONS THAT TESTING IS COMPLETE

Monitoring organization   Contact: _____   Time: _____

Building management   Contact: _____   Time: _____

Building occupants   Contact: _____   Time: _____

Authority having jurisdiction   Contact: _____   Time: _____

Other, if required   Contact: _____   Time: _____

9. SYSTEM RESTORED TO NORMAL OPERATION

Date: _____   Time: _____

10. CERTIFICATION

10.1 Inspector Certification:

This system, as specified herein, has been inspected and tested according to all NFPA standards cited herein.

Signed: _____   Printed name: _____   Date: _____

Organization: _____   Title: _____   Phone: _____

10.2 Acceptance by Owner or Owner's Representative:

The undersigned has a service contract for this system in effect as of the date shown below.

Signed: _____   Printed name: _____   Date: _____

Organization: _____   Title: _____   Phone: _____

     NFPA 72 (p. 10 of 11)

(continues)

DEVICE TEST RESULTS

(Attach additional sheets if required)

Device Type	Address	Location	Test Results

NFPA 72 (p. 11 of 11)

FIGURE 14.6.2.4 Continued

FIRE ALARM AND EMERGENCY COMMUNICATION SYSTEM INSPECTION AND TESTING FORM

To be completed by the system inspector or tester at the time of the inspection or test.
It shall be permitted to modify this form as needed to provide a more complete and/or clear record.
Insert N/A in all unused lines.
Attach additional sheets, data, or calculations as necessary to provide a complete record.

Date of this inspection or test: ___12/22/2010___   Time of inspection or test: ___8:00 AM___

1. PROPERTY INFORMATION

Name of property: ___Main Street Towers___

Address: ___12345 Main Street, Pleasantville, NY 01111___

Description of property: ___40-story high-rise building with an adjacent 1-story parking structure___

Occupancy type: ___B1___

Name of property representative: ___Mary Morris, Property Manager, Mary's Management Company___

Address: ___12345 Main Street, Pleasantville, NY 01111___

Phone: ___222/222-2222___   Fax: ___333/333-3333___   E-mail: ___mm@mmc.com___

Authority having jurisdiction over this property: ___Inspector Jack Jones, Pleasantville Fire Department___

Phone: ___444/444-4444___   Fax: ___555/555-5555___   E-mail: ___jackjones@pfd.org___

2. INSTALLATION, SERVICE, AND TESTING CONTRACTOR INFORMATION

Service and/or testing organization for this equipment: ___Fred's Fine Fire Alarm Systems___

Address: ___789 Broad Street, Pleasantville, NY 01113___

Phone: ___888/888-8888___   Fax: ___999/999-9999___   E-mail: ___fredfriendly@fffas.com___

Service technician or tester: ___Fred Friendly___

Qualifications of technician or tester: ___NICET IV No 888888___

A contract for test and inspection in accordance with NFPA standards is in effect as of: ___6/11/2010___

The contract expires: ___6/11/2011___ Contract number: ___45678___ Frequency of tests and inspections: ___Quarterly___

Monitoring organization for this equipment: ___Manny's Monitoring___

Address: ___899 First Street, Pleasantville, NY 01114___

Phone: ___777/777-7777___   Fax: ___777/777-7771___   E-mail: ___manny@mannys.com___

Entity to which alarms are retransmitted: ___Pleasantville Fire Department___   Phone: ___444/444-4444___

3. TYPE OF SYSTEM OR SERVICE

❏ Fire alarm system (nonvoice)

❏ Fire alarm with in-building fire emergency voice alarm communication system (EVACS)

❏ Mass notification system (MNS)

☑ Combination system, with the following components:

   ☑ Fire alarm   ☑ EVACS   ☑ MNS   ☑ Two-way, in-building, emergency communication system

❏ Other (specify): ___N/A___

NFPA 72 (p. 1 of 11)

FIGURE A.14.6.2.4 *Example of a Filled-Out Inspection and Testing Form.*

3. TYPE OF SYSTEM OR SERVICE *(continued)*

NFPA 72 edition: ____2010____   Additional description of system(s): ____N/A____

3.1 Control Unit

Manufacturer: ____Megasystems____   Model number: ____AZ–1230____

3.2 Mass Notification System
❑ This system does not incorporate an MNS.

3.2.1 System Type:

☑ In-building MNS — combination

❑ In-building MNS — stand-alone   ❑ Wide-area MNS   ❑ Distributed recipient MNS

❑ Other (specify): ____N/A____

3.2.2 System Features:

☑ Combination fire alarm/MNS   ❑ MNS ACU only   ❑ Wide-area MNS to regional national alerting interface

❑ Local operating console (LOC)   ❑ Direct recipient MNS (DRMNS)   ❑ Wide-area MNS to DRMNS interface

❑ Wide-area MNS to high-power speaker array (HPSA) interface   ❑ In-building MNS to wide-area MNS interface

❑ Other (specify): ____N/A____

3.3 System Documentation

☑ An owner's manual, a copy of the manufacturer's instructions, a written sequence of operation, and a copy of the record drawings are stored on site. Location: ____Building management office, Suite 2222____

3.4 System Software
❑ This system does not have alterable site-specific software.

Software revision number: ____4.567____   Software last updated on: ____June 26, 2010____

☑ A copy of the site-specific software is stored on site. Location: ____Building management office, Suite 2222____

4. SYSTEM POWER

4.1 Control Unit

4.1.1 Primary Power

Input voltage of control panel: ____120 VAC____   Control panel amps: ____6.2____

4.1.2 Engine-Driven Generator
❑ This system does not have a generator.

Location of generator: ____Lower level generator room____

Location of fuel storage: ____Sub basement fuel storage room____   Type of fuel: ____Diesel____

4.1.3 Uninterruptible Power System
☑ This system does not have a UPS.

Equipment powered by a UPS system: ____

Location of UPS system: ____

Calculated capacity of UPS batteries to drive the system components connected to it:

In standby mode (hours): ____   In alarm mode (minutes): ____

FIGURE A.14.6.2.4 *Continued*

4. SYSTEM POWER *(continued)*

4.1.4 Batteries

Location: __Fire control room__   Type: __Gel cell__   Nominal voltage: __24 VDC__   Amp/hour rating: __30__

Calculated capacity of batteries to drive the system:

In standby mode (hours): __38__   In alarm mode (minutes): __11__

☑ Batteries are marked with date of manufacture.

4.2 In-Building Fire Emergency Voice Alarm Communication System or Mass Notification System

❏ This system does not have an EVACS or MNS.

4.2.1 Primary Power

Input voltage of EVACS or MNS panel: __120 VAC__   EVACS or MNS panel amps: __11.9__

4.2.2 Engine-Driven Generator   ❏ This system does not have a generator.

Location of generator: __Lower level generator room__

Location of fuel storage: __Sub basement fuel storage room__   Type of fuel: __Diesel__

4.2.3 Uninterruptible Power System   ☑ This system does not have a UPS.

Equipment powered by a UPS system: _____

Location of UPS system: _____

Calculated capacity of UPS batteries to drive the system components connected to it:

In standby mode (hours): _____   In alarm mode (minutes): _____

4.2.4 Batteries

Location: __Fire control room__   Type: __Gel cell__   Nominal voltage: __24 VDC__   Amp/hour rating: __120__

Calculated capacity of batteries to drive the system:

In standby mode (hours): __30__   In alarm mode (minutes): __8__

☑ Batteries are marked with date of manufacture.

4.3 Notification Appliance Power Extender Panels   ❏ This system does not have power extender panels.

4.3.1 Primary Power

Input voltage of power extender panel(s): __120 VAC__   Power extender panel amps: __2__

4.3.2 Engine-Driven Generator   ❏ This system does not have a generator.

Location of generator: __Lower level generator room__

Location of fuel storage: __Sub basement fuel storage room__   Type of fuel: __Diesel__

4.3.3 Uninterruptible Power System   ☑ This system does not have a UPS.

Equipment powered by a UPS system: _____

Location of UPS system: _____

Calculated capacity of UPS batteries to drive the system components connected to it:

In standby mode (hours): _____   In alarm mode (minutes): _____

(continues)

4. SYSTEM POWER *(continued)*

4.3.4 Batteries

Location: _____Inside each panel_____ Type:___Gel cell___ Nominal voltage:___24 VDC___ Amp/hour rating:____14____

Calculated capacity of batteries to drive the system:

In standby mode (hours): _____ In alarm mode (minutes): ___See attached calculations___

☑ Batteries are marked with date of manufacture.

5. ANNUNCIATORS

❑ This system does not have annunciators.

5.1 Location and Description of Annunciators

Annunciator 1: _____Fire control room_____

Annunciator 2: _____Front lobby at east entrance doors_____

Annunciator 3: _____Engineering office on P1 level_____

6. NOTIFICATIONS MADE PRIOR TO TESTING

Monitoring organization	Contact: ___Manny Monitor___	Time:___8:10 AM___
Building management	Contact: ___Mary Morris___	Time:___8:00 AM___
Building occupants	Contact: ___By PA Announcement___	Time:___8:15 AM___
Authority having jurisdiction	Contact: ___Pleasantville Fire Dept___	Time:___8:15 AM___
Other, if required	Contact: ___N/A___	Time:___N/A___

7. TESTING RESULTS

7.1 Control Unit and Related Equipment

Description	Visual Inspection	Functional Test	Comments
Control unit	☑	☑	
Lamps/LEDs/LCDs	☑	☑	
Fuses	☑	☑	
Trouble signals	☑	☑	
Disconnect switches	☑	❑	Did not test
Ground-fault monitoring	☑	☑	
Supervision	☑	☑	
Local annunciator	☑	☑	
Remote annunciators	☑	☑	
Power extender panels	☑	☑	
Isolation modules	☑	☑	
Other (specify)	❑	❑	

NFPA 72 (p. 4 of 11)

FIGURE A.14.6.2.4 *Continued*

7. TESTING RESULTS *(continued)*

7.2 Control Unit Power Supplies

Description	Visual Inspection	Functional Test	Comments
120-volt power	☑	☑	
Generator or UPS	☑	☑	
Battery condition	☑	☑	
Load voltage	☑	☑	
Discharge test	☑	☑	
Charger test	☑	☑	
Other (specify)	❑	❑	

7.3 In-Building Fire Emergency Voice Alarm Communications Equipment

Description	Visual Inspection	Functional Test	Comments
Control unit	☑	☑	
Lamps/LEDs/LCDs	☑	☑	
Fuses	☑	☑	
Primary power supply	☑	☑	
Secondary power supply	☑	☑	
Trouble signals	☑	☑	
Disconnect switches	☑	☑	
Ground-fault monitoring	☑	☑	
Panel supervision	☑	☑	
System performance	☑	☑	

Sound pressure levels
Occupied ❑ Yes ❑ No
  Ambient _____ dBA
  Alarm _____ dBA
(attach report with locations, values, and weather conditions)
	☑	☑	Tested by ear only

System intelligibility ❑ CSI ❑ STI (attach report with locations, values, and weather conditions)	☑	☑	Tested by ear only
Other (specify)	❑	❑	

NFPA 72 (p. 5 of 11)

(continues)

7. TESTING RESULTS *(continued)*

7.4 Notification Appliance Power Extender Panels

Description	Visual Inspection	Functional Test	Comments
Lamps/LEDs/LCDs	☑	☑	
Fuses	☑	☑	
Primary power supply	☑	☑	
Secondary power supply	☑	☑	
Trouble signals	☑	☑	
Ground-fault monitoring	☑	☑	
Panel supervision	☑	☑	
Other (specify)	❑	❑	

7.5 Mass Notification Equipment

Description	Visual Inspection	Functional Test	Comments
Functional test	☑	☑	
Reset/power down test	☑	☑	
Fuses	☑	☑	
Primary power supply	☑	☑	
UPS power test	❑	❑	Did not test
Trouble signals	☑	☑	
Disconnect switches	❑	❑	Did not test
Ground-fault monitoring	☑	☑	
CCU security mechanism	❑	❑	N/A
Prerecorded message content	☑	☑	
Prerecorded message activation	☑	☑	
Software backup performed	❑	❑	No
Test backup software	☑	☑	
Fire alarm to MNS interface	☑	☑	
MNS to fire alarm interface	☑	☑	
In-building MNS to wide-area MNS	❑	❑	N/A

NFPA 72 (p. 6 of 11)

FIGURE A.14.6.2.4 Continued

7. TESTING RESULTS *(continued)*

7.5 Mass Notification Equipment *(continued)*

Description	Visual Inspection	Functional Test	Comments
MNS to direct recipient MNS	❏	❏	N/A
Sound pressure levels Occupied ❏ Yes ❏ No Ambient _____ dBA Alarm _____ dBA (attach report with locations, values, and weather conditions)	❏	❏	Did not test
System intelligibility ❏ CSI ❏ STI (attach report with locations, values, and weather conditions)	❏	❏	Did not test
Other (specify)	❏	❏	

7.6 Two-Way Communications Equipment

Description	Visual Inspection	Functional Test	Comments
Phone handsets	☑	☑	
Phone jacks	☑	☑	
Off-hook indicator	☑	☑	
Call-in signal	☑	☑	
System performance	☑	☑	
System audibility	☑	☑	
System intelligibility	☑	☑	
Radio communications enhancement system	❏	❏	N/A
Area of refuge communication system	❏	❏	N/A
Elevator emergency communications system	❏	❏	N/A
Other (specify)	❏	❏	

(continues)

7. TESTING RESULTS *(continued)*

7.7 Combination Systems

Description	Visual Inspection	Functional Test	Comments
Fire extinguishing monitoring devices/system	❏	❏	N/A
Carbon monoxide detector/system	❏	❏	N/A
Combination fire/ security system	❏	❏	N/A
Other (specify)	❏	❏	

7.8 Special Hazard Systems

Description (specify)	Visual Inspection	Functional Test	Comments
24th floor preaction	☑	❏	Visually checked but did not test
	❏	❏	
	❏	❏	

7.9 Emergency Communications System

❏ Visual

❏ Functional

❏ Simulated operation

❏ Ensure predischarge notification appliances of special hazard systems are not overridden by the MNS. See *NFPA 72,* 24.4.1.7.1.

7.10 Monitored Systems

Description (specify)	Visual Inspection	Functional Test	Comments
Engine-driven generator	☑	❏	Visually checked but did not test
Fire pump	☑	❏	Visually checked but did not test
Special suppression systems	❏	❏	N/A
Other (specify)	❏	❏	

FIGURE A.14.6.2.4 *Continued*

7. TESTING RESULTS *(continued)*

7.11 Auxiliary Functions

Description	Visual Inspection	Functional Test	Comments
Door-releasing devices	☑	☑	
Fan shutdown	☑	☑	
Smoke management/ Smoke control	❏	❏	N/A
Smoke damper operation	☑	☑	
Smoke shutter release	❏	❏	N/A
Door unlocking	☑	☑	
Elevator recall	☑	☑	
Elevator shunt trip	☑	☑	
MNS override of FA signals	☑	☑	
Other (specify)	❏	❏	

7.12 Alarm Initiating Device

☑ Device test results sheet attached listing all devices tested and the results of the testing

7.13 Supervisory Alarm Initiating Device

☑ Device test results sheet attached listing all devices tested and the results of the testing

7.14 Alarm Notification Appliances

☑ Appliance test results sheet attached listing all appliances tested and the results of the testing

7.15 Supervisory Station Monitoring

Description	Yes	No	Time	Comments
Alarm signal	☑	❏	4:30 PM	
Alarm restoration	☑	❏	4:40 PM	
Trouble signal	☑	❏	4:30 PM	
Trouble restoration	☑	❏	4:40 PM	
Supervisory signal	☑	❏	4:30 PM	
Supervisory restoration	☑	❏	4:40 PM	

(continues)

8. NOTIFICATIONS THAT TESTING IS COMPLETE

Monitoring organization   Contact: _Manny Monitor_   Time: _4:20 PM_

Building management   Contact: _Mary Morris_   Time: _4:20 PM_

Building occupants   Contact: _By PA Announcement_   Time: _4:20 PM_

Authority having jurisdiction   Contact: _Pleasantville Fire Dept_   Time: _4:20 PM_

Other, if required   Contact: _N/A_   Time: _N/A_

9. SYSTEM RESTORED TO NORMAL OPERATION

Date: _12/22/2010_   Time: _4:40 PM_

10. CERTIFICATION

10.1 Inspector Certification:

This system, as specified herein, has been inspected and tested according to all NFPA standards cited herein.

Signed: _Fred Friendly_   Printed name: _Fred Friendly_   Date: _12/22/2010_

Organization: _Fred's Fine Fire Alarm Syst._   Title: _President_   Phone: _888/888-8888_

10.2 Acceptance by Owner or Owner's Representative:

The undersigned has a service contract for this system in effect as of the date shown below.

Signed: _Mary Morris_   Printed name: _Mary Morris_   Date: _12/30/2010_

Organization: _Mary's Management_   Title: _Property Manager_   Phone: _222/222-2222_

   NFPA 72 (p. 10 of 11)

FIGURE A.14.6.2.4 *Continued*

DEVICE TEST RESULTS

(Attach additional sheets if required)

Device Type	Address	Location	Test Results
Smoke detector	L1D4	1st floor fire control room	OK
Manual fire alarm box	L1M6	1st floor main lobby	OK

* * * * Continue with a complete listing of all devices tested * * * *

14.6.2.4* A record of all inspections, testing, and maintenance shall be provided that includes the following information regarding tests and all the applicable information requested in Figure 14.6.2.4:

(1) Date
(2) Test frequency
(3) Name of property
(4) Address
(5) Name of person performing inspection, maintenance, tests, or combination thereof, and affiliation, business address, and telephone number
(6) Name, address, and representative of approving agency(ies)
(7) Designation of the detector(s) tested
(8) Functional test of detectors
(9)*Functional test of required sequence of operations
(10) Check of all smoke detectors
(11) Loop resistance for all fixed-temperature, line-type heat detectors
(12) Functional test of mass notification system control units
(13) Functional test of signal transmission to mass notification systems
(14) Functional test of ability of mass notification system to silence fire alarm notification appliances
(15) Tests of intelligibility of mass notification system speakers
(16) Other tests as required by the equipment manufacturer's published instructions
(17) Other tests as required by the authority having jurisdiction
(18) Signatures of tester and approved authority representative
(19) Disposition of problems identified during test (e.g., system owner notified, problem corrected/successfully retested, device abandoned in place)

A.14.6.2.4 Figure A.14.6.2.4 provides an example of a filled-out Inspection and Testing Form.

A.14.6.2.4(9) One method used to define the required sequence of operations and to document the actual sequence of operations is an input/output matrix. [See Figure A.14.6.2.4(9).]

14.6.3 Supervising Station Records. For supervising station alarm systems, records pertaining to signals received at the supervising station that result from maintenance, inspection, and testing shall be maintained for not less than 12 months.

14.6.3.1 Records shall be permitted to be maintained on either paper or electronic media.

14.6.3.2 Upon request, a hard copy record shall be provided to the authority having jurisdiction.

14.6.4 Simulated Operation Note. If the operation of a device, circuit, fire alarm control unit function, or special hazard system interface is simulated, it shall be noted on the inspection/test form that the operation was simulated.

For future reference in determining overall system reliability, it is important to document whether the interfaced system operation was fully tested by actual operation of the interfaced system or if its operation was simulated.

REFERENCES CITED IN COMMENTARY

NFPA 12, *Standard on Carbon Dioxide Extinguishing Systems*, 2008 edition, National Fire Protection Association, Quincy, MA.

NFPA 720, *Standard for the Installation of Carbon Monoxide (CO) Detection and Warning Equipment*, 2009 edition, National Fire Protection Association, Quincy, MA.

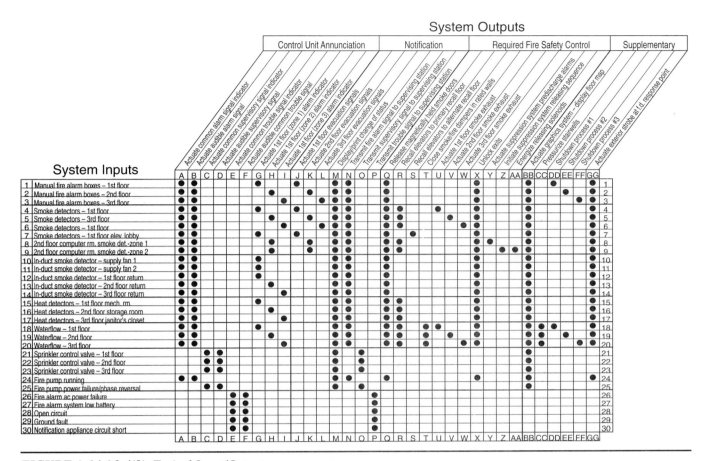

FIGURE A.14.6.2.4(9) *Typical Input/Output*

ANSI S3.2, *Method for Measuring the Intelligibility of Speech Over Communications Systems*, 1995 edition, American National Standards Institute, Inc., New York, NY.

IEC 60849, *Sound Systems for Emergency Purposes*, 1998 edition, International Electrotechnical Commission, Geneva, Switzerland.

Intelligibility of Fire Alarm and Emergency Communication Systems, November 2008, Fire Protection Research Foundation, Quincy, MA. Available on-line at *http://www.nfpa.org/assets/files//PDF/Research/intelligibilityFireAlarm.pdf*

"Cry Wolf," *NEMA Magazine*, Fall 2003, National Electrical Manufacturers Association, Rosslyn, VA.

Reserved

In this 2010 edition of *NFPA 72®*, *National Fire Alarm and Signaling Code*, Chapter 15 is reserved for future use.

Reserved

In this 2010 edition of *NFPA 72®*, *National Fire Alarm and Signaling Code*, Chapter 16 is reserved for future use.

Initiating Devices

CHAPTER 17

Chapter 17 (Chapter 5 in previous editions of the Code) covers the design and installation criteria for all sensors and devices that recognize or are used to provide recognition of the existence of a fire or the status of a protected space and fire protection systems within that space. The term *initiating device* includes all forms of signal input devices and sensors, ranging from manually operated fire alarm boxes to automatic fire detectors to switches that detect the operation of a fire extinguishing or fire suppression system to valve status supervisory switches. In short, this chapter covers any device that provides an incoming signal to the fire alarm control unit.

The following list is a summary of significant changes to the chapter on initiating devices in the 2010 edition:

- Revised 17.7.1.11 addressing protection of smoke detectors during construction
- New 17.7.3.1.4 permitting a detector(s) to be installed in close proximity to the object it protects
- Revised 17.7.3.2.3.1 providing an enforceable spacing criterion for spot-type smoke detectors with interpretive guidance in A.17.7.3.2.3.1
- Revised criteria, based on new research, in 17.7.3.2.4.2 through 17.7.3.2.4.5 for spacing smoke detectors on ceilings with beams and waffle-type ceilings
- New Section 17.10 addressing detectors used to detect flammable gases or combustible vapors

Performance-based detection designs continue to play a prominent role in the application of fire alarm systems, and the option of using performance-based design has been retained in the 2010 edition. In the sections dealing with heat detectors and smoke detectors, the designer has the option of selecting either a prescriptive- or a performance-based design. Once the design option has been selected, the designer follows the criteria outlined for that option. In 17.7.7, Video Image Smoke Detection, and Section 17.8, Radiant Energy-Sensing Fire Detectors, the performance-based design method is the only permissible option. This has been the case for radiant energy-sensing fire detectors since the 1990 edition of NFPA 72E, *Standard on Automatic Fire Detectors*.

In general, the sooner a fire is detected, the better, simply because small fires are easier to extinguish and produce less damage than large fires. The objective of the system design is to achieve sufficient speed and surety of response to a fire or supervised condition with minimal probability that such signals are the result of a non-fire stimulus or spurious source. System designers can achieve this objective only if they select the proper type of detector for each application. This selection process requires a thorough understanding of how each type of detector operates and how it is affected by its environment. The mission effectiveness of the fire alarm system depends heavily on this choice.

Automatic fire detectors do not actually respond to the fire itself but rather to some change in the ambient conditions in the immediate vicinity of the detector that is the result of the fire. A heat detector responds to an increase in the ambient temperature in its immediate vicinity. A smoke detector responds to the presence of smoke in the air in its immediate vicinity. A flame detector responds to the influx of radiant energy that has traveled from the fire to the detector. In each case, heat, smoke, or electromagnetic radiation (light) must travel from the fire to the detector before the detector initiates an alarm signal.

The placement and spacing of both smoke detectors and heat detectors depend on the transfer of combustion products (heat, smoke, etc.) from the location of the fire to the vicinity of the detector. A set of physical principles, generally called *fire plume dynamics,* describes this transfer of smoke aerosol or of heated combustion product gases and air. The combustion reactions of the fire heat the air immediately above it as hot combustion product gases and radiant energy are released. The hot air and combustion product gas mixture rises in an expanding buoyant column, or *plume,* from the fire to the ceiling. As the fire burns, it continues to produce additional hot combustion product gases, which flow upward as a buoyant plume. When the hot gases in the plume collide with the ceiling, the momentum of the gas plume is conserved. The plume turns and flows horizontally beneath the ceiling. This horizontal flow of combustion product gases beneath the ceiling is called a *ceiling jet.* The ceiling jet consists of a layer of hot air and combustion gases that expand radially away from the fire plume centerline, as shown in Exhibit 17.1.

EXHIBIT 17.1 *Ceiling Jet Formed by Fire Plume. (Source: J. M. Cholin Consultants, Inc., Oakland, NJ)*

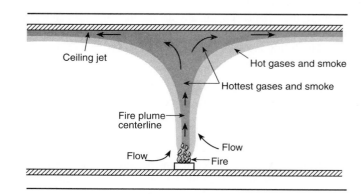

The ceiling jet carries the heat and combustion product gases (smoke) to the heat detector or smoke detector mounted on the ceiling. The location and spacing criteria for heat and smoke detectors in Chapter 17 are derived from an understanding of how the ceiling jet forms and how it behaves. The speed of response of a system using heat detectors or smoke detectors is determined, in part, by two factors. The first is the velocity of the ceiling jet as it conveys heat and smoke from the fire plume to the detector. The second is the distance the ceiling jet must travel from the fire plume centerline to the nearest detector.

Radiant energy–sensing detectors respond to the electromagnetic radiation from the fire. The fire emits radiation in all directions. All materials in the environment, including the air through which the radiation must travel, reflect, diffract, absorb, and transmit radiant energy. As the distance between the fire and the detector increases, the intensity of the radiant energy available to the detector diminishes. The speed of response of the radiant energy–sensing detectors is determined, in part, by the distance between the detector and the fire and the effect the air has on the transmission of radiant energy from the fire to the detector.

Manual fire alarm boxes provide a means for human observers to initiate a fire alarm signal. They are distributed in a manner that provides both relatively short travel time and ease of operation while occupants are leaving the building. The speed of response is determined largely by the speed with which the occupants can travel and the distance they must travel to reach a manual fire alarm box.

The prescriptive system design requirements in this chapter of *NFPA 72®, National Fire Alarm and Signaling Code,* are intended to provide the minimum criteria sufficient to fulfill generally accepted response expectations. However, the Code does not quantify those response expectations. Where the needed response differs from the generally accepted expectations or where conditions are different from those presumed by the prescriptive criteria, this chapter permits the use of performance-based design methods. Refer to Supplement 1, Performance-Based Design and Fire Alarm Systems, and Annex B, Engineering Guide for Automatic Fire Detector Spacing.

17.1 Application

17.1.1 The performance, selection, use, and location of automatic fire detection devices, sprinkler waterflow detectors, manually activated fire alarm stations, and supervisory signal–initiating devices (including guard tour reporting used to ensure timely warning for the purposes of life safety and the protection of a building, a space, a structure, an area, or an object) shall comply with the minimum requirements of this chapter.

Section 17.1 addresses the applicability of the requirements of Chapter 17. The basic scope of the chapter is established in 17.1.1. An understanding of the scope limitations of Chapter 17 is crucial. Where the Code is referenced in laws or ordinances, the requirements of the Code assume the effect of law. The established scope determines whether the provisions of this chapter apply.

17.1.2 The requirements of Chapters 10, 12, 21, 23, and 24 shall also apply unless they are in conflict with this chapter.

Chapter 17 provides the installation requirements regarding fire alarm signal and supervisory signal–initiating devices. Chapters 10, 12, 21, 23, and 24 include some requirements that relate to where and under what circumstances such devices are required. The designer must refer to Chapter 10 and Chapter 12 for requirements relating to the means of connection. Chapters 21, 23, and 24 have criteria that are implemented by referring to Chapter 17.

17.1.3 The requirements of Chapter 14 shall apply.

Chapter 14 covers the inspection, testing, and maintenance criteria for the fire alarm system, including all initiating devices.

17.1.4 The requirements of single- and multiple-station alarms and household fire alarm systems shall be determined in accordance with Chapter 29.

17.1.5 The material in this chapter shall be applied by persons knowledgeable in the application of fire detection and fire alarm systems and services.

In 17.1.5, the phrase "persons knowledgeable in the application of fire detection and fire alarm systems and services" refers to someone of a higher skill and knowledge level than that which is necessary to simply read the Code. The user is expected to understand the role that the fire alarm system plays in the overall fire safety strategy for the site. Knowing the limitations of the types of detectors is as important as knowing which detector is the right choice for the application. Understanding which type of system will meet the owner's goals is as important as understanding how the system will operate. Many jurisdictions have licensure or certification requirements for persons working on fire protection equipment. See also the requirements for the system designer in Section 10.4.

17.1.6 The interconnection of initiating devices with control equipment configurations and power supplies, or with output systems responding to external actuation, shall be as detailed elsewhere in this Code or in other NFPA codes and standards.

The interconnection of initiating devices to the fire alarm control unit via system wiring is subject to requirements that relate to both the initiating device and the fire alarm control unit. Consequently, the user must apply the requirements of this chapter and Chapters 10, 12, 21, 23, and 24, as well as requirements in any relevant occupancy standards in the design process.

17.2 Purpose

Automatic and manual initiating devices shall contribute to life safety, fire protection, and property conservation by providing a reliable means to signal other equipment arranged to monitor the initiating devices and to initiate a response to those signals.

FAQ ▶
Does Chapter 17 establish the need for the installation of initiating devices?

Chapter 17 does not require that a building owner install detectors of any particular type in any particular location, nor does it address which types of facilities need a particular type of initiating device. Where some other code or standard, such as NFPA *101®*, *Life Safety Code®*, or a local or state adopted building code requires a building owner to install fire detectors, Chapter 17 establishes the design and installation requirements for systems. Where an owner elects to install detection devices as part of a nonrequired fire alarm system, the requirements of this chapter are also intended to apply.

The requirement for some form of fire or supervisory signal initiation is established in the codes and standards that cover a specific class of occupancy or, in some cases, a specific class of fire protection system. The property owner, property insurance carrier, or other authority having jurisdiction might also establish requirements for fire alarm or supervisory signal initiation. Once a requirement has been established by some other code or authority, the designer then refers to this Code for the specifics of selection, installation, and placement.

For example, NFPA 664, *Standard for the Prevention of Fires and Explosions in Wood Processing and Woodworking Facilities*, requires the use of spark/ember detectors in certain instances. The designer using NFPA 664 must then refer to Chapter 17 of the Code for the relevant installation requirements for spark/ember detectors.

As another example, Chapter 40 of NFPA *101*, which covers industrial occupancies, requires a fire alarm system where 100 or more people are on-site and 25 or more people are on a floor other than the exit discharge–level floor. Chapter 40 also addresses the means (manual initiation, automatic fire detection, automatic sprinkler operation) needed to initiate the fire alarm system and the requirements for occupant notification. (Refer to Supplement 4 for a summary of requirements for various occupancies based on the 2009 edition of NFPA *101*.) The fire protection designer of such an industrial site must then refer to *NFPA 72* for the relevant requirements for that fire alarm system and to Chapter 17 for the determination of the type, quantity, and placement of the fire detection devices. The designer must also refer to Chapter 17 for the installation requirements for waterflow switches, pressure switches, and other initiating devices that might be required by NFPA 13, *Standard for the Installation of Sprinkler Systems*; NFPA 12, *Standard on Carbon Dioxide Extinguishing Systems*; or other standards.

Chapter 17 establishes the selection and placement criteria for initiating devices. These criteria ultimately establish the number and type of initiating devices. When a designer places detection in a specific area or in a manner to protect from a specific hazard, the detection devices to be installed must follow the requirements outlined in this Code.

17.3* Performance-Based Design

The process of performance-based design is described in Supplement 1. The three areas where fire alarm systems lend themselves to performance-based design methods are initiation, notification, and maintenance. This chapter provides a performance-based design alternative to the prescriptive criteria for the design of the initiating part of the fire alarm system and includes specific requirements that pertain to the review and approval of performance-based designs in Section 17.3. Usually, a performance-based design is deemed "engineering," and those performing this work are subject to the licensure requirements of the governing jurisdiction.

A.17.3 Annex B, Engineering Guide for Automatic Fire Detector Spacing, provides a detailed design guide for the implementation of the performance-based design of fire alarm systems.

17.3.1 Performance-based designs submitted to the authority having jurisdiction for review and approval shall include documentation, in an approved format, of each performance objective and applicable scenario, together with any calculations, modeling, or other technical substantiation used in establishing the proposed design's fire and life safety performance.

17.3.2 The authority having jurisdiction shall determine whether such identified performance objectives are appropriate and have been met.

17.3.3 The authority having jurisdiction shall approve modifications to or variations from the approved design or design basis in advance.

17.4 General Requirements

17.4.1 These requirements shall apply to all initiating devices.

As used in this Code, the term *initiating device* covers not only fire detection devices such as manual fire alarm boxes, heat detectors, smoke detectors, and radiant energy–sensing detectors, but also other devices monitoring conditions related to fire safety. These devices include sprinkler system waterflow switches, pressure switches, valve tamper switches, building temperature monitoring devices, and any signaling switches used to monitor special extinguishing systems. The requirements in Section 17.4 apply to all monitoring devices that provide information in the form of binary, digital, or analog data transmitted to a fire alarm control unit. See also the definition of *initiating device* in 3.3.122.

17.4.2 Initiating devices shall not be installed in inaccessible areas.

This requirement has been included to prevent the installation of initiating devices where they cannot be maintained during the life of the system. If the initiating devices are inaccessible, the maintenance contractor will not be able to maintain them in accordance with Chapter 14. If the initiating devices cannot be maintained in accordance with Chapter 14, they cannot be expected to provide reliable service. *Inaccessible* is not defined in the Code; however, *NFPA 70®, National Electrical Code® (NEC®)*, has three definitions that may be useful in determining the acceptability of a device location:

Accessible (as applied to equipment). Admitting close approach; not guarded by locked doors, elevation, or other effective means. [70:100]

Accessible (as applied to wiring methods). Capable of being removed or exposed without damaging the building structure or finish or not permanently closed in by the structure or finish of the building. [70:100]

Accessible, Readily (Readily Accessible). Capable of being reached quickly for operation, renewal, or inspections without requiring those to whom ready access is requisite to climb over or remove obstacles or to resort to portable ladders, and so forth. [70:100]

17.4.3 Where subject to mechanical damage, an initiating device shall be protected. A mechanical guard used to protect a smoke, heat, or radiant energy–sensing detector shall be listed for use with the detector.

A prudent designer and installer would apply the requirement in 17.4.3 to every component of the fire alarm system. The cause of many unwanted alarms as well as system failures has been found to be the result of damage to a detector or other initiating device.

Mechanical damage is not necessarily limited to catastrophic destruction. Mechanical damage can occur over an extended period of time from vibration, extremes in temperature, corrosive atmospheres, other chemical reactions, or excessive humidity. The designer and the installer must be sure that the initiating device is appropriate for the environment in which it is to be installed.

FAQ ▶
Why must mechanical guards be listed for use with the detector?

Subsection 17.4.3 requires that mechanical guards used to protect smoke detectors, heat detectors, and radiant energy–sensing detectors be listed for that purpose. Because both smoke detectors and heat detectors rely on the ceiling jet to convey smoke and hot combustion product gases from the fire plume to the detector, any object that impedes that flow retards the response of the detector. Similarly, any object that impedes the transmission of radiant energy to radiant energy–sensing detectors would have an adverse effect on the response of the detector. The only means to be certain the mechanical guard is not a material impediment to detector response is to require that a qualified testing laboratory test and list the guard for the specific make and model detector. The listing will indicate the reduction in spacing or sensitivity that will result from use of the guard. See Exhibit 17.2 for an example of a protected detector.

17.4.4 Initiating devices shall be supported independently of their attachment to the circuit conductors.

Subsection 17.4.4 applies to all types of initiating devices. The copper used in the wiring conductors is not formulated to serve as a mechanical support. Copper fatigues over time if placed under a mechanical stress, resulting in increasing brittleness and electrical resistance. Ultimately, the fatigued conductor breaks or its resistance becomes too high to allow the circuit to function properly. In either case, the operation of the circuit is impaired, and a loss of life or property could conceivably result because of fire alarm system failure.

Initiating devices must always be mounted as shown in the manufacturer's instructions. The requirements for listing include a method for mounting that adequately supports the initiating device so that no mechanical stresses are applied to the circuit conductors. Listing also requires that no electrical shock hazard exists if the device is mounted according to the instructions. If the instructions show the use of an electrical device or outlet box, then installation of the device with a box is a requirement of the listing, and the specific type of box shown must be used. If not shown, the use of an electrical box is determined by field conditions and the requirements of the *NEC*. See also the requirements of 10.3.1 regarding the installation of listed equipment.

17.4.5 Initiating devices shall be installed in a manner that provides accessibility for periodic maintenance.

As noted in 17.4.2, the term *accessible* is defined in *NFPA 70* as "admitting close approach: not guarded by locked doors, elevation, or other effective means." Prudent designers and installers should consider this for all system components requiring maintenance and where security is not an issue. If special equipment, such as a manlift, is necessary to install any detection devices, the designer should ensure that the owner understands that this special equipment will be needed for future testing and maintenance of those devices. The accessibility of a detector or other initiating device will ultimately be reflected in the ability of serv-

EXHIBIT 17.2 *Smoke Detector with Protective Mechanical Guard. (Source: Safety Technology International, Inc., Waterford, MI)*

ice personnel to perform the required testing and maintenance in accordance with Chapter 14. See also 1.3.4 regarding the meaning of terms and the reference to *NFPA 70*.

17.4.6 Initiating devices shall be installed in all areas, compartments, or locations where required by other NFPA codes and standards or as required by other governing laws, codes, or standards.

Subsection 17.4.6 provides correlation between the *National Fire Alarm and Signaling Code* and other codes and standards. Initiating devices must be used wherever required by another code or standard. Chapter 17 answers the questions of how many devices and how they should be installed. Note that the authority having jurisdiction may require initiating devices in areas where they are not necessarily required by other codes or standards. If the authority having jurisdiction makes such a requirement, those initiating devices must also be installed in a manner consistent with Chapter 17.

17.4.7* Duplicate terminals, leads, or connectors that provide for the connection of installation wiring shall be provided on each initiating device for the express purpose of connecting into the fire alarm system to monitor the integrity of the signaling and power wiring.

Exception: Initiating devices connected to a system that provides the required monitoring.

Traditionally, fire alarm system control units have used a small monitoring current to recognize a break in a conductor or the removal of a detector from the circuit. Under normal conditions, the monitoring current flows through the circuit. When a detector is removed or a conductor is broken, the current path is interrupted and the flow of current stops. The control unit translates this action into a trouble signal.

A common practice in the electrical trade in the installation of electrical outlets has been to remove a short section of insulation from the conductor and loop the wire beneath the screw terminal without ever cutting the conductor. This method of installation of fire alarm initiating devices is unacceptable. If this method is used, the connection to the initiating device (detector) could loosen over time and the detector could become disconnected from the circuit. If this situation were to occur, the control unit would not recognize this as a break in the circuit and a loss of a detection device. Subsection 17.4.7 was incorporated into the Code to preclude this practice.

Systems using addressable detectors and addressable control units are available. A microcomputer in the control unit maintains a list of the binary code that serves as the "name" of each initiating device in the system. The control unit sequentially addresses each device by name (binary code) and verifies the response from that device. The control unit recognizes when an initiating device fails to respond when it has been addressed, indicating that the device either has failed or has been removed or that a break has occurred in the wiring. This method does not depend on the continuous flow of current. Therefore, these systems are exempt from the duplicate terminal requirement unless a Class A circuit is used. See also the commentary following A.10.17.1.

See Exhibits 17.3 and 17.4 for examples of duplicate terminals.

◄ FAQ
Are duplicate leads required for initiating devices that are interrogated by an addressable system?

A.17.4.7 The monitoring of circuit integrity relies on the interruption of the wiring continuity when the connection to the initiating device is lost. Terminals and leads, as illustrated in Figure A.17.4.7(a) and Figure A.17.4.7(b), monitor the presence of the device on the initiating device circuit.

A review of the equivalent circuit inside the detector is helpful when considering Figure A.17.4.7(b).

The generic four-wire detector has power supply terminals, terminals for a normally closed (n.c.) trouble contact, and terminals for a normally open (n.o.) alarm contact. Exhibit 17.5 shows the equivalent schematic of the detector (initiating device). Note that the num-

EXHIBIT 17.3 *Smoke Detector with Base Showing Incoming and Outgoing Terminals. (Source: Hochicki America Corp., Buena Park, CA; photo courtesy of Mammoth Fire Alarms, Inc., Lowell, MA)*

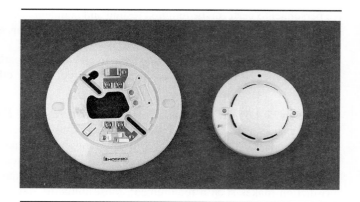

EXHIBIT 17.4 *Connections for a Manual Fire Alarm Box Showing Incoming and Outgoing Leads. (Source: Edwards Signaling & Security Systems, Plainville, CT)*

bering of the terminals shown in Exhibit 17.5 is strictly illustrative and will not necessarily be consistent with the numbering of commercially available detectors. Also note that the circuitry (shaded area) is divided into two parts — a sensing part (a), which operates the alarm-operated contact, and a trouble indicating part (t), which operates the trouble-operated contact. Using Exhibit 17.5, one can follow the flow of current through the circuit in Figure A.17.4.7(b).

As shown by the designations in Exhibit 17.5, the operating potential (voltage) for the detector is supplied to terminals 7 and 8. Within the detector, connections exist from terminal 7 to terminal 4 and from terminal 8 to terminal 3. Terminals 4 and 3 are wired to terminals 7 and 8, respectively, of the next detector on the circuit, providing operating potential

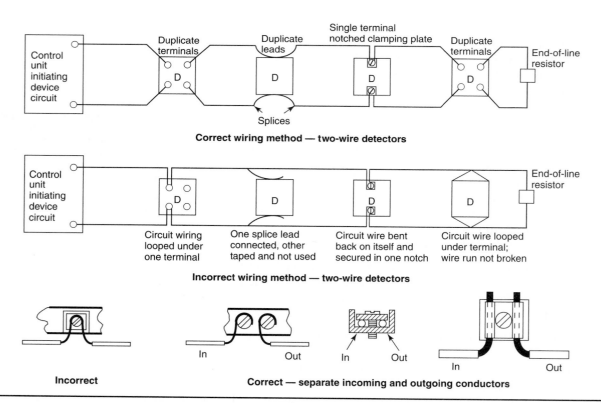

FIGURE A.17.4.7(a) *Correct (and Incorrect) Wiring Methods.*

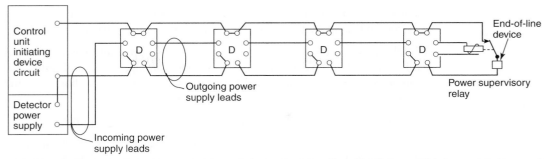

Illustrates four-wire smoke detector employing a three-wire connecting arrangement. One side of power supply is connected to one side of initiating device circuit. Wire run broken at each connection to smoke detector to provide supervision.

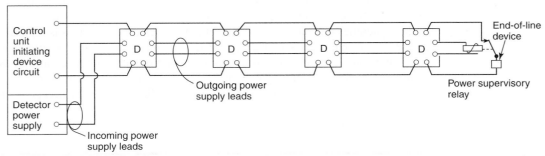

Illustrates four-wire smoke detector employing a four-wire connecting arrangement. Incoming and outgoing leads or terminals for both initiating device and power supply connections. Wire run broken at each connection to provide supervision.

D = Detector

FIGURE A.17.4.7(b) *Wiring Arrangements for Four-Wire Detectors.*

(voltage) to the subsequent detectors. The application of operating potential (voltage) in the proper polarity closes a normally closed trouble contact between terminals 5 and 6. Within the detector, a jumper is between terminals 2 and 1. Thus, under normal operational conditions, terminals 1, 2, 5, and 6 provide a circuit path for the monitoring current. Between terminals 1 and 6, a normally open alarm contact closes when the detector senses the byproducts of fire.

The normally closed contacts allow a monitoring current to flow from the control unit into terminal 6, out terminal 5, on through each detector, through the end-of-line device, and back through terminals 1 and 2 of each detector to the control unit. If an initiating device (detector) loses its source of operating potential (voltage), the trouble contact between terminals 5 and 6 opens, interrupting the current flow. If an initiating device senses a fire, the alarm contact between terminals 1 and 6 closes, bypassing the end-of-line device, which increases the current flowing through the initiating device circuit. The control unit interprets the larger flow of current as a fire alarm.

The ability to use the three-wire format or the four-wire format is determined by the initiating device input circuit of the fire alarm control unit, not the detector. Some control units use one side of the power supply as part of the initiating device circuit and others do not. The system must be wired according to the instructions provided by the manufacturer of the fire alarm system control unit. In addition, the only circuit-powered detectors that are permitted to be connected to a fire alarm control unit are those that have been listed as being compatible with the specific make and model control unit.

17.4.8 Where smoke detectors are installed in concealed locations more than 10 ft (3.0 m) above the finished floor or in arrangements where the detector's alarm or supervisory indicator

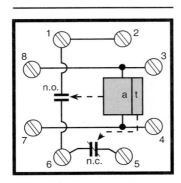

EXHIBIT 17.5 *Equivalent Circuit of a Generic Four-Wire Detector. (Source: J. M. Cholin Consultants, Inc., Oakland, NJ)*

is not visible to responding personnel, the detectors shall be provided with remote alarm or supervisory indication in a location acceptable to the authority having jurisdiction.

17.4.9 Where required by 17.4.8 and unless the specific detector alarm or supervisory signal is indicated at the control unit, remote alarm or supervisory indicators shall be installed in an accessible location and shall be clearly labeled to indicate both their function and the air-handling unit(s) associated with each detector.

Subsection 17.4.9 was added by a tentative interim amendment (TIA).

In earlier editions of the Code, the requirements contained in 17.4.8 and 17.4.9 were originally associated only with the use of duct-type smoke detectors. In the 2010 edition, they are now applicable to all initiating devices.

Identification of which initiating device is activated is a chronic problem wherever devices are installed in facilities with unfinished ceilings or in the above-ceiling space because of the difficulties typically involved in getting to such detectors. This is especially true where duct-type smoke detectors are used for heating, ventilation, and air-conditioning (HVAC) system shutdown or damper actuation. Because the fire causing activation may be located far from the detector location, rapid identification of the individual activated detector is critical. The location of the remote alarm or supervisory indication must be acceptable to the authority having jurisdiction.

17.5 Requirements for Smoke and Heat Detectors

Because both heat detectors and smoke detectors rely on the fire plume and the ceiling jet, many requirements are equally applicable to both heat and smoke detectors. These requirements are grouped together in Section 17.5.

17.5.1 Recessed Mounting.

Unless tested and listed for recessed mounting, detectors shall not be recessed into the mounting surface.

Both heat and smoke detectors rely on the flow of the ceiling jet to convey the heat and smoke, respectively, to the detector. Recessing smoke and heat detectors that are not tested and listed for recessed mounting would locate the detector out of the prevailing flow of the ceiling jet and hence would have an adverse effect on the ability of the detector to perform as intended.

A heat detector must absorb heat from the hot gases of the ceiling jet, as shown in Exhibit 17.1, before it can respond. Approximately 92 percent to 98 percent of the heat that a heat detector receives is carried to the detector in the hot air and combustion product gases of the ceiling jet that are created by the fire. This process is called *convection* or *convective heat transfer*. Note that the velocity, temperature, and smoke concentration are not uniform across the thickness of the ceiling jet. At the surface of the ceiling, the ceiling jet moves more slowly due to frictional losses and is slightly cooler due to heat transfer to the ceiling. A heat detector that is recessed is removed from the flow of air; consequently, the quantity of heat it receives per unit of time is reduced. The heat detector's response slows, allowing the fire to grow larger before it is detected. A heat detector also receives a small percentage of radiated heat. If the detector is recessed, less of this radiated heat energy can strike the detector. Consequently, if heat detectors are installed recessed into the ceiling, contrary to the Code, the system will likely respond more slowly, if at all, than if the heat detectors are mounted as required by the Code.

The effect is the same with smoke detectors. Smoke detectors depend on air movement to convey smoke from the fire to the detector. Usually this air movement is the ceiling jet produced by the fire. Smoke detectors are typically mounted on the ceiling to take advantage of fire plume dynamics and the ceiling jet. However, because of frictional energy loss between the ceiling jet and the ceiling surface, a very thin layer of air immediately beneath the ceiling surface is flowing more slowly than the layer a little farther down. The force that pushes the smoke into the sensing chamber is a function of the ceiling jet velocity. If the velocity at the detector is low, smoke moves into the detector slowly. If a smoke detector is recessed, this more slowly moving air immediately beneath the ceiling surface is the only flow impinging upon the detector. Because a recessed detector is in a no-flow or low-flow location, relative to the ceiling jet, it will be very slow to respond — if it responds at all — compared with the same detector mounted on the ceiling surface.

17.5.2* Partitions. Where partitions extend to within 15 percent of the ceiling height, the spaces separated by the partitions shall be considered as separate rooms.

Research on fire plumes and ceiling jets indicates that the thickness of the ceiling jet under most conditions is approximately 10 percent of the distance from the floor to the ceiling in the fire compartment. Refer to Exhibit 17.6. Keep in mind that the ceiling jet does not have an abrupt boundary. The ceiling jet velocity varies with the distance from the ceiling, and the 10 percent depth criterion is the depth above which the majority of the flow occurs. Some flow exists below the upper 10 percent of the floor-to-ceiling height. Once the ceiling jet collides with the walls of the compartment, it forms an "upper layer." This layer will increase in thickness as the fire grows. However, during the time period in which a fire alarm system should respond, the 10 percent ceiling jet thickness is generally valid.

◄ **FAQ**
What is the reason for the value of 15 percent when considering the effect of partitions?

EXHIBIT 17.6 *Partitions Extending Higher Than 85 Percent of the Floor-to-Ceiling Height, Necessitating the Addition of Detectors for Each Partitioned-Off Area. (Source: J. M. Cholin Consultants, Inc., Oakland, NJ)*

The technical committee increased the 10-percent number by 50 percent to provide for a margin of safety and to address the fact that the ceiling jet does not have an abrupt lower boundary. This results in a clearance criterion of 15 percent of the floor-to-ceiling height. Partitions that are more than 85 percent of the floor-to-ceiling height are expected to interfere with the natural flow of the ceiling jet and retard detector response.

In the case of a fire with an established plume, the plume jet is the dominant air mover and produces a ceiling jet. The objective is to ensure that the partition does not interfere with the smoke travel across the ceiling to the detector location.

In the case of a small, low-energy fire, whether the partition affects detection system response depends entirely on the extent to which the partitions impede the flow of smoke entrained in the normal air currents.

The treatment of partitions in the Code is very different from the treatment of partitions in NFPA 13, where the principal concern is the discharge pattern of the sprinkler head and the impact of the partition on that discharge pattern and, thus, on the control of the fire.

A.17.5.2 This requirement is based on the generally accepted principle that the ceiling jet is approximately 10 percent of the distance from the base of the fire to the ceiling. To this figure, an additional safety factor of 50 percent has been added. Performance-based methods are available to predict the impact of partitions on the flow of smoke to detectors and can be used to substantiate a less restrictive design criterion.

17.5.3* Detector Coverage.

A.17.5.3 The requirement of 17.5.3 recognizes that there are several different types of detector coverage.

For years, locally adopted codes have required smoke detection in specific parts of the building but not necessarily in all compartments, as sound fire protection engineering usually dictates. Subsection 17.5.3 describes different detection coverage concepts, allowing the designer alternatives for the application under consideration. The extent of detection coverage is generally related to the tacit performance expectations in the relevant building code. These tacit performance expectations can be inferred from the prescribed coverage requirements based on the occupancy.

Where the locally adopted code is not specific about the type and extent of the automatic detection coverage required, the owner and the designer should consult with the local authority having jurisdiction and establish the type and extent of coverage to be provided. The type of coverage established for the system must be documented as a part of the Fire Alarm System Record of Completion, Figure 10.18.2.1.1.

The designer should consider that whenever a fire is ignited in a building compartment that is not equipped with detection, the smoke and/or heat must travel a longer distance before it impinges upon a detector that can initiate an alarm signal. This scenario usually results in a substantial — and often critical — delay in the detection of the fire. This delay allows the fire time to grow much larger before detection than would have been the case if detection were installed in the compartment of fire origin.

This Code is silent as to the type of detection (heat, smoke, flame, etc.) required for any specific type of occupancy. The relevant building code or the performance objectives of the owner establish the type and extent of required coverage. If the governing, adopted building code does not dictate the type of detection or its required coverage, then the designer should develop the detection strategy (type of detection and spacing) based on the loss control objectives of the owner.

17.5.3.1 Total (Complete) Coverage. Where required by laws, codes, or standards, and unless otherwise modified by 17.5.3.1.1 through 17.5.3.1.5, total coverage shall include all rooms, halls, storage areas, basements, attics, lofts, spaces above suspended ceilings, and other subdivisions and accessible spaces, as well as the inside of all closets, elevator shafts, enclosed stairways, dumbwaiter shafts, and chutes.

FAQ ▶
What does "total coverage" mean?

The concept of total, or complete, detector coverage is effectively defined by 17.5.3.1. Total coverage means that detectors are installed in all accessible compartments or spaces. The underlying premise is that if an enclosed compartment is accessible, it might be used to store combustible materials. The requirement set forth in 17.5.3.1 is parallel to that of Section 4.1 of NFPA 13, as follows:

> **4.1 Level of Protection.** A building, where protected by an automatic sprinkler system installation, shall be provided with sprinklers in all areas except where specific sections of this standard permit the omission of sprinklers. [**13**:4.1]

17.5.3.1.1 Where inaccessible areas are constructed of or contain combustible material, unless otherwise specified in 17.5.3.1.2, they shall be made accessible and shall be protected by a detector(s).

Under the concept of total coverage, detectors must be located in all compartments. An inaccessible compartment that contains combustible material is a potential fire location and must be equipped with detection if total coverage is to be provided. Since all detectors must be accessible, the inaccessible compartment that contains combustible materials must be made accessible.

17.5.3.1.2 Detectors shall not be required in combustible blind spaces if any of the following conditions exist:

(1) Where the ceiling is attached directly to the underside of the supporting beams of a combustible roof or floor deck
(2) Where the concealed space is entirely filled with a noncombustible insulation (In solid joist construction, the insulation shall be required to fill only the space from the ceiling to the bottom edge of the joist of the roof or floor deck.)
(3) Where there are small concealed spaces over rooms, provided that any space in question does not exceed 50 ft^2 (4.6 m^2) in area
(4) In spaces formed by sets of facing studs or solid joists in walls, floors, or ceilings, where the distance between the facing studs or solid joists is less than 6 in. (150 mm)

Combustible blind spaces include a number of boxed-in spaces that are common in stud-wall, curtain-wall, and frame construction. These spaces are in place as a result of construction or where renovations have created void spaces with no access, thus preventing the storage of combustible materials. Furthermore, if a space is inaccessible, the probability of ignition becomes extremely remote. Consequently, 17.5.3.1.2 excludes these specific spaces from the total coverage requirement.

17.5.3.1.3 Detectors shall not be required below open grid ceilings if all of the following conditions exist:

(1) Openings of the grid are $\frac{1}{4}$ in. (6.4 mm) or larger in the least dimension.
(2) Thickness of the material does not exceed the least dimension.
(3) Openings constitute at least 70 percent of the area of the ceiling material.

All three of the criteria must be met for a compartment or room with an open grid ceiling to qualify for an exemption for detectors under the concept of total coverage. Where true open grid ceilings complying with the criteria of 17.5.3.1.3 exist, the ceiling does not represent a significant barrier to the movement of smoke and fire gases. In most facilities with suspended ceilings, the grid is not sufficiently open to permit smoke to travel through the grid, and the compartment does not comply with the criteria of 17.5.3.1.3. Furthermore, the above-ceiling space often contains combustibles, resulting in the need for detection both above and beneath the ceiling plane where total coverage is required.

17.5.3.1.4 Detectors shall not be required in concealed, accessible spaces above suspended ceilings that are used as a return air plenum meeting the requirements of NFPA 90A, *Standard for the Installation of Air-Conditioning and Ventilating Systems*, where equipped with smoke detection at each connection from the plenum to the central air-handling system.

Paragraph 17.5.3.1.4 addresses above-ceiling spaces used, as defined in *NFPA 70*, as "other space used for environmental air." Where these above-ceiling, return air spaces meet the requirements of NFPA 90A, *Standard for the Installation of Air-Conditioning and Ventilating Systems*, and are equipped with smoke detection at each connection to the central air-handling system, then 17.5.3.1.4 waives the requirement for detectors throughout the above-ceiling space. The relevant sections of NFPA 90A limit the types and quantities of combustible materials that can be included within the above-ceiling return air space. This exemption relies on the construction limitations and the limitations on combustibles imposed by NFPA 90A.

Detectors in the above-ceiling space do *not* supplant detectors installed on the compartment ceiling for general area protection. Consequently, area detection at the ceiling plane is still required.

17.5.3.1.5 Detectors shall not be required underneath open loading docks or platforms and their covers and for accessible under-floor spaces if all of the following conditions exist:

(1) Space is not accessible for storage purposes or entrance of unauthorized persons and is protected against the accumulation of windborne debris.
(2) Space contains no equipment such as steam pipes, electric wiring, shafting, or conveyors.
(3) Floor over the space is tight.
(4) No flammable liquids are processed, handled, or stored on the floor above.

All the criteria enumerated in 17.5.3.1.5 must exist if detectors are to be omitted from underneath open loading docks or platforms where total coverage is to be provided for a facility.

17.5.3.2* Partial or Selective Coverage. Where codes, standards, or laws require the protection of selected areas only, the specified areas shall be protected in accordance with this Code.

A.17.5.3.2 If there are no detectors in the room or area of fire origin, the fire could exceed the design objectives before being detected by remotely located detectors. When coverage other than total coverage is required, partial coverage can be provided in common areas and work spaces such as corridors, lobbies, storage rooms, equipment rooms, and other tenantless spaces. The intent of selective coverage is to address a specific hazard only.

Where a specific area is to be protected, all points within that area should be within 0.7 × the adjusted detector spacing for spot-type detectors as required by 17.6.3 and 17.7.3.2. Note that an area does not necessarily mean an entire room. It is possible to provide properly spaced detectors to provide detection for only part of a room. Similarly, the Code permits protection of a specific hazard. In that case, detectors within a radius of 0.7 × the adjusted detector spacing from the hazard provide the required detection. An example of protection of specific risk is the smoke detector required by Section 21.3 to be within 21 ft (6.4 m) of an elevator, where elevator recall is required.

It should also be noted that fire detection by itself is not fire protection. Also, protection goals could be such that detection being provided for a specific area or hazard might require a form of total coverage for that particular area or hazard. That is, it might be necessary to provide detectors above suspended ceilings or in small closets and other ancillary spaces that are a part of, or an exposure to, the area or hazard being protected.

FAQ ▶
What is meant by the terms
partial coverage and *selective
coverage?*

Many locally adopted building codes require an automatic fire alarm system in all corridors, foyers, common spaces, mechanical equipment rooms, and other tenantless spaces. Where the building code itemizes the portions of a building required to be equipped with smoke detection, it is effectively establishing a requirement for partial coverage. Selective coverage is intended to address only a specific hazard.

Partial or selective coverage allows for the protection of the selected compartments or areas without requiring additional detection in other compartments or areas of the building. However, the detectors used for this coverage must be installed in the selected compartments or areas in conformance with the appropriate prescriptive spacing and location criteria in the Code. If the prescriptive criteria in the Code results in an excessive equipment burden, performance-based design methods can be used to tailor the detection system design to a specific performance objective.

The building owner or operator must keep in mind that although partial or selective coverage might fulfill a minimum compliance requirement, it does not necessarily provide sound fire protection, and careful consideration should be given to the logic of placing detection in only part of the building. A fire alarm system cannot be expected to detect a fire in a timely manner if detectors are not in the compartment of fire origin. Building codes often require smoke detectors in a corridor without requiring detection within the rooms served by that corridor. The tacit objective served by that requirement is to notify building occupants that the tenability of the route to the means of egress is being compromised by smoke. The detectors are *not* there to detect fires in the rooms served by the corridor. Where smoke detectors are required in a corridor but not in the rooms served by that corridor, a substantial delay is to be expected in detecting a fire that has been ignited in one of the rooms, especially if the door to the room or compartment of fire origin is closed when the fire is ignited. When a fire is ignited in a building compartment that is not equipped with detection, it will grow undetected until it becomes sufficiently large to pressurize the compartment and force smoke out past the closed door into an adjoining compartment that is equipped with detectors. Such a scenario can result in a substantial delay in warning occupants and initiating response to the fire. Doors, ceiling irregularities, ventilation supplies and returns, and distance all retard the flow of smoke and heat toward a building compartment equipped with detection. The resulting delays in response have been critical in some fires. In addition, where selective coverage is provided only for a specific hazard, it will provide little protection for personnel or assets outside the room, compartment, or immediate vicinity of the detectors, depending on the circumstances.

As further concern, where any detection coverage other than total or complete is used in a system design, the designer should be aware that the interconnecting wiring between the devices, appliances, and the fire alarm control unit will often pass through unprotected areas of the building. The designer should consider the potential for thermal impact of a fire on the detection system wiring prior to the initiation of a fire alarm signal. The designer should consider protecting the fire alarm system wiring in those areas through which fire alarm system wiring passes. Generally, installation in a 2-hour-rated enclosure or using 2-hour-rated circuit integrity cable is deemed sufficient for most hazard areas.

17.5.3.3* Nonrequired Coverage.

The term *nonrequired* is not the same as the terms *supplementary* or *selective*. Refer to the definitions of *nonrequired* and *supplementary* found in 3.3.158 and 3.3.272 along with their associated commentary.

The subparagraphs of 17.5.3.3 address the circumstances in which a need exists for fire detection to serve purposes or achieve objectives not established by a locally adopted, minimum-compliance building or fire code. Often a user has specific fire protection goals or objectives that can be achieved only by using automatic fire detection. For example, a building operator might have a mission continuity objective and intends to use a special extinguishing system, actuated by automatic detection, to achieve that objective. Such a system is a nonrequired system because it would be installed at the option of the owner or operator and not because of a building or fire code requirement.

The language of 17.5.3.3 subparagraphs provides the necessary latitude in design for systems that are being installed to meet an objective other than the minimum requirements for property protection and life safety provided in the local building code. Although the requirements in 17.5.3.3.1 and 17.5.3.3.2 are specified in prescriptive terms, designs for some objectives may be best achieved through the use of the performance-based design option in this chapter. The process of performance-based design involves a documented formal analysis that serves as the basis for design decisions. This process is outlined in Supplement 1 and in Annex B.

A.17.5.3.3 The requirement of 17.5.3.3 recognizes there will be instances where, for example, a facility owner would want to apply detection to meet certain performance goals and to address a particular hazard or need, but that detection is not required. Once installed, of course, acceptance testing, annual testing, and ongoing maintenance in accordance with this Code is expected. The intent of this section is to allow the use of a single detector, or multiple detectors provided for specific protection, with spacing to meet specific fire safety objectives as determined in accordance with 17.6.1.1 and 17.7.1.1.

Where the building owner elects to install fire detection systems or components that are not required by the relevant building codes, the systems still must be installed in accordance with the minimum-compliance criteria of this Code. Designers would be well advised to consider the additional concerns addressed in the commentary following A.17.5.3.2.

17.5.3.3.1 Detection installed for reasons of achieving specific fire safety objectives, but not required by any laws, codes, or standards, shall meet all of the requirements of this Code, with the exception of the prescriptive spacing criteria of Chapter 17.

FAQ ▶
What requirements apply to installations of nonrequired coverage?

Even where detection is not required by some applicable law, code, or standard, 17.5.3.3.1 requires that detection must still comply with all the requirements of *NFPA 72,* including the specific detector location, installation, operation, and maintenance requirements for the type of detector being used. The technical committee adopted this requirement to help ensure that purchasers of nonrequired systems receive systems that work. Decades of experience in fire alarm system design, installation, and maintenance have demonstrated that compliance with the criteria in this Code results in systems that have a high probability of providing consistent, reliable service. The exception in 17.5.3.3.1 permits the use of detector spacing that is different from the spacing specified in the prescriptive sections of this Code. This exception was adopted because with some system objectives, using detection at the spacings found elsewhere in this Code is not necessary in order to attain the performance intended for the nonrequired system.

Whenever any system is designed, 17.6.1.1, 17.7.1.1, 17.8.1.1, and 17.8.3.3.2 require that the objectives for that system be stipulated in the design documentation. Consequently, these sections apply to nonrequired systems. Although the exception in 17.5.3.3.1 exempts nonrequired detection from the prescriptive spacing rules of Chapter 17, the spacing selected must still be substantiated in the design documentation to show that design objectives for the system will be satisfied when the detectors are selected and installed on the spacing selected.

17.5.3.3.2 Where nonrequired detectors are installed for achieving specific fire safety objectives, additional detectors not necessary to achieve the objectives shall not be required.

The concept of nonrequired coverage addresses situations such as the possible placement of detection to protect a valuable asset in one portion of a much larger compartment where complete coverage is not required or desired. Generally, the objective is to attain an early warning of a fire involving that valuable asset but not necessarily some other portion of the compartment. Under these circumstances, providing detection for the portion of the compartment where the asset is actually located, rather than throughout the entire compartment or building, might be sufficient. Exhibits 17.7 and 17.8 represent special application detection devices.

17.6 Heat-Sensing Fire Detectors

Heat-sensing fire detectors are addressed in Section 17.6. The relationship between heat and temperature must be understood if heat-sensing detectors are to be applied properly. Heat is energy and is quantified in terms of an amount usually measured in British thermal units (Btu) or joules (J). Temperature is a measure of the quantity of heat in a given mass of material and is measured as an intensity, quantified in terms of degrees Fahrenheit or Celsius.

The majority of the heat flowing into or absorbed by a heat detector is from the hot gases that make up the ceiling jet. This process is called *convective heat transfer*. A much smaller portion of the heat absorbed by a heat detector is transferred by radiation, which is a process called *radiant heat transfer*. Heat detectors operate on one or more of three different principles. These operating principles are categorized as fixed temperature, rate compensation, and rate-of-rise. Most heat detectors are devices that change in some way when the temperature

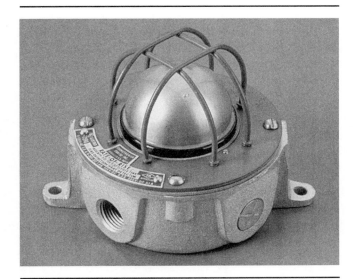

EXHIBIT 17.7 *Explosionproof Spot-Type Heat Detector. (Source: Kidde-Fenwal, Ashland, MA)*

EXHIBIT 17.8 *Typical Line-Type Heat Detector Installed in Cable Tray Applications. (Source: The Protectowire Co., Inc., Plymouth, MA)*

at the detector achieves a particular level or a set point. These detectors are classified as *fixed-temperature* heat detectors. Another type of detector adjusts its set point temperature in response to the rate of increase in the temperature. These heat detectors are classified as *rate compensation* heat detectors. Other detectors respond to the rate of temperature change and are classified as *rate-of-rise* heat detectors. Each principle has its performance advantages and can be used in either a *spot-type device* or a *line-type device*, which are two general types of heat detectors. Spot-type devices occupy a specific spot or point, while line-type devices are linear and extend over a distance, sensing temperature along their entire length.

A number of different technologies can be used to detect the heat from a fire, including the following:

1. Expanding bimetallic components
2. Eutectic solders
3. Eutectic salts
4. Melting insulators
5. Thermistors
6. Temperature-sensitive semiconductors
7. Expanding air volume
8. Expanding liquid volume
9. Temperature-sensitive resistors
10. Thermopiles

The Code has been written to allow the development and use of new technologies. The designer must be careful not to confuse the terms *type* and *principle* with *technology*, which is the method used to achieve heat detection.

See Exhibits 17.9 through 17.16 for examples of typical heat detectors. A precise definition and explanation of the mode of operation for each type of heat detector can be found in 3.3.59.

EXHIBIT 17.9 *Electronic Spot-Type Heat Detector. (Source: System Sensor Corp., St. Charles, IL)*

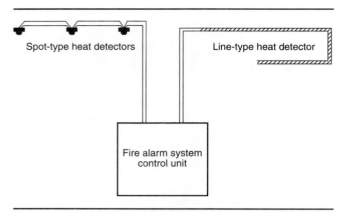

EXHIBIT 17.10 *Two Types of Heat Detectors: Spot-Type and Line-Type. (Source: J. M. Cholin Consultants, Inc., Oakland, NJ)*

EXHIBIT 17.11 *"Low-Profile" Rate-of-Rise and Fixed-Temperature Heat Detectors. (Source: Top, GE Security, Bradenton, FL. Bottom, Kidde-Fenwal, Ashland, MA; photo courtesy of Mammoth Fire Alarms, Inc., Lowell, MA)*

EXHIBIT 17.12 *Spot-Type Fixed-Temperature Heat Detector. (Source: Kidde-Fenwal, Ashland, MA; photo courtesy of Mammoth Fire Alarms, Inc., Lowell, MA)*

17.6.1 General.

17.6.1.1* The heat detection design documentation shall state the required performance objective of the system.

A.17.6.1.1 The performance objective statement should describe the purpose of the detector placement and the intended response of the fire alarm control unit to the detector activation. This statement can include a narrative description of the required response time of the detectors, a narrative of the sequence of operations, a tabular list of programming requirements or some other method.

The performance objective of a fire detection system is usually expressed in terms of time and the size fire the system is intended to detect, measured in British thermal units per second (Btu/sec) or kilowatts (kW). Typically, the fire alarm system designer does not establish this criterion. It is usually obtained from the design documentation prepared by the designer responsible for the strategy of the structure as a whole. Where a prescriptive design is being provided, this requirement is fulfilled by stating in the design documentation that the design conforms to the prescriptive provisions of this Code.

FAQ ▶
When is design documentation required to include a statement of the performance objective of the system?

With the increasingly widespread acceptance of performance-based design, the Code incorporates a performance-based design alternative for the design of fire detection systems using heat detectors. The designer is afforded two alternative routes in the design process. One route is the prescriptive process, in which the designer follows the prescribed spacing and location criteria provided in the Code. The second route is to use the performance-based design methods that are outlined in Annex B. In either case, 17.6.1.1 requires the performance objective of the system to be stated in the heat detection design documentation.

17.6.1.2 Designs not in accordance with 17.6.1.3 shall be deemed prescriptive designs and shall be designed in accordance with the prescriptive requirements of this chapter.

17.6.1.3* Performance-based designs shall be executed in accordance with Section 17.3.

EXHIBIT 17.13 *Line-Type Heat Detector. (Source: The Protectowire Co., Inc., Plymouth, MA)*

EXHIBIT 17.14 *Rate Compensation Heat Detector — Horizontal Mounting. (Source: Kidde-Fenwal, Ashland, MA)*

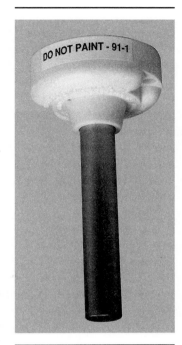

EXHIBIT 17.15 *Rate Compensation Heat Detector — Vertical Mounting. (Source: Thermotech Inc., Ogden, UT; photo courtesy of Mammoth Fire Alarms, Inc., Lowell, MA)*

A.17.6.1.3 In a performance-based design environment, the performance objectives for the fire alarm system are not established by the fire alarm system designer.

A fire protection strategy is developed to achieve those goals. General performance objectives are developed for the facility. These general objectives give rise to specific performance objectives for each fire protection system being employed in the facility. Consequently, the performance objectives and criteria for the fire alarm system are part of a much larger strategy that often relies on other fire protection features, working in concert with the fire alarm system to attain the overall fire protection goals for the facility.

In the performance-based design environment, the designer uses computational models to demonstrate that the spacing used for automatic fire detectors connected to the fire alarm system will achieve the objectives established by the system, by showing that the system meets the performance criteria established for the system in the design documentation. Consequently, it is imperative that the design objectives and performance criteria to which the system has been designed are clearly stated in the system documentation.

Performance-based design as described in A.17.6.1.1 and A.17.6.1.3 is a holistic process that leads to a design from a starting point of stated, agreed-upon, quantified objectives. In most cases concerning fire detection system design, the objective is to detect a fire of a specified size, assuming a growing fire. Supplement 1 and Annex B provide an overview of the process and the methods employed in that process.

17.6.1.4* Spot-type heat detectors shall include in their installation instructions, technical data, and listing documentation the operating temperature and response time index (RTI) as determined by the organization listing the device.

A.17.6.1.4 In order to predict the response of a heat detector using current fire modeling programs and currently published equations describing plume dynamics, two parameters must be known: operating temperature and response time index (RTI). The RTI is the quantification of the rate of heat transfer from the ceiling jet to the detector sensing element per unit of time, expressed as a function of ceiling jet temperature, ceiling jet velocity, and time. Spot-type heat detectors manufactured prior to July 1, 2008, were not required to be marked with an RTI.

Two performance parameters must be quantified in order to predict the operation of a heat detector for a fire scenario in a given compartment or building environment: set-point temperature and response time index (RTI). These two operating parameters are the result of the physical design of the detector.

EXHIBIT 17.16 *Spot-Type Combination Rate-of-Rise and Fixed-Temperature Heat Detector. (Source: Kidde-Fenwal, Ashland, MA; photo courtesy of Mammoth Fire Alarms, Inc., Lowell, MA)*

Set-point temperature is well understood. It is the temperature at which the detector is designed to operate. RTI is a measure of the speed of response of the detector and is quantified during the listing evaluation.

17.6.2 Temperature.

In general, where a heat detector with a lower operating temperature is used, the system will produce a faster response to a fire. However, when the detector operating temperature is too close to the maximum ambient temperature, the probability of an unwarranted alarm increases. The prudent designer makes certain that the heat detector operating temperature stipulated is consistent with the criteria in Table 17.6.2.1.

17.6.2.1 Classification. Heat-sensing fire detectors of the fixed-temperature or rate-compensated, spot type shall be classified as to the temperature of operation in accordance with Table 17.6.2.1.

TABLE 17.6.2.1 *Temperature Classification and Color Code for Heat-Sensing Fire Detectors*

Temperature Classification	Temperature Rating Range		Maximum Ceiling Temperature		Color Code
	°F	°C	°F	°C	
Low*	100–134	39–57	80	28	Uncolored
Ordinary	135–174	58–79	115	47	Uncolored
Intermediate	175–249	80–121	155	69	White
High	250–324	122–162	230	111	Blue
Extra high	325–399	163–204	305	152	Red
Very extra high	400–499	205–259	380	194	Green
Ultra high	500–575	260–302	480	249	Orange

*Intended only for installation in controlled ambient areas. Units shall be marked to indicate maximum ambient installation temperature.

FAQ ▶
What two factors must be considered in the selection of a heat detector temperature classification?

Spot-type heat detectors are currently the most widely used type of heat detector for general purpose use. Paragraph 17.6.2.1 requires these detectors to be classified as to the temperature of operation. Table 17.6.2.1 presents specific criteria for the nominal temperature classification versus the maximum expected normal temperature for the location of the detector. Both Table 17.6.2.1 and 17.6.2.3 require that the designer select a detector temperature classification that provides at least a 20°F (11°C) difference between the temperature classification of the detector and the maximum expected normal ceiling temperature. This requirement is in place to minimize the likelihood of unwarranted responses to normal fluctuations in the ambient environment where the detector is installed. Also, the detector selected should not have a detector temperature classification higher than necessary. This decision is crucial because the higher the temperature classification, the longer the detector will take to initiate an alarm — a larger fire will be needed to produce the higher temperatures at the detector location. Consequently, the designer must consider both the detector operating temperature and the extremes in the ambient temperature during the design process.

The color code for heat detectors is very similar to that used for sprinkler heads, as described in NFPA 13. Manufacturers also provide this information in their data sheets for each type of heat detector.

17.6.2.2 Marking.

17.6.2.2.1 Color Coding.

17.6.2.2.1.1 Heat-sensing fire detectors of the fixed-temperature or rate-compensated, spot type shall be marked with a color code in accordance with Table 17.6.2.1.

17.6.2.2.1.2 If the overall color of a heat-sensing fire detector is the same as the color code marking required for that detector, one of the following arrangements, applied in a contrasting color and visible after installation, shall be employed:

(1) Ring on the surface of the detector
(2) Temperature rating in numerals at least $\frac{3}{8}$ in. (9.5 mm) high

Not all heat detector manufacturers use a color code. Some manufacturers simply provide a label on the side or bottom of the detector. Using the unified color coding of heat detectors facilitates inspections because it allows a person standing on the floor to identify the temperature rating of a ceiling-mounted heat detector.

See Exhibits 17.17 and 17.18 for examples of heat detector marking.

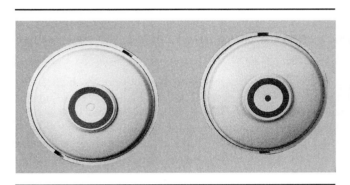

EXHIBIT 17.17 *Heat Detectors with Color-Coded Rings. (Source: Kidde-Fenwal, Ashland, MA; photo courtesy of Mammoth Fire Alarms, Inc., Lowell, MA)*

EXHIBIT 17.18 *Heat Detector Temperature Marked with Numerals. (Source: GE Security, Bradenton, FL; photo courtesy of Mammoth Fire Alarms, Inc., Lowell, MA)*

17.6.2.2.2 Operating Temperature.

17.6.2.2.2.1 Heat-sensing fire detectors shall be marked with their listed operating temperature.

17.6.2.2.2.2 Heat-sensing fire detectors where the alarm threshold is field adjustable shall be marked with the temperature range.

The commercial availability of solid-state thermal sensors and analog/addressable fire alarm system control units has made the development of analog/addressable heat detectors possible. These detectors permit the designer to adjust the alarm threshold temperature at the fire alarm control unit and select a unique threshold temperature based on an analysis of the compartment and the fire hazard. A color code would be meaningless for this technology and, consequently, is waived. Clearly, where analog/addressable technology is used, an alternative means for facilitating inspection should be in place.

17.6.2.2.2.3 Spot-type heat detectors shall also be marked with their RTI.

RTI is a measure of the speed with which heat can flow into the detector and raise the temperature of the heat-sensing component. RTI can be thought of as a measure of the sensitivity of the heat-sensing element responding to rising temperature. Commercially available heat detectors generally exhibit RTIs with values less than 100, with 10 indicating a more rapid response than 100. The response time of a heat detector to a given fire in a given compartment can be predicted if and only if both the operating temperature and the RTI are known. The computational method for predicting heat detector response is outlined in Annex B with design examples provided in B.3.3. RTI is measured in units of $(m \cdot sec)^{1/2}$ — the computational method that uses RTI requires that only SI units be employed. The only method for determining RTI is the "plunge test" as outlined in FM Approval Standard 3210, *Heat Detectors for Automatic Fire Alarm Signaling*.

The reader should note that small differences in the numerical value of RTI suggest only small differences in response time. No basis exists for a conclusion that a heat detector with an RTI of 15 is significantly faster than one with a published RTI of 16. However, a heat detector with an RTI of 5 will respond substantially faster than one with an RTI of 50, if all other factors affecting response are held constant.

While other testing laboratories are free to perform the test to quantify the RTI for a heat detector, the testing laboratory must correlate its test procedure and instrumentation so it produces a numerical value consistent with that obtained by FM Approvals using FM Approval Standard 3210. At this time, the only recognized test method that has been validated is the method outlined in and performed in accordance with FM Approval Standard 3210.

17.6.2.3* Ambient Ceiling Temperature. Detectors having fixed-temperature or rate-compensated elements shall be selected in accordance with Table 17.6.2.1 for the maximum expected ambient ceiling temperature. The temperature rating of the detector shall be at least 20°F (11°C) above the maximum expected temperature at the ceiling.

Paragraph 17.6.2.3 establishes a minimum temperature difference between the highest expected ceiling temperature and the temperature set point of the detector. The intent of this requirement is to prevent unwarranted alarms due to variations in the ambient temperature. Selecting a detector with a higher set point temperature means that the fire will have to grow larger before an alarm is achieved. Consequently, prudent design dictates that the detector should be selected that has a set point temperature that is higher than, but as close as practical to, the requirements of this section.

A.17.6.2.3 Detectors should be selected to minimize this temperature difference in order to minimize response time. However, a heat detector with a temperature rating that is somewhat in excess of the highest normally expected ambient temperature is specified in order to avoid the possibility of premature operation of the heat detector to non-fire conditions.

17.6.3 Location and Spacing.

Subsection 17.6.3 prescribes the proper location and spacing of heat detectors for general purpose, open area detection. The distance between the fire and the nearest heat detector establishes the response time of the fire detection system. The hot combustion product gases must rise to the ceiling plane and then move horizontally across the ceiling to the detector location. Detectors that are closer to the fire will give a more rapid response. Since it is usually not known where a fire will occur in the compartment, detectors are placed according to a geometric spacing with a defined "spacing" between detectors. The smaller the spacing, the more rapid the anticipated response of the system.

Another factor that governs response time is the shape of the ceiling. Smooth ceilings allow the ceiling jet gases to flow without impediment from the fire toward the detectors. Joists, beams, or other downward projecting features on the ceiling will impede the flow of the ceiling jet gases and increase the time needed for the hot gases to reach the first detector, retarding system response. Consequently, if equivalent response time is desired in such a compartment (and presumably it is), then the presence of joists and beams necessitates the reduction of the detector spacing.

17.6.3.1 Smooth Ceiling.

17.6.3.1.1* Spacing. One of the following requirements shall apply:

(1) The distance between detectors shall not exceed their listed spacing, and there shall be detectors within a distance of one-half the listed spacing, measured at right angles from all walls or partitions extending upward to within the top 15 percent of the ceiling height.
(2) All points on the ceiling shall have a detector within a distance equal to or less than 0.7 times the listed spacing (0.7S).

The number of detectors required is a function of the spacing factor, S, of the chosen detector. S is established through a series of fire tests conducted in the course of the listing evaluation by the organization listing the detector. The spacing is an approximation of the relative sensitivity of the detector.

◀ **FAQ**
What is the basis of the spacing factor, *S*, for heat detectors?

The spacing derived from the fire tests relates the response of the heat detector to the response of a specially chosen 160°F (71.1°C) automatic sprinkler head. The fire test room has a ceiling height of 15 ft, 9 in. (4.8 m) above the floor and has no airflow. The test fire is situated at the center of a square array of the test sprinkler heads, installed on 10 ft by 10 ft (3 m by 3 m) centers. This arrangement places the centerline of the test fire 7.07 ft (2.2 m) from the test sprinklers.

Heat detectors are mounted in square arrays that are centered about the test fire with progressively increased spacing. The fire is located approximately 3.0 ft (0.9 m) above the floor and consists of a number of pans of an ethanol/methanol mixture yielding an output of approximately 1138 Btu/sec (1200 kW). The height of the test fire and the fire area are adjusted to produce a time versus temperature curve at the test sprinklers that falls within the envelope established for the test and causes the activation of the test sprinkler at 2 minutes ± 10 seconds. The greatest detector spacing that produces an alarm signal before a test sprinkler actuates is the listed spacing for the heat detector.

With this method of measuring heat detector performance, heat detector response is defined relative to the distance at which it could detect the same fire that fused the test sprinkler head in 2 minutes ± 10 seconds. For example, a heat detector installed on a 50 ft by 50 ft (15.2 m by 15.2 m) array receives a 50 ft (15.2 m) listed spacing if it responds to the test fire just before the test sprinkler head operates.

It is important to keep in mind that the listed spacing for a heat detector is a "lumped" parameter, meaning that a number of unrelated variables are lumped together into a single parameter. These variables include fire size, fire growth rate, ambient temperature, ceiling height, and RTI. All these factors are lumped into a single parameter called the *listed spacing*. The listed spacing is sufficiently accurate to compare two heat detectors, but it cannot be used to predict when a given detector will respond, except in the context of the fire test in the test room under test conditions. Outside the context of the listing test, the listed spacing is only a relative indication of the detector thermal response. When using the prescriptive design rules of the Code, the designer uses a spacing based on the listed spacing of the heat detector to be used.

The number of detectors necessary for a given application also depends on the ceiling height, the type of ceiling (whether it has exposed joists or beams), and other features that may affect the flow of air or the accumulation of heat from a fire. All these factors are addressed in the spacing design rules that are provided in 17.6.3.

If a quantitative prediction of detector performance is needed either for analysis or for the basis of a design, the alternative design method in Annex B should be used. (See 17.6.1.3.) In this case, fairly precise predictions of heat detector response time can be developed using the RTI of the heat detector, its operating temperature, and the prediction calculations in Section B.3.

A.17.6.3.1.1 Maximum linear spacings on smooth ceilings for spot-type heat detectors are determined by full-scale fire tests. *[See Figure A.17.6.3.1.1(c).]* These tests assume that the detectors are to be installed in a pattern of one or more squares, each side of which equals the maximum spacing as determined in the test, as illustrated in Figure A.17.6.3.1.1(a). The detector to be tested is placed at a corner of the square so that it is positioned at the farthest possible distance from the fire while remaining within the square. Thus, the distance from the detector to the fire is always the test spacing multiplied by 0.7 and can be calculated as shown in Table A.17.6.3.1.1. Figure A.17.6.3.1.1(b) illustrates the smooth ceiling spacing layout for line-type heat detectors.

Once the correct maximum test distance has been determined, it is valid to interchange the positions of the fire and the detector. The detector is now in the middle of the square, and the listing specifies that the detector is adequate to detect a fire that occurs anywhere within that square — even out to the farthest corner.

In laying out detector installations, designers work in terms of rectangles, as building areas are generally rectangular in shape. The pattern of heat spread from a fire source, however, is not rectangular in shape. On a smooth ceiling, heat spreads out in all directions in an

TABLE A.17.6.3.1.1 *Test Spacing for Spot-Type Heat Detectors*

Test Spacing		*Maximum Test Distance from Fire to Detector (0.7D)*	
ft	*m*	*ft*	*m*
50 × 50	15.2 × 15.2	35.0	10.7
40 × 40	12.2 × 12.2	28.0	8.5
30 × 30	9.1 × 9.1	21.0	6.4
25 × 25	7.6 × 7.6	17.5	5.3
20 × 20	6.1 × 6.1	14.0	4.3
15 × 15	4.6 × 4.6	10.5	3.2

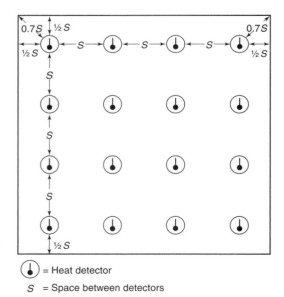

⬤ = Heat detector

S = Space between detectors

FIGURE A.17.6.3.1.1(a) *Spot-Type Heat Detectors.*

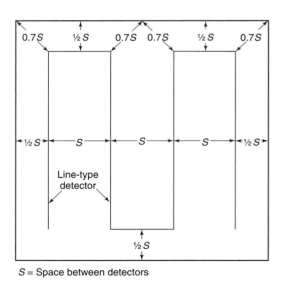

S = Space between detectors

FIGURE A.17.6.3.1.1(b) *Line-Type Detectors — Spacing Layouts, Smooth Ceiling.*

ever-expanding circle. Thus, the coverage of a detector is not, in fact, a square, but rather a circle whose radius is the linear spacing multiplied by 0.7.

This is graphically illustrated in Figure A.17.6.3.1.1(d). With the detector at the center, by rotating the square, an infinite number of squares can be laid out, the corners of which create the plot of a circle whose radius is 0.7 times the listed spacing. The detector will cover any of these squares and, consequently, any point within the confines of the circle.

So far this explanation has considered squares and circles. In practical applications, very few areas turn out to be exactly square, and circular areas are extremely rare. Designers deal generally with rectangles of odd dimensions and corners of rooms or areas formed by wall intercepts, where spacing to one wall is less than one-half the listed spacing. To simplify the rest of this explanation, the use of a detector with a listed spacing of 30 ft × 30 ft (9.1 m × 9.1 m) should be considered. The principles derived are equally applicable to other types.

Figure A.17.6.3.1.1(g) illustrates the derivation of this concept. In Figure A.17.6.3.1.1(g), a detector is placed in the center of a circle with a radius of 21 ft (0.7 × 30 ft) [6.4 m (0.7 × 9.1 m)]. A series of rectangles with one dimension less than the permitted maximum of 30 ft (9.1 m) is constructed within the circle. The following conclusions can be drawn:

(1) As the smaller dimension decreases, the longer dimension can be increased beyond the linear maximum spacing of the detector with no loss in detection efficiency.

(2) A single detector covers any area that fits within the circle. For a rectangle, a single, properly located detector may be permitted, provided the diagonal of the rectangle does not exceed the diameter of the circle.

(3) Relative detector efficiency actually is increased, because the area coverage in square meters is always less than the 900 ft² (84 m²) permitted if the full 30 ft × 30 ft (9.1 m × 9.1 m) square were to be utilized. The principle illustrated here allows equal linear spacing between the detector and the fire, with no recognition for the effect of reflection from walls or partitions, which in narrow rooms or corridors is of additional benefit. For detectors that are not centered, the longer dimension should always be used in laying out the radius of coverage.

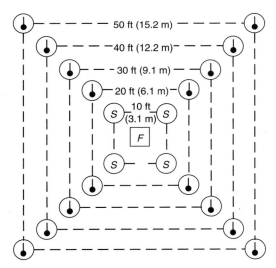

F = Test fire, denatured alcohol, 190 proof. Pan located approximately 36 in. (0.9 m) above floor.
S = Indicates normal sprinkler spacings on 10 ft (3.1 m) schedules.
= Indicates normal heat detector spacing on various spacing schedules.

FIGURE A.17.6.3.1.1(c) *Fire Test Layout.*

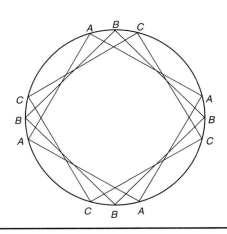

FIGURE A.17.6.3.1.1(d) *Detector Covering any Square Laid Out in the Confines of a Circle in Which the Radius Is 0.7 Times the Listed Spacing.*

Areas so large that they exceed the rectangular dimensions given in Figure A.17.6.3.1.1(g) require additional detectors. Often proper placement of detectors can be facilitated by breaking down the area into multiple rectangles of the dimensions that fit most appropriately *[see Figure A.17.6.3.1.1(e) and Figure A.17.6.3.1.1(f)]*. For example, refer to Figure A.17.6.3.1.1(h). A corridor 10 ft (3.0 m) wide and up to 82 ft (25.0 m) long can be covered with two 30 ft (9.1 m) spot-type detectors. An area 40 ft (12.2 m) wide and up to 74 ft (22.6 m) long can be covered with four spot-type detectors. Irregular areas need more careful planning to make certain that no spot on the ceiling is more than 21 ft (6.4 m) away from a detector. These points can be determined by striking arcs from the remote corner. Where any part of the area lies beyond the circle with a radius of 0.7 times the listed spacings, additional detectors are required.

Figure A.17.6.3.1.1(h) illustrates smoke or heat detector spacing layouts in irregular areas.

FAQ ▶
Why is reduced spacing required?

The spacing criteria established by 17.6.3.1.1 determine how many detectors of a given type are necessary to provide heat detection for a compartment of a given area. The designer must reduce the spacing used for design from the listed spacing to compensate for the impact that variations in the specific compartment can have on the temperature and velocity of the ceil-

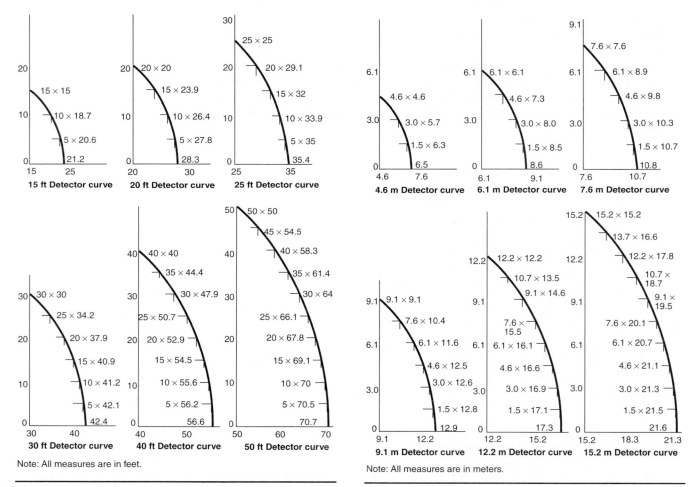

Note: All measures are in feet.

Note: All measures are in meters.

FIGURE A.17.6.3.1.1(e) *Typical Rectangles for Detector Curves of 15 ft to 50 ft.*

FIGURE A.17.6.3.1.1(f) *Typical Rectangles for Detector Curves of 4.6 m to 15.2 m.*

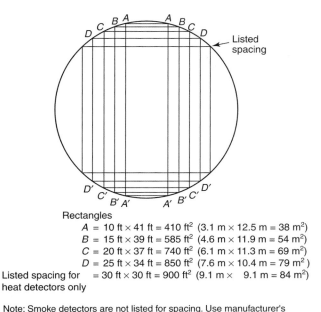

Rectangles

$A = 10\ \text{ft} \times 41\ \text{ft} = 410\ \text{ft}^2$ (3.1 m × 12.5 m = 38 m²)
$B = 15\ \text{ft} \times 39\ \text{ft} = 585\ \text{ft}^2$ (4.6 m × 11.9 m = 54 m²)
$C = 20\ \text{ft} \times 37\ \text{ft} = 740\ \text{ft}^2$ (6.1 m × 11.3 m = 69 m²)
$D = 25\ \text{ft} \times 34\ \text{ft} = 850\ \text{ft}^2$ (7.6 m × 10.4 m = 79 m²)

Listed spacing for = 30 ft × 30 ft = 900 ft² (9.1 m × 9.1 m = 84 m²)
heat detectors only

Note: Smoke detectors are not listed for spacing. Use manufacturer's coverage recommendations and this figure.

FIGURE A.17.6.3.1.1(g) Detector Spacing, Rectangular Areas.

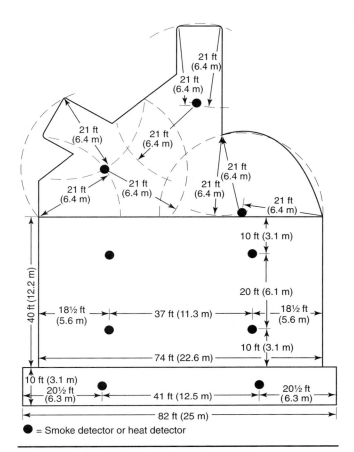

● = Smoke detector or heat detector

FIGURE A.17.6.3.1.1(h) Smoke or Heat Detector Spacing Layout in Irregular Areas.

ing jet. These spacing reductions, addressed in 17.6.3.2 through 17.6.3.5, are intended to compensate for environmental impacts on the detector performance and provide response roughly equivalent to that attainable from the same detectors installed on smooth, level ceilings 10 ft (3 m) in height using the listed spacing.

17.6.3.1.2 Irregular Areas. For irregularly shaped areas, the spacing between detectors shall be permitted to be greater than the listed spacing, provided that the maximum spacing from a detector to the farthest point of a sidewall or corner within its zone of protection is not greater than 0.7 times the listed spacing.

In Figure A.17.6.3.1.1(h), an arc having a radius of 0.7S has been drawn about each detector to verify that no point in the room is more than a distance of 0.7S from the nearest detector. If the room has an irregular shape, this method often results in detectors being located in an asymmetrical pattern.

17.6.3.1.3 Location.

17.6.3.1.3.1* Unless otherwise modified by 17.6.3.2.2, 17.6.3.3.2, or 17.6.3.7, spot-type heat-sensing fire detectors shall be located on the ceiling not less than 4 in. (100 mm) from the sidewall or on the sidewalls between 4 in. and 12 in. (100 mm and 300 mm) from the ceiling.

A.17.6.3.1.3.1 Figure A.17.6.3.1.3.1 illustrates the proper mounting placement for detectors.

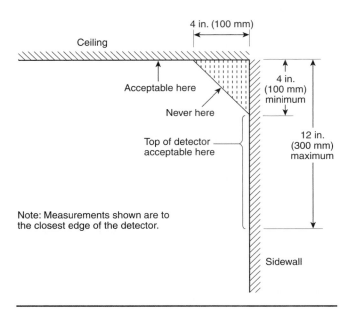

FIGURE A.17.6.3.1.3.1 *Example of Proper Mounting for Heat Detectors.*

Paragraph 17.6.3.1.3.1 applies only to spot-type heat detectors. Subsection 3.3.33 defines ceiling surfaces and the terms *solid joist construction* and *beam construction* for use in this context.

Subsection 3.3.31 defines a *ceiling* as "the upper surface of a space, regardless of height."

In compartments equipped with heat detection, spot-type heat detectors must be located on the ceiling at a distance 4 in. (100 mm) or more from a vertical side wall or on the side wall between 4 in. (100 mm) and 12 in. (300 mm) from the ceiling, measured to the top of the detector.

FAQ ▶
What is the best location for the installation of heat detectors?

The ceiling location derives the maximum benefit from the upward flow of the fire plume and the flow of the ceiling jet beneath the ceiling plane. The best currently available research data support the existence of a dead air space where the walls meet the ceiling in a typical room [Fire Protection Research Foundation, 1993]. Figure A.17.6.3.1.3.1 shows this dead air space extending 4 in. (100 mm) in from the wall and 4 in. (100 mm) down from the ceiling. Consequently, the Code excludes detectors from those areas. As the ceiling jet approaches the wall, its velocity declines. Lower ceiling jet velocities result in slower heat transfer to the detector and, therefore, a retarded response. The prudent designer will keep detectors further from the wall than the 4 in. (100 mm) minimum distance criterion established by the Code. Prudent design practice would also allow this minimum distance criterion to downward projecting obstructions such as beams.

17.6.3.1.3.2 Unless otherwise modified by 17.6.3.2.2, 17.6.3.3.2, or 17.6.3.7, line-type heat detectors shall be located on the ceiling or on the sidewalls not more than 20 in. (510 mm) from the ceiling.

Line-type heat detectors are generally considered to be equivalent to a row of spot-type detectors for the purposes of spacing and location. However, different manufacturers of line-type detection have had their products listed with different mounting techniques. The location of line-type detection must always be in conformance with the manufacturer's installation instructions. Keep in mind that attaching a line-type detector directly to and in contact with a structural building component that can absorb heat will retard response of the detector — the building component will act as a "heat sink" and retard the increase in detector temperature as a function of time.

17.6.3.2* Solid Joist Construction.

The definition of the term *joist* must be inferred from the definition, in 3.3.33.4, of *solid joist construction*. Joists are solid projections, whether structural or not, extending downward from the ceiling that are more than 4 in. (100 mm) in depth and are spaced on centers of 3.0 ft (0.9 m) or less. The commonly encountered 2 in. by 10 in. (50 mm by 250 mm) rafter installed on 16 in. (400 mm) centers supporting a roof deck is typical of solid joist construction as used in *NFPA 72*.

The structural component commonly called a *bar joist* is actually an open web beam. If the upper web member of an open web beam is less than 4 in. (100 mm) deep, the beam is ignored. If it is more than 4 in. (100 mm) deep, it is called either a joist or a beam, depending on the center-to-center spacing.

A.17.6.3.2 In addition to the special requirements for heat detectors that are installed on ceilings with exposed joists, reduced spacing also could be required due to other structural characteristics of the protected area, such as possible drafts or other conditions that could affect detector operation.

See Figure A.17.6.3.2 for an example of reduced spacing for solid joist construction.

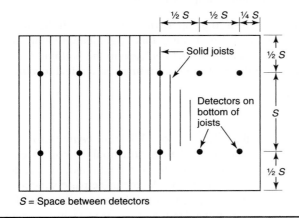

FIGURE A.17.6.3.2 Detector Spacing Layout, Solid Joist Construction.

17.6.3.2.1 Spacing. The spacing of heat detectors, where measured at right angles to the solid joists, shall not exceed 50 percent of the listed spacing.

Paragraph 17.6.3.2.1 establishes the effect of joists on detector spacing. The hot combustion product gases and smoke from a fire rise vertically in a plume until the plume impinges on the ceiling. There, the hot combustion product gases and entrained air of the fire plume change direction and move horizontally across the ceiling, becoming a ceiling jet.

Where the joists are running parallel to the direction of travel of the ceiling jet, they have little effect on the speed with which the hot gases of the ceiling jet move across the ceiling. However, where the joists are perpendicular to the direction of gas flow from the fire to the detector, they produce turbulence and thus reduce the ceiling jet velocity, as depicted in Exhibit 17.19. Consequently, a closer spacing for heat detectors in the direction perpendicular to the joists is necessary to attain uniform performance.

An important point to remember is that joists are solid members extending more than 4 in. (100 mm) down from the ceiling and are installed on centers of 3.0 ft (0.9 m) or less. If

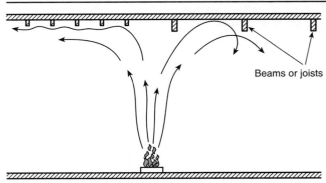

EXHIBIT 17.19 *Effect of Joists and Beams on the Ceiling Jet. (Source: J. M. Cholin Consultants, Inc., Oakland, NJ)*

Beams or joists

Joists: 3 ft (0.9 m) or less on center, more than 4 in. (100 mm) deep
Beams: More than 3 ft (0.9 m) on center, more than 4 in. (100 mm) deep

the solid members extending down from the ceiling are on centers larger than 3.0 ft (0.9 m), they are beams. Also, bar joists have no effect on spacing unless the top cord is greater than 4 in. (100 mm) deep.

17.6.3.2.2 Location. Detectors shall be mounted at the bottom of the joists.

The thickness of the ceiling jet is usually taken to be approximately one-tenth the floor-to-ceiling height. In a normal room with an 8 ft (2.4 m) ceiling, this height leads to a presumed ceiling jet thickness of 9.6 in. (244 mm). Locating a heat detector on the bottom of a 4 in. (100 mm) joist would place the detector in the center of the ceiling jet, an ideal location for undelayed response.

17.6.3.3* Beam Construction.

A definition of *beam* must be inferred from the definition, in 3.3.33.1, of *beam construction*. Beams are effectively defined as solid projections, whether structural or not, extending downward from the ceiling that are more than 4 in. (100 mm) in depth and are spaced on centers of more than 3.0 ft (0.9 m). In the context of the Code, the principal distinction between a joist and a beam is the center-to-center spacing. Unlike joists, the location of detectors in an area with beams varies depending upon the depth and center-to-center spacing of the beams.

Due to their increased depth, beams are expected to create barriers to the horizontal flow of the ceiling jet because they project more than 4 in. (100 mm) from the ceiling and are on center-to-center spacing greater than 3.0 ft (0.9 m). The bay created by the beams and the walls at either end or by the purlins (cross beams) extending from beam to beam fills up with smoke and hot combustion product gases before spilling into the next bay. This fill-and-spill progression of the ceiling jet is slower than the velocity attained on a smooth, flat ceiling.

Because the rate of heat transfer from the ceiling jet gases to the detector is proportional to the velocity of the ceiling jet flow, slower flow results in slower detector response. Consequently, for the design to attain consistent performance, the detector spacing in the direction perpendicular to the beams must be reduced to compensate for the reduced ceiling jet velocity and the reduced speed of response.

Open web beams and trusses have little effect on the passage of air currents that are caused by fire. Generally, open web beams and trusses are not considered in determining the proper spacing of detectors unless the solid part of the top cord extends more than 4 in. (100 mm) down from the ceiling.

A.17.6.3.3 The location and spacing of heat detectors should consider beam depth, ceiling height, beam spacing, and fire size.

If the ratio of beam depth (*D*) to ceiling height (*H*), (*D/H*), is greater than 0.10 and the ratio of beam spacing (*W*) to ceiling height (*H*), (*W/H*), is greater than 0.40, heat detectors should be located in each beam pocket.

If either the ratio of beam depth to ceiling height (*D/H*) is less than 0.10 or the ratio of beam spacing to ceiling height (*W/H*) is less than 0.40, heat detectors should be installed on the bottom of the beams.

The criteria included in A.17.6.3.3 make some tacit assumptions regarding the thickness of the ceiling jet under varied conditions. In general, research has shown that, to a first-order approximation, the ceiling jet can be thought of as occupying the upper 10 percent of the compartment volume [Alpert, 1972; Heskestad and Delichatsios, 1989]. If the downward extension of the beams is less than 10 percent of the ceiling height, the impact of the beams on the flow of the hot combustion product gases in the ceiling jet will be lessened, because a significant portion of the ceiling jet will pass beneath the beams.

Research also shows that as the plume rises from the fire, it expands [Heskestad, 1975; Morton, Taylor, and Turner, 1956; Schifiliti, 1986]. Generally, a first-order approximation of the plume diameter at the ceiling is 40 percent of the ceiling height (0.4 *H*). Therefore, when relatively narrow center-to-center beam spacing is encountered with a beam spacing-to-ceiling height ratio of less than 0.4, the plume will be wider than the bay formed by the beams and purlins in at least one direction when it impinges upon the ceiling.

Because more than one bay will be filling from the plume and the bays will fill rapidly, the fill part of the fill-and-spill propagation of the ceiling jet causes only a relatively short delay in time. Where the beam depths are relatively large or the bay volumes that are proportional to beam center-to-center spacing are large, the fill delay is significant and detectors must be located in each bay.

Exhibit 17.20 shows the measurements that affect the location of heat detectors where beamed ceilings are encountered.

◀ FAQ
What effects do beam spacing and depth have on detection?

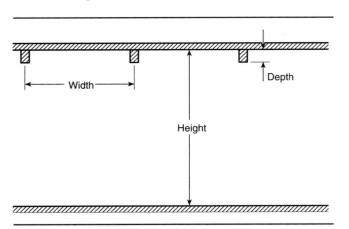

EXHIBIT 17.20 *Beam Measurements for Predicting Effects on Detection. (Source: J. M. Cholin Consultants, Inc., Oakland, NJ)*

17.6.3.3.1 Spacing.

17.6.3.3.1.1 A ceiling shall be treated as a smooth ceiling if the beams project no more than 4 in. (100 mm) below the ceiling.

Beams of depths less than 4 in. (100 mm) have insufficient effect on the overall flow of the ceiling jet to materially affect system response.

17.6.3.3.1.2 Where the beams project more than 4 in. (100 mm) below the ceiling, the spacing of spot-type heat detectors at right angles to the direction of beam travel shall be not more than two-thirds of the listed spacing.

17.6.3.3.1.3 Where the beams project more than 18 in. (460 mm) below the ceiling and are more than 96 in. (2.44 m) on center, each bay formed by the beams shall be treated as a separate area.

17.6.3.3.2 Location. Where beams are less than 12 in. (300 mm) in depth and less than 96 in. (2.44 m) on center, detectors shall be permitted to be installed on the bottom of beams.

Paragraph 17.6.3.3.2 permits the installation of heat detectors on the beam bottoms only where the beams are less than 12 in. (300 mm) deep and only where the beams are on centers of less than 96 in. (2.44 m). If the beams are more than 12 in. (300 mm) deep, they will likely project downward far enough to completely obstruct the ceiling jet. Additionally, if the beams are spaced more than 96 in. (2.44 m) apart, the volume enclosed by the bay formed by the beams will be of a sufficient size that a large quantity of ceiling jet gases must accumulate in that bay before they will spill into the adjacent bay. These two factors will retard detector response; consequently, the detectors must be placed on the ceiling surface between the beams.

Finally, the only permitted location for spot-type heat detectors is at or in close proximity to the ceiling plane, consistent with the stipulations in 17.6.3.1.3.1. Detectors are not allowed to be mounted on the bottoms of open web beams. Research is not available to provide guidance for detector placement in areas without ceilings. By inference, if the hazard area does not have a ceiling on which to locate heat detectors, heat detection cannot be installed in compliance with the prescriptive requirements of the Code.

17.6.3.4* Sloping Ceilings (Peaked and Shed).

When the fire plume impinges on a sloped ceiling, the development of the ceiling jet is affected by the slope of the ceiling. The plume is buoyant and flows upward due to the force of cooler and denser ambient air beneath. When the plume impinges upon a sloped ceiling, the buoyancy forces continue to accelerate the plume up the sloped ceiling. Furthermore, less energy is needed to turn the flow of combustion product gases and entrained air up a sloped ceiling than to turn it 90 degrees for a flat ceiling. These two effects result in the ceiling jet moving much more rapidly up a sloped ceiling and much more slowly down the slope than it would across a level ceiling. When the ceiling jet reaches the peak of the roof, its flow stops.

In the design of detection for sloped ceilings, two spacings must be applied. The first is the spacing perpendicular to the slope of the ceiling. All the detectors on this row are the same height from the floor, and the spacing is determined by the ceiling height criteria in 17.6.3.4.1.1 or 17.6.3.4.1.2, depending on the slope of the ceiling. For shallow slopes, the designer assumes the ceiling height established by the peak of the roof. For steeper slopes, the designer uses the average height to calculate the spacing.

The second spacing is in the up-slope direction. To compensate for the slope, the horizontal projection down onto the floor is used. The actual distance between the detectors will be greater as the slope gets steeper, but the buoyancy effects will also be greater, accelerating the ceiling jet up the slope.

A.17.6.3.4 Figure A.17.6.3.4(a) illustrates smoke or heat detector spacing for peaked-type sloped ceilings.

Figure A.17.6.3.4(b) illustrates smoke or heat detector spacing for shed-type sloped ceilings.

17.6.3.4.1 Spacing.

17.6.3.4.1.1 Ceiling Slope Less Than 30 Degrees. For a ceiling slope of less than 30 degrees, all detectors shall be spaced using the height at the peak.

Sloping ceilings are defined in 3.3.31.2 as ceilings that have a slope of more than 1 in 8, which means 1 in. (25.4 mm) rise (vertical) over 8 in. (200 mm) of run (horizontal). This slope corresponds to a rise-over-run ratio of 0.125, or an angle of about 7.2 degrees. Any slope less than or equal to 1 in 8 is deemed equivalent to a level ceiling.

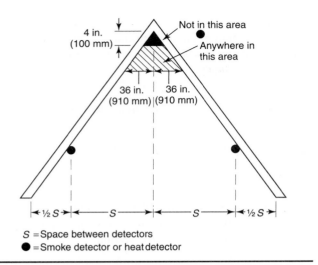

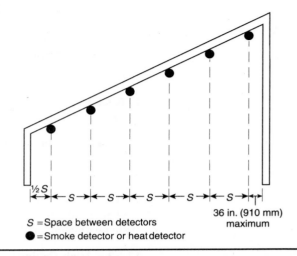

FIGURE A.17.6.3.4(a) Smoke or Heat Detector Spacing Layout, Sloped Ceilings (Peaked Type).

FIGURE A.17.6.3.4(b) Smoke or Heat Detector Spacing Layout, Sloped Ceilings (Shed Type).

Since the buoyancy of the ceiling jet gases accelerates the ceiling jet beneath a sloped ceiling, the spacing of detectors along the slope can be increased. A spacing based on the horizontal projection down from the ceiling provides a response roughly equivalent to that of a horizontal ceiling.

17.6.3.4.1.2 Ceiling Slopes of 30 Degrees or Greater. All detectors, other than those located in the peak, shall be spaced using the average slope height or the height of the peak.

Where the slope of the ceiling is 30 degrees or greater, the acceleration of the ceiling jet due to buoyancy becomes a dominant factor. Less cooling of the ceiling jet occurs as it flows up the ceiling slope. Consequently, less compensation is necessary and the average ceiling height is used for the determination of detector spacing.

17.6.3.4.1.3 Spacing shall be measured along a horizontal projection of the ceiling in accordance with the type of ceiling construction.

The acceleration of the ceiling jet up the sloped ceiling is accounted for by using the horizontal projection of the ceiling onto the floor. The horizontal projection is the cosine of the slope angle. For a ceiling slope of 30 degrees and a design spacing of 30 ft (9.1 m) (projected onto the floor), divide 30 ft (9.1 m) by cos 30° to obtain the actual distance along the ceiling between detectors:

$$\frac{30 \text{ ft } (9.1 \text{ m})}{0.866} = 34.6 \text{ ft } (10.5 \text{ m})$$

Thus, adjacent detectors will be 34.6 ft (10.5 m) apart when measured along the ceiling surface.

17.6.3.4.2 Location.

The buoyancy of the fire plume and ceiling jet affects the location of heat detectors as well as the spacing. The spacing is affected in the up/down slope direction and is adjusted for buoyancy by using the horizontal projection measurements between detectors. At the peak, the ceiling jet collides with a mass of the hottest air that normally exists beneath the ceiling. The ceiling jet usually displaces this air because the ceiling jet is usually hotter than the air at the peak of the roof. Because the volume of the roof peak area is relatively small, it rapidly fills with the hottest gas from the plume. Usually the speed of response for a heat detector is a factor of both the temperature of the ceiling jet gases and the velocity of the ceiling jet flow. The hotter the gas and the faster the flow, the more rapid the detector response. At the peak of the roof, even though the ceiling jet velocity decreases, the temperature remains high. The high temperature of the gas at the peak offsets the ceiling jet velocity decrease at the peak. Consequently, a row of spot-type detectors is required in the peak of the roof.

17.6.3.4.2.1 A row of detectors shall first be located at or within 36 in. (910 mm) of the peak of the ceiling.

17.6.3.4.2.2 Additional detectors shall be located as determined in 17.6.3.4.1.

The process of design starts with a row of detectors, spaced in accordance with 17.6.3.1, 17.6.3.2, or 17.6.3.3, as appropriate at the peak, within 36 in. (910 mm) of the ridge beam. Then additional rows of detectors are located downslope from the peak, with spacing measured across the floor in a horizontal projection from the roof, until a row of detectors is installed within one-half the design spacing of the ceiling-wall intersection.

17.6.3.5 High Ceilings.

FAQ ▶
What is the reason that detector spacing must be reduced for ceilings higher than 10 ft (3 m)?

The speed of response of a heat detector is dependent on both the temperature of the ceiling jet gas and the speed of the ceiling jet flow. The higher the gas temperature and flow velocity are, the more rapid the heat detector response. As the fire plume rises, it cools due to fresh air entrainment and volumetric expansion. As the plume cools, its buoyancy is reduced and its upward velocity decreases. These cooling and velocity loss phenomena continue after the plume turns and forms a ceiling jet. The ceiling jet entrains cool air as it moves across the ceiling. As the ceiling jet moves further from the plume centerline, its velocity decreases, as does its temperature.

In compartments with higher than normal ceilings, the plume gases undergo increased cooling due to the increased cool air entrainment and expansion as the plume travels the increased distance to the ceiling. When the plume reaches the ceiling and turns due to its momentum, it becomes a ceiling jet. In the case of a room with a high ceiling, the plume is cooler and slower, yielding a ceiling jet that is both cooler and moving at a slower initial velocity. Consequently, if all other variables are held constant, heat detectors installed on high ceilings experience cooler ceiling jet flows at lower velocities than when they are installed on lower ceilings.

One way to compensate for the cooler and slower flow of the ceiling jet at high ceiling elevations is to move the detectors closer to the fire plume centerline, where velocity and temperature will be higher. This is the basis for the reduction in heat detector spacings based on ceiling height. At high ceilings, to attain a roughly equivalent response to one obtained at normal ceiling heights, the detector spacing must be reduced.

17.6.3.5.1* On ceilings 10 ft to 30 ft (3.0 m to 9.1 m) high, heat detector spacing shall be reduced in accordance with Table 17.6.3.5.1 prior to any additional reductions for beams, joists, or slope, where applicable.

Exception: Table 17.6.3.5.1 shall not apply to the following detectors, which rely on the integration effect:

(1) Line-type electrical conductivity detectors (see 3.3.59.10)
(2) Pneumatic rate-of-rise tubing heat detectors (see 3.3.59.14)

In these cases, the manufacturer's published instructions shall be followed for appropriate alarm point and spacing.

A.17.6.3.5.1 Both 17.6.3.5.1 and Table 17.6.3.5.1 are constructed to provide detector performance on higher ceilings [to 30 ft (9.1 m) high] that is essentially equivalent to that which would exist with detectors on a 10 ft (3.0 m) ceiling.

TABLE 17.6.3.5.1 *Heat Detector Spacing Reduction Based on Ceiling Height*

Ceiling Height Above		Up to and Including		Multiply Listed Spacing by
ft	m	ft	m	
0	0	10	3.0	1.00
10	3.0	12	3.7	0.91
12	3.7	14	4.3	0.84
14	4.3	16	4.9	0.77
16	4.9	18	5.5	0.71
18	5.5	20	6.1	0.64
20	6.1	22	6.7	0.58
22	6.7	24	7.3	0.52
24	7.3	26	7.9	0.46
26	7.9	28	8.5	0.40
28	8.5	30	9.1	0.34

The Fire Detection Institute Fire Test Report *(see Annex H)* is used as a basis for Table 17.6.3.5.1. The report does not include data on integration-type detectors. Pending development of such data, the manufacturer's published instructions will provide guidance.

Table 17.6.3.5.1 provides for spacing modification to take into account different ceiling heights for generalized fire conditions. Information regarding a design method that allows the designer to take into account ceiling height, fire size, and ambient temperatures is provided in Annex B.

The spacing factor for a given detector is a rough measure of how far the ceiling jet can travel from the test fire (used in the listing evaluation) before the jet has cooled and slowed down too much to provide reliable detection in the required time period. As hot combustion product gases in the fire plume rise from the fire, the gases expand, giving off energy and cooling down. Furthermore, cool air becomes entrained into the plume, cooling it more. This process leaves less energy available to continue accelerating the plume toward the ceiling. Once the ceiling plane has been reached, the remaining plume momentum is the only force available to accelerate the ceiling jet horizontally across the ceiling.

Increased ceiling height has a significant effect on the ceiling jet temperature and velocity. The reduction of detector spacing with increased ceiling height places detectors closer to the fire plume centerline, thus allowing the hot combustion product gas, air, and radiated heat to travel a shorter distance before encountering a detector.

The inverse square law predicts that when the distance between the fire and the detector is doubled, the amount of radiated heat reaching the detector will be reduced by a factor of 4. To the extent that some contribution may be from radiant heat transfer, this factor also increases the need to reduce the detector spacing as the ceiling height is increased.

An important note is that Table 17.6.3.5.1 covers ceiling heights up to 30 ft (9.1 m). This ceiling is the highest for which the Technical Committee on Initiating Devices for Fire Alarm Systems had test data. (See references in Annex B.) Where ceilings are higher than 30 ft (9.1 m), the designer must act with the knowledge that those conditions are beyond the limits of the testing that provided the basis for the requirements of the Code. The temptation is to extrapolate for higher ceiling heights. However, a theoretical basis for doing so has yet to be reviewed by the Technical Committee on Initiating Devices for Fire Alarm Systems. The considerable research that is ongoing in this area eventually might yield important new insights.

The computational method in Annex B can be used in conjunction with performance-based design methods in accordance with 17.6.1.3 to account for ceiling height. The predicted response obtained from Annex B calculations is preferable to the predictions obtained from the table because the calculations are based on the actual RTI of the detector rather than an average.

The Code neither prohibits nor permits the use of heat detectors on ceilings higher than 30 ft (9.1 m). Computer models such as FPETool and Fire Dynamic Simulator have been used to predict detector performance at higher ceiling heights. Some studies have confirmed the predictions derived from these models. However, in the context of an exponentially growing fire, a much larger fire will be necessary to actuate the detectors on higher ceilings. The fire allowed by the delayed detection might be considerably larger than that normally assumed. In some cases, this delay will mean that the detection system will not meet the protection goals of the owner nor the intent of the Code. The final decision as to whether a design is acceptable rests with the appropriate authority having jurisdiction.

17.6.3.5.2* Spacing Minimum. The minimum spacing of heat detectors shall not be required to be less than 0.4 times the height of the ceiling.

A.17.6.3.5.2 The width of uniform temperature of the plume when it impinges on the ceiling is approximately 0.4 times the height above the fire, so reducing spacing below this level will not increase response time. For example, a detector with a listed spacing of 15 ft (4.6 m) or 225 ft² (21 m²) need not be spaced closer than 12 ft (3.7 m) on a 30 ft (9.1 m) ceiling, even though Table 17.6.3.5.1 states that the spacing should be 0.34 × 15 ft (0.34 × 4.6 m), which equals 5.1 ft (1.6 m).

Research shows that as the plume rises from the fire it expands. Generally, a first-order approximation of the plume diameter at the ceiling is 40 percent of the ceiling height (0.4 *H*), as shown in Exhibit 17.21. Consequently, no performance advantage is accrued where heat detectors are installed with spacings smaller than 40 percent of the ceiling height.

EXHIBIT 17.21 *Generally Accepted Behavior of an Unperturbed Fire Plume and Ceiling Jet. (Source: J. M. Cholin Consultants, Inc., Oakland, NJ)*

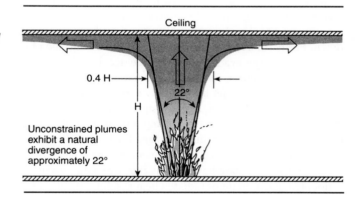

17.6.3.6* Integral Heat Sensors on Combination and Multi-Sensor Detectors. A heat-sensing detector integrally mounted on a smoke detector shall be listed for not less than 50 ft (15.2 m) spacing.

A.17.6.3.6 The linear space rating is the maximum allowable distance between heat detectors. The linear space rating is also a measure of the heat detector response time to a standard test fire where tested at the same distance. The higher the rating, the faster the response time. This Code recognizes only those heat detectors with ratings of 50 ft (15.2 m) or more.

Some commonly used smoke detectors are equipped with an integral heat sensor as mentioned in 17.6.3.6. Because the customary spacing of smoke detectors is 30 ft (9.1 m), and because smoke detectors are primarily considered to be fulfilling an early warning role, the heat detector, if deemed a necessary addition to the smoke detector, should be sufficiently sensitive to provide a response before the fire has grown to an excessive size. For the heat sensor portion of the detector to fulfill this expectation, it must have a minimum 50 ft (15.2 m) spacing factor.

See Exhibit 17.22 for an example of a combination smoke and heat detector. In this example, the entrance to the smoke-sensing chamber is shown at the center with heat-sensing thermistors located on either side.

EXHIBIT 17.22 *Smoke Detector with 50 ft (15.2 m) Listed Heat Detection. (Source: System Sensor Corp., St. Charles, IL)*

Heat sensor

17.6.3.7 Other Applications. Where a detector is used in an application other than open area protection, the manufacturer's published instructions shall be followed.

17.6.3.8 Alternative Design Methods. Annex B shall be permitted to be used as one alternative design method for determining detector spacing.

The computational method for heat detection system design presented in Annex B is based on first principles of physics and experimental correlations. This method serves as an alternative design to the prescriptive criteria in 17.6.3. Designers who elect to use Annex B should involve the authorities having jurisdiction. The design method in Annex B can lead to detector spacings that exceed the listed spacing in many cases. This difference does not mean the spacings are wrong. Where the design objectives, fire behavior, and compartment dimensions differ from those in the UL fire test room, one would expect to obtain different spacing. This difference is to be expected when a designer uses the design methods of Annex B; the performance that characterizes a particular fire will likely be quite different from the characteristics of the test fire used to evaluate the detector for listing.

17.7 Smoke-Sensing Fire Detectors

The definition of *smoke detector* can be found in 3.3.59.19. Also refer to the definitions in 3.3.252 for the mode of operation of each type of smoke detection.

17.7.1 General.

17.7.1.1* The smoke detection design documentation shall state the required performance objective of the system.

A.17.7.1.1 The performance objective statement should describe the purpose of the detector placement and the intended response of the fire alarm control unit to the detector activation. This statement can include a narrative description of the required response time of the detectors, a narrative of the sequence of operations, a tabular list of programming requirements, or some other method.

The performance objective of a fire detection system is usually expressed in terms of time and the size fire the system is intended to detect, measured in British thermal units per second (Btu/sec) or kilowatts (kW). Typically, the fire alarm system designer does not establish this criterion. It is usually obtained from the design documentation prepared by the designer responsible for the strategy of the structure as a whole. Where a prescriptive design is being provided, this requirement is fulfilled by stating in the design documentation that the design conforms to the prescriptive provisions of this Code.

With the increasingly widespread acceptance of performance-based design, the Code incorporates a performance-based design alternative for the design of fire detection systems using smoke detectors. The designer is afforded two alternative routes in the design process. One route is the prescriptive process, in which the designer follows the prescribed spacing and location criteria provided in the Code. The second route is the use of the performance-based design methods outlined in Annex B. In either case, 17.7.1.1 requires the performance objective of the system to be stated in the smoke detection design documentation.

Smoke detectors are required by the relevant building code where a life safety objective is to be achieved. Smoke detectors are often also used where a property conservation objective justifies "early warning." "Early warning" is not defined and often means different things to different people. Usually, fires are measured by their heat release rate, in British thermal units per second or kilowatts. Is the detection of a 100 kW fire early enough? Customarily, smoke detectors are spaced using a 30 ft (9.1 m) spacing. The experience in the industry suggests that this spacing is adequate to achieve the life safety objectives implied by the building codes. If the objective for the fire detection system is other than life safety, some other spacing could conceivably be more appropriate, meaning that it would achieve the response objectives with the minimum number of smoke detectors. Consequently, it is imperative that the design documentation explicitly state what objectives the system is intended to achieve.

FAQ ▶
What types of fire are assumed in the methods in Annex B for predicting the actuation of smoke detectors?

Annex B gives two methods for predicting the actuation of smoke detectors for fires that produce a buoyant plume, such as flaming fires. The limitation on the applicability of Annex B to buoyant plume fires for smoke detector design comes from the fact that both methods use conservation of momentum and energy relationships to infer temperature at a given location relative to the fire centerline. The methodology then uses correlations to temperature to infer the probable optical density or mass density at the detector locations. Because both methods assume a buoyant plume and a ceiling jet as the mechanism of smoke transfer, the validity of these methods is limited to a flaming fire.

Popular computer models such as FPETool and FastLite model the smoke detector as a very sensitive (RTI = 1) heat detector. These models usually presume that a smoke detector will actuate when a temperature rise of 20°F (13°C) occurs at the detector. This simplified assumption of a correlation of temperature to smoke density, introduced in early research [Schifiliti, 1986], has persisted since the 1980s. Today, many researchers consider this estimate extremely conservative. There are algorithms now being used in Fire Dynamics Simulator (FDS) that track temperature, mass, and velocity that also infer the operation of a smoke detector.

In some applications, the computational methods in Annex B yield smoke detector spacings that are considerably greater than the customary 30 ft (9.1 m) spacing permitted in the prescriptive section of this Code. The computational methods outlined in Annex B are derived from testing performed under the auspices of the Fire Detection Institute [Heskestad and Delichatsios, 1986, 1995; Heskestad and Delichatsios, 1989]. This procedure provides a more analytical and precise method of determining detector spacing if a specific fire-size criterion has been established for smoke detection system response.

The designer must understand the behaviors of the fire plume and the ceiling jet in order to understand how the building structure can affect the flow of smoke through the compartment and from one compartment to others. The site evaluation includes an audit of all combustibles within the compartment, as well as all ignition sources, including transient ones [Babrauskas, Lawson, Walton, and Twilley, 1982; Heskestad and Delichatsios, 1986, 1995; 47 CFR 1934]. The designer models the fires to obtain an estimate of the rate of fire growth for each combustible and ignition source scenario and then compares the fire scenarios to the performance objectives for the compartment. This procedure leads to a basis for design.

Without sound performance metrics and validated modeling methods for smoke detectors, the selection of detector locations often becomes more of an art than a science. Most manufacturers recommend a spacing of 30 ft (9.1 m) on center. This recommendation is purported to have been derived from the size of the room in which the testing laboratories perform full-scale fire tests. Detailed analysis of the ANSI/UL 268, *Standard for Smoke Detectors for Fire Alarm Systems*, test criteria tends to refute that idea. The convention of using a 30 ft (9.1 m) spacing for smoke detectors can only be attributed to observations over many years that when used on that spacing, listed detectors seem to provide the level of performance expected of them.

17.7.1.2* Designs not in accordance with 17.7.1.3 shall be deemed prescriptive designs and shall be designed in accordance with the prescriptive requirements of this chapter.

A.17.7.1.2 The person designing an installation should keep in mind that, in order for a smoke detector to respond, the smoke has to travel from the point of origin to the detector. In evaluating any particular building or location, likely fire locations should be determined first. From each of these points of origin, paths of smoke travel should be determined. Wherever practicable, actual field tests should be conducted. The most desired locations for smoke detectors are the common points of intersection of smoke travel from fire locations throughout the building.

NOTE: This is one of the reasons that specific spacing is not assigned to smoke detectors by the testing laboratories.

17.7.1.3* Performance-based designs shall be executed in accordance with Section 17.3.

A.17.7.1.3 In a performance-based design environment, the performance objectives for the fire alarm system are not established by the fire alarm system designer.

A fire protection strategy is developed to achieve those goals. General performance objectives are developed for the facility. These general objectives give rise to specific performance objectives for each fire protection system being employed in the facility. Consequently, the performance objectives and criteria for the fire alarm system are part of a much larger strategy that often relies on other fire protection features, working in concert with the fire alarm system to attain the overall fire protection goals for the facility.

In the performance-based design environment, the designer uses computational models to demonstrate that the spacing used for automatic fire detectors connected to the fire alarm system will achieve the objectives established by the system, by showing that the system meets the performance criteria established for the system in the design documentation. Consequently, it is imperative that the design objectives and performance criteria to which the system has been designed are clearly stated in the system documentation.

Performance-based design as described in A.17.7.1.1 and A.17.7.1.3 is a holistic process that leads to a design from a starting point of stated, agreed-upon, quantified objectives. In most cases concerning fire detection system design, the objective is to detect a fire of a specified size, assuming a growing fire. Supplement 1 and Annex B provide an overview of the process and the methods employed within that process.

17.7.1.4 The prescriptive requirements in this section shall be applied only where detectors are installed in ordinary indoor locations.

Paragraph 17.7.1.4 limits the applicability of the prescriptive requirements and recommendations of Section 17.7 to "ordinary indoor locations." The authority having jurisdiction must decide whether a hazard area falls into this category. The Code assumes that users understand what is meant by ordinary indoor locations. The term is not defined in the Code.

Where the application falls outside the conditions assumed for the prescriptive requirements of Section 17.7, the designer must consider the impact of those conditions on the operability and reliability of the detector. In evaluating the reasons why the conditions are not appropriate, the designer might identify an alternative design approach that solves the problem. Some authorities having jurisdiction establish additional requirements for specific types of occupancies that go above and beyond the requirements of Section 17.7. To protect extremely valuable assets, the designer might also choose a closer spacing in certain areas, such as in a data center or where the owner's fire protection goals demand a closer spacing of smoke detectors. In some cases, the situation might warrant the use of a more fully developed performance-based approach or the use of a different type of fire detection than smoke-sensing fire detection.

Finally, the common interpretation of 17.7.1.4 usually does not include special compartments, such as switchgear enclosures, laboratories, or wafer fabrication facilities. Although a particular design might use detectors in these and similar locations, the designer should carefully consider the impact of the intended environment on both detector response and stability.

17.7.1.5 Where smoke detectors are being installed to control the spread of smoke, they shall be installed in accordance with the requirements of 17.7.5.

Early in the second half of the 20th century, several fires in high-rise buildings demonstrated the difficulty of trying to evacuate all the occupants. Concurrently, smoke inhalation became well known to be the principal cause of death associated with fires. Designers developed a new strategy of protecting in place or using areas of refuge. Now, to protect occupants in place, HVAC system or an engineered smoke control system automatically controls the flow of smoke. Designers typically employ smoke detectors to actuate such systems. As stated in 17.7.1.5, the use of smoke detectors for that purpose is covered in 17.7.5.

17.7.1.6 Smoke detectors shall be installed in all areas where required by other governing laws, codes, or standards or by other parts of this Code.

FAQ ▶
Where does *NFPA 72* require the installation of smoke detectors?

Paragraph 17.7.1.6 has been included to correlate with national and state adopted codes that reference this Code. *NFPA 72* does not stipulate where or in which occupancies detection must be installed. Rather, the Code establishes how detection must be designed and installed once an applicable law, code, or standard has established the requirement for detection in the occupancy in question. Refer to Supplement 4 for a summary of requirements for various occupancies based on the 2009 edition of NFPA *101*.

17.7.1.7 The selection and placement of smoke detectors shall take into account both the performance characteristics of the detector and the areas into which the detectors are to be installed to prevent nuisance alarms or improper operation after installation.

The logic used by the designer in the process of detector selection should be documented as part of the project file. How the design addresses the criteria outlined in A.17.7.1.8 and A.17.7.1.9 should also be documented. Paragraph 17.7.1.7 relates to the requirement in 17.7.1.1 for a statement of the objective being achieved by the system. If the system fails at some time in the future, the designer will have to show that a logical process was followed in selecting the type of detector and the detector locations.

17.7.1.8* Unless specifically designed and listed for the expected conditions, smoke detectors shall not be installed if any of the following ambient conditions exist:

(1) Temperature below 32°F (0°C)
(2) Temperature above 100°F (38°C)

(3) Relative humidity above 93 percent
(4) Air velocity greater than 300 ft/min (1.5 m/sec)

The temperature, humidity, and airflow criteria cited in 17.7.1.8 reflect the test criteria in the test standards used by the listing agency in the process of the listing evaluation. Different detection technologies are affected differently by these environmental extremes. Different makes and models within each group may be affected more or less than others. Apart from the generalities presented here, identifying these effects is beyond the scope of this handbook. However, the designer must recognize that some detector designs are inherently more forgiving than others.

The tests performed in the process of listing ascertain that a detector meets minimum performance criteria. Design features in specific devices that allow them to be effectively used in extreme environments can be beyond those considered in the listing evaluation. The manufacturer should be consulted if such an application is contemplated.

Environmental limits may require the designer to consider alternative detection methods. Although smoke detection may be preferable from the standpoint of the anticipated first evidence of a fire, heat- or radiant energy–sensing detection might be a better choice where the hazard area is one that undergoes too broad a range of environmental conditions to allow the use of smoke detection.

A.17.7.1.8 Product-listing standards include tests for temporary excursions beyond normal limits. In addition to temperature, humidity, and velocity variations, smoke detectors should operate reliably under such common environmental conditions as mechanical vibration, electrical interference, and other environmental influences. Tests for these conditions are also conducted by the testing laboratories in their listing program. In those cases in which environmental conditions approach the limits shown in Table A.17.7.1.8, the detector manufacturer's published instructions should be consulted for additional information and recommendations.

TABLE A.17.7.1.8 *Environmental Conditions that Influence Smoke Detector Response*

Protection	*Air Velocity* *>300 ft/min* *(>91.44 m/min)*	*Altitude* *>3000 ft* *(>914.4 m)*	*Humidity* *>93% RH*	*Temp.* *<32°F > 100°F* *(<0°C>37.8°C)*	*Color of* *Smoke*
Ion	X	X	X	X	O
Photo	O	O	X	X	X
Beam	O	O	X	X	O
Air sampling	O	O	X	X	O

X: Can affect detector response. O: Generally does not affect detector response.

17.7.1.9* The location of smoke detectors shall be based on an evaluation of potential ambient sources of smoke, moisture, dust, or fumes, and electrical or mechanical influences, to minimize nuisance alarms.

A.17.7.1.9 Smoke detectors can be affected by electrical and mechanical influences and by aerosols and particulate matter found in protected spaces. The location of detectors should be such that the influences of aerosols and particulate matter from sources such as those in Table A.17.7.1.9(a) are minimized. Similarly, the influences of electrical and mechanical factors shown in Table A.17.7.1.9(b) should be minimized. While it might not be possible to isolate environmental factors totally, an awareness of these factors during system layout and design favorably affects detector performance.

TABLE A.17.7.1.9(a) *Common Sources of Aerosols and Particulate Matter Moisture*

Moisture	Humid outside air Humidifiers Live steam Showers Slop sink Steam tables Water spray	Atmospheric contaminants	Corrosive atmospheres Dust or lint Excessive tobacco smoke Heat treating Linen and bedding handling Pneumatic transport Sawing, drilling, and grinding Textile and agricultural processing
Combustion products and fumes	Chemical fumes Cleaning fluids Cooking equipment Curing Cutting, welding, and brazing Dryers Exhaust hoods Fireplaces Machining Ovens Paint spray	Engine exhaust	Diesel trucks and locomotives Engines not vented to the outside Gasoline forklift trucks
		Heating element with abnormal conditions	Dust accumulations Improper exhaust Incomplete combustion

TABLE A.17.7.1.9(b) *Sources of Electrical and Mechanical Influences on Smoke Detectors*

Electrical Noise and Transients	Airflow
Vibration or shock Radiation Radio frequency Intense light Lightning Electrostatic discharge Power supply	Gusts Excessive velocity

In applications where the factors listed in Table A.17.7.1.9(a) and Table A.17.7.1.9(b) cannot be sufficiently limited to allow reasonable stability and response times, alternative modes of fire detection should be considered.

17.7.1.10* The effect of stratification below the ceiling shall be taken into account. The guidelines in Annex B shall be permitted to be used.

A.17.7.1.10 Stratification of air in a room can hinder air containing smoke particles or gaseous combustion products from reaching ceiling-mounted smoke detectors or fire–gas detectors.

Stratification occurs when air containing smoke particles or gaseous combustion products is heated by smoldering or burning material and, becoming less dense than the surrounding cooler air, rises until it reaches a level at which there is no longer a difference in temperature between it and the surrounding air.

Stratification also can occur when evaporative coolers are used, because moisture introduced by these devices can condense on smoke, causing it to fall toward the floor. Therefore, to ensure rapid response, it might be necessary to install smoke detectors on sidewalls or at locations below the ceiling.

In installations where detection of smoldering or small fires is desired and where the possibility of stratification exists, consideration should be given to mounting a portion of the detectors below the ceiling. In high-ceiling areas, projected beam–type or air sampling–type detectors at different levels also should be considered. *(See Figure A.17.7.1.10.)*

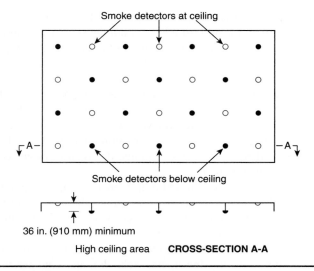

FIGURE A.17.7.1.10 *Smoke Detector Layout Accounting for Stratification.*

The requirements in 17.7.1.10 are not limited to certain conditions of room dimensions or temperature. The potential for stratification must be consciously considered whenever and wherever smoke detectors are being employed.

When gaseous combustion products (smoke) form in a fire, they are hot and, consequently, begin expanding. These expanded gases are less dense than the surrounding air and are buoyed upward. According to the ideal gas law, as a gas expands, it loses heat. In addition, the rising plume gases mix with the surrounding air, entraining the air as the plume flows upward. The entrainment of ambient air also contributes to the cooling of the plume. As long as the plume remains hotter than the surrounding air, despite some cooling due to expansion and entrainment, it continues to expand and rise. This process results in a V-shaped fire plume that is small at the bottom and grows larger in diameter the higher it rises. Eventually, the gaseous combustion products in the fire plume decrease in temperature due to expansion and entrainment until they are no longer hotter than the surrounding air, and the plume loses buoyancy and spreads out in a layer. If that happens before the fire plume impinges on the ceiling, the layer of smoke will be below the ceiling-mounted smoke detectors and response will be delayed until the fire grows sufficiently large to drive the smoke up to the ceiling plane.

A ceiling jet is formed when the plume hits the ceiling with sufficient momentum. The radial flow of the ceiling jet from the plume centerline is the result of the residual momentum of the upward flowing plume gases. This momentum conveys smoke to the detector location. Without a ceiling jet, the smoke and heat from the fire will not move horizontally beneath the ceiling. Most of the spacing criteria for smoke and heat detectors are based on the assumption that a ceiling jet exists and that it is moving the smoke and heat horizontally in a layer immediately beneath the ceiling. Stratification affects the performance of the detection system because the smoke forms a layer too far below the ceiling-mounted smoke detectors.

FAQ ▶
What considerations can affect the height at which stratification occurs?

The height at which the stratification occurs depends on both the size of the fire and the ambient temperature and temperature gradient of the space. Stratification is most likely to occur when the fire is small and the ceiling high. However, HVAC systems designed to form a layer of cool air at some given distance above the floor can create exactly the same conditions as naturally occurring stratification. This phenomenon can have the same profound effects on the performance of a detection system.

Where stratification can be expected, the location and spacing of smoke detectors must be adjusted. The design of a smoke detection system must address both the spectrum of ambient conditions and the range of fire scenarios for the space. In areas of high ceilings, layering of detectors or combining detectors to address all possible fire scenarios is often necessary. If a second "layer" of detectors is contemplated, remember that the spacing rules *assume* the existence of a ceiling jet to move smoke horizontally to the detector. A layer of smoke detectors suspended a number of feet (meters) from the ceiling does not have the benefit of a ceiling jet, and the conventional spacing rules are irrelevant. Far more detectors will probably be necessary. Selecting a detector spacing equivalent to no more than 0.4 times the detector height above the floor can be justified on the basis of plume divergence. Projected beam smoke detectors can also be used to great benefit.

The objective of detecting the fire before it has achieved a high-energy output requires additional insight into the placement of detectors. The high-energy output flaming fire produces a fire plume that propels smoke and hot air upward. The larger the fire, the higher the plume extends and the greater the air velocity within the plume.

In the smoldering, low-energy-output fire often encountered in residential (e.g., homes, hotels, apartments), institutional (e.g., hospitals, nursing homes, schools), and commercial (e.g., offices, stores) occupancies, significant quantities of smoke may be produced before an energetic fire plume develops. This smoke may lack the energy to rise up to ceiling-mounted smoke detectors where the ceilings are higher than normally encountered. This situation must be addressed in any fire alarm system designed for residential, institutional, or commercial occupancies. The addition of smoke detectors at some distance below the ceiling generally does not eliminate the requirement for ceiling-mounted detectors.

17.7.1.11* Protection During Construction.

Many needless alarms are caused by smoke detectors installed too early in the construction process. Construction activities produce airborne dust that inevitably finds its way into detectors, contaminating them and making them prone to false alarms. History, however, shows that fires often occur during renovation and construction because these activities include numerous fire ignition sources. Often smoke detection is required in areas under construction for that very reason. If smoke detection is required in the area under construction or renovation, 17.7.1.11 establishes the requirements for cleaning and sensitivity measurement or replacement.

Where the authority having jurisdiction requires early installation, detectors installed prior to the completion of final finish work must be cleaned and measured for their normal operating sensitivity. Those detectors found outside their design sensitivity range must be replaced.

A.17.7.1.11 Construction debris, dust (especially gypsum dust and the fines resulting from the sanding of drywall joint compounds), and aerosols can affect the sensitivity of smoke detectors and, in some instances, cause deleterious effects to the detector, thereby significantly reducing the expected life of the detector.

17.7.1.11.1 Where detectors are installed for signal initiation during construction, they shall be cleaned and verified to be operating in accordance with the listed sensitivity, or they shall be replaced prior to the final commissioning of the system.

17.7.1.11.2 Where detectors are installed but not operational during construction, they shall be protected from construction debris, dust, dirt, and damage in accordance with the manufacturer's recommendations and verified to be operating in accordance with the listed sensitivity, or they shall be replaced prior to the final commissioning of the system.

The requirement in 17.7.1.11.2 is new in the 2010 edition. If detectors are installed before completion of construction cleanup, they must be protected in accordance with the manufacturer's instructions.

Many smoke detectors are shipped with a thin plastic cover over the sensing portion of the detector. It is widely assumed that these covers are suitable for protecting the detector from construction dust, dirt, and debris. In actuality, most of the "covers" supplied are merely for shipping and are not intended to be used in lieu of proper protection from construction debris.

In some cases, the authority having jurisdiction may allow the installation of protective covers. However, these covers cannot be relied on to keep the detector entirely free of contaminants. Therefore, sensitivity measurement and cleaning of the detectors after all construction trades have finished their work will probably still be necessary. If covers are used, the contractor must also have a means of verifying that they all have been removed when the construction trades have completed their work. If the authority having jurisdiction requires the covers to be removed at the end of each day, a good practice is to number the covers to ensure that all have been removed and then to replace them the next morning. Again, if the covers are removed during the construction process, it will be necessary to inspect the detectors closely, cleaning them when necessary, and testing them to ensure that their sensitivity is within the listed and marked sensitivity range. See Exhibit 17.23 for an example of a smoke detector protective cover.

EXHIBIT 17.23 *Smoke Detector with Protective Plastic Cover. (Source: Hochiki America Corp., Buena Park, CA)*

17.7.1.11.3 Where detection is not required during construction, detectors shall not be installed until after all other construction trades have completed cleanup.

Many needless alarms are caused by smoke detectors installed too early in the construction process. Construction activities produce airborne dust that inevitably finds its way into detectors, contaminating them and making them prone to false alarms. Unless detection is required while the area is under construction, experience has shown that the best practice is to not install smoke detectors until all construction cleanup is completed.

17.7.2* Sensitivity.

A.17.7.2 Throughout this Code, smoke detector sensitivity is referred to in terms of the percent obscuration required to alarm or produce a signal. Smoke detectors are tested using various smoke sources that have different characteristics (e.g., color, particle size, number of particles, particle shape). Unless otherwise specified, this Code, the manufacturers, and the listing agencies report and use the percent obscuration produced using a specific type of gray smoke. Actual detector response will vary when the characteristics of the smoke reaching the detector are different from the smoke used in testing and reporting detector sensitivity.

Listing agencies base the listings of smoke detectors on repeatable laboratory tests. These tests do not necessarily correlate to actual fires in actual applications. Consequently, the listing agencies do not provide a listed spacing for smoke detectors as they do for heat detectors. With this edition of *NFPA 72*, the technical committee has adopted a prescriptive spacing for smoke detectors (see 17.7.3.2.3.1).

The tests conducted in the course of a listing investigation by the organization providing the listing include a sensitivity measurement in a smoke box using a cotton lamp wick under controlled airflow to produce a light gray smoke with a controlled rate of optical density increase per unit of time. The manufacturer marks the detector with its sensitivity, based on the response obtained in the smoke box test as outlined in the listing investigation standard used. However, the sensitivity measurements obtained from the test are relevant only in the context of the smoke box and smoke used. The measurements are not intended to predict performance in any other context. Consequently, a marking of a nominal smoke obscuration of 0.6 percent to 4.0 percent obscuration per foot does not necessarily mean that an installed detector will respond to a real fire at that level of optical obscuration. The combustibles in a real fire environment bear little resemblance to the dry cotton lamp wicking used in smoke box tests. Consequently, the level of optical obscuration at which an alarm signal is generated can be very different in a real compartment fire from that obtained in a smoke box. Therefore, a designer should not base a design on the marked sensitivity.

Full-scale room fire tests are also conducted by the listing organization during the listing evaluation of a smoke detector. In accordance with UL 268, smoke detectors are required to render an alarm when subjected to fires that ultimately produce smoke obscurations of 37 percent per foot for the paper fire, 17 percent per foot for the wood fire, 21 percent per foot for the heptane/toluene fire, and 10 percent per foot for a smoldering wood fire. These pass/fail tests also do not provide a meaningful basis for predicting smoke detector performance.

17.7.2.1* Smoke detectors shall be marked with their nominal production sensitivity and tolerance (percent per foot obscuration), as required by the listing.

A.17.7.2.1 The production sensitivity range should only be used as a benchmark for testing and should not be used as the sole basis for selection of devices. The percent per foot sensitivity marked on the smoke detector is derived from testing in a smoke chamber, usually referred to as the UL 268 Smoke Box. The measurements derived from this measurement apparatus are only valid in the context of the apparatus and cannot be used outside the context of the smoke box. The polychromatic light source employed in the smoke box results in measurements that are highly dependent upon smoke color and does not account for variations in light transmission as a function of wavelength that occurs as fuels and fire ventilation rates change or as smoke ages. Furthermore, the measurement apparatus uses a measurement of light obscuration by smoke to infer a measure of light reflectance when there is no correlation between these two optical characteristics.

FAQ ▶
To what does percent per foot obscuration relate?

Because the mission of most smoke detection systems is the protection of human life, the response of a smoke detector is usually defined in human terms. The percent per foot obscuration method of measuring sensitivity relates to a person's ability to see well enough to escape from a fire. Smoke is composed of both visible and invisible gases and particulate matter. Although the portion of the smoke that is invisible has little immediate impact on an individual's ability to escape, it can constitute the majority of the smoke mass under some fire conditions.

Refer to the commentary following A.17.7.2 for an explanation of how the sensitivity marked on a smoke detector is obtained and what it means with respect to performance in actual fires.

The marking of the detector with its sensitivity does allow for the testing of the unit and comparison of its present sensitivity to its initial nominal production sensitivity.

17.7.2.2 Smoke detectors that have provision for field adjustment of sensitivity shall have an adjustment range of not less than 0.6 percent per foot obscuration.

The adjustment of detector sensitivity over a range of less than 0.6 percent per foot has little, if any, practical benefit. Even where smoke detectors are used for property protection (as in data centers), the difference in response represented by an adjustment range of less than 0.6 percent per foot is minor. This consideration is reflected in the requirement of 17.7.2.2.

17.7.2.3 If the means of adjustment of sensitivity is on the detector, a method shall be provided to restore the detector to its factory calibration.

Some smoke detectors have a feature that allows the adjustment of detector sensitivity to accommodate the immediate ambient conditions in the area of the detector. If maintenance personnel use the adjustment feature between cleaning intervals to maintain stability, they should restore the detector to its original design sensitivity after it has been cleaned. Chapter 14 covers the maintenance of smoke detectors.

17.7.2.4 Detectors that have provision for program-controlled adjustment of sensitivity shall be permitted to be marked with their programmable sensitivity range only.

Most addressable/analog smoke detectors have provisions for detector sensitivity adjustment by means of the system software. These smoke detectors send a voltage or current value back to the control unit that is proportional to the concentration of smoke sensed by the detector. In such a case, the trip point of the detector is often a voltage or current level stored in the control unit memory. Consequently, the adjustment of the activation point of a detector is actually the adjustment of the activation value stored in memory for that detector. When a provision for the adjustment of the detector sensitivity is at the control unit, there must be a means to restore the detector to its factory sensitivity. The manufacturer must mark the detector to show the sensitivity range. If maintenance personnel use the adjustment feature between cleaning intervals to maintain stability, they should restore the detector to its original design sensitivity after the detector has been cleaned. Chapter 14 covers the maintenance of smoke detectors.

17.7.3 Location and Spacing.

As with heat detectors, smoke detectors rely primarily on plume and ceiling jet flows to transport the smoke from a fire to the detector. Note the similarity in the location criteria between smoke detectors and heat detectors.

All the criteria for a given type of detector are organized in a single section of the Code. All the spot-type detector criteria are collected in 17.7.3.2 through 17.7.3.5. The criteria for air sampling–type detectors are collected in 17.7.3.6, and the criteria for projected beam–type detectors are collected in 17.7.3.7. Refer to Exhibits 3.19, 17.27 through 17.30, and 3.16 and 3.17, respectively, for examples of these three different types of smoke-sensing fire detectors.

17.7.3.1* General.

A.17.7.3.1 Except in the case of smoldering, low-energy fires, all smoke detectors, regardless of the type of technology, usually rely on the plume and ceiling jet produced by the fire to transport the smoke upward and across the ceiling to the detector, sampling port, or projected sensing light beam. Once sufficient concentration is attained at the detector, sampling port, or sensing light beam location and, in the case of spot-type detectors, sufficient flow velocity is attained to overcome the flow resistance into the sensing chamber, the detector responds with an alarm signal. Detectors are usually mounted at the ceiling plane to take advantage of the flow provided by the plume and the ceiling jet. A hot, energetic fire produces large plume velocities and temperatures and hot, fast ceiling jets. This minimizes the time it takes for the smoke to travel to the detector. A smoldering fire produces little, if any, plume and no appreciable ceiling jet. Far more time elapses between ignition and detection under this circumstance.

17.7.3.1.1 The location and spacing of smoke detectors shall be based upon the anticipated smoke flows due to the plume and ceiling jet produced by the anticipated fire, as well as any pre-existing ambient airflows that could exist in the protected compartment.

When determining the location and spacing of smoke detectors, the designer must consider how smoke is likely to flow. The likely flow of smoke depends on the ambient conditions as well as the fire. In some cases, the ambient airflow can be deduced by inspection. In other cases, the use of a velometer or an anemometer can be helpful in determining the direction and the speed of ambient air currents that constitute the dominant ambient air movement in the compartment or space. The flow of the plume and the ceiling jet depends on the fuel load, the ambient conditions, and the location of the fire within the space. Usually, the behavior of the fire plume cannot be determined by direct measurements. Computational fluid dynamics (CFD) programs can be used to model airflows if necessary.

Under smoldering, low-energy-output fire conditions, the fire does not achieve an energy output (heat release rate) sufficient to serve as the primary source of propulsion for the smoke. Existing air currents through the hazard area dominate the flow of smoke with little, if any, contribution from the fire. The prediction of flow is far more dependent on site-specific airflow variables, meaning that prediction of detection becomes much more difficult.

The Code requires that the designer consciously analyze the space as part of the design process even when using a prescriptive design. The prudent designer will document this analysis for future reference. If the air movement patterns are changed in the protected space after the system has been installed, the relocation of smoke detectors might be advisable.

17.7.3.1.2 The design shall account for the contribution of the following factors in predicting detector response to the anticipated fires to which the system is intended to respond:

(1) Ceiling shape and surface
(2) Ceiling height
(3) Configuration of contents in the protected area
(4) Combustion characteristics and probable equivalence ratio of the anticipated fires involving the fuel loads within the protected area
(5) Compartment ventilation
(6) Ambient temperature, pressure, altitude, humidity, and atmosphere

The general criteria listed in 17.7.3.1.2 are far less specific than those established for heat detectors. The reasoning can be understood by a review of the importance of fire plume dynamics in the location and spacing of heat detectors versus smoke detectors.

Heat detectors depend on the fire plume and ceiling jet to carry hot gaseous combustion products and entrained air to the detector where heat can flow from the ceiling jet into the detector, resulting in an alarm. Although not explicitly stated in the Code, heat detectors are generally used where response is needed once the fire has achieved an energy output of at least 1.2 MW, which is the size fire used in determining the listed spacing for a heat detector. This size fire liberates a significant quantity of energy, which serves as the engine that creates its own air currents. The energy from the fire propels the hot air and smoke mixture across the ceiling; thus, the fire is the dominant air mover in the compartment.

FAQ ▶
What is the dominant factor in predicting smoke flow under smoldering, low-energy-output fire conditions?

Under smoldering, low-energy-output fire conditions, the fire does not yet represent an energy output (heat release rate) sufficient to serve as the primary source of propulsion for the smoke. Existing air currents through the hazard area dominate the flow of smoke with little, if any, contribution from the fire. The prediction of flow is far more dependent on site-specific airflow variables, meaning that prediction of detection becomes much more difficult.

Modeling the flow of the fire plume and ceiling jet is possible with computer programs such as Fire Dynamics Simulator (FDS) that apply the rules of fluid flow physics and thermodynamics to the plume from a fire. If the plume and ceiling jet correlations are used to predict the response of smoke detectors, it can be seen that smoke detectors will provide response significantly before heat detectors will. Because the space-specific variables are dominant factors in predicting plume behavior, the location and spacing of smoke detectors, if explicit modeling is not used, must be determined subject to the judgment of the designer on how the site-specific environmental features enumerated in 17.7.3.1.2 will affect the flow of smoke from early-stage, low-energy-output fires.

17.7.3.1.3 If the intent is to protect against a specific hazard, the detector(s) shall be permitted to be installed closer to the hazard in a position where the detector can intercept the smoke.

Usually, the design process begins by locating detectors so that they will provide general area protection. Additional detectors are added or positions adjusted to take into account known or anticipated ignition sources and known air currents. Paragraph 17.7.3.1.3 is generally cited when detectors are placed closer to hazards like switchgear enclosures, power supplies, and similar assets with known histories of ignition.

17.7.3.1.4* If the intent is to initiate action when smoke/fire threatens a specific object or space, the detector shall be permitted to be installed in close proximity to that object or space.

A.17.7.3.1.4 There are some applications that do not require full area protection, but do require detection, to initiate action when specific objects or spaces are threatened by smoke or fire, such as at elevator landings that have ceilings in excess of 15 ft (4.6 m) and for protection of fire alarm control units. In high-ceiling areas, to achieve the desired initiation, such as for elevator recall and protection of fire alarm control units (FACUs), detection should be placed on the wall above and within 60 in. (1.52 m) from the top of the elevator door(s) or FACU.

17.7.3.2* Spot-Type Smoke Detectors.

This section on spot-type smoke detectors has been substantially revised based on research conducted under the auspices of the Fire Protection Research Foundation that specifically addressed questions regarding smoke detector spacing on ceilings with beams and bays.

A.17.7.3.2 In high-ceiling areas, such as atriums, where spot-type smoke detectors are not accessible for periodic maintenance and testing, projected beam–type or air sampling–type detectors should be considered where access can be provided.

The importance of accessibility and the maintenance of a smoke detection system cannot be overemphasized. The designer must exercise judgment and discretion to provide a system that can be maintained pursuant to the criteria established in Chapter 14. Paragraph A.17.7.3.2 clarifies 17.4.5, which requires that all initiating devices, including smoke detectors, be installed in such a manner that they can be effectively maintained.

Atria and other areas with exceptionally high ceilings (such as auditoriums, gymnasiums, exhibit halls, storage facilities, and some manufacturing facilities) represent very difficult situations for the use of spot-type smoke detection. Stratification, maintenance concerns, accessibility for testing, and smoke dissipation may warrant the use of other types of detection. Paragraph A.17.7.3.2 advises the designer to consider either air sampling or linear projected beam–type photoelectric light obscuration smoke detection as alternatives. However, note that the air-sampling ports of an air sampling–type detector are treated as individual spot-type detectors. Air sampling–type detectors rely on the plume and ceiling jet to carry smoke to the sampling ports. Consequently, where stratification is a concern, this type of detection (air-sampling detectors) might not represent an advantage over traditional spot-type detectors. Furthermore, where stratification is a concern, the beams of projected-beam smoke detection must be carefully located to ensure that the design fire will be detected. Annex B provides additional information on how to predict the elevation of a stratification plane under known conditions.

17.7.3.2.1* Spot-type smoke detectors shall be located on the ceiling or, if on a sidewall, between the ceiling and 12 in. (300 mm) down from the ceiling to the top of the detector.

A.17.7.3.2.1 Refer to Figure A.17.7.3.2.1 for an example of proper mounting for detectors. Sidewall detectors mounted closer to the ceiling will respond faster.

In earlier editions of the Code, ceiling-mounted smoke detectors were not permitted within 4 in. (100 mm) of a sidewall, and sidewall-mounted smoke detectors were not permitted within 4 in. (100 mm) of the ceiling. The concern was that smoke flow would be compromised in a "dead-air space" in the corner where the ceiling and the wall meet.

Earlier experimentation showed that a significant delay in the increase in air temperature occurred at this location compared with other locations in the room. This difference in

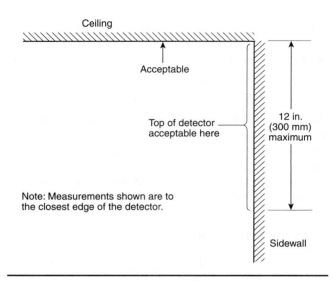

FIGURE A.17.7.3.2.1 Example of Proper Mounting for Smoke Detectors.

temperature was interpreted to indicate that the ceiling jet was not effectively extending into this space. What the experimentation did not show was just how far from the wall the detector should be placed. As the ceiling jet approaches a wall, it necessarily slows down. The rate of smoke entry is a function of ceiling jet velocity: Slow ceiling jet velocity produces slow response.

Recent experimentation and CFD investigations have challenged this conventional wisdom. CFD simulations have shown smoke flowing into such corners for a limited range of room geometries. With conflicting test data, the technical committee elected to drop the prohibition from installing detectors in the corner where the ceiling and a wall meet. [Note that the 4 in. (100 mm) prohibition still applies to heat-sensing fire detectors. See 17.6.3.1.3.1.]

The location requirement in 17.7.3.2.1 is valid for both the low-energy incipient fire and a high-energy-output fire that is immediately life threatening. Either the normally existing air currents or the fire plume and ceiling jet from the larger fire convey smoke to ceiling-mounted detectors. While the ceiling-wall corner is permitted, it is not the most desirable location. For the detectors to be able to respond, they must be installed in the working air volume of the compartment. A prudent designer will endeavor to keep ceiling-mounted spot-type smoke detectors as close to the center of the protected compartment as possible or in the direction that prevailing air currents would carry smoke from a low-energy, incipient fire.

17.7.3.2.2* To minimize dust contamination, smoke detectors, where installed under raised floors, shall be mounted only in an orientation for which they have been listed.

A.17.7.3.2.2 Figure A.17.7.3.2.2 illustrates under-floor mounting installations.

The fast-moving air in a data center under-floor space has sufficient energy to suspend dust. As that air enters the detector, it slows down and the suspended dust settles in the detector. The accumulation of dust within a smoke detector has a effect similar to that of smoke. In an ionization smoke detector, the dust impedes the flow of current within the chamber. In a spot-type photoelectric detector, the dust increases the reflectance within the chamber. Thus, dust causes each type of detector to become more sensitive, increasing the likelihood of unwarranted alarms. The permitted orientations shown in Figure A.17.7.3.2.2 (top) minimize the possibility of dust falling into the detector from the floor and also minimize the effect of air-conveyed dust on the detector.

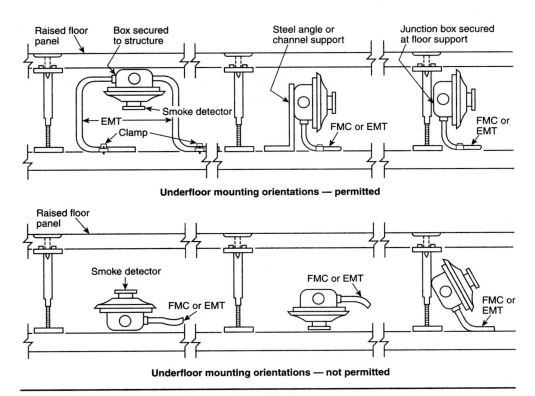

FIGURE A.17.7.3.2.2 *Mounting Installations Permitted (top) and Not Permitted (bottom).*

Other concerns reinforce the benefits of positioning detectors as shown in Figure A.17.7.3.2.2 (top). The detector is placed in the upper half of the under-floor volume. Because the purpose of the under-floor space is to allow for the routing of cables between machines, the floor is usually covered with cable. This cable has the same effect on the flow of air in the under-floor volume that joists have on airflow in a room. The cables create turbulence and force the flow to be concentrated in the upper half of the under-floor volume. Placing the detector in the upper half of the under-floor volume improves the system's ability to respond to an early-stage fire.

Another reason for positioning detectors as shown in Figure A.17.7.3.2.2 (top) is that detectors mounted in the upper half of the under-floor volume are far less likely to be damaged as new cables are installed or old cables are rerouted through the under-floor space. Where water-cooled computers are in use, the detectors are less likely to become wet if the computer cooling system leaks. Also, when air is not flowing, the detectors will be in the best orientation for detection. Finally, Figure A.17.7.3.2.2 (top) shows the detectors in the orientation for which they have been tested and listed.

17.7.3.2.3 On smooth ceilings, spacing for spot-type smoke detectors shall be in accordance with 17.7.3.2.3.1 through 17.7.3.2.3.5.

17.7.3.2.3.1* In the absence of specific performance-based design criteria, smooth ceiling smoke detector spacing shall be a nominal 30 ft (9.1 m).

A.17.7.3.2.3.1 The 30 ft (9.1 m) spacing is a guide for prescriptive designs. The use of such a spacing is based upon customary practice in the fire alarm community.

Where there are explicit performance objectives for the response of the smoke detection system, the performance-based design methods outlined in Annex B should be used.

For the purposes of this section, "nominal 30 ft (9.1 m)" should be determined to be 30 ft (9.1 m) +/–5 percent [+/–18 in. (460 mm)].

Paragraph 17.7.3.2.3.1 has been changed for the 2010 edition of the Code. In earlier editions, the 30 ft (9.1 m) spacing criterion was stipulated in permissive language. It has been changed to an explicit requirement in view of the fact that 17.7.1.3 effectively allows designers to use any other spacing they deem appropriate as a performance-based alternative.

The concept of detector spacing was developed in the context of heat detectors, where the testing laboratories have test standards that compare the response of a given make and model of heat detector with that of a fire suppression sprinkler head. [See Figure A.17.6.3.1.1(c).] The results of the test establish a listed spacing for the detector under test. Since the fire in the listing fire tests is located in the center of a square array of detectors, the distance between the fire and the detectors is equivalent to 0.707 times the spacing between detectors. Consequently, one can think of the detector as covering a circular area that encompasses the square array. This concept, called the *circle of coverage*, is shown in Figure A.17.6.3.1.1(d).

If the detector is capable of covering any point within the circle of coverage, then detectors can be placed in rectilinear arrays so long as the rectangular area assigned to each detector falls within that same circle of coverage. This arrangement is shown in Figure A.17.6.3.1.1(g). Consequently, a detector spacing of 30 ft (9.1 m) does not necessarily mean that the space between adjacent detectors cannot be greater than 30 ft (9.1 m). As shown in Figure A.17.6.3.1.1(g), if a detector is assigned a coverage area of 10 ft (3.1 m) by 41 ft (12.5 m), permitted under a 30 ft (9.1 m) "spacing," and two such rectangular areas are stacked end-to-end, such as might be encountered in a corridor, there will be a distance of 42 ft (12.8 m) between adjacent detectors. The distance of 42 ft (12.8 m) between adjacent detectors in a corridor is consistent with the 30 ft (9.1 m) "spacing" for the detectors. This arrangement makes intuitive sense when the effect that walls have on channeling the ceiling jet produced by a fire is considered.

FAQ ▶
What is the reason for the 30 ft (9.1 m) "spacing" requirement for spot-type smoke detectors?

In the listing investigations performed on smoke detectors, no full-scale fire test establishes a listed spacing for smoke detectors. One reason is because a sufficiently explicit response criterion against which a smoke detector can be measured has not been established. However, experience has shown that installing smoke detectors using a nominal 30 ft (9.1 m) spacing criterion works — it achieves the necessary life safety objectives. Where the owner and other relevant stakeholders have objectives other than life safety, a different spacing criterion might be appropriate. That criterion would be developed using the performance-based methods outlined in Annex B.

Finally, it is important to keep in mind that the technical committee does *not* intend for enforcement authorities to measure smoke detector–to–smoke detector spacings with critical precision. The nominal plus or minus 5 percent criterion set forth in Annex A is intended to provide some latitude in enforcement. The development of a fire and the extension of smoke through a real space is highly variable. The assertion that a difference in smoke detector spacing of 2 or 3 ft (0.61 to 0.91 m) will have a material affect on the ultimate performance of the system is highly speculative at best.

17.7.3.2.3.2 In all cases, the manufacturer's published instructions shall be followed.

When a manufacturer, through its own testing and research program, publishes a specific spacing recommendation that is different from the 30 ft (9.1 m) spacing, that spacing recommendation becomes an enforceable part of this Code.

17.7.3.2.3.3 Other spacing shall be permitted to be used depending on ceiling height, different conditions, or response requirements.

In the prescriptive design environment, a spacing other than 30 ft (9.1 m) can be used provided the justification for doing so is based on the fire dynamics, environment, compartment dimensions, and response objectives. The criteria in 17.7.3.2.3.3 imply, but do not explicitly require, a formal design process such as that required by 17.7.1.3. The designer should document the basis for selecting a spacing other than 30 ft (9.1 m), and that document should become a permanent part of the project file. Finally, the spacing selected will be subject to review and approval by the relevant authority having jurisdiction.

17.7.3.2.3.4 For the detection of flaming fires, the guidelines in Annex B shall be permitted to be used.

Currently, there are no computational models designed to develop predictions of smoke flow for nonflaming fires. Where the design objective is the detection of a smoldering fire, the designer should model ambient compartment air currents and the power commitment to them to determine to what extent they will dominate the flow of smoke.

Two analytical methods are provided in Annex B. Because these methods rely on plume and ceiling jet dynamics, their use must be limited to scenarios involving flaming fires that produce a buoyant plume. For smoldering fire scenarios, other methods must be used until open flaming commences. Then Annex B methods can be used.

Several available computer models (including FPETool, FastLite, and Hazard 1) predict smoke detector activation to the flaming fire scenario. However, it must be noted that these computer models use a temperature rise model, not optical density or mass density of smoke, to predict the activation of smoke detectors. Their credibility is limited by the validity of the temperature correlation plugged into the model for smoke detector response.

In this regard, the Fire Detection Institute sponsored a research paper entitled *Fire Detection Modeling, State of the Art*, by Robert P. Schifiliti and William E. Pucci. This paper analyzes the various ways the computer fire models predict smoke detector operation and points out the advantages and disadvantages of each method [Schifiliti and Pucci, 1998].

More recently, Fire Dynamics Simulator, a computational fluid dynamics model, has become popular for modeling the flow of smoke and fire plumes in rooms and buildings. However, this computer model is not simple to operate and requires considerable skill to generate reliable simulations. FDS tracks mass, velocity, and temperature. Users of the FDS model must, again, set numerical values for these parameters, which are then used to infer smoke detector activation.

17.7.3.2.3.5* For smooth ceilings, all points on the ceiling shall have a detector within a distance equal to 0.7 times the selected spacing.

A.17.7.3.2.3.5 This is useful in calculating locations in corridors or irregular areas *[see A.17.6.3.1.1 and Figure A.17.6.3.1.1(h)]*. For irregularly shaped areas, the spacing between detectors can be greater than the selected spacing, provided the maximum spacing from a detector to the farthest point of a sidewall or corner within its zone of protection is not greater than 0.7 times the selected spacing (0.7S).

The concepts behind the spacing of smoke detectors follow directly from the concepts developed for heat detectors. Paragraph A.17.6.3.1.1 develops the concepts that enable a designer to determine the area that will be covered by a detector. That area can vary in shape as long as the distance from the detector to the farthest point to be covered by the detector does not exceed 0.7 times the selected spacing. See Figure A.17.6.3.1.1(a) through Figure A.17.6.3.1.1(h) for a graphical representation of these mathematical concepts.

17.7.3.2.4* For solid joist and beam construction, spacing for spot-type smoke detectors shall be in accordance with 17.7.3.2.4.1 through 17.7.3.2.4.6.

The paragraphs in 17.7.3.2.4 have been completely rewritten for the 2010 edition of the Code. The technical committee considered research from a number of different sources, including Schirmer Engineering, Hughes Associates, and Combustion Science and Engineering. The technical committee selected bounding condition design parameters that should provide detector response at roughly the same time that would be attained were the beams and bays not present.

A.17.7.3.2.4 Detectors are placed at reduced spacings at right angles to joists or beams in an attempt to ensure that detection time is equivalent to that which would be experienced on a flat ceiling. It takes longer for the combustion products (smoke or heat) to travel at right angles to beams or joists because of the phenomenon wherein a plume from a relatively hot fire with significant thermal lift tends to fill the pocket between each beam or joist before moving to the next beam or joist.

Though it is true that this phenomenon might not be significant in a small smoldering fire where there is only enough thermal lift to cause stratification at the bottom of the joists, reduced spacing is still recommended to ensure that detection time is equivalent to that which would exist on a flat ceiling, even in the case of a hotter type of fire.

17.7.3.2.4.1 Solid joists shall be considered equivalent to beams for smoke detector spacing guidelines.

When the rules for spacing of spot-type smoke detectors in 17.7.3.2.4 are applied, solid joists and solid beams are treated the same. At the fire sizes normally associated with the response of a smoke detection system, the ceiling jet velocities are relatively low and produce less turbulence at the beam and joist bottoms. Consequently, the effects of beams and joists on the ceiling jet flow are expected to be essentially the same.

17.7.3.2.4.2 For level ceilings, the following shall apply:

(1) For ceilings with beam depths of less than 10 percent of the ceiling height (0.1 H), smooth ceiling spacing shall be permitted. Spot-type smoke detectors shall be permitted to be located on ceilings or on the bottom of beams.

Since the thickness of the ceiling jet is generally taken to be equal to the upper 10 percent of the floor-to-ceiling height, beams and joists extending down a depth of less than this thickness are not expected to have a significant effect on the response time of the smoke detector, especially in view of the fact that the farthest a detector should be from the fire is 0.7 times the 30 ft (9.1 m) spacing. Consequently, the Code permits the designer to use smooth ceiling spacing where the beams and joists extend less than 10 percent of the floor-to-ceiling height down from the ceiling surface regardless of the beam spacing. Detectors can be located on either the ceiling or the bottom of the beam. Also see 17.7.3.2.4.6 where applicable. Refer to Exhibit 17.24.

EXHIBIT 17.24 *Smoke Detector Spacing with Beams Less Than 0.1 H. (Source: J. M. Cholin Consultants, Inc., Oakland, NJ)*

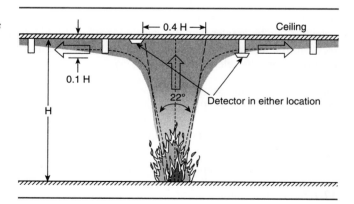

(2) For ceilings with beam depths equal to or greater than 10 percent of the ceiling height (0.1 H), the following shall apply:

    (a) Where beam spacing is equal to or greater than 40 percent of the ceiling height (0.4 H), spot-type detectors shall be located on the ceiling in each beam pocket.

(b) Where beam spacing is less than 40 percent of the ceiling height (0.4 *H*), the following shall be permitted for spot detectors:

  i. Smooth ceiling spacing in the direction parallel to the beams and at one-half smooth ceiling spacing in the direction perpendicular to the beams

  ii. Location of detectors either on the ceiling or on the bottom of the beams

When the beams extend down from a level ceiling more than 10 percent of the floor-to-ceiling height, they are expected to obstruct the ceiling jet flow. The obstruction of the ceiling jet delays the arrival of the smoke at the detector location. Furthermore, the speed with which smoke enters the sensing chamber of the detector is controlled by the speed of the ceiling jet past the detector. When ceiling jet flow is obstructed, it flows more slowly, increasing the smoke entry time once it arrives at the detector location.

Since it is generally accepted that the smoke plume from the fire will diverge at a nominal 22 degrees from the vertical axis (see Exhibit 17.21), the plume will cover an area on the ceiling equal to 40 percent of the floor-to-ceiling height (0.4 *H*). When the beam spacing exceeds 40 percent of the floor-to-ceiling height, the entire plume can be surrounded by beams. See Exhibit 17.25. If a smoke detector is not located in the bay created by the beams, the entire bay must fill with smoke before there is fill-and-spill propagation to an adjacent bay where a smoke detector might be located. This phenomenon will result in a delayed response. In the case where the beams are *both* equal to or more than 10 percent of the floor-to-ceiling height in depth *and* spaced equal to or more than 40 percent of the floor-to-ceiling height, a detector must be installed in each beam pocket.

Where the beams are greater than 10 percent of the floor-to-ceiling height and are spaced less than 40 percent of the floor-to-ceiling height, the plume will fill more than one bay regardless of where the plume is located relative to the beams. The presence of the beams will retard the flow of the ceiling jet in the direction perpendicular to the beams and channel the flow in the direction parallel to the beams. See Exhibit 17.26.

◀ **FAQ**
What spacing should be used when beam spacing is greater than 40 percent of the floor-to-ceiling height (0.4 *H*)?

(3)* For beam pockets formed by intersecting beams, including waffle or pan-type ceilings, the following shall apply:

  (a) For beam depths less than 10 percent of the ceiling height (0.1 *H*), spacing shall be in accordance with 17.7.3.2.4.2(1).

  (b) For beam depths greater than or equal to 10 percent of the ceiling height (0.1 *H*), spacing shall be in accordance with 17.7.3.2.4.2(2).

(4)* For corridors 15 ft (4.6 m) in width or less having ceiling beams or solid joists perpendicular to the corridor length, the following shall apply:

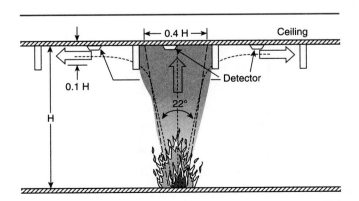

EXHIBIT 17.25 *Smoke Detector Spacing with Beam Depths Greater Than 0.1 H and Spaced More Than 0.4 H. (Source: J. M. Cholin Consultants, Inc., Oakland, NJ)*

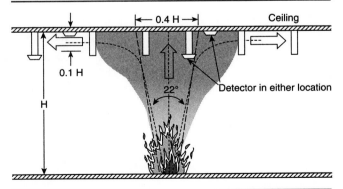

EXHIBIT 17.26 *Smoke Detector Spacing with Beam Depths Greater Than 0.1 H and Spaced Less Than 0.4 H. (Source: J. M. Cholin Consultants, Inc.)*

(a) Smooth ceiling spacing shall be permitted.

(b) Location of spot-type smoke detectors on ceilings, sidewalls, or the bottom of beams or solid joists

(5) For rooms of 900 ft² (84 m²) or less, the following shall be permitted:

(a) Use of smooth ceiling spacing

(b) Location of spot-type smoke detectors on ceilings or on the bottom of beams

Where smoke detectors are being used to fulfill a life safety objective, a room of only 900 ft² (8.4 m²) constrains the ceiling jet such that even when ceiling beams are present, the fire can be detected sufficiently early to achieve the objective. Where other objectives demand more rapid response, performance-based design methods should be employed.

Paragraph 17.7.3.2.4.2(5) was added to address small mechanical rooms with unfinished ceilings that might have deep beams yet constitute a modest fire risk. It is not the intent of the technical committee that this section be applied to 5 ft (1.5 m) wide passageways 180 ft (54.9 m) in length, 10 ft (3.1 m) wide corridors 90 ft (27.4 m) in length, or other compartments where the fire hazard and risk are nominally equivalent to the rest of the normally occupied portion of the building.

A.17.7.3.2.4.2(3) The geometry and reservoir effect is a significant factor that contributes to the development of velocity, temperature, and smoke obscuration conditions at smoke detectors located on the ceiling in beam pocket areas or at the bottom of beams as smoke collected in the reservoir volume spills into adjacent pockets. The waffle- or pan-type ceiling created by beams or solid joists, although retarding the initial flow of smoke, results in increased optical density, temperature rise, and gas velocities comparable to unconfined smooth ceilings.

For waffle- or pan-type ceilings with beams or solid joists, an alternative smoke detector grid arrangement (such as a shifted grid), with detectors located to take advantage of the channeling effect due to the reservoirs created by the beam pockets, will improve detector response and might allow greater spacing. See Figure A.17.7.3.2.4.2(3)(a) and Figure A.17.7.3.2.4.2(3)(b) for an example of shifted grids. The alternative smoke detector grid arrangement and spacing should be justified by an engineering analysis comparing the alternative smoke detector grid arrangement with the performance of smoke detectors on a level ceiling of equal height using 30 ft (9.1 m) smoke detector spacing.

Figure A.17.7.3.2.4.2(3)(a) illustrates the reservoir and channeling effect that results from the deep beam configuration. The strongest gas flows occur in a direction perpendicu-

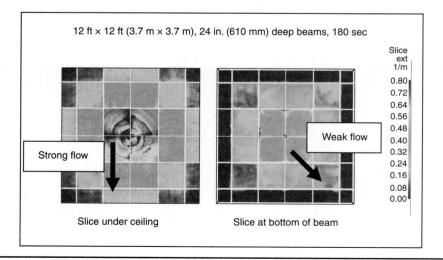

FIGURE A.17.7.3.2.4.2(3)(a) *Reservoir and Channeling Effect of Deep Beams.*

lar to the beam opposite the fire location. The weaker flow occurs in a directional 45 degrees off the beam grid; however, the reservoir effect accounts for higher concentrations of smoke eventually flowing from the strong area reservoirs into the weak area reservoirs.

Figure A.17.7.3.2.4.2(3)(b) is a generic example illustrating how a smoke detection grid using 30 ft (9.1 m) spacing can be shifted to take advantage of the channeling and reservoir effect to optimize detection response. In the circle, the fire is split into four beam bays that must fill with smoke before appreciable flows occur into the next adjoining eight beam bays. This represents the worst case scenario for smoke to reach the detectors on the circle. The three other fire locations shown require the fire to initially fill only one or two bays before spilling to adjacent bays.

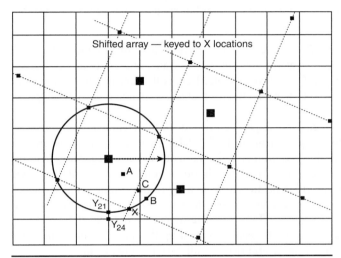

FIGURE A.17.7.3.2.4.2(3)(b) *Shifted Smoke Detection Grid to Optimize Detection for Deep Beam Effects.*

Recent research conducted under the auspices of the Fire Protection Research Foundation using Fire Dynamics Simulator (FDS) initially suggested that the relatively small volume of 12 ft high by 12 ft wide by 2 ft deep (3.7 m by 3.7 m by 0.6 m) bays present in waffle- or pan-type ceilings did not adversely affect system response. However, further study indicated that the revisions in the 2007 edition of the Code were not sufficiently conservative to establish design criteria that would be valid in all cases. Subsection 17.7.3 has now been revised to bound all sets of conditions of beam depth and spacing. Where the waffle-type ceiling consists of beam-equivalent elements that are less than the ceiling jet thickness, bounding smooth ceiling spacings is appropriate. However, when the beam elements of a waffle ceiling exceed the ceiling jet thickness in depth, spacing reductions are needed to achieve response equivalent to that for flat ceilings.

A.17.7.3.2.4.2(4) Corridor geometry is a significant factor that contributes to the development of velocity, temperature, and smoke obscuration conditions at smoke detectors located along a corridor. This is based on the fact that the ceiling jet is confined or constrained by the nearby walls without opportunity for entrainment of air. For corridors of approximately 15 ft (4.6 m) in width and for fires of approximately 100 kW or greater, modeling has demonstrated that the performance of smoke detectors in corridors with beams has been shown to be comparable to spot smoke detector spacing on an unconfined smooth ceiling surface.

17.7.3.2.4.3* For sloping ceilings with beams running parallel up slope, the following shall apply:

(1) Spot-type detector(s) shall be located on the ceiling within beam pocket(s).
(2) The ceiling height shall be taken as the average height over slope.
(3) Spacing shall be measured along a horizontal projection of the ceiling.
(4) Smooth ceiling spacing shall be permitted within beam pocket(s) parallel to the beams.
(5) For beam depths less than or equal to 10 percent of the ceiling height (0.1 H), spot-type detectors shall be located with smooth ceiling spacing perpendicular to the beams.
(6) For beam depths greater than 10 percent of the ceiling height (0.1 H), the following shall apply for spacing perpendicular to the beams:

   (a) For beam spacing greater than or equal to 40 percent of the ceiling height (0.4 H), spot-type detectors shall be located in each beam pocket.
   (b) For beam spacing less than 40 percent of the ceiling height (0.4 H), spot-type detectors shall not be required in every beam pocket but shall be spaced not greater than 50 percent of smooth ceiling spacing.

Sloping ceilings are defined in 3.3.31.2 as ceilings that have a slope of more than 1 in 8. A slope of 1 in 8 corresponds to a rise-over-run ratio of 0.125 or an angle of about 7.2 degrees. Any slope less than or equal to 1 in 8 is a level ceiling. Beams that are parallel to the slope are perpendicular to the ridge beam of the roof. (Beams that are perpendicular to the slope are parallel to the ridge beam.)

New research has been conducted on sloped ceilings since the technical committee action on the 2007 edition. The new requirements in 17.7.3.2.4.3 are based on that research.

The concept behind these design requirements is analogous to those regarding heat detectors. When a buoyant plume from a flaming fire impinges on a sloped ceiling, it will progress rapidly upward toward the ridge beam. The buoyancy of the ceiling jet gases accelerates the ceiling jet up the slope. This acceleration provides for faster response by detectors that are up-slope from the fire. Computer CFD modeling demonstrated that the beams are very effective in channeling the smoke in the beam channel up the slope to the peak of the roof. This rapid upward flow reduces the lateral flow parallel to the ridge beam.

A.17.7.3.2.4.3 A smoke detector should be placed within each beam channel. Computer modeling has shown that parallel beams (upslope) are very effective at channeling smoke, and smoke spillover is rarely detectable in adjacent parallel pockets.

17.7.3.2.4.4* For sloping ceilings with beams running perpendicular across slope, the following shall apply:

(1) Spot-type detector(s) shall be located at the bottom of the beams.
(2) The ceiling height shall be taken as the average height over slope.
(3) Spacing shall be measured along a horizontal projection of the ceiling.
(4) Smooth ceiling spacing shall be permitted within beam pocket(s).
(5) For beam depths less than or equal to 10 percent of the ceiling height (0.1 H), spot-type detectors shall be located with smooth ceiling spacing.
(6) For beam depths greater than 10 percent of the ceiling height (0.1 H), spot-type detectors shall not be required to be located closer than (0.4 H) and shall not exceed 50 percent of smooth ceiling spacing.

Beams that are perpendicular to the slope are parallel to the ridge beam. These beams form dams that prevent the smoke from flowing up the ceiling slope toward the ridge beam. When the smoke encounters a beam running across the slope, the ceiling jet will begin forming a smoke layer. Smoke will flow laterally as the depth of the smoke layer increases. Eventually the smoke layer will become deep enough to spill over the beam and begin filling the next bay. This process is a much slower propagation than when the beams run up the slope. However, the damming effect of the beams will tend to channel smoke across the roof, parallel to the beams. The spacing adjustments in this section are the result of a detailed analysis of the computer CFD modeling research that was conducted to investigate this issue.

A.17.7.3.2.4.4 Irregular area spacing guidance for level beam ceilings can be used. Computer modeling has shown that spot-type detectors should be located on the bottom of perpendicular beams.

17.7.3.2.4.5* For sloped ceilings with beam pockets formed by intersecting beams, the following shall apply:

(1) Spot-type detector(s) shall be located at the bottom of the beams.
(2) The ceiling height shall be taken as the average height over slope.
(3) Spacing shall be measured along a horizontal projection of the ceiling.
(4) For beam depths less than or equal to 10 percent of the ceiling height (0.1 *H*), spot-type detectors shall be spaced with not more than three beams between detectors and shall not exceed smooth ceiling spacing.
(5) For beam depths greater than 10 percent of the ceiling height (0.1 *H*), spot-type detectors shall be spaced with not more than two beams between detectors, but shall not be required to be spaced closer than (0.4 *H*), and shall not exceed 50 percent of smooth ceiling spacing.

A.17.7.3.2.4.5 Computer modeling has shown that spot-type detectors should be located on the bottom of perpendicular beams and should be aligned with the center of pocket, as shown, in Figure A.17.7.3.2.4.5.

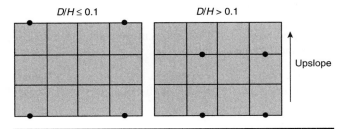

FIGURE A.17.7.3.2.4.5 *Spot-Type Detector Spacing for Sloping Ceilings with Beam Pockets.*

17.7.3.2.4.6 For sloped ceilings with solid joists, the detectors shall be located on the bottom of the joist.

The relatively small volume of the channel between joists results in smoke filling this volume quickly. Once filled, the smoke flows across the bottom of the joists. Locating smoke detectors at the bottom of the joist places them where the dominant flow of smoke is expected to occur. Paragraph 17.7.3.2.4.1 specifies that solid joists be treated as beams for smoke detector spacing guidelines. However, where the beams are actually joists, that is, greater than 4 in. (100 mm) in depth and on centers 3.0 ft (0.9 m) or less, the detectors *must* be placed on the bottoms of the joists. Keep in mind that bar joists or open web beams do not affect smoke flow unless the top plate exceeds 4 in. (100 mm) in depth.

17.7.3.3* Peaked. Detectors shall first be spaced and located within 36 in. (910 mm) of the peak, measured horizontally. The number and spacing of additional detectors, if any, shall be based on the horizontal projection of the ceiling.

A.17.7.3.3 Refer to Figure A.17.6.3.4(a).

The criteria in 17.7.3.3 are applicable to all types of smoke detection. Where the ceiling is not level, the plume and the resulting ceiling jet will concentrate smoke in the highest portion of the interior volume. By requiring that the location of detectors begin with a row of detectors, or their equivalent, at the peak of the peaked roof and space rows of detectors, or their equivalent, down the sloping ceiling from that high point, an optimally responsive design is ensured.

17.7.3.4* Shed. Detectors shall first be spaced and located within 36 in. (910 mm) of the high side of the ceiling, measured horizontally. The number and spacing of additional detectors, if any, shall be based on the horizontal projection of the ceiling.

A.17.7.3.4 Refer to Figure A.17.6.3.4(b).

17.7.3.5 Raised Floors and Suspended Ceilings. Spaces beneath raised floors and above suspended ceilings shall be treated as separate rooms for smoke detector spacing purposes. Detectors installed beneath raised floors or above suspended ceilings, or both, including raised floors and suspended ceilings used for environmental air, shall not be used in lieu of providing detection within the room.

When total coverage is required by the authority having jurisdiction or other codes, 17.5.3.1 requires detection in all accessible spaces (combustible or noncombustible) and in inaccessible combustible spaces. The spaces beneath raised floors and above suspended ceilings usually fall into that category and, hence, require detection using the same location and spacing concepts as required for the occupied portion of a building.

17.7.3.5.1 For raised floors, the following shall apply:

(1) Detectors installed beneath raised floors shall be spaced in accordance with 17.7.3.1, 17.7.3.1.3, and 17.7.3.2.2.
(2) Where the area beneath the raised floor is also used for environmental air, detector spacing shall also conform to 17.7.4.1 and 17.7.4.2.

Although the requirements of Chapter 17, particularly Section 17.7, apply as a whole, the referenced paragraphs have a specific bearing on smoke detector applications in these spaces.

17.7.3.5.2 For suspended ceilings, the following shall apply:

(1) Detector spacing above suspended ceilings shall conform to the requirements of 17.7.3 for the ceiling configuration.
(2) Where detectors are installed in ceilings used for environmental air, detector spacing shall also conform to 17.7.4.1 and 17.7.4.2.

17.7.3.6 Air Sampling–Type Smoke Detector.

Air sampling–type detector, addressed in 17.7.3.6, is defined in 3.3.59.1. These detectors use one or more sampling tubes and draw a sample of air from the hazard area to the detector, where the presence of visible smoke or invisible combustion products is determined. These detectors include a number of cloud chamber–type smoke detectors and several varieties of high sensitivity, photoelectric-type smoke detectors. Air sampling–type smoke detectors consist of a sampling tube network, an aspirating fan, and a highly sensitive centralized detector.

Air sampling–type detectors are used in a variety of applications where the designer is concerned with very early smoke detection and where increased sensitivity is needed to meet the owner's fire protection goals. Because of their sensitivity ranges, air-sampling detectors are often used in areas that house valuable equipment. See Exhibits 17.27 through 17.30 for examples of air sampling–type smoke detectors.

17.7.3.6.1 Each sampling port of an air sampling–type smoke detector shall be treated as a spot-type detector for the purpose of location and spacing.

The International Fire Detection Research Project considered an issue directly relating to air sampling–type detectors when it evaluated the flow velocity field in the immediate vicinity of the sampling port. This research showed that the sampling port does *not* produce the effect of drawing the smoke up to the sampling port from lower down in the compartment. Conse-

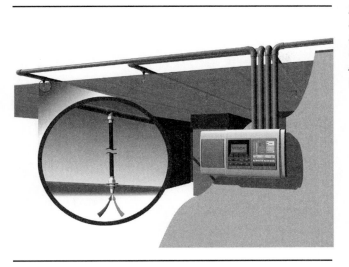

EXHIBIT 17.27 *Use of Sampling Tubes to Convey Smoke-Laden Air to the Central Detection Unit of an Air-Sampling Detector. (Source: Xtralis, Norwell, MA)*

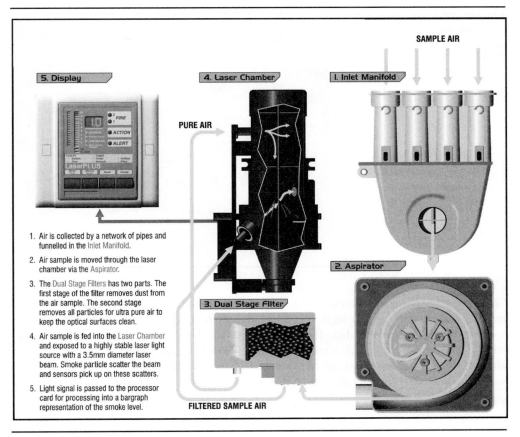

EXHIBIT 17.28 *How an Optical Air-Sampling System Works. (Source: Xtralis, Norwell, MA)*

1. Air is collected by a network of pipes and funnelled in the Inlet Manifold.

2. Air sample is moved through the laser chamber via the Aspirator.

3. The Dual Stage Filters has two parts. The first stage of the filter removes dust from the air sample. The second stage removes all particles for ultra pure air to keep the optical surfaces clean.

4. Air sample is fed into the Laser Chamber and exposed to a highly stable laser light source with a 3.5mm diameter laser beam. Smoke particle scatter the beam and sensors pick up on these scatters.

5. Light signal is passed to the processor card for processing into a bargraph representation of the smoke level.

quently, when air-sampling detectors are used to protect rooms and other large compartments, they rely on either ambient air currents or the fire plume and ceiling jet as much as spot-type smoke detectors.

17.7.3.6.2 Maximum air sample transport time from the farthest sampling port to the detector shall not exceed 120 seconds.

EXHIBIT 17.29 *Air Sampling–Type Smoke Detectors. (Source: Xtralis, Norwell, MA)*

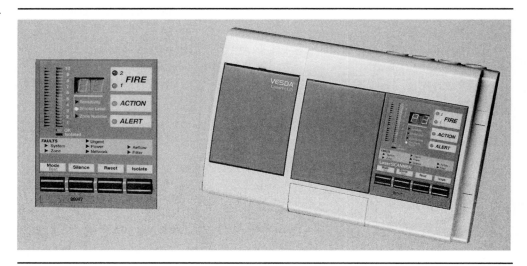

EXHIBIT 17.30 *Air Sampling–Type Smoke Detector with Cover Removed. (Source: Fenwal Protection Systems, Ashland, MA)*

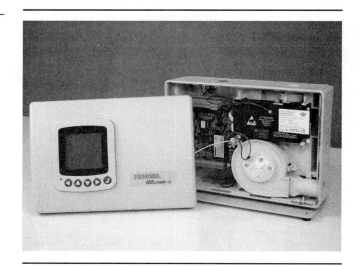

FAQ ▶
What effect does limiting the transport time have on the system design?

The air transport time criterion in 17.7.3.6.2 places an effective limit on the design of the fan and the maximum distance from the detector to the farthest sampling port, as well as the size and layout of the sampling tubes. The manufacturer's listing and instructions provide the details on how the particular product must be used in order to comply with this limitation. Some air sampling–type smoke detectors have a means to detect changes in airflow, which provides some measure of monitoring the integrity of the tubing or piping network.

17.7.3.6.3* Sampling pipe networks shall be designed on the basis of, and shall be supported by, sound fluid dynamic principles to ensure required performance.

A.17.7.3.6.3 A single-pipe network has a shorter transport time than a multiple-pipe network of similar length pipe; however, a multiple-pipe system provides a faster smoke transport time than a single-pipe system of the same total length. As the number of sampling holes in a pipe increases, the smoke transport time increases. Where practicable, pipe run lengths in a multiple-pipe system should be nearly equal, or the system should be otherwise pneumatically balanced.

The manufacturers of air sampling–type smoke detectors provide engineering guidelines in their installation manuals that ensure that the products meet the criteria of 17.7.3.6.3. These guidelines are evaluated by testing laboratories as part of the listing evaluation procedure. The factors in A.17.7.3.6.3 are generalizations that the designer can use as guidance in deciding the type of piping network that best serves the application under consideration.

17.7.3.6.4 Sampling pipe network design details shall include calculations showing the flow characteristics of the pipe network and each sample port.

The transport time is determined by flow calculations. Flow calculations provide the only way to be certain that sufficient pressure and flow volume are available at all the sampling ports and that the air sampling–type detector will provide detection over the entire area it is to cover.

17.7.3.6.5 Air-sampling detectors shall give a trouble signal if the airflow is outside the manufacturer's specified range.

The detection of a flow rate outside the manufacturer's design range is indicative of a failure of the physical integrity of the sampling tubes. This requirement is analogous to the monitoring for integrity of the initiating device circuit wiring.

17.7.3.6.6* The sampling ports and in-line filter, if used, shall be kept clear in accordance with the manufacturer's published instructions.

A.17.7.3.6.6 The air sampling–type detector system should be able to withstand dusty environments by either air filtering or electronic discrimination of particle size. The detector should be capable of providing optimal time delays of alarm outputs to eliminate nuisance alarms due to transient smoke conditions. The detector should also provide facilities for the connection of monitoring equipment for the recording of background smoke level information necessary in setting alert and alarm levels and delays.

Dust from the protected space can cause clogging of the sampling tubes as well as the sampling ports of those makes of detectors that employ a filter at the sampling port. Both clogging and filter loading can lead to reduced sampling flow from the affected portions of the sampling network.

17.7.3.6.7 Air-sampling network piping and fittings shall be airtight and permanently fixed.

Although Article 760 of the *NEC* has detailed criteria for detection system wiring, no national consensus standards are published for sampling tube installation. Each manufacturer makes its own recommendations that establish the minimum compliance criteria for that product. The integrity of the sampling tube network is just as important to the air sampling–type detector as the integrity of the wiring is to the spot-type smoke detector. The installation methods used for air-sampling tubing should provide equivalent security and mechanical protection.

17.7.3.6.8 Sampling system piping shall be conspicuously identified as "SMOKE DETECTOR SAMPLING TUBE — DO NOT DISTURB," as follows:

(1) At changes in direction or branches of piping
(2) At each side of penetrations of walls, floors, or other barriers
(3) At intervals on piping that provide visibility within the space, but no greater than 20 ft (6.1 m)

Numerous building systems are often installed in the above-ceiling space. If the sampling tubing is damaged by some other trade at a later time, a break in the air-sampling detector piping could result in the detector sampling the above-ceiling air rather than the air beneath the ceiling plane, as intended. This possibility necessitates that tubing be clearly marked in a manner that will endure for the lifetime of the unit.

17.7.3.7* Projected Beam–Type Smoke Detectors.

A.17.7.3.7 On smooth ceilings, a spacing of not more than 60 ft (18.3 m) between projected beams and not more than one-half that spacing between a projected beam and a sidewall (wall parallel to the beam travel) should be used as a guide. Other spacing should be determined based on ceiling height, airflow characteristics, and response requirements.

In some cases, the light beam projector is mounted on one end wall, with the light beam receiver mounted on the opposite wall. However, it is also permitted to suspend the projector and receiver from the ceiling at a distance from the end walls not exceeding one-quarter the selected spacing (*S*). *(See Figure A.17.7.3.7.)*

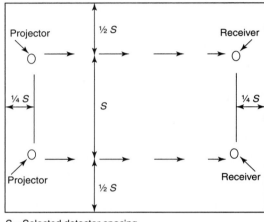

S = Selected detector spacing

FIGURE A.17.7.3.7   Maximum Distance at Which Ceiling-Suspended Light Projector and Receiver Can Be Positioned from End Wall Is One-Quarter Selected Spacing (S).

17.7.3.7.1 Projected beam–type smoke detectors shall be located in accordance with the manufacturer's published instructions.

Each make and model of linear projected beam–type smoke detector has specific installation limitations as well as performance capabilities. Most notable of these limitations are the maximum and the minimum beam lengths. The designer should make certain that the contemplated installation is consistent with the criteria established in the published installation instructions of the product the designer plans to use.

17.7.3.7.2 The effects of stratification shall be evaluated when locating the detectors.

As with other types of smoke detection, the location selected for detectors must account for the effects of stratification. In high-ceiling areas where stratification is probable and a serious concern, detectors can be positioned at several levels. Alternatively, the methods in Annex B can be used to calculate the plume divergence at the detector mounting height. The plume width at the detector mounting height can then be used as the "spacing" between adjacent beams in a performance-based design.

Why is the observance of the manufacturer's beam length limitations important?

FAQ ▶

17.7.3.7.3 The beam length shall not exceed the maximum permitted by the equipment listing.

Linear projected beam–type smoke detectors have limitations on both the minimum and the maximum beam lengths over which they will operate properly. The minimum beam length limitation is established by the lowest smoke concentration that can be detected at that minimum beam length. The maximum beam length is determined by the maximum distance at which the detector can maintain its design stability even when some normal light obscuration is present. The projected beam–type smoke detector must be able to identify a low concentration of smoke distributed along a substantial portion of the beam and a high concentration of smoke localized in a short segment of the beam. Each manufacturer obtains a listing from a qualified testing laboratory that sets the upper and lower limits on the beam length. Failure to observe these limits could result in an unstable detector or the failure to detect a fire consistent with the performance objectives.

17.7.3.7.4 If mirrors are used with projected beams, the mirrors shall be installed in accordance with the manufacturer's published instructions.

Mirrors used with linear projected beam–type smoke detectors must also be listed for use with the detector.

17.7.3.7.5 A projected beam–type smoke detector shall be considered equivalent to a row of spot-type smoke detectors for level and sloping ceiling applications.

The similarity between the installation and spacing concepts developed for line-type heat detectors and projected-beam smoke detectors should be noted. The logic behind the design rules remains consistent. When spacing strategies are being developed, just as a line-type heat detector can be thought of as a row of spot-type heat detectors, it is often helpful to think of a linear projected-beam detector as equivalent to a row of spot-type smoke detectors, as stated in 17.7.3.7.5. The distance between the linear projected beams is analogous to the distance between rows of spot-type smoke detectors.

17.7.3.7.6 Projected beam–type detectors and mirrors shall be mounted on stable surfaces to prevent false or erratic operation due to movement.

17.7.3.7.7 The beam shall be designed so that small angular movements of the light source or receiver do not prevent operation due to smoke and do not cause nuisance alarms.

Contrary to popular belief, buildings move under normal, everyday conditions. Portions of buildings vibrate due to traffic on nearby streets. Buildings sway due to wind or uneven thermal expansion; even the ebb and flow of the tides can cause oceanfront buildings to flex. Modern curtain wall/steel frame buildings are designed to flex. This movement, however, places a demand on fire alarm systems, especially fire alarm systems using projected-beam smoke detection. The detectors must be able to accommodate the natural or designed movement of the building. The manufacturers of projected beam–type detectors provide installation instructions that address the potential for this type of difficulty. Because of the physical instability of mounting surfaces and building movement, some manufacturers do not allow the use of mirrors. Often a limiting factor on beam length is the diameter of the projected beam and the receiver in relation to the expected flexure of the building.

17.7.3.7.8* The light path of projected beam–type detectors shall be kept clear of opaque obstacles at all times.

A.17.7.3.7.8 Where the light path of a projected beam–type detector is abruptly interrupted or obscured, the unit should not initiate an alarm. It should give a trouble signal after verification of blockage.

Modern projected beam–type detectors use obscuration algorithms in their software that can distinguish the progressive obscuration that occurs during a fire with the step-wise obscuration that usually indicates interference in the path of the beam by an opaque object. However, in spite of the most sophisticated software, Christmas decorations, party balloons, and hanging plants have been known to cause problems. Obstructions that can gradually grow and block a beam detector, such as trees in an atrium, should also be considered a potential problem.

17.7.4 Heating, Ventilating, and Air-Conditioning (HVAC).

17.7.4.1* In spaces served by air-handling systems, detectors shall not be located where airflow prevents operation of the detectors.

A.17.7.4.1 Detectors should not be located in a direct airflow or closer than 36 in. (910 mm) from an air supply diffuser or return air opening. Supply or return sources larger than those commonly found in residential and small commercial establishments can require greater clearance to smoke detectors. Similarly, smoke detectors should be located farther away from high velocity air supplies.

For years, the rule in 17.7.4.1 had been applied only to air supplies. In research conducted under the International Fire Detection Research Project, managed by the Fire Protection Research Foundation, the computer modeling conducted by the National Institute of Standards and Technology (NIST) identified situations where areas of nonactuation extended almost 11 ft (3.4 m) from some supply diffusers. In addition, the research showed that a smoke dilution effect occurred near air returns. An air return pulls air up from levels in the room that are beneath the ceiling jet, which has the effect of diluting smoke concentration near the air return grille. Consequently, the designer should arrange the detection so that detectors are not adjacent to either air supplies or air returns.

Situations may exist where even a 3 ft (0.9 m) separation is not adequate. This situation would depend on the air velocity (supply air and return air) and the throw characteristics of the supply diffuser and diffuser size. Unfortunately, because the research did not address wide variations in HVAC flow rates, the minimum distance between a detector and the HVAC system supply or return recommended in A.17.7.4.1 might not be valid in all cases. Where in doubt, airflow in the vicinity of the detector should be mapped with a velometer or anemometer. Certainly, the ambient airflow at the detector location should be only a fraction of that used in the UL 268 smoke box of 30 ft/min (0.152 m/sec).

17.7.4.2 Detectors installed in plenums shall comply with 17.7.4.2.1 and 17.7.4.2.2.

17.7.4.2.1 In under-floor spaces and above-ceiling spaces that are used as HVAC plenums, detectors shall be listed for the anticipated environment as required by 17.7.1.8. Detector spacings and locations shall be selected on the basis of anticipated airflow patterns and fire type.

To cool a room to 70°F (21°C), the introduction of extremely frigid air into the room may be necessary. Conversely, heating a room sometimes requires introducing extremely hot air into a room. Consequently, HVAC plenums usually have ambient conditions that are far more extreme than the spaces they support.

Smoke detectors are electronic sensors. Ambient temperature, the relative humidity, and, especially in the case of spot-type ionization detectors, the velocity of the air around the detector all affect detector operation. Not all smoke detectors are listed for the range of conditions found in HVAC plenums or in under-floor or above-ceiling spaces. It is the designer's responsibility to verify that the detector is listed for use in the range of environmental conditions that will be encountered where it is to be installed. See also 17.7.1.8 and A.17.7.1.8.

17.7.4.2.2* Detectors placed in environmental air ducts or plenums shall not be used as a substitute for open area detectors. Where detectors are used for the control of smoke spread, the requirements of 17.7.5 shall apply. Where open area protection is required, 17.7.3 shall apply.

In most buildings, there are times when the HVAC system is not moving significant quantities of air from the compartments it serves. This is typical of variable air volume (VAV) systems. Consequently, the fire detection system cannot be designed to rely on the HVAC system operation for the transport of smoke to smoke detectors.

A.17.7.4.2.2 Smoke might not be drawn into the duct or plenums when the ventilating system is shut down. Furthermore, when the ventilating system is operating, the detector(s) can be less responsive to a fire condition in the room of fire origin due to dilution by clean air.

17.7.5* Smoke Detectors for Control of Smoke Spread.

A.17.7.5 Refer to NFPA *101, Life Safety Code*, for the definition of smoke compartment; NFPA 90A, *Standard for the Installation of Air-Conditioning and Ventilating Systems*, for the definition of duct systems; and NFPA 92A, *Standard for Smoke-Control Systems Utilizing Barriers and Pressure Differences*, for the definition of smoke zone.

Between 1960 and 1971, several fires in high-rise buildings demonstrated the difficulty of trying to evacuate an entire building. Not only did occupants incur injuries during the evacuation, but also the means of egress often became untenable due to heavy smoke concentrations.

As improved building codes resulted in structures that could maintain their integrity in spite of the complete combustion of the interior fire load through passive fire-resistive construction and compartmentation, defending occupants in place became a viable option. Strategies for establishing smoke compartments and areas of refuge and for managing the flow of smoke by directing it away from the occupants were developed. Experiences with high-rise fires indicate that the proactive control of smoke with either automatic smoke detectors and HVAC systems or engineered smoke control systems is a viable strategy for occupant protection in high-rise buildings.

Subsection 17.7.5 does not require the installation of smoke detectors for smoke control. The purpose of 17.7.5 is to describe the performance and installation requirements for smoke detectors being used for smoke control, as required by some other code or standard.

◄ **FAQ**
Does 17.7.5 require the installation of smoke detectors for smoke control?

17.7.5.1* Classifications. Smoke detectors installed and used to prevent smoke spread by initiating control of fans, dampers, doors, and other equipment shall be classified in the following manner:

(1) Area detectors that are installed in the related smoke compartments
(2) Detectors that are installed in the air duct systems
(3) Video image smoke detection that is installed in related smoke compartments

Either dedicated detectors installed in the HVAC system or area detectors can be used to control smoke spread. With modern addressable/analog detection technology, individual ceiling-mounted spot-type detectors produce discrete alarm signal codes that are logged by the fire alarm control unit. This technology permits the use of area detection without the incremental cost of large numbers of detector relays, as was the case decades ago. Both projected beam smoke detectors and video image smoke detectors are also used as area detection and can be used as an input signal for the control of the HVAC system serving the related smoke compartments.

A.17.7.5.1 Smoke detectors located in an open area(s) should be used rather than duct-type detectors because of the dilution effect in air ducts. Active smoke management systems installed in accordance with NFPA 92A, *Standard for Smoke-Control Systems Utilizing Barriers and Pressure Differences*, or NFPA 92B, *Standard for Smoke Management Systems in Malls, Atria, and Large Spaces*, should be controlled by total coverage open area detection.

Paragraph 17.5.3.1 identifies all the spaces that must have smoke detectors if total coverage is to be achieved.

17.7.5.2* Limitations.

A.17.7.5.2 Dilution of smoke-laden air by clean air from other parts of the building or dilution by outside air intakes can allow high densities of smoke in a single room with no appreciable smoke in the air duct at the detector location. Smoke might not be drawn from open areas if air-conditioning systems or ventilating systems are shut down.

17.7.5.2.1 Detectors that are installed in the air duct system in accordance with 17.7.5.1(2) shall not be used as a substitute for open area protection.

All too often, uninformed designers attempt to use air duct–type smoke detectors to provide open area protection. This strategy does not address the potential for a fire during those times when the HVAC system is not running, nor does it address the delay in detection due to smoke dilution. Paragraph 17.7.5.2.1 specifically prohibits the use of duct smoke detection in lieu of area detection installed pursuant to Section 17.7.

17.7.5.2.2 Where open area protection is required, 17.7.3 shall apply.

17.7.5.3* Purposes.

A.17.7.5.3 Smoke detectors can be applied in order to initiate control of smoke spread for the following purposes:

(1) Prevention of the recirculation of dangerous quantities of smoke within a building
(2) Selective operation of equipment to exhaust smoke from a building
(3) Selective operation of equipment to pressurize smoke compartments
(4) Operation of doors and dampers to close the openings in smoke compartments

17.7.5.3.1 To prevent the recirculation of dangerous quantities of smoke, a detector approved for air duct use shall be installed on the supply side of air-handling systems as required by NFPA 90A, *Standard for the Installation of Air-Conditioning and Ventilating Systems*, and 17.7.5.4.2.1.

17.7.5.3.2 If smoke detectors are used to initiate selectively the operation of equipment to control smoke spread, the requirements of 17.7.5.4.2.2 shall apply.

17.7.5.3.3 If detectors are used to initiate the operation of smoke doors, the requirements of 17.7.5.6 shall apply.

17.7.5.3.4 If duct detectors are used to initiate the operation of smoke dampers within ducts, the requirements of 17.7.5.5 shall apply.

17.7.5.4 Application.

17.7.5.4.1 Area Smoke Detectors Within Smoke Compartments. Area smoke detectors within smoke compartments shall be permitted to be used to control the spread of smoke by initiating operation of doors, dampers, and other equipment.

Paragraph 17.7.5.4.1 allows area detectors to serve the additional purpose of providing signals to initiate the control of the spread of smoke. Although this approach might not have been very practical when the only available technology was conventional detection on an initiating device circuit, now addressable/analog detectors, whose principal function is area protection, can be used effectively to provide signals that are then used to control smoke spread. Existing detectors can perform double duty through the programming of the fire alarm control unit. When area smoke detectors are used, smoke detectors are needed where they can identify the presence of smoke at a particular location or the movement of smoke past a particular location. The locations for area smoke detectors are a function of building geometry, anticipated fire locations, and intended goals of smoke control functions.

FAQ ▶
Is complete area smoke detection always required?

Except where used as permitted in 17.7.5.4.2.2(B), complete area smoke detection is not necessary to provide for such control features. Specific locations are often identified for specific fire scenarios. For example, smoke detectors are often placed at the perimeter of an atrium to detect smoke movement into the atrium space from a corridor that opens into the atrium. Another example is the use of smoke detectors to release smoke doors only as their associated smoke detector is actuated, thus avoiding premature release of all other doors. Selective door release is sometimes chosen to prevent the premature release of doors needed to facilitate rapid evacuation.

Paragraph 17.7.5.4.1 also allows complete area coverage to be used for the control of smoke spread. In this case, when a compartment detector actuates in the smoke compartment, it signals the fire alarm control unit, which, in turn, signals the HVAC control system or smoke door release system. The HVAC controller operates or controls fans and dampers to prevent the introduction of smoke into other smoke compartments and to vent the smoke from the fire compartment, facilitating occupant egress. The smoke door release system either closes all doors in the building or all doors in the smoke zone.

17.7.5.4.2* Smoke Detection for the Air Duct System.

A.17.7.5.4.2 Smoke detectors are designed to sense the presence of particles of combustion, but depending on the sensing technology and other design factors, different detectors respond to different types of particles. Detectors based on ionization detection technology are most responsive to smaller, invisible sub-micron sized particles. Detectors based on photoelectric technology, by contrast, are most responsive to larger visible particles.

It is generally accepted that particle size distribution varies from sub-micron diameter particles predominant in the proximity of the flame of a flaming fire to particles one or more orders of magnitude larger, which are characteristic of smoke from a smoldering fire. The actual particle size distribution depends on a host of other variables including the fuel and its physical make-up, the availability of oxygen including air supply and fire–gas discharge, and other ambient conditions, especially humidity. Moreover, the particle size distribution is not constant, but as the fire gases cool, the sub-micron particles agglomerate and the very large ones precipitate. In other words, as smoke travels away from the fire source, the particle size distribution shows a relative decrease in smaller particles. Water vapor, which is abundantly present in most fires, when cooled sufficiently will condense to form fog particles — an effect frequently seen above tall chimneys. Because water condensation is basically clear in color, when it is mixed with other smoke particles, it can be expected to lighten the color of the mixture.

In almost every fire scenario in an air-handling system, the point of detection will be some distance from the fire source; therefore, the smoke will be cooler and more visible because of the growth of sub-micron particles into larger particles due to agglomeration and recombination. For these reasons, photoelectric detection technology has advantages over ionization detection technology in air duct system applications.

17.7.5.4.2.1 Supply Air System. Where the detection of smoke in the supply air system is required by other NFPA standards, a detector(s) listed for the air velocity present and that is located in the supply air duct downstream of both the fan and the filters shall be installed.

Exception: Additional smoke detectors shall not be required to be installed in ducts where the air duct system passes through other smoke compartments not served by the duct.

The NFPA standards relevant to 17.7.5.4.2.1 are NFPA 90A; NFPA 92A, *Standard for Smoke-Control Systems Utilizing Barriers and Pressure Differences*; and NFPA *101*. The purpose of supply-side smoke detection is the sensing of smoke that might be contaminating the area served by the duct but not as a result of a fire in that area. The smoke might be coming from another area via return air ducts, from outside via fresh air mixing ducts, or from a fire within the duct (such as in a filter or fan belt). If the source of the smoke is from outside or from within the duct, a fire alarm response for area detection within the space would not normally be expected to produce the most appropriate set of responses.

Different airflow management programs are required for supply-side smoke inflow as opposed to smoke generated within the compartment. Furthermore, compartment area detection cannot be relied on to respond to a supply duct smoke inflow, because of the expected dilution of smoke-laden air with fresh air as it enters the smoke compartment where the area detection is installed. This expected condition necessitates the use of detectors downstream of the fan and filters in the supply air duct.

The exception to 17.7.5.4.2.1 is based on the fire resistance of HVAC ducts and the unlikelihood of smoke escaping from the HVAC duct into a compartment not served by the duct.

Refer to the following excerpt from NFPA 90A for supply and return air smoke detection requirements.

> **6.4.2* Location. [90A:6.4.2]**
>
> **6.4.2.1** Smoke detectors listed for use in air distribution systems shall be located as follows:
> (1) Downstream of the air filters and ahead of any branch connections in air supply systems having a capacity greater than 944 L/sec (2000 ft³/min)
> (2) At each story prior to the connection to a common return and prior to any recirculation or fresh air inlet connection in air return systems having a capacity greater than 7080 L/sec (15,000 ft³/min) and serving more than one story [**90A:**6.4.2.1]
>
> **6.4.2.2** Return system smoke detectors shall not be required where the entire space served by the air distribution system is protected by a system of area smoke detectors. [**90A:**6.4.2.2]
>
> **6.4.2.3** Smoke detectors shall not be required for fan units whose sole function is to remove air from the inside of the building to the outside of the building. [**90A:**6.4.2.3]

17.7.5.4.2.2* Return Air System. Unless otherwise modified by 17.7.5.4.2.2(A) or 17.7.5.4.2.2(B), if the detection of smoke in the return air system is required by other NFPA standards, a detector(s) listed for the air velocity present shall be located where the air leaves each smoke compartment, or in the duct system before the air enters the return air system common to more than one smoke compartment.

(A) Additional smoke detectors shall not be required to be installed in ducts where the air duct system passes through other smoke compartments not served by the duct.

Paragraph 17.7.5.4.2.2(A) is based on the same reasoning used in the exception to 17.7.5.4.2.1. With reference to Figure A.17.7.5.4.2.2(c), the top duct does not need additional detectors and/or dampers where it passes through either the center compartment or the right compartment.

(B) Where total coverage smoke detection is installed in all areas of the smoke compartment served by the return air system, installation of air duct detectors in the return air system shall not be required, provided that their function is accomplished by the design of the area detection system.

The key phrase in 17.7.5.4.2.2(B) is "provided that their function is accomplished by the design of the area detection system." When an engineering analysis shows that the area smoke detection addresses all the smoke ingress paths from the compartment into the return air duct, this allowance is operative. Naturally, the analysis must be fully documented and made part of the permanent fire alarm system design file.

A.17.7.5.4.2.2 Detectors listed for the air velocity present can be permitted to be installed at the opening where the return air enters the common return air system. The detectors should be installed up to 12 in. (300 mm) in front of or behind the opening and spaced according to the following opening dimensions *[see Figure A.17.7.5.4.2.2(a) through Figure A.17.7.5.4.2.2(c)]*:

(1) *Width.*

    (a) Up to 36 in. (910 mm) — One detector centered in opening
    (b) Up to 72 in. (1.83 m) — Two detectors located at the one-quarter points of the opening
    (c) Over 72 in. (1.83 m) — One additional detector for each full 24 in. (610 mm) of opening

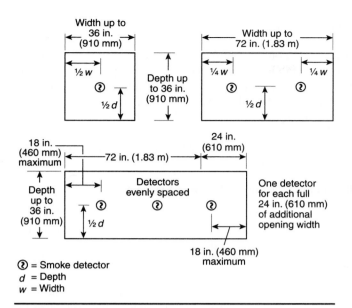

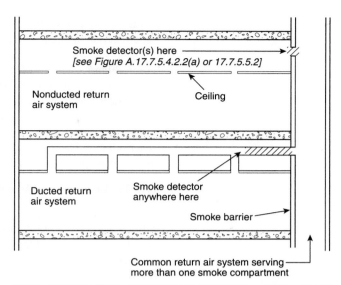

FIGURE A.17.7.5.4.2.2(a) *Location of a Smoke Detector(s) in Return Air System Openings for Selective Operation of Equipment.*

FIGURE A.17.7.5.4.2.2(b) *Location of a Smoke Detector(s) in Return Air Systems for Selective Operation of Equipment.*

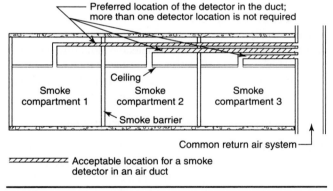

FIGURE A.17.7.5.4.2.2(c) *Detector Location in a Duct that Passes Through Smoke Compartments Not Served by the Duct.*

(2) *Depth.* The number and spacing of the detector(s) in the depth (vertical) of the opening should be the same as those given for the width (horizontal) in A.17.7.5.4.2.2(1).

(3) *Orientation.* Detectors should be oriented in the most favorable position for smoke entry with respect to the direction of airflow. The path of a projected beam–type detector across the return air openings should be considered equivalent in coverage to a row of individual detectors.

The objective of HVAC system return detection is to prevent the recirculation of smoke-laden air to other, smoke-free portions of the building via the HVAC system. While use of complete area detection is preferable because it provides the earliest possible response, the use of return duct detection is permitted and most often used.

If duct detection is used for control of smoke spread, detectors must be installed only where the return air duct leaves the smoke compartment or before the duct joins a return air

Where must detectors be installed if duct detection is used in return air applications?

◄ **FAQ**

plenum serving more than one smoke compartment. These locations are intended to minimize the effects of smoke dilution.

The specific detector location criteria outlined in A.17.7.5.4.2.2 are intended to achieve a representative sample of the air flowing into the system. The HVAC system return will draw air from a portion of the room volume based on its location. Ceiling returns pull fresh air up from lower elevations in the room, through the ceiling jet, diluting the smoke. Wall-mounted returns also tend to draw in air from a range of elevations in the room, reducing the relative smoke concentration. Consequently, dilution is almost always present and almost always delays response. Therefore, dilution is one of the reasons that duct-type smoke detection will be slower than spot detection in the area of the fire.

17.7.5.5 Location and Installation of Detectors in Air Duct Systems.

Sampling tubes provide a flow of air through the detector enclosure due to a pressure differential that results from the flow of air across the tubes. Small errors in the orientation of the sampling tubes can reduce the pressure differential, rendering them ineffective in drawing air into the detector enclosure, especially at low air velocities in variable air volume (VAV) HVAC systems.

For sampling tubes to take a representative sample of the air passing through the duct, they must be fabricated and installed in a manner consistent with their listing. The pressure differential between the inflow and outflow tubes is usually measured with either a manometer or pressure gauges. (See Exhibit 14.11.) If the flow of air through the sampling tube and the detector enclosure assembly cannot be verified, as required by 17.7.5.5, there is no basis to presume that the air within the duct is being sampled by the detector. Prudent practice dictates that the pressure differential be measured at the lowest air velocity anticipated for the duct where the detector is located in a VAV HVAC system.

Finally, duct-type smoke detectors usually consist of a standard production smoke detector and a specially designed enclosure equipped with a smoke detector mounting base and sampling tube fittings already installed. However, not all detectors are listed for use in a duct smoke detector enclosure that uses sampling tubes. Care should be taken to make certain that the detector is listed for use in the duct smoke detector housing as an assembly.

17.7.5.5.1 Detectors shall be listed for the purpose for which they are being used.

The listing of the detector stipulates the range of air velocities over which it can operate, as well as the temperature and the relative humidity range. These last two criteria are particularly important where a general purpose detector is being installed in a duct detector housing. Often HVAC system fans and ducts are located in penthouses and mechanical rooms, where comfort heating and cooling are not provided. Consequently, it is possible that a smoke detector will be inadvertently installed where the ambient conditions exceed its design range. The location of the duct detector must be maintained within the operating range of the detector used.

17.7.5.5.2* Air duct detectors shall be installed in such a way as to obtain a representative sample of the airstream. This installation shall be permitted to be achieved by any of the following methods:

(1) Rigid mounting within the duct

Support of the detector by the conduit or raceway containing wiring conductors is not permitted by *NFPA 70* unless the box is specifically listed for the purpose and installed in accordance with the listing.

(2) Rigid mounting to the wall of the duct with the sensing element protruding into the duct
(3) Installation outside the duct with rigidly mounted sampling tubes protruding into the duct
(4) Installation through the duct with projected light beam

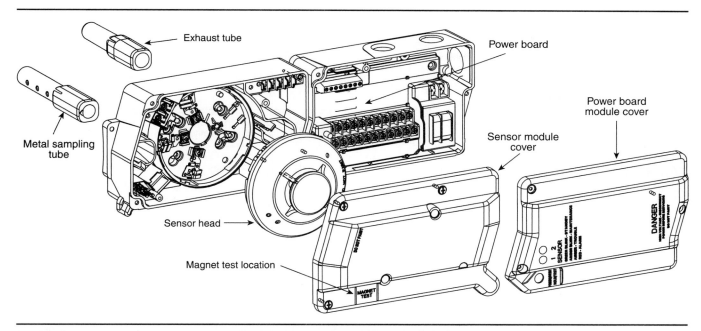

EXHIBIT 17.31 *Internal View of a Duct-Type Smoke Detector. (Source: System Sensor Corp., St. Charles, IL)*

The flow of air through a duct is not necessarily uniform. Bends and changes in cross-sectional area and cross-sectional shape of the duct produce regions of reduced flow velocity and, hence, reduced flow volume. The flow in a duct can also become divided into layers depending on differing temperatures, resulting in smoke being concentrated in a portion of the duct cross-section and not uniformly dispersed across the duct area. The options in 17.7.5.5.2(1) and 17.7.5.5.2(2) are often most appropriate for smaller ducts or where an engineering analysis shows that smoke concentrations will be even across the duct cross-section and that laminar flow is not going to produce a nonuniform smoke concentration. Option (3) is more suited to larger ducts. The use of sampling tubes enables the duct detector to sample the air across the entire duct cross-section rather than a small portion of it. The designer should consult the manufacturer's technical bulletin for installation limitations.

See Exhibits 17.31 and 17.32 for examples of typical duct-type smoke detectors.

A.17.7.5.5.2 Where duct detectors are used to initiate the operation of smoke dampers, they should be located so that the detector is between the last inlet or outlet upstream of the damper and the first inlet or outlet downstream of the damper.

In order to obtain a representative sample, stratification and dead air space should be avoided. Such conditions could be caused by return duct openings, sharp turns, or connections, as well as by long, uninterrupted straight runs.

In return air systems, the requirements of 17.7.5.4.2.2 take precedence over these considerations. *[See Figure A.17.7.5.5.2(a) and Figure A.17.7.5.5.2(b).]*

Usually, it is necessary to manage smoke flow in buildings. Duct smoke detectors are used to shut down HVAC systems or initiate smoke management.

Filters have a serious effect on the performance of duct smoke detectors. The location of the detector relative to the filter and the source of smoke must be considered during the design process. Where smoke detectors are installed downstream from filters, they should be deemed to serve the purpose of providing an alarm indication of the occurrence of a fire in the HVAC unit (filters, belts, heat exchangers, etc.). These detectors usually serve the purpose of protecting building occupants from the smoke produced by an HVAC unit fire, or smoke

EXHIBIT 17.32 *Duct-Type Smoke Detector. (Source: Hochiki America Corp., Buena Park, CA)*

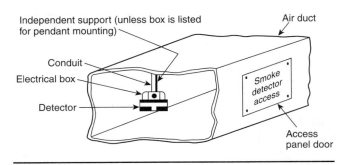

FIGURE A.17.7.5.5.2(a) *Pendant-Mounted Air Duct Installation.*

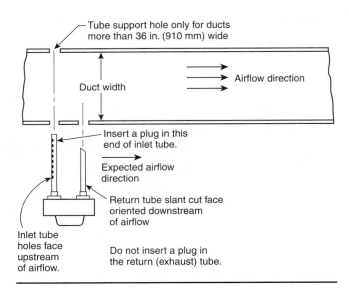

FIGURE A.17.7.5.5.2(b) *Inlet Tube Orientation.*

ingress via the fresh air intake for the unit. They cannot be expected to serve the purpose of providing detection for the return side of the system.

Where return side detection is required, that requirement should be fulfilled with separate detectors from those monitoring the supply side. In order to be effective, return air duct smoke detectors should be located such that there are no filters between them and the source of the smoke.

Sampling tubes should be oriented to overcome thermal stratification due to buoyancy of the smoke in the upper half of the duct. This condition occurs where duct velocities are low, buoyancy exceeds flow inertia, or the detector is installed close to the fire compartment. A vertical orientation of sampling tubes overcomes the effects of differential buoyancy.

Where a detector is installed on a duct serving a single fire compartment, where the buoyancy exceeds the flow inertia of the air in the duct and the sampling tube cannot be oriented vertically, then the effects of thermal stratification can be minimized by locating the detector sampling tube in the upper half of the duct.

The thermal stratification is not a concern where the detector is installed far from the fire compartment or where the smoke is at or close to the average temperature in the duct.

FAQ ▶
According to the research, what orientation has been shown to improve detector performance?

This portion of the Code was substantially revised for the 2007 edition. For years, the Code had recommended that duct detector sampling tubes be located at least 6 to 10 duct diameters downstream of a bend or change in dimension. Research conducted under the auspices of the Fire Detection Institute discovered that the recommendation had no technical basis.

The research also showed that in most cases detector performance would be improved by mounting sampling tubes in a vertical orientation rather than the horizontal orientation most often seen in actual practice. The vertical orientation would provide for effective sampling when thermal stratification in the duct caused variations in smoke concentration. However, the validity of this generalization becomes less reliable when ducts are encountered that are much wider than they are tall in cross-section.

The requirements in 17.7.5.5.2 and the guidance in A.17.7.5.5.2 are provided to ensure that the detectors in the air duct are suitably located to obtain an adequate sampling of air. These location guidelines should be followed to maximize the probability that smoke will be evenly distributed throughout the duct cross-section at the detector location.

17.7.5.5.3 Detectors shall be mounted in accordance with the manufacturer's published instructions and shall be accessible for cleaning by providing access doors or control units in accordance with NFPA 90A, *Standard for the Installation of Air-Conditioning and Ventilating Systems.*

Chapter 14 provides inspection and testing schedules for each type of detector. The accessibility of detectors is critical in order to facilitate cleaning. Poor or neglected maintenance is a dominant cause of unwarranted alarm in smoke detectors.

17.7.5.5.4 The location of all detectors in air duct systems shall be permanently and clearly identified and recorded.

A permanent placard placed outside the first point of access is advisable to indicate that a detector is accessible from that point. For example, the placard might be mounted on the wall beneath the ceiling tile that must be removed to access the duct. HVAC and fire alarm drawings should clearly show the actual as-built locations of the detectors. In most cases, one drawing that shows only the smoke detector locations is useful. The location can also be included in the display descriptor of addressable systems.

17.7.5.5.5 Detectors mounted outside of a duct that employs sampling tubes for transporting smoke from inside the duct to the detector shall be designed and installed to allow verification of airflow from the duct to the detector.

17.7.5.5.6 Detectors shall be listed for operation over the complete range of air velocities, temperature, and humidity expected at the detector when the air-handling system is operating.

The listing requirements of 17.7.5.5.6 are important to ensure proper operation of a detector in its installed location. Often HVAC system fans and ducts are located in penthouses and mechanical rooms, where comfort heating and cooling are not provided. Consequently, the environment of the detector might exceed the limits observed in the listing investigation. In addition, when warm moist air is circulated through a cold duct smoke detector housing, condensation can occur in the duct smoke detector housing. These conditions can seriously degrade detector performance and stability. Where these extremes are likely, provisions must be made to maintain the operating environment of the detector within its operating range.

17.7.5.5.7 All penetrations of a return air duct in the vicinity of detectors installed on or in an air duct shall be sealed to prevent entrance of outside air and possible dilution or redirection of smoke within the duct.

Subsection 17.7.5.5.8 was deleted by a tentative interim amendment (TIA).

17.7.5.6 Smoke Detectors for Door Release Service.

Two general methods of controlling doors with smoke detectors are available. The first is to use area smoke detectors to control the doors for that area. Either smoke detectors served by a selected circuit of a fire alarm control unit or specific addressable detectors are programmed to operate magnetic door release devices via the fire alarm system control unit. When one of the area smoke detectors renders an alarm, the control unit transfers to the alarm state and energizes the output circuit that controls the door holders. The requirements for such a system are addressed in Chapter 21. The second method is to control the door holder mechanism directly with a dedicated smoke detector or smoke detectors.

The requirements in 17.7.5.6 apply equally to both design concepts. When the open area protection system is used, 17.7.5.6.1 allows the spacing in the corridors as normally required for area protection in conformance with 17.7.3 to be considered acceptable for smoke door release service. In that case, the explicit spacing requirements of 17.7.5.6.2 do not apply. When dedicated smoke detectors are used for door release service, the requirements of 17.7.5.6.3 through 17.7.5.6.6 apply.

17.7.5.6.1 Smoke detectors that are part of an open area protection system covering the room, corridor, or enclosed space on each side of the smoke door and that are located and spaced as required by 17.7.3 shall be permitted to accomplish smoke door release service.

FAQ ▶
What location and spacing
requirements apply when an
open area detection system is
used?

Area detection installed in accordance with 17.7.3 is permitted to be used as long as area detection is provided on both sides of the doors to be closed. Discrete and dedicated smoke detectors separate from the area protection are not required to be used when the area detectors are wired or programmed to actuate the door release. Furthermore, the requirements of 17.7.5.6.5.1 through 17.7.5.6.5.4, which stipulate the quantities of detectors used for door release service, do not apply where both sides of the door are protected by open area smoke detection in accordance with 17.7.3.

17.7.5.6.2 Smoke detectors that are used exclusively for smoke door release service shall be located and spaced as required by 17.7.5.6.

Where area detection per 17.7.3 is not provided and where automatic closure of doors upon the presence of smoke is required, smoke detectors must be installed according to the prescriptive requirements in 17.7.5.6.3 through 17.7.5.6.6.2.

17.7.5.6.3 Where smoke door release is accomplished directly from the smoke detector(s), the detector(s) shall be listed for releasing service.

17.7.5.6.4 Smoke detectors shall be of the photoelectric, ionization, or other approved type.

17.7.5.6.5 The number of detectors required shall be determined in accordance with 17.7.5.6.5.1 through 17.7.5.6.5.4.

The placement requirements outlined in 17.7.5.6.5 have been derived from a qualitative understanding of the expected behavior of a ceiling jet, similar to the physical principles from which the rules for location and placement of area smoke detection have been derived. As research continues, additional insight may be developed for this application.

The original reason for this application of smoke detectors at smoke doors in corridors was simply to control smoke movement in the corridors. Early designs often used stand-alone smoke detectors that did not connect to a fire alarm system. Generally, this type of design is not used today because area smoke detector coverage in the corridors perform the same function more rapidly than waiting for the smoke to travel to the doorway.

If smoke detectors are installed only for door release, designers should consider the added benefit of using these detectors as part of the fire alarm system (if the building has one) and connect them to a fire alarm control unit to actuate notification appliances when smoke is detected.

If the smoke detectors from the fire alarm system corridor detection are used to control the doors, they are covered under 17.7.5.6.1 and the spacing requirements at the doors outlined in 17.7.5.6.5 are no longer applicable.

17.7.5.6.5.1 If doors are to be closed in response to smoke flowing in either direction, the requirements of 17.7.5.6.5.1(A) through 17.7.5.6.5.1(D) shall apply.

Paragraphs 17.7.5.6.5.1(A) through 17.7.5.6.5.1(D) and Figure 17.7.5.6.5.1(A) recognize that both ceiling and wall-mounted detectors can be used. The prescribed locations for smoke detectors to control doors are depicted in Figure 17.7.5.6.5.1(A).

(A) If the depth of wall section above the door is 24 in. (610 mm) or less, one ceiling-mounted smoke detector shall be required on one side of the doorway only, or two wall-mounted detectors shall be required, one on each side of the doorway. Figure 17.7.5.6.5.1(A), part A or B, shall apply.

The requirements in 17.7.5.6.5.1(A) are intended to address the same issues as the requirements regarding smoke detectors and ceilings with deep beams (see 17.7.3.2.4). However, the requirements have been amended to permit the use of wall-mounted smoke detectors for door release service.

In the editions of the Code prior to 2007, there was no mention of the use of wall-mounted smoke detectors, implying that wall-mounted detectors were not to be used. The

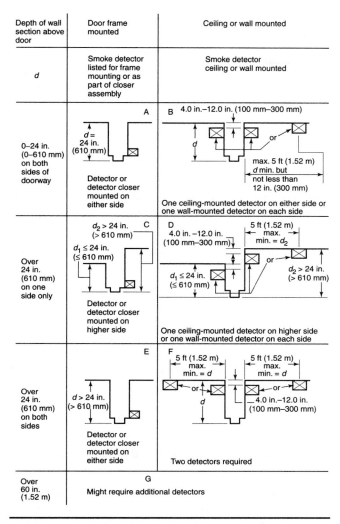

FIGURE 17.7.5.6.5.1(A) *Detector Location Requirements for Wall Sections.*

technical committee determined that there was no research to support the exclusion of the use of wall-mounted detectors in a minimum-compliance design standard.

The requirements in 17.7.5.6.5.1(A) have been derived from a qualitative assessment of anticipated smoke flows in a corridor where smoke flow is channeled by the corridor walls. For the case described in 17.7.5.6.5.1(A), only one ceiling-mounted detector is required. It can be located on either side of the smoke control door. Under the worst-case scenario, the door-control smoke detector is on the far side of the smoke-control door relative to the source of smoke. As smoke begins to flow into a corridor, it forms a layer of smoke immediately beneath the corridor ceiling. The upper portion of the corridor will fill with smoke until it begins to spill beneath the top of the door opening. As soon as this spillage occurs, the ceiling-mounted smoke detector on the far side of the door responds, closing the door and preventing further ingress of smoke. Since the wall section is less than 24 in. (610 mm), it does not produce an inordinately long delay in response, even when the detector is on the far side of the door. However, under the same worst-case scenario, if only one wall-mounted smoke detector is used, response is delayed until smoke fills both the corridor with the source of smoke *and* the far side corridor to the level of the smoke detector. Under that circumstance,

◄ **FAQ**
Why are two wall-mounted detectors required as opposed to a single ceiling-mounted detector?

the smoke control doors have already failed in their intended mission: to prevent the ingress of smoke into the corridor. Consequently, if the smoke detectors for door closure are mounted on the corridor walls, a smoke detector must be mounted on each side of the door.

(B) If the depth of wall section above the door is greater than 24 in. (610 mm) on one side only, one ceiling-mounted smoke detector shall be required on the higher side of the doorway only, or one wall-mounted detector shall be required on both sides of the doorway. Figure 17.7.5.6.5.1(A), part D, shall apply.

This paragraph was added in the 2002 edition of the Code and modified in the 2007 edition to address the condition illustrated in Figure 17.7.5.6.5.1(A), part D, where the depth of the wall section is greater than 24 in. (610 mm) on one side of the door only.

(C)* If the depth of wall section above the door is greater than 24 in. (610 mm) on both sides, two ceiling-mounted or wall-mounted detectors shall be required, one on each side of the doorway. Figure 17.7.5.6.5.1(A), part F, shall apply.

A.17.7.5.6.5.1(C) If the depth of wall section above the door is 60 in.(1.52 m) or greater, additional detectors might be required as indicated by an engineering evaluation.

Because the average door height is a nominal 84 in. to 96 in. (2.1 m to 2.4 m), the addition of 60 in. (1.5 m) above the door results in a ceiling height as high as 13 ft (3.9 m). The data in Annex B suggest that when the ceiling height exceeds 10 ft (3 m), reduced spacing for heat detectors is required if there is to be no reduction in performance due to the higher ceilings. In the modeling of smoke detectors, a similar logic is accepted. Thus, when the height above the door exceeds 60 in. (1.52 m), an engineering evaluation should be performed to determine if reduced smoke detector spacing is appropriate for the specific application under consideration.

(D) If a detector is specifically listed for door frame mounting, or if a listed combination or integral detector–door closer assembly is used, only one detector shall be required if installed in the manner recommended by the manufacturer's published instructions. Figure 17.7.5.6.5.1(A), parts A, C, and E, shall apply.

17.7.5.6.5.2 If door release is intended to prevent smoke transmission from one space to another in one direction only, detectors located in the space to which smoke is to be confined, regardless of the depth of wall section above the door, shall be in accordance with 17.7.5.6.6. Alternatively, a smoke detector conforming with 17.7.5.6.5.1(D) shall be permitted to be used.

Occasionally, there is a need to limit smoke spread in only one direction. When that is the case, 17.7.5.6.5.2 allows the elimination of some detectors that would otherwise be required.

17.7.5.6.5.3 If there are multiple doorways, additional ceiling-mounted detectors shall be required as specified in 17.7.5.6.5.3(A) through 17.7.5.6.5.3(C).

(A) If the separation between doorways exceeds 24 in. (610 mm), each doorway shall be treated separately. Figure 17.7.5.6.5.3(A), part E, shall apply.

(B) Each group of three or more doorway openings shall be treated separately. Figure 17.7.5.6.5.3(B) shall apply.

(C) Each group of doorway openings that exceeds 20 ft (6.1 m) in width, measured at its overall extremes, shall be treated separately. Figure 17.7.5.6.5.3(C) shall apply.

17.7.5.6.5.4 If there are multiple doorways and listed door frame–mounted detectors, or if listed combination or integral detector–door closer assemblies are used, there shall be one detector for each single or double doorway.

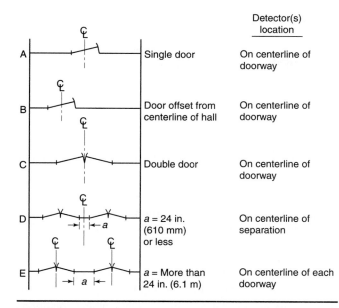

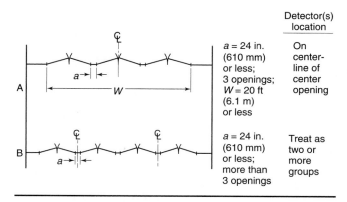

FIGURE 17.7.5.6.5.3(B) *Detector Location Requirements for Group Doorways.*

FIGURE 17.7.5.6.5.3(A) *Detector Location Requirements for Single and Double Doors.*

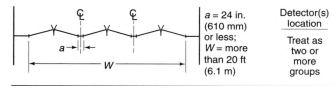

FIGURE 17.7.5.6.5.3(C) *Detector Location Requirements for Group Doorways over 20 ft (6.1 m) in Width.*

17.7.5.6.6 The locations of detectors shall be determined in accordance with 17.7.5.6.6.1 and 17.7.5.6.6.2.

17.7.5.6.6.1 If ceiling-mounted smoke detectors are to be installed on a smooth ceiling for a single or double doorway, they shall be located as follows *(Figure 17.7.5.6.5.3(A) shall apply)*:

(1) On the centerline of the doorway
(2) No more than 5 ft (1.5 m), measured along the ceiling and perpendicular to the doorway *(Figure 17.7.5.6.5.1(A) shall apply.)*
(3) No closer than shown in Figure 17.7.5.6.5.1(A), parts B, D, and F

17.7.5.6.6.2 If ceiling-mounted detectors are to be installed in conditions other than those outlined in 17.7.5.6.6.1, an engineering evaluation shall be made.

17.7.6 Special Considerations.

It is important for the designer to recognize that in presenting minimum requirements, the Code might not cover those special considerations that are unique to a specific application. The Code also might not address a particular product that allows the system to fulfill its design objective aside from the minimum prescriptive criteria in the Code. Although the Code makes every effort to establish minimum compliance criteria to address problems that have a documented history of affecting smoke detection systems, the issues addressed by the requirements of 17.7.6 cannot be assumed to be exhaustive and cover every conceivable contingency. The designer should consider all known factors in the protected area that have the potential to contribute to unwanted alarms or that could prevent the successful conveyance of smoke to the detector.

17.7.6.1 Spot-Type Detectors.

17.7.6.1.1 Combination and multi-sensor smoke detectors that have a fixed-temperature element as part of the unit shall be selected in accordance with Table 17.6.2.1 for the maximum ceiling temperature expected in service.

Refer to the definitions of *combination detector* and *multi-sensor detector* in 3.3.59.4 and 3.3.59.12, respectively. While the requirement in 17.7.6.1.1 was originally developed for application to smoke detectors that also have a heat sensor, its applicability was broadened in the 2007 edition of the Code.

The temperature rating of a fixed-temperature heat sensor incorporated into a combination or multi-sensor detector does not necessarily imply that the detector is listed for installation in spaces where the ambient temperature is as high as permitted by Table 17.6.2.1. For combination and multi-sensor detectors, care must be taken to ensure that ambient conditions fall within those listed for the detector as a whole.

In most fires, smoke detectors respond much sooner than either automatic sprinklers or heat detectors. Even in flaming fire tests, smoke detectors actuate long before typical fixed-temperature heat detectors. The difference in the speed of response becomes even more dramatic with low-energy fires. Because of this profound difference in the speed of response, adding a fixed-temperature heat detector to a smoke detector adds little to overall fire detection performance, particularly when the design criteria imply a life safety objective.

FAQ ▶

What advantage can multi-sensor detectors sometimes provide in smoke detection applications?

In the past few years, multi-sensor detectors have become available that employ ionization, photoelectric, and thermistor-type thermal sensors in a single device that utilizes a microcomputer algorithm to match the sensed conditions to known fire "signatures" stored in memory. While these detectors are tested to the same criteria in UL 268 as conventional smoke detectors, the multi-sensor architecture provides improved immunity to known false alarm sources.

17.7.6.1.2* Holes in the back of a detector shall be covered by a gasket, sealant, or equivalent means, and the detector shall be mounted so that airflow from inside or around the housing does not prevent the entry of smoke during a fire or test condition.

A.17.7.6.1.2 Airflow through holes in the rear of a smoke detector can interfere with smoke entry to the sensing chamber. Similarly, air from the conduit system can flow around the outside edges of the detector and interfere with smoke reaching the sensing chamber. Additionally, holes in the rear of a detector provide a means for entry of dust, dirt, and insects, each of which can adversely affect the detector's performance.

The conditions stated in A.17.7.6.1.2 have been encountered frequently enough to warrant inclusion of the requirements in 17.7.6.1.2. However, the list of installation-related problems in A.17.7.6.1.2 cannot be assumed to be exhaustive. Once again, the designer should be aware of any factor in the protected area that could contribute to unwanted alarms or that could prevent the successful conveyance of smoke to the detector and then take steps consistent with the manufacturer's installation instructions to address it.

17.7.6.2* High-Rack Storage. The location and spacing of smoke detectors for high-rack storage shall address the commodity, quantity, and configuration of the rack storage.

A.17.7.6.2 For the most effective detection of fire in high-rack storage areas, detectors should be located on the ceiling above each aisle and at intermediate levels in the racks. This is necessary to detect smoke that is trapped in the racks at an early stage of fire development when insufficient thermal energy is released to carry the smoke to the ceiling. Earliest detection of smoke is achieved by locating the intermediate level detectors adjacent to alternate pallet sections as shown in Figure A.17.7.6.2(a) and Figure A.17.7.6.2(b). The detector manufacturer's published instructions and engineering judgment should be followed for specific installations.

A projected beam–type detector can be permitted to be used in lieu of a single row of individual spot-type smoke detectors.

Sampling ports of an air sampling–type detector can be permitted to be located above each aisle to provide coverage that is equivalent to the location of spot-type detectors. The manufacturer's published instructions and engineering judgment should be followed for the specific installation.

Fire protection for high-rack storage warehouses is a particularly difficult problem. The fuel load per unit of floor area is extremely high, and the accessibility to the fuel is relatively low. Also, the combustibility of the materials in any given rack can vary from nominally noncombustible to flammable.

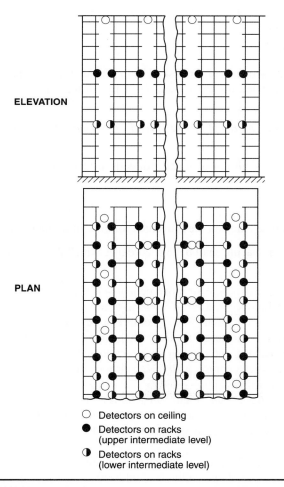

○ Detectors on ceiling
● Detectors on racks
   (upper intermediate level)
◐ Detectors on racks
   (lower intermediate level)

FIGURE A.17.7.6.2(a) *Detector Location for Solid Storage (Closed Rack) in Which Transverse and Longitudinal Flue Spaces Are Irregular or Nonexistent, as for Slatted or Solid Shelved Storage.*

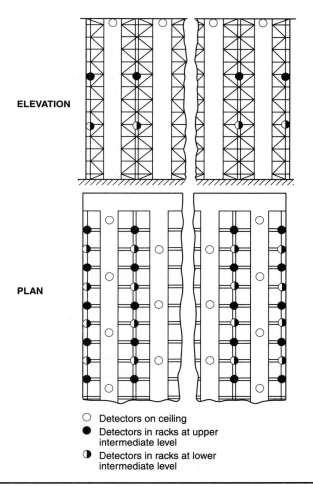

○ Detectors on ceiling
● Detectors in racks at upper
   intermediate level
◐ Detectors in racks at lower
   intermediate level

FIGURE A.17.7.6.2(b) *Detector Location for Palletized Storage (Open Rack) or No Shelved Storage in Which Regular Transverse and Longitudinal Flue Spaces Are Maintained.*

The orientation of the fuel also creates vertical flues between the combustibles that produce ideal conditions for the propagation of the fire and the worst possible conditions for extinguishment. Likewise, the presence of solid shelving can create horizontal flues that materially aid in horizontal fire spread. The shelves also tend to shield the fire from water discharged by the automatic fire suppression sprinkler system and hose streams intended to extinguish the fire. These factors make early detection highly desirable so that rapid extinguishment of the fire in the incipient stages is possible. Once the fire becomes well established, it is virtually impossible to extinguish. A number of catastrophic total losses have occurred in high-rack storage facilities in the past decade.

The guidance provided for locating detectors in rack storage arrays strives to ensure that any vertical flue spaces created by the stored commodities and solid shelves are covered with a detector at some level. Care must also be used in installing detectors in these applications because they are vulnerable to damage as commodities are moved into and out of the storage racks.

Although maintaining accessibility for service and maintenance while locating detectors for both maximum speed of response and minimum exposure to damage from operations may seem impossible, it is not. System designs exist that have satisfied all three of these apparently conflicting requirements. Air sampling–type smoke detectors, with the piping network extended throughout each rack, as well as projected beam detectors, have been used successfully in this application.

17.7.6.3 High Air Movement Areas.

17.7.6.3.1 General. The purpose and scope of 17.7.6.3 shall be to provide location and spacing guidance for smoke detectors intended for early warning of fire in high air movement areas.

Exception: Detectors provided for the control of smoke spread are covered by the requirements of 17.7.5.

17.7.6.3.2 Location. Smoke detectors shall not be located directly in the airstream of supply registers.

17.7.6.3.3* Spacing.

A.17.7.6.3.3 Smoke detector spacing depends on the movement of air within the room.

17.7.6.3.3.1 Spot-type smoke detector spacing shall be in accordance with Table 17.7.6.3.3.1 and Figure 17.7.6.3.3.1.

The most regularly encountered example of a high air movement area is the data center (computer room). Because of the very high concentration of value in a data center, reducing the spacing of spot-type smoke detectors is common. This spacing can be derived from Table 17.7.6.3.3.1 and Figure 17.7.6.3.3.1. In some cases, an authority having jurisdiction, such as an insurance carrier, will establish a spacing criterion for such locations. Data centers are by no means the only areas that fall into this category. Usually, high air movement areas are characterized by six or more air changes per hour.

FAQ ▶
What provisions in the Code apply to smoke detection in under-floor or above-floor spaces used for environmental air?

It should be noted that Table 17.7.6.3.3.1 and Figure 17.7.6.3.3.1 are not intended to be used to compute detector spacing for spaces under the floor or above the ceiling. Under-floor and above-ceiling spaces used for environmental air are addressed in 17.7.3.5, 17.7.4.1, and 17.7.4.2.

Table 17.7.6.3.3.1 and Figure 17.7.6.3.3.1 provide the detector spacing for high air movement ambient conditions in areas other than above-ceiling and under-floor spaces. These data were developed in the early 1980s and have not been reviewed with current technology detectors.

As air movement in these spaces increases, air currents disrupt the formation of a ceiling jet and mixing can result in dilution and other effects that can impact detection. For this rea-

TABLE 17.7.6.3.3.1 *Smoke Detector Spacing Based on Air Movement*

Minutes per Air Change	Air Changes per Hour	Spacing per Detector	
		ft²	m²
1	60	125	12
2	30	250	23
3	20	375	35
4	15	500	46
5	12	625	58
6	10	750	70
7	8.6	875	81
8	7.5	900	84
9	6.7	900	84
10	6	900	84

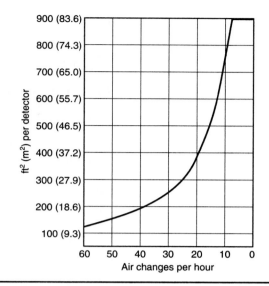

FIGURE 17.7.6.3.3.1 *High Air Movement Areas (Not to Be Used for Under-Floor or Above-Ceiling Spaces).*

son, detector spacing is reduced as the number of air changes increases. In the majority of very high air movement areas, spot-type detectors might not be the best detectors for the application. Air-sampling detectors can offer increased sensitivity and have been used for such spaces quite successfully.

High air movement areas might not necessarily mean high air velocity at the detector or detection location. Airflow patterns at the detector locations should be measured and recorded in the system documentation.

The velocity of the air stream from supply registers supplying high air movement areas is likely to exceed 300 ft/min (1.5 m/sec), which is the maximum for which most detectors are listed. See 17.7.1.8. It is important to remember that when detectors are tested for a listing that includes high airflow environments, they are tested to ensure they do not render a false alarm in high airflow conditions. No test verifies that they will detect fires as quickly as they would in a non–high airflow condition. The designer should take into consideration any potential effects of high air velocity at the detector location on the ability of the detector to sense smoke from the fires it is intended to detect as well as the effect the air velocity might have on the detector stability and maintenance needs.

Some authorities having jurisdiction compute the rate of air change based on the entire air volume, including the room, under-floor plenum, and above-ceiling plenum. In other circumstances, the above-ceiling space is not part of the working air volume of the hazard area, and only the volumes of the room and the under-floor space are used to compute air changes per hour. Before the design process is begun, the HVAC system must be well understood and the designer and the authorities having jurisdiction must agree on what air volume the calculations are to be based.

17.7.6.3.3.2 Air-sampling or projected beam smoke detectors shall be installed in accordance with the manufacturer's published instructions.

The spacing adjustments in Table 17.7.6.3.3.1 and Figure 17.7.6.3.3.1 were developed from experimental data developed in the 1980s using spot-type detectors. No research has been found that allows the development of analogous spacing reductions, if any, for air sampling or projected beam smoke detection. On a qualitative basis, it is suspected that the principal impact of high air movement is on the disruption of the plume and the distortion or prevention of the formation of a ceiling jet. The fire must compete with the normal extant air movement to establish the flow effects on which smoke detection normally relies. Since smoke detection is usually placed in high air movement areas to achieve property protection and mission continuity objects, a performance-based approach should be considered.

17.7.6.3.4 HVAC Mechanical Rooms. Where HVAC mechanical rooms are used as an air plenum for return air, the spacings of smoke detectors shall not be required to be reduced based on the number of air changes.

Where smoke detection is employed in HVAC mechanical rooms, the objective is to detect a fire involving the HVAC units. This objective does not require a spacing reduction. Where HVAC mechanical rooms are used as a plenum for return air, the HVAC system is the dominant mechanism for smoke transport, and reduced spacing of detectors would not improve detection response.

17.7.7 Video Image Smoke Detection.

Recently, video cameras have been used, in conjunction with frame capture and comparison software in a computer, for the purposes of detecting smoke. As with any new technology, the Code recognizes that video cameras offer a potentially viable solution to a particular set of fire detection problems. At least one manufacturer of this type of detection technology has had its product listed. Consequently, a section was added to the Code in the 2007 edition to establish the requirement to follow the manufacturer's application guidelines as accepted by the listing organization's testing and listing process. As with any new technology, application and device location information will develop through the product's use, and additional requirements may appear in future editions of the Code. See Exhibit 17.33 for an example of a conceptual video detection system.

17.7.7.1 Video image smoke detection systems and all of the components thereof, including hardware and software, shall be listed for the purpose of smoke detection.

The listing requirement in 17.7.7.1 places the responsibility on the organization providing the listing to evaluate the efficacy of the equipment and software for appropriateness for a defined scope of applications. The limits on the size of the monitored compartment versus the size of the fire that can be reliably detected and the limitations on the environment within the compartment necessary to permit reliable detection have not yet been established by the technical committee.

17.7.7.2 Video image smoke detection systems shall comply with all of the applicable requirements of Chapters 1, 10, 14, 17, and 23 of this Code.

A video image smoke detection system consists of one or more video cameras, a signal router or interface, and a computer to analyze the individual video image frames in real time. Chapters 1, 10, 14, 17, and 23 include requirements that are applicable to such a system because the system that serves the role of a smoke detector is a large assemblage of components with the same level of complexity as a fire alarm system. For example, all these components require power and must comply with the power supply criteria in Chapter 10. All the interconnections between cameras, interfaces, and computers must be monitored for integrity. All the components in the system must be listed for the purpose for which they are used. The alarm signal must be conveyed to a fire alarm control unit via a circuit that is monitored for integrity. The requirements in Chapters 1, 10, 14, 17, and 23 address these and many other issues that are relevant to the video image smoke detection system and are applicable in much the same way they are applicable to an air-sampling smoke detection system.

17.7.7.2.1 Systems shall be designed in accordance with the performance-based design requirements of Section 17.3.

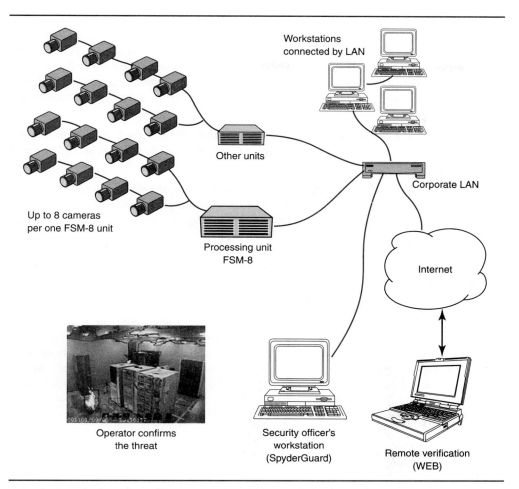

EXHIBIT 17.33 *Conceptual Video Detection System. (Source: axonX LLC, Sparks, MD)*

Since prescriptive design criteria have not yet been developed for video image smoke detection, each video image smoke detection system should be designed with complete documentation, including the basis of the design, calculations demonstrating the capability of detecting the design fire over the entire volume covered by the system, and reliability calculations demonstrating that the system will be adequately reliable over the maintenance interval for the system. Section B.2 in Annex B provides guidance on the performance-based design method.

17.7.7.2.2 The location and spacing of video image smoke detectors shall comply with the requirements of 17.11.5.

Section 17.11 provides general rules for detection technologies that are not explicitly itemized in this chapter. Subsection 17.11.5 establishes general spacing and location rules that are deemed applicable to video image smoke detection systems.

17.7.7.3* Video signals generated by cameras that are components of video image smoke detection systems shall be permitted to be transmitted to other systems for other uses only through output connections provided specifically for that purpose by the video system manufacturer.

A.17.7.7.3 Facility owners and managers might desire to use cameras and their images for purposes other than smoke detection. The intent of this paragraph is not to prohibit additional uses, but to ensure the integrity of the life safety smoke detection mission of the equipment.

FAQ ▶
What types of applications are
suitable for video detection
systems?

Video image smoke detection systems are best suited for large open spaces with high value assets that warrant such protection. In many cases, the facility security system includes cameras to monitor the space during unoccupied times to maintain surveillance. There is little basis for two sets of cameras, one for smoke detection and a second for surveillance. Paragraph 17.7.7.3 allows the video signal to be shared as long as the equipment and the software that allow the sharing are listed for the purpose and the system ensures that the security use of the signal does not interfere with the fire safety use of the signal.

17.7.7.4* All component controls and software shall be protected from unauthorized changes. All changes to the software or component settings shall be tested in accordance with Chapter 14.

A.17.7.7.4 Video image smoke detection control and software should be protected from tampering by passwords, software keys, or other means of limiting access to authorized/qualified personnel. Component settings include any control or programming that might affect the operation of coverage of the detection. This includes, but is not limited to, camera focus, field of view, motion sensitivity settings, and change of camera position. Any changes in component settings or ambient conditions that affect the design performance of the detector should initiate a trouble signal.

Since this technology is new and experience with it is limited, only a general requirement has been established by the technical committee. Video image smoke detection systems operate by comparing the view of the hazard area to earlier views of the hazard area and initiate alarm signals when the changes in groups of pixels are consistent with the presence of smoke in the monitored space. Changes in camera position, focus, contrast setting, field of view, ambient lighting, and the criteria in the software for a smoke detection decision all can affect the reliability of the system as a smoke detection means. The system must be designed to provide protection against unauthorized changes that could affect the system's performance or reliability. Any intentional changes must be subject to the acceptance testing criteria in Chapter 14.

17.8 Radiant Energy–Sensing Fire Detectors

The term *radiant energy–sensing fire detectors* encompasses both flame detectors and spark/ember detectors. (See the definitions in 3.3.59.8, 3.3.59.16, and 3.3.59.20.) The physics that govern the operation of both types of detectors is largely the same. However, the applications of the two different types of radiant energy–sensing detectors are radically different. Flame detectors are generally employed in large open spaces where lines of sight from the detector to the anticipated fire location are clear and ambient lighting is normal. Such spaces include fuel loading racks, aircraft hangars, electrostatic paint booths, and petroleum production and processing facilities. Spark/ember detectors are usually used on pneumatic-conveying system duct work, enclosed belt conveyors and other normally dark locations found in wood processing and woodworking plants, refuse-derived fuel plants, chemical plants, and other facilities where combustible particulate solids are processed or conveyed.

The design approach recognized for radiant energy–sensing fire detectors is a performance-based approach. This type of detector has no prescriptive spacing nor a uniform test standard that results in detectors from different manufacturers all having roughly equivalent sensitivities. The opposite is the case. Each make and model detector has unique performance attributes and the system design must take into account those design attributes.

For each type of radiant energy–sensing detector, the fire to be detected must be quantified in terms of an energy release rate (power), usually measured in terms of British thermal units per second or kilowatts for flame detectors and microwatts for spark/ember detectors. A worst-case scenario is considered where the "design fire" is situated in the least favorable location relative to the detector. The universal response equation is solved using the sensitivity parameter published for the detector (and verified by the organization providing the listing) to determine whether the detector will respond to the worst-case scenario. This process is repeated with each location or detector in the design. This design method is the only one recognized by the Code. A detailed description of the design method is provided in Annex B.

17.8.1* General.

A.17.8.1 For the purpose of this Code, radiant energy includes the electromagnetic radiation emitted as a by-product of the combustion reaction, which obeys the laws of optics. This includes radiation in the ultraviolet, visible, and infrared portions of the spectrum emitted by flames or glowing embers. These portions of the spectrum are distinguished by wavelengths as shown in Table A.17.8.1.

The radiant emissions from an ember and a flame are very different. Furthermore, flame detectors and spark/ember detectors are used in very different contexts. Although they share similar physical principles, the ways in which they are applied differ. Paragraphs 3.3.59.8 and 3.3.59.20 provide definitions for these two types of detectors.

Subsection A.17.8.1 clarifies the distinction drawn in the Code between heat (which is commonly detected with heat detectors using convective heat transfer) and radiant energy (which is detected with either flame or spark/ember detectors using electro-optical methods to sense sparks, embers, and flames). See 3.3.294 for the definition of *wavelength* and A.3.3.294 for associated explanatory material.

17.8.1.1 The radiant energy detection design documentation shall state the required performance objective of the system.

The design documentation should clearly state the performance objective of the system and the criteria that are used to demonstrate attainment of that objective. This language parallels the language of 17.6.1.1 and 17.7.1.1. The requirements in Section 17.8 establish criteria for radiant energy–sensing detectors in performance-based terms that can be addressed only through a performance-based design.

17.8.1.2 The purpose and scope of Section 17.8 shall be to provide requirements for the selection, location, and spacing of fire detectors that sense the radiant energy produced by burning substances. These detectors shall be categorized as flame detectors and spark/ember detectors.

17.8.2* Fire Characteristics and Detector Selection.

When using radiant energy–sensing detectors, the designer must match the detector to the radiant emissions, or signature, of the flame or spark/ember to be detected. The designer must do so with a degree of precision and attention to detail that is not generally required with other types of detectors.

The requirements of Chapter 17 effectively direct the system designer to work through an analysis to arrive at the most appropriate detector for the fire hazard under consideration. The first decision is whether flame detection or spark/ember detection is the most appropriate type of radiant energy–sensing fire detector. The type of detector is often determined by the physical state of the material involved in the fire.

Combustion occurs in the gas phase and in the solid phase. Flammable gases, flammable liquids, combustible liquids, and many combustible solids will support the formation of a flame (see the definition of *flame* in 3.3.103). With a flame, the combustion takes place in the gas phase, regardless of the physical state of the unburned fuel. The heat from the combustion gasifies the fuel, allowing it to mix with air, supporting the flame. Because gas molecules are free to vibrate in free space, the flame spectra show typical emission spikes that indicate flame intermediates and products. Flame detectors respond to the radiant emissions

TABLE A.17.8.1 *Spectrum Wavelength Ranges*

Radiant Energy	μ*m*
Ultraviolet	0.1–0.35
Visible	0.36–0.75
Infrared	0.76–220

Conversion factors: 1.0 μm = 1000 nm = 10,000 Å.

◄ **FAQ**
What is the difference between gas-phase combustion and solid-phase combustion?

that occur as the result of gas-phase chemical combustion reactions that take place in the flame.

Many solids also burn in the solid phase as embers (see the definition of *ember* in 3.3.77). In solid-phase combustion, the molecules on the surface of the fuel particle are oxidized off the surface of the particle without the development of a layer of gasified fuel, which could produce a true flame. Therefore, combustion intermediates (partially oxidized molecules) and often combustion products are locked up on the surface of the fuel particle and are not free to assume the diverse vibrational states of a gas-phase molecule. Consequently, the radiant emissions in solid-phase combustion are profoundly different from those in gas-phase combustion. This difference in combustion radiant emissions necessitates different types of radiant energy–sensing detectors for the different physical combustion states. Spark/ember detectors are designed to respond to the infrared emissions that occur as the result of solid-phase combustion reactions that occur in the surface of a solid fuel. While most spark/ember detectors will respond to a flame, most flame detectors will not respond to a glowing ember.

In an effort to reduce unwanted alarms from non-fire radiant-emission sources, flame detector designers have developed detectors that look for specific radiant-emission wavelengths that are uniquely associated with the combustion process of particular fuels. The result is detectors that will detect one type of radiant emissions from one class of fuels but will be virtually blind to fires involving other combustibles. A thorough understanding of how these detectors operate is necessary if they are to be properly applied. See Exhibits 17.34 through 17.39 for examples of spectral response characteristics of commonly encountered flame detector architectures.

A.17.8.2 Following are operating principles for two types of detectors:

(1) *Flame Detectors.* Ultraviolet flame detectors typically use a vacuum photodiode Geiger–Muller tube to detect the ultraviolet radiation that is produced by a flame. The photodiode allows a burst of current to flow for each ultraviolet photon that hits the active area of the tube. When the number of current bursts per unit time reaches a predetermined level, the detector initiates an alarm.

A single wavelength infrared flame detector uses one of several different photocell types to detect the infrared emissions in a single wavelength band that are produced by a

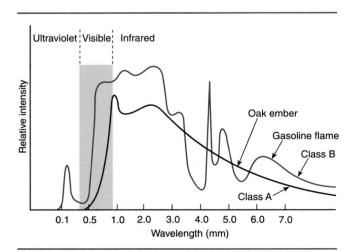

EXHIBIT 17.34 *Emission Spectral Response of Class A and Class B Combustibles. (Source: J. M. Cholin Consultants, Inc., Oakland, NJ)*

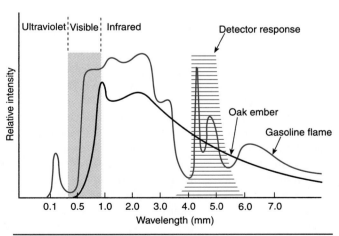

EXHIBIT 17.35 *Spectral Response of a Single Wavelength Infrared Flame Detector Superimposed on the Spectrum of Typical Radiators. (Source: J. M. Cholin Consultants, Inc., Oakland, NJ)*

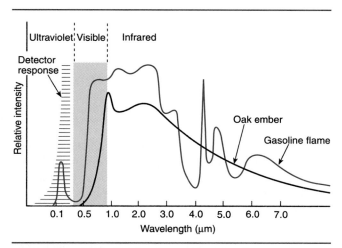

EXHIBIT 17.36 *Spectral Response of an Ultraviolet (UV) Flame Detector Superimposed on the Spectrum of Typical Radiators. (Source: J. M. Cholin Consultants, Inc., Oakland, NJ)*

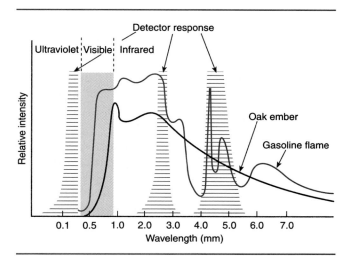

EXHIBIT 17.37 *Spectral Response of an Ultraviolet/Infrared (UV/IR) Flame Detector Superimposed on the Spectrum of Typical Radiators. (Source: J. M. Cholin Consultants, Inc., Oakland, NJ)*

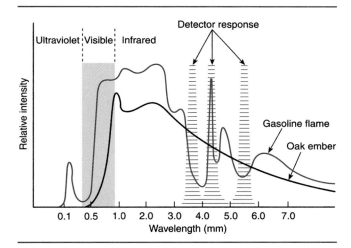

EXHIBIT 17.38 *Spectral Response of a Multiple Wavelength Infrared (IR/IR) Flame Detector Superimposed on the Spectrum of Typical Radiators. (Source: J. M. Cholin Consultants, Inc., Oakland, NJ)*

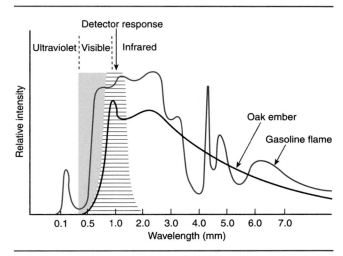

EXHIBIT 17.39 *Spectral Response of an Infrared Spark/Ember Detector Superimposed on the Spectrum of Typical Radiators. (Source: J. M. Cholin Consultants, Inc., Oakland, NJ)*

flame. These detectors generally include provisions to minimize alarms from commonly occurring infrared sources such as incandescent lighting or sunlight. An ultraviolet/ infrared (UV/IR) flame detector senses ultraviolet radiation with a vacuum photodiode tube and a selected wavelength of infrared radiation with a photocell and uses the combined signal to indicate a fire. These detectors need exposure to both types of radiation before an alarm signal can be initiated. A multiple wavelength infrared (IR/IR) flame detector senses radiation at two or more narrow bands of wavelengths in the infrared spectrum. These detectors electronically compare the emissions between the bands and initiate a signal where the relationship between the two bands indicates a fire.

Some UV/IR flame detectors require radiant emissions at 0.2 microns (µm) (UV) and 2.5 µm (IR). Other UV/IR flame detectors require radiant emissions at 0.2 µm (UV) and nominal 4.7 µm (IR).

Some IR/IR flame detectors compare radiant emissions at 4.3 µm (IR) to a reference at nominal 3.8 µm (IR). Other IR/IR flame detectors use a nominal 5.6 µm (IR) reference.

Different products use different slices of the spectrum for detection. The designer must verify that the fuels in the hazard area emit radiation at the wavelengths the detectors use for detection.

(2) *Spark/Ember Detectors.* A spark/ember-sensing detector usually uses a solid state photodiode or phototransistor to sense the radiant energy emitted by embers, typically between 0.5 microns and 2.0 microns in normally dark environments. These detectors can be made extremely sensitive (microwatts), and their response times can be made very short (microseconds).

17.8.2.1* The type and quantity of radiant energy–sensing fire detectors shall be determined on the basis of the performance characteristics of the detector and an analysis of the hazard, including the burning characteristics of the fuel, the fire growth rate, the environment, the ambient conditions, and the capabilities of the extinguishing media and equipment.

A.17.8.2.1 The radiant energy from a flame or spark/ember is comprised of emissions in various bands of the ultraviolet, visible, and infrared portions of the spectrum. The relative quantities of radiation emitted in each part of the spectrum are determined by the fuel chemistry, the temperature, and the rate of combustion. The detector should be matched to the characteristics of the fire.

Almost all materials that participate in flaming combustion emit ultraviolet radiation to some degree during flaming combustion, whereas only carbon-containing fuels emit significant radiation at the 4.35 micron (carbon dioxide) band used by many detector types to detect a flame. *(See Figure A.17.8.2.1.)*

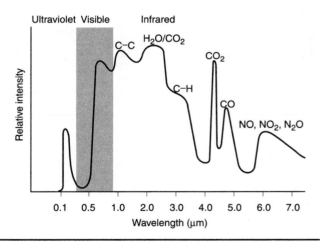

FIGURE A.17.8.2.1 *Spectrum of a Typical Flame (Free-Burning Gasoline).*

The radiant energy emitted from an ember is determined primarily by the fuel temperature (Planck's law emissions) and the emissivity of the fuel. Radiant energy from an ember is primarily infrared and, to a lesser degree, visible in wavelength. In general, embers do not emit ultraviolet energy in significant quantities (0.1 percent of total emissions) until the ember achieves temperatures of 3240°F (1727°C or 2000°K). In most cases, the emissions are included in the band of 0.8 microns to 2.0 microns, corresponding to temperatures of approximately 750°F to 1830°F (398°C to 1000°C).

Most radiant energy detectors have some form of qualification circuitry within them that uses time to help distinguish between spurious, transient signals and legitimate fire alarms. These circuits become very important where the anticipated fire scenario and the ability of the detector to respond to that anticipated fire are considered. For example, a detector that uses an integration circuit or a timing circuit to respond to the flickering light from a fire might not respond well to a deflagration resulting from the ignition of accumulated combustible vapors and gases, or where the fire is a spark that is traveling up to 328 ft/sec (100 m/sec) past the detector. Under these circumstances, a detector that has a high-speed response capability is most appropriate. On the other hand, in applications where the development of the fire is slower, a detector that uses time for the confirmation of repetitive signals is appropriate. Consequently, the fire growth rate should be considered in selecting the detector. The detector performance should be selected to respond to the anticipated fire.

The radiant emissions are not the only criteria to be considered. The medium between the anticipated fire and the detector is also very important. Different wavelengths of radiant energy are absorbed with varying degrees of efficiency by materials that are suspended in the air or that accumulate on the optical surfaces of the detector. Generally, aerosols and surface deposits reduce the sensitivity of the detector. The detection technology used should take into account those normally occurring aerosols and surface deposits to minimize the reduction of system response between maintenance intervals. It should be noted that the smoke evolved from the combustion of middle and heavy fraction petroleum distillates is highly absorptive in the ultraviolet end of the spectrum. If using this type of detection, the system should be designed to minimize the effect of smoke interference on the response of the detection system.

The environment and ambient conditions anticipated in the area to be protected impact the choice of detector. All detectors have limitations on the range of ambient temperatures over which they will respond, consistent with their tested or approved sensitivities. The designer should make certain that the detector is compatible with the range of ambient temperatures anticipated in the area in which it is installed. In addition, rain, snow, and ice attenuate both ultraviolet and infrared radiation to varying degrees. Where anticipated, provisions should be made to protect the detector from accumulations of these materials on its optical surfaces.

17.8.2.2* The selection of the radiant energy–sensing detectors shall be based on the following:

(1) Matching of the spectral response of the detector to the spectral emissions of the fire or fires to be detected
(2) Minimizing the possibility of spurious nuisance alarms from non-fire sources inherent to the hazard area

A.17.8.2.2 Normal radiant emissions that are not from a fire can be present in the hazard area. When selecting a detector for an area, other potential sources of radiant emissions should be evaluated. Refer to A.17.8.2.1 for additional information.

The designer must select the most appropriate detector model or technology only after the type of combustion has been determined and the decision regarding type of detector to be used has been made.

The expected emission spectrum from the fuel is matched to the wavelength bands of the candidate detector to ensure response to the fire, using the criteria stated in the detector manufacturer's engineering manual. The performance capabilities of the detector must be matched with the known radiant emissions of the fuel. To ascertain that the detector is appropriate for the fuels to be detected, the designer can use the performance attributes that were verified by a qualified testing laboratory during the listing evaluation.

◄ **FAQ**
What must be determined before the designer can select the most appropriate detector?

The candidate detector must then be evaluated for its unwanted alarm immunity with respect to the ambient or false alarm sources anticipated in the hazard area. The information provided in A.17.8.2.1 also relates to 17.8.2.2(2) and should be used as guidance.

Finally, the designer must consider the impact of the full range of expected ambient conditions on both the detection capability and the stability of the candidate detector. Both flame detectors and spark/ember detectors are routinely installed outdoors, where they are exposed to the weather and fluctuations in temperature.

Special attention must be given to the temperature range limits and other limiting weather-related conditions that are specified by the manufacturer. Such attention will help ensure that the detector has been qualified for the anticipated extremes. The prudent designer will document the decision-making process in writing for future reference.

17.8.3 Spacing Considerations.

The spacing considerations for radiant energy–sensing fire detectors in 17.8.3 are derived from the physics of light transmission. This method contrasts with fire plume dynamics and fluid flow physics, which govern the spacing of heat and smoke detectors. Consequently, when using radiant energy–sensing fire detectors, the designer must determine the spacing of the detectors by the location and aiming of the devices.

In turn, the location and the aiming of the detectors are determined by two critical factors: the field of view of the detector (see the definition in 3.3.90) and the sensitivity of the detector (see the definitions in 3.3.105 and 3.3.260).

17.8.3.1 General Rules.

17.8.3.1.1* Radiant energy–sensing fire detectors shall be employed consistent with the listing or approval and the inverse square law, which defines the fire size versus distance curve for the detector.

A.17.8.3.1.1 All optical detectors respond according to the following theoretical equation:

$$S = \frac{kP^{-e\zeta d}}{d^2}$$

where:

S = radiant power reaching the detector

k = proportionality constant for the detector

P = radiant power emitted by the fire

e = Naperian logarithm base (2.7183)

ζ = extinction coefficient of air

d = distance between the fire and the detector

The sensitivity (S) typically is measured in nanowatts. This equation yields a family of curves similar to the one shown in Figure A.17.8.3.1.1.

The curve defines the maximum distance at which the detector consistently detects a fire of defined size and fuel. Detectors should be employed only in the shaded area above the curve.

Under the best of conditions, with no atmospheric absorption, the radiant power reaching the detector is reduced by a factor of 4 if the distance between the detector and the fire is doubled. For the consumption of the atmospheric extinction, the exponential term zeta (ζ) is added to the equation. Zeta is a measure of the clarity of the air at the wavelength under consideration. Zeta is affected by humidity, dust, and any other contaminants in the air that are absorbent at the wavelength in question. Zeta generally has values between –0.001 and –0.1 for normal ambient air.

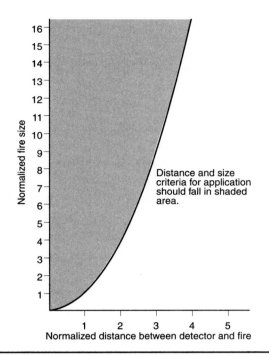

FIGURE A.17.8.3.1.1 *Normalized Fire Size vs. Distance.*

The inverse square law modeled by the relationship shown in A.17.8.3.1.1 relates the size of the fire, the detector sensitivity, and the distance between the fire and the detector. The inverse square law applies to all radiant energy–sensing detectors. However, two tacit assumptions are made when the inverse square law is used for modeling the performance of flame detectors.

The first assumption is that the fire is small and far away from the detector. This assumption permits modeling the fire as a point source. When the fire is modeled as a point source, all of the radiant power is thought of as emanating from a single point. The alternative would be to model the fire as a portion of the field of view. This alternative approach requires the use of advanced calculus and is far more difficult for the average designer.

The second assumption is that the flame is assumed to be "optically dense," meaning that radiation from the back side of the flame does not pass through the flame. Generally, because flame intermediates absorb radiation at the same wavelengths at which they emit radiation, this assumption holds true.

Using the inverse square law enables the design engineer to compute with considerable precision how large the fire must get before enough radiant energy hits the detector to cause an alarm. These calculations are critical because they help determine the number of detectors of given sensitivity, location, and aiming that are necessary to detect a fire of given size.

It is important to remember that fire size is quantified in units of power output, either British thermal units per second or kilowatts, regardless of the type of radiant energy–sensing fire detector under consideration. Also the normally assumed 35 percent radiative fraction used in other fire calculations is not used when quantifying the power output of a fire in this context. The sensitivity of radiant energy–sensing detectors is derived from listing evaluations performed by the listing agency. The listing evaluations use the whole fire output as the metric.

Finally, for flame detectors, the numerical value of zeta (ζ) is determined by the set of wavelengths that were chosen for sensing and reference in the detector architecture and the atmospheric absorption at those wavelengths. The numerical value for ζ should be stated on the detector engineering and installation documentation. A design cannot be performed in accordance with this Code if the value of ζ for the detector is not provided. Keep in mind that if the air is contaminated with vapors or gases not normally in the air, the value of ζ has probably changed. Consult the detector manufacturer for guidance. Refer to Section B.5 for the design process.

In the design of spark/ember detectors, the extinction factor, ζ, is the measure of the opacity of the fuel particulate at the detector operating wavelengths. The extinction relation is used to address the absorption of ember radiation by the nonburning fuel particles between the ember and the detector. In the spark/ember detection context, ζ is determined by the combustible.

17.8.3.1.2 Detector quantity shall be based on the detectors being positioned so that no point requiring detection in the hazard area is obstructed or outside the field of view of at least one detector.

A flame detector or spark/ember detector cannot detect what it cannot "see." The definition of the term *field of view* in 3.3.90 has a sensitivity criterion attached to it. Field of view is the angle off the optical axis of the detector where the effective sensitivity is 50 percent of the on-axis sensitivity.

All points where a fire can exist in the hazard area must be within the field of view of at least one detector, as required by 17.8.3.1.2. This requirement also effectively demands that the manufacturer provide sensitivity versus angle of incidence data in its engineering manual.

FAQ ▶
What is usually required when flame detectors are used to release extinguishing agents?

When flame detectors are used to release extinguishing agents, such as aqueous film-forming foam (AFFF), alarm signals from two or more detectors are usually required before the agent is released. Under those circumstances, the designer should apply 17.8.3.1.2 in a manner that requires all points in the hazard area where a fire can exist to be within the fields of view of the number of detectors required to discharge the extinguishing agent. Otherwise, the fire could occur in a portion of the hazard area that is within the field of view of only one detector. The release of the extinguishing agent would be delayed until the fire grows to a size sufficient to alarm the additional confirmation detector(s). This situation would result in far more fire damage and a greater threat of loss of life.

The requirements in 17.8.3.1.1 and 17.8.3.1.2 pertain to both flame and spark/ember detectors. Other design considerations are more specific to one type of detector or the other. These considerations are addressed in 17.8.3.2 for flame detectors and 17.8.3.3 for spark/ember detectors, respectively.

17.8.3.2 Spacing Considerations for Flame Detectors.

17.8.3.2.1* The location and spacing of detectors shall be the result of an engineering evaluation that includes the following:

(1) Size of the fire that is to be detected
(2) Fuel involved
(3) Sensitivity of the detector
(4) Field of view of the detector
(5) Distance between the fire and the detector
(6) Radiant energy absorption of the atmosphere
(7) Presence of extraneous sources of radiant emissions
(8) Purpose of the detection system
(9) Response time required

In the context of 17.8.3.2.1, the term *spacing* includes the number, location, and aiming of the detectors selected for the hazard area. In every system design using flame detectors, the location of each unit in the system must address the criteria listed in 17.8.3.2.1. Exhibit 17.40 depicts a typical flame detector application.

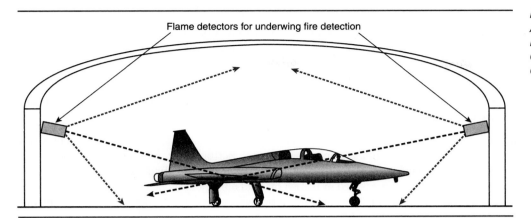

Flame detectors for underwing fire detection

EXHIBIT 17.40 *A Typical Application for Flame Detection. (Source: J. M. Cholin Consultants, Inc., Oakland, NJ)*

Product development in the field of radiant energy–sensing fire detection has been vigorous. New design concepts are introduced frequently. Consequently, at the current rate of change, providing an exhaustive list of the available technologies in the Code or the Code handbook is impossible.

Recently, microcomputer-based multi-spectrum flame detectors have become available that use a microcomputer to evaluate emissions from four, five, and possibly six different bands in the UV, visible, and IR regions. However, the wavelength bands and operational architecture of these multi-spectrum devices have not yet been disclosed in sufficient detail to provide the Technical Committee on Initiating Devices for Fire Alarm Systems with the requisite information for inclusion in this edition of the Code.

Paragraph 17.8.3.2.1 states the criteria that must be considered during the decision-making process the designer uses to select a flame detector and then apply it to a given location. The commentary following 17.8.3.2.2 provides additional insight into how the decision-making process is driven by the detector performance criteria and the anticipated fire and hazard environment.

A.17.8.3.2.1 The following are types of application for which flame detectors are suitable:

(1) High-ceiling, open-spaced buildings such as warehouses and aircraft hangars
(2) Outdoor or semioutdoor areas where winds or drafts can prevent smoke from reaching a heat or smoke detector
(3) Areas where rapidly developing flaming fires can occur, such as aircraft hangars, petrochemical production areas, storage and transfer areas, natural gas installations, paint shops, or solvent areas
(4) Areas needing high fire risk machinery or installations, often coupled with an automatic gas extinguishing system
(5) Environments that are unsuitable for other types of detectors

Some extraneous sources of radiant emissions that have been identified as interfering with the stability of flame detectors include the following:

(1) Sunlight
(2) Lightning
(3) X-rays
(4) Gamma rays
(5) Cosmic rays
(6) Ultraviolet radiation from arc welding
(7) Electromagnetic interference (EMI, RFI)
(8) Hot objects
(9) Artificial lighting

A single detector type or model is unlikely to be susceptible to all or even a majority of the unwanted alarm sources listed in A.17.8.3.2.1. Different types and models of flame detectors exhibit different degrees of susceptibility to some of these sources. Despite the best intentions and ardent efforts of flame detector manufacturers, the completely nuisance alarm–proof radiant energy–sensing detector has not yet been invented.

17.8.3.2.2 The system design shall specify the size of the flaming fire of given fuel that is to be detected.

Paragraph 17.8.3.2.2 is a performance-based code requirement. Because of the complexities inherent in the design of flame detection systems, a performance criterion must drive the design. The performance criterion is the detection of a fire of specified size and fuel.

Fire size is usually measured in British thermal units per second or in kilowatts, but more information is necessary in this context because flames are optically dense radiators. With optically dense radiators, the radiation from the back side of the flame does not travel through the flame toward the detector. Instead, the radiation is reabsorbed by the flame. Consequently, the flame detector "sees" only the profile of the fire, that is, its width and height.

The flame height is proportional to the heat release rate (British thermal units per second or kilowatts). Consequently, both fire width and heat release rate are necessary to quantify the size of a fire. Many designers have not yet made the conversion from simply stipulating a fire size criterion in terms of a pool fire of given fuel and area.

Annex B outlines a detailed design method for flame detection systems. The design fire is specified and the fire flame height calculated. The radiating area of the fire is then calculated. Next, the radiant output of the fire is correlated to the sensitivity tests performed by a testing laboratory in the course of the listing evaluation. The correlated radiant density per unit of flame area is then assigned to the design fire, and the radiant output is calculated based on the radiant output per unit area times the radiating area of the fire. The design fire is then modeled as a point source radiator having the calculated radiant output. See Section B.5.

17.8.3.2.3* In applications where the fire to be detected could occur in an area not on the optical axis of the detector, the distance shall be reduced or detectors shall be added to compensate for the angular displacement of the fire in accordance with the manufacturer's published instructions.

A.17.8.3.2.3 The greater the angular displacement of the fire from the optical axis of the detector, the larger the fire must become before it is detected. This phenomenon establishes the field of view of the detector. Figure A.17.8.3.2.3 shows an example of the effective sensitivity versus angular displacement of a flame detector.

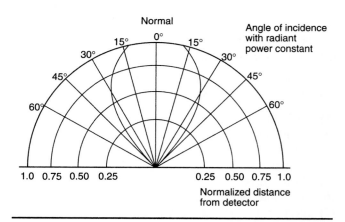

FIGURE A.17.8.3.2.3 *Normalized Sensitivity vs. Angular Displacement.*

17.8.3.2.4* In applications in which the fire to be detected is of a fuel that differs from the test fuel used in the process of listing or approval, the distance between the detector and the fire shall be adjusted consistent with the fuel specificity of the detector as established by the manufacturer.

A.17.8.3.2.4 Virtually all radiant energy–sensing detectors exhibit some kind of fuel specificity. If burned at uniform rates [W (J/sec)], different fuels emit different levels of radiant power in the ultraviolet, visible, and infrared portions of the spectrum. Under free-burn conditions, a fire of given surface area but of different fuels burns at different rates [W (J/sec)] and emits varying levels of radiation in each of the major portions of the spectrum. Most radiant energy detectors designed to detect flame are qualified on the basis of a defined fire under specific conditions. If employing these detectors for fuels other than the defined fire, the designer should make certain that the appropriate adjustments to the maximum distance between the detector and the fire are made consistent with the fuel specificity of the detector.

In an effort to make flame detectors more sensitive yet more immune to unwanted alarms, manufacturers began designing detectors that concentrated on very specific features of the flame spectrum. These features include the emissions of the flame across the range of wavelengths from UV to IR. In concept, such flame detectors infer that a flame exists if an emission of a specific wavelength or set of wavelengths is detected. However, one fuel emits a different radiant intensity at a given wavelength than another fuel. This characteristic gives rise to detectors that are fuel-specific. In some cases, a flame detector may be several times more sensitive to one fuel than to another.

The language of 17.8.3.2.4 effectively requires the designer to obtain flame spectra of potential fuels in the hazard area and response curves from the detector manufacturer to make certain the detector will respond to the fuel(s) involved. Furthermore, if the detector chosen for the system is less sensitive to one of the fuels in the hazard area, the spacing (including quantity, location, and aiming) of the detectors must be adjusted for the fuel to which the detector is least sensitive.

◄ **FAQ**
What must the designer obtain in order to ensure the proper spacing of the detectors?

17.8.3.2.5 Because flame detectors are line-of-sight devices, their ability to respond to the required area of fire in the zone that is to be protected shall not be compromised by the presence of intervening structural members or other opaque objects or materials.

Some atmospheric contaminants, including vapors and gases, are absorptive at the wavelengths used by some flame detectors, which can have a significant effect on the performance of the system. See A.17.8.3.1.1 for the relationship of fire size and distance from a detector. The extinction coefficient, ζ, is multiplied by the distance between the detector and the design fire to determine the portion of the emitted radiation that is lost due to atmospheric absorption. The design calculations should state the expected concentrations of absorptive air contaminants and their effect on the value for ζ that is being used. Contaminants on detector windows can often adversely affect performance. Also, a window material that is clear in the visible portion of the spectrum might be opaque in either the UV or the IR portion of the spectrum. Common glass is opaque in both the UV and the IR. Consequently, 17.8.3.2.5 must be applied to any window material that is not specifically listed for use with the detector in question.

17.8.3.2.6* Provisions shall be made to sustain detector window clarity in applications where airborne particulates and aerosols coat the detector window between maintenance intervals and affect sensitivity.

A.17.8.3.2.6 This requirement has been satisfied by the following means:

(1) Lens clarity monitoring and cleaning where a contaminated lens signal is rendered
(2) Lens air purge

The need to clean detector windows can be reduced by the provision of air purge devices. These devices are not foolproof, however, and are not a replacement for regular inspection and testing. Radiant energy–sensing detectors should not be placed in protective housings (e.g., behind glass) to keep them clean, unless such housings are listed for the purpose. Some optical materials are absorptive at the wavelengths used by the detector.

17.8.3.3 Spacing Considerations for Spark/Ember Detectors.

17.8.3.3.1* The location and spacing of detectors shall be the result of an engineering evaluation that includes the following:

(1) Size of the spark or ember that is to be detected
(2) Fuel involved
(3) Sensitivity of the detector
(4) Field of view of the detector
(5) Distance between the fire and the detector
(6) Radiant energy absorption of the atmosphere
(7) Presence of extraneous sources of radiant emissions
(8) Purpose of the detection systems
(9) Response time required

A.17.8.3.3.1 Spark/ember detectors are installed primarily to detect sparks and embers that could, if allowed to continue to burn, precipitate a much larger fire or explosion. Spark/ember detectors are typically mounted on some form of duct or conveyor, monitoring the fuel as it passes by. Usually, it is necessary to enclose the portion of the conveyor where the detectors are located, as these devices generally require a dark environment. Extraneous sources of radiant emissions that have been identified as interfering with the stability of spark/ember detectors include the following:

(1) Ambient light
(2) Electromagnetic interference (EMI, RFI)
(3) Electrostatic discharge in the fuel stream

Exhibit 17.41 shows typical applications where spark/ember detectors are used. Spark/ember detectors are usually used on conveyance ducts and conveyors to detect embers in particulate solids as they are transported. The top drawing in Exhibit 17.41 shows the general concept of spark/ember detectors. The middle drawing illustrates the application of spark/ember detectors to protect a dust collector. The bottom drawing illustrates the protection of a conveyor.

It should be noted that the detectors are located at a point along the duct or conveyor, monitoring the cross-section of the duct or conveyor at that one point by essentially "looking across" the duct. Commercially available, listed spark/ember detectors are designed to monitor a fuel stream as it moves past the detector. These detectors are not designed to "look down the duct." The capacitive nature of the circuitry of this type of detector generally makes it incapable of detecting a slowly growing radiator; the radiator must move past the detector rapidly if it is to be detected.

Annex B provides a more detailed design guide for spark detection system design.

17.8.3.3.2* The system design shall specify the size of the spark or ember of the given fuel that the detection system is to detect.

A.17.8.3.3.2 There is a minimum ignition power (watts) for all combustible dusts. If the spark or ember is incapable of delivering that quantity of power to the adjacent combustible material (dust), an expanding dust fire cannot occur. The minimum ignition power is determined by the fuel chemistry, fuel particle size, fuel concentration in air, and ambient conditions such as temperature and humidity.

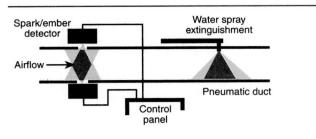

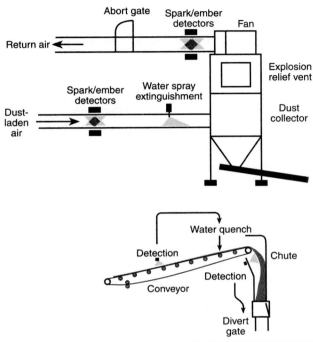

EXHIBIT 17.41 *Spark/Ember Detector Applications. (Source: J. M. Cholin Consultants, Inc., Oakland, NJ)*

The size of an ember is measured in terms of watts or milliwatts. The radiant energy from an ember and hence its size cannot be accurately inferred from a description that states diameter and temperature only. See the definition for *spark/ember detector sensitivity* in 3.3.260. Furthermore, the equation for the inverse square law in A.17.8.3.1.1 cannot be used to calculate the ability of the detector to detect the ember in question unless both the detector sensitivity and the ember size are specified in the same terms of radiant power: watts, milliwatts, or microwatts.

As with 17.8.3.2.2 regarding flame detectors, 17.8.3.3.2 is a performance-based design criterion that drives the entire system design. However, sparks are so close to actually being a point source radiator in real life that calculating radiating area, as is done with flames, is not necessary. The radiant output of the spark is used directly.

As with 17.8.3.2 dealing with flame detectors, the selected decision-making process brings the designer to this section on spark detection that is based on the analysis of the radiant characteristics of the combustible and the environmental factors applicable to the hazard area. The hazard analysis begins with the determination of whether the combustible will burn in the solid phase as an ember or in the gas phase as a flame. That determination then points the designer toward the spark/ember detector (for solid-phase combustion) or the flame detector (for gas-phase combustion). The engineering manuals provided by the manufacturers of the various detectors under consideration should be used to determine the usefulness of a particular device for the hazard under consideration.

17.8.3.3.3 Spark detectors shall be positioned so that all points within the cross section of the conveyance duct, conveyor, or chute where the detectors are located are within the field of view *(as defined in 3.3.90)* of at least one detector.

FAQ ▶
How many detectors are needed to ensure proper coverage for each location on a pneumatic conveyance duct?

Most makes of spark detection require a minimum of two detectors at each location on a pneumatic conveyance duct requiring detection. The need for this quantity of detectors is determined by the detector's field of view. Unless the field of view is 180 degrees, at least two devices are needed to cover the inside of a duct. As the duct diameter increases, using that portion of the field of view where the detector is most sensitive is necessary to offset the absorption of the radiant emission from the spark by the nonburning material. Consequently, most spark detection systems require additional detectors as duct size increases.

17.8.3.3.4* The location and spacing of the detectors shall be adjusted using the inverse square law, modified for the atmospheric absorption and the absorption of nonburning fuel suspended in the air in accordance with the manufacturer's published instructions.

A.17.8.3.3.4 As the distance between the fire and the detector increases, the radiant power reaching the detector decreases. Refer to A.17.8.3.1.1 for additional information.

The equation used for spark detection design is the same as that used for flame detection design. However, the atmospheric extinction coefficient, ζ (zeta), is determined by the optical absorbance of the nonburning material in the band of wavelengths used by the detector and by the concentration of the nonburning material per unit of air volume. The conservative design approach is to assume an emissivity (absorbance) of 1.0, which means that the material is 100 percent absorbent and does not reflect any radiation that strikes a nonburning fuel particle.

17.8.3.3.5* In applications where the sparks to be detected could occur in an area not on the optical axis of the detector, the distance shall be reduced or detectors shall be added to compensate for the angular displacement of the fire in accordance with the manufacturer's published instructions.

A.17.8.3.3.5 The greater the angular displacement of the fire from the optical axis of the detector, the larger the fire must become before it is detected. This phenomenon establishes the field of view of the detector. Figure A.17.8.3.2.3 shows an example of the effective sensitivity versus angular displacement of a flame detector.

17.8.3.3.6* Provisions shall be made to sustain the detector window clarity in applications where airborne particulates and aerosols coat the detector window and affect sensitivity.

A.17.8.3.3.6 This requirement has been satisfied by the following means:

(1) Lens clarity monitoring and cleaning where a contaminated lens signal is rendered
(2) Lens air purge

17.8.4 Other Considerations.

The requirements in 17.8.4 are intended to be applied to all radiant energy–sensing detectors, regardless of type.

17.8.4.1 Radiant energy–sensing detectors shall be protected either by design or installation to ensure that optical performance is not compromised.

Because radiant energy–sensing detectors are usually installed where they must endure the rigors of difficult industrial environments, the designer is cautioned to consider the long-term impact of the environment on the optical performance of the detectors to ensure compliance with 17.8.4.1.

Atmospheric contaminants are often opaque at detector operating wavelengths. Structures are often modified after detector placement and aiming. Snow and ice can accumulate on either the detector or the adjacent structure, obscuring the field of view. These factors as well as others might affect the clear view of the hazard area or impede the required routine maintenance of detectors. Finally, unless a detector has been specifically listed for use with a particular window material, the installation of a detector behind a protective window violates the operational characteristics as outlined in the listing of the detector. Most detectors employ windows made of optical material other than glass, selected for their transmittance in nonvisible portions of the spectrum. Glass is not transmittant at either UV or mid-IR wavelengths and would "blind" most flame detectors.

17.8.4.2 If necessary, radiant energy–sensing detectors shall be shielded or otherwise arranged to prevent action from unwanted radiant energy.

In some cases, shielding a detector from radiant emissions coming from a portion of its field of view — where the sole source of radiant emissions is a spurious source — can be an effective way of dealing with the source of unwanted alarms. Many detectors are available with scoops or baffles to limit the field of view to a small portion of the total viewing area. Scoops or baffles provide the detector the ability to operate in spite of the presence of a spurious alarm source. When considering such methods, the designer should consult the manufacturer. The designer should also keep in mind that reflected radiant emissions can cause alarms as well.

All surfaces are not uniformly reflective at all wavelengths. Unwanted alarms are often traced to reflections from radiant sources that are outside the actual field of view of the detector.

17.8.4.3 Where used in outdoor applications, radiant energy–sensing detectors shall be shielded or otherwise arranged in a fashion to prevent diminishing sensitivity by conditions such as rain or snow and yet allow a clear field of vision of the hazard area.

Both water and snow are highly absorptive in both the UV and IR portions of the spectrum. Where detectors are exposed to interference from streaming water or snow, their ability to respond to the design fire can be seriously compromised. Water can also initiate false alarms by causing the modulation of background radiant emissions, simulating the modulated emissions of a flame.

17.8.4.4 A radiant energy–sensing fire detector shall not be installed in a location where the ambient conditions are known to exceed the extremes for which the detector has been listed.

17.8.5 Video Image Flame Detection.

New products have recently been introduced that use a video camera and image recognition software to detect flames. These systems consist of a set of video cameras, a signal router/interface, and a computer with frame capture and image recognition software that result in the recognition of a flame. An output signal is then initiated that serves to initiate an alarm signal in the connected fire alarm control unit.

17.8.5.1 Video image flame detection systems and all of the components thereof, including hardware and software, shall be listed for the purpose of flame detection.

The listing requirement in 17.8.5.1 places the responsibility on the organization providing the listing to evaluate the efficacy of the equipment and software for appropriateness for a defined scope of applications. The limits on the size of the monitored compartment versus the size of the fire that can be reliably detected and the limitations on the environment within the compartment necessary to permit reliable detection have not yet been established by the technical committee.

17.8.5.2 Video image flame detection systems shall comply with all of the applicable requirements of Chapters 1, 10, 14, 17, and 23 of this Code.

A video image flame detection system consists of one or more video cameras, a signal router or interface, and a computer to analyze the individual video image frames in real time. Requirements in Chapters 1, 10, 14, 17, and 23 are applicable to such a system because the system that serves the role of a flame detector is a large assemblage of components with the same level of complexity as a fire alarm system. For example, all these components require power and must comply with the power supply criteria in Chapter 10. All the interconnections between cameras, interfaces, and computers must be monitored for integrity. All the components in the system must be listed for the purpose for which they are used. The alarm signal must be conveyed to a fire alarm control unit via a circuit that is monitored for integrity. The requirements in Chapters 1, 10, 14, 17, and 23 address these and many other issues that are relevant to the video image flame detection system and are applicable in much the same way they are applicable to an air-sampling smoke detection system.

17.8.5.3* Video signals generated by cameras that are components of video image flame detection systems shall be permitted to be transmitted to other systems for other uses only through output connections provided specifically for that purpose by the video system manufacturer.

A.17.8.5.3 Facility owners and managers might desire to use cameras and their images for purposes other than flame detection. The intent of this paragraph is not to prohibit additional uses, but to ensure the integrity of the life safety flame detection mission of the equipment.

Video image flame detection systems are best suited for large open spaces with high value assets that warrant such protection. In many cases, the facility security system includes cameras to monitor the space during unoccupied times to maintain surveillance. There is little basis for two sets of cameras, one for flame detection and a second for surveillance. Paragraph 17.8.5.3 allows the video signal to be shared as long as the equipment and the software that allows the sharing are listed for the purpose and the system ensures that the security use of the signal does not interfere with the fire safety use of the signal.

17.8.5.4* All component controls and software shall be protected from unauthorized changes. All changes to the software or component settings shall be tested in accordance with Chapter 14.

A.17.8.5.4 Video image flame detection control and software should be protected from tampering by passwords, software keys, or other means of limiting access to authorized/qualified personnel. Component settings include any control or programming that might affect the operation of coverage of the detection. This includes, but is not limited to, camera focus, field of view, motion sensitivity settings, and change of camera position. Any changes in component settings or ambient conditions that affect the design performance of the detector should initiate a trouble signal.

Since this technology is new and experience with it is limited, only a general requirement has been established by the technical committee. Video image flame detection systems operate by comparing the view of the hazard area to earlier views of the hazard area and initiate alarm signals when the changes in groups of pixels are consistent with the presence of flame in the monitored space. Changes in camera position, focus, contrast setting, field of view, ambient lighting, and the criteria in the software for recognition of a flame all can affect the reliability of the system as a flame detection means. The system must be designed to provide protection against unauthorized changes that could affect the system's performance or reliability. Any intentional changes must be subject to the acceptance testing criteria in Chapter 14.

17.9 Combination, Multi-Criteria, and Multi-Sensor Detectors

This section was added in the 2007 revision cycle. Detectors that respond to a number of different stimuli in order to detect a hostile fire have recently entered the fire alarm market. This section was added to address those products.

17.9.1 General. Section 17.9 provides requirements for the selection, location, and spacing of combination, multi-criteria, and multi-sensor detectors.

17.9.2 Combination Detectors.

17.9.2.1 A combination detector shall be listed for each sensor.

Since, by definition, a *combination detector* is two or more separate detectors combined into a single unit, each capable of producing its own, individual signal, each of the detectors within the combination detector has the ability to operate alone, respond independently of the others, and initiate its own signal. (See 3.3.59.4.) Consequently, the individual detection devices within the combination detector must be listed as if they were stand-alone devices. For example, a combination smoke/heat detector would be listed as a smoke detector under UL 268 and a heat detector under ANSI/UL 521, *Standard for Heat Detectors for Fire Protective Signaling Systems.*

◄ **FAQ**
What is the reason for requiring that each sensor of a combination detector be listed?

17.9.2.2 The device listings shall determine the locations and spacing criteria in accordance with Chapter 17.

With earlier versions of combination detectors, there is the distinct possibility that a combination detector containing a smoke sensor and a heat sensor could have a listed spacing as a heat detector that is smaller than the conventionally used 30 ft (9.1 m) spacing for smoke detectors in this chapter. In that case, the designer could use the most conservative spacing as the design spacing for the combination detector. [Note that 17.6.3.6 currently requires a listed spacing of at least 50 ft (15.2 m) for an integral heat sensor on a smoke detector.] Historically, the heat detector was considered by some authorities having jurisdiction to be a back-up to the smoke sensor should the smoke sensor fail. However, if the generation of a heat detection signal relies on any of the electronic processing or switching circuitry of the smoke detector, it cannot serve that function. If the primary purpose of the detector is to provide life safety, the spacing should be based on the smoke detector spacing rules in the Code.

17.9.3 Multi-Criteria Detectors.

17.9.3.1 A multi-criteria detector shall be listed for the primary function of the device.

Multi-criteria detectors are defined in 3.3.59.11. While the detector utilizes multiple sensors to measure multiple criteria, it produces only a single alarm signal. In most cases, these detection devices include (1) both a photoelectric smoke sensor and a thermistor heat sensor, (2) an ionization smoke sensor and a thermistor heat sensor, or (3) both an ionization and photoelectric smoke sensor and a thermistor heat sensor. These detection devices are usually listed under UL 268 as smoke detectors. They can be designed as addressable/analog devices or as conventional (on/off) initiating devices.

17.9.3.2 Because of the device-specific, software-driven solution of multi-criteria detectors to reduce unwanted alarms and improve detector response to a nonspecific fire source, location and spacing criteria included with the detector installation instructions shall be followed.

If the unit is listed under UL 268 as a smoke detector, it is to be located, spaced, and installed in accordance with Section 17.7.

17.9.4 Multi-Sensor Detectors.

17.9.4.1 A multi-sensor detector shall be listed for each sensor.

Multi-sensor detectors are defined in 3.3.59.12. In addition to utilizing multiple criteria, these detectors can initiate an alarm signal as a result of any one of the sensors achieving its alarm threshold. These detectors can produce a number of alarm signals. In most cases, these detection devices include (1) a photoelectric smoke sensor, (2) a thermistor heat sensor, (3) an ionization smoke sensor, (4) a carbon monoxide sensor, and (5) a carbon dioxide sensor and a set of fire algorithms in a microcomputer that matches the detected levels to fire signatures in memory. If a multi-sensor detector uses an ionization chamber, a photoelectric chamber, a thermistor heat sensor, and a carbon monoxide sensor to arrive at a single alarm signal, then it is listed as a single multi-criteria detector. However, if that same detector is capable of sending the individual signals to the fire alarm control unit (FACU) and the FACU can initiate a fire alarm on the basis of any one of those sensing means, then the multi-sensor detector is actually serving as a group of individual detectors and must be listed for each detection mode. These detectors are usually designed as addressable/analog devices, and the control unit often performs signature matching to generate the alarm signals.

17.9.4.2 Because of the device-specific, software-driven solution of multi-sensor detectors to reduce unwanted alarms and improve detector response to a nonspecific fire source, location and spacing criteria included with the detector installation instructions shall be followed.

17.10 Gas Detection

Section 17.10 was added to the 2010 edition of the Code. Its development was precipitated by the recognition that flammable gas and combustible vapor detection systems were being required by numerous occupancy standards. If the fire safety of a particular occupancy relies on a flammable gas or combustible vapor detection system, then that system should be installed to the same level of reliability as the fire protection signaling system.

17.10.1 General. The purpose and scope of Section 17.10 shall be to provide requirements for the selection, installation, and operation of gas detectors.

17.10.2 Gas Characteristics and Detector Selection.

17.10.2.1 Gas detection equipment shall be listed for detection of the specific gas or vapor to be encountered.

Different sensing technologies are used for the detection of different gases. While most flammable hydrocarbon gases and combustible hydrocarbon vapors are detected using a catalytic bead technology, the catalyst varies depending on the target gas to be detected. Some flammable gases are detected best with electrochemical sensors. In other cases, semiconductor sensors are used. The sensor must be matched and calibrated to the specific gas to be detected. While there are some broad-spectrum flammable hydrocarbon gas sensors available on the market, their sensitivity and output vary considerably with the specific gas present. The gas detector must be carefully matched to the gas or vapor that is present. When a mixture of gases or vapors is present, the detector must be calibrated for that mixture.

Gas detectors generally do not have a fixed alarm threshold. Usually a gas detection system consists of a sensor located where the gas is expected to be present, wired to a controller in a safe location. The controller has adjustable alarm thresholds, usually expressed as a percentage of the lower flammable limit (LFL), the lowest concentration of the gas in air that will propagate a flame. For a general review of gas and vapor detection systems and monitors, refer to Section 14, Chapter 8, of the *Fire Protection Handbook®*, 20th edition.

17.10.2.2 Any gas detection systems installed on a fire alarm system shall comply with all the applicable requirements of Chapters 1, 10, 14, 17, and 23 of this Code.

Fire losses have occurred that were ultimately traced back to the failure of a flammable gas or combustible vapor detection system. The referenced chapters establish the minimum compliance criteria for a gas detection system installed to provide part of the fire safety for a compartment of a building.

17.10.2.3 The requirements of this Code shall not apply to gas detection systems used solely for process control.

Where the gas detection system is not providing a fire safety function but is limited only to process control, the requirements of this Code are not applicable. The gas detection systems in those applications are designed by the persons responsible for the design of the process. The process designers are in the best position to know what is necessary to control that process. Once the presence of the gas or vapor detection system begins serving a fire safety function, the requirements of this Code become applicable.

The design of gas detection systems is inherently different from the design of smoke detection systems. In a smoke detection system, the fire produces a buoyant plume that forms a ceiling jet, and the fire sends the smoke to a predictable location — the ceiling. Consequently, smoke detectors are installed on the ceiling in an array, the spacing of which is derived from a response time criterion. With a gas or vapor leak, there is not necessarily a buoyant plume. The gases or vapors are carried by the ambient air movement unless there is a substantial difference in the density between the gases or vapors and the ambient air. Consequently, a detailed engineering analysis of the ambient air in the compartment or compartments to be served by the gas detection system is necessary to determine where to locate the sensors. That analysis will include a three-dimensional map of the airflow currents under the entire range of operating scenarios to ensure that sensors are located where the air currents will convey the gas or vapor to be detected.

17.10.2.4* The selection and placement of the gas detectors shall be based on an engineering evaluation.

A.17.10.2.4 The engineering evaluation should include, but is not limited to, the following:

(1) Structural features, size, and shape of the rooms and bays
(2) Occupancy and uses of areas
(3) Ceiling heights
(4) Ceiling shape, surface, and obstructions
(5) Ventilation
(6) Ambient environment
(7) Gas characteristics of the gases present
(8) Configuration of the contents in the area to be protected
(9) Response time(s)

17.11 Other Fire Detectors

The intent of the Code is to provide for the development of new technologies and to allow the use of such technologies consistent with sound principles of fire protection engineering. A number of aerosol-sensing detectors do not yet conform to the response criteria of UL 268 and for that reason are not called "smoke detectors." One detector senses hydrogen chloride; another senses carbon monoxide. The requirements in Section 17.11 provide for methods not explicitly described in other sections of the chapter to accommodate new technology developed during Code cycles.

17.11.1 Detectors that operate on principles different from those covered by Sections 17.6 through 17.8 shall be classified as "other fire detectors."

Chapter 14 outlines the required maintenance procedures and schedules for all components of a fire alarm system, including the initiating devices. Initiating devices covered by Section 17.11 must be maintained pursuant to Chapter 14 and the manufacturer's recommendations.

17.11.1.1 Such detectors shall be installed in all areas where they are required either by other NFPA codes and standards or by the authority having jurisdiction.

17.11.2* "Other fire detectors" shall operate where subjected to the abnormal concentration of combustion effects that occur during a fire.

A.17.11.2 Examples of such combustion effects are water vapor, ionized molecules, or other phenomena for which they are designed. The performance characteristics of the detector and the area into which it is to be installed should be evaluated to minimize nuisance alarms or conditions that would interfere with operation.

17.11.3 Detection layout shall be based upon the size and intensity of fire to provide the necessary quantity of required products and related thermal lift, circulation, or diffusion for operation.

17.11.4 Room sizes and contours, airflow patterns, obstructions, and other characteristics of the protected hazard shall be taken into account.

17.11.5 Location and spacing of detectors shall comply with 17.11.5.1 through 17.11.5.3.

17.11.5.1 The location and spacing of detectors shall be based on the principle of operation and an engineering survey of the conditions anticipated in service.

17.11.5.1.1 The manufacturer's published instructions shall be consulted for recommended detector uses and locations.

17.11.5.2 Detectors shall not be spaced beyond their listed or approved maximums.

17.11.5.2.1 Closer spacing shall be used where the structural or other characteristics of the protected hazard warrant.

17.11.5.3 The location and sensitivity of the detectors shall be based on a documented engineering evaluation that includes the manufacturer's installation instructions and the following:

(1) Structural features, size, and shape of the rooms and bays
(2) Occupancy and uses of the area
(3) Ceiling height
(4) Ceiling shape, surface, and obstructions
(5) Ventilation
(6) Ambient environment
(7) Burning characteristics of the combustible materials present
(8) Configuration of the contents in the area to be protected

17.12 Sprinkler Waterflow Alarm-Initiating Devices

17.12.1* The provisions of Section 17.12 shall apply to devices that initiate an alarm indicating a flow of water in a sprinkler system.

A.17.12.1 Piping between the sprinkler system and a pressure actuated alarm-initiating device should be galvanized or of nonferrous metal or other approved corrosion-resistant material of not less than $\frac{3}{8}$ in.(9.5 mm) nominal pipe size.

17.12.2* Activation of the initiating device shall occur within 90 seconds of waterflow at the alarm-initiating device when flow occurs that is equal to or greater than that from a single sprinkler of the smallest orifice size installed in the system.

The 90-second response criterion addresses only the time lag between the initial flow of water and the issuance of the electronic signal to the fire alarm control unit by the switch. The criterion does not include any polling delays introduced by the fire alarm control unit.

The water in a wet pipe automatic sprinkler system riser is not static; it moves upward and downward in the riser, depending on differences in pressure between the sprinkler system riser and the municipal water supply. Any air trapped in the sprinkler system piping provides a compressible gas cushion, enhancing the tendency for flow to occur as a result of variance of pressures in the water supply system. The alarm check valve in the sprinkler system tends to slow down, but not eliminate, this flow. Consequently, the majority of sprinkler systems require a means to retard the initiation of a sprinkler waterflow signal to prevent the small flows that are the artifact of pressure variations from generating a waterflow alarm. The prevention of small flows is accomplished with a "retard" feature. This feature can be part of the sprinkler system or it can be incorporated into the flow switch.

Some waterflow alarm–initiating devices are implemented as pressure switches installed on the wet pipe sprinkler system alarm trim, rather than with paddle- or vane-type switches located on the riser itself. If a valve is installed in the connection between the sprinkler system and the waterflow initiating device, it must be supervised and transmit a supervisory signal if in the off-normal (full open) state. In general, pressure-type flow switches should not be installed on the top of a retard chamber, because a valve is always located between the alarm check valve and the retard chamber that is difficult if not impossible to supervise or lock open. Furthermore, false alarms can occur if the retard chamber drain on the sprinkler system trim becomes clogged.

Because of their design, dry pipe, pre-action, and deluge sprinkler systems do not suffer from the phenomenon of riser flow from pressure variations. However, these types of sprinkler systems should always be equipped with pressure-type flow switches rather than paddle or vane type. If a paddle- or vane-type flow switch is installed downstream of a dry pipe, pre-action, or deluge-type system, the paddle or vane is likely to be damaged when the valve opens.

◄ **FAQ**
What type of flow switch should be used in a dry pipe, pre-action, or deluge-type system?

A.17.12.2 The waterflow device should be field adjusted so that an alarm is initiated no more than 90 seconds after a sustained flow of at least 10 gpm (40 L/min).

Features that should be investigated to minimize alarm response time include the following:

(1) Elimination of trapped air in the sprinkler system piping
(2) Use of an excess pressure pump
(3) Use of pressure drop alarm-initiating devices
(4) A combination thereof

Care should be used when choosing waterflow alarm-initiating devices for hydraulically calculated looped systems and those systems using small orifice sprinklers. Such systems might incorporate a single point flow of significantly less than 10 gpm (40 L/min). In such cases, additional waterflow alarm-initiating devices or the use of pressure drop-type waterflow alarm-initiating devices might be necessary.

Care should be used when choosing waterflow alarm-initiating devices for sprinkler systems that use on–off sprinklers to ensure that an alarm is initiated in the event of a waterflow condition. On–off sprinklers open at a predetermined temperature and close when the temperature reaches a predetermined lower temperature. With certain types of fires, waterflow might occur in a series of short bursts of a duration of 10 seconds to 30 seconds each. An alarm-initiating device with retard might not detect waterflow under these conditions. An excess pressure system or a system that operates on pressure drop should be considered to facilitate waterflow detection on sprinkler systems that use on–off sprinklers.

Excess pressure systems can be used with or without alarm valves. The following is a description of one type of excess pressure system with an alarm valve.

An excess pressure system with an alarm valve consists of an excess pressure pump with pressure switches to control the operation of the pump. The inlet of the pump is connected to the supply side of the alarm valve, and the outlet is connected to the sprinkler system. The pump control pressure switch is of the differential type, maintaining the sprinkler system pressure above the main pressure by a constant amount. Another switch monitors low sprinkler system pressure to initiate a supervisory signal in the event of a failure of the pump or other malfunction. An additional pressure switch can be used to stop pump operation in the event of a deficiency in water supply. Another pressure switch is connected to the alarm outlet of the alarm valve to initiate a waterflow alarm signal when waterflow exists. This type of system also inherently prevents false alarms due to water surges. The sprinkler retard chamber should be eliminated to enhance the detection capability of the system for short duration flows.

In many facilities, the sprinkler system is used as both a suppression system and a detection system. The flow of water initiates an alarm. In a large wet pipe system with large sprinkler risers, depending on the amount of trapped air, the flow from a single head has proved hard to detect. The air acts as a gas cushion, allowing pulsating variations in water pressure within the riser when a single head discharges. This action can prevent the vane of a vane-type waterflow switch from lifting, or the clapper of an alarm check valve from opening, long enough to overcome the pneumatic, electronic, or mechanical retard mechanism of the switch. (Rising and falling water supply pressure over the course of any 24-hour period causes the pressure entering the wet pipe sprinkler system to change. This pressure change can cause unwanted alarms. Consequently, most flow switches are equipped with a retard feature that delays the transmission of a signal until after stable waterflow has been achieved.) With pulsating flow in the riser, flow from one or two sprinkler heads can go undetected. Consequently, the acceptance testing for systems with large risers should include flowing the system from the inspector's test connection at the most remote point on the sprinkler system to verify that the flow from a single head does, indeed, initiate an alarm signal within the maximum 90-second criterion. Often, exhausting the entrapped air in the sprinkler system is necessary to reduce this effect.

Meeting the 90-second criterion can be challenging. If the sprinkler system uses on–off sprinklers, a waterflow alarm-initiating device must be used that can sense a possible flow of shorter duration. Meeting the 90-second criterion also can be a challenge with large systems using conventional sprinklers.

Finally, the designer must be familiar with NFPA 13.

17.12.3 Movement of water due to waste, surges, or variable pressure shall not initiate an alarm signal.

17.13* Detection of the Operation of Other Automatic Extinguishing Systems

The operation of fire extinguishing systems or suppression systems shall initiate an alarm signal by alarm-initiating devices installed in accordance with their individual listings.

A.17.13 Alarm initiation can be accomplished by devices that detect the following:

(1) Flow of water in foam systems
(2) Pump activation
(3) Differential pressure
(4) Pressure (e.g., clean agent systems, carbon dioxide systems, and wet/dry chemical systems)
(5) Mechanical operation of a release mechanism

The operation of any automatic fire extinguishing system is a clear indication of a fire. Currently listed automatic fire extinguishing systems include electric switching devices that are intended to be used to transmit a fire alarm signal to the building fire alarm system.

Discharge pressure switches or actuation mechanism microswitches are the usual means of providing the extinguishing system operation signal to the fire detection control unit. Due to the critical function these switches perform, they must be listed for use with the specific make and model of extinguishing system. The connection of a listed extinguishing agent release initiating device to an appropriate initiating device circuit on the fire alarm control unit, consistent with the listings of both the unit and the initiating device, is critical for the successful operation of most special extinguishing systems. See Exhibit 17.42 for an example of a pressure-actuated discharge switch.

Many extinguishing systems include emergency mechanical manual release capability. This feature provides for the release of the extinguishing agent, bypassing the operation of the fire detection system that is used to actuate the extinguishing system. Provisions must be in place to ensure that any automatic functions necessary for the proper operation of the extinguishing agent, including shutdown of local HVAC, actuation of HVAC dampers, closing doors, interruption of production equipment, shutoff of fuel flow, and so on — functions normally accomplished by means of electrical switching in the extinguishing system control panel — also occur when the mechanical manual release is used. See Exhibit 17.43 for an example of a manual agent release device.

The designer should review the following standards for more information on alarm initiation requirements that are unique to the various extinguishing agents covered by these standards:

NFPA 12, *Standard on Carbon Dioxide Extinguishing Systems*

NFPA 12A, *Standard on Halon 1301 Fire Extinguishing Systems*

NFPA 16, *Standard for the Installation of Foam-Water Sprinkler and Foam-Water Spray Systems*

NFPA 17, *Standard for Dry Chemical Extinguishing Systems*

NFPA 2001, *Standard on Clean Agent Fire Extinguishing Systems*

◄ **FAQ**
What are usual means to signal operation of the extinguishing system?

EXHIBIT 17.42 *Typical Extinguishing System Pressure-Actuated Discharge Switch. (Source: Kidde-Fenwal, Ashland, MA)*

EXHIBIT 17.43 *Emergency Manual Cable Release for Extinguishing Systems. (Source: Kidde-Fenwal, Ashland, MA)*

17.14 Manually Actuated Alarm-Initiating Devices

The user should note that many fire alarm systems are not equipped with an automatic off-site signal transmission capability to a supervising station. In those buildings where the fire alarm system is not equipped with automatic off-site signal transmission to a supervising station system, activation of the manual fire alarm box only notifies other occupants in the building of the presence of a fire. The manual fire alarm box does not notify the fire service. For those buildings, explicit instructions to the operator of the manual fire alarm box to also notify the fire department from outside the building are desirable and might be required by local ordinance or code to be placed at each manual fire alarm box location.

17.14.1 Manual fire alarm boxes shall be used only for fire alarm initiating purposes.

The requirement in 17.14.1 stems from two concerns: credibility and reliability.

If manual fire alarm boxes are used for some other purpose, for the actuation of a special extinguishing system, for example, then someone unfamiliar with the facility could actuate the wrong manual fire alarm box in response to a fire incident. Consequently, manual fire alarm boxes are permitted to be used only for initiation of a fire alarm signal. A manual alarm-initiating device other than a manual *fire* alarm initiation device must be used for those other purposes. This requirement limits the potential for occupant confusion during a fire.

When manual alarm-initiating devices are installed to initiate some other type of emergency response, such as for toxic release or spill, the manual alarm-initiating device should be obviously different from those used to report a fire to minimize the probability of confusion during an emergency. Refer to Chapter 24 for guidance on manual initiation devices used for mass notification systems.

17.14.1.1* Unless installed in an environment that precludes the use of red paint or red plastic, manual fire alarm boxes shall be red in color.

A.17.14.1.1 In environments where red paint or red plastic is not suitable, an alternative material, such as stainless steel, could be used as long as the box meets the requirements of 17.14.5.

17.14.1.2 Manual pull stations for initiating other than fire alarm shall be permitted if the devices are differentiated from the manual fire alarm boxes by a color other than red and labeling.

Paragraph 17.14.1.1 reserves the color red for the manual initiating device that initiates a fire signal. If manual initiating devices are used to initiate some other emergency signal (e.g., toxic release, radiological release, medical emergency, hazardous weather), they must be differentiated from each other and from the fire alarm boxes by both color and labeling. No consensus has been reached yet on a color code for manual emergency reporting initiating devices.

17.14.1.3 Manual fire alarm boxes shall be mounted on a background of contrasting color.

17.14.2 Combination manual fire alarm boxes and guard's signaling stations shall be permitted.

If the manual fire alarm box is incorporated into some other non-fire-related assembly (with the single exception of guard's tour supervisory stations), the probability of unwarranted operation is increased. This arrangement leads to false alarms and erodes the occupants' confidence in the system. Also, when manual fire alarms are combined with non-fire-related functions, the probability that a failure in the non-fire-related function will compromise the fire alarm system increases.

17.14.3 Each manual fire alarm box shall be securely mounted.

17.14.4 The operable part of each manual fire alarm box shall be not less than 42 in. (1.07 m) and not more than 48 in. (1.22 m) above floor level.

Subsection 17.14.4 addresses the historical "side reach" accessibility requirement of 54 in. (1.37 m) that resulted from the adoption of the Americans with Disabilities Act (ADA). As a minimum-compliance standard, the Code must permit the use of the widest range deemed acceptable. However, the accessibility requirements have been under review for some time. The final draft of the *Americans with Disabilities Act and Architectural Barriers Act Accessibility*

Guidelines (July 23, 2004) specifies a maximum unobstructed "side reach" of 48 in. (1.22 m). The guidelines also retain the maximum value of 48 in. (1.22 m) for unobstructed "forward reach." Refer to the specific details of the guidelines for what constitutes obstructed versus unobstructed approach. Information concerning the current policy of the Architectural and Transportation Barriers Compliance Board and the final draft of the guidelines can be found at the access board website *www.access-board.gov.*

See Exhibit 17.44 for an example of a manual fire alarm box.

Manual fire alarm boxes mounted in damp or wet locations must be listed for such use.

17.14.5 Manual fire alarm boxes shall be installed so that they are conspicuous, unobstructed, and accessible.

The objective behind 17.14.5 is to ensure that, as they leave the building, occupants can find manual fire alarm–initiating devices without searching. It is the authority having jurisdiction that decides if the manual fire alarm–initiating devices are sufficiently conspicuous, unobstructed, and accessible.

Subsection 17.14.5 addresses the issue of items of interior décor being placed in front of or adjacent to manual fire alarm boxes. The manual fire alarm box must be clearly identifiable from a distance, and nothing can hinder a person from operating the manual fire alarm box as that person proceeds to the means of egress.

Plastic covers are permitted to protect manual fire alarm boxes and provide relief from accidental or malicious unwarranted alarms. These covers must be listed for such use. Some provide a local signal that sounds at the device when the cover is lifted. In the event that an audible signal is incorporated into a cover, care must be taken to educate users that the opening of the cover does *not* constitute the initiation of a fire alarm signal and that the fire alarm box must still be actuated. See Exhibit 17.45 for an example of a manual fire alarm box protective cover.

17.14.6 Manual fire alarm boxes shall be located within 60 in. (1.52 m) of the exit doorway opening at each exit on each floor.

17.14.7 Manual fire alarm boxes shall be mounted on both sides of grouped openings over 40 ft (12.2 m) in width, and within 60 in. (1.52 m) of each side of the opening.

The objective of 17.14.7 is to provide a manual fire alarm box within easy reach in the normal exit path of the occupants. When multi-leaf door sets are installed, the actual exitway can become sufficiently wide that the departing occupant might not notice the fire alarm box on the far side of a wide set of doors, or the occupant would have to delay departure in order to cross the doors to activate the manual fire alarm box. The consensus of the technical committee was that when door sets attain this width, fire alarm boxes are needed on both sides of the means of egress. In the 1999 edition, the Technical Committee on Initiating Devices for Fire Alarm Systems clarified this requirement to ensure that the number and the location of the manual fire alarm boxes required for multi-leaf doors are consistent where there are groups of exit doors.

17.14.8* Additional manual fire alarm boxes shall be provided so that the travel distance to the nearest fire alarm box will not be in excess of 200 ft (61.0 m), measured horizontally on the same floor.

A.17.14.8 It is not the intent of 17.14.8 to require manual fire alarm boxes to be attached to movable partitions or to equipment, nor to require the installation of permanent structures for mounting purposes only.

The criterion described in 17.14.8 is derived from the requirements established in NFPA *101.*

EXHIBIT 17.44 *Manual Fire Alarm Box. (Source: SimplexGrinnell, Westminster, MA)*

◄ **FAQ**

What is the reason for requiring manual fire alarm boxes on both sides of group openings?

EXHIBIT 17.45 *Protective Cover for Manual Fire Alarm Box. (Source: Safety Technology International, Inc., Waterford, MI)*

EXHIBIT 17.46 *Fire Extinguisher Monitored by a Fire Extinguisher Monitoring Device. (Source: MIJA Inc., Rockland, MA)*

17.15 Fire Extinguisher Electronic Monitoring Device

A fire extinguisher electronic monitoring device shall indicate those conditions for a specific fire extinguisher required by NFPA 10, *Standard for Portable Fire Extinguishers*, to a fire alarm control unit or other control unit.

Note that this section does not require that fire extinguisher monitoring devices be provided. Section 17.15 requires that if and where they are provided that they monitor those conditions required by the inspection criteria of NFPA 10, *Standard for Portable Fire Extinguishers*. The signals provided to the fire alarm control unit or other control unit are intended to serve in lieu of the regular, routine inspection of fire extinguishers as required by NFPA 10, and an off-normal condition should initiate a supervisory signal at the control unit. Chapter 23 provides further information on these devices, in 23.8.4.8. See Exhibit 17.46.

17.16 Supervisory Signal–Initiating Devices

17.16.1 Control Valve Supervisory Signal–Initiating Device.

Control valve supervisory signal–initiating devices, addressed in 17.16.1, have traditionally been switches specifically designed and listed for service as valve-monitoring devices. See Exhibit 17.47 for an example of a valve supervisory switch. The requirement for two distinct signals does not necessarily mean two switches. A switch that transfers when the valve begins to close and stays transferred while the valve remains closed, then returns to normal when the valve is reopened, satisfies the requirement. The initial transfer is the first signal. The return to normal is the second signal.

For example, assume the switch on the valve is a normally open contact. As the operator begins to turn the valve, the switch closes, indicating an off-normal condition. The switch stays in the closed, off-normal position as the operator continues to close the valve. When the operator reopens the valve, the closed contact transfers back to the open state when the valve is completely open. The opening of the contact provides the second, distinct signal.

17.16.1.1 Two separate and distinct signals shall be initiated: one indicating movement of the valve from its normal position (off-normal), and the other indicating restoration of the valve to its normal position.

17.16.1.2 The off-normal signal shall be initiated during the first two revolutions of the hand-wheel or during one-fifth of the travel distance of the valve control apparatus from its normal position.

17.16.1.3 The off-normal signal shall not be restored at any valve position except normal.

17.16.1.4 An initiating device for supervising the position of a control valve shall not interfere with the operation of the valve, obstruct the view of its indicator, or prevent access for valve maintenance.

17.16.2 Pressure Supervisory Signal–Initiating Device.

17.16.2.1 Two separate and distinct signals shall be initiated: one indicating that the required pressure has increased or decreased (off-normal), and the other indicating restoration of the pressure to its normal value.

As with supervisory signal–initiating devices for valve operation, water pressure supervisory signal–initiating devices may consist of a single switch.

See Exhibit 17.48 for an example of a pressure supervisory switch.

17.16.2.2 The following requirements shall apply to pressure supervisory signal–initiating devices:

17.16.2.2.1 Pressure Tank.

(1) A pressure tank supervisory signal–initiating device for a pressurized limited water supply, such as a pressure tank, shall indicate both high- and low-pressure conditions.
(2) The off-normal signal shall be initiated when the required pressure increases or decreases by 10 psi (70 kPa).

17.16.2.2.2 Dry-Type Sprinkler.

(1) A pressure supervisory signal–initiating device for a dry-pipe sprinkler system shall indicate both high- and low-pressure conditions.
(2) The off-normal signal shall be initiated when the pressure increases or decreases by 10 psi (70 kPa).

17.16.2.2.3 Steam Pressure.

(1) A steam pressure supervisory signal–initiating device shall indicate a low pressure condition.
(2) The off-normal signal shall be initiated prior to the pressure falling below 110 percent of the minimum operating pressure of the steam-operated equipment supplied.

17.16.2.2.4 Other Sources. An initiating device for supervising the pressure of sources other than those specified in 17.16.2.2.1 through 17.16.2.2.3 shall be provided as required by the authority having jurisdiction.

17.16.3 Water Level Supervisory Signal–Initiating Device.

17.16.3.1 Two separate and distinct signals shall be initiated: one indicating that the required water level has been lowered or raised (off-normal), and the other indicating restoration.

As with supervisory signal–initiating devices for valve operation, water level supervisory signal–initiating devices may consist of a single switch.
See Exhibit 17.49 for an example of a tank water level supervisory switch.

EXHIBIT 17.47 Outside Screw and Yoke (OS&Y) Valve Supervisory Switch. (Source: Potter Electric Signal Company, LLC, St. Louis, MO)

EXHIBIT 17.48 Pressure Supervisory Switch. (Source: Potter Electric Signal Company, LLC, St. Louis, MO)

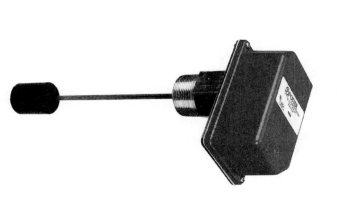

EXHIBIT 17.49 Tank Water Level Supervisory Switch. (Source: Potter Electric Signal Company, LLC, St. Louis, MO)

17.16.3.2 A pressure tank signal-initiating device shall indicate both high and low water level conditions.

17.16.3.2.1 The off-normal signal shall be initiated when the water level falls 3 in. (70 mm) or rises 3 in. (70 mm).

EXHIBIT 17.50 *Tank Water Temperature Supervisory Switch. (Source: Potter Electric Signal Company, LLC, St. Louis, MO)*

EXHIBIT 17.51 *Room Temperature Supervisory Switch. (Source: Potter Electric Signal Company, LLC, St. Louis, MO)*

17.16.3.3 A supervisory signal–initiating device for other than pressure tanks shall initiate a low water level signal when the water level falls 12 in. (300 mm).

17.16.4 Water Temperature Supervisory Signal–Initiating Device.

17.16.4.1 A temperature supervisory device for a water storage container exposed to freezing conditions shall initiate two separate and distinctive signals, as specified in 17.16.4.2.

Water temperature supervisory signal–initiating devices may consist of a single switch. See Exhibit 17.50 for a tank water temperature supervisory switch.

17.16.4.2 One signal shall indicate a decrease in water temperature to 40°F (4.4°C), and the other shall indicate its restoration to above 40°F (4.4°C).

17.16.5 Room Temperature Supervisory Signal–Initiating Device. A room temperature supervisory device shall indicate a decrease in room temperature to 40°F (4.4°C) and its restoration to above 40°F (4.4°C).

As with the other supervisory signal-initiating devices mentioned in Section 17.16, room temperature supervisory signal–initiating devices may also consist of a single switch. See Exhibit 17.51 for a typical room temperature supervisory switch.

REFERENCES CITED IN COMMENTARY

Alpert, R., "Ceiling Jets," *Fire Technology* (August) 1972.

Americans with Disabilities Act and Architectural Barriers Act Accessibility Guidelines. (July 23, 2004), United States Access Board, Washington, DC. www.access-board.gov.

ANSI/UL 268, *Standard for Smoke Detectors for Fire Alarm Systems*, Underwriters Laboratories Inc., Northbrook, IL, 2006; available from www.Comm2000.com.

ANSI/UL 521, *Standard for Heat Detectors for Fire Protective Signaling Systems*, Underwriters Laboratories Inc., Northbrook, IL, 2005; available from www.Comm2000.com.

Babrauskas, V., Lawson, J. R., Walton, W. D., and Twilley, W. H., "Upholstered Furniture Heat Release Rates Measured with a Furniture Calorimeter" [NBSIR 82-2604 (December)], National Institute of Standards and Technology (formerly National Bureau of Standards), Center for Fire Research, Gaithersburg, MD, 1982.

Cote, A. E., ed., *Fire Protection Handbook*®, 20th edition, National Fire Protection Association, Quincy, MA, 2008.

Fire Protection Research Foundation, *International Fire Detection Research Project,* Technical Report Year 1 (April), National Fire Protection Association, Quincy, MA, 1993.

Fire Protection Research Foundation, *International Fire Detection Research Project,* Technical Report Year 2 (October), National Fire Protection Association, Quincy, MA, 1994.

Fire Protection Research Foundation, *International Fire Detection Research Project,* Technical Report Year 3 (April), National Fire Protection Association, Quincy, MA, 1996.

Fire Protection Research Foundation, *International Fire Detection Research Project,* Technical Report Year 4 (June), National Fire Protection Association, Quincy, MA, 1998.

FM Approval Standard 3210, *Heat Detectors for Automatic Fire Alarm Signaling*, FM Approvals, Norwood, MA, 2007.

Heskestad, G., "Characterization of Smoke Entry and Response for Products-of-Combustion Detectors," Proceedings of the 7th International Conference on Problems of Automatic Fire Detection, Rheinish-Westfalischen Technischen Hochschule Aachen (March 1975).

Heskestad, G., and Delichatsios, M. A., "Environments of Fire Detectors — Phase 1: Effect of Fire Size, Ceiling Height and Material," Measurements vol. I (NBS-GCR-77-86), Analysis vol. II (NBS-GCR-77-95), National Technical Information Service (NTIS), Springfield, VA, 1986, 1995.

Heskestad, G., and Delichatsios, M. A., "Update: The Initial Convective Flow in Fire," *Fire Safety Journal*, vol. 15(5), 1989.

Morton, B. R., Taylor, G., and Turner, J. S., "Turbulent Gravitational Convection from Maintained and Instantaneous Sources," *Proc. Royal Society A,* 234:1–23, 1956.

NFPA 10, *Standard for Portable Fire Extinguishers,* 2007 edition, National Fire Protection Association, Quincy, MA.

NFPA 12, *Standard on Carbon Dioxide Extinguishing Systems*, 2008 edition, National Fire Protection Association, Quincy, MA.

NFPA 12A, *Standard on Halon 1301 Fire Extinguishing Systems*, 2009 edition, National Fire Protection Association, Quincy, MA.

NFPA 13, *Standard for the Installation of Sprinkler Systems*, 2010 edition, National Fire Protection Association, Quincy, MA.

NFPA 16, *Standard for the Installation of Foam-Water Sprinkler and Foam-Water Spray Systems*, 2007 edition, National Fire Protection Association, Quincy, MA.

NFPA 17, *Standard for Dry Chemical Extinguishing Systems*, 2009 edition, National Fire Protection Association, Quincy, MA.

NFPA 70®, National Electrical Code®, 2008 edition, National Fire Protection Association, Quincy, MA.

NFPA 72E, *Standard on Automatic Fire Detectors*, 1990 edition, National Fire Protection Association, Quincy, MA.

NFPA 90A, *Standard for the Installation of Air-Conditioning and Ventilating Systems*, 2009 edition, National Fire Protection Association, Quincy, MA.

NFPA 92A, *Standard for Smoke-Control Systems Utilizing Barriers and Pressure Differences*, 2009 edition, National Fire Protection Association, Quincy, MA.

NFPA *101®, Life Safety Code®*, 2009 edition, National Fire Protection Association, Quincy, MA.

NFPA 664, *Standard for the Prevention of Fires and Explosions in Wood Processing and Woodworking Facilities*, 2007 edition, National Fire Protection Association, Quincy, MA.

NFPA 2001, *Standard on Clean Agent Fire Extinguishing Systems*, 2008 edition, National Fire Protection Association, Quincy, MA.

Schifiliti, R., "Use of Fire Plume Theory in the Design and Analysis of Fire Detector and Sprinkler Response," Master's Thesis, Worcester Polytechnic Institute, Center for Fire-safety Studies, Worcester, MA, 1986.

Schifiliti, R. P., and Pucci, W. E., *Fire Detection Modeling, State of the Art*, Fire Detection Institute, Windsor, CT, 1998.

Notification Appliances

Chapter 18 (Chapter 7 in previous editions of the Code) includes requirements for audible and visible notification appliances for all types of systems. The use of notification appliances is not limited to occupant notification. Notification appliances are also used to alert and inform emergency services personnel and staff. In addition to notification equipment, this chapter includes equipment used to signal or present information to operators and other users of alarm and emergency communications systems (ECSs).

One significant change is a broadening of the chapter to accommodate ECSs. This change began in the 2007 edition with removal of the word *fire* in many locations where the term *fire alarm* had been used. This allowed the requirements of Chapter 18 to be used in the application of notification appliances for any system. An important addition in the 2010 edition of the Code is the concept of acoustically distinguishable spaces (ADSs), which are addressed in 18.4.10, Voice Intelligibility.

Dimensions and other numerical values have been reviewed to ensure that they express the intended level of precision for design, installation, and enforcement. (See Section 1.6, Units and Formulas, for more discussion on the subject of precision.) Values converted to metric units are rounded to convey the same approximate level of precision as the original U.S. units. Due to rounding, the two values might not convert exactly because of the intended precision of the measurement. For example, in the 2007 edition, the metric equivalent of 90 in. was given as 2290 mm, not 2286 mm, because measurements are not intended to be made to the exact millimeter. In the 2010 edition, 90 in. is converted and rounded to 2.29 m to better convey the intended precision. Where a measurement had been in inches, the intended precision is approximately 1 in., not 1 mm. By rounding the millimeter conversion to the nearest 10, the precision implied is 10 mm ÷ 25.4 mm/in. = 0.4 in. Users, however, might question whether the zero in 2290 was considered a "significant digit." By expressing the value in meters as 2.29, there is no confusion — the 9 is the significant digit, and the number has a precision of 0.01 m.

The following list is a summary of significant changes to the chapter on notification appliances in the 2010 edition:

- New 18.4.2 containing requirements for the standard audible evacuation signal
- New 18.4.5.3, effective January 1, 2014, requiring all system-activated audible appliances in sleeping areas to use a low frequency 520 Hz square wave
- New 18.4.10.1 through 18.4.10.3 requiring designers of voice systems to designate ADSs

18.1* Application

A.18.1 Notification appliances should be sufficient in quantity, audibility, intelligibility, and visibility so as to reliably convey the intended information to the intended personnel during an emergency.

Notification appliances in conventional commercial and industrial applications should be installed in accordance with the specific requirements of Section 18.4 and Section 18.5.

The Code recognizes that it is not possible to identify specific criteria sufficient to ensure effective occupant notification in every conceivable application. If the specific criteria of Section 18.4 and Section 18.5 are determined to be inadequate or inappropriate to provide the performance recommended, approved alternative approaches or methods are permitted to be used.

18.1.1 The requirements of this chapter shall apply where required by the enforcing authority; governing laws, codes, or standards; or other parts of this Code.

FAQ ▶
Where are the requirements for occupant notification or staff notification?

The requirement to provide notification of occupants or staff is not found in this chapter. If an enforcing authority; governing laws, codes, or standards; or other parts of this Code require notification of occupants or staff, this chapter contains methods to accomplish that task. For example, requirements for having notification appliances are found in other codes, such as NFPA *101*®, *Life Safety Code*®. Also, some other sections of this Code contain requirements for alerting occupants or staff. For example, Section 10.12 and 10.17.3.1.1 require an audible and visible trouble indication upon failure of either primary or secondary power supply voltage. The required location for the signal is given in 10.12.6 and 10.12.7. Chapter 18 of *NFPA 72*® , *National Fire Alarm and Signaling Code*, covers the installation and performance requirements for that required signal and the appliance that generates the signal. Also note that if audible occupant notification is required (by some other code) and if the noise level is high (105 dBA), then 18.4.1.1 requires that visible signaling be added even if the enabling codes do not require visible appliances.

Supplement 4 provides a summary of requirements, including requirements for occupant notification, for various occupancies based on the 2009 edition of NFPA *101*.

18.1.2 The requirements of this chapter shall address the reception of a notification signal and not the signal's information content.

As noted in 18.1.2, the requirements in Chapter 18 do not address the content of a textual message or a message contained in a coded audible or visible signal. Rather, the requirements address the ability of notification appliances to deliver a message. Chapter 18, in 18.4.2, does require the use of the ANSI S3.41, *American National Standard Audible Emergency Evacuation Signal*, 1996 edition, where evacuation of an area is intended. This chapter also requires that signal to meet certain audibility and installation requirements.

18.1.3 The performance, location, and mounting of notification appliances used to initiate or direct evacuation or relocation of the occupants, or for providing information to occupants or staff, shall comply with this chapter.

This Code recognizes that a building's fire emergency plan may require evacuation of the building or relocation of occupants within the protected premises.

18.1.4 The performance, location, and mounting of annunciators, displays, and printers used to display or record information for use by occupants, staff, responding emergency personnel, or supervising station personnel shall comply with this chapter.

The scope of the chapter includes the types of notification appliances noted in 18.1.4 that provide information to occupants, staff, responding emergency personnel, or supervising station personnel.

18.1.5* The requirements of this chapter shall apply to the areas, spaces, or system functions where required by the enforcing authority; governing laws, codes, or standards; or other parts of this Code requiring compliance with this chapter.

A.18.1.5 Chapter 18 establishes the means, methods, and performance requirements of notification appliances and systems. Chapter 18 does not require the installation of notification appliances or identify where notification signaling is required. Authorities having jurisdiction, other codes, other standards, and chapters of this Code require notification signaling and might specify areas or intended audiences.

For example, Chapter 10 requires audible and visible trouble signals at specific locations. A building or fire code might require audible and visible occupant notification throughout all occupiable areas. In contrast, a building or fire code might require complete coverage with audible signaling, but might only require specific areas or spaces to have visible signaling. It is also possible that a referring code or standard might require compliance with mounting and notification appliance performance requirements without requiring complete notification signaling system performance. An example might be where an appliance is specifically located to provide information or notification to a person at a specific desk within a larger room.

In some cases, other parts of this Code may require notification of occupants or staff. The audible or visible notification appliances referred to in other chapters of this Code are described in detail in this chapter. An example is the requirement in Chapter 10 that a fault on a circuit produce an audible trouble signal at certain locations. As another example, requirements in Chapter 23 for occupant notification refer to Chapter 18 for requirements on the use of notification appliances to alert occupants of the need for evacuation or relocation. Similarly, notification appliances required by Chapter 26 to alert supervising station personnel must meet the requirements of Chapter 18.

18.1.6 The requirements of Chapters 10, 14, 23, and 24 and shall apply to the interconnection of notification appliances, the control configurations, the power supplies, and the use of the information provided by notification appliances.

18.1.7 Notification appliances shall be permitted to be used within buildings or outdoors and to target the general building, area, or space, or only specific parts of a building, area, or space designated in specific zones and sub-zones.

This paragraph explicitly recognizes the broader role of emergency communications systems (ECSs). While most fire alarm systems provide general evacuation of an entire building, some may provide only partial evacuation or relocation. An ECS used for both fire and other emergencies may be required to communicate with a small subset of building occupants or even with an entire community.

18.2 Purpose

Notification appliances shall provide stimuli for initiating emergency action and provide information to users, emergency response personnel, and occupants.

18.3 General

18.3.1 Listing. All notification appliances installed in conformity with Chapter 18 shall be listed for the purpose for which they are used.

The requirement in 18.3.1 states that the listing of notification appliances must be use-specific. This provision means that the listing of an appliance must relate to the exact manner in which it will be used. This requirement correlates with the rules of 10.3.1 and 10.3.2, which also require fire alarm system components to be installed in accordance with manufacturers' published instructions. These instructions generally are taken into consideration by the listing organization. For example, visible notification appliances listed for wall mounting are not permitted to be installed on a ceiling because they are designed, tested, and listed for a

EXHIBIT 18.1 *Listed Audible Notification Appliances (Bells). (Source: GE Security, Bradenton, FL)*

specific orientation to cover a specific area. Visible notification appliances that are listed for wall mounting but that are mounted on ceilings will produce inadequate coverage. Appliances listed for ceiling mounting would be required for that application.

See Exhibit 18.1 for examples of typical notification appliances listed for fire alarm use.

18.3.2 Nameplates.

18.3.2.1 Notification appliances shall include on their nameplates reference to electrical requirements and rated audible or visible performance, or both, as defined by the listing authority.

18.3.2.2 Audible appliances shall include on their nameplates reference to their parameters or reference to installation documents (supplied with the appliance) that include the parameters in accordance with 18.4.3 or 18.4.4.

18.3.2.3 Visible appliances shall include on their nameplates reference to their parameters or reference to installation documents (supplied with the appliance) that include the parameters in accordance with 18.5.2.1 or Section 18.6.

To guide designers and installers of fire alarm systems so that the system will deliver audible and visible information with appropriate intensity, the nameplate must state the capabilities of the appliance, as determined through tests conducted by the listing organization. The nameplate information also assists inspectors in verifying compliance with approved documents.

Notification appliance circuits (NACs) require special treatment to ensure that the voltage supplied to all the connected appliances will be within the limits specified for proper operation of each appliance. Voltage that is below the operating range of the appliance can cause the appliances to produce visible signal intensities or sound pressure levels (SPLs) that are below the levels assumed in the design of the system.

FAQ ▶
What is the purpose of voltage drop calculations?

Voltage drop calculations must be performed to ensure proper performance of the appliance and, on request, must be provided to the authority having jurisdiction in accordance with 10.18.1.2. In developing voltage drop calculations, the designer of the NAC should consider the following questions:

- What are the current and voltage limits of the power source for the circuit?
- Do these limits include the effects of any reduced voltage due to extended operation of the system on the secondary power supply?
- How many appliances can be connected to the NAC?
- What is the size planned for the field-wiring conductors?
- What is the total length of the NAC?
- Is the wire gauge selected appropriate for termination to the notification appliance?

The following examples use nominal 24 volt fire alarm systems. The same method of calculating voltage drop can be applied to 12 volt fire alarm systems using the appropriate corresponding values of 12 volt control units and appliances.

Under all operating conditions, the voltage on the NAC must be sufficient to operate all the notification appliances so that they deliver the proper signal intensity. Often, the worst-case operating condition is when the control unit's primary power supply has failed and the battery capacity is at its lowest point. ANSI/UL 864, *Standard for Control Units and Accessories for Fire Alarm Systems*, indicates a minimum value of 20.4 volts (end of useful battery life). This value then becomes the starting point for the voltage drop calculations.

NOTE: If unique power supplies are used that maintain control unit voltage higher than 20.4 volts for the conditions mentioned in the previous paragraph, consult the manufacturer's instructions for the allowable voltage to be used as the starting voltage.

Product Test Standard The particular edition of the Underwriter Laboratories Inc. (UL) standards to which the notification appliance has been tested and listed (for public mode, ANSI/UL 1971, *Standard for Signaling Devices for the Hearing Impaired*; for private mode, ANSI/UL

1638, *Standard for Visual Signaling Appliances — Private Mode Emergency and General Utility Signaling*; and ANSI/UL 464, *Standard for Audible Signal Appliances*) determines the voltage range and maximum current that can be used in voltage drop calculations.

In the past, notification appliances were marked with a rated (nameplate) range (e.g., 22–29 volts dc). For instance, in the case of visible appliances (strobes), testing laboratories tested notification appliances at 80 percent and 110 percent of their rated (nameplate) voltage to ensure proper signal intensity and flash rate. This testing provided a reasonable level of assurance that the appliances would operate at lower voltages, which might occur when incoming ac power nears brownout conditions or when the system has been operating on battery near the end of a required 24-hour time period. For example, if an appliance was rated for operation between 22 volts and 29 volts (nameplate voltage range), testing laboratories would test the output of the notification appliance at 17.6 volts and 31.9 volts. This range is called the *operating range* and is different (wider range) from the nameplate range. In this example, this particular NAC must be designed and installed to provide no less than 17.6 volts at any appliance in order to deliver the required light output (intensity) and flash rate. In this example, the maximum voltage drop between the NAC terminals and the last appliance must be 2.8 volts or less (20.4 starting voltage at the control unit less the 17.6 volts required at the appliance equals 2.8 volts maximum voltage drop).

More current editions of UL standards relating to notification appliances eliminate the 80 percent to 110 percent testing that established the operating range and instead require a standard operating voltage range for notification appliances. In the case of 24 volt appliances, when the voltage drop is being calculated, both the listed and the nameplate operating voltage ranges will be 16–33 volts, unless the appliance has been listed as a "special applications" appliance. Therefore, 16 volts should be considered the minimum voltage that must be delivered to any appliance. (Appliances for 12 volt systems will have a standard operating range of 8–17.5 volts.) In the case of a "special applications" appliance, the operating voltage range will be identified on both the appliance and its installation instructions.

When new appliances are added to older NACs or when the fire alarm control unit is replaced, compatibility must be ensured. The appliance manufacturer should be contacted if any questions relating to the electrical specifications or listing of the product arise.

Calculation Methods Several methods exist for calculating the voltage drop between the control unit and the last notification appliance on the NAC. Two possible methods are center load calculations and point-to-point calculations. However, these methods require knowledge of actual appliance current draws at the minimum operating voltage and fairly accurate measurements of conductor length between the appliances as well as total conductor length. Because these data are generally not reliable during the design phase, another method, the lump sum method, is recommended and should be used because of the margin of safety it provides for unknowns.

The simplest voltage drop calculation method is to assume that the entire appliance loads are *at the end of the circuit* (lump sum). Based on the earlier UL standards, most manufacturers did not usually provide the current draw of an appliance at the minimum listed operating voltage. Therefore, the current draw at the minimum nameplate rated voltage should be used for those calculations. Ohm's law is used to calculate the voltage drop for the circuit. The relationship is as follows:

$$V_{load} = V_{terminals} - (I_{load} R_{conductors})$$

where:

V_{load} = 16 volts minimum operating voltage of the appliance (unless it has been listed as a "special applications" appliance)

$V_{terminals}$ = 20.4 volts (unless otherwise specified by the manufacturer and the listing)

I_{load} = total current draw in amperes of the connected appliances*

$R_{conductors}$ = total conductor resistance in ohms

*The total current draw is the sum of the rated current draw for all the appliances on the circuits. The rated current is the maximum current measured by the listing agency over the operating voltage range of the appliance. The product listing standards for notification appliances specify that only the maximum current be marked on the appliance. See Exhibit 18.2.

EXHIBIT 18.2 *Lump Sum Model for Voltage Drop Calculations. (Source: R. P. Schifiliti Associates, Inc., Reading, MA)*

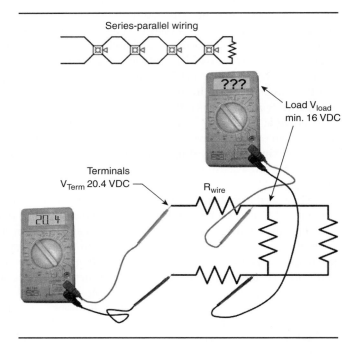

Solving for $R_{conductors}$ and using Table 8 of Chapter 9 in *NFPA 70®*, *National Electrical Code®* (*NEC®*), 2008 edition, the required conductor size can be determined. Table 8 provides resistance per 1000 m and per 1000 ft for solid or stranded conductors at 167°F (75°C). The conductor resistance at other temperatures can be calculated or obtained from the wire manufacturer's data sheet. However, the temperature used should be representative of the ambient temperature where the conductors are located. Note that the calculated total conductor resistance ($R_{conductors}$) includes the resistance of both outgoing and return circuit conductors.

FAQ ▶
What resistance must be included in the calculated total conductor resistance?

The actual length of the circuit run (the routing path between the control unit and the farthest appliance) used in the determination of conductor size is only half of the total conductor length, since the total path is from the control unit out to the last appliance and then back to the control unit. Assuming a minimum appliance operating voltage (V_{load}) of 16 volts and a total current draw (I_{load}) of 5.0 amperes, the resulting (maximum) total conductor resistance ($R_{conductors}$) is calculated as follows:

$$R_{conductors} = \frac{20.4 - 16}{5} = 0.88 \text{ ohm}$$

For a circuit that is 100 ft from end to end, the total conductor length would be 200 ft (out and back). (For simplicity, measurements in this example are presented only in U.S. units.) The permitted resistance per foot would be 0.88 ohm ÷ 200 ft = 0.0044 ohm/ft, or 4.4 ohms/1000 ft. Per Table 8 of the *National Electrical Code*, Chapter 9, this calculated resistance-per-foot limit would require a 14 AWG wire size (assuming stranded, coated copper at 167°F), which has a resistance of 3.26 ohms/1000 ft, which is less than the maximum calculated resistance of 4.4 ohms/1000 ft. A larger-size conductor or a reduction in total current draw would be needed to increase the length of the circuit. Note that the total current draw might also be limited by the capability of the control unit output circuit. For example, many power-limited NACs have a maximum current output of 2.0 amperes. The length that circuit could be if wired using 18 AWG stranded, coated copper at 167°F is calculated as follows:

$$\frac{20.4 - 16}{2} = 2.2 \text{ ohms}$$

$$\frac{2.2 \text{ ohms}}{0.00845 \text{ ohms/ft}} = \frac{260 \text{ ft max. conductor length or } 130 \text{ ft}}{\text{from the control unit to the last appliance.}}$$

This method of voltage drop calculation applies to NACs that are laid out and installed in a true series-parallel configuration, as are most of today's NACs. See Exhibit 18.2. However, Class B addressable notification appliances are permitted to be installed in signaling line circuits that have T-taps; refer to the manufacturer's installation instructions. If the circuit has T-taps, it is not a true series-parallel circuit. The lump sum calculation method can still be used if the longest path is used as a length and the total current for all appliances is used for the load. However, the calculations will be very conservative. More sophisticated calculation methods and tools would be more accurate.

It is acceptable to use the actual current draw, that is, the amount of current based on the actual load intended to be on the circuit. However, if any appliances must be added to the circuit at a later date, the wire size might be incorrect unless some factor of safety is used. It is recommended that the control unit manufacturer's maximum current be used as the load. That way, the circuit is calculated at its maximum capacity. A factor of safety should also be used in estimating the circuit length. Some owners, engineers, and authorities might require factors of safety in the calculations.

◄ **FAQ**
What load (current draw) should be used in the calculations?

18.3.3 Physical Construction.

18.3.3.1 Appliances intended for use in special environments, such as outdoors versus indoors, high or low temperatures, high humidity, dusty conditions, and hazardous locations, or where subject to tampering, shall be listed for the intended application.

Maintaining the operational integrity of audible and visible notification appliances is essential despite their possible location in relatively hostile environments. Use of appliances not listed for the type of environment in which the appliance is to be placed is a violation of 18.3.1.

18.3.3.2* Notification appliances used for signaling other than fire shall not have the word FIRE, or any fire symbol, in any form (i.e., stamped, imprinted, etc.) on the appliance visible to the public. Notification appliances with multiple visible elements shall be permitted to have fire markings only on those visible elements used for fire signaling.

A.18.3.3.2 The intent is to prohibit labeling that could give an incorrect message. Wording such as "Emergency" would be acceptable for labeling because it is generic enough not to cause confusion. Fire alarm systems are often used as emergency notification systems, and therefore attention should be given to this detail.

Combination audible and visible units may have several visible appliances, each labeled differently or not labeled at all.

An ECS can use the same appliances for signaling both fire and other emergencies. If that is the case, the appliance should not have "FIRE" markings. Some ECSs use multiple visible appliances. In those cases, one visible appliance is labeled "FIRE" and is used to signal the need for immediate evacuation, while another visible appliance is used during more complex situations to signal the need for occupants to get additional information from other sources. For example, during a chemical release or bomb threat, communicating specific evacuation or relocation instructions might be necessary to prevent undesired exposure to occupants. The use of different types or colors of notification appliances on a system to influence occupant

EXHIBIT 18.3 *Notification Appliance Showing Mechanical Baffle. (Source: Cooper Wheelock, Inc., Long Branch, NJ)*

behavior should be carefully considered but might be advisable only where the occupants are not transient and are well trained and drilled in the required response.

18.3.4* Mechanical Protection.

A.18.3.4 Situations exist where supplemental enclosures are necessary to protect the physical integrity of a notification appliance. Protective enclosures should not interfere with the performance characteristics of the appliance. If the enclosure degrades the performance, methods should be detailed in the manufacturer's published instructions of the enclosure that clearly identify the degradation. For example, where the appliance signal is attenuated, it might be necessary to adjust the appliance spacings or appliance output.

The protection described in 18.3.4 is usually provided by an enclosure that protects the actual audible or visible mechanism. In the case of speakers, a mechanical baffle protects the cone from being punctured by a sharp object. See Exhibit 18.3 for an example of a typical notification appliance with a mechanical baffle.

Guards placed over an audible or visible appliance can degrade the level of the audible signal or the light intensity of the appliance. For that reason, the guard or protective device must be tested with the specific appliance, and its effect must be measured and reported. System designers, installers, and inspectors can then de-rate the appliance performance and make corrections when using the appliance with the guard in a design. Exhibit 18.4 is an example of a typical protective guard for an audible/visible appliance.

EXHIBIT 18.4 *Protective Guard for an Audible/Visible Appliance. (Source: Safety Technology International, Inc., Waterford, MI)*

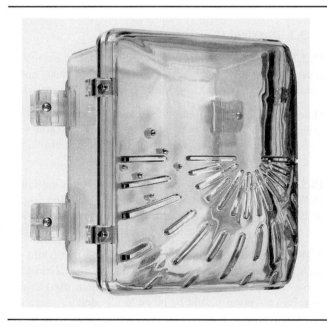

18.3.4.1 Appliances subject to mechanical damage shall be suitably protected.

18.3.4.2 If guards, covers, or lenses are employed, they shall be listed for use with the appliance.

In the case of an appliance such as that shown in Exhibit 18.3, the integral mechanical baffle is a normal part of the appliance, and its effect is accounted for in the product listing. The guard shown in Exhibit 18.4 is an after-market product that must be listed for use with the appliance. That listing will state the performance restrictions, if any.

18.3.4.3 The effect of guards, covers, or lenses on the appliance's field performance shall be in accordance with the listing requirements.

18.3.5 Mounting.

18.3.5.1 Appliances shall be supported independently of their attachments to the circuit conductors.

18.3.5.2 Appliances shall be mounted in accordance with the manufacturer's published instructions.

Physically supporting the appliance by means of the conductors that connect the appliance to the NAC of the fire alarm system is not permitted. Constant strain on terminal connections can cause conductors to pull free or to break. See Exhibit 18.5 for an example of independent support for a notification appliance.

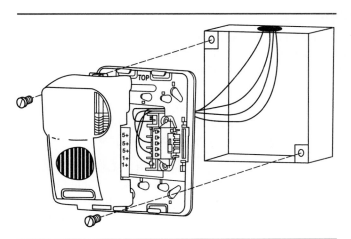

EXHIBIT 18.5 *Notification Appliance with Independent Support. (Source: Gentex Corp., Zeeland, MI)*

18.3.6* Connections. Terminals, leads, or addressable communication, that provide for monitoring the integrity of the notification appliance connections shall be provided.

A.18.3.6 For hardwired appliances, terminals or leads, as described in 18.3.6, are necessary to ensure that the wire run is broken and that the individual connections are made to the leads or other terminals for signaling and power.

A common terminal can be used for connection of incoming and outgoing wires. However, the design and construction of the terminal should not permit an uninsulated section of a single conductor to be looped around the terminal and to serve as two separate connections. For example, a notched clamping plate under a single securing screw is acceptable only if separate conductors of a notification circuit are intended to be inserted in each notch. *[See Figure A.17.4.7(a).]*

Another means to monitor the integrity of a connection is to establish communication between the appliance and the fire alarm control unit. The integrity of the connection is verified by the presence of communication. Monitoring integrity in this fashion might not require multiple terminals or leads as previously described.

It should be noted that monitoring the integrity of the installation conductors and their connection to an appliance does not guarantee the integrity of the appliance or that it is operational. Appliances can be damaged and become inoperable or a circuit can be overloaded, resulting in failure when the appliances are called upon to work. Presently, only testing can establish the integrity of an appliance.

FAQ ▶
What is required to ensure the monitoring for integrity of the NAC?

To provide system reliability and availability, NACs are monitored for integrity in accordance with the requirements of Chapter 10. The appliances themselves are neither monitored nor supervised. To comply with the requirements of Chapter 10, especially for appliances that are not addressable, the appliance must have the correct number and type of screw terminals or pigtail leads to permit proper connection to the circuit. See Figure A.17.4.7(a). Although Figure A.17.4.7(a) shows initiating devices, the figure is equally applicable to notification appliances. The correct type of terminals or leads, combined with correct installation practice, results in the circuit opening if a connection to an appliance is broken. This open circuit results in a trouble signal at the fire alarm control unit.

As with initiating devices, addressable notification appliances produced by some manufacturers monitor circuit integrity using digital communication rather than current flow.

18.4 Audible Characteristics

18.4.1 General Requirements.

18.4.1.1* An average ambient sound level greater than 105 dBA shall require the use of a visible notification appliance(s) in accordance with Section 18.5 where the application is public mode or Section 18.6 where the application is private mode.

In some occupancies, the ambient sound level is so high that the sole reliance on audible notification appliances would be impractical. A drop forge shop, a large casino, a rock music dance hall, or a newspaper press room are all candidates for the addition of visible signal appliances to help ensure that the signals will be perceived by the occupants. See Exhibits 18.6 and 18.7 for examples of typical visible notification appliances.

Visible signaling is required by this Code when the ambient sound pressure levels exceed 105 dBA, as noted in 18.4.1.1, because trying to overcome that level with audible fire alarm signals is difficult and possibly harmful. In some occupancies, such as theaters, concert halls, and nightclubs, it may be possible to turn off the ambient noise when the fire alarm system is activated as permitted by 18.4.3.5.

EXHIBIT 18.6 *One Type of Visible Notification Appliance. (Source: Cooper Wheelock, Inc., Long Branch, NJ)*

A.18.4.1.1 The Code does not require that all audible notification appliances within a building be of the same type. However, a mixture of different types of audible notification appliances within a space is not the desired method. Audible notification appliances that convey a similar audible signal are preferred. For example, a space that uses mechanical horns and bells might not be desirable. A space that is provided with mechanical horns and electronic horns with similar audible signal output is preferred.

However, the cost of replacing all existing appliances to match new appliances can impose substantial economic impact where other methods can be used to avoid occupant confusion of signals and signal content. Examples of other methods used to avoid confusion include, but are not limited to, training of occupants, signage, consistent use of temporal code signal pattern, and fire drills.

Hearing protection can attenuate both the ambient noise level and the audible fire alarm signal. Specifications from hearing protection manufacturers might allow the effect of hearing protection devices to be evaluated. In spaces where hearing protection is worn due to high ambient noise conditions, visible signal appliances should be considered.

In addition, where hearing protection is worn due to high ambient noise conditions, the audible fire alarm signal and ambient noise measurements can be analyzed and the audible fire alarm signal can be adjusted to account for attenuation caused by the hearing protection devices.

EXHIBIT 18.7 *Another Type of Visible Notification Appliance. (Source: Simplex-Grinnell, Westminster, MA)*

18.4.1.2* The total sound pressure level produced by combining the ambient sound pressure level with all audible notification appliances operating shall not exceed 110 dBA at the minimum hearing distance.

A.18.4.1.2 The maximum sound pressure level permitted in a space is 110 dBA, reduced from 120 dBA in previous editions. The change from 120 dBA to 110 dBA is to coordinate with other laws, codes, and standards.

In addition to the danger of exposure to a high sound level, long-term exposure to lower levels may also be a problem when, for example, occupants must traverse long egress paths to exit or technicians test large systems over extended time periods.

This Code does not presume to know how long a person will be exposed to an audible notification system. The limit of 110 dBA has been set as a reasonable upper limit for the performance of a system. For workers who may be exposed to high sound levels over the course of a 40-year employment history, OSHA (Occupational, Health and Safety Administration) has established a maximum permitted dose before a hearing conservation program must be implemented. A worker exposed to 120 dBA for 7.5 minutes a day for 40 years might be in danger of suffering a hearing impairment. The OSHA regulation includes a formula to calculate a dose for situations where a person is exposed to different sound levels for different periods of time. The maximum permitted by the regulation is an 8-hour equivalent dose of 90 dBA. It is possible to calculate the dose a person experiences when traversing an egress path where the sound pressure level varies as he/she passes close to, then away from, audible appliances. Table A.18.4.1.2 depicts OSHA permissible noise exposures.

TABLE A.18.4.1.2 *Permissible Noise Exposures*

Duration (hr)	L_A (dBA)
8	90
6	92
4	95
3	97
2	100
1.5	102
1	105
0.5	110
0.25	115
0.125 (7.5 minutes)	120

Source: OSHA, 29 CFR 1910.5, Table G-16, Occupational Noise Exposure.

Prior to the 2007 edition, the audible limit was set at 120 dBA. In the 2007 edition, the limit in 18.4.1.2 was changed to 110 dBA as a reasonable upper limit for the performance of a system. The reduction was made to correlate with other codes and standards. Note that the limit is for the sound pressure level at any location with the entire system operating, not just any one appliance. The "minimum hearing distance" is not defined but for most installations can be assumed to result when a person is standing directly under or next to one appliance or noise source.

18.4.1.3* Sound from normal or permanent sources, having a duration greater than 60 seconds, shall be included when measuring maximum ambient sound level. Sound from temporary or abnormal sources shall not be required to be included when measuring maximum ambient sound level.

The intent of the Code for all audible signaling is that the worst-case conditions be used for all ambient and alarm sound level measurements. This might require testing with doors and other barriers opened and closed to determine the worst case. However, it is not necessary to open a door to get the worst-case noise and then close the door to get the worst-case alarm level — or vice versa. Instead, the difference between ambient and alarm can be measured with the door open and then again with the door closed to ensure that the required levels are met in both situations. See also 18.4.5.2.

A.18.4.1.3 In determining maximum ambient sound levels, sound sources that should be considered include air-handling equipment and background music in a typical office environment, office cleaning equipment (vacuum cleaner), noisy children in a school auditorium, car engines in an auto shop, conveyor belts in a warehouse, and a running shower and fan in a hotel bathroom. Temporary or abnormal sound sources that can be excluded would include internal or external construction activities (i.e., office rearrangements and construction equipment).

18.4.1.4 Audible notification appliances for alert and evacuation signal tones shall meet the requirements of 18.4.3 (Public Mode Audible Requirements), 18.4.4 (Private Mode Audible Requirements), 18.4.5 (Sleeping Area Requirements), or 18.4.6 (Narrow Band Tone Signaling for Exceeding Masked Thresholds), as applicable.

18.4.1.5* Voice messages shall not be required to meet the audibility requirements of 18.4.3 (Public Mode Audible Requirements), 18.4.4 (Private Mode Audible Requirements), 18.4.5 (Sleeping Area Requirements), or 18.4.6 (Narrow Band Tone Signaling for Exceeding Masked Thresholds), but shall meet the intelligibility requirements of 18.4.10 where voice intelligibility is required.

FAQ ▶
Why are audibility measurements not required for textual (voice) signals?

The Technical Committee on Notification Appliances for Fire Alarm Systems wanted to clarify the following two facts:

- Sound pressure level requirements within Chapter 18 are for tone signals only, not for voice messages.
- Intelligible voice messages are dependent on more than just adequate loudness.

Additional requirements for textual audible appliances are covered in Section 18.8. If a textual audible notification appliance produces a signal of adequate sound level, but the message is not intelligible, then such a signal is not adequate. Chapter 14, which covers inspection, testing, and maintenance, does not require voice signals to be measured for audibility because the sound being produced is modulated and would not result in a meaningful measurement. See also the definitions of *intelligibility* and *intelligible* in 3.3.125 and 3.3.126.

Additional discussion of voice system intelligibility, the factors that affect it, and how it is evaluated and measured can be found in Supplement 3, Voice Intelligibility for Emergency Voice/Alarm Communications Systems, and in Annex D, Speech Intelligibility.

A.18.4.1.5 Because voice is composed of modulated tones, it is not valid to compare loudness measurements of tone signals with loudness measurements of voice signals. A voice signal that is subjectively judged to be equally as loud as a tone signal will actually produce a dB reading below that of the tone signal. The modulated tones of a voice signal can have the same or greater peak amplitude as that of a tone signal. However, because they are modulated meters with fast or slow time, constants will show a lower dB or dBA reading.

A voice signal must have sufficient audibility to result in intelligible communication. Intelligibility modeling/measurements (subject based and instrument based) include audibility as well as many other factors when determining whether a voice signal is adequate or not adequate.

Where a voice signal includes an audible alert or evacuation tone, the tone portion of the signal should meet the audible signal requirements listed in 18.4.3.

18.4.1.6 Audible notification appliances used for exit marking shall not be required to meet the audibility requirements of 18.4.3 (Public Mode Audible Requirements), 18.4.4 (Private Mode Audible Requirements), 18.4.5 (Sleeping Area Requirements), or 18.4.6 (Narrow Band

Tone Signaling for Exceeding Masked Thresholds), except as required by 18.4.7 (Exit Marking Audible Appliance Requirements).

The technical committee recognizes that exit marking systems (see 18.4.7) may have "targeted" areas where specific appliances should be heard to direct occupant movement.

18.4.2 Distinctive Evacuation Signal.

The requirement for and definition of a distinctive evacuation signal has been relocated to this chapter to provide one place for the systems chapters to reference. In previous editions, that requirement was in the Protected Premises Fire Alarm Systems chapter and simply referenced ANSI S3.41. The functional requirements for the three-pulse temporal code have been explicitly placed in the body of the Code rather than simply referencing ANSI S3.41.

18.4.2.1* To meet the requirements of Section 10.7, the alarm audible signal pattern used to notify building occupants of the need to evacuate (leave the building) shall be the standard alarm evacuation signal consisting of a three-pulse temporal pattern. The pattern shall be in accordance with Figure 18.4.2.1 and shall consist of the following in this order:

(1) "On" phase lasting 0.5 second ±10 percent
(2) "Off" phase lasting 0.5 second ±10 percent for three successive "on" periods
(3) "Off" phase lasting 1.5 seconds ±10 percent

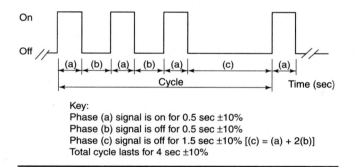

Key:
Phase (a) signal is on for 0.5 sec ±10%
Phase (b) signal is off for 0.5 sec ±10%
Phase (c) signal is off for 1.5 sec ±10% [(c) = (a) + 2(b)]
Total cycle lasts for 4 sec ±10%

FIGURE 18.4.2.1 *Temporal Pattern Parameters.*

Exception: Where approved by the authority having jurisdiction, continued use of the existing consistent evacuation signaling scheme shall be permitted.

A.18.4.2.1 Paragraph 10.7 requires that alarm signals be distinctive in sound from other signals and that this sound not be used for any other purpose. The use of the distinctive three-pulse temporal pattern fire alarm evacuation signal required by 18.4.2.1 became effective July 1, 1996, for new systems installed after that date. It is not the intent to prohibit continued use of an existing consistent evacuation signaling scheme, subject to approval by the authority having jurisdiction. It is also not the intent that the distinct pattern be applied to visible appliances.

The temporal pattern can be produced by any audible notification appliance, as illustrated in Figure A.18.4.2.1(a) and Figure A.18.4.2.1(b).

18.4.2.2 A single-stroke bell or chime sounded at "on" intervals lasting 1 second ±10 percent, with a 2-second ±10 percent "off" interval after each third "on" stroke, shall be permitted.

18.4.2.3 The signal shall be repeated for a period appropriate for the purposes of evacuation of the building, but for not less than 180 seconds. The minimum repetition time shall be permitted to be manually interrupted.

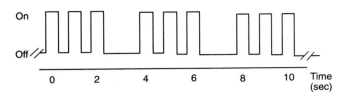

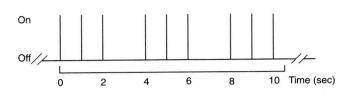

FIGURE A.18.4.2.1(a) *Temporal Pattern Imposed on Signaling Appliances That Emit a Continuous Signal While Energized.*

FIGURE A.18.4.2.1(b) *Temporal Pattern Imposed on a Single-Stroke Bell or Chime.*

18.4.2.4 The use of the standard evacuation signal shall be restricted to situations where it is desired that all occupants hearing the signal evacuate the building immediately. It shall not be used where, with the approval of the authority having jurisdiction, the planned action during an emergency is not evacuation, but rather is the relocation of occupants or their protection in place, as directed by the building emergency response plan or as directed by emergency personnel.

18.4.2.5* The standard evacuation signal shall be synchronized within a notification zone.

A.18.4.2.5 Coordination or synchronization of the audible signal within a notification zone is needed to preserve the temporal pattern. It is unlikely that the audible signal in one evacuation/notification zone will be heard in another at a level that will destroy the temporal pattern. Thus, it would not normally be necessary to provide coordination or synchronization for an entire system. Caution should be used in spaces such as atriums, where the sounds produced in one notification zone can be sufficient to cause confusion regarding the temporal pattern.

18.4.3* Public Mode Audible Requirements.

The requirement that audible appliances produce some minimum sound pressure level (75 dBA at 10 ft) was removed in 2002 to permit signaling in small, enclosed spaces as well as targeted signaling. The audible notification requirements found in this chapter are performance-based. In many instances performance requirements can be met using appliances rated at less than 75 dBA at 10 ft.

A.18.4.3 The typical average ambient sound level for the occupancies specified in Table A.18.4.3 are intended only for design guidance purposes. The typical average ambient sound levels specified should not be used in lieu of actual sound level measurements.

FAQ ▶
What do the values in Table A.18.4.3 represent?

The sound levels shown in Table A.18.4.3 are defined in 3.3.25 as "the root mean square, A-weighted, sound pressure level." This value can be experimentally determined (measured) for a particular occupancy by using an integrating, sound pressure level meter. Exhibit 18.8 shows two examples of meters that can be used to measure the total integrated sound pressure level in dBA or to analyze the dB at specific frequency bands (see 18.4.6). These particular meters can also be used to measure the voice intelligibility score discussed in the sections on speech intelligibility.

Measurements taken by a major manufacturer of fire alarm equipment in a large sampling of hotel rooms with through-the-wall air-conditioning units determined that the average ambient sound level in those rooms with the air conditioners operating was 55 dBA.

The suggested value of 85 dBA for mechanical rooms is only an example, as are all the other table entries. Some mechanical equipment rooms might have an average ambient sound level that exceeds this value, and others might be lower. Based on the average ambient sound level of 85 dBA, the audible notification appliances would need to deliver 100 dBA throughout the room. See Exhibits 18.9 and 18.10 for examples of typical audible notification appli-

TABLE A.18.4.3 *Average Ambient Sound Level According to Location*

Location	Average Ambient Sound Level (dBA)
Business occupancies	55
Educational occupancies	45
Industrial occupancies	80
Institutional occupancies	50
Mercantile occupancies	40
Mechanical rooms	85
Piers and water-surrounded structures	40
Places of assembly	55
Residential occupancies	35
Storage occupancies	30
Thoroughfares, high-density urban	70
Thoroughfares, medium-density urban	55
Thoroughfares, rural and suburban	40
Tower occupancies	35
Underground structures and windowless buildings	40
Vehicles and vessels	50

EXHIBIT 18.8 *Combination Sound Pressure Level Meter/Analyzer and Speech Intelligibility Meter (left) and AL1 Meter Displaying Basic STI-PA Result (right). [Sources: (left) Gold Line, West Redding, CT; (right) NTI Americas, Tigard, OR]*

ances for high ambient noise areas, such as might be found in some mechanical rooms or some industrial occupancies.

18.4.3.1* To ensure that audible public mode signals are clearly heard, unless otherwise permitted by 18.4.3.2 through 18.4.3.5, they shall have a sound level at least 15 dB above the average ambient sound level or 5 dB above the maximum sound level having a duration of at

EXHIBIT 18.9 Audible Notification Appliance for High Ambient Noise Areas. (Source: Signal Communications Corp., Woburn, MA)

EXHIBIT 18.10 Cluster Speakers. (Source: Cooper Notification, Long Branch, NJ)

least 60 seconds, whichever is greater, measured 5 ft (1.5 m) above the floor in the area required to be served by the system using the A-weighted scale (dBA).

Care must be exercised in selection of the source of the maximum sound level for each occupancy to ensure that it is the maximum. The average ambient sound level is more difficult to determine than the maximum sound level that lasts at least 60 seconds. In addition, if the maximum level is not at least 10 dB above the average ambient sound level, the sound level from an audible notification system designed to produce 5 dB over the maximum sound level will not comply fully with the requirements of 18.4.3.1.

Measurements are made at 5 ft (1.5 m) above the floor to reduce the effects of sound wave reinforcement and cancellation due to walls and surfaces.

Additional appliances might be required so that the signal will be heard clearly throughout the target area. The technical committee has changed the text to indicate that the audibility requirement is in the "area required to be served by the system." In the past, the requirement addressed the "occupiable" or "occupied" area. However, those terms created confusion and misapplication, with some authorities requiring full audibility in small closets and other similar spaces because they *could* be occupied. The technical committee's intent is that other codes and standards specify where a system must be audible. However, where those codes do not give specific examples of where the full audible performance requirement must be met, common sense should apply.

Audible appliance ratings, as measured by the manufacturer and qualified testing laboratories, are specified as a decibel rating at a predetermined distance, usually 10 ft (3 m). The rule of thumb is that the output of an audible notification appliance is reduced by 6 dB if the distance between the appliance and the listener is doubled. The accuracy of this rule of thumb depends on many intervening variables, particularly the acoustic properties of the materials in the listening space, such as ceiling materials and floor and wall coverings.

The use of the appliance's rating along with this rule allows system designers to estimate audible levels in occupiable spaces before a system is installed. See Exhibit 18.11 for an example of how this rule of thumb is applied.

More complex situations require calculating sound attenuation through doors and walls. See *The SFPE Handbook of Fire Protection Engineering* for appropriate calculation methods.

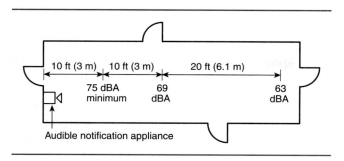

EXHIBIT 18.11 *Estimating Audible Levels Using the 6 dBA Rule of Thumb Method. (Source: R. P. Schifiliti Associates, Inc., Reading, MA)*

A.18.4.3.1 Audio levels are commonly measured using units of decibels, or $\frac{1}{10}$ Bell, abbreviated dB. When measured using a sound level meter, the operator can select either an A-weighted, B-weighted, or C-weighted measurement. The C-weighted measurement is nominally flat from 70 Hz to 4000 Hz, and the B-weighted measurement is nominally flat from 300 Hz to 4000 Hz. The A-weighted measurement filters the input signal to reduce the measurement sensitivity for frequencies to which the human ear is less sensitive and is relatively flat from 600 Hz to 7000 Hz. This results in a measurement that is weighted to simulate the segment of the audio spectrum that provides the most significant intelligibility components heard by the human ear. The units used for measurement are still dB, but the shorthand for specifying use of the A-weighted filter is typically dBA. The difference between any two sound levels measured on the same scale is always expressed in units of dB, not dBA.

The constantly changing nature of pressure waves, which are detected by ear, can be measured by electronic sound meters, and the resulting electronic waveforms can be processed and presented in a number of meaningful ways. Most simple sound level meters have a fast or slow time constant (125 ms and 1000 ms, respectively) to quickly average a sound signal and present a root mean square (RMS) level to the meter movement or display. This is the type of measurement used to determine "the maximum sound level having a duration of at least 60 seconds." Note that Chapter 14 requires this measurement to be made using the FAST time setting on the meter. However, this quick average of impressed sound results in fast movements of the meter's output that are best seen when talking into the microphone; the meter quickly rises and falls with speech. However, when surveying the ambient sound levels to establish the increased level at which a notification appliance will properly function, the sound source needs to be averaged over a longer period of times. See 3.3.25, Average Ambient Sound Level. Moderately priced sound level meters have such a function, usually called L_{eq} or "equivalent sound level." For example, an L_{eq} of speech in a quiet room would cause the meter movement to rise gradually to a peak reading and slowly fall well after the speech is over. L_{eq} measurements are made over a specified time period and reported as $L_{eq,t}$, where t is the time period. For example, a measurement taken over 24 hours is reported as L_{eq24}.

L_{eq} readings can be misapplied in situations where the background ambient noises vary greatly during a 24-hour period. L_{eq} measurements should be taken over the period of occupancy. This is clarified by the definition of Average Ambient Sound Level, 3.3.25. Note that average in this context is the integrated average at a particular measurement location, not the average of several readings taken at different locations. For example, it would be incorrect to take a reading in a quiet bathroom and average it with a reading taken near a noisy machine to get an average to use for the alarm signal design. The alarm would probably be excessively loud in the quiet bathroom and not loud enough near the noisy machine.

In areas where the background noise is generated by machinery and is fairly constant, a frequency analysis can be warranted. It might be found that the high sound levels are predominantly in one or two frequency bandwidths — often lower frequencies. Fire alarm notification appliances producing sound in one or two other frequency bandwidths can adequately penetrate the background noise and provide notification. The system would still be designed to produce or have a sound level at the particular frequency or frequency bandwidth of at least 15 dB above the average ambient sound level or 5 dB above the maximum sound level having a duration of at least 60 seconds, whichever is greater.

In very high noise areas, such as theaters, dance halls, nightclubs, and machine shops, sound levels during occupied times can be 100 dBA and higher. Peak sounds might be 110 dBA or greater. At other occupied times, the sound level might be below 50 dBA. A system designed to have a sound level of at least 15 dB above the average ambient sound level or 5 dB above the maximum sound level having a duration of at least 60 seconds might result in a required fire alarm level in excess of the maximum of 115 dBA. A viable option is to reduce or eliminate the background noise. Professional theaters or other entertainment venues can have road show connection control units (see NFPA 70, National Electrical Code, Section 520.50) for troupes to connect their light and sound systems to. These power sources can be controlled by the fire alarm system. In less formal applications, such as many nightclubs, designated power circuits could be controlled. Diligence needs to be exercised to ensure that the controlled circuits are used.

Also, in occupancies such as machine shops or other production facilities, care must be exercised in the design to ensure that the removal of power to the noise source does not create some other hazard. As with other emergency control functions, control circuits and relays would be monitored for integrity in accordance with Chapter 10, Chapter 12, and Chapter 23.

Appropriate audible signaling in high ambient noise areas is often difficult. Areas such as automotive assembly areas, machining areas, paint spray areas, and so on, where the ambient noise is caused by the manufacturing process itself, require special consideration. Adding additional audible notification appliances that merely contribute to the already noisy environment might not be appropriate. Other alerting techniques such as visible notification appliances, for example, could be more effectively used.

Other codes, standards, laws or regulations, and the authority having jurisdiction determine where a signal must be audible. This Code section describes the performance requirement needed for a signal to be considered reliably audible.

18.4.3.2 Where approved by the authority having jurisdiction or other governing codes or standards, the requirements for audible signaling shall be permitted to be reduced or eliminated when visible signaling is provided in accordance with Section 18.5.

FAQ ▶
What conditions must be satisfied to reduce or eliminate audible signaling?

The provision in 18.4.3.2 was added to previous editions of the Code for both public and private mode signaling. Audible signaling can be reduced or eliminated only where allowed by the authority having jurisdiction or other governing codes or standards, and only where public mode visible signaling is also provided. Use of this allowance should be for cases specifically addressed by an occupancy code or where supported by careful evaluation of the special conditions that warrant its use. Refer to 18.4.4.2 and A.18.4.4.2 for additional insight.

18.4.3.3 Audible alarm notification appliances installed in elevator cars shall be permitted to use the audibility criteria for private mode appliances detailed in 18.4.4.1.

18.4.3.4 If approved by the authority having jurisdiction, audible alarm notification appliances installed in restrooms shall be permitted to use the audibility criteria for private mode appliances detailed in 18.4.4.1.

18.4.3.5 A fire alarm system arranged to stop or reduce ambient noise shall comply with 18.4.3.5.1 through 18.4.3.5.3.

Where acceptable to the authority having jurisdiction, reducing the background noise is a viable alternative to providing a fire alarm system with a high level of audio output. In fact, in some situations, such as nightclubs, concert halls, and theaters, an advisable action is to stop the background noise and control the lighting to create a sudden and noticeable change in the environment to get people's attention. However, care must be exercised to ensure that the shutdown mechanism is reliable and will not damage the equipment being shut down.

18.4.3.5.1 A fire alarm system arranged to stop or reduce ambient noise shall produce a sound level at least 15 dB above the reduced average ambient sound level or 5 dB above the maximum sound level having a duration of at least 60 seconds after reduction of the ambient noise level, whichever is greater, measured 5 ft (1.5 m) above the floor in the area required to be served by the system using the A-weighted scale (dBA).

18.4.3.5.2 Visible notification appliances shall be installed in the affected areas in accordance with Sections 18.5 or 18.6.

18.4.3.5.3 Relays, circuits, or interfaces necessary to stop or reduce ambient noise shall meet the requirements of Chapters 10, 12, 21 and 23.

18.4.4 Private Mode Audible Requirements.

18.4.4.1* To ensure that audible private mode signals are clearly heard, they shall have a sound level at least 10 dB above the average ambient sound level or 5 dB above the maximum sound level having a duration of at least 60 seconds, whichever is greater, measured 5 ft (1.5 m) above the floor in the area required to be served by the system using the A-weighted scale (dBA).

A.18.4.4.1 See A.18.4.3.1 for additional information on sound measurements and weighting scales.

18.4.4.2* Where approved by the authority having jurisdiction or other governing codes or standards, the requirements for audible signaling shall be permitted to be reduced or eliminated when visible signaling is provided in accordance with Section 18.5.

A.18.4.4.2 For example, in critical care patient areas, it is often desirable to not have an audible fire alarm even at reduced private mode levels. Each case requires consideration by the governing authority. Another example would be high noise work areas where an audible signal needed to overcome background noise at one time of day would be excessively loud and potentially dangerous at another time of lower ambient noise. A sudden increase of more than 30 dB over 0.5 seconds is considered to cause sudden and potentially dangerous fright.

A hospital patient care area is one example of where a code or an authority having jurisdiction can permit private mode signaling. The public occupants include patients who might not be able to respond to a fire alarm signal. In some cases, alerting them directly with audible (and possibly visible) signals might even be dangerous. For this reason, the system is designed to alert trained staff.

Areas that use private mode signaling (such as certain areas in a hospital) often have a less intense average ambient sound level and a lower maximum sound level, making the reduced level cited in 18.4.4.1 appropriate. In the delivery of private mode signals, it is important that the sound level of the audible notification appliance be adequate but not so loud as to startle the occupants.

Lower audible levels are permitted because part of the staff's job is to listen for and respond appropriately to the fire alarm signals. In addition, they must communicate among themselves to be able to implement emergency procedures; a louder alarm might interfere with that communication.

In a few cases, such as operating rooms or critical care patient areas, other codes and authorities having jurisdiction may permit elimination of audible (and possibly visible) signaling altogether.

18.4.4.3 A system arranged to stop or reduce ambient noise shall comply with 18.4.4.3.1 through 18.4.4.3.3.

18.4.4.3.1 A system arranged to stop or reduce ambient noise shall be permitted to produce a sound level at least 10 dB above the reduced average ambient sound level or 5 dB above the maximum sound level having a duration of at least 60 seconds after reduction of the ambient noise level, whichever is greater, measured 5 ft (1.5 m) above the floor, using the A-weighted scale (dBA).

18.4.4.3.2 Visible notification appliances shall be installed in the affected areas in accordance with Sections 18.5 or 18.6.

18.4.4.3.3 Relays, circuits, or interfaces necessary to stop or reduce ambient noise shall meet the requirements of Chapters 10, 12, 21 and 23.

18.4.5 Sleeping Area Requirements.

18.4.5.1* Where audible appliances are installed to provide signals for sleeping areas, they shall have a sound level of at least 15 dB above the average ambient sound level or 5 dB above the maximum sound level having a duration of at least 60 seconds or a sound level of at least 75 dBA, whichever is greater, measured at the pillow level in the area required to be served by the system using the A-weighted scale (dBA).

A.18.4.5.1 See A.18.4.3.1 for additional information on sound measurements and weighting scales.

FAQ ▶
What additional condition must be satisfied for sleeping areas, compared with the requirements in 18.4.3.1?

Paragraph 18.4.5.1 requires that the sound level delivered by the audible notification system in rooms where people sleep be either 15 dB above the average ambient sound level, 5 dB above any peak sound level lasting 60 seconds or more, or at least 75 dBA, whichever is greatest. If the average ambient sound level in the sleeping area is 40 dBA, then the audible notification appliances must deliver at least 75 dBA (40 + 15 = 55, which is less than the 75 dBA minimum). If the average ambient sound level in the sleeping area is 65 dBA, then the audible notification appliances must deliver at least 80 dBA (65 + 15 = 80).

Note that 75 dBA is a change from the requirement of 70 dBA prior to the 2002 edition. Some studies suggest a minimum of 75 dBA, while others suggest 70 dBA. These levels are for people without hearing impairments and without incapacitation due to drugs, alcohol, or exhaustion. Also, a certain sound pressure level does not instantly awaken all test subjects. There is a distribution of time to alert some or all of the occupants. Obviously, as the sound level increases, the time to alert the majority of people decreases. The time it takes to awaken someone and the time it takes for the person to act must be considered by designers with respect to the development of hazardous conditions.

18.4.5.2 If any barrier, such as a door, curtain, or retractable partition, is located between the notification appliance and the pillow, the sound pressure level shall be measured with the barrier placed between the appliance and the pillow.

Although 18.4.5.2 applies only to sleeping areas, the intent of the Code for all audible signaling is that the worst-case conditions be used for all ambient and alarm sound level measurements. This might require testing with doors and other barriers opened and closed to determine the worst case. However, it would not be necessary to open a door to get the worst-case noise and then close the door to get the worst-case alarm level — or vice versa. Instead, the difference between ambient and alarm can be measured with the door open and then again with the door closed to ensure that the required levels are met in both situations.

18.4.5.3* Effective January 1, 2014, where audible appliances are provided to produce signals for sleeping areas, they shall produce a low frequency alarm signal that complies with the following:

(1) The alarm signal shall be a square wave or provide equivalent awakening ability.
(2) The wave shall have a fundamental frequency of 520 Hz ± 10 percent.

Two research programs and their resultant reports (*Optimizing Fire Alarm Notification for High Risk Groups, Summary Report*; *Waking Effectiveness of Alarms for Adults Who Are Hard of Hearing*; and *Waking Effectiveness of Alarms for the Alcohol Impaired*), which were supported by the Fire Protection Research Foundation under the umbrella of "optimizing notification systems," have led to new requirements for tones used to awaken people. Previous editions of the Code have not specified any particular frequency content for audible tones. Most fire alarm and smoke alarm tones for new equipment use sounders that produce high frequency tones on the order of 3150 Hz. That frequency band is also the one at which most adults experience hearing loss. The Foundation's research programs have shown that a low frequency, 520 Hz square wave signal can awaken and alert people with hearing loss and alcohol-impaired adults.

The Technical Committee on Notification Appliances for Fire Alarm Systems has written this Code requirement that all sleeping area signals are to use the new low frequency signal effective January 1, 2014. This requirement applies to new system-activated signals. The use of speakers and amplifiers that also provide voice capability is one way to accommodate this need. Other hardware solutions can also be used. The effective date allows time for system product development and listing. The Technical Committee on Single- and Multiple-Station Alarms and Household Fire Alarm Systems (Chapter 29) has incorporated the same low frequency signal requirement for residential protection without an effective date, which would be applicable when the 2010 edition is adopted in the particular jurisdiction. Refer to 29.3.8 for the requirements and conditions that apply in household applications.

A.18.4.5.3 It is not the intent of this section to preclude devices that have been demonstrated through peer reviewed research to awaken occupants with hearing loss as effectively as those using the frequency and amplitude specified in this section.

Fundamental frequency: 520 Hz ± 10 percent. Odd harmonic frequency components 3, 5, 7 and 9 times the fundamental frequency should be present in appropriate magnitude defined by the Fourier transform of a square wave (see below) ± 20 percent.

On a linear scale where X is the peak magnitude of the fundamental frequency component, the harmonic frequencies should have the following peak magnitudes with the tolerance defined above:

(1) 520 Hz X
(2) 1560 Hz $\frac{1}{3}$ X
(3) 2600 Hz $\frac{1}{5}$ X
(4) 3640 Hz $\frac{1}{7}$ X
(5) 4680 Hz $\frac{1}{9}$ X

A square wave contains only the odd integer harmonics. In general, a square wave can be expressed using the Fourier series. As presented by Wolfram MathWorld, the general mathematical expression for the function of an ideal square wave as an infinite series is

$$\chi_{\text{square}}(t) = \frac{4}{\pi} \sum_{n=1,3,5,\ldots}^{\infty} \frac{1}{n} \sin(2n\pi ft)$$

Where $\chi_{\text{square}}(t)$ is the square wave as a function of time, t, sin( ) is the sine wave function, f is the frequency, π is pi, the relationship between the circumference and the diameter of a circle, and *n* is the odd harmonics. An expanded expression for the 1st, 3rd, 5th, 7th, and 9th harmonics is

$$\chi_{square}(t) = \frac{4}{\pi}\left(\frac{1}{1}\sin(2\pi ft) + \frac{1}{3}\sin(6\pi ft) + \frac{1}{5}\sin(10\pi ft) + \frac{1}{7}\sin(14\pi ft) + \frac{1}{9}\sin(18\pi ft)\right)$$

An example of a 520 Hz square wave audio signal is presented as a spectrograph in Figure A.18.4.5.3. Note the dBA scale and weighting.

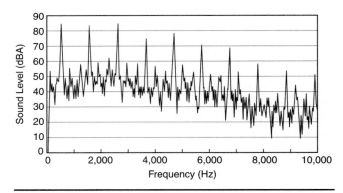

FIGURE A.18.4.5.3 *Spectrograph of a 520 Hz Square Wave Audio Signal.*

Additional harmonics for the square wave beyond the 9th harmonic can be present in the signal, but should not contribute more than 10 percent of the integrated-averaged sound level.

18.4.6* Narrow Band Tone Signaling for Exceeding Masked Thresholds.

A.18.4.6 This subsection permits a more rigorous analysis and design for audible signaling. Acoustic design practice and psychoacoustic research have long recognized that for a signal to be audible, it need only penetrate the background noise in a one-third or a one octave band. The averaging resulting from A-weighted analysis and design is a simplification that often results in systems being overdesigned. This overdesign is not dangerous but can be costly and is certainly not needed for effective system performance.

18.4.6.1 Masked Threshold Allowance. Audible tone signaling shall be permitted to comply with the masked threshold requirements in this subsection in lieu of the A-weighted signaling requirements in 18.4.3 and 18.4.4.

18.4.6.2* Calculation Method. The effective masked threshold shall be calculated in accordance with ISO 7731, *Danger signals for work places — Auditory danger signals.*

A.18.4.6.2 Noise at a lower frequency can mask a signal at an adjacent higher frequency. Thus, it is necessary to calculate the effective masked level of the noise in accordance with established procedures. Figure A.18.4.6.2 shows an example of an octave band analysis of noise along with the calculated effective masked threshold and the proposed fire alarm signal.

The effective masked threshold can be thought of as the adjusted ambient noise. The actual ambient noise level is adjusted to account for the masking effect that a lower frequency band has on a higher, adjacent frequency band.

The example of narrow band signaling shown in Figure A.18.4.6.2 uses a line plot for the noise and the masked threshold signal. This graphically shows that the masking of a higher frequency by a lower frequency results in a minimum slope of –7.5 dB per octave. This mask-

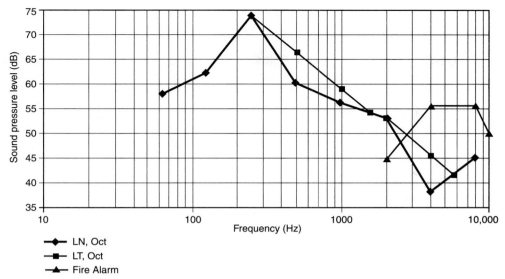

At the first octave band center frequency, the masked threshold of hearing, LT, Oct is equal to the noise level. For each subsequent center frequency, LT, Oct is the greater of either the noise level at that octave band, LN, Oct, or the masked threshold of the previous band less 7.5 dB.

FIGURE A.18.4.6.2 *Threshold Masking Level Example.*

ing level is specified in the referenced document ISO 7731, *Danger Signals for Work Places — Auditory Danger Signals.*

Note that the masking line is plotted as a negative slope (−7.5 dB per octave) until it intersects the noise line rather than connecting at the next data point. This method for determining the masked threshold is shown graphically in ISO 7731. The masked threshold is difficult (but possible) to define mathematically but is easy to determine graphically as shown in Figure A.18.4.6.2. Because octave and one-third octave band analysis is not continuous, the analysis is better represented as a bar graph. For further explanation, refer to the commentary following 18.4.6.5.2 and related Exhibit 18.12.

ISO 7731 defines the effective masked threshold in a particular octave band as the greater of the noise level at that band or the masked threshold of the previous band less 7.5 dB. For one-third octave band analysis, the requirement is a minimum slope of −2.5 dB per one-third octave. Thus, the effective masked threshold in a particular one-third octave band is the greater of the noise level at that band or the masked threshold of the previous band less 2.5 dB.

Also refer to the definitions of *effective masked threshold* in 3.3.75 and *octave band* and *one-third octave band* in 3.3.163 and 3.3.163.1.

18.4.6.3 Noise Data. Noise data for calculating the effective masked threshold shall be the peak value of noise lasting 60 seconds or more for each octave or one-third octave band.

18.4.6.4 Documentation. Analysis and design documentation shall be submitted to the authority having jurisdiction and shall contain the following information:

(1) Frequency data for the ambient noise, including the date, time, and location where measurements were taken for existing environments, or projected data for environments not yet constructed
(2) Frequency data of the audible notification appliance
(3) Calculations of the effective masked threshold for each set of noise data
(4) A statement of the sound pressure level that would be required by 18.4.3 or 18.4.4 if masked threshold signaling had not been done

COMMENTARY TABLE 18.1 *Compressor Room One-Third Octave Noise Data and Calculated Masked Threshold*

Center Frequency (Hz)	Noise (dB)	Masked Threshold (dB)	Center Frequency (Hz)	Noise (dB)	Masked Threshold (dB)	Center Frequency (Hz)	Noise (dB)	Masked Threshold (dB)
25	71	71.0	315	84	84.0	4,000	68	**68.5**
32	73	73.0	400	83	83.0	5,000	69	69.0
40	72	72.0	500	80	**80.5**	6,300	67	67.0
50	74	74.0	630	76	**78.0**	8,000	66	66.0
63	76	76.0	800	78	78.0	10,000	64	64.0
80	75	75.0	1,000	77	77.0	12,500	63	63.0
100	78	78.0	1,250	79	79.0	16,000	67	67.0
125	79	79.0	1,600	78	78.0	20,000	65	65.0
160	80	80.0	2,000	76	76.0	L_P	92	
200	80	80.0	2,500	70	**73.5**	L_A	88	
250	81	81.0	3,150	65	**71.0**			

Source: R. P. Schifiliti Associates, Inc., Reading, MA.

COMMENTARY TABLE 18.2 *Dominant Frequency Distribution of a Typical Piezo-Electric Fire Alarm Sounder*

Center Frequency (Hz)	Alarm (dB)
1,600	30
2,000	36
2,500	73
3,150	85
4,000	67
5,000	49
L_P	85
L_A	87

Source: R. P. Schifiliti Associates, Inc., Reading, MA.

In the example provided, how do the results of the one-third octave band analysis compare to the result noted above, using the requirements of 18.4.3.1?

FAQ ▶

18.4.6.5 Sound Pressure Level. For masked threshold signaling, the audible signal tone shall meet the requirements of either 18.4.6.5.1 or 18.4.6.5.2 but not for the reproduction of prerecorded, synthesized, or live messages.

18.4.6.5.1 The sound pressure level of the audible tone signal shall exceed the masked threshold in one or more octave bands by at least 10 dB in the octave band under consideration.

18.4.6.5.2 The sound pressure level of the audible tone signal shall exceed the masked threshold in one or more one-third octave bands by at least 13 dB in the one-third octave band under consideration.

The human ear can discriminate distinct frequency bands. These bands can be thought of as pickets in a fence. Commentary Table 18.1 shows a particular compressor room one-third octave band noise data (unweighted) and the resulting calculated masked threshold. Bold entries show frequency bands where the masked level is greater than the measured noise level. The total integrated sound pressure level (L_p) is 92 dB (unweighted). When adjusted for the way the human ear hears different frequencies, the total A-weighted sound pressure level (L_A) is shown as 88 dBA. The peak sound pressure level is approximately 84 dB at 315 Hz. If these data were the average ambient sound level in the space, 18.4.3.1 would require a fire alarm signal of 88 + 15 = 103 dBA.

Commentary Table 18.2 shows the dominant frequency distribution of a typical piezo-electric fire alarm sounder. The data have been adjusted using the 6 dB rule (see Exhibit 18.12) for the distance from the planned mounting location to the point where the noise data in Commentary Table 18.1 were measured.

Exhibit 18.12 uses a bar graph to show the noise, the threshold masked level, and the fire alarm signal. The noise and resulting threshold masked level can be thought of as a picket fence trying to obscure our view of the fire alarm signal. To know that the fire alarm signal is there, we need only "see" one of its pickets behind the adjusted noise data (threshold masked level).

In this example, the noise measured at 3150 Hz is 65 dB, but the masked threshold at that frequency is 71 dB (73.5 at the previous band minus 2.5). The fire alarm signal produces 85 dB at 3150 Hz, resulting in a signal-to-noise ratio of 14 dB. This ratio meets the requirement of 18.4.6.5.2 for a minimum 13 dB for one-third octave band signaling.

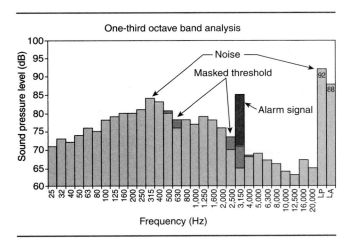

EXHIBIT 18.12 Noise Data, Threshold Masked Level (Adjusted Noise Data), and the Fire Alarm Signal. (Source: R. P. Schifiliti Associates, Inc., Reading, MA)

Measured using an integrating meter set to the A scale, this system would not meet the Code's requirements. However, using a one-third octave band analysis, the system passes.

18.4.7 Exit Marking Audible Notification Appliance Requirements.

Refer to the definition of *exit marking audible notification appliance* in 3.3.160.1.1.

18.4.7.1* Exit marking audible notification appliances shall meet or exceed the frequency and sound level settings and guidelines specified in the manufacturer's documented instructions.

A.18.4.7.1 The sound content of directional sounders is very different from that of the traditional fire alarm sounders. Traditional fire alarm sounders have a strong tonal content, usually centered near the 3 kHz region. Directional sounders use broadband frequency content, usually covering most of the human audible frequency range, 20 Hz to 20 kHz. Figure A.18.4.7.1(a) compares the frequency content of a traditional fire alarm sounder to a directional sounder. This figure shows that while the fire alarm sounder clearly dominates the 3 kHz and upper harmonics, the broadband content of the directional sounder is 20 dB to 30 dB in other frequency bands or ranges. The fire alarm has an overall A-weighted sound level greater than the directional sounder and will be perceived as being louder. However, since the directional sounder has a wide spectral range, the signal penetrates the fire alarm signal in several other frequency bands as permitted by 18.4.6.

There are three main types of information that allow the brain to identify the location of a sound. The first two are known as binaural cues because they make use of the fact that we have two ears, separated by the width of our head. A sound that emanates from either side of the mid-line will arrive first at the ear closer to it and will be loudest at the ear closer to it. At low frequencies the brain recognizes differences in the arrival time of sound between the ears (interaural time differences). At higher frequencies the salient signal is the loudness/intensity difference between the sounds at each ear (interaural intensity differences). Refer to Figure A.18.4.7.1(b). For single frequencies, these cues are spatially ambiguous.

The inherent ambiguity has been described as the "cone of confusion." This arises from the fact that for any given frequency there are numerous spatial positions that generate identical timing/intensity differences. These can be graphically represented in the form of a cone, the apex of which is at the level of the external ear. The cone of confusion is the main reason for our not being able to localize pure tones.

The final piece of sound localization information processed by the brain is the head-related transfer function (HRTF). The HRTF refers to the effect the external ear has on sound.

Directional sound = 66 dB(A)*; Fire alarm = 86 dB(A)*

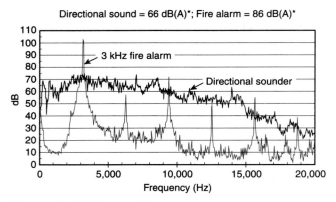

* Measured at 10 ft in an anechoic room.

FIGURE A.18.4.7.1(a) *Comparison of Frequency Content of a Traditional Fire Alarm Sounder to a Directional Sounder.*

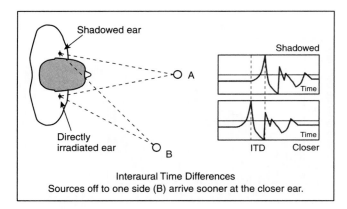

Interaural Time Differences
Sources off to one side (B) arrive sooner at the closer ear.

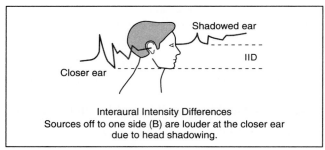

Interaural Intensity Differences
Sources off to one side (B) are louder at the closer ear due to head shadowing.

FIGURE A.18.4.7.1(b) *Interaural Time and Intensity Differences of Sound.*

As a result of passing over the bumps or convolutions of the pinna, the sound is modified so that some frequencies are attenuated and others are amplified. Refer to Figure A.18.4.7.1(c). Although there are certain generalities in the way the pinnae modify sound, the HRTF is unique to each individual. The role of the HRTF is particularly important when determining whether a sound is in front of or behind us. In this instance the timing and intensity differences are negligible, and there is consequently very little information available to the central nervous system on which to base this decision. To locate the direction of a sound source, the larger the frequency content to overcome the ambiguities inherent to single tones, the better the accuracy.

18.4.7.2* In addition to 18.4.7.1, as a minimum, to ensure that exit marking audible notification appliance signals are clearly heard and produce the desired directional effects for 50 ft (15.24 m) within an unobstructed egress path, they shall meet the audibility requirements of 18.4.6 in at least one one-third octave band or one octave band within the effective frequency ranges of the interaural time difference (ITD), interaural level or intensity difference (ILD or IID), and anatomical transfer function or head-related transfer function (ATF or HRTF) localization cues. The signal shall penetrate both the ambient noise and the fire alarm signal.

A.18.4.7.2 *ITD*: A difference in arrival times of waveform features (such as peaks and positive-going zero crossings) at the two ears is known as the interaural time difference, or ITD. The binaural physiology is capable of using phase information from ITD cues only at low frequencies below about 1500 Hz. However, the binaural system can successfully register an ITD that occurs at a high frequency such as 4000 Hz if the signal is modulated. The modulation, in turn, must have a rate that is less than about 1000 Hz.

ILD: Comparison between intensities in the left and right ears is known as the interaural level difference, or ILD. ILD cues exist physically only for frequencies above about 500 Hz.

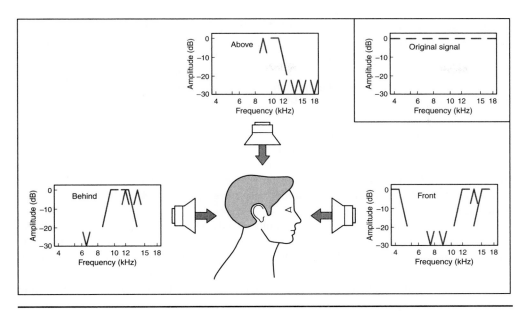

FIGURE A.18.4.7.1(c) *Examples of Frequency-Dependent Attenuation for Sources in Front, Above, and Behind the Listener.*

They become large and reliable for frequencies above 3000 Hz, making ILD cues most effective at high frequencies.

ATF: The anatomical transfer function (ATF), also known as the head-related transfer function (HRTF), is used by listeners to resolve front–back confusion and to determine elevation. Waves that come from behind tend to be boosted in the 1000 Hz frequency region, whereas waves that come from the forward direction are boosted near 3000 Hz. The most dramatic effects occur above 4000 Hz.

These localization cues can be implemented simultaneously when the source signal is a broadband sound containing a range of low to high frequencies. For example, octave bands of 1 kHz (707–1414 Hz) for ITD, 4 kHz (2828–5856) Hz for ILD, and 8 kHz (5657–11314 Hz) for ATF would fall within the effective frequency ranges required in 18.4.6.

Additional information on sound localization and auditory localization cues is contained in the following article: http://www.aip.org/pt/nov99/locsound.html, H.1.2.14.2.

The ability to pinpoint the location of a sound source is based on the physics of sound and the physiology of the human hearing mechanism. The brain processes a large amount of neural signals, some of which provide cues to the sound source's location. People are able to hear sound ranging from about 20 Hz to 20,000 Hz. Unfortunately, pure tones in this frequency range provide only limited localization information. The primary localization cues are provided by interaural time differences (ITDs) (lower frequencies), interaural intensity differences (IIDs) (mid to higher frequencies), and the head-related transfer function (HRTF) (higher frequencies). In enclosed spaces that can be somewhat reverberant, the precedence effect (PE) also provides directional information.

The interaural time difference (ITD) and interaural intensity difference (IID) are termed binaural cues because they depend on both ears separated by the width of the head. At lower frequencies (longer wavelength), the time delay between arriving sound signals is detectable. ITD is most evident in frequencies below about 500 Hz with clicks or short bursts of sound. At higher frequencies (shorter wavelength), the loudness/intensity differences between the ears is more noticeable because of partial shielding of the more distant ear by the head. IID is most evident for frequencies above 3000 Hz.

The head-related transfer function (HRTF) relies on the effect of the external ear on perceived sound. The HRTF describes the transforming effect of the head, torso, and external ear on sound as it travels from the sound source to the ear canals. The HRTF changes depending on sound source location, providing an additional localization cue. HRTF operates over a range of frequencies but seems to be most effective in the 5000 Hz to 10,000 Hz range. Combined with the listener's head motion, HRTF provides an independent localization method to complement ITD and IID capabilities.

The precedence effect (PE) is important for discriminating between the direct sound signal and reflected sound, a common situation within buildings. The ear is capable of discerning and fixating on the first sound received (line-of-sight direct signal) and disregarding later signals (reflected sound). The acoustical signal arriving first at the ears suppresses the ability to hear other signals (including reverberation) that arrive up to about 40 milliseconds after the initial signal.

All of the preceding cues are utilized simultaneously when the source signal is broadband sound containing a range of low and high frequencies, and when the sound arrives in bursts rather than as steady state sound. The combination of different cues provides reinforcement and redundancy of information to enhance the ability to locate the sound source. Broadband sound tends to eliminate potential ambiguities that occur for pure tone or narrowband sound sources.

Other types of sound patterns can be used as directional sounders that can be used for audible exit marking. Some scientific research has been performed to develop a directional sounder that utilizes a tonal sound different from the example above. As with the directional sound example presented above, the development of this alternative signal is similarly rooted in the vast research data that exists for sound localization and directional auditory cues.

An example of an alternative directional sound signal can be a sequence of two harmonic two-tone complexes. This sequence starts with a complex of low fundamental frequencies of 262 and 330 Hz having duration of 200 ms. This sound is then followed by a 200-ms silence. Next the sequence continues with a second sound that is a complex of low fundamental frequencies of 330 and 392 Hz having a duration of 200 ms. After another 200-ms silence, this whole pattern is repeated.

Localizability was ensured by the dense harmonic structure of the signal, with closely spaced harmonics up to 20 kHz. In addition sharp signal onsets were included to aid the detection of interaural time differences, thus increasing localizability.

Requirements for exit marking systems were added in the 2007 edition. Exit marking systems use sound to direct occupants to exits. The intent is for the sound to be directional, allowing the occupant to distinctly identify the location and direction where the sound originates. To accomplish this, the signal must have very specific characteristics. The technical committee added performance-based requirements derived from underlying research on directional sound.

18.4.7.3 Where required by the enforcing authority; governing laws, codes, or standards; or other parts of this Code, exit marking audible notification appliances shall be installed in accordance with the manufacturer's instructions.

18.4.7.4* Where required by the enforcing authority; governing laws, codes, or standards; or other parts of this Code, exit marking audible notification shall be located at the entrance to all building exits and areas of refuge as defined by the applicable building or fire code.

A.18.4.7.4 Where directional sounders are used, they should not be located on only a single exit. They should be located at all of the identified exits in the building. This is to ensure that in an evacuation or relocation the occupants utilize all of the exits and areas of refuge, not just those that have directional sounders located near them. Some examples of exits would include the following:

(1) Code-complying exterior doors and exit discharge
(2) Code-complying exit passageway
(3) Code-complying interior stairs, including smokeproof enclosures
(4) Code-complying outside stairs
(5) Code-complying ramps
(6) Code-complying fire escapes
(7) Code-complying horizontal exits

Note that the terms *exit* and *area of refuge* have very specific definitions in building, fire, and life safety codes.

18.4.7.5 Where exit marking audible notification appliances are utilized to mark areas of refuge, they shall provide an audible signal distinct from that used for other exits that do not have areas of refuge.

18.4.8 Location of Audible Notification Appliances for a Building or Structure.

18.4.8.1 If ceiling heights allow, and unless otherwise permitted by 18.4.8.2 through 18.4.8.5, wall-mounted appliances shall have their tops above the finished floors at heights of not less than 90 in. (2.29 m) and below the finished ceilings at distances of not less than 6 in. (150 mm).

18.4.8.2 Ceiling-mounted or recessed appliances shall be permitted.

18.4.8.3 If combination audible/visible appliances are installed, the location of the installed appliance shall be determined by the requirements of 18.5.4.

Paragraph 18.4.8.3 requires that the location of a combination audible/visible notification appliance comply with the requirements for the mounting of visible notification appliances in 18.5.4. The height limitation specified in 18.5.4 is intended to keep visible notification appliances at a height that ensures that the light pattern covers the intended area.

18.4.8.4 Appliances that are an integral part of a smoke detector, smoke alarm, or other initiating device shall be located in accordance with the requirements for that device.

Refer to 18.5.4.6 regarding the installation of combination smoke detectors and visible notification appliances installed in sleeping areas.

18.4.8.5 Mounting heights other than required by 18.4.8.1 and 18.4.8.2 shall be permitted, provided that the sound pressure level requirements of 18.4.3 for public mode or 18.4.4 for private mode, or 18.4.5 for sleeping areas, based on the application, are met.

The purpose of the mounting height requirements for audible appliances is to prevent common furnishings from blocking appliances after installation. However, the required sound pressure levels (see 18.4.3, 18.4.4, 18.4.5, and 18.4.6) are performance requirements. Thus, the Code requires authorities to permit audible appliances at other mounting heights as long as the system ultimately provides the required sound pressure level. The system must pass the testing requirements of Chapter 14. Remember that the appliances must also be accessible for repair and maintenance and that they should not be located where they would be subjected to mechanical damage or harsh environmental conditions. This allowance for other mounting heights applies only to audible appliances, not to visible or combination appliances. The mounting heights for visible or combination appliances can deviate from the Code requirements but require a corresponding adjustment for their area of coverage. See 18.5.4.1, A.18.5.4.1, and 18.5.4.5.

◄ FAQ
What is the purpose of the mounting height requirements for audible appliances?

18.4.9 Location of Audible Notification Appliances for Wide Area Signaling.
Audible notification appliances for wide area signaling shall be installed in accordance with

the requirements of the authority having jurisdiction, approved design documents, and the manufacturer's installation instruction to achieve the required performance.

18.4.10* Voice Intelligibility. Within the acoustically distinguishable spaces (ADS) where voice intelligibility is required, voice communications systems shall reproduce prerecorded, synthesized, or live (e.g., microphone, telephone handset, and radio) messages with voice intelligibility.

A.18.4.10 See Annex D, Speech Intelligibility.

The concept of acoustically distinguishable space (ADS) is new in the 2010 edition. See the definition in 3.3.2.

18.4.10.1* ADSs shall be determined by the system designer during the planning and design of all emergency communications systems.

A.18.4.10.1 See the definition of acoustically distinguishable space in 3.3.2.

The intent is that all parts of a building or space be divided up into definable ADSs.

18.4.10.2 Each ADS shall be identified as requiring or not requiring voice intelligibility.

Because more facilities are now incorporating voice communications for ECS and general paging and communication systems, there is a greater need to educate designers, installers, testing personnel, and authorities having jurisdiction about intelligible voice communications. The Fire Protection Research Foundation conducted a program to develop a guide test protocol. The final report also addresses certain planning and design factors. Much of that report has been incorporated as the new Annex D, Speech Intelligibility.

A significant change in the body of the Code that resulted from the study is the requirement for designers to plan and designate acoustically distinguishable spaces (ADSs). Designers must establish and document which spaces, if any, will require intelligible voice communications. Considerable discussion in Annex D and in A.3.3.2 points out that intelligible voice communication is not necessary in all spaces and that it might not be possible in certain circumstances. By requiring designers to list or otherwise document these spaces and conditions, the Code ensures that system goals are documented and agreed to by all interested parties.

For each ADS, the designer must identify the spaces where occupant notification is needed. If occupant notification is required, the designer must decide if it will be by tone only or will include voice. If it is tone only, the audibility requirements of 18.4.3, 18.4.4, 18.4.5, or 18.4.6 apply. If the notification will be by voice with a tone alert, the same audibility requirements apply to the tone. The last decision is whether the voice component in the ADS must be intelligible. The decision tree in Exhibit 18.13 can be used for each ADS. Though not required, a similar process might be used for visible notification and communication.

FAQ ▶
Why would a system have voice capability and the Code not *require* that voice to be intelligible?

Note that the Code does not require the voice to be intelligible. The key is that voice communications might not *need* to be intelligible in *all* ADSs. Of course, there will be ADSs where the system has to be intelligible if it is to serve any useful purpose. An example is an office building that has small offices around the perimeter and some combination of open plan and circulation corridors in the core. By definition, each small office is an ADS. As an example, if the ECS also is to be used as a paging or music system, a designer might choose to require intelligible communications in the small offices. However, if the ECS is to be used only for emergencies, the designer might not design for intelligible communications in each of the small offices. The ADSs in the small offices would still have to receive an audible alert meeting the Code requirements for audibility. Occupants would then have to open their office doors and possibly move out to another ADS to receive intelligible voice communications.

FAQ ▶
Why not require all ADSs to have intelligible voice communications?

Cost is one reason to not require all ADSs to have intelligible voice communications. Another might be if the system is used to provide background music in the core areas that is not wanted in the smaller office spaces in the preceding example.

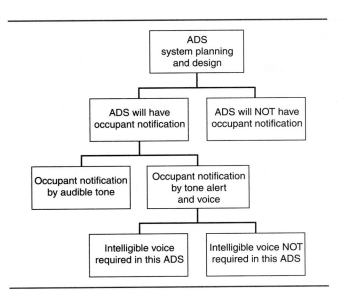

EXHIBIT 18.13 *ADS Planning and Design Decision Tree. (Source: R. P. Schifiliti Associates, Inc., Reading, MA)*

Another example of a design that might not require intelligibility throughout is a corridor or tunnel. Good speech intelligibility can be achieved in the direct field of ceiling-mounted speakers if the system is properly designed. The speakers can be spaced so that someone walking the length of the corridor is always in an area with acceptable speech intelligibility. However, it might also be an acceptable design to space the speakers farther apart. In that case, there might be small distances where the system is audible but not intelligible. In ADSs that have a lot of hard surfaces, resulting in high reverberation, speakers would have to be close together and powered at very low wattages to reduce reverberation and increase intelligibility. It might be perfectly acceptable and effective to use the alternative design in which the system would not be intelligible along the entire path. A reason the speakers are spaced more widely in the tunnel example is to reduce overall sound energy and attendant reverberation in the hard-finished space, which could improve intelligibility within the direct speaker field. The direct field is generally taken as the cone where the sound level is within 6 dB of the on-axis dB; it will vary with frequency and is usually taken at 2000 Hz for voice communications. It is also a function of angle from the speaker axis and distance from the speaker.

18.4.10.3* Where required by the authority having jurisdiction, ADS assignments shall be submitted for review and approval.

A.18.4.10.3 ADS assignments should be a part of the original design process. See the discussion in A.3.3.2. The design drawings should be used to plan and show the limits of each ADS where there is more than one.

All areas that are intended to have audible occupant notification, whether by tone only or by voice should be designated as one or more ADSs. Drawings or a table listing all ADSs should be used to indicate which ADSs will require intelligible voice communications and those that will not. The same drawings or table could be used to list audibility requirements where tones are used and to list any forms of visual or other notification or communications methods being employed in the ADS.

If a table is used, as suggested in A.18.4.10.3, it is not always necessary to list each ADS. In the office example given in the commentary on 18.4.10.2, the small, individual offices could be listed as "Offices 201 through 212" or "Perimeter Offices." On drawings, the offices could be outlined and a note could indicate that each is an ADS with common characteristics.

18.5* Visible Characteristics — Public Mode

Following passage of the Americans with Disabilities Act (ADA) and the Architectural Barriers Act (ABA), a great deal of debate ensued about visible signaling requirements. In the past, the *National Fire Alarm Code* differed from the *Americans with Disabilities Act Accessibility Guidelines* (ADAAG) and other accessibility standards, such as ICC/ANSI 117.1, *Standard on Accessible and Usable Buildings and Facilities*. The fire alarm industry has worked with the various code and advocacy groups to develop reasonable, safe, and effective visible notification requirements.

The requirements in the 2002 edition of the *National Fire Alarm Code* have been accepted as "equivalent facilitation" (and in some cases superior) to the original ADAAG requirements. Subsequently, the ADAAG has been revised to become the *Americans with Disabilities Act and Architectural Barriers Act Accessibility Guidelines* and now references the 1999 and 2002 editions of *NFPA 72*. See Exhibit 18.14.

The 2007 and 2010 editions of *NFPA 72* are expected to be accepted as equivalent because the maximum sound pressure level of 120 dBA in the 1999 and 2002 editions has been reduced to 110 dBA, as in the revised guidelines.

A.18.5 The mounting height of the appliances affects the distribution pattern and level of illumination produced by an appliance on adjacent surfaces. It is this pattern, or effect, that provides occupant notification by visible appliances. If mounted too high, the pattern is larger but at a lower level of illumination (measured in lumens per square foot or foot-candles). If mounted too low, the illumination is greater (brighter) but the pattern is smaller and might not overlap correctly with that of adjacent appliances.

A qualified designer could choose to present calculations to an authority having jurisdiction showing that it is possible to use a mounting height greater than 96 in. (2.44 m) or less than 80 in. (2.03 m), provided that an equivalent level of illumination is achieved on the adjacent surfaces. This can be accomplished by using listed higher intensity appliances or closer spacing, or both.

Engineering calculations should be prepared by qualified persons and should be submitted to the authority having jurisdiction, showing how the proposed variation achieves the same or greater level of illumination provided by the prescriptive requirements of Section 18.5.

The calculations require knowledge of calculation methods for high-intensity strobes. In addition, the calculations require knowledge of the test standards used to evaluate and list the appliance.

18.5.1* Visible Signaling. Public mode visible signaling shall meet the requirements of Section 18.5 using visible notification appliances.

A.18.5.1 There are two methods of visible signaling. These are methods in which notification of an emergency condition is conveyed by direct viewing of the illuminating appliance or by means of illumination of the surrounding area.

Visible notification appliances used in the public mode must be located and must be of a type, size, intensity, and number so that the operating effect of the appliance is seen by the intended viewers regardless of the viewer's orientation.

In the same manner that signals produced by audible notification appliances must be clearly heard, the signals produced by visible notification appliances must be clearly seen without regard to the viewer's position within the protected area, as noted in A.18.5.1. This does not mean that an appliance must be seen from any location in a space but rather that the operating effect must be seen. For example, if a single visible notification appliance in an L-shaped area is properly located and sized, the visible appliance may not be seen from all parts of the room, but the flash from the appliance will be seen. Also note that there is no requirement to

Excerpts from Americans with Disabilities Act (ADA) and Architectural Barriers Act (ABA) Accessibility Guidelines for Buildings and Facilities

Published in the *Federal Register* July 23, 2004 and amended August 5, 2005.

-----------ADA APPLICATION AND SCOPING (excerpts)-----------

105 Referenced Standards

105.2.5 NFPA. Copies of the referenced standards may be obtained from the National Fire Protection Association, 1 Batterymarch Park, Quincy, Massachusetts 02169-7471, (http://www.nfpa.org).

NFPA 72 National Fire Alarm Code, 1999 Edition (see 702.1 and 809.5.2).

NFPA 72 National Fire Alarm Code, 2002 Edition (see 702.1 and 809.5.2).

> Advisory 105.2.5 NFPA. NFPA 72-1999 and NFPA 72-2002 address the application, installation, performance, and maintenance of protective signaling systems and their components. The NFPA 72 incorporates Underwriters Laboratory (UL) 1971 by reference. The standard specifies the characteristics of audible alarms, such as placement and sound levels. However, Section 702 of these requirements limits the volume of an audible alarm to 110 dBA, rather than the maximum 120 dBA permitted by NFPA 72-1999.
>
> NFPA 72 specifies characteristics for visible alarms, such as flash frequency, color, intensity, placement, and synchronization. However, Section 702 of this document requires that visual alarm appliances be permanently installed. UL 1971 specifies intensity dispersion requirements for visible alarms. In particular, NFPA 72 requires visible alarms to have a light source that is clear or white and has polar dispersion complying with UL 1971.

215 Fire Alarm Systems

215.1 General. Where fire alarm systems provide audible alarm coverage, alarms shall comply with 215.

EXCEPTION: In existing facilities, visible alarms shall not be required except where an existing fire alarm system is upgraded or replaced, or a new fire alarm system is installed.

> Advisory 215.1 General. Unlike audible alarms, visible alarms must be located within the space they serve so that the signal is visible. Facility alarm systems (other than fire alarm systems) such as those used for tornado warnings and other emergencies are not required to comply with the technical criteria for alarms in Section 702. Every effort should be made to ensure that such alarms can be differentiated in their signal from fire alarms systems and that people who need to be notified of emergencies are adequately safeguarded. Consult local fire departments and prepare evacuation plans taking into consideration the needs of every building occupant, including people with disabilities.

215.2 Public and Common Use Areas. Alarms in public use areas and common use areas shall comply with 702.

215.3 Employee Work Areas. Where employee work areas have audible alarm coverage, the wiring system shall be designed so that visible alarms complying with 702 can be integrated into the alarm system.

215.4 Transient Lodging. Guest rooms required to comply with 224.4 shall provide alarms complying with 702.

215.5 Residential Facilities. Where provided in residential dwelling units required to comply with 809.5, alarms shall comply with 702.

-----------ABA APPLICATION AND SCOPING (excerpts)-----------

F105 Referenced Standards

F105.2.5 NFPA. Copies of the referenced standards may be obtained from the National Fire Protection Association, 1 Batterymarch Park, Quincy, Massachusetts 02169-7471, (http://www.nfpa.org).

NFPA 72 National Fire Alarm Code, 1999 Edition (see 702.1 and 809.5.2).

NFPA 72 National Fire Alarm Code, 2002 Edition (see 702.1 and 809.5.2).

> Advisory F105.2.5 NFPA. NFPA 72-1999 and NFPA 72-2002 address the application, installation, performance, and maintenance of protective signaling systems and their components. The NFPA 72 incorporates Underwriters Laboratory (UL) 1971 by reference. The standard specifies the characteristics of audible alarms, such as placement and sound levels. However, Section 702 of these requirements limits the volume of an audible alarm to 110 dBA, rather than the maximum 120 dBA permitted by NFPA 72-1999.
>
> NFPA 72 specifies characteristics for visible alarms, such as flash frequency, color, intensity, placement, and synchronization. However, Section 702 of this document requires that visual alarm appliances be permanently installed. UL 1971 specifies intensity dispersion requirements for visible alarms. In particular, NFPA 72 requires visible alarms to have a light source that is clear or white and has polar dispersion complying with UL 1971.

F215 Fire Alarm Systems

F215.1 General. Where fire alarm systems provide audible alarm coverage, alarms shall comply with F215.

EXCEPTION: In existing facilities, visible alarms shall not be required except where an existing fire alarm system is upgraded or replaced, or a new fire alarm system is installed.

> Advisory F215.1 General. Unlike audible alarms, visible alarms must be located within the space they serve so that the signal is visible. Facility alarm systems (other than fire alarm systems) such as those used for tornado warnings and other emergencies are not required to comply with the technical criteria for alarms in Section 702. Every effort should be made to ensure that such alarms can be differentiated in their signal from fire alarms systems and that people who need to be notified of emergencies are adequately safeguarded. Consult local fire departments and prepare evacuation plans taking into consideration the needs of every building occupant, including people with disabilities

------------------TECHNICAL CHAPTERS (excerpt)------------------

702 Fire Alarm Systems

702.1 General. Fire alarm systems shall have permanently installed audible and visible alarms complying with NFPA 72 (1999 or 2002 edition) (incorporated by reference, see "Referenced Standards" in Chapter 1), except that the maximum allowable sound level of audible notification appliances complying with section 4-3.2.1 of NFPA 72 (1999 edition) shall have a sound level no more than 110 dB at the minimum hearing distance from the audible appliance. In addition, alarms in guest rooms required to provide communication features shall comply with sections 4-3 and 4-4 of NFPA 72 (1999 edition) or sections 7.4 and 7.5 of NFPA 72 (2002 edition).

EXCEPTION: Fire alarm systems in medical care facilities shall be permitted to be provided in accordance with industry practice.

EXHIBIT 18.14 *Excerpts from the ADA and ABA Accessibility Guidelines.*

place an appliance so that it can be directly viewed by the majority of occupants or by any occupant in particular.

18.5.2 Light, Color, and Pulse Characteristics.

18.5.2.1 The flash rate shall not exceed two flashes per second (2 Hz) nor be less than one flash every second (1 Hz) throughout the listed voltage range of the appliance.

18.5.2.2 A maximum pulse duration shall be 0.2 second with a maximum duty cycle of 40 percent.

18.5.2.3 The pulse duration shall be defined as the time interval between initial and final points of 10 percent of maximum signal.

The light intensity of a pulsed source can be graphed as a curve ascending to a peak and then decaying. The duration of the pulse as defined in 18.5.2.3 is measured beginning at the point where the upward side of the curve exceeds 10 percent of the maximum intensity to the point where the downward side of the curve drops below 10 percent of the maximum intensity. See Exhibit 18.15 for an example of a graph showing these phenomena. While an actual appliance output curve might be shaped differently, the exhibit illustrates the general concept.

EXHIBIT 18.15 *Peak Versus Effective Intensity. (Source: R. P. Schifiliti Associates, Inc., Reading, MA)*

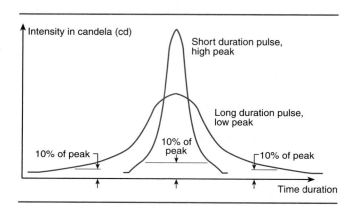

18.5.2.4* Lights used for fire alarm signaling only or to signal the intent for complete evacuation shall be clear or nominal white and shall not exceed 1000 cd (effective intensity).

A.18.5.2.4 Effective intensity is the conventional method of equating the brightness of a flashing light to that of a steady-burning light as seen by a human observer. The units of effective intensity are expressed in candelas (or candlepower, which is equivalent to candelas). For example, a flashing light that has an effective intensity of 15 cd has the same apparent brightness to an observer as a 15 cd steady-burning light source.

Measurement of effective intensity is usually done in a laboratory using specialized photometric equipment. Accurate field measurement of effective intensity is not practical. Other units of measure for the intensity of flashing lights, such as peak candela or flash energy, do not correlate directly to effective intensity and are not used in this standard.

Strobe lights might be used to signal fire or other emergencies and might be intended to initiate evacuation, relocation, or some other behavior. Lights intended to initiate evacuation due to fire are required by the Code to be clear or white. Colored lights, such as amber/yellow lights, might be used in a combination system for any emergency (fire, bomb, chemical, weather, etc.) when the intent is for the signal recipient to seek additional information from other sources (voice, text displays, and so on).

Example Scenario 1: A building has a fire alarm system used for general evacuation. A separate mass notification system is used to provide voice instructions and information in the event of non-fire emergencies. The fire alarm system would have white/clear strobes intended to alert occupants of the need to evacuate. The mass notification system would have amber/yellow strobes that are intended to signal the need to get additional information from either audible voice announcements, text or graphical displays, or other information sources controlled or operated from the mass notification system. In the event that both systems are activated at the same time, the strobes should be synchronized per 18.5.4.3.2.

Example Scenario 2: A building has a mass notification system that provides information and instructions for a variety of emergency situations, including fire. Fire alarm initiation might be by a stand-alone fire detection system or might be an integral part of the mass notification system. In the event of an emergency, textual audible appliances are used to provide information. Visible alerting could be accomplished using one set of clear or colored strobes to indicate the need to get additional information. Visible textual information can be provided by text or graphic display or other visible information appliances. The content of the audible and visible messages will vary depending on the emergency.

Source intensity is a measure of the light output of the appliance. As noted in A.18.5.2.4, the unit of measure is the candela (cd). (This unit was formerly called candlepower. There is a one-to-one relationship between candela and candlepower.) As you move away from any light source, its illumination decreases. Illumination is measured in units of lumens per square foot or lumens (lm) per square meter (also called lux). [Formerly, the unit used to describe illumination was the footcandle — 1 footcandle = 1 lm/ft^2 (0.0926 footcandle = 1 lm/m^2)]. See Exhibit 18.16 for graphic definitions of these terms and a mathematical relationship showing their use.

Because strobe lights flash very briefly, the perceived brightness can vary depending on the actual peak source strength and the duration of the flash. Whereas one appliance might reach a peak intensity of 1000 cd in 0.1 second and another 750 cd in 0.2 second, the human eye might perceive both as being equally bright. A mathematical relationship is used to relate the perceived brightness of a strobe light to that of a constantly burning light. The result is called the effective intensity (candela effective, or cd eff.).

◀ **FAQ**
What is source intensity?

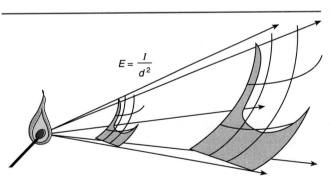

$$E = \frac{I}{d^2}$$

EXHIBIT 18.16 *Definitions of Light Source, Intensity, and Illumination. (Source: R. P. Schifiliti Associates, Inc., Reading, MA)*

E = illumination [1 lumen/ft^2 or 1 footcandle (1 lumen/m^2 or 1 lux or 0.0926 footcandle)]

I = intensity of source (1 cd or 12.57 lumens)

d = distance from source to object (ft or m)

18.5.2.5 Lights used to signal occupants to seek information or instructions shall be clear, nominal white, or other color as required by the emergency plan and the authority having jurisdiction for the area or building.

As required by 18.3.3.2, notification appliances used for signaling other than fire cannot be labeled with the word "FIRE" or with any fire symbol, in any form. An ECS may use the same appliances for signaling both fire and other emergencies. Some ECSs may use multiple visible appliances. In that case, one visible appliance would be labeled "FIRE" and would be used to signal the need for immediate evacuation, and another visible appliance would be used during more complex situations to signal the need for occupants to get additional information from other sources. There is some flexibility in Chapter 24 as to how visible appliances are to be used with ECSs. Unfortunately, visible appliance use in mass notification systems do not provide enough information for the hearing impaired to take appropriate action. Textual graphic or video displays can be used to serve that purpose.

The Technical Committee on Notification Appliances for Fire Alarm Systems chose to require clear or nominal white for fire alarm signaling only or when the intent is for complete evacuation. Where visible notification appliances are intended to elicit a different response, other colors are permitted, although clear or nominal white is still permitted provided the intent is clarified by the emergency plan. Signage and training of regular occupants might be necessary. The use of different types or colors of visible notification appliances on a system to influence occupant behavior should be carefully considered but might be advisable only where the occupants are not transient and are well trained and drilled in the required response.

18.5.2.6* The strobe synchronization requirements of this chapter shall not apply where the visible notification appliances located inside the building are viewed from outside of the building.

A.18.5.2.6 It is not the intent to establish viewing and synchronization requirements for viewing locations outdoors. As an example, there is no need for floor No. 1 to be synchronized with floor No. 2 if there is no visible coupling as in an atrium.

Studies have shown that the effect of strobes on photosensitive epilepsy lessens with distance and viewing angle.

As long as the composite flash rate is no greater than that produced by two listed strobes as allowed by 18.5.4.3.2, compliance is achieved.

Example: A ballroom has multiple synchronized strobes operating during an emergency, the doors exiting the ballroom are opened, and the strobes outside in the lobby and corridor are also operating. The strobes in the corridor and lobby are synchronized with each other, but the strobes outside the ballroom are not synchronized with the strobes inside the ballroom. This would be an acceptable application because the composite flash rate does not exceed that allowed by 18.5.4.3.2.

18.5.3* Appliance Photometrics. The light output shall comply with the polar dispersion requirements of ANSI/UL 1971, *Standard for Signaling Devices for the Hearing Impaired*, or equivalent.

FAQ ▶
Why are the polar dispersion characteristics of visible appliances important?

The polar dispersion characteristics of the appliance are very important for compliance with Chapter 18, because the effectiveness of visible signaling is based on tests in which the viewers responded to the illumination of their surroundings. Thus, it is important that the appliance produces a pattern of light on adjacent surfaces, such as walls, floors, desks, and so forth. Appliances listed to standards other than ANSI/UL 1971 and not having specified polar dispersion requirements might produce most of their light on axis and very little down or off to the side. Thus, the appliance might not produce a noticeable pattern sufficient to alert occupants.

A.18.5.3 The prescriptive requirements of Section 18.5 assume the use of appliances having very specific characteristics of light color, intensity, distribution, and so on. The appliance and application requirements are based on extensive research. However, the research was limited to typical residential and commercial applications such as school classrooms, offices, hallways, and hotel rooms. While these specific appliances and applications will likely work in other spaces, their use might not be the most effective solution and might not be as reliable as other visible notification methods.

For example, in large warehouse spaces and large distribution spaces such as super stores, it is possible to provide visible signaling using the appliances and applications of this chapter. However, mounting strobe lights at a height of 80 in. to 96 in. (2.03 m to 2.44 m) along aisles with rack storage subjects the lights to frequent mechanical damage by forklift trucks and stock. Also, the number of appliances required would be very high. It might be possible to use other appliances and applications not specifically addressed by this chapter at this time. Alternative applications must be carefully engineered for reliability and function and would require permission of the authority having jurisdiction.

Tests of a system in large warehouse/super stores designed using the prescriptive approach of 18.5.4.3 showed that high ambient light levels resulted in both indirect and direct signaling effects. The signal-to-noise ratio produced by the operating visible notification appliances was low in many locations. However, with visible notification appliances located over the aisles or unobstructed by stock, indirect and some direct notification was sometimes achieved. Direct notification occurs even when occupants do not look up toward the ceiling-mounted visible notification appliances due to the extended cone of vision shown in Figure A.18.5.3(a). The visible notification appliance intensity and spacing resulting from the prescriptive design was generally sufficient for occupant notification by a combination of direct and indirect signaling. Testing showed that the best performance was achieved where visible notification appliances were directly over aisles or where visible notification appliances in adjacent aisles were not obstructed by stock. The performance-based design method will almost always result in aisles not having a line of visible notification appliances in them, because the spacing of visible notification appliances can be greater than the spacing of aisles. Also, it is recognized that aisles might be relocated after installation of the system. Good design practice is to place visible notification appliances over aisles, especially those that are likely to remain unchanged such as main aisles, and over checkout areas. Where reorganization of aisles results in visible notification appliances not in or over an aisle, or where that is the base design, it is important to have a clear view from that aisle to a nearby visible notification appliance. See Figure A.18.5.3(b). Some spaces might have marginal visible notification appliance effect (direct or indirect). However, occupants in these large stores and storage occupancies move frequently and place themselves in a position where they receive notification via the visible notification appliances. In addition, complete synchronization of the visible notification appliances in the space produced a desirable effect.

Visible notification using the methods contained in 18.5.4.3 is achieved by indirect signaling. This means the viewer need not actually see the appliance, just the effect of the appliance. This can be achieved by producing minimum illumination on surfaces near the appliance, such as the floor, walls, and desks. There must be a sufficient change in illumination to be noticeable. The tables and charts in Section 18.5 specify a certain candela-effective light intensity for certain size spaces. The data were based on extensive research and testing. Appliances do not typically produce the same light intensity when measured off-axis. To ensure that the appliance produces the desired illumination (effect), it must have some distribution of light intensity to the areas surrounding the appliance. ANSI/UL 1971, *Standard for Signaling Devices for the Hearing Impaired*, specifies the distribution of light shown to provide effective notification by indirect visible signaling.

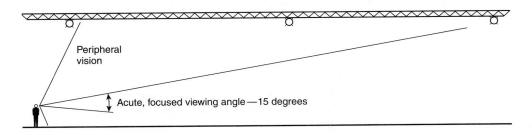

FIGURE A.18.5.3(a) *Extended Cone of Vision. (Courtesy of R. P. Schifiliti Associates, Inc.)*

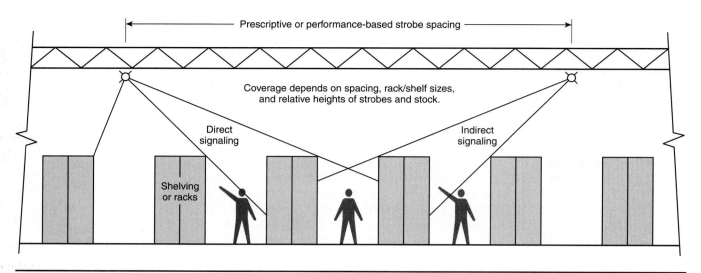

FIGURE A.18.5.3(b) *Visible Notification Appliances in Stores. (Courtesy of R. P. Schifiliti Associates, Inc.)*

The technical committee added discussion and examples of possible visible signaling methods in large warehouse-type spaces. These guidelines are based on testing done under a grant from the Fire Protection Research Foundation (*www.rpsa-fire.com/strobeproject*).

18.5.4 Appliance Location.

18.5.4.1* Wall-mounted appliances shall be mounted such that the entire lens is not less than 80 in. (2.03 m) and not greater than 96 in. (2.44 m) above the finished floor or at the mounting height specified using the performance-based alternative of 18.5.4.5.

A.18.5.4.1 The requirements for the location of appliances within a building or structure are intended to apply to strobe lights applied in accordance with 18.5.4.3, 18.5.4.4, and 18.5.4.6. The mounting and location of appliances installed using the performance-based alternative of 18.5.4.5 can be located differently, provided they meet the intended performance requirements. Other appliances, such as graphic displays, video screens, and so on, should be located so that they meet their intended performance.

Where low ceiling heights or other conditions do not permit mounting at a minimum of 80 in. (2.03 m), visible appliances can be mounted at a lower height. However, lowering the mounting height reduces the area of coverage for that strobe. The performance-based methods of 18.5.4.5 can be used to determine the area of coverage. Strobe light mounting height should not be lowered below the plane of normal human viewing [approximately 5 ft (1.5 m)] except where ceiling heights limit the mounting position.

The mounting height requirement of 80 in. to 96 in. (2.03 m to 2.44 m) does not address the possibility of conditions where ceiling heights are less than 80 in. (2.03 m). The range that is permitted [80 in. to 96 in. (2.03 m to 2.44 m)] ensures that strobes are not mounted too high, which would result in lower levels of illumination on surrounding walls and on the floor. The lower limit of the range ensures that a minimum percentage of the surrounding surfaces is illuminated and that the top of the illuminated pattern is at or above the plane of normal human viewing [approximately 5 ft (1.5 m)]. Wall mounting of strobe lights, which are listed only for wall mounting, can result in little or no illumination above the plane of the strobe light. In the case of lower ceiling heights and mounting close to the ceiling, the level of illumination on the floor and surrounding walls is not reduced but the walls have a near 100 percent illuminated or "painted" area because the strobe is close to the ceiling. That is, there is little or no wall surface above the plane of the strobe that is not illuminated when the strobe is mounted close to the ceiling. Thus, when a strobe is mounted lower than the minimum [80 in. (2.03 m)] but still close to the ceiling, the only loss of signal is the smaller pattern produced on the horizontal plane (floor).

In the case where the only change is a lower mounting height due to a lower ceiling height, the room size covered by a strobe of a given value should be reduced by twice the difference between the minimum mounting height of 80 in. (2.03 m) and the actual, lower mounting height. For example, if a 15 cd effective strobe that normally covers a 20 ft (6.1 m) square space is being used and the height of the space is 63 in. (1.6 m) and the strobe is mounted at 59 in. (1.5 m), the strobe can only cover a 16.5 ft (5.03 m) square space: 20 ft − 2 (80 in. − 59 in.) (1 ft/12 in.) = 16.5 ft (5.03 m).

The room size reduction assumes that the horizontal pattern on each side of the strobe is reduced by the same amount that the strobe height is reduced.

18.5.4.2 Where low ceiling heights do not permit mounting at a minimum of 80 in. (2.03 m), visible appliances shall be mounted within 6 in. (150 mm) of the ceiling. The room size covered by a strobe of a given value shall be reduced by twice the difference between the minimum mounting height of 80 in. (2.03 m) and the actual, lower mounting height.

In rooms with sufficient ceiling height, the entire lens of the visible appliance must be at least 80 in. (2.03 m) above the floor but not more than 96 in. (2.44 m) above the floor.

The minimum mounting height is intended to locate appliances so they are not blocked by common furnishings or equipment and, more important, to ensure a light pattern large enough to cover the intended space. The maximum mounting height is important because the illumination from a visible appliance reduces drastically with distance and angle from a horizontal plane through the appliance. Proof of this reduction can be determined by the mathematical relationship in Exhibit 18.16.

◄ **FAQ**
What is the purpose of the minimum and maximum mounting heights for wall-mounted visible notification appliances?

For this reason, wall-mounted appliances are limited by 18.5.4 such that the entire lens is not less than 80 in. (2.03 m) and not more than 96 in. (2.44 m) above the floor. Ceiling mounting is permitted; however, the appliances must be specifically listed for ceiling mounting. See also A.18.5.

Where low ceilings do not permit wall-mounted appliances to be installed within the specified range, 18.5.4.2 has a method to alter the allowable coverage based on the actual mounting height. The allowance for lower ceiling heights is illustrated in the fourth paragraph of A.18.5.4.1.

In many cases, an authority having jurisdiction has required a contractor to relocate appliances that were mounted 1 or 2 inches lower or higher than the height listed in 18.5.4.1. However, it is important to remember that where a dimension is listed in inches, the intended precision is 1 inch (see A.1.6.5). For that reason, there is room for small errors. Also, it is permitted to use 18.5.4.2 and 18.5.4.5 to show that a different mounting height, whether intentional or accidental, still meets the Code's intent.

18.5.4.3* Spacing in Rooms.

A.18.5.4.3 The strobe intensities listed in Table 18.5.4.3.1(a) or Table 18.5.4.3.1(b), 18.5.4.4, Table 18.5.4.6.2 or determined in accordance with the performance requirements of 18.5.4.5 are the minimum required intensities. It is acceptable to use a higher intensity strobe in lieu of the minimum required intensity.

Areas large enough to exceed the rectangular dimensions given in Figure A.18.5.4.3(a) through Figure A.18.5.4.3(c) require additional appliances. Often, proper placement of appliances can be facilitated by breaking down the area into multiple squares and dimensions that fit most appropriately [see Figure A.18.5.4.3(a) through Figure A.18.5.4.3(d)]. An area that is 40 ft (12.2 m) wide and 80 ft (24.4 m) long can be covered with two 60 cd appliances. Irregular areas and areas with dividers or partitions need more careful planning to make certain that at least one 15 cd appliance is installed for each 20 ft × 20 ft (6.1 m × 6.1 m) area and that light from the appliance is not blocked.

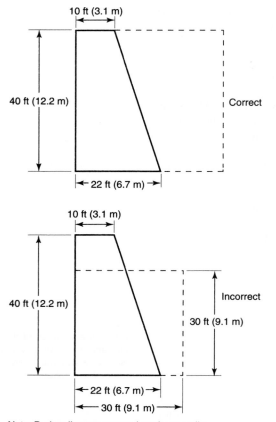

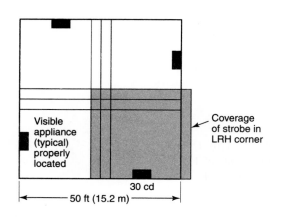

Note: Broken lines represent imaginary walls.

FIGURE A.18.5.4.3(a) *Irregular Area Spacing.*

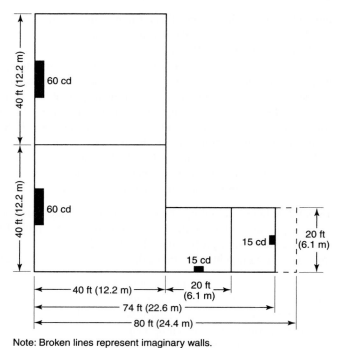

Note: Broken lines represent imaginary walls.

FIGURE A.18.5.4.3(b) *Spacing of Wall-Mounted Visible Appliances in Rooms.*

FIGURE A.18.5.4.3(c) *Room Spacing Allocation —*
Correct.

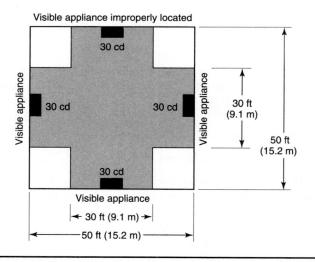

FIGURE A.18.5.4.3(d) *Room Spacing Allocation —*
Incorrect.

Figure A.18.5.4.3(a) through Figure A.18.5.4.3(d) help to avoid misinterpretation of the text. Figure A.18.5.4.3(a) demonstrates how a nonsquare or nonrectangular room can be fitted into the spacing allocation of Table 18.5.4.3.1(a) and Table 18.5.4.3.1(b). Figure A.18.5.4.3(b) demonstrates how to divide a room or area into smaller areas to enable the use of lower intensity visible notification appliances. Figure A.18.5.4.3(c) and Figure A.18.5.4.3(d) show the correct and incorrect placement of multiple visible notification appliances in a room.

Table 18.5.4.3.1(a) for wall mounting of visible notification appliances was expanded and edited for the 2002 edition and again for the 2007 edition. In 2002, entries were added for commonly manufactured strobe intensities, and the entry for a 30 ft square room was modified to correct a rounding error. In 2007, entries were made in the column for four lights per room where the table previously listed "unknown."

Note that the historical record is incomplete concerning the development of table entries for multiple visible notification appliances in a room, ceiling appliances, and the use of visible notification appliances to cover square spaces without bounding (reflecting) walls. For that reason, the technical committee in the past chose to not add entries for two and four lights per room. In the 2007 edition, the committee added the entries for the four lights per room column by assuming that the large space was divided into four imaginary parts. See also 18.5.4.5.2 and associated commentary.

18.5.4.3.1 Spacing shall be in accordance with either Table 18.5.4.3.1(a) and Figure 18.5.4.3.1 or Table 18.5.4.3.1(b).

18.5.4.3.2 Visible notification appliances shall be installed in accordance with Table 18.5.4.3.1(a) or Table 18.5.4.3.1(b) using one of the following:

(1) A single visible notification appliance
(2) Two visible notification appliances located on opposite walls

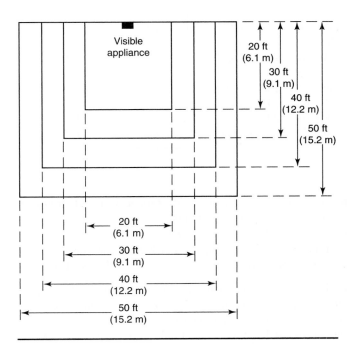

FIGURE 18.5.4.3.1 *Room Spacing for Wall-Mounted Visible Appliances.*

TABLE 18.5.4.3.1(a) *Room Spacing for Wall-Mounted Visible Appliances*

Maximum Room Size		Minimum Required Light Output [Effective Intensity (cd)]		
			Two Lights per Room (Located on Opposite Walls)	Four Lights per Room (One Light per Wall)
ft	m	One Light per Room		
20 × 20	6.10 × 6.10	15	NA	NA
28 × 28	8.53 × 8.53	30	Unknown	NA
30 × 30	9.14 × 9.14	34	15	NA
40 × 40	12.2 × 12.2	60	30	15
45 × 45	13.7 × 13.7	75	Unknown	19
50 × 50	15.2 × 15.2	94	60	30
54 × 54	16.5 × 16.5	110	Unknown	30
55 × 55	16.8 × 16.8	115	Unknown	28
60 × 60	18.3 × 18.3	135	95	30
63 × 63	19.2 × 19.2	150	Unknown	37
68 × 68	20.7 × 20.7	177	Unknown	43
70 × 70	21.3 × 21.3	184	95	60
80 × 80	24.4 × 24.4	240	135	60
90 × 90	27.4 × 27.4	304	185	95
100 × 100	30.5 × 30.5	375	240	95
110 × 110	33.5 × 33.5	455	240	135
120 × 120	36.6 × 36.6	540	305	135
130 × 130	39.6 × 39.6	635	375	185

NA: Not allowable.

TABLE 18.5.4.3.1(b) *Room Spacing for Ceiling-Mounted Visible Appliances*

Maximum Room Size		Maximum Lens Height		Minimum Required Light Output (Effective Intensity); One Light (cd)
ft	m	ft	m	
20 × 20	6.1 × 6.1	10	3.0	15
30 × 30	9.1 × 9.1	10	3.0	30
40 × 40	12.2 × 12.2	10	3.0	60
44 × 44	13.4 × 13.4	10	3.0	75
50 × 50	15.2 × 15.2	10	3.0	95
53 × 53	16.2 × 16.2	10	3.0	110
55 × 55	16.8 × 16.8	10	3.0	115
59 × 59	18.0 × 18.0	10	3.0	135
63 × 63	19.2 × 19.2	10	3.0	150
68 × 68	20.7 × 20.7	10	3.0	177
70 × 70	21.3 × 21.3	10	3.0	185
20 × 20	6.1 × 6.1	20	6.1	30
30 × 30	9.1 × 9.1	20	6.1	45
44 × 44	13.4 × 13.4	20	6.1	75
46 × 46	14.0 × 14.0	20	6.1	80
50 × 50	15.2 × 15.2	20	6.1	95
53 × 53	16.2 × 16.2	20	6.1	110
55 × 55	16.8 × 16.8	20	6.1	115
59 × 59	18.0 × 18.0	20	6.1	135
63 × 63	19.2 × 19.2	20	6.1	150
68 × 68	20.7 × 20.7	20	6.1	177
70 × 70	21.3 × 21.3	20	6.1	185
20 × 20	6.1 × 6.1	30	9.1	55
30 × 30	9.1 × 9.1	30	9.1	75
50 × 50	15.2 × 15.2	30	9.1	95
53 × 53	16.2 × 16.2	30	9.1	110
55 × 55	16.8 × 16.8	30	9.1	115
59 × 59	18.0 × 18.0	30	9.1	135
63 × 63	19.2 × 19.2	30	9.1	150
68 × 68	20.7 × 20.7	30	9.1	177
70 × 70	21.3 × 21.3	30	9.1	185

(3)* Two groups of visible notification appliances, where visual appliances of each group are synchronized, in the same room or adjacent space within the field of view. This shall include synchronization of strobes operated by separate systems

(4) More than two visible notification appliances or groups of synchronized appliances in the same room or adjacent space within the field of view that flash in synchronization

A.18.5.4.3.2(3) The field of view is based on the focusing capability of the human eye specified as 120 degrees in the *Illuminating Engineering Society (IES) Lighting Handbook Reference and Application*. The apex of this angle is the viewer's eye. In order to ensure compliance with the requirements of 18.5.4.3.2, this angle should be increased to approximately 135 degrees.

Testing has shown that high flash rates of high-intensity strobe lights can pose a potential risk of seizure to people with photosensitive epilepsy. To reduce this risk, more than two visible appliances are not permitted in any field of view unless their flashes are synchronized. This does not preclude synchronization of appliances that are not within the same field of view.

In 1996, the Code was modified to reduce the chances that visible notification appliances would induce seizures in persons with photosensitive epilepsy. The flash rate was adjusted so that two appliances (or groups of synchronized appliances) not flashing in unison cannot produce a flash rate that is considered dangerous. If more than two appliances or groups of synchronized appliances can be viewed at the same time, they must be synchronized. The option of spacing more than two appliances a minimum of 55 ft (16.8) apart in large rooms in lieu of synchronization is no longer permitted by the Code. In 2007, the intent was clarified by noting that groups or zones of visible notification appliances may be synchronized and that it is the perceived composite flash rate that is important.

Prior to the 1999 edition, the table corresponding to the current Table 18.5.4.3.1(a) did not permit more than two visible notification appliances in a room unless the room was at least 80 ft × 80 ft (24.4 m × 24.4 m), even if they were synchronized. Since the 1999 edition, the use of more than two visible notification appliances in any size space is permitted, provided they are synchronized.

In the 2010 edition, 18.5.4.3.2 has been revised to include reference to ceiling-mounted visible notification appliances. In prior editions, the missing reference could have been interpreted to not require ceiling-mounted visible notification appliances to be synchronized, even though the technical committee did intend that they be synchronized.

Because visible signaling is a complex topic, the Code presents prescriptive requirements rather than performance requirements, such as those for audible signaling. In essence, the Code provides preset designs that can be used for a variety of actual field conditions requiring these appliances. The prescriptive requirements contained in the Code are based, in part, on tests performed by Underwriters Laboratories Inc. in developing ANSI/UL 1971. Paragraph 18.5.4.5 contains a performance-based method for determining visible notification appliance coverage that is actually more stringent when compared with Table 18.5.4.3.1(a) and Table 18.5.4.3.1(b).

A visible notification appliance intensity greater than that specified for a certain room size is permitted, provided the limit of 18.5.2.4 is not exceeded.

18.5.4.3.3 Room spacing in accordance with Table 18.5.4.3.1(a) and Figure 18.5.4.3.1 for wall-mounted appliances shall be based on locating the visible notification appliance at the halfway distance of the wall.

18.5.4.3.4 In square rooms with appliances not centered or in nonsquare rooms, the effective intensity (cd) from one visible wall-mounted notification appliance shall be determined by maximum room size dimensions obtained either by measuring the distance to the farthest wall or by doubling the distance to the farthest adjacent wall, whichever is greater, as required by Table 18.5.4.3.1(a) and Figure 18.5.4.3.1.

18.5.4.3.5 If a room configuration is not square, the square room size that allows the entire room to be encompassed or allows the room to be subdivided into multiple squares shall be used.

Figure 18.5.4.3.1, Tables 18.5.4.3.1(a), and Table 18.5.4.3.1(b) help to ensure that a sufficient number of properly sized visible notification appliances are installed in each protected space to provide complete coverage. The key to proper coverage in irregular spaces is to divide the space into a series of squares and provide proper coverage for each square as if it were an independent space. Exhibit 18.17 illustrates this concept. Synchronization might be required per 18.5.4.3.2. The practice of using multiple visible notification appliances per room has been permitted by the Code since the visible notification appliance tables were first added in 1993. However, for additional insight comparing the prescriptive requirements of these tables

◄ **FAQ**
What method can be used to provide proper coverage for irregular spaces?

EXHIBIT 18.17 Irregular Floor Plan Showing Notification Appliances for Required Locations.

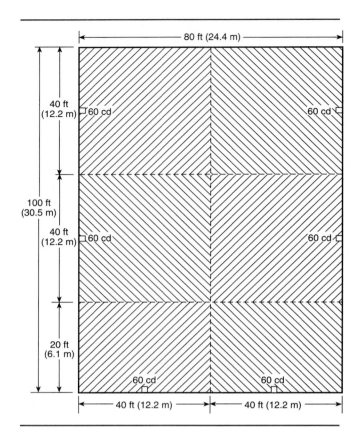

with the performance requirements now addressed in the Code, see 18.5.4.5.2 and associated commentary.

18.5.4.3.6* If ceiling heights exceed 30 ft (9.14 m), ceiling-mounted visible notification appliances shall be suspended at or below 30 ft (9.14 m) or at the mounting height determined using the performance-based alternative of 18.5.4.5, or wall-mounted visible notification appliances shall be installed in accordance with Table 18.5.4.3.1(a).

A.18.5.4.3.6 This subsection is also intended to permit ceiling-mounted strobes to be suspended below the ceiling, provided the strobe height is not below the viewing plane for any ceiling height.

The Code currently does not have guidance or requirements for spaces with high ceilings. In some high-ceiling spaces, such as a gymnasium or a large atrium, suspending or wall mounting appliances in accordance with the prescriptive requirements of the Code might not be feasible. Performance-based calculations or alternative methods for notification might need to be considered. Examples of alternatives are high-intensity revolving beacons, high-intensity indirect viewing appliances, or even the flashing of some or all of the building lights. One study showed that flashing only 20 percent of the lights in an office space would result in 100 percent alerting of persons who are not blind. Most of these methods are not yet recognized by the Code because the technical committees have not seen test data to support their use or because of other potential issues of reliability and use. Nevertheless, careful engineering might show these methods to be effective and more reliable than suspending standard appliances from the ceiling or wall mounting them in large congested spaces, such as warehouse stores or convention halls. Some methods, such as the use of building lighting systems, might use circuits that are not directly monitored for integrity. However, the large number of lighting units versus the number required for effective alerting combined with the use of branch circuits and daily operation might actually result in higher overall system availability and reliability. In applying alternative methods, the requirements of Section 1.5 must be observed.

Another possible solution for high-ceiling spaces is a performance-based design using a combination of direct and indirect signaling as described in A.18.5.3 for warehouse-type spaces.

Paragraph 18.5.4.3.6 was revised in the 2010 edition to clarify that performance-based methods are permitted for horizontally mounted visible notification appliances. The text is intended to allow visible notification appliances to be mounted at any height above the floor even if the appliance is below the ceiling. See Exhibit 18.18.

EXHIBIT 18.18 *Visible Notification Appliance Suspended Below a Ceiling. (Source: R. P. Schifiliti Associates, Inc., Reading, MA)*

18.5.4.3.7 Table 18.5.4.3.1(b) shall be used if the ceiling-mounted visible notification appliance is at the center of the room. If the ceiling-mounted visible notification appliance is not located at the center of the room, the effective intensity (cd) shall be determined by doubling the distance from the appliance to the farthest wall to obtain the maximum room size.

18.5.4.4* Spacing in Corridors.

A.18.5.4.4 Because the occupants are usually alert and moving, and because their vision is focused by the narrowness of the space, corridor signaling is permitted to be by direct viewing of lower-intensity (15 cd) appliances. That is, the alerting is intended to be done by direct viewing of the strobe, not necessarily by its reflection off of surfaces (indirect viewing) as required for rooms in 18.5.4.3.

Note that it is acceptable to use 18.5.4.3 (Spacing in Rooms) to determine the number and location of strobes in corridors. If 18.5.4.3 is used, it is not necessary to have a corridor strobe within 15 ft (4.5 m) of the end of the corridor.

See Figure A.18.5.4.4 for corridor spacing for visible appliances.

18.5.4.4.1 The installation of visible notification appliances in corridors 20 ft (6.1 m) or less in width shall be in accordance with the requirements of either 18.5.4.3 or 18.5.4.4.

The allowance to use the more stringent requirements of indirect signaling for corridor applications in lieu of the requirements of 18.5.4.4 was included in the 2002 edition. In the 2007 edition, this allowance was relocated to the beginning of 18.5.4.4 to emphasize that alternative methods are acceptable.

18.5.4.4.2 Paragraph 18.5.4.4 shall apply to corridors not exceeding 20 ft (6.1 m) in width.

18.5.4.4.3 In a corridor application, visible appliances shall be rated not less than 15 cd.

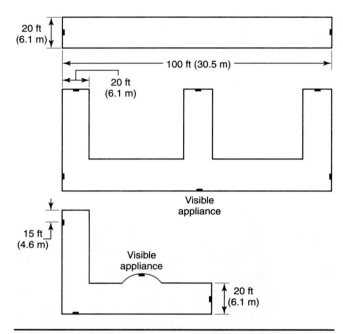

FIGURE A.18.5.4.4 *Corridor Spacing for Visible Appliances.*

18.5.4.4.4 Corridors greater than 20 ft (6.1 m) wide shall comply with the spacing requirements for rooms in accordance with 18.5.4.3.

FAQ ▶
Are the spacing requirements for corridors based on direct or indirect viewing of appliances?

The intensity and spacing requirements for visible notification appliances located in corridors less than 20 ft (6.1 m) wide are less stringent than for those in rooms and are based on direct viewing rather than indirect viewing of appliances. A person in a corridor is usually moving and alert. Because the occupants usually are alert, fewer appliances are required, which results in greater spacing in long corridors. Only 15 cd appliances are required in corridors less than 20 ft (6.1 m) wide. Corridors that are more than 20 ft (6.1 m) wide are treated the same as rooms.

18.5.4.4.5* Visible notification appliances shall be located not more than 15 ft (4.57 m) from the end of the corridor with a separation not greater than 100 ft (30.5 m) between appliances.

A.18.5.4.4.5 Visible appliances in corridors are permitted to be mounted on walls or on ceilings in accordance with 18.5.4.4. Where there are more than two appliances in a field of view, they need to be synchronized.

   Note that it is acceptable to use 18.5.4.3 (Spacing in Rooms) to determine the number and location of strobes in corridors. If 18.5.4.3 is used, it is not necessary to have a corridor strobe within 15 ft (4.5 m) of the end of the corridor. It is not the intent of this section to require strobes at or near every exit or exit access from a corridor.

   It might be possible to share notification appliances under some conditions where corridors change direction or intersect. This arrangement will result in the proper coverage with fewer appliances. See also 18.5.4.4.8.

18.5.4.4.6 If there is an interruption of the concentrated viewing path, such as a fire door, an elevation change, or any other obstruction, the area shall be treated as a separate corridor.

18.5.4.4.7 In corridors where more than two visible notification appliances are in any field of view, they shall flash in synchronization.

In most cases where room visible notification appliances are required to be synchronized and where corridor visible notification appliances require synchronization, the corridor appliances may also be synchronized with the room appliances. However, as permitted by 18.5.4.3.2(4), the overall system would be acceptable provided that the viewer does not see more than two unsynchronized *groups* of visible notification appliances, where the synchronized room appliances would be one group and the synchronized corridor appliances would be the second group.

18.5.4.4.8 Wall-mounted visible notification appliances in corridors shall be permitted to be mounted on either the end wall or the side wall of the corridor in accordance with spacing requirements of 18.5.4.4.5.

18.5.4.5* Performance-Based Alternative.

A.18.5.4.5 A design that delivers a minimum illumination of 0.0375 lumens/ft^2 (footcandles) [0.4037 lumens/m^2 (lux)] to all occupiable spaces where visible notification is required is considered to meet the minimum light intensity requirements of 18.5.4.3.2(1). This level of illumination has been shown to alert people by indirect viewing (reflected light) in a large variety of rooms with a wide range of ambient lighting conditions.

The illumination from a visible notification appliance at a particular distance is equal to the effective intensity of the appliance divided by the distance squared (the inverse square law). Table 18.5.4.3.1(a) and Table 18.5.4.3.1(b) are based on applying the inverse square law to provide an illumination of at least 0.0375 lumens/ft^2 (0.4037 lumens/m^2) throughout each room size. For example, a 60 cd effective intensity appliance in a 40 ft × 40 ft (12.2 m × 12.2 m) room produces 0.0375 lumens/ft^2 (0.4037 lumens/m^2) on the opposite wall 40 ft (12.2 m) away [60 ÷ (40 ft)^2 or (60 ÷ (12.2 m)^2)]. This same 60 cd effective intensity appliance produces 0.0375 lumens/ft^2 (0.4037 lumens/m^2) on the adjacent wall 20 ft (6.1 m) away [60 × 25% ÷ (20 ft)^2 or (60 × 25% ÷ (12.2 m)^2)] where the minimum light output of the appliance at 90 degrees off-axis is 25 percent of rated output per ANSI/UL 1971, *Standard for Safety Signaling Devices for the Hearing Impaired*. Similarly, a 110 cd strobe will produce at least 0.0375 lumens/ft^2 (0.4037 lumens/m^2) in a 54 ft × 54 ft (16.5 m × 16.5 m) room. Calculated intensities in Table 18.5.4.3.1(a) and Table 18.5.4.3.1(b) have been adjusted to standardize the intensity options of presently available products and take into account additional reflections in room corners and higher direct viewing probability when there is more than one appliance in a room.

The application of visible notification appliances in outdoor areas has not been tested and is not addressed in this standard. Visible appliances that are mounted outdoors should be listed for outdoor use (under ANSI/UL 1638, *Visual Signaling Appliances — Private Mode Emergency and General Utility Signaling*, for example) and should be located for direct viewing because reflected light will usually be greatly reduced.

The tables and charts for visible notification appliances form a prescriptive solution for visible signaling and are relatively easy to apply. The subparagraphs of 18.5.4.5 offer an alternative, performance-based method for designing visible notification systems.

18.5.4.5.1 Any design that provides a minimum of 0.0375 lumens/ft^2 (0.4036 lumens/m^2) of illumination at any point within the covered area at all angles specified by the polar dispersion planes for wall- or ceiling-mounted visual appliances in ANSI/UL 1971, *Standard for Signaling Devices for the Hearing Impaired*, or equivalent, as calculated for the maximum distance from the nearest visual notification appliance, shall be permitted in lieu of the requirements of 18.5.4, excluding 18.5.4.6.

The stated performance goal is a level of illumination equal to or greater than 0.0375 lm/ft^2 (0.4036 lm/m^2). The Code text says this level must be achieved at "any" point in the covered space. It is clear from 18.5.4.5.2(1) and 18.5.4.5.2(2) that the technical committee did not intend to mean "any one point." The minimum level of illumination applies to points within the covered area at each angle specified in the product test standard. These are the only points for which listing test data might be available for use in the calculations.

18.5.4.5.2 Documentation provided to the authority having jurisdiction shall include the following:

(1) Inverse Square Law calculations using each of the vertical and horizontal polar distribution angles in ANSI/UL 1971, *Standard for Signaling Devices for the Hearing Impaired*, or equivalent.
(2) The calculations shall account for the effects of polar distribution using one of the following:

    (a) The percentages from the applicable table(s) in ANSI/UL 1971, *Standard for Signaling Devices for the Hearing Impaired*, or equivalent
    (b) The actual results of laboratory tests of the specific appliance to be used as recorded by the listing organization

The performance objective must be achieved throughout the covered area. However, as noted in 18.5.4.5.2(1) and 18.5.4.5.2(2), proof of compliance is met by providing calculations for the space at a discrete number of points as defined by the product listing standard. One can use the minimum intensities permitted by the product standard for a given visible notification appliance rating or use actual polar dispersion intensities provided by the manufacturer. Proof of compliance is not intended to be achieved by testing at the installation site. Calculation and subsequent inspection of the installation are considered sufficient.

FAQ ▶
In applying the performance-based method of 18.5.4.5, what angles must be considered?

The required performance level must be calculated for each of the angles specified in ANSI/UL 1971 product standard. For wall-mounted units, the angles include 12 horizontal angles on the plane of the visible notification appliance, 14 vertical angles, and 2 compound angles. For a given visible notification appliance, it is possible to develop a three-dimensional shape that defines the maximum volume or space that can be covered by the appliance. However, the actual illumination of a surface requires that the illumination level be adjusted for the angle at which it strikes the surface. This angle is different from the angle at which the light ray leaves the appliance. Thus, the shape of the room (square, rectangular, etc.) will affect the calculations.

Exhibit 18.19 shows the results of calculations for a typical wall-mounted visible notification appliance. The plot is for the horizontal plane (parallel to the floor) through the appliance and is for a square room. The outer data points show the distance from the appliance at which the required 0.0375 lm/ft² (0.4036 lm/m²) level of illumination perpendicular to the light ray is achieved. The inner data points account for the shape of the room and show the distance to the walls of a square room where the required illumination is achieved after adjusting for the angle at which the light ray strikes the surface. The superimposed square is the room size listed in the prescriptive Table 18.5.4.3.1(a). Note that these calculations show that the prescriptive requirements of the Code fall short of the performance requirements. From 0 to 45 degrees off-axis, the level of illumination on the walls (after correcting for the angle of incidence) is less than the stated performance objective. If the visible notification appliance is a 15 cd eff. appliance, the maximum room size, based on the performance calculations for the horizontal plane, is approximately 12.2 ft × 12.2 ft (3.7 m × 3.7 m) not 20 ft × 20 ft (6.1 m × 6.1 m) as listed in the prescriptive table.

Why is there a discrepancy between the prescriptive requirements and the performance requirements? The technical committee reviewed the research report and NFPA records and found a gap in the documentation leading to the development of the product standard — including the polar dispersion requirements — and the *NFPA 72* prescriptive tables. Various sources have stated that the intended performance was a level of 0.0375 lm/ft² (0.4036 lumens/m²) illumination at each of the angles. However, calculations show this not to be the case for the tables. Another suggestion was that light reflection between

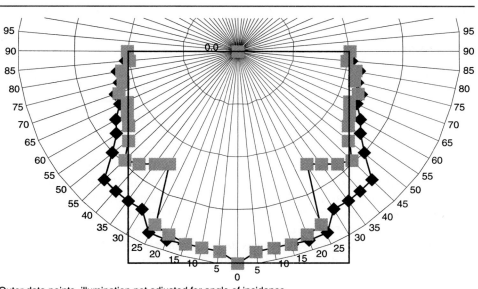

EXHIBIT 18.19 Polar Plot Showing a Horizontal Plane Through a Visible Notification Appliance Located in the Center of a Wall of a Square Room. (Source: R. P. Schifiliti Associates, Inc., Reading, MA)

◆ Outer data points–illumination not adjusted for angle of incidence

▪ Inner data points–illumination after adjustment for angle of incidence

walls in the corners increased the illumination to meet the performance requirements. An additive value of 10 percent was suggested. However, as shown in Exhibit 18.19, the values fall short by more than 10 percent. Also, in large open-plan spaces, no walls are there to reflect light.

The confidence level is high that the on-axis illumination of 0.0375 lm/ft^2 (0.4036 lm/m^2) is correct. The question is whether that level should be achieved at all angles or if the decreased levels consistent with the prescriptive requirements are sufficient. The fact that the prescriptive requirements of *NFPA 72* do not result in a level of 0.0375 lm/ft^2 (0.4036 lm/m^2) on the walls does not lead to the conclusion that the *NFPA 72* tables are in error. Thus, the committee did not have sufficient information to change or delete the prescriptive tables. However, the committee wanted to provide a performance-based approach and chose to include a conservative requirement.

18.5.4.6 Sleeping Areas.

18.5.4.6.1 Combination smoke detectors and visible notification appliances or combination smoke alarms and visible notification appliances shall be installed in accordance with the applicable requirements of Chapters 17, 18, and 29.

The requirement in 18.5.4.6.1 reinforces the detector coverage requirements of Chapters 17 and 29 as well as those of Chapter 18.

18.5.4.6.2* Table 18.5.4.6.2 shall apply to sleeping areas.

A.18.5.4.6.2 For sleeping areas, the use of lights with other intensities at distances different than within 16 ft (4.9 m) has not been researched and is not addressed in this Code.

This section on strobes for alerting sleeping persons intends that stand-alone strobes be located in accordance with 18.5.4. If the strobe is an integral part of a smoke detector or smoke alarm, the unit must be mounted in accordance with the requirements for the smoke detector or smoke alarm. In either case (stand-alone or combination), Table 18.5.4.6.2 is then consulted to determine the minimum required intensity. Where the appliance is mounted less

TABLE 18.5.4.6.2 *Effective Intensity Requirements for Sleeping Area Visible Notification Appliances*

Distance from Ceiling to Top of Lens		Intensity (cd)
in.	*mm*	
≥24	≥610	110
<24	<610	177

than 24 in. (610 mm) from the ceiling, it must have a minimum 177 cd effective rating because it might be in a smoke layer at the time it is called upon to operate. If the appliance is 24 in. (610 mm) or more from the ceiling, it is permitted to be rated 110 cd effective or more. Note that the requirement for increasing the intensity when mounted close to the ceiling applies only to strobes used in sleeping areas to awaken sleeping people. It is assumed that in nonsleeping situations, a strobe is not needed to alert someone if there is a developing smoke layer.

In sleeping rooms, smoke can accumulate at the ceiling without a person who is asleep being aware of it. If a visible notification appliance is being used to awaken the person in the room, smoke might partially obscure the appliance and reduce the effective intensity. Thus, if the visible notification appliance is less than 24 in. (610 mm) from the ceiling, it must have a higher rating (177 cd eff.). Obviously, this requirement does not apply to nonsleeping spaces because a visible notification appliance should not be needed to notify an alert person that the space is filling with smoke.

The requirement in 18.5.4.6.2 does not change the mounting height requirement for wall-mounted visible notification appliances in 18.5.4. The hierarchy is as follows:

1. If the visible notification appliance is part of a smoke detector or smoke alarm, the unit must be mounted per the requirements for smoke detectors and smoke alarms. This requirement places the appliance either on the ceiling or on the wall within 12 in. (300 mm) of the ceiling. Therefore the visible notification appliance must be a 177 cd eff. appliance and listed for wall or ceiling mounting as required.
2. If the visible notification appliance is not part of a smoke detector or smoke alarm, and the unit is to be wall mounted, it must be located at least 80 in. (2.03 m) above the floor but not more than 96 in. (2.44 m) above the floor. If that places it within 24 in. (610 mm) of the ceiling, it must have a 177 cd eff. rating. If it is 24 in. (610 mm) or more from the ceiling, it can be a 110 cd eff. appliance.
3. If the visible notification appliance is not part of a smoke detector or smoke alarm, and the unit is to be ceiling mounted, it must be a 177 cd eff. appliance.

In the unlikely situation where the ceiling height of a sleeping area is less than 80 in. (2.03 m), the visible notification appliance should be located as high as possible — at ceiling level whether wall mounted or ceiling mounted. The visible notification appliance must then be a 177 cd eff. appliance. The critical measurement is the distance to the pillow, which cannot exceed 16 ft (4.87 m) measured horizontally.

18.5.4.6.3 For rooms with a linear dimension greater than 16 ft (4.87 m), the visible notification appliance shall be located within 16 ft (4.87 m) of the pillow.

18.5.5 Location of Visible Notification Appliances for Wide Area Signaling. Visible notification appliances for wide area signaling shall be installed in accordance with the requirements of the authority having jurisdiction, approved design documents, and the manufacturer's instructions to achieve the required performance.

18.6* Visible Characteristics — Private Mode

Visible notification appliances used in the private mode shall be of a sufficient quantity and intensity and located so as to meet the intent of the user and the authority having jurisdiction.

Visible notification appliances in the private mode, addressed in Section 18.6, are often used in conjunction with an audible notification appliance to call the viewer's attention to the visible appliance. Many visible appliances in the private mode provide annunciated information that helps the viewer to locate the source of an alarm or a supervisory or trouble signal. A remote annunciator is an example of this usage.

◀ FAQ
What are the uses of many private mode visible notification appliances?

A.18.6 Though the number of visible notification appliances might be reduced in private operating mode settings, visible notification appliances might still need to be considered in spaces occupied by the public or the hearing impaired or subject to other laws or codes.

18.7 Supplementary Visible Signaling Method

A supplementary visible notification appliance shall be intended to augment an audible or visible signal.

A supplementary visible notification appliance is not intended to serve as one of the required visible notification appliances. Examples are nonrequired remote annunciators and nonrequired flashing appliances located in the security or maintenance office. See the definition of *supplementary* in 3.3.272.

18.7.1 A supplementary visible notification appliance shall comply with its marked rated performance.

Recognizing that this appliance is not satisfying a requirement but is providing a supplemental function, 18.7.1 mandates that the appliance function be marked and rated. This requirement discourages manufacturers from overrating the marking, which might not be detected because the appliances are supplementary, and gives the authority having jurisdiction a basis for verifying the performance of such appliances.

18.7.2 Supplementary visible notification appliances shall be permitted to be located less than 80 in. (2.03 m) above the floor.

Because such an appliance is supplementary, it does not need to meet the mandatory mounting height requirement for visible appliances.

18.8 Textual Audible Appliances

18.8.1 Speaker Appliances.

18.8.1.1 Speaker appliances shall comply with Section 18.4.

18.8.1.2* The sound pressure level, in dBA, of the fire alarm speaker appliance evacuation tone signals of the particular mode installed (public or private) shall comply with all the requirements in 18.4.3 (public) or 18.4.4 (private).

A.18.8.1.2 The evacuation tone signal is used to evaluate the audibility produced by fire alarm speaker appliances because of the fluctuating sound pressure level of voice or recorded messages.

EXHIBIT 18.20 *Loudspeaker Used as Textual Audible Appliance. (Source: Cooper Wheelock, Inc., Long Branch, NJ)*

Speaker appliances are called textual audible appliances, not speakers, because the term *speaker* might also refer to a person who is speaking.

In addition to conveying textual information, textual audible appliances are used to produce tones to warn occupants to evacuate the protected premises. Textual audible appliances are audible appliances and must comply with the audibility and mounting requirements of Section 18.4, which also includes the intelligibility requirements of 18.4.1.5 and 18.4.10. The audibility (sound pressure level) requirement applies to tone signals put through the appliance, not to voice signals, because voice is modulated. See also 18.4.1.5, A.18.4.1.5, the testing requirements for audible appliances in Chapter 14, and Annex D. Exhibit 18.20 shows a typical textual audible appliance.

18.8.2 Telephone Appliances.

18.8.2.1 Telephone appliances shall be in accordance with EIA Tr 41.3, *Telephones*.

The Electronic Industries Alliance (EIA) standard helps to ensure the quality and technical suitability of a telephone handset. EIA Tr 41.3, *Telephones*, in 18.8.2.1, is available from the Electronics Industries Alliance, 2500 Wilson Blvd., Arlington, VA 22201-3834, *www.eia.org*.

18.8.2.2 Wall-mounted telephone appliances or related jacks shall be not less than 36 in. (910 mm) and not more than 66 in. (1.68 m) above floor level with clear access to the appliance that is at least 30 in. (760 mm) wide.

18.8.2.3 If accessible to the general public, one telephone appliance per location shall be not more than 48 in. (1.22 m) above floor level.

The term *accessible* in the context of 18.8.2.3 means "available to and intended to be used by the general public." This includes use by floor or section fire wardens who might be required to communicate with the building emergency communications center by means of the fire alarm system telephones.

18.9* Textual Visible Appliances

Examples of textual visible appliances addressed in Section 18.9 are annunciators, panel displays (LED and LCD), CRTs, screens, and signs. See Exhibit 18.21 for an annunciator that represents a typical textual visible appliance.

Additional information on textual visible notification can be found in 24.4.2.21.

A.18.9 Textual visible appliances are selected and installed to provide temporary text, permanent text, or symbols. Textual visible appliances are most commonly used in the private mode. The use of microprocessors with computer monitors and printers has resulted in the ability to provide detailed fire alarm system information in the form of text and graphics to persons charged with directing emergency response and evacuation. Textual visible appliances are also used in the public mode to communicate emergency response and evacuation information directly to the occupants or inhabitants of the area protected by the fire alarm system. Because textual visible appliances do not necessarily have the ability to alert, they should only be used to supplement audible or visible notification appliances.

Textual visible information should be of a size and visual quality that is easily read. Many factors influence the readability of textual visible appliances, including the following:

EXHIBIT 18.21 *Textual Visible Appliance (Annunciator). (Source: Silent Knight by Honeywell, Maple Grove, MN)*

(1) Size and color of the text or graphic
(2) Distance from the point of observation
(3) Observation time
(4) Contrast
(5) Background luminance

(6) Lighting

(7) Stray lighting (glare)

(8) Shadows

(9) Physiological factors

While many of these factors can be influenced by the fire alarm equipment manufacturer and by the building designers, there is no readily available method to measure legibility.

18.9.1 Application. Textual visible appliances shall be permitted for fire alarm signaling if used in addition to audible or visible, or both, notification appliances.

18.9.2 Performance. The information produced by textual visible appliances shall be legible.

18.9.3 Location.

18.9.3.1 Private Mode. Unless otherwise permitted by the authority having jurisdiction, all textual visible notification appliances in the private mode shall be located in rooms that are accessible only to those persons directly concerned with the implementation and direction of emergency action initiation and procedure in the areas protected by the system.

Paragraph 18.9.3.1 intends to limit access to private mode textual visible displays to only those persons authorized to obtain such information. The authority having jurisdiction is permitted to specify a more public location for the textual visible appliance, presumably for use by responding emergency personnel.

18.9.3.2 Public Mode. Textual visible notification appliances used in the public mode shall be located to ensure readability by the occupants or inhabitants of the protected area.

Table 24.4.2.21.14.5 provides character size and viewing distance criteria.

18.10 Tactile Appliances

In a study by Ashley et al., "Waking Effectiveness of Audible, Visual and Vibratory Emergency Alarms Across All Hearing Levels" (funded by the National Institutes of Health, National Institute on Deafness and Other Communicative Disorders), tactile signaling was shown to be more effective than strobes for awakening hearing-impaired and deaf persons. However, the technical committee felt that the use of tactile appliances should not permit the elimination of visible appliances that cover a larger volume of space.

18.10.1 Application. Tactile appliances shall be permitted if used in addition to audible or visible, or both, notification appliances.

18.10.2* Performance. Tactile appliances shall meet the performance requirements of ANSI/UL 1971, *Standard for Signaling Devices for the Hearing Impaired*, or equivalent.

During the 2010 Code development cycle, proposals were made to require tactile signaling for certain risk groups. However, the technical committees determined that while this is a common method used in the deaf and hearing-loss community, additional research and performance specifications were needed before code language could be developed. Many variables that might affect the reliability of tactile appliance performance have not been tested or documented. Some of the tactile appliance variables include the mass of the appliance, frequency of vibration, and the throw or displacement of the vibrating mass as well as any pattern to the vibration. Occupant variables that might affect the reporting of test results and the effectiveness of the appliance include the person's age, whether a person has a profound hearing loss versus a partial hearing loss, how long a person has lived with hearing loss, and what sleep stage the person is experiencing when the appliance operates. The type of mattress might also have an effect on the performance of certain tactile appliances. Mattress variables include thickness, firmness, memory foam, pillow tops, water beds, and motion isolation mattresses. Until additional research is done, performance requirements for the manufacture, listing, installation, and use of tactile appliances cannot be specified with a sufficient degree of confidence.

A.18.10.2 Notification appliances are available for the deaf and hard of hearing. These appliances include, but are not limited to, supplemental tactical notification appliances. Such tactile notification appliances may be capable of awakening people. Tactile appliances can initiate in response to the activation of an audible smoke alarm, through hard wiring into the fire alarm system or by wireless methods.

Some tests show that strobes might not be effective in awakening some sleeping individuals during an emergency. Some tactile devices may be more effective in awakening individuals, regardless of hearing levels, from sleep.

18.11* Standard Emergency Service Interface

Where required by the enforcing authority; governing laws, codes, or standards; or other parts of this Code, annunciators, information display systems, and controls for portions of a system provided for use by emergency service personnel shall be designed, arranged, and located in accordance with the requirements of the organizations intended to use the equipment.

A.18.11 *Standard Emergency Service Interface.* Annunciators, information display systems, and controls for portions of a system provided for use by emergency service personnel should be designed, arranged, and located in accordance with the needs of the organizations intended to use the equipment.

Where annunciators, information display systems, and controls for portions of the system are provided for use by emergency service personnel, these should have a common design and operation to avoid confusion of users.

See Annex E, NEMA Standards Publication SB 30–2005, *Fire Service Annunciator and Interface.*

FAQ ▶
What is the purpose of the standard emergency service interface?

The requirement in Section 18.11 for a standard emergency service interface is intended to help serve the needs of the fire service and other emergency service personnel. The ability of emergency service personnel to understand and use the information can play a key role in incident command and resource allocation. The standard emergency service interface is intended to provide information in a consistent manner for all systems. The information in A.18.11 will help to provide the intended consistency.

REFERENCES CITED IN COMMENTARY

Americans with Disabilities Act and Architectural Barriers Act Accessibility Guidelines, published in the *Federal Register,* U.S. Government Printing Office, Washington, DC, July 23, 2004 and amended August 5, 2005.

ANSI S3.41, *American National Standard Audible Emergency Evacuation Signal,* 1996, American National Standards Institute, Inc., New York, NY.

ANSI/UL 464, *Standard for Audible Signal Appliances,* 2003 edition, Underwriters Laboratories Inc., Northbrook, IL.

ANSI/UL 864, *Standard for Control Units and Accessories for Fire Alarm Systems,* 2003, revised 2006, Underwriters Laboratories Inc. Northbrook, IL.

ANSI/UL 1971, *Standard for Signaling Devices for the Hearing Impaired*, 2002, revised 2008, Underwriters Laboratories Inc., Northbrook, IL.

ANSI/UL 1638, *Standard for Visual Signaling Appliances — Private Mode Emergency and General Utility Signaling*, 2001 edition, Underwriters Laboratories Inc., Northbrook, IL.

Ashley, E., Du Bois, J., Klassen, M., and Roby, R., "Waking Effectiveness of Audible, Visual and Vibratory Emergency Alarms Across All Hearing Levels," *Fire Safety Science — Proceedings of the Eighth International Symposium,* International Association for Fire Safety Science, 2005.

EIA Tr 41.3, *Telephones*, Electronic Industries Alliance, 2500 Wilson Blvd., Arlington, VA 22201-3834, *www.eia.org.*

ICC/ANSI 117.1, *Standard on Accessible and Usable Buildings and Facilities*, 2003 edition, International Code Council, 5203 Leesburg Pike, Suite 600, Falls Church, VA 22041.

ISO 7731, *Danger Signals for Work Places — Auditory Danger Signals*, 2003 edition, International Standards Organization, Geneva, Switzerland.

NFPA 70®, National Electrical Code®, 2008 edition, National Fire Protection Association, Quincy, MA.

NFPA *101®, Life Safety Code®*, 2009 edition, National Fire Protection Association, Quincy, MA.

Optimizing Fire Alarm Notification for High Risk Groups, Summary Report, Fire Protection Research Foundation, Quincy, MA, June 2007.

The SFPE Handbook of Fire Protection Engineering, 4th edition, National Fire Protection Association, Quincy, MA, and Society of Fire Protection Engineers, Bethesda, MD, 2008, pp. 4-32–4-42.

Waking Effectiveness of Alarms for Adults Who Are Hard of Hearing, Fire Protection Research Foundation, Quincy, MA, June 2007.

Waking Effectiveness of Alarms for the Alcohol Impaired, Fire Protection Research Foundation, Quincy, MA, June 2007.

BIBLIOGRAPHY

Butler, B., et al., *Locating Fire Alarm Sounders for Audibility*, Building Services Research and Information Association, Berkshire, UK, 1981.

IEC 60268-16, *Sound system equipment — Part 16: Objective rating of speech intelligibility by speech transmission index*, International Electrotechnical Commission, Geneva, Switzerland, 22 May 2003.

IEC 60849, *Sound Systems for Emergency Purposes*, 1998 edition, International Electrotechnical Commission, Geneva, Switzerland.

ISO 7240-19, *Fire Detection and Alarm Systems – Part 19: Design, Installation, Commissioning and Service of Sound Systems for Emergency Purposes*, 1st edition, International Organization for Standardization, Geneva, Switzerland, 15 Aug 2007.

Jacob, K., "Understanding Speech Intelligibility and the Fire Alarm Code," Bose™ Professional Systems, 2001. Available at *www.rpsa-fire.com.*

Myles, M., *Analysis of Acoustic Signals Produced by Residential Fire Alarms*, National Fire Protection Association, Quincy, MA, 1979 Annual Meeting.

NEMA Standards Publication SB 50-2008, "Emergency Communications Audio Intelligibility Applications Guide," National Electrical Manufacturers Association, Rosslyn, VA, 2008.

Schifiliti, R. P., "Audibility and Audible Signaling, Selected Bibliography," March 2001. Available at *www.rpsa-fire.com.*

Schifiliti, R. P., "Designing Fire Alarm Audibility," *Fire Technology*, May 1988.

Schifiliti, R. P., "Intelligibility — Selected Bibliography," January 2002. Available at *www.rpsa-fire.com.*

Schifiliti, R. P., "Mass Notification Systems," NEMA Supplement in *Fire Protection Engineering*, Society of Fire Protection Engineers, Bethesda, MD, Fall 2005.

Schifiliti, R. P., "The Mosquito and the Picket Fence — A Modern Day Fire Alarm Fable About Broad-band versus Narrow-band Signaling," NEMA Supplement (three parts) in *Fire Protection Engineering*, Society of Fire Protection Engineers, Bethesda, MD, Winter, Spring, and Summer 2005.

Schifiliti, R. P., "Visual Signaling as a Means for Occupant Notification in Large Spaces," Fire Protection Research Foundation, Quincy, MA, January 2006.

Reserved

CHAPTER 19

In this 2010 edition of *NFPA 72*®, *National Fire Alarm and Signaling Code*, Chapter 19 is reserved for future use.

Reserved

CHAPTER 20

In this 2010 edition of *NFPA 72*®, *National Fire Alarm and Signaling Code*, Chapter 20 is reserved for future use.

Emergency Control Functions and Interfaces

CHAPTER 21

Chapter 21 is new in the 2010 edition of the Code. This chapter contains the information that was in Section 6.16, Protected Premises Fire Safety Functions, in the 2007 edition of the Code. Because many of the fire safety functions might also be performed by an emergency signaling system under conditions other than a fire, the requirements were moved to a separate chapter. Although the term *emergency control function* is now generally used in the Code instead of *fire safety function*, the latter term is still used for the time being in Chapter 23, Protected Premises Fire Alarm Systems, to provide continuity within the chapter for fire alarm systems.

The following list is a summary of significant changes to the chapter on emergency control functions and interfaces in the 2010 edition:

- Term *fire safety function* changed to *emergency control function*.
- New requirements added in Section 21.5, First Responders Use Elevators
- New requirements added in Section 21.6, Elevators for Occupant-Controlled Evacuation

21.1 Application

The provisions of Chapter 21 shall cover the minimum requirements for the interconnection of emergency control functions to the fire alarm system and emergency communications systems in accordance with and 21.2.1 through 21.2.3 and 23.8.1.1

The control of protected premises emergency control (fire safety) functions is automatically initiated by the fire alarm system in response to fire alarm signals. Some emergency control functions can be initiated as a result of nonspecific system alarm signals, while other fire emergency control can be initiated only from a specific device or zone (e.g., fire or smoke door release or fans shut down on the floor of fire origin only).

21.1.1 The requirements of Chapters 10, 17, 18, 23, 24 and 26 shall also apply, unless they are in conflict with this chapter.

21.1.2 The requirements of Chapter 14 shall apply.

21.1.3 The requirements of this chapter shall not apply to Chapter 29 unless otherwise noted.

21.2 General

21.2.1* Emergency control functions shall be permitted to be performed automatically.

A.21.2.1 The performance of automatic emergency control functions refers to their normal operation. For instance, it is all right to shut down elevator mainline power when the system has been designed to do so.

21.2.2 The performance of automatic emergency control functions shall not interfere with power for lighting or for operating elevators.

21.2.3 The performance of automatic emergency control functions shall not preclude the combination of fire alarm services with other services requiring monitoring of operations.

21.2.4* A listed relay or other listed appliance connected to the fire alarm system used to initiate control of protected premises emergency control functions shall be located within 3 ft (1 m) of the controlled circuit or appliance.

A.21.2.4 Control devices (fire alarm relays) can be located at a motor control center that is located floors away from the device to be activated, such as air-handling units and exhaust fans located on the roof. The requirement for monitoring for integrity only applies to the installation wiring between the fire alarm control unit and the auxiliary fire alarm relay. It does not apply to the wiring between the auxiliary fire alarm relay and the emergency control device (e.g., motor stop/start control relay), or between the emergency control device and the equipment to be controlled (e.g., air-handling units and exhaust fans). For example, although the auxiliary fire alarm relay is required to be located within 36 in. (915 mm) of the emergency control device, there is no limit specified for the distance between the emergency control device and the equipment to be controlled.

FAQ ▶
Where must the fire alarm system control device be located?

An emergency control (fire safety) function may involve turning on a fan through the operation of a motor controller located remote from the fan. This action is accomplished through the operation of a listed relay connected as an output from the fire alarm system. Subsection 21.2.4 requires this fan control relay to be located within 3 ft (1 m) of the controlled circuit or appliance. The distance between the fan control relay and the fan control circuit at the motor controller should not exceed 3 ft (1 m). Positioning the relay within 3 ft (1 m) of the fan is unnecessary. However, as the distance between the fan motor controller and the fan increases, so does the potential for interruption of power to the fan.

21.2.5 The relay or other appliance shall function within the voltage and current limitations of the fire alarm control unit.

The appliance used for actuating an emergency control (fire safety) function is usually an auxiliary relay. These relays must be listed specifically to operate with the fire alarm control unit and not be off-the-shelf items from an electronics supply store.

21.2.6 The installation wiring between the fire alarm control unit and the relay or other appliance shall be Class A, Class B, Class D, or Class X in accordance with Chapter 12.

This subsection has been modified to specify the allowable pathway class designations that can be used for these circuits. In previous editions, the requirement was to monitor the installation wiring for integrity unless the circuit was arranged to perform its function on loss of power. Each of the class designations permitted by 21.2.6, except Class D, includes a provision to annunciate conditions that are adverse to the operation of the circuit or pathway. This change essentially preserves the original requirement and correlates with 21.2.8 and 21.2.11. The Class D designation corresponds to the previous allowance to exclude monitoring for integrity if the circuit operated in a fail-safe manner. Refer to 23.4.3 for requirements related to the designation of pathways for fire alarm system applications. Pathway class designations and their intended performance can be found in Section 12.3.

21.2.7 Emergency control functions shall not interfere with other operations of the fire alarm system.

The requirement in 21.2.7 is similar to the requirements for combination systems. One way to ensure that the emergency control (fire safety) functions do not interfere with other operations of the fire alarm system is to use auxiliary relays listed for use with the fire alarm control unit to isolate the emergency control function from the control unit.

21.2.8 The method(s) of interconnection between the fire alarm system and controlled electrical and mechanical systems shall be monitored for integrity in accordance with Section 10.17.

21.2.9 The method(s) of interconnection between the fire alarm system and controlled electrical and mechanical systems shall comply with the applicable provisions of *NFPA 70, National Electrical Code.*

21.2.10 The method(s) of interconnection between the fire alarm system and controlled electrical and mechanical systems shall be achieved by one of the following recognized means:

(1) Electrical contacts listed for the connected load
(2) Data communications over a signaling line circuit(s) dedicated to the fire alarm or shared with other premises operating systems
(3) Other listed methods

21.2.11 If a fire alarm system is a component of a life safety network and it communicates data to other systems providing life safety functions, or it receives data from such systems, the following shall apply:

(1) The path used for communicating data shall be monitored for integrity. This shall include monitoring the physical communication media and the ability to maintain intelligible communications.
(2) Data received from the network shall not affect the operation of the fire alarm system in any way other than to display the status of life safety network components.
(3) Where non-fire alarm systems are interconnected to the fire alarm system using a network or other digital communication technique, a signal (e.g., heartbeat, poll, ping, query) shall be generated between the fire alarm system and the non-fire alarm system. Failure of the fire alarm system to receive confirmation of the transmission shall cause a trouble signal to indicate within 200 seconds.

Life safety network is defined in 3.3.131 as "a type of combination system that transmits fire safety control data through gateways to other building system control units." Subsection 21.2.11 applies where data are communicated between the fire alarm system and other systems providing life safety functions. This communications path requires a level of monitoring for integrity consistent with that required for other fire alarm circuits.

21.2.12 The operation of all fire safety emergency control functions shall be verified by an operational test at the time of system acceptance.

A complex fire alarm system may do much more than detect a fire and sound the alarm. The many emergency control (fire safety) functions that can be initiated by the fire alarm system can make the building a much safer environment for the building occupants as well as fire fighters responding to an alarm. The proper design and installation of a complete "fire safety system" (fire alarm system and all interfaced systems) are usually dependent on multiple system designers and installers. Testing the fire safety system as a whole is critical. If the fire alarm system is designed to recall and shut down the elevators, a test of the complete system should be conducted to make sure that these functions occur as intended. That means actuating the system to see that the elevators are recalled or shut down as appropriate. Simply attaching a meter to output contacts to prove the presence of electrical power does not ensure that the final connections to the elevator will be completed properly. The same holds true for

HVAC systems, smoke control systems, and any other building system interfaced with the fire alarm system. Chapter 14 has been updated to include a specific provision in 14.2.6 to emphasize the testing of emergency control (fire safety) functions.

Representatives from all involved systems (HVAC, sprinkler, elevators, etc.) should be present when the authority having jurisdiction witnesses the final acceptance test.

21.3* Elevator Recall for Fire Fighters' Service

Elevator recall involves removing elevators from normal service by having them automatically travel to a predetermined level upon activation of specific smoke detectors (or other automatic fire detection devices as permitted by 21.3.7). This feature is a requirement of ANSI/ASME A17.1a/CSA B44a, Addenda, *Safety Code for Elevators and Escalators*, and serves to provide a means of leaving elevator cars in a safe location for passengers to exit and for subsequent use by fire fighters. Some of the signals used for elevator recall are also used to provide appropriate warning to emergency personnel concerning the use of the elevators after they have been recalled.

A.21.3 The terms *machinery space*, *control space*, *machine room*, and *control room* are defined in *NFPA 70, National Electrical Code*, and ANSI/ASME A17.1/CSA B44.

21.3.1 All initiating devices used to initiate fire fighters' service recall shall be connected to the building fire alarm system.

FAQ ▶
The requirement for the installation of initiating devices for elevator recall comes from which code?

The rules in 21.3.1 apply to the elevator recall functions of the fire alarm system. The requirement to install initiating devices for elevator recall comes from ANSI/ASME A17.1a/CSA B44a. All initiating devices associated with elevator recall must be connected to the building fire alarm system or, where there is no building fire alarm system, to a dedicated function fire alarm control unit in accordance with 21.3.2.

ANSI/ASME A17.1a/CSA B44a requires a fire alarm initiating device at each floor served by the elevator; in the associated elevator machine room, control space, or control room; and in the elevator hoistway if sprinklers are located in the hoistway. The terms *control room* and *control space* refer to elevators that use *machine-room-less* elevator designs. These machine-room-less designs can have various configurations of elevator controller and equipment locations. These terms are defined and illustrated in ANSI/ASME A17.1a/CSA B44a. When machine-room-less elevators are used, the elevator code requires a fire alarm initiating device to be installed at these locations. Exhibit 21.1 provides an excerpt from ANSI/ASME A17.1a/CSA B44a showing the related elevator recall requirements.

Subsection 21.3.1 uses the term *initiating devices*. Previous editions of the Code used the phrase "system-type smoke detectors, or other automatic fire detection permitted by 6.16.3.7" (now 21.3.7). The revisions to 21.3.1 in the 2010 edition of the Code were made to simplify the Code language. However, the intended type of initiating device for elevator recall is still a system-type smoke detector, unless ambient conditions dictate the need for another type of automatic fire detection in accordance with 21.3.7, or unless other initiating devices associated with elevator shutdown are also used to initiate elevator recall. Refer to the commentary following 21.3.3 for additional discussion.

21.3.2* In facilities without a building fire alarm system, initiating devices used to initiate fire fighters' service recall shall be connected to a dedicated function fire alarm control unit that shall be designated as "elevator recall control and supervisory control unit," permanently identified on the dedicated function fire alarm control unit and on the record drawings.

A.21.3.2 In facilities without a building alarm system, dedicated function fire alarm control units are required by 21.3.2 for elevator recall in order that the elevator recall systems be mon-

2.27.3.2 Phase I Emergency Recall Operation by Fire Alarm Initiating Devices

2.27.3.2.1 In jurisdictions not enforcing the NBCC, fire alarm initiating devices used to initiate Phase I Emergency Recall Operation shall be installed in conformance with the requirements of NFPA 72, and shall be located

(a) at each floor served by the elevator
(b) in the associated elevator machine room, control space, or control room
(c) in the elevator hoistway, when sprinklers are located in those hoistways

2.27.3.2.2 In jurisdictions enforcing the NBCC, smoke detectors, or, if applicable, the building fire alarm system (fire alarm initiating devices), used to initiate Phase I Emergency Recall Operation, shall be installed in conformance with the requirements of the NBCC, and shall be located in

(a) each elevator lobby
(b) the machine room
NOTE (2.27.3.2.2): Fire alarm initiating devices are referred to as fire detectors in the NBCC.

2.27.3.2.3 Phase I Emergency Recall Operation to the designated level shall conform to the following:

(a) The activation of a fire alarm initiating device specified in 2.27.3.2.1 or 2.27.3.2.2(a) at any floor, other than at the designated level, shall cause all elevators that serve that floor, and any associated elevator of a group automatic operation, to be returned nonstop to the designated level.

(b) The activation of a fire alarm initiating device specified in 2.27.3.2.1(b) or 2.27.3.2.2(b) shall cause all elevators having any equipment located in that machine room, and any associated elevators of a group automatic operation, to be returned nonstop to the designated level. If the machine room is located at the designated level, the elevator(s) shall be returned nonstop to the alternate level.

(c) In jurisdictions not enforcing NBCC, the activation of a fire alarm initiating device specified in 2.27.3.2.1(c) or in jurisdictions enforcing NBCC, the initiation of a fire detector in the hoistway shall cause all elevators having any equipment in that hoistway, and any associated elevators of a group automatic operation, to be returned nonstop to the designated level, except that initiating device(s) installed at or below the lowest landing of recall shall cause the car to be sent to the upper recall level.

(d) The Phase I Emergency Recall Operation to the designated level shall conform to 2.27.3.1.6(a) through (n).

2.27.3.2.4 Phase I Emergency Recall Operation to an alternate level (see 1.3) shall conform to the following:

(a) the activation of a fire alarm initiating device specified in 2.27.3.2.1(a) or 2.27.3.2.2(b) that is located at the designated level, shall cause all elevators serving that level to be recalled to an alternate level, unless Phase I Emergency Recall is in effect

(b) the requirements of 2.27.3.1.6(f), (j), (m), and (n)

(c) the requirements of 2.27.3.1.6(a), (b), (c), (d), (e), (g), (h), (i), (k), and (l), except that all references to the "designated level" shall be replaced with "alternate level"

2.27.3.2.5 The recall level shall be determined by the first activated fire alarm initiating device for that group (see 2.27.3.2.1 or 2.27.3.2.2).
If the car(s) is recalled to the designated level by the "FIRE RECALL" switch(es) [see also 2.27.3.1.6(j)], the recall level shall remain the designated level.

2.27.3.2.6 When a fire alarm initiating device in the machine room, control space, control room, or hoistway initiates Phase I Emergency Recall Operation, as required by 2.27.3.2.3 or 2.27.3.2.4, the visual signal [see 2.27.3.1.6(h) and Fig. 2.27.3.1.6(h)] shall illuminate intermittently only in a car(s) with equipment in that machine room, control space, control room, or hoistway.

EXHIBIT 21.1 *Elevator Recall Requirements. [Excerpt from ANSI/ASME A17.1a/CSA B44a] (Reprinted from ANSI/ASME A17.1a-08/CSA B44a-08 by permission of The American Society of Mechanical Engineers. All rights reserved)*

itored for integrity and have primary and secondary power meeting the requirements of this Code.

The fire alarm control unit used for this purpose should be located in an area that is normally occupied and should have audible and visible indicators to annunciate supervisory (elevator recall) and trouble conditions; however, no form of general occupant notification or evacuation signal is required or intended by 21.3.2.

Where elevator recall is required in buildings that do not have and are not required to have a fire alarm system, a fire alarm control unit designated and permanently labeled as the "Elevator Recall Control and Supervisory Control Unit" must be used. This control unit serves the initiating devices used for elevator recall or shutdown and is intended solely to provide signals to the elevator controller for elevator recall or shutdown. Installation of this dedicated function fire alarm control unit does not trigger the need to install any additional alarm-initiating devices other than those specifically required by *NFPA 72*.

The elevator recall control and supervisory control unit should be placed in an area that is constantly attended for monitoring, especially when it is installed as a stand-alone control.

21.3.3 Unless otherwise required by the authority having jurisdiction, only the elevator lobby, elevator hoistway, and elevator machine room smoke detectors, or other automatic fire detection as permitted by 21.3.7, and initiating devices used to initiate shutdown of elevator power in accordance with Section 21.4 shall be used to recall elevators for fire fighters' service.

Except for initiating devices associated with elevator shutdown in accordance with Section 21.4, elevator lobby, elevator hoistway, and elevator machine room smoke detectors (or other automatic fire detection devices as permitted by 21.3.7) are the only initiating devices permitted to initiate elevator recall (subject to the requirement of the authority having jurisdiction). Detectors serving the machinery space (containing a motor controller or electric driving machine), control room, and control space locations identified in 21.3.9 are also intended to be included in the list of "machine room" initiating devices permitted to be used to recall elevators.

In the 2010 edition of *NFPA 72*, 21.3.3 was modified to correlate with changes anticipated for ANSI/ASME A.17.1a/CSA B44a that would require elevator recall to be initiated by initiating devices used to shut down elevator power in accordance with Section 21.4. However, to date, these anticipated provisions have not been incorporated. The revision of 21.3.3 allows these initiating devices to be used for elevator recall even though the elevator code does not require it. However, until such time that ANSI/ASME A.17.1a/CSA B44a includes clear provisions addressing elevator recall from initiating devices used to shut down elevator power, extreme caution is advised. This should be done only with a clear understanding of the implications involved, careful attention to the requirements for elevator shutdown in ANSI/ASME A.17.1a/CSA B44a and to the requirements in NFPA 13, *Standard for the Installation of Sprinkler Systems*, and with the concurrence and permission of the authority having jurisdiction. If such elevator shutdown is permitted, coordination and timing are extremely important and may require the use of a pre-action sprinkler system. Also see A.21.4.2.

21.3.4 Each initiating device used to initiate fire fighters' service recall shall be capable of initiating elevator recall when all other devices on the same initiating device circuit have been manually or automatically placed in the alarm condition.

Some systems cannot guarantee that the individual smoke detector or relay responsible for initiating recall will be able to actuate if other devices on the circuit have already actuated.

Unless the smoke detectors are installed on individual initiating device circuits without any other fire alarm devices installed on those circuits, the smoke detectors should be powered separately from the initiating device circuit. Smoke detectors installed on most signaling line circuits will not be affected.

21.3.5* A lobby smoke detector shall be located on the ceiling within 21 ft (6.4 m) of the centerline of each elevator door within the elevator bank under control of the detector.

Exception: For lobby ceiling configurations exceeding 15 ft (4.6 m) in height or that are other than flat and smooth, detector locations shall be determined in accordance with Chapter 17.

A.21.3.5 Smoke detectors should not be installed in outdoor locations or locations that are open to the weather (such as unenclosed elevator lobbies in open parking structures), because such environments can exceed the parameters of the detector listing and can result in unwanted alarms. *(See 21.3.7.)*

FAQ ▶
What is the basis of the 21 ft (6.4 m) requirement in 21.3.5?

The spacing rules for smoke detectors in Chapter 17 require that for smooth ceilings all points along the ceiling have a smoke detector within 0.7 times the selected spacing of the detector. On smooth ceilings, 17.7.3.2.3.1 requires a nominal spacing of 30 ft (9.1 m) (unless performance-based criteria require something different). The value of 21 ft (6.4 m) specified in 21.3.5 correlates with this spacing (30 ft × 0.7 = 21 ft) and ensures that a smoke detector will be within 21 ft (6.4 m) of the centerline of the elevator door. High or non-smooth ceilings may require a different spacing. The Code does not require that the smoke detector be located immediately adjacent to the elevator doors. The Code also does not require that an individual smoke detector be provided for each elevator in a bank of elevators, as long as a detector is within 21 ft (6.4 m) of the centerline of each door. See Exhibit 21.2 for an illustration of the 21 ft (6.4 m) rule.

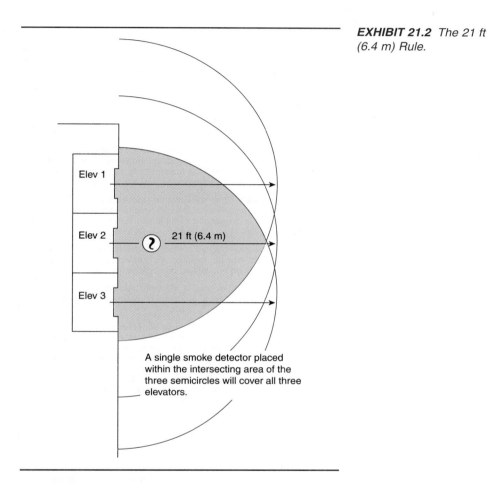

EXHIBIT 21.2 *The 21 ft (6.4 m) Rule.*

21 ft (6.4 m)

A single smoke detector placed within the intersecting area of the three semicircles will cover all three elevators.

The exception to 21.3.5 directs users to Chapter 17 for detector locations where ceiling configurations are other than level, smooth ceilings and where ceiling heights exceed 15 ft (4.5 m). A new provision has been added in 17.7.3.1.4 to address situations such as elevator lobbies with high ceilings. It permits locating smoke detectors in close proximity to an object or a space if it is the intent that action be initiated when smoke or fire threatens that object or space. Refer to A.17.7.3.1.4 for further explanation.

21.3.6 Smoke detectors shall not be installed in unsprinklered elevator hoistways unless they are installed to activate the elevator hoistway smoke relief equipment.

Most elevator hoistways are not environments suitable for the installation of smoke detectors. Although 17.5.3.1 mentions elevator hoistways as one of the areas where detection must be installed where total coverage is specified, smoke detectors installed in hoistways require continuous maintenance and are a common source of false or nuisance alarms. The environmental conditions in the hoistway typically exceed those permitted for smoke detectors. If total coverage is the fire protection design goal, then the hoistway could be protected by a heat detector(s) to meet that goal. Subsection 21.3.6 specifically prohibits the installation of smoke detectors in elevator hoistways unless the hoistway is protected by an automatic sprinkler system or unless they are required to activate hoistway smoke relief equipment. If sprinklers are installed in the hoistway, then the smoke detector (or other automatic fire detection) is needed to provide the required recall feature.

Whether the hoistway requires sprinklers depends on 8.15.5 of NFPA 13. See Exhibit 21.3 for an excerpt from NFPA 13.

EXHIBIT 21.3 *Elevator Hoistways and Machine Rooms. [Excerpt from NFPA 13, 2010 edition]*

8.15.5 Elevator Hoistways and Machine Rooms.

8.15.5.1* Sidewall spray sprinklers shall be installed at the bottom of each elevator hoistway not more than 2 ft (0.61 m) above the floor of the pit.

A.8.15.5.1 The sprinklers in the pit are intended to protect against fires caused by debris, which can accumulate over time. Ideally, the sprinklers should be located near the side of the pit below the elevator doors, where most debris accumulates. However, care should be taken that the sprinkler location does not interfere with the elevator toe guard, which extends below the face of the door opening.

ASME A17.1, *Safety Code for Elevators and Escalators*, allows the sprinklers within 2 ft (0.65 m) of the bottom of the pit to be exempted from the special arrangements of inhibiting waterflow until elevator recall has occurred.

8.15.5.2 The sprinkler required at the bottom of the elevator hoistway by 8.15.5.1 shall not be required for enclosed, noncombustible elevator shafts that do not contain combustible hydraulic fluids.

8.15.5.3* Automatic sprinklers in elevator machine rooms or at the tops of hoistways shall be of ordinary– or intermediate–temperature rating.

A.8.15.5.3 ASME A17.1, *Safety Code for Elevators and Escalators*, requires the shutdown of power to the elevator upon or prior to the application of water in elevator machine rooms or hoistways. This shutdown can be accomplished by a detection system with sufficient sensitivity that operates prior to the activation of the sprinklers (*see also NFPA 72, National Fire Alarm and Signaling Code*). As an alternative, the system can be arranged using devices or sprinklers capable of effecting power shutdown immediately upon sprinkler activation, such as a waterflow switch without a time delay. This alternative arrangement is intended to interrupt power before significant sprinkler discharge.

8.15.5.4* Upright, pendent, or sidewall spray sprinklers shall be installed at the top of elevator hoistways.

A.8.15.5.4 Passenger elevator cars that have been constructed in accordance with ASME A17.1, *Safety Code for Elevators and Escalators*, Rule 204.2a (under A17.1a-1985 and later editions of the code) have limited combustibility. Materials exposed to the interior of the car and the hoistway, in their end-use composition, are limited to a flame spread index of 0 to 75 and a smoke developed index of 0 to 450, when tested in accordance with ASTM E 84, *Standard Test Method of Surface Burning Characteristics of Building Materials*.

8.15.5.5 The sprinkler required at the top of the elevator hoistway by 8.15.5.4 shall not be required where the hoistway for passenger elevators is noncombustible or limited-combustibe and the car enclosure materials meet the requirements of ASME A17.1, *Safety Code for Elevators and Escalators*.

21.3.7* If ambient conditions prohibit installation of automatic smoke detection, other automatic fire detection shall be permitted.

A.21.3.7 The objective of Phase I Emergency Recall Operation is to have the elevator automatically return to the recall level before fire can affect the safe operation of the elevator. This includes both the safe mechanical operation of the elevator, as well as the delivery of passengers to a safe lobby location. Where ANSI/ASME A17.1a/CSA B44a, *Safety Code for Elevators and Escalators*, specifies the use of smoke detectors, these devices are expected to provide the earliest response to situations that would require Phase I Emergency Recall Operations. The use of other automatic fire detection is only intended where smoke detection would not be appropriate due to the environment. Where ambient conditions prohibit the installation of smoke detectors, the selection and location of other automatic fire detection should be evaluated to ensure the best response is achieved. When heat detectors are used, consideration should be given to both detector temperature and time lag characteristics. The consideration of a low temperature rating alone might not provide the earliest response.

Many elevator lobbies, hoistways, and machine rooms are not suitable environments for the installation of spot-type smoke detectors. Dust, dirt, humidity, and temperature extremes may exceed the operating parameters of the smoke detector. Unheated parking garages normally have elevators, but a spot-type smoke detector installed in the lobby would likely experience problems due to vehicle exhaust, dust, dirt, humidity, and temperature extremes. The intent of 21.3.7 is to prevent nuisance alarms from smoke detectors installed in such areas. Another type of fire detector may be substituted for a smoke detector where the authority having jurisdiction or another code requires detection in an area with ambient conditions unsuitable for a smoke detector. Also refer to A.21.3.5.

21.3.8 When actuated, any detector that has initiated fire fighters' recall shall also be annunciated at the building fire alarm control unit, or other fire alarm control unit as described in 21.3.2, and at required remote annunciators.

21.3.9 Actuation from the elevator hoistway, elevator machine room, elevator machinery space, elevator control space, or elevator control room smoke detectors, or other automatic fire detection as permitted by 21.3.7, shall cause separate and distinct visible annunciation at the building fire alarm control unit, or the fire alarm control unit described in 21.3.2, and at required annunciators to alert fire fighters and other emergency personnel that the elevators are no longer safe to use.

The Code requires that the elevator hoistway smoke detector (if one is present) and the elevator machine room, elevator machinery space, elevator control space, or elevator control room smoke detector(s) be connected to the building fire alarm control unit or the elevator recall control and supervisory control unit and any required annunciator to cause a separate and distinct indication to alert emergency responders that the elevators may no longer be safe to use. This requirement also correlates with the requirement in 21.3.12.3 for the elevator visual warning signal.

21.3.10 Where approved by the authority having jurisdiction, the detectors used to initiate elevator recall shall be permitted to initiate a supervisory signal in lieu of an alarm signal.

21.3.11 Where lobby detectors are used for other than initiating elevator recall, the signal initiated by the detector shall also initiate an alarm signal.

Signals from fire alarm–initiating devices fall in the category of alarm signals. With the permission of the authority having jurisdiction, 21.3.10 permits signals used to initiate elevator recall to be supervisory signals unless, in accordance with 21.3.11, the signal is also used for something else, such as part of an open area protection system. This allowance is provided to minimize the nuisance alarms from smoke detectors in these areas. This option should be used only where trained personnel are constantly in attendance and can immediately respond to the supervisory signal. A means should be provided to initiate the fire alarm signal if investigation of the supervisory signal indicates that building evacuation is necessary.

21.3.12* Separate outputs from the fire alarm systems to the elevator controller(s) shall be provided to implement elevator Phase I Emergency Recall Operation in accordance with Section 2.27 of ANSI/ASME A17.1a/CSA B44a, *Safety Code for Elevators and Escalators*, as required in 21.3.12.1 through 21.3.12.3.

A.21.3.12 It is recommended that the installation be in accordance with Figure A.21.3.12(a) and Figure A.21.3.12(b). Figure A.21.3.12(a) should be used where the elevator is installed at the same time as the building fire alarm system. Figure A.21.3.12(b) should be used where the elevator is installed after the building fire alarm system.

Subsection 21.3.12 addresses requirements for fire alarm system outputs to the elevator controller(s) and correlates with the requirements of ANSI/ASME A17.1a/CSA B44a. This subsection is divided into three subparagraphs to address the three basic outputs involved: designated level recall, alternate level recall, and visual warning indicator. The rules given in ANSI/ASME A17.1a/CSA B44a, Sections 2.27.3.2.3 and 2.27.3.2.4, specify the conditions required to cause recall to the designated level or to the alternate level. As indicated in ANSI/ASME A17.1a/CSA B44a, Section 2.27.3.2.5, the location of the initial alarm-initiating device actuated determines which of the two recall levels will be used. Requirements for the elevator visual warning indicator are provided in ANSI/ASME A17.1a/CSA B44a, Section 2.27.3.2.6. Refer to Exhibit 21.1 for an excerpt of the related ANSI/ASME A17.1a/CSA B44a rules.

FAQ ▶
How are the designated and alternate levels determined?

As a point of information, the building code or enforcement authority assigns which floors are to be used as the "designated level" and the "alternate level." Note that the designated level is usually, but might not always be, the lowest recall level.

In the commentary following 21.3.12.1, 21.3.12.2, and 21.3.12.3, it might be helpful to refer to Exhibit 21.4. This exhibit shows a typical arrangement in which the designated level is the lowest recall level, the machine room is not located at the designated level, and the hoistway initiating devices are not at or below the designated level. (Note: This exhibit is intended to show the relationship of signals and should not be used as a wiring diagram.)

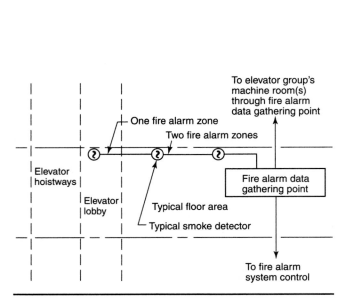

FIGURE A.21.3.12(a) *Elevator Zone — Elevator and Fire Alarm System Installed at Same Time.*

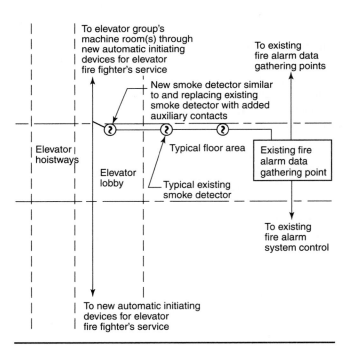

FIGURE A.21.3.12(b) *Elevator Zone — Elevator Installed After Fire Alarm System.*

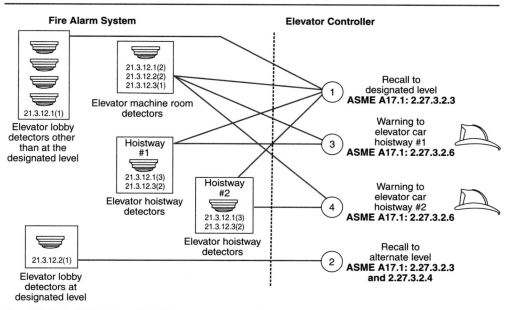

EXHIBIT 21.4 *Detectors for Control of Elevator. (Source: SimplexGrinnell, Westminster, MA)*

Note: NFPA 72, NFPA 13, and ASME A17.1 must be used jointly.

21.3.12.1 Designated Level Recall. For each elevator or group of elevators, an output shall be provided to signal elevator recall to the designated level in response to the following:

(1) Activation of smoke detectors, or other automatic fire detection as permitted by 21.3.7, located at any elevator lobby served by the elevator(s) other than the lobby at the designated level

(2) Activation of smoke detectors, or other automatic fire detection as permitted by 21.3.7, located at any elevator machine room, elevator machinery space, elevator control space, or elevator control room serving the elevator(s), except where such rooms or spaces are located at the designated level

(3) Activation of smoke detectors, or other automatic fire detection as permitted by 21.3.7, located in the elevator hoistway serving the elevator where sprinklers are located in the hoistway, unless otherwise specified in 21.3.12.2(3)

The fire alarm system output for designated level recall is required when any of the three conditions described in 21.3.12.1(1) through 21.3.12.1(3) occur. These conditions relate to ANSI/ASME A17.1a/CSA B44a, Section 2.27.3.2.1(a), (b), and (c), as shown in Exhibit 21.1.

21.3.12.2 Alternate Level Recall. For each elevator or group of elevators, an output shall be provided to signal elevator recall to the alternate level in response to the following:

(1) Activation of smoke detectors, or automatic fire detection as permitted by 21.3.7, located at the designated level lobby served by the elevator(s)

(2) Activation of smoke detectors, or other automatic fire detection as permitted by 21.3.7, located in the elevator machine room, elevator machinery space, elevator control space, or elevator control room serving the elevator(s) if such rooms or spaces are located at the designated level

(3)*Activation of the initiating devices identified in 21.3.12.1(3) if they are installed at or below the lowest level of recall in the elevator hoistway and the alternate level is located above the designated level

The fire alarm system output for alternate level recall is required when any of the three conditions described in 21.3.12.2(1) through 21.3.12.2(3) occur. The first two conditions are similar to those of 21.3.12.1(1) and 21.3.12.1(2), except they apply where the locations are at the dedicated level. The condition in 21.3.12.2(3) is somewhat unique in that it applies where initiating devices are installed in the hoistway below the lowest level of recall and the lowest level of recall is the designated level. Paragraph A.21.3.12.2(3) provides further explanation concerning this condition.

In regard to 21.3.12.1(3), the installation in hoistways of smoke detectors, or other automatic fire detection as permitted by 21.3.7, depends on whether or not sprinklers are located in the hoistways. The need to have sprinklers in a hoistway is determined by the requirements of NFPA 13. Refer to Exhibit 21.3 for an excerpt of NFPA 13.

A.21.3.12.2(3) Where initiating devices are located in the elevator hoistway at or below the lowest level of recall, ANSI/ASME A17.1a/CSA B44a, *Safety Code for Elevators and Escalators*, requires that the elevator be sent to the upper recall level. Note that the lowest level of recall could be the "designated level" or "alternate level" as determined by the local authority for the particular installation. Also note that the elevator hoistway, as defined in ASME A.17.1, includes the elevator pit.

Where heat detectors are installed in elevator pits to recall elevators, they should be, whenever practicable, installed in accordance with Chapter 17. In situations that preclude installation of heat detectors in accordance with Chapter 17, detectors should be installed using best judgment so that the detector will stand the best chance of earliest detection of fire and also be readily available for testing and servicing.

21.3.12.3* Visual Warning. For each elevator or group of elevators, an output(s) shall be provided for the elevator visual warning signal in response to the following:

(1) Activation of the elevator machine room, elevator machinery space, elevator control space, or elevator control room initiating devices identified in 21.3.12.1(2) or 21.3.12.2(2)
(2) Activation of the elevator hoistway initiating devices identified in 21.3.12.1(3) or 21.3.12.2(3)

A.21.3.12.3 ANSI/ASME A17.1a/CSA B44a, *Safety Code for Elevators and Escalators*, requires differentiation between separate hoistways that share a common elevator machine room. For instance, in a situation where there is more than one single hoistway sharing the same elevator machine room, a separate signal must be derived from each hoistway.

Each elevator car is equipped with a special visual signal in the form of a fire fighter's fire hat. The fire hat illuminates whenever the elevator is on Phase I Emergency Recall Operation. However, when recall is initiated by an initiating device located in the elevator machine room, machinery space, control space, control room or hoistway, the fire hat illuminates intermittently (flashes) as a warning to fire fighters that conditions in these locations could be adverse to the continued operation of the elevator. Fire fighters are permitted to use their own judgment as to whether to continue to use the elevator based on their knowledge of fire conditions.

21.4 Elevator Shutdown

FAQ ►
What is the purpose of elevator shutdown?

Provisions must be made to automatically disconnect power to the elevator (elevator shutdown) upon or prior to the application of water wherever a sprinkler system is installed in the elevator machine room, machinery space, control space, control room, or hoistway, as specified in 2.8.3.3 of ANSI/ASME A17.1a/CSA B44a. An excerpt of this rule is shown in Exhibit 21.5.

The primary purpose of elevator shutdown is to avoid the potential hazards of a wet elevator braking system and other effects. If the elevator brakes are wet and cannot hold, the elevator can potentially move uncontrolled to the top or bottom of the hoistway, depending on the load in the car and the type of elevator control system.

2.8.3.3 Sprinkler systems conforming to NFPA 13 or the NBCC, whichever is applicable (see Part 9), shall be permitted to be installed in the hoistway, machinery space, machine room, control space, or control room subject to 2.8.3.3.1 through 2.8.3.3.4.

2.8.3.3.1 All risers shall be located outside these spaces. Branch lines in the hoistway shall supply sprinklers at not more than one floor level. When the machinery space, machine room, control space, or control room is located above the roof of the building, risers and branch lines for these sprinklers shall be permitted to be located in the hoistway between the top floor and the machinery space, machine room, control space, or control room.

2.8.3.3.2 In jurisdictions not enforcing the NBCC, where elevator equipment is located or its enclosure is configured such that application of water from sprinklers could cause unsafe elevator operation, means shall be provided to automatically disconnect the main line power supply to the affected elevator and any other power supplies used to move the elevator upon or prior to the application of water.

(a) This means shall be independent of the elevator control and shall not be self-resetting.
(b) Heat detectors and sprinkler flow switches used to initiate main line elevator power shutdown shall comply with the requirements of NFPA 72.
(c) The activation of sprinklers outside of such locations shall not disconnect the main line elevator power supply. See also 2.27.3.3.6.

2.8.3.3.3 Smoke detectors shall not be used to activate sprinklers in these spaces or to disconnect the main line power supply.

2.8.3.3.4 In jurisdictions not enforcing the NBCC, when sprinklers are installed not more than 600 mm (24 in.) above the pit floor, 2.8.3.3.4(a) and (b) apply to elevator electrical equipment and wiring in the hoistway located less than 1 200 mm (48 in.) above the pit floor, except earthquake protective devices conforming to 8.4.10.1.2(d); and on the exterior of the car at the point where the car platform sill and the lowest landing hoistway door sill are in vertical alignment.

(a) Elevator electrical equipment shall be weatherproof (Type 4 as specified in NEMA 250).
(b) Elevator wiring, except traveling cables, shall be identified for use in wet locations in accordance with the requirements in NFPA 70.

EXHIBIT 21.5 Disconnection Requirement. [Excerpt from ANSI/ASME A17.1a/CSA B44a]. (Reprinted from ANSI/ASME A17.1a-08/CSA B44a-08 by permission of The American Society of Mechanical Engineers. All rights reserved)

21.4.1* Where heat detectors are used to shut down elevator power prior to sprinkler operation, the detector shall have both a lower temperature rating and a higher sensitivity as compared to the sprinkler.

A.21.4.1 When determining desired performance, consideration should be given to the temperature and time lag characteristics of both the sprinkler head and the heat detector to ensure as much as possible that the heat detector will operate prior to the sprinkler head, because a lower temperature rating alone might not provide earlier response. The listed spacing rating of the heat detector should be 25 ft (7.6 m) or greater.

A seldom understood concept is that a 135°F (57.2°C) heat detector may not respond before a 165°F (73°C) sprinkler head despite the obvious differences in temperature rating. The response time of a heat detector or sprinkler head is based on the response time index (RTI) of each device. The RTI must be known before the design and installation of heat detectors for elevator shutdown. Until the RTI for heat detectors is readily available, a sensitive fixed-temperature heat detector with a listed spacing equal to or greater than 25 ft (7.6 m) must be used.

Note that the excerpt shown in Exhibit 21.5 includes language that is much more general with regard to the location of sprinklers that may affect the elevator operation. Previously, the requirements limited power shutdown to applications where sprinklers were located in the elevator machine room or where they were located in the hoistway more than 24 in. (600 mm) above the pit floor. The current language reflects the broader range of equipment locations that can occur for machine-room-less elevators.

21.4.2* If heat detectors are used to shut down elevator power prior to sprinkler operation, they shall be placed within 24 in. (610 mm) of each sprinkler head and be installed in accordance with the requirements of Chapter 17. Alternatively, engineering methods, such as those specified in Annex B, shall be permitted to be used to select and place heat detectors to ensure response prior to any sprinkler head operation under a variety of fire growth rate scenarios.

A.21.4.2 Upon activation of the heat detector used for elevator power shutdown, there should be a delay in the activation of the power shunt trip. This delay should be the time that it takes the elevator cab to travel from the top of the hoistway to the lowest recall level.

21.4.3* If pressure or waterflow switches are used to shut down elevator power immediately upon, or prior to, the discharge of water from sprinklers, the use of devices with time-delay switches or time-delay capability shall not be permitted.

A.21.4.3 Care should be taken to ensure that elevator power cannot be interrupted due to water pressure surges in the sprinkler system. The intent of the Code is to ensure that the switch and the system as a whole do not have the capability of introducing a time delay into the sequence. The use of a switch with a time delay mechanism set to zero does not meet the intent of the Code, because it is possible to introduce a time delay after the system has been accepted. This might occur in response to unwanted alarms caused by surges or water movement, rather than addressing the underlying cause of the surges or water movement (often due to air in the piping). Permanently disabling the delay in accordance with the manufacturer's printed instructions should be considered acceptable. Systems that have software that can introduce a delay in the sequence should be programmed to require a security password to make such a change.

21.4.4* Control circuits to shut down elevator power shall be monitored for the presence of operating voltage. Loss of voltage to the control circuit for the disconnecting means shall cause a supervisory signal to be indicated at the control unit and required remote annunciators.

Cases have occurred where the operating power for the elevator shunt trip circuit has been de-energized or never connected to a power source. This situation prevents shutdown of the elevator when automatic sprinklers operate in the machine room or hoistway. Monitoring the integrity of the control power as required by 21.4.4 is similar to monitoring the integrity of the power for an electric motor–driven fire pump.

A.21.4.4 Figure A.21.4.4 illustrates one method of monitoring elevator shunt trip control power for integrity.

21.4.5 The initiating devices described in 21.4.2 and 21.4.3 shall be monitored for integrity by the fire alarm control unit required in 21.3.1 and 21.3.2.

The requirement in 21.4.5 makes it clear that initiating devices used for elevator shutdown must be connected to a fire alarm system.

21.5 First Responders Use Elevators

Where one or more elevators are specifically designated and marked for use by first responders during fires, the conditions specified in 21.5.1 for the elevators, associated lobbies, and machine rooms shall be continuously monitored and displayed during any such use.

In some cases, specific elevators may be marked and designated for use by the fire department and other emergency responders. The requirements of Section 21.5 are intended to pro-

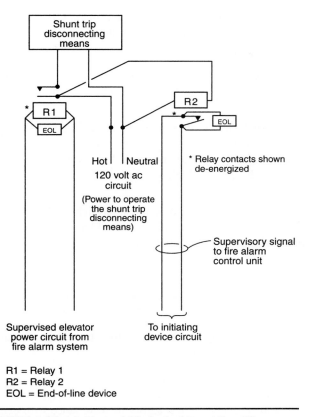

Shunt trip
disconnecting
means

R1

EOL

R2

EOL

Hot   Neutral

120 volt ac
circuit

(Power to operate
the shunt trip
disconnecting
means)

* Relay contacts shown
de-energized

Supervisory signal
to fire alarm
control unit

Supervised elevator
power circuit from
fire alarm system

To initiating
device circuit

R1 = Relay 1
R2 = Relay 2
EOL = End-of-line device

FIGURE A.21.4.4 *Typical Method of Providing Elevator Power Shunt Trip Supervisory Signal.*

vide information to emergency responders concerning the safety of continued use of the elevator(s) during the course of the emergency.

21.5.1 The conditions monitored and displayed shall include, but are not limited to, the following:

(1) Availability of main and emergency power to operate the elevator(s), elevator controller(s), and machine room (if provided) ventilation
(2) Status of the elevator(s), including location within the hoistway, direction of travel, position of landing doors, and whether they are occupied
(3) Temperature and presence of smoke in associated lobbies and machine room (if provided)

21.5.2 The conditions shall be displayed on a standard emergency services interface complying with Section 18.11.

21.6 Elevators for Occupant-Controlled Evacuation

Specific elevators may be marked and designated for occupant-controlled evacuation during an emergency. The requirements of Section 21.6 are intended to provide information to the occupants concerning the availability of the elevator(s) for evacuation during the course of the emergency.

21.6.1 Where one or more elevators are specifically designated and marked for use by occupants for evacuation during fires, they shall comply with all of the provisions of Section 21.5.

21.6.2 The lobbies of elevators required by other governing codes or standards for use by occupants for evacuation in fires shall be provided with a status indicator complying with Chapter 18.

21.6.2.1 The required status indicator shall display an illuminated green light and the message "Elevators available for occupant evacuation" while the elevators are operating under normal service and the fire alarm system is in an alarm condition, but before Phase I Emergency Recall Operation in accordance with ANSI/ASME A.17.1a/CSA B44a, *Safety Code for Elevators and Escalators*, has been initiated.

21.6.2.2 The required status indicator shall display an illuminated red light and the message "Elevators out of service, use exit stairs" once the elevators are under Phase I or Phase II operation in accordance with ANSI/ASME A.17.1a/CSA B44a, *Safety Code for Elevators and Escalators*.

21.7 Heating, Ventilating and Air-Conditioning (HVAC) Systems

21.7.1 The provisions of Section 21.7 shall apply to the basic method by which a fire alarm system interfaces with the heating, ventilating, and air-conditioning (HVAC) systems.

21.7.2* If connected to the fire alarm system serving the protected premises, all detection devices used to cause the operation of HVAC systems smoke dampers, fire dampers, fan control, smoke doors, and fire doors shall be monitored for integrity in accordance with Section 10.17.

A.21.7.2 See A.21.7.3.

Where the devices are connected to the fire alarm system, the wiring to these devices must be monitored for integrity the same as any other system detector. Stand-alone detectors, including 120 VAC-powered, single-station smoke detectors used to control HVAC equipment, that are not connected to the fire alarm system cannot be monitored for integrity.

FAQ ▶
Does *NFPA 72* require detection devices to be connected to the building fire alarm system?

NFPA 72 does not specifically require detection devices used for HVAC system control to be connected to the building fire alarm system. The requirements for this connection would be established by other codes, standards, or sources. As an example, NFPA 90A, *Standard for the Installation of Air-Conditioning and Ventilating Systems,* requires these smoke detectors to be connected to the fire alarm system if an approved system is installed in the building. Refer to Exhibit 21.6 for requirements from NFPA 90A. Based on the requirement from NFPA 90A for new installations, stand-alone detectors would be permitted only if the building does not have a building fire alarm system.

21.7.3* Connections between fire alarm systems and the HVAC system for the purpose of monitoring and control shall operate and be monitored in accordance with applicable NFPA standards.

A.21.7.3 This standard does not specifically require detection devices used to cause the operation of HVAC system smoke dampers, fire dampers, fan control, smoke doors, and fire doors to be connected to the fire alarm system.

21.7.4 Smoke detectors mounted in the air ducts of HVAC systems shall initiate either an alarm signal at the protected premises or a supervisory signal at a constantly attended location or supervising station.

The purpose of a duct-mounted smoke detector is to shut down the air handler so it will not move smoke throughout the building. The use of duct-mounted smoke detectors is not intended as a method of detecting a fire in the open area covered by the HVAC system. In accordance with NFPA 90A, a duct smoke detector used solely to close dampers or shut down HVAC equipment is not required to activate the building evacuation alarm. Subsection 21.7.4 correlates with the requirements in NFPA 90A. The option to allow the duct smoke detector to initiate a supervisory signal is provided to minimize nuisance alarms. The option can be used only where trained personnel are constantly in attendance or the signal is transmitted to a supervising station. See Exhibit 21.6 for an excerpt from NFPA 90A.

6.4* Smoke Detection for Automatic Control.

A.6.4 The use of smoke detectors in relationship to HVAC systems and high air movement areas and the details regarding their optimum installation are covered in Section 5.7 of *NFPA 72, National Fire Alarm Code*.

Protection provided by the installation of smoke detectors and related requirements is intended to prevent the distribution of smoke through the supply air duct system and, preferably, to exhaust a significant quantity of smoke to the outside. Neither function, however, guarantees either the early detection of fire or the detection of smoke concentrations prior to dangerous smoke conditions where smoke movement is other than through the supply air system.

Where smoke-control protection for a facility is determined to be needed, see NFPA 92A, *Recommended Practice for Smoke-Control Systems*.

6.4.1 Testing. All automatic shutdown devices shall be tested at least annually.

6.4.2* Location.

A.6.4.2 The summation of the capacities of individual supply-air fans should be made where such fans are connected to a common supply air duct system (i.e., all fans connected to a common air duct supply system should be considered as constituting a single system with respect to the applicability of the Chapter 6 provisions that are dependent on system capacity).

6.4.2.1 Smoke detectors listed for use in air distribution systems shall be located as follows:

(1) Downstream of the air filters and ahead of any branch connections in air supply systems having a capacity greater than 944 L/sec (2000 ft³/min)

(2) At each story prior to the connection to a common return and prior to any recirculation or fresh air inlet connection in air return systems having a capacity greater than 7080 L/sec (15,000 ft³/min) and serving more than one story

6.4.2.2 Return system smoke detectors shall not be required where the entire space served by the air distribution system is protected by a system of area smoke detectors.

6.4.2.3 Smoke detectors shall not be required for fan units whose sole function is to remove air from the inside of the building to the outside of the building.

6.4.3* Function.

A.6.4.3 Where automatic water sprinklers are provided and zoned to coordinate with the HVAC zones, their water flow switches should initiate devices for the functions described in Chapter 6.

Sprinklers are often tested weekly. Where it is desirable to prevent the accompanying automatic shutdown of the fan system(s) referred to in 6.4.3, a means can be permitted to be used to avoid such shutdown temporarily, provided one of the following occurs:

(1) A trouble signal is sustained in the sprinkler supervisory system until the automatic shutdown provision is restored.

(2) The automatic shutdown provision is restored at the end of the time period necessary to test the sprinkler system, its alarms, and related elements.

6.4.3.1 Smoke detectors provided as required by 6.4.2 shall automatically stop their respective fan(s) on detecting the presence of smoke.

6.4.3.2 Where the return air fan is functioning as part of an engineered smoke-control system and a different mode is required, the smoke detectors shall not be required to automatically stop their respective fans.

6.4.4 Installation.

6.4.4.1 Smoke detectors shall be installed, tested, and maintained in accordance with *NFPA 72®, National Fire Alarm Code®*.

6.4.4.2 In addition to the requirements of 6.4.3, where an approved fire alarm system is installed in a building, the smoke detectors required by the provisions of Section 6.4 shall be connected to the fire alarm system in accordance with the requirements of *NFPA 72, National Fire Alarm Code*.

6.4.4.2.1 Smoke detectors used solely for closing dampers or for heating, ventilating, and air-conditioning system shutdown shall not be required to activate the building evacuation alarm.

6.4.4.3 Where smoke detectors required by Section 6.4 are installed in a building not equipped with an approved fire alarm system as specified by 6.4.4.2, the following shall occur:

(1) Smoke detector activation required by Section 6.4 shall cause a visual and audible signal in a normally occupied area.

(2) Smoke detector trouble conditions shall be indicated visually or audibly in a normally occupied area and shall be identified as air duct detector trouble.

6.4.4.4 Smoke detectors powered separately from the fire alarm system for the sole function of stopping fans shall not require standby power.

EXHIBIT 21.6 *Smoke Detection for Automatic Control. [Excerpt from NFPA 90A, 2009 edition]*

21.7.5 If the fire alarm control unit actuates the HVAC system for the purpose of smoke control, the automatic alarm-initiating zones shall be coordinated with the smoke-control zones they actuate.

21.7.6 Where interconnected as a combination system, a firefighter's smoke control station (FSCS) shall be provided to perform manual control over the automatic operation of the system's smoke control strategy.

A firefighter's smoke control station (FSCS) permits responding fire fighters to manually control the operation of fans, dampers, and other equipment installed for controlling smoke movement within the building.

21.7.7 Where interconnected as a combination system, the smoke control system programming shall be designed such that normal HVAC operation or changes do not prevent the intended performance of the smoke control strategy.

21.8 Door Release Service

21.8.1 The provisions of Section 21.8 shall apply to the methods of connection of door hold-open release devices and to integral door hold-open release, closer, and smoke detection devices.

21.8.2 All detection devices used for door hold-open release service shall be monitored for integrity in accordance with Section 10.17.

Exception: Smoke detectors used only for door release and not for open area protection.

Monitoring for integrity is not required for detectors integral to the door assembly or stand-alone detectors not connected to the fire alarm system.

21.8.3 All door hold-open release and integral door release and closure devices used for release service shall be monitored for integrity in accordance with Section 21.2.

Generally, magnetic door release appliances are installed so that they release on loss of power. Where Class D circuits or pathways are used in accordance with 21.2.6, fail-safe operation is provided and monitoring for integrity is not required. Refer to the commentary following 21.2.6.

21.8.4 Magnetic door holders that allow doors to close upon loss of operating power shall not be required to have a secondary power source.

The purpose of a magnetic door release appliance is to hold doors open under normal conditions and allow the doors to close during smoke and fire conditions. If the designer or the authority having jurisdiction wants the doors to remain open even under a primary power failure, the magnetic door holders must be connected to a circuit with secondary power. The Code does not require secondary power for this optional method of operation, as stated in 21.8.4. In addition, using this option increases the battery size and standby power requirements without providing additional fire safety. Exhibit 21.7 shows examples of typical magnetic door hold-open release appliances.

21.9 Electrically Locked Doors

21.9.1 Any device or system intended to electrically lock a required means of egress door in the direction of egress shall be connected to the fire alarm system serving the protected premises.

EXHIBIT 21.7 *Magnetic Door Hold-Open Release Appliances. (Source: GE Security)*

Revisions have been made to Section 21.9 for the 2010 edition of the Code to correlate with the requirements of NFPA *101®, Life Safety Code®*. Previously, the requirements were expressed in terms of devices used to actuate the locking or unlocking of exits. The requirements are now expressed in terms of electrically locked required means of egress doors where locking occurs in the direction of egress. Means of egress doors are not limited to doors at exits.

NFPA *101* specifies the requirements for means of egress for each occupancy and defines and explains the term "means of egress" as follows:

> **3.3.161* Means of Egress.** A continuous and unobstructed way of travel from any point in a building or structure to a public way consisting of three separate and distinct parts: (1) the exit access, (2) the exit, and (3) the exit discharge. [*101,* 2009]

> **A.3.3.161 Means of Egress.** A means of egress comprises the vertical and horizontal travel and includes intervening room spaces, doorways, hallways, corridors, passageways, balconies, ramps, stairs, elevators, enclosures, lobbies, escalators, horizontal exits, courts, and yards. [*101,* 2009]

21.9.2* Electrically locked doors in a required means of egress shall unlock in the direction of egress as prescribed by other laws, codes, and governing standards.

Previous editions of the Code required unlocking of exits on any fire alarm signal unless permitted otherwise by the authority having jurisdiction. The 2010 edition requires unlocking as prescribed by other laws, codes, and governing standards. Examples of how other laws, codes, and standards may prescribe unlocking requirements are provided in A.21.9.2. Other codes, standards, and authorities having jurisdiction may also include or provide specific permission for doors to remain locked in certain situations. Examples include detention and correctional facilities and psychiatric wards in a health care facility.

A.21.9.2 Doors are commonly locked for various security reasons. Though doors are permitted to be locked to prevent ingress, doors are generally not permitted to be locked to restrict egress unless specifically permitted by governing laws, codes, and standards. Examples of special locking arrangements include delayed-egress locking and access control locking. Approved locking requirements by governing laws, codes, and standards can vary extensively. For example, some might require all fire alarm initiating devices to immediately unlock electrically locked egress doors, while others might permit such doors to remain locked when a single manual fire alarm box is activated. Some codes might also permit electrically locked doors to remain locked when a single smoke detector has activated. These allowances are typically permitted only in sprinklered buildings and are generally used as additional safeguards to counter efforts to breach security, without compromising occupant safety.

21.9.3* For all means of egress doors connected in accordance with 21.9.1, and where batteries are used in accordance with 10.5.6.1.1(1) as the secondary power supply, the batteries shall not be utilized to maintain these doors in the locked condition, unless the fire alarm control unit is arranged with circuitry and sufficient secondary power to ensure the exits will unlock within 10 minutes of loss of primary power.

A.21.9.3 A problem could exist when batteries are used as a secondary power source if a fire alarm control unit having 24 hours of standby operating power were to lose primary power and be operated for more than 24 hours from the secondary power source (batteries). It is possible that sufficient voltage would be available to keep the doors locked, but not enough voltage would be available to operate the fire alarm control unit to release the locks.

FAQ ▶
Under what circumstances does *NFPA 72* permit the use of the fire alarm system secondary power supply batteries to maintain doors in a locked condition?

In general, life safety concerns dictate that means of egress doors unlock immediately on actuation of the fire alarm system as prescribed in other laws, codes, or standards. However, circumstances sometimes exist where unlocking the doors (e.g., unlocking cell doors in a jail) could cause a security problem that poses a greater life safety risk than maintaining the exit doors locked. A change in the 2007 edition of the Code permitted batteries used as the secondary power supply in accordance with 10.5.6.1.1(1) to maintain the doors locked as long as sufficient power is provided to unlock the doors within 10 minutes. This time period is intended to permit security or other personnel to investigate the situation and take appropriate action to ensure an adequate level of security before the doors are unlocked.

21.9.4 Locks powered by independent power supplies dedicated to lock power and access control functions, and that unlock upon loss of power, shall not be required to comply with 21.9.3.

21.9.5 If means of egress doors are unlocked by the fire alarm system, the unlocking function shall occur prior to, or concurrent with, activation of any public-mode notification appliances in the area(s) served by the normally locked means of egress doors.

The intent of 21.9.5 is to prevent a possible panic situation where the fire alarm system has actuated and notification appliances are signaling the occupants to evacuate, but they cannot exit because the doors are still locked.

21.9.6 All doors that are required to be unlocked by the fire alarm system in accordance with 21.9.1 shall remain unlocked until the fire alarm condition is manually reset.

21.10* Exit Marking Audible Notification Systems

A.21.10 When a fire alarm evacuation signal activates, the exit marking system will be activated. In some cases, the activation might be sequenced to meet the fire safety plan of the property.

21.10.1 Where required by other governing laws, codes, standards, or the authority having jurisdiction, exit marking audible notification appliances shall be activated by the building fire alarm system.

21.10.2 Exit marking systems shall meet the requirements of Chapter 18.

Exit marking audible notification systems are designed to provide audible cues to assist building occupants to locate an exit during an emergency. The systems are not required by the Code, but Section 21.10, along with 18.4.7, details the requirements for their installation as part of a building fire alarm system if the exit marking audible notification system is required by other codes or the authority having jurisdiction. If exit marking systems are required by another code, standard, or authority having jurisdiction, the intent of the Code is that the system be actuated by the building fire alarm system.

REFERENCES CITED IN COMMENTARY

ANSI/ASME A17.1a/CSA B44a, *Safety Code for Elevators and Escalators*, 2007 edition and 2008 Addenda, American Society of Mechanical Engineers, New York, NY.

NFPA 13, *Standard for the Installation of Sprinkler Systems*, 2010 edition, National Fire Protection Association, Quincy, MA.

NFPA 90A, *Standard for the Installation of Air-Conditioning and Ventilating Systems*, 2009 edition, National Fire Protection Association, Quincy, MA.

NFPA *101®*, *Life Safety Code®*, 2009 edition, National Fire Protection Association, Quincy, MA.

Reserved

CHAPTER 22

In this 2010 edition of *NFPA 72®*, *National Fire Alarm and Signaling Code*, Chapter 22 is reserved for future use.

Protected Premises Fire Alarm Systems

CHAPTER 23

Chapter 23 (Chapter 6 in previous editions of the Code) covers the requirements for the installation and performance of protected premises fire alarm systems. *Protected premises (local) fire alarm system* is defined in 3.3.95.4 as simply "a fire alarm system located at the protected premises." *Building fire alarm system*, *dedicated function fire alarm system*, and *releasing fire alarm system* are subcategories of *protected premises (local) fire alarm system*. Chapter 23 is a focal chapter of the Code in that it contains requirements common to all local fire alarm systems (excluding household fire alarm systems).

In addition to the renumbering of the chapter from 6 to 23, some of the requirements formerly contained in this chapter have been relocated to new chapters, because the requirements are common to more than just protected premises fire alarm systems. These relocated sections are included in the summary of changes below.

The following list is a summary of significant changes to the chapter on protected premises fire alarm systems in the 2010 edition:

- Relocation of requirements and information on the performance of circuits and pathways to Chapter 12, Circuits and Pathways
- Relocation of information and performance criteria for emergency voice/alarm communications systems to Chapter 24, Emergency Communications Systems (24.4.1)
- Relocation of information and performance criteria on fire-fighter two-way telephone communications systems and two-way in-building radio communications enhancement systems to Chapter 24 (24.5.1 and 24.5.2, respectively)
- Relocation of information and performance criteria for protected premises fire safety functions to Chapter 21, Emergency Control Functions and Interfaces
- Relocation of information and performance criteria concerning the distinctive evacuation signal to Chapter 18, Notification Appliances (18.4.2)
- Revision of 23.2.2 providing new requirements for software and firmware compatibility
- Revision of Sections 23.5, 23.6, and 23.7 providing updated performance requirements for initiating device circuits, signaling line circuits, and notification appliance circuits
- New 23.8.4.3 providing more detailed performance requirements for non-fire alarm equipment used in combination systems

Annex I provides a cross-reference of section and paragraph numbers from the 2007 edition to the 2010 edition. Users may find this table useful in determining the disposition of the 2007 requirements.

23.1 Application

23.1.1* The application, installation, and performance of fire alarm systems within protected premises, including fire alarm and supervisory signals, shall comply with the requirements of this chapter.

A.23.1.1 It is intended that fire alarm systems and their components used for mass notification applications be covered by Chapter 23.

FAQ ▶
How is the need for a fire alarm system and its features established?

Chapter 23 does not require the installation of a protected premises (local) fire alarm system or any type of fire safety control functions. Required systems are basically those systems that are needed due to the requirements of other applicable codes or statutes that have been adopted by the enforcing jurisdiction (see 23.3.1). Typically, the need for these systems and their features is established by enabling codes such as the local building code or NFPA *101*®, *Life Safety Code*®. Those codes are the source of any requirements for the installation of a fire alarm system, supervisory functions, or other fire safety functions controlled by a protected premises (local) fire alarm system. For nonrequired systems, the system designer is responsible for determining the functions and features that the system will include. Chapter 23 explains the methods of accomplishing these functions where required by some other code, standard, or authority having jurisdiction or where selected by the system designer to meet the goals of the system owner. Refer to 23.2.3 and Section 23.3 and associated commentary.

In-building mass notification systems, defined in 3.3.79.1.3, are systems used to provide appropriate information and instructions to occupants in emergency situations, including terrorist threats, chemical or biological hazards, and natural disasters. These systems can be separate from the fire alarm system, or they can be integrated with fire alarm systems. When a fire alarm system is also used for mass notification, the system is considered a *combination system,* as defined in 3.3.95.1, and the requirements of 23.8.4 for combination systems apply in particular. Because the system is also used for mass notification, the requirements of Chapter 24, Emergency Communications Systems, also apply.

23.1.2 The requirements of Chapters 10, 12, 17, 18, 21, 24 and 26 shall also apply, unless they are in conflict with this chapter.

The requirements of Chapter 1, the references in Chapter 2, and the definitions in Chapter 3 apply throughout the Code, including Chapter 23.

Subsection 23.1.2 ensures that all fire alarm systems installed within the protected premises first comply with Chapter 23 and then comply with the requirements of other chapters. The other chapters may add to the requirements for protected premises system installations. If conflicts exist between the requirements of Chapter 23 and other chapters of the Code, the requirements of Chapter 23 prevail.

Chapter 10 addresses the fundamental requirements, such as power supplies and monitoring for integrity, applicable to all types of fire alarm systems. Chapter 12 applies to the class and survivability requirements of fire alarm system circuits and pathways. Chapter 17 applies to the initiating devices installed within a protected premises. Chapter 18 applies to the notification appliances installed within a protected premises. The requirements for emergency control functions are covered in Chapter 21, and the requirements for transmission of signals to a supervising station are contained in Chapter 26. If a protected premises (local) fire alarm system sends a signal to a supervising station, in accordance with 26.1.1, the entire system becomes a supervising station alarm system. However, as explained in A.26.1.1, the requirements of Chapter 23 still apply to the portions of the system located at the premises, including the signaling between the transmitter and the balance of the protected premises portion of the system. Chapter 26 requirements apply to off-site signaling functions of the transmitter located at the protected premises, the transmission channel, and the remotely located supervising station. Chapter 27 covers signals transmitted to a communications center by means of an auxiliary alarm system.

Two choices can be made where a multiple-building, contiguous property has its proprietary supervising station in one of the on-site buildings. Each building can have its own protected premises system and be connected to the on-site supervising station through a transmitter and transmission channel that meets the requirements of Section 26.6. Alternatively, the individual building systems can be directly connected to a master fire alarm control unit (FACU) that is co-located within the supervising station. These systems must comply with the requirements of 23.8.2.1, 23.8.2.2, and 23.8.2.5 for interconnected FACUs. In addition, they must comply with the requirements for multiple buildings in 10.16.6 and 26.6.2.3.

For a single-building property, the initiating devices and notification appliances are either directly connected or connected through zone or floor fire alarm system control units to the proprietary supervising station using initiating device circuits or signaling line circuits. Where other interconnected control units are used, the requirements of 23.8.2.1, 23.8.2.2, and 23.8.2.5 apply. Regardless of the method of connection, the proprietary supervising station facilities for both single- and multiple-building properties must comply with the requirements of Section 26.4.

Where signals from a multiple-building, campus-style protected premises are sent to a central supervising station or remote supervising station, they can be sent directly from each building if each building has its own separate fire alarm system, or they can be sent from the premises (campus) main FACU where a single fire alarm system serves the entire campus. The single fire alarm system can comprise multiple interconnected FACUs or a single FACU that serves the entire premises. Compliance with 10.16.6, 23.8.2.1, 23.8.2.2, 23.8.2.5, and 26.6.2.3 must be considered when deciding on an appropriate configuration. The consideration of any control or display location requirements from the applicable building code would be prudent. Refer to the commentary following A.10.16.3.

23.1.3 The requirements of Chapter 14 shall apply.

Chapter 14 covers inspection, testing, and maintenance. Regular testing of a fire alarm system provides ongoing assurance that equipment is performing as intended and improves overall system reliability by minimizing the time interval between the occurrence of a problem and when it is discovered. Subsection 23.1.3 applies to all installed fire alarm systems. Some jurisdictions feel the need to develop and enforce their own fire alarm system testing requirements. However, the purpose of 23.1.3 is to provide the authority having jurisdiction with an enforceable, mandatory requirement to test all fire alarm systems in accordance with the Code. Note that the requirements of Chapter 14 apply to both new and existing fire alarm system installations.

23.1.4 The requirements of this chapter shall not apply to Chapter 29 unless otherwise noted.

Chapter 29 covers single- and multiple-station alarms and household fire alarm systems and contains specific requirements for the installation of fire warning equipment in residential occupancies. Refer to the introductory commentary in Chapter 29 regarding that chapter's scope and to the definition of the term *fire warning equipment* in 3.3.100.

Fire alarm systems as discussed in Chapter 23 may be used in single living units or as dwelling fire warning systems if the requirements of Chapter 29 are satisfied. Where a fire alarm system is installed in an apartment building to serve the common areas, smoke detectors and notification appliances connected to the system may be used within individual dwelling units in place of the required smoke alarms unless prohibited by the adopted building, occupancy, or fire code or by the authority having jurisdiction. The system functions within each dwelling unit would need to be arranged to mimic requirements specified in terms of smoke alarms, and the installation within the dwelling unit would still need to comply with the requirements of Chapter 29.

23.1.5 The requirements of 24.4.1 shall apply where in-building fire emergency voice/alarm communications systems are used.

23.2 General

23.2.1* Purpose. The systems covered in Chapter 23 shall be for the protection of life or property, or both, by indicating the existence of heat, fire, smoke, or other emergencies impacting the protected premises.

A.23.2.1 Systems can be installed for the purposes of life safety, property protection, or both. Evacuation or relocation is not a required output action for every system installed in accordance with Chapter 23.

FAQ ▶
Do all fire alarm systems require the installation of notification appliances for occupant notification?

Subsection 23.2.1 clearly states that the primary purpose of the systems covered in Chapter 23 is "the protection of life or property, or both." Subsection 23.2.1 gives the protection of both life and property equal and full consideration. Occupant notification for evacuation or relocation is not a required output action of every fire alarm system installed in accordance with this chapter. Refer to 23.8.6.1 and related commentary regarding requirements for systems where occupant notification is required. Fire alarm systems are often installed for reasons other than occupant notification such as systems intended for the supervision and actuation of extinguishing systems.

The phrase "or other emergencies impacting the protected premises" at the end of 23.2.1 reflects the role that fire alarm systems interfaced with mass notification systems can play in signaling for other emergencies such as terrorist threats, chemical or biological hazards, or natural disasters.

23.2.2 Software and Firmware Control.

Special requirements are provided in 23.2.2 for computerized or microprocessor-based fire alarm systems. Two types of software are defined in the Code: executive software and site-specific software. *Executive software* is defined in 3.3.255.1 as "control and supervisory program, which manages the execution of all other programs and directly or indirectly causes the required functions of the product to be performed. Executive software is sometimes referred to as firmware, BIOS, or executive program." This type of software usually resides on a read only memory (ROM) integrated circuit that is programmed at the factory, is considered a component of a listed fire alarm control panel, and cannot be modified in the field by the installer or user. *Site-specific software* is defined in 3.3.255.2 as a "program that is separate from, but controlled by, the executive software, which allows inputs, outputs, and system configuration to be selectively defined to meet the needs of a specific installation." Site-specific software contains information such as the operations matrix and device addresses. The installer programs site-specific software.

23.2.2.1 A record of installed software and firmware version numbers shall be maintained at the location of the fire alarm control unit.

Generally, the version numbers are recorded on the permanently attached diagram in the control unit and on the as-built record drawings for the system. The record of completion form required in Chapter 10 (see Figure 10.18.2.1.1) must also show the current software version installed. A record copy of the actual site-specific software must be provided to the system owner in accordance with 10.18.2.3 and 14.6.1.2.1.

23.2.2.1.1* Software and firmware within the fire alarm control system that interfaces to other required software or firmware shall be functionally compatible.

A.23.2.2.1.1 Compatibility between software systems is necessary to ensure that the systems can communicate correctly and that the overall system can function as intended. Unfortunately, software that is compatible can become incompatible when the software is updated. Newer revisions of software might not maintain compatibility with older revisions. This paragraph requires that the fire alarm software or firmware that interfaces with software or firmware in another system is compatible. An example might be a smoke control system that gets information from the fire alarm system. The term "required" indicates that this compatibility requirement is intended for required functions (e.g., smoke control) and not for supplemental functions that are not part of the required operation of the fire alarm system. An example of a supplemental function might be an RS-232 port that connects to a terminal emulator program used for maintenance purposes. The term "functionally" is intended to ensure that the intended functionality is maintained by the software. It is trying to avoid a situation where a change in software revision might still be compatible but changes the available functionality so that the two systems no longer perform the intended functions, even though the software communicates correctly.

23.2.2.1.2* The compatible software or firmware versions shall be documented at the initial acceptance test and at any reacceptance tests.

A.23.2.2.1.2 Compatibility between systems will be documented in one or the other (or both) of the manufacturer's installation documents for the compatible products and controlled by the listings agencies. This documentation will be referenced in the marking on the product. The documentation might be paper copy or electronic media (disk, web site, etc.). When a software revision changes, the documentation can be consulted to ensure that it is still compatible with the software or firmware on the other side of the interface.

23.2.2.2* All software and firmware shall be protected from unauthorized changes.

A.23.2.2.2 A commonly used method of protecting against unauthorized changes can be described as follows (in ascending levels of access):

(1) *Access Level 1.* Access by persons who have a general responsibility for safety supervision, and who might be expected to investigate and initially respond to a fire alarm or trouble signal
(2) *Access Level 2.* Access by persons who have a specific responsibility for safety, and who are trained to operate the control unit
(3) *Access Level 3.* Access by persons who are trained and authorized to do the following:

    (a) Reconfigure the site-specific data held within the control unit, or controlled by it
    (b) Maintain the control unit in accordance with the manufacturer's published instructions and data

(4) *Access Level 4.* Access by persons who are trained and authorized either to repair the control unit or to alter its site-specific data or operating system program, thereby changing its basic mode of operation

As required in 23.2.2.2, the software and firmware must be protected from unauthorized changes. As anyone with any experience in the use of computer software knows, a single change in the software has the potential of affecting the operation of the entire fire alarm system. In terms of reliability, software is the least reliable component of the fire alarm system, and care must be taken to ensure that the system is programmed to match the requirements of the Code, the authority having jurisdiction, project specifications, and the owner's fire protection goals.

23.2.2.3 All changes shall be tested in accordance with 14.4.1.2.

Paragraph 14.4.1.2 specifies testing that must be performed if changes are made to site-specific software. When software is revised, the record of completion form must be updated to reflect the changes. If the authority having jurisdiction examines a control unit or record of completion form and finds a version of software or firmware that is different from the version installed at the time of the acceptance test, the results of the reacceptance test required by 14.4.1.2 should be reviewed.

23.2.3* Nonrequired (Voluntary) Systems and Components.

A.23.2.3 Nonrequired fire alarm features are defined in 3.3.158. These are fire alarm systems or components that are not required by the building or fire codes and are installed voluntarily by a building owner to meet site-specific fire safety objectives. There is a need to properly document the nonrequired system and components. Nonrequired components must be operationally compatible in harmony with other required components and must not be detrimental to the overall system performance. It is for this reason that 23.2.3.1 mandates that nonrequired (voluntary) systems and components meet the applicable installation, testing, and maintenance requirements of this Code. It is not the intent of the Code to have the installation of nonrequired (voluntary) systems or components trigger a requirement for the installation of additional fire alarm components or features in the building. For example, if a building owner voluntarily installs a fire alarm control unit to transmit sprinkler waterflow signals to a central station, that does not trigger a requirement to install other fire alarm system components or features, such as manual fire alarm boxes, occupant notification, or electronic supervision of sprinkler control valves. See also A.17.5.3.3 and A.18.1.5.

Alternatively, supervision and power requirements are required to be taken into account for the nonrequired components/systems on the required fire alarm systems.

FAQ ▶
What is a nonrequired system, and what requirements must it meet?

Nonrequired systems, addressed in 23.2.3 and 23.3.2, are systems that are installed to meet specific performance criteria desired by the owner. The building code, the fire code, or other NFPA standards may not mandate this performance; however, the system still must meet the requirements of *NFPA 72®, National Fire Alarm and Signaling Code*. The intended performance needs to be documented so that the authority having jurisdiction can approve the final installation. Nonrequired systems that do not meet the requirements of the Code can create a false sense of security for owners and among occupants who think they are protected by a code-compliant fire alarm system. Also important to understand is that the term *nonrequired* and the term *supplementary* have different meanings and are not interchangeable. Refer to the definitions of these terms in 3.3.158 and 3.3.272.

The requirements of 23.2.3 do not mean that a building owner who wants to install a fire alarm system in a particular area of a building for property protection must install a complete fire alarm system throughout the building. The Code contains specific guidance on the use of dedicated function fire alarm systems. See 3.3.95.4.2 for the definition of *dedicated function fire alarm system*. For example, if a building owner installs a fire detection and alarm system in a computer room for protection of the computer equipment, that system would have to meet the requirements of the Code for the area it protects. Documenting the rationale and design basis of the system is critical. Otherwise, an authority having jurisdiction may see the fire alarm system installed in the computer room and, not understanding that it was installed for specific property protection purposes, require the installation of additional devices and equipment throughout the building that extend coverage of the system beyond the original intent.

23.2.3.1 Nonrequired protected premises systems and components shall meet the requirements of this Code.

All fire alarm system installations are required to comply with the requirements of *NFPA 72* regardless of the reason that they are installed.

23.2.3.2 Nonrequired systems and components shall be identified on the record drawings required in 10.18.2.3(2).

This paragraph requires nonrequired systems and components to be identified on the record drawings. Note that Section 23.3 requires that the system features for both required and nonrequired systems be documented as a part of the system design. Nonrequired systems and components are often installed because the building owner has specific fire safety objectives, such as early fire detection in a computer room, warehouse, or other high-hazard or high-value area. The purpose and design basis of the system also should be documented for future reference if questions arise about why the system was installed. If the owner wishes to install a nonrequired building fire alarm system, then all the applicable Code requirements would apply.

23.3 System Features

The features required for a protected premises fire alarm system shall be documented as a part of the system design and shall be determined in accordance with 23.3.1 through 23.3.3.

This section of the Code requires the system designer to document the features and purposes of the fire alarm system. For small, uncomplicated systems, documentation might be accomplished by providing information on the record drawings. For other systems, the information is usually documented in a formal analysis. Whether the written analysis is called a design narrative, design analysis, basis of design report, or design brief, it should clearly explain the design objectives for the system and the decisions made to ensure that the design objectives are met.

23.3.1 Required Systems. Features for required systems shall be based on the requirements of other applicable codes or statutes that have been adopted by the enforcing jurisdiction.

23.3.2 Nonrequired Systems. The features for a nonrequired system shall be established by the system designer on the basis of the goals and objectives intended by the system owner.

A nonrequired system is installed for a specific purpose. Whoever makes the decision to install a nonrequired system must have specific reasons for installing the system. The designer must discuss fire protection goals with the owner to ensure they are in agreement with the type of fire alarm system and the expected performance of the system. This subsection requires the system designer to ensure that the nonrequired system meets the objectives of the system owner.

23.3.3 Required Features.

The functions of a fire alarm system vary depending on the requirements of the applicable codes, the requirements of the authority having jurisdiction, and the objectives of the system owner. The Code does not require the provision of any specific features. The features of any particular system can include any or all of the features listed in 23.3.3.1.

23.3.3.1 Building Fire Alarm Systems. Protected premises fire alarm systems that serve the general fire alarm needs of a building or buildings shall include one or more of the following systems or functions:

(1) Manual fire alarm signal initiation
(2) Automatic fire alarm and supervisory signal initiation
(3) Monitoring of abnormal conditions in fire suppression systems
(4) Activation of fire suppression systems
(5) Activation of fire safety functions
(6) Activation of fire alarm notification appliances
(7) In-building fire emergency voice/alarm communications
(8) Guard's tour supervisory service
(9) Process monitoring supervisory systems
(10) Activation of off-premises signals
(11) Combination systems

A *protected premises (local) fire alarm system,* as defined in 3.3.95.4, is simply "a fire alarm system located at the protected premises." A *building fire alarm system,* as defined in 3.3.95.4.1, is "a protected premises fire alarm system that includes any of the features identified in 23.3.3.1 and that serves the general fire alarm needs of a building or buildings and that provides fire department or occupant notification or both." Note that in order to be a building fire alarm system, occupant notification, fire department notification, or both must be provided.

◄ **FAQ**
What is the purpose of a building fire alarm system?

Remember that the Code does not require the installation of any type of fire alarm system in any type of occupancy. The requirements for installation of a fire alarm system come from other enabling codes or local requirements as explained in the commentary following A.23.1.1. This paragraph of the Code simply reinforces this fact.

23.3.3.2* Dedicated Function Fire Alarm Systems.

The term *dedicated function fire alarm system* was introduced in the 2007 Code, but the idea is not new. Several editions of the Code have contained provisions for installation of an FACU, designated as an "elevator recall control and supervisory control unit," to accomplish elevator recall and power shutdown. This paragraph of the Code applies to other functions that may require the use of a fire alarm system to accomplish specific objectives in buildings that are not otherwise required to have a fire alarm system. See 3.3.95.4.2 for the definition of a *dedicated function fire alarm system.*

A.23.3.3.2 Examples of dedicated function fire alarm systems would include an elevator recall control and supervisory control unit, as addressed in 21.3.2, or a system used specifically to monitor sprinkler waterflow and supervisory functions.

23.3.3.2.1 In facilities without a building fire alarm system, a dedicated function fire alarm system shall be permitted and shall not be required to include other functions or features of a building fire alarm system.

23.3.3.2.2 Where a dedicated function fire alarm system exists and a building fire alarm system is subsequently installed, the systems shall be interconnected and comply with 23.8.2.

The intent of the Code is that the building fire alarm system monitor the operation of all other fire alarm systems or control units in the building.

23.4 System Performance and Integrity

23.4.1 Purpose. Section 23.4 provides information that shall be used in the design and installation of protected premises fire alarm systems for the protection of life and property.

23.4.2 Circuit Designations. Initiating device circuits, notification appliance circuits, and signaling line circuits shall be designated by class, depending on the circuit's capability to continue to operate during specified fault conditions as indicated in Sections 23.5 through 23.7.

FAQ ▶
Who is responsible for selection of a circuit class?

The Code requires the class of circuits to be designated in accordance with the classes of circuits and pathways defined in Chapter 12 but does not require the use of any specific class circuit. Unless another code or the authority having jurisdiction designates a class of circuit to be used, the designer is responsible for designating the circuit classifications. Significant revisions have been made to this portion of the Code. The performance tables have been removed and replaced by the information contained in Chapter 12, Circuits and Pathways. Where previous editions of the Code designated circuits by class and style, only class is used now. Additionally, where previous editions of the Code only designated Class A and Class B circuits, the 2010 edition describes the performance requirements for Class A, Class B, Class C, Class D, Class E, and Class X circuits. Another change is that the circuit class designations can now be applied to all types of fire alarm circuits, not just initiating device circuits, notification appliance circuits, and signaling line circuits.

The type of circuit selected by the designer should be based on consideration of the number of devices connected to the circuit, the amount of detection that would be lost during a fault condition, and the impact that the loss of detection would have on life safety or property protection. Furthermore, the selections can be based on the number and condition of occupants, the length of the circuit, and other factors.

The designer must carefully consider the performance objectives of the system and the influences listed in 23.4.3.2 when selecting the class for fire alarm system circuits. It is not required that a single class be selected and used throughout the system. Differing classes can be used in a system depending on the capabilities of the FACU and the design objectives for the system.

As mentioned, the circuit class and style tables have been removed. Tables 6.5, 6.6.6.1, and 6.7 in the 2007 edition of the Code, which had been a fixture for many editions of the Code, have been removed entirely and replaced by the requirements of Chapter 12.

The performance of a circuit depends on two factors: how the circuit is physically wired and how the FACU operates during the specified fault conditions. Chapter 12 provides the requirements for operation of the circuit under fault conditions as well as any specific physical arrangement of the circuit, such as requirements for a redundant pathway.

In addition to describing the performance characteristics of circuits and pathways by class, Chapter 12 also designates levels of survivability for circuits and pathways. Although Chapter 23 does not require the provision of any level of survivability of fire alarm system circuits and pathways, there are applications where it would be prudent design practice to provide a level of survivability. For example, circuits and pathways that control the actuation of a remote extinguishing system or the actuation of a critical fire safety control function may necessitate a level of survivability to meet site-specific fire safety objectives. Chapter 12 provides the means to designate the desired level of survivability.

23.4.2.1 Specified fault conditions shall result in the annunciation of a trouble signal at the protected premises within 200 seconds as required in Section 10.17.

23.4.2.2* Class A and Class X circuits using physical conductors (e.g., metallic, optical fiber) shall be installed such that the outgoing and return conductors, exiting from and returning to the control unit, respectively, are routed separately. The outgoing and return (redundant) circuit conductors shall be permitted in the same cable assembly (i.e., multi-conductor cable), enclosure, or raceway only under the following conditions:

(1) For a distance not to exceed 10 ft (3.0 m) where the outgoing and return conductors enter or exit the initiating device, notification appliance, or control unit enclosures
(2) For single raceway drops to individual devices or appliances
(3) For single raceway drops to multiple devices or appliances installed within a single room not exceeding 1000 ft^2 (93 m^2) in area

In general, the intent of the Code is that the redundant pathways provided by a Class A and Class X circuit be physically separated to provide some protection against a single point of failure from disabling the entire circuit or pathway. For example, providing separation between cables, conduits, and raceways minimizes the potential loss of all circuit functionality due to severing of a single cable, conduit, or raceway. The exceptions to this section address situations in which a single event might disrupt operation of a single device or appliance or all devices and appliances in a limited area but would not generally result in loss of function for the entire circuit.

Paragraph 23.4.2.2(1) applies to cable assemblies, enclosures, and raceways. Exhibit 23.1 illustrates 23.4.2.2(1).

Paragraph 23.4.2.2(2) applies only to conduit/raceway systems and not to cables. A drop to a single device or appliance limits exposure of the conductors. Even if all four conductors to the device or appliance were cut or damaged by fire, only the single device or appliance would be lost. Exhibit 23.2 illustrates 23.4.2.2(2).

Paragraph 23.4.2.2(3) applies only to conduit/raceway systems and not to cables. A drop to a room of 1000 ft^2 (93 m^2) or less in size limits exposure of the circuit. Even if all four

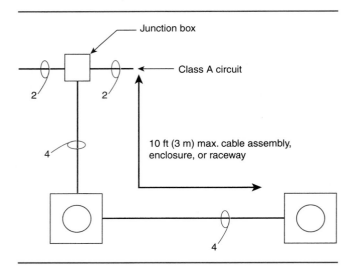

EXHIBIT 23.1 *Illustration of Paragraph 23.4.2.2(1), Distances Not to Exceed 10 ft (3.0 m).*

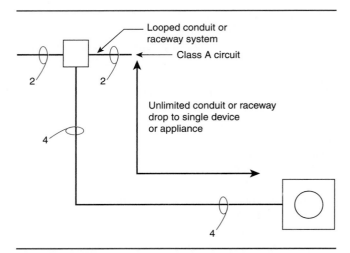

EXHIBIT 23.2 *Illustration of Paragraph 23.4.2.2(2), Drops to Individual Devices or Appliances.*

conductors to the room are cut or damaged, only a small number of devices or appliances are likely to be lost. Exhibit 23.3 illustrates 23.4.2.2(3).

EXHIBIT 23.3 *Illustration of Paragraph 23.4.2.2(3), Single Room Not Exceeding 1000 ft^2 (93 m^2).*

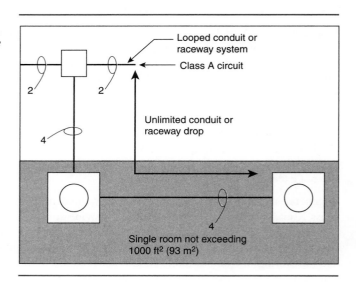

A.23.4.2.2 A goal of 23.4.2.2 is to provide adequate separation between the outgoing and return cables. This separation is required to help ensure protection of the cables from physical damage. The recommended minimum separation to prevent physical damage is 12 in. (300 mm) where the cable is installed vertically and 48 in. (1.22 m) where the cable is installed horizontally.

Separation of the outgoing and return conductors of a Class A or Class X circuit minimizes the potential for complete loss of the circuit due to mechanical damage at a single location. Installing all the conductors in one cable or conduit subjects the circuit to complete loss if the cable or conduit is cut or otherwise damaged. Chapter 23 does not require survivability from attack by fire, but Chapter 12 addresses means of providing this protection if desired.

The separation distances in A.23.4.2.2 are recommended minimums. The 12 in. (305 mm) separation distance in vertical installations was selected because this spacing would be the minimum size of most vertical pipe or wiring chases in existing buildings. The minimum 48 in. (1.22 m) separation recommended for horizontal installations is the minimum width of most corridors in existing buildings. In both cases, the idea is that in the worst case the outgoing conductors would follow one side of the chase or corridor, and the return conductor would follow the opposite side. Ideally, the conductors would be separated as far as possible to ensure protection from mechanical damage.

23.4.2.3* Where the power to a device is supplied over a separate circuit from the signaling line circuit or initiating device circuit, the operation of the power circuit shall meet the performance requirements of the initiating device circuit or signaling line circuit, unless different performance requirements are established in accordance with the evaluation in 23.4.3 and approved by the authority having jurisdiction.

In some cases, a fire alarm device is connected to a signaling line circuit but is supplied with operating power by a separate power circuit. Paragraph 23.4.2.3 requires that the power circuit meet the same performance requirements as the signaling line circuit. For example, if the signaling line circuit to which a smoke detector is attached is a Class A pathway as defined by Chapter 12, the power circuit to the smoke detector would have to be arranged in a manner that provides the same level of performance under the specified fault conditions as the signaling line circuit. The Code also recognizes that different performance requirements might be acceptable where an evaluation and approval of the authority having jurisdiction are provided.

A.23.4.2.3 The intent of this paragraph is to prevent situations where the signaling line circuit to a device is required to be one class of operation, while the power circuits, running in the same raceways and subject to the same threats, are wired to a lower class of operation. This means that it is possible to have power wiring connected to a device that is of a different class than the signaling line or initiating device circuits. One example of where meeting the same minimum performance requirements would still allow different classes of wiring is where the performance requirements are based on distance or the number of devices attached to the wires. For example, if the signaling line circuit supplies 200 devices and the performance requirement is that not more than 10 devices be lost to a wiring fault, then the class of wiring on the signaling line circuit will be Class A, with isolators to protect against shorts. Where the power wires never supply more than 10 devices, the power wires could be wired as Class B.

23.4.3 Pathway Classification.

See 3.3.174 for the definition of *path (pathway)*. Also see Section 12.3 for pathway class designations.

23.4.3.1 The class of pathways shall be determined from an evaluation based on the path performance as required by governing laws, codes, standards, and a site-specific engineering analysis.

The Code does not require the use of any particular class of circuits. Unless a building code, the *Life Safety Code*, the building owner, or the authority having jurisdiction requires a specific circuit class, the choice is a design decision. The selection should be based on a careful evaluation of the site-specific conditions and needs of the facility. Establishing the performance objectives of the system in terms of life safety, property protection, and mission continuity is the first step in conducting the evaluation required by 23.4.3.1. (Also refer to the commentary following 23.4.2.) This evaluation should be documented in the design analysis, basis of design report, design narrative, or other documentation prepared by the designer as part of the overall system design documentation and included with the documentation required by Section 10.18.

Separate but related requirements concerning the reliability of the interconnecting signaling path are contained in Section 10.17 and involve monitoring the integrity of installation conductors. The concept of "T-tapping" is addressed in the related commentary (see 10.17.1). Although T-tapping is permitted for some types of fire alarm circuits and may offer some wiring convenience, this allowance should not dissuade the selection of circuits with a higher level of fault tolerance when the evaluation determines the need for them. Note that the designer may also choose to prohibit T-tapping of circuits that might permit it, such as Class B signaling line circuits.

A surge suppression device should protect any fire alarm circuit that extends outside the building envelope. At a minimum, the type and arrangement of the surge suppression should be as recommended by the manufacturer of the FACU.

23.4.3.2 When determining the integrity and reliability of the interconnecting signaling paths (circuits) installed within the protected premises, the following influences shall be considered:

(1) Transmission media used
(2) Length of the circuit conductors
(3) Total building area covered by, and the quantity of initiating devices and notification appliances connected to, a single circuit
(4) Effect of a fault in the fire alarm system that would hinder the performance objectives of the system that protects the occupants, mission, and property of the protected premises
(5) Nature of hazards present within the protected premises
(6) Functional requirements of the system necessary to provide the level of protection required for the system
(7) Size and nature of the population of the protected premises

FAQ ▶
What minimum factors must be considered in the evaluation required by 23.4.3.1?

The evaluation required in 23.4.3.1 must consider the factors in 23.4.3.2. The list in 23.4.3.2 is not all-inclusive, as the site-specific conditions may dictate that other factors be considered as well. Designers should avoid "putting all their eggs in one basket." For example, installing all initiating devices on a single signaling line circuit might be possible, but it may not be a good design practice in very large area facilities where all devices on the circuit could be affected by a single fault.

23.4.3.3 Results of the evaluation required by 23.4.3.1 shall be included with the documentation required by 10.18.1.2.

Paragraph 23.4.3.3 requires the system designer to record the evaluation required in 23.4.3.1 in the system documentation required by 10.18.1.2. The documentation should explain the rationale for selecting the class or style of each circuit.

23.5 Performance of Initiating Device Circuits (IDCs)

23.5.1 The assignment of class designations to initiating device circuits shall be based on their performance capabilities under abnormal (fault) conditions in accordance with the requirements for Class A or Class B pathways specified in Chapter 12, as well as the requirements specified in 23.5.2 and 23.5.3.

Subsection 23.5.1 requires that initiating device circuits be Class A or Class B as described by Chapter 12. The circuits must also meet the performance requirements of 23.5.2 and 23.5.3.

23.5.2 An open or ground condition shall result in the annunciation of a trouble signal.

23.5.3 The circuit shall maintain alarm receipt capability during the application of a single ground fault.

23.6* Performance of Signaling Line Circuits (SLCs)

A.23.6 Subsection 23.6.5 requires a trouble indication on the loss of data communications for all styles. Loss of data communications means that a device or subsystem connected to the signaling line circuit is unable to send or receive information to another device or subsystem connected to the same signaling line circuit. In practical operation this means that a device or subsystem cannot be removed from the signaling line circuit or made completely inoperable without a trouble indication at the system.

23.6.1 The assignment of class designations to signaling line circuits shall be based on their performance capabilities under abnormal (fault) conditions in accordance with the requirements for Class A, Class B, or Class X pathways specified in Chapter 12 and the requirements of 23.6.2 through 23.6.5.

Subsection 23.6.1 requires that signaling line circuits meet the requirements of Class A, Class B, or Class X as described by Chapter 12. The circuits must also meet the requirements of 23.6.2 through 23.6.5.

23.6.2 An open, short circuit, or ground fault shall result in the annunciation of a trouble signal.

23.6.3 Class B pathways shall maintain alarm capability during the application of a single ground fault.

23.6.4 Class A and Class X pathways shall maintain alarm capability during the application of a single ground fault, and also during the combination of a single open and a single ground fault.

23.6.5 Where digital communications are used, inability to send or receive digital signals over a signaling line circuit shall be indicated by a trouble signal.

23.7 Performance of Notification Appliance Circuits (NACs)

23.7.1 The assignment of class designations to notification appliance circuits shall be based on their performance capabilities under abnormal (fault) conditions in accordance with the requirements for Class A or Class B pathways specified in Chapter 12, as well as the requirements specified in 23.7.2 and 23.7.3.

Subsection 23.7.1 requires that notification appliance circuits be Class A or Class B as described by Chapter 12. The circuits must also meet the performance requirements of 23.7.2 and 23.7.3.

23.7.2 An open or ground condition shall result in the annunciation of a trouble signal.

23.7.3 The circuit shall maintain alarm capability during the application of a single ground fault.

23.8 System Requirements

23.8.1 General.

23.8.1.1* Actuation Time. Actuation of alarm notification appliances or emergency voice communications, fire safety functions, and annunciation at the protected premises shall occur within 10 seconds after the activation of an initiating device.

FAQ ►
What time limit must be met for current fire alarm system response?

The requirement in 23.8.1.1 is derived from the requirements found in 1-5.4.1.2 and 1-5.4.2.2 of the 1999 edition of the Code, which were added in the 1996 edition. The maximum time delay was changed from 90 seconds to 20 seconds for the 1999 Code because occupant notification and critical fire safety control functions, such as smoke control, elevator recall, and suppression system actuation, should not be delayed once a fire is detected. The 1999 edition required the time delay to be further reduced to a maximum of 10 seconds by January 1, 2002. This gradual reduction in the maximum time delay allowed manufacturers time to develop the technology to meet the new 10-second requirement. Only new systems installed after January 1, 2002, are required to meet the 10-second requirement. Existing systems using older control equipment might not meet this requirement and would be grandfathered under the Code in force when the system was originally installed.

A.23.8.1.1 Actuation of an initiating device is usually the instant at which a complete digital signal is achieved at the device, such as a contact closure. For smoke detectors or other automatic initiating devices, which can involve signal processing and analysis of the signature of fire phenomena, actuation means the instant when the signal analysis requirements are completed by the device or fire alarm control unit software.

A separate fire alarm control unit contemplates a network of fire alarm control units forming a single large system as defined in Section 23.8.

For some analog initiating devices, actuation is the moment that the fire alarm control unit interprets that the signal from an initiating device has exceeded the alarm threshold programmed into the fire alarm control unit.

For smoke detectors working on a system with alarm verification, where the verification function is performed in the fire alarm control unit, the moment of actuation of smoke detectors is sometimes determined by the fire alarm control unit.

It is not the intent of this paragraph to dictate the time frame for the local fire safety devices to complete their function, such as fan wind-down time, door closure time, or elevator travel time.

23.8.1.2* Presignal Feature.

A.23.8.1.2 A system provided with an alarm verification feature as permitted by 23.8.5.4.1 is not considered a presignal system, since the delay in the signal produced is 60 seconds or less and requires no human intervention.

23.8.1.2.1 Systems that have a presignal feature complying with 23.8.1.2 shall be permitted if approved by the authority having jurisdiction.

23.8.1.2.2 A presignal feature shall meet the following conditions:

(1) The initial fire alarm signals sound only in department offices, control rooms, fire brigade stations, or other constantly attended central locations.
(2) Where there is a connection to a remote location, the transmission of the fire alarm signal to the supervising station activates upon the initial alarm signal.
(3) Subsequent system operation is by either of the following means:

    (a) Human action that activates the general fire alarm
    (b) A feature that allows the control equipment to delay the general alarm by more than 1 minute after the start of the alarm processing

The remote location referred to in 23.8.1.2.2(2) is a supervising station or other location to which signals are transmitted. Presignal systems generally rely on human intervention to actuate the general alarm. Building or occupancy codes should be consulted to determine if the presignal feature is permitted. *NFPA 72* requires specific permission of the authority having jurisdiction to use the presignal feature, because this feature can delay the general alarm more than 1 minute. Delaying the operation of the fire alarm system during a fire can have disastrous consequences. The presignal feature should be used only in very special situations where well-trained operators are on duty at all times. In many cases where a presignal feature is used, an immediate response to the fire area by a well-trained, fully equipped emergency response team is also provided. The following excerpt from NFPA *101* is provided for reference.

> **9.6.3.3** Where permitted by Chapter 11 through Chapter 43, a presignal system shall be permitted where the initial fire alarm signal is automatically transmitted without delay to a municipal fire department, to a fire brigade (if provided), and to an on-site staff person trained to respond to a fire emergency. [*101:*9.6.3.3] [Presignal feature is referred to as "presignal system" in NFPA *101*.]

Supplement 4 provides a summary of higher level requirements for various occupancies based on the 2009 edition of NFPA *101*.

23.8.1.3 Positive Alarm Sequence.

The positive alarm sequence addressed by 23.8.1.3 provides a timed delay of a general alarm signal in a building and at a supervising station. This delay gives a trained responder up to 3 minutes to investigate the cause of an alarm signal. The time limits to acknowledge the alarm signal and reset the system are designed to help eliminate the total reliance on human intervention (as typical in presignal systems) to actuate the alarm especially when personnel are not available to acknowledge, investigate, and reset the alarm. Building or occupancy codes should be consulted to determine if a positive alarm sequence is permitted; *NFPA 72* requires specific permission of the authority having jurisdiction to use a positive alarm sequence. The following excerpt from NFPA *101* is provided for reference.

> **9.6.3.4** Where permitted by Chapter 11 through Chapter 43, a positive alarm sequence shall be permitted, provided that it is in accordance with *NFPA 72, National Fire Alarm Code.* [*101:*9.6.3.4]

Supplement 4 provides a summary of higher level requirements for various occupancies based on the 2009 edition of NFPA *101*.

Exhibit 23.4 illustrates the positive alarm sequence.

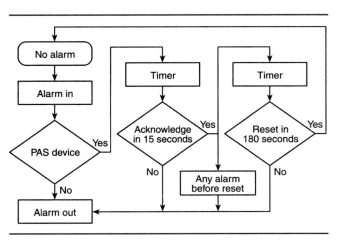

EXHIBIT 23.4 *Positive Alarm Sequence (PAS) Flow Chart. (Source: R. P. Schifiliti Associates, Inc., Reading, MA)*

23.8.1.3.1 Systems that have positive alarm features complying with 23.8.1.3 shall be permitted if approved by the authority having jurisdiction.

23.8.1.3.1.1 The positive alarm sequence operation shall comply with the following:

(1) To initiate the positive alarm sequence operation, the signal from an automatic fire detection device selected for positive alarm sequence operation shall be acknowledged at the fire alarm control unit by trained personnel within 15 seconds of annunciation.
(2) If the signal is not acknowledged within 15 seconds, notification signals in accordance with the building evacuation or relocation plan and remote signals shall be automatically and immediately activated.
(3) If the positive alarm sequence operation is initiated in accordance with 23.8.1.3.1.1(1), trained personnel shall have an alarm investigation phase of up to 180 seconds to evaluate the fire condition and reset the system.
(4) If the system is not reset during the alarm investigation phase, notification signals in accordance with the building evacuation or relocation plan and remote signals shall be automatically and immediately activated.
(5) If a second automatic fire detector selected for positive alarm sequence is actuated during the alarm investigation phase, notification signals in accordance with the building evacuation or relocation plan and remote signals shall be automatically and immediately activated.
(6)*If any other fire alarm initiating device is actuated, notification signals in accordance with the building evacuation or relocation plan and remote signals shall be automatically and immediately activated.

A.23.8.1.3.1.1(6) "Immediately activated" means there are no delays imposed by the system other than the processing of the signal in accordance with 23.8.1.1.

23.8.1.3.1.2* The system shall provide means for bypassing the positive alarm sequence.

A.23.8.1.3.1.2 The bypass means is intended to enable automatic or manual day, night, and weekend operation.

FAQ ▶
What is the purpose of the positive alarm sequence bypass means?

After acknowledgment of the alarm, actuation of the alarm functions is delayed for up to 180 seconds. The bypass provides a method for staff members to actuate the alarm as soon as they determine it is required, without needing to wait for the delay to expire.

23.8.2* Fire Alarm Control Units.

A.23.8.2 This Code addresses field installations that interconnect two or more listed control units, possibly from different manufacturers, that together fulfill the requirements of this Code.

Such an arrangement should preserve the reliability, adequacy, and integrity of all alarm, supervisory, and trouble signals and interconnecting circuits intended to be in accordance with the provisions of this Code.

Where interconnected control units are in separate buildings, consideration should be given to protecting the interconnecting wiring from electrical and radio frequency interference.

The term *fire alarm control unit* is defined in 3.3.92 as "a component of the fire alarm system, provided with primary and secondary power sources, which receives signals from initiating devices or other FACUs, and processes these signals to determine part or all of the required fire alarm system output function(s)." This equipment must comply with the requirements of 23.8.2 and be interconnected so that the system functions as a whole. The requirements of 23.8.2 cover the interconnection, monitoring, and compatibility of FACUs. The requirements apply to the interconnection of two or more FACUs regardless of whether the control units are from the same or different manufacturers.

23.8.2.1 Fire alarm systems shall be permitted to combine all detection, notification, and auxiliary functions in a single system or be a combination of component subsystems.

23.8.2.2 Except as permitted in 23.8.2.3, the fire alarm systems components shall be permitted to share control equipment or shall be able to operate as stand-alone subsystems, but, in any case, they shall be arranged to function as a single system.

Many reasons can be given for having multiple fire alarm subsystems and control units in a building. A building may need additional notification appliances and power supplies to conform to new requirements, such as those of the Americans with Disabilities Act and the Architectural Barriers Act (*ADA-ABA Guidelines*), and the existing fire alarm system cannot accommodate the changes. A lack of spare parts, manufacturer support, or simple economics may also make modifying or expanding an existing FACU or system configuration unfeasible. As a consequence, a building addition or upgrade might be designed with a new, separate FACU. The new unit must function as if it were part of the original building fire alarm system. In addition, some newer systems consist of two or more subsystems (control units) connected to a single- or multiple-master control unit(s). These newer systems must also be arranged to function as a single system. Also note that dedicated function FACUs and releasing service FACUs, defined in 3.3.92.2.1 and 3.3.92.2.2, respectively, fall under the scope of 23.8.2 and are required to be interconnected with the building's master FACU if a building fire alarm system exists or is being installed.

The intent of 23.8.2.2 is not to propose the installation of multiple small, interconnected FACUs to avoid installation of a single, larger FACU in a new fire alarm system installation. The intent of the Code is that the system designer use appropriately sized equipment designed to meet the site-specific needs of the facility. For some applications a single control unit may be the most appropriate design approach. In other situations, a distributed system using multiple interconnected control units may best meet the design objectives. Paragraph 23.8.2.2 of the Code simply details the requirement that all connected control units must function as a single fire alarm system.

23.8.2.3 Where the building is not served by a building fire alarm system, independent dedicated function fire alarm systems and/or releasing fire alarm systems shall not be required to be interconnected to function as a single system.

Connecting multiple dedicated function FACUs in the absence of a building fire alarm system serves little purpose since each dedicated function fire alarm system is designed to function as a stand-alone system to accomplish its assigned tasks.

23.8.2.4 All component subsystems shall be capable of simultaneous, full-load operation without degradation of the required overall system performance.

It is not acceptable to design a fire alarm system with multiple components, such as multiple FACUs, and to size individual components, such as circuits or batteries, based on the assumption that only a portion(s) of the system will be operating at any one time. For example, the amplifiers serving an in-building fire emergency voice/alarm communications system typically installed in a high-rise building must be designed to power all the speakers that it supports under full-load conditions, not just the speakers on the fire floor, the floor above, and the floor below.

23.8.2.5 The method of interconnection of fire alarm control units shall meet the monitoring requirements of Section 10.17 and *NFPA 70, National Electrical Code*, Article 760, and shall be achieved by the following recognized means:

(1) Electrical contacts listed for the connected load
(2) Data communications over a signaling line circuit(s) dedicated to the fire alarm or shared with other premises operating systems
(3) Other listed methods

The Code recognizes that signaling line circuits are the predominant means for interconnecting multiple FACUs and other premises control and management systems, which is reflected in 23.8.2.5(2). The requirements in 23.8.2.6 address connections to other premises systems.

23.8.2.6 Where the signaling line circuit is shared by other premises operating systems, operation shall be in accordance with 23.8.4.

Where a signaling line circuit is shared by another premises operating system, it must comply with the requirements for combination systems in 23.8.4 in addition to the requirements of 23.8.2.6.1 and 23.8.2.6.2.

Fire alarm systems can be connected to or be part of an integrated building management system. Such systems may control energy management, heating, ventilation, air conditioning, security, fire alarm, mass notification, and other functions. The requirements are intended to ensure that when fire alarm system functions are part of a larger, integrated system or network, fire alarm service is not impaired by a malfunction of another system or network component. Fire alarm systems combined with the functions of other building systems must still meet all the requirements of a stand-alone fire alarm system, including performance, power supplies, and response times.

All signal control and transport equipment (routers and servers) must be listed for fire alarm service or comply with the conditions listed in 23.8.2.6.1(1) through 23.8.2.6.1(5). Paragraph 23.8.2.6.2 requires the use of a listed barrier gateway. Refer to the definition of *gateway* in 3.3.107.

23.8.2.6.1 All signal control and transport equipment (such as routers, servers) located in a critical fire alarm or fire safety function signaling path shall be listed for fire alarm service, unless the following conditions are met:

(1) The equipment meets the performance requirements of 10.14.1.
(2) The equipment is provided with primary and secondary power and monitored for integrity as required in Sections 10.5 and 10.17.
(3) All programming and configuration ensure a fire alarm system actuation time as required in 23.8.1.1.
(4) System bandwidth is monitored to confirm that all communications between equipment that is critical to the operation of the fire alarm system or fire safety functions take place within 10 seconds; failure shall be indicated within 200 seconds.
(5) Failure of any equipment that is critical to the operation of the fire alarm system or fire safety functions is indicated at the master fire alarm control unit within 200 seconds.

23.8.2.6.2 A listed barrier gateway, integral with or attached to each control unit or group of control units, as appropriate, shall be provided to prevent the other systems from interfering with or controlling the fire alarm system.

23.8.2.7 Each interconnected fire alarm control unit shall be separately monitored for alarm, supervisory, and trouble conditions.

FAQ ▶
If a remote FACU experiences a trouble condition, what type of signal should be indicated at the master FACU?

Each interconnected FACU must be monitored for alarm signals first, then each interconnected FACU must be monitored for supervisory conditions. This requirement means that if the satellite FACU interconnected to the master FACU experiences a trouble condition for any reason, that trouble condition reports to the master FACU as a supervisory condition, indicating the interconnected FACU is off-normal.

The interconnection between the FACUs is monitored for integrity, and if that circuit experiences a fault condition, a trouble condition for that circuit (zone or point) is indicated at the master FACU. See also Section 10.7 for descriptions of the distinct signal requirements and the priority of the signals.

23.8.2.8 Interconnected fire alarm control unit alarm signals shall be permitted to be monitored by zone or by combined common signals.

The protected premises may be a single building or a group of buildings, such as a campus setting that includes office, research, or educational buildings. In a campus setting where multiple buildings are considered to be the protected premises, each building may have an FACU that reports to a master FACU in one of the buildings. Due to renovations at different times, a single building may have multiple FACUs. A building may also have a master FACU serving the building along with FACUs that control specific fire safety functions, such as release of a special extinguishing system (dedicated function or releasing fire alarm system), as noted previously.

Where multiple FACUs are within the protected premises, the Code permits the designation of a main or master fire alarm panel for the building, with other FACUs reporting to the master FACU as if they were single initiating devices. For example, an FACU in a computer room that controls fire detection and actuation of a clean agent fire suppression system may report to the main building FACU as a single zone or component. In other words, when the computer room system has an alarm, supervisory, or trouble signal, it would annunciate the appropriate signal on the main building FACU as "Computer Room alarm, supervisory, or trouble." Going to the computer room control unit would then be necessary to determine the specific alarm, supervisory, or trouble condition indicated on the computer room control unit. It is important to note that where zoning and annunciation are a concern or where signals are transmitted to a supervising station, the requirements of 10.16.6 and 26.6.2.3 apply and each building must be indicated separately for these functions.

23.8.2.9 Protected premises fire alarm control units shall be capable of being reset or silenced only from the fire alarm control unit at the protected premises, unless otherwise permitted by 23.8.2.10.

Remotely resetting fire alarm control equipment without first investigating the premises is a dangerous practice. A serious fire could be in progress that is not evident at the remote reset location. Delayed alarms are a contributing factor to many large loss-of-life and large property-loss fires. Paragraph 23.8.2.9 requires on-site restoration to normal of fire alarm systems. If a fire alarm system is in alarm or trouble, a technician should be required to investigate the cause of that alarm or trouble first and then reset the FACU. In most cases, the desire for remote reset capability is to accommodate a method of conveniently handling false alarms. A much better way to eliminate false or unwanted alarms is to properly design, install, and maintain the system.

Exhibit 23.5 illustrates a case in which the control unit was remotely reset when a fire was actually in progress. In this situation, attempts to reset the alarm from a remote location delayed notification of the public fire department. The fire caused extensive property damage and extended interruption of telephone service for an entire metropolitan area.

23.8.2.10 Remote resetting and silencing of a fire alarm control unit from other than the protected premises shall be permitted with the approval of the authority having jurisdiction.

Under very unusual circumstances, the capability to reset or silence the fire alarm system from a remote location may be necessary. Paragraph 23.8.2.10 permits this feature only when the authority having jurisdiction has been provided with the reasons for permitting remote reset and agrees with the reasons. Few situations would warrant remote reset capability, and the authority having jurisdiction should be thoroughly convinced that the remote silence or reset capability will not compromise immediate response to an alarm signal.

23.8.3 Protected Premises Fire Alarm Systems Interconnected with Dwelling Unit Fire Warning Equipment.

23.8.3.1 A protected premises fire alarm system shall be permitted to be interconnected to a household fire alarm system(s) for the purpose of activating the notification appliances connected to the household fire alarm system(s).

Where dwelling units, such as apartments or condominiums, are equipped with systems that comply with Chapter 29, the protected premises fire alarm system serving the apartment building as a whole may be used to actuate the notification appliances connected to the individual household fire alarm systems located in the dwelling units, as permitted by 23.8.3.1. Without this provision, the installation of both "building system" and "dwelling system" notification appliances might be required. Paragraph 23.8.3.1 permits notification appliances to be used as part of both the building fire alarm system and the household fire alarm system. Note that this provision applies to *household fire alarm systems,* defined in 3.3.95.2, and not to single- and multiple-station alarms.

23.8.3.2 The status of dwelling unit smoke alarms shall be permitted to be displayed at the protected premises control unit and annunciators.

Paragraph 23.8.3.2 permits, but does not require, the display of alarm signals on the protected premises FACU. The dwelling smoke alarms are not required to actuate the building fire alarm system, and in most cases this would not be desirable or permitted, because every accidental alarm in an individual dwelling unit would cause actuation of the building fire alarm system. However, some building codes require the smoke alarms to be connected to the building fire alarm system and arranged to initiate a supervisory signal when actuated. Also refer to 23.8.3.5.

Single- and multiple-station smoke alarms are not part of a fire alarm system, and the interconnecting circuits of these alarms are not monitored for integrity in the same manner that system components are monitored. One means for connecting smoke alarms with a building fire alarm system is through the use of an auxiliary output module furnished separately from the individual smoke alarms. The auxiliary output module is typically interconnected in the smoke alarm circuit in the same way as the individual smoke alarms. The module usually provides a relay contact output that can be used to operate equipment such as visual notification appliances or be used for remote annunciation. The use of these modules is subject to any limitations stated in the manufacturer's published instructions and to the limits of the number of devices specified in 29.8.2.

23.8.3.3 If interconnected, an alarm condition at the protected premises fire alarm system shall cause the fire alarm notification appliance(s) within the family living unit of the dwelling unit fire warning system to become energized. The notification appliances shall remain energized until the protected premises fire alarm system is silenced or reset.

23.8.3.4 The interconnection circuit or path from the protected premises fire alarm system to the dwelling unit fire warning system shall be monitored for integrity by the protected premises fire alarm system in accordance with Section 10.17.

23.8.3.5 An alarm condition occurring at the dwelling unit fire warning system or the operation of any test switches provided as part of the dwelling unit fire warning equipment shall not cause an alarm condition at the protected premises fire alarm system.

23.8.4 Combination Systems.

A *combination system*, as defined in 3.3.95.1, is a fire alarm system in which components are used, in whole or in part, in common with a non–fire signaling system. Also refer to A.3.3.95.1.

23.8.4.1* Fire alarm systems shall be permitted to share components, equipment, circuitry, and installation wiring with non–fire alarm systems.

A.23.8.4.1 The provisions of 23.8.4.1 apply to types of equipment used in common for fire alarm systems, such as fire alarm, sprinkler supervisory, or guard's tour service, and for other systems, such as burglar alarm or coded paging systems, and to methods of circuit wiring common to both types of systems. The intent of connecting non-fire systems with the fire alarm system is often to cause the non-fire systems to react appropriately when signaled by the fire alarm system.

Virtually anything can be combined with a fire alarm system as long as it does not interfere with the operation of the fire alarm system. Combined features can include security functions, HVAC control, paging, lighting, and more. The *only* exception to this noninterference requirement is when a mass notification system either is installed as a stand-alone system interfaced with the fire alarm system or is integrated with the fire alarm system. (The mass notification system is permitted to override a fire alarm signal in accordance with 23.8.4.5 and Section 10.6.) Typically, only fire alarm system performance (and now mass notification system performance) is regulated by codes and standards because failure of other systems does not normally have an adverse impact on life safety in the building. New building network communications technologies such as BACnet and LONWorks have blurred the lines between fire alarm systems and other building systems.

◀ FAQ
What requirements apply when fire alarm signaling line circuits are shared with other systems?

As a minimum, where fire alarm system signaling line circuits are shared with other systems, the requirements of 23.8.2.6 and 23.8.4.3 apply and wiring for other systems must comply with the requirements of *NFPA 70®, National Electrical Code® (NEC®)*. Special care must be taken to ensure that the function or malfunction of other systems does not interfere with the operation of the fire alarm system.

23.8.4.2 Operation of a non–fire system function(s) originating within a connected non–fire system shall not interfere with the required operation of the fire alarm system, unless otherwise permitted by this Code.

While fire alarm systems are permitted to share circuits with non–fire alarm systems or components, 23.8.4.2 requires the circuits to be arranged such that operation of the non–fire alarm system equipment or a non–fire alarm system component does not impair the operation of the fire alarm system. For example, actuation of a security device on a shared circuit must not impair operation of the fire alarm system. Extensive testing may be required to ensure that this requirement is met under all possible operating conditions and all possible combinations of events. In other words, on a shared circuit, fire alarm functions must take priority over operation of the other equipment or components on the circuit. The only exception to this requirement is where signals dealing with another life safety system, such as a mass notification system, might take priority over fire alarm signals, as addressed in 23.8.4.5 and Section 10.6.

23.8.4.3 Non–Fire Alarm Equipment.

Requirements for non–fire alarm equipment used in a combination system are addressed in two parts. Equipment that is listed to the performance requirements of 10.14.1 is addressed in 23.8.4.3.1, and equipment that is not listed to the performance requirements of 10.14.1 is addressed in 23.8.4.3.2.

23.8.4.3.1* For non–fire alarm equipment listed to the performance requirements specified in 10.14.1, the requirements of 23.8.4.3.1.1 through 23.8.4.3.1.3 shall apply.

A.23.8.4.3.1 For systems such as carbon monoxide detection, fire extinguisher electronic monitoring device, emergency communication (mass notification), or intrusion, much of the benefit of a combination system comes from being able to use common wiring. If the equipment in the combination system is of equivalent quality to fire alarm equipment, and the system monitors the wiring and equipment in the same way as fire alarm equipment, then sharing of wiring is permitted. If the equipment is not of equivalent quality, isolation between the systems would be required.

23.8.4.3.1.1 The equipment shall be permitted to be attached to a fire alarm circuit, either among the fire alarm devices or as a branch or extension of the fire alarm pathways, when the following requirements are met:

(1) All the equipment and pathways shall meet the monitoring for integrity requirements of Section 10.17.
(2) All the equipment and pathways shall be maintained by a single service organization.
(3) All the equipment and pathways shall be installed in accordance with the requirements of this Code.
(4) All the equipment shall be listed as compatible with the fire alarm equipment or shall have a contact closure interface listed for the connected load.

For equipment that is not listed for fire alarm service, 23.8.4.3.1 requires that it be demonstrated that it is not possible for the connected equipment to adversely affect the operation of the fire alarm system under any circumstance. Maintenance operations or failure of systems connected to the fire alarm system could result in impairment of the fire alarm system. Equipment that is not required for the operation of the fire alarm system must not impair operation of the fire alarm system if it is removed or malfunctions.

In order to display more detailed information than may be available from the fire alarm system alone, users have been known to connect fire alarm systems to supplementary equipment (such as desktop computers and monitors) that are not listed for fire alarm use. In some installations, software or firmware changes or other repairs to the non–fire alarm equipment have delayed fire alarm signals or prevented their display altogether. Improperly interconnected systems can prevent one or more fire alarm system functions from operating as intended.

Where a non–fire alarm system component is listed as being compatible with fire alarm equipment, the listing agency investigates compatibility with a fire alarm system, as well as electrical characteristics and other factors, to ensure that the product is suitable for the purpose.

23.8.4.3.1.2 If the equipment is attached to the fire alarm system via separate pathways, then short circuits or open circuits in this equipment, or between this equipment and the fire alarm system pathways, shall not impede or impair the monitoring for integrity of the fire alarm system or prevent alarm, supervisory, or fire safety control signal transmissions.

23.8.4.3.1.3 Grounds in this equipment, or between this equipment and the fire alarm system pathways, shall be reported, annunciated, and corrected in the same manner as grounds in the rest of the fire alarm system.

23.8.4.3.2 For non-fire equipment not listed to the performance requirements specified in 10.14.1, the requirements of 23.8.4.3.2.1 through 23.8.4.3.2.3 shall apply.

23.8.4.3.2.1 Short circuits or open circuits in the equipment, or between the equipment and the fire alarm system pathways, shall not impede or impair the monitoring for integrity of the fire alarm system or prevent alarm, supervisory, or fire safety control signal transmissions.

Common wiring can include circuits supplying device power, initiating device circuits, signaling line circuits, or notification appliance circuits. A short, ground, or open circuit caused by the non–fire alarm equipment in the common wiring must not prevent the receipt of alarm, supervisory, or trouble signals or prevent the fire alarm system notification appliances from operating.

23.8.4.3.2.2 Grounds in this equipment, or between this equipment and the fire alarm system pathways, shall be reported, annunciated, and corrected in the same manner as grounds in the rest of the fire alarm system.

23.8.4.3.2.3 Removal, replacement, failure, maintenance procedures, or ground on this hardware, software, or circuits shall not impair the required operation of the fire alarm system.

23.8.4.4 Speakers used as alarm notification appliances on fire alarm systems shall also be permitted to be used for emergency communications systems when installed in accordance with Chapter 24.

Fire alarm speakers can be used for other emergency communications provided they are installed in accordance with the requirements of Chapter 24. Chapter 24 also permits the use of the speakers for general paging, music, and other nonemergency functions provided the requirements of 24.3.4.2 are met. For the 2010 edition of the Code, all requirements for voice-capable systems have been moved to Chapter 24.

23.8.4.5* In combination systems, fire alarm signals shall be distinctive, clearly recognizable, and shall be indicated as follows in descending order of priority, except where otherwise required by other governing laws, codes or standards, or by other parts of this Code:

(1) Signals associated with life safety
(2) Signals associated with property protection
(3) Trouble signals associated with life and/or property protection
(4) All other signals

A.23.8.4.5 Examples of signal classification are provided in Table A.23.8.4.5. This is not all-inclusive or prescriptive but is meant to illustrate a potential classification scheme. Actual schemes may vary depending upon the response plan and/or requirements of the authority having jurisdiction. Mass notification systems are allowed to take priority over the fire alarm audible notification message or signal. This is intended to allow the mass notification system to prioritize emergency signals on the basis of risk to building occupants. The designer should specify the desired operation, in particular, as to what should occur immediately after the mass notification message has completed.

Exhibit 23.6 shows a combination system that includes mass notification system components.
     The requirement in 23.8.4.5 does not necessarily mean that separate notification appliances are required. A single appliance may be used if it can provide different, distinctive signals and the fire alarm signal takes precedence over all other signals (with the exception of emergency signals from a mass notification system). Where speakers are used, the

◄ **FAQ**
Must separate notification appliances always be used for non–fire functions?

TABLE A.23.8.4.5 *Examples of Signal Classification*

Life Safety	Property Protection	Trouble	Other
Fire alarm signals	Security signals	Battery fault	HVAC signals
Holdup alarm signals	Supervisory signals	AC power failure	Occupancy
Code blue signals	Access control	IDC faults	
Panic alarms		NAC faults	
Hazmat signals		SLC faults	
Severe weather warnings			
Flood alarms			
Mass notification signals			

EXHIBIT 23.6 *Combination Fire and Mass Notification System (MNS). (Source: Cooper Notification, Long Branch, NJ)*

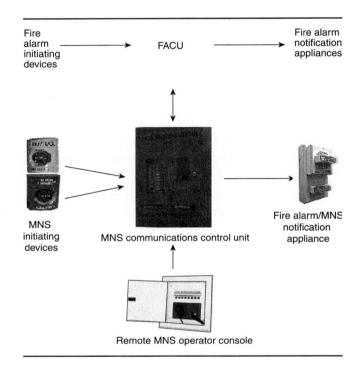

requirements of 23.8.4.4 must be observed. Note that visible notification appliances for fire alarm signaling only or to signal complete evacuation must be clear or nominal white in accordance with 18.5.2.4. The use of another color for other applications would require a separate appliance. See A.18.5.2.4 and 18.5.2.5.

Specific reference to mass notification systems has been removed from 23.8.4.5 for this edition of the Code. However, other parts of the Code still address the allowance for mass notifications systems to take priority over fire alarm signals. (See Section 10.6 and 24.4.2.16.) This recognizes that emergency situations such as terrorist attacks can be more of a priority than even a fire and that the fire alarm signal may need to be overridden by signals from the mass notification system. Table A.23.8.4.5 provides examples of how various types of signals should be prioritized for compliance with 23.8.4.5. System integration and event prioritization add extensively to the complexity of the system, and careful planning and coordination will be required to ensure that the system will properly respond to these situations.

23.8.4.6 If the authority having jurisdiction determines that the information being displayed or annunciated on a combination system is excessive and is causing confusion and delayed response to a fire emergency, the authority having jurisdiction shall be permitted to require that the display or annunciation of information for the fire alarm system be separate from, and have priority in accordance with, 23.8.4.5, over information for the non–fire alarm systems.

Causing an operator to scroll through many non–fire alarm system events, such as door opening or closure signals, can result in a delay in identifying and responding to fire alarm signals. If fire alarm signals cannot be easily identified and displayed on a priority basis, the authority having jurisdiction may require a separate display for the fire alarm signals. Under the new requirements for listing FACUs to ANSI/UL 864, *Standard for Control Units and Accessories for Fire Alarm Systems,* the person at the FACU must now manually scroll the alarms list to determine if all alarms have been investigated. A first responder may not be aware of this new requirement and assume that the last alarm displayed is the only alarm. For example, in one recent case, fire department personnel in the northeastern United States found no fire where a manual fire alarm box had been actuated. The manual fire alarm box was reset, but the control unit remained in the alarm condition. Personnel then manually scrolled the alarm screen and found that a smoke detector in an office had alarmed and that indeed there was a fire in the office.

23.8.4.7* Signals from carbon monoxide detectors and carbon monoxide detection systems transmitted to a fire alarm system shall be permitted to be supervisory signals.

A.23.8.4.7 See NFPA 720, *Standard for the Installation of Carbon Monoxide (CO) Detection and Warning Equipment*, for more information.

If carbon monoxide detectors are connected to the fire alarm system, 23.8.4.7 permits the detector to initiate a supervisory signal instead of an alarm signal. However, caution is advised here. NFPA 720, *Standard for the Installation of Carbon Monoxide (CO) Detection and Warning Equipment*, generally requires occupant notification throughout the protected premises (see NFPA 720, 5.5.6.2) and requires carbon monoxide alarm signals to be a distinctive alarm signal pattern (see NFPA 720, 5.5.6.5).

23.8.4.8* Fire Extinguisher Electronic Monitoring Devices and Systems. Signals from a fire extinguisher electronic monitoring device or fire extinguisher monitoring system transmitted to a fire alarm system shall be permitted to be supervisory signals.

A.23.8.4.8 See NFPA 10, *Standard for Portable Fire Extinguishers*, for more information on portable fire extinguishers.

Fire extinguisher electronic monitoring devices and systems are designed to monitor the presence of a fire extinguisher, obstructions in front of, and the pressure inside a portable fire extinguisher. The Code treats these devices and systems the same as other fire protection systems monitored by the fire alarm system. See Exhibit 23.7.

23.8.5 Fire Alarm System Inputs.

The requirements of the Code exist not in a vacuum but rather within a framework that involves many other codes, standards, and jurisdictional documents that work together for the protection of life and property against the ravages of fire.

With this framework in mind, the types of inputs (and outputs) required for the fire alarm system are selected primarily to meet the requirements of a model building code; federal, state, or local ordinance; insurance company requirements; corporate policies; or other organizational policies (both private and public). To be clear, this framework can include the criteria used by the designer to meet the goals of the system owner. In the rare cases where the *National Fire and Signaling Alarm Code* requires certain inputs, they are usually related to supporting the reliability of the system or are based on requirements from other codes or standards.

EXHIBIT 23.7 *Wireless Fire Extinguisher Monitoring Device. (Source: MIJA Inc., Rockland, MA)*

23.8.5.1 General.

23.8.5.1.1 All initiating devices shall be installed in accordance with Chapter 17 and tested in accordance with Chapter 14.

The term *device* generally means input is provided to the system. Refer to the definition of *initiating device* in 3.3.122 along with specific types of initiating devices also defined in 3.3.122.

The phrase *listed for the intended application* was deleted from the paragraph in the 2007 edition because equipment listing is already addressed in Chapter 10. However, an important point to emphasize is that if a device is used in a low-temperature environment or a wet location, it must be listed not only for fire alarm system use but also for installation in that specific environment. Fire alarm system control units used for actuation of an extinguishing system must be specifically listed for releasing service. Ensuring that a device is listed is not sufficient. The device must be listed for the specific application, which is also referred to as *listed for the purpose*. Refer to 10.3.1 and its associated commentary.

23.8.5.1.2* Where connected to a supervising station, fire alarm systems employing automatic fire detectors or waterflow detection devices shall include a manual fire alarm box to initiate a signal to the supervising station.

Exception: Fire alarm systems dedicated to elevator recall control and supervisory service as permitted in Section 21.3.

Any fire alarm system that uses automatic fire detectors or sprinkler waterflow switches must be provided with at least one manual fire alarm box if the system is connected to a supervising station. This requirement applies to all types of systems except dedicated function systems installed to provide elevator recall control and supervisory service.

A.23.8.5.1.2 The manual means required by 23.8.5.1.2 is intended to provide a backup means to manually activate the fire alarm system when the automatic fire detection system or waterflow devices are out of service due to maintenance or testing, or where human discovery of the fire precedes automatic sprinkler system or automatic detection system activation.

The manual fire alarm box required by 23.8.5.1.2 should be connected to a separate circuit that is not placed "on test" when the detection or sprinkler system is placed "on test." The manual means is only intended for use by the system technician or the building owner and should be located by the sprinkler riser or fire alarm control unit.

FAQ ▶
What is the reason the Code requires at least one manual fire alarm box?

Information and guidance have been added in A.23.8.5.1.2 to help users understand the purpose of requiring at least one manual fire alarm box. One reason is to allow an alarm to be transmitted if the automatic fire detectors or sprinkler system is out of service during repairs or during a test. This requirement presumes that a contingency plan exists to address a fire emergency during the out-of-service time or during a test. It also presumes that personnel within the facility and at the supervising station to which the premises is connected are aware of the plan and will acknowledge receipt of the alarm.

Although not required by the Code, locating manual fire alarm boxes electrically ahead of all other initiating devices, depending on the design of the circuit, ensures that the alarm signal will be initiated even if an open circuit condition occurs downstream of the manual fire alarm box. In addition, A.23.8.5.1.2 recommends placing the manual fire alarm box on a separate circuit that will not be placed "on test."

23.8.5.2 Fire Alarm Signal Initiation — Manual. Manual fire alarm signal initiation shall comply with the requirements of Section 17.14.

23.8.5.2.1 If signals from manual fire alarm boxes and other fire alarm initiating devices within a building are transmitted over the same signaling line circuit, there shall be no interference with manual fire alarm box signals when both types of initiating devices are operated at the same time.

The requirement in 23.8.5.2.1 applies only to signaling line circuits. The requirement does not apply to systems that use initiating device circuits, because those circuits do not distinguish which device initiated the alarm. The requirement originally addressed spring-wound, coded devices that transmitted a fixed number of rounds of code. Although circuits of this type are still in service in older facilities, few if any new circuits of this type are installed today. Two or more devices operating simultaneously could interfere with one another, resulting in the transmission of garbled signals. Paragraph 23.8.5.2.1 does not preclude the installation of manual fire alarm boxes on initiating device circuits with other initiating devices such as smoke detectors or heat detectors.

23.8.5.2.2 Provision of the shunt noninterfering method of operation shall be permitted for this performance.

The shunt noninterfering method of operation is one way to prevent the signals from publicly accessible alarm boxes from interfering with one another. This same system can be used where coded fire alarm systems are used as the protected premises fire alarm system. The operation of a shunt system is described in 27.6.3.2 and related annex material. As mentioned in the commentary following 23.8.5.2.1, while circuits of this type are still in service in various facilities, few if any new circuits of this type are installed today.

23.8.5.3 Fire Alarm Signal Initiation — Initiating Devices with Separate Power and Signaling Wiring.

23.8.5.3.1 Automatic fire alarm signal initiating devices that have integral trouble signal contacts shall be connected to the initiating device circuit so that a trouble condition within a device does not impair alarm transmission from any other initiating device.

Exception: Where the trouble condition is caused by electrical disconnection of the device or by removing the initiating device from its plug-in base.

If a device with integral trouble contacts is incorrectly connected to an initiating device circuit, disabling the initiating device circuit when the device experiences a trouble condition is possible.

The initiating device circuit must first connect to all the alarm contacts of the initiating devices. Then, after the alarm contacts of the last initiating device, the circuit must route back through the trouble contacts. This places the trouble contacts beyond the alarm contacts of all the initiating devices. Exhibits 23.8 and 23.9 show the incorrect and correct methods of connection.

At one time, photoelectric smoke detectors used a tungsten filament lamp as a light source. The Code required the detector to monitor the integrity of the filament. An open filament would cause a relay within the detector to open a normally closed trouble contact. This

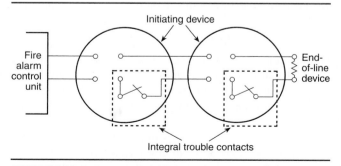

EXHIBIT 23.8 *Incorrect Method of Connecting Integral Trouble Contacts. (Source: Hughes Associates, Inc., Warwick, RI)*

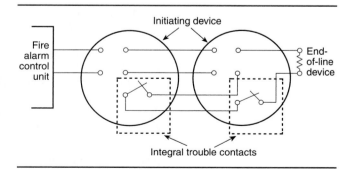

EXHIBIT 23.9 *Correct Method of Connecting Integral Trouble Contacts. (Source: Hughes Associates, Inc., Warwick, RI)*

contact was wired in series with the initiating device circuit. Few initiating devices, other than radiant energy–sensing fire detectors, have integral trouble contacts.

Disconnection or removal of any initiating device from a plug-in base opens the circuit and results in a circuit trouble signal. The exception to 23.8.5.3.1 recognizes this expected circuit trouble signal and exempts it from the requirement.

23.8.5.3.2* Automatic fire alarm signal initiating devices that use a nonintegral device to monitor the integrity of the power supply wiring to the individual initiating devices shall have the nonintegral device connected to the initiating device circuit so that a fault on the power supply wiring does not impair alarm transmission from any operational initiating device.

A.23.8.5.3.2 Where power is supplied separately to the individual initiating device(s), multiple initiating circuits are not prohibited from being monitored for integrity by a single power supervision device.

FAQ ▶
How must the power circuit be arranged if the detection device receives power from an external power circuit?

Some detection devices receive their power from an external power circuit. Paragraph 23.8.5.3.2 requires that where detection devices receive their power from an external power circuit, the power circuit must be arranged such that its failure does not impair the operation of any other fire detectors. Exhibit 23.10 shows an example of how this monitoring should be accomplished.

EXHIBIT 23.10 *Four-Wire Smoke Detectors Supervised for the Absence of Operating Power by an End-of-Line Power Supervision Relay.*

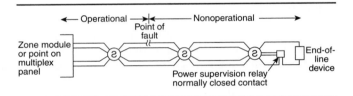

23.8.5.4 Fire Alarm Signal Initiation — Detection Devices.

23.8.5.4.1* Systems equipped with alarm verification features shall be permitted under the following conditions:

(1) The alarm verification feature is not initially enabled, unless conditions or occupant activities that are expected to cause nuisance alarms are anticipated in the area that is protected by the smoke detectors. Enabling of the alarm verification feature shall be protected by password or limited access.
(2) A smoke detector that is continuously subjected to a smoke concentration above alarm threshold does not delay the system functions of Sections 10.6 through 10.13, 23.8.1.1, or 21.2.1 by more than 1 minute.
(3) Actuation of an alarm-initiating device other than a smoke detector causes the system functions of Sections 10.6 through 10.13, 23.8.1.1, or 21.2.1 without additional delay.
(4) The current status of the alarm verification feature is shown on the record of completion *(see Figure 10.18.2.1.1, item 5.2.8).*

Alarm verification feature, defined in 3.3.12, is a feature that introduces a time period in which to confirm a valid signal with the objective of reducing unwanted alarms. The feature is permitted only for smoke detectors. Because smoke detectors manufactured today are far more stable and less prone to nuisance alarms than previous generations, the Code restricts the use of this feature to situations in which transient conditions or activities that would cause nuisance alarms are anticipated.

The alarm verification feature should not be used to compensate for a poor design that places the wrong type of smoke detector in locations prone to unwanted alarms. The feature is also not intended to eliminate unwanted alarms resulting from failure to properly test and maintain smoke detectors. In some cases, the feature is automatically programmed into the fire alarm system control unit. The record of completion form (see Figure 10.18.2.1.1) must show whether alarm verification is enabled. If the status of the alarm verification feature changes, the record of completion form must be updated after the reacceptance test.

A.23.8.5.4.1 The alarm verification feature should not be used as a substitute for proper detector location/applications or regular system maintenance. Alarm verification features are intended to reduce the frequency of false alarms caused by transient conditions. They are not intended to compensate for design errors or lack of maintenance.

Alarm verification can be very useful in reducing false or unwanted alarms caused by transient conditions. This feature can reduce accidental false alarms caused by the casual spraying of aerosols into a smoke detector, a gust of wind blowing dust or contaminants into the detector, and similar situations. Verification does not reduce false alarms from conditions that remain relatively constant, such as high humidity, high air velocities, insect infestation, and where people maliciously and persistently initiate false alarms. Alarm verification should not be installed or programmed in a system that experiences false alarms without the specific cause(s) of the false alarms being determined.

Alarm verification is a specific operation and timing sequence of smoke detector/system operation. Verification must be listed as part of the control unit, device, or circuit card. Exhibit 23.11 illustrates the alarm verification timing sequence.

23.8.5.4.2 If automatic drift compensation of sensitivity for a fire detector is provided, the fire alarm control unit shall identify the affected detector when the limit of compensation is reached.

Outside sources, such as dust, dirt, or environmental changes, can affect the sensitivity of a smoke detector. Automatic drift compensation helps keep the detector within its original range of sensitivity. If the compensated value places the detector outside its listed window of sensitivity, the control unit indicates that maintenance is needed.

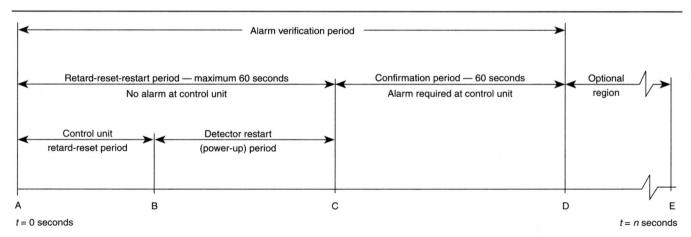

A — Smoke detector goes into alarm.

AB — Retard-reset period (control unit) — Control unit senses detector in alarm and retards (delays) alarm signal, usually by de-energizing power to the detector. Length of time varies with design.

BC — Restart period (detector power-up time) — Power to the detector is reapplied and time is allowed for detector to become operational for alarm. Time varies with detector design.

AC — Retard-reset-restart period — No alarm obtained from control unit. Maximum permissible time is 60 seconds.

CD — Confirmation period — Detector is operational for alarm at point C. If detector is still in alarm at point C, control unit will alarm. If detector is not in alarm, system returns to standby. If the detector re-alarms at any time during the confirmation period, the control unit will alarm.

DE — Optional region — Either an alarm can occur at control unit or restart of the alarm verification cycle can occur.

AD — Alarm verification period — Consists of the retard-reset-restart and confirmation periods.

EXHIBIT 23.11 *Alarm Verification Timing Diagram. (Source: Underwriters Laboratories Inc., Northbrook, IL)*

23.8.5.4.3 Systems that require the operation of two automatic detectors to initiate the alarm response shall be permitted, provided that the following conditions are satisfied:

(1) The systems are not prohibited by the authority having jurisdiction.
(2) At least two automatic detectors are in each protected space.
(3) The alarm verification feature is not used.

The configuration described in 23.8.5.4.3 can be called cross-zoning or priority matrix zoning. This configuration is most commonly used for the actuation of extinguishing systems. The potential for accidental discharge is minimized because actuation of more than one detector is required to initiate discharge of the extinguishing system. An important note is that, in addition to the conditions listed in 23.8.5.4.3, detector spacing must also comply with the requirements of 23.8.5.4.4 and 23.8.5.4.5.

23.8.5.4.4 For systems that require the operation of two automatic detectors to initiate fire safety functions or to actuate fire extinguishing or suppression systems, the detectors shall be installed at the spacing determined in accordance with Chapter 17.

For applications involving the initiation of fire safety functions or the actuation of extinguishing or suppression systems, detector spacing cannot exceed the limits determined in accordance with Chapter 17. Although a requirement for reduced spacing is not specified in 23.8.5.4.4, some applications and designs might use detector spacing that would be significantly less than that required by Chapter 17, since actuation of two detectors is required for system discharge. Using a reduced spacing may speed actuation of the extinguishing system and may be required by the system designer to achieve a desired performance goal.

23.8.5.4.5 For systems that require the operation of two automatic detectors to actuate public mode notification, the detectors shall be installed at a linear spacing not more than 0.7 times the linear spacing determined in accordance with Chapter 17.

Applications that require the actuation of two detectors to actuate public mode notification are rare. This method should not be used to minimize unwanted or false alarms that are the result of the improper application of detectors or poor system design. In addition, for these applications, 23.8.5.4.5 requires detector spacing to be reduced. The linear spacing determined in accordance with Chapter 17 must be effectively reduced by at least 30 percent, increasing the number of detectors that would otherwise be needed.

23.8.5.5* Fire Alarm Signal Initiation — Sprinkler Systems.

A.23.8.5.5 This Code does not specifically require a waterflow alarm-initiating device to be connected to the building fire alarm system. Connection to the building fire alarm system would be determined by the requirements established by the authority having jurisdiction. See A.1.2.4.

FAQ ▶
Does *NFPA 72* require connection of a waterflow alarm–initiating device to a fire alarm system?

The requirement to have a fire alarm system input from a waterflow alarm–initiating device(s) is established by the requirements of other codes or sources within the framework described in the general discussion following 23.8.5. For example, where a *supervised* automatic sprinkler system is provided in accordance with the provisions of NFPA *101*, that system is required to transmit a waterflow alarm to a supervising station or the fire department by means of a fire alarm system. Refer to Exhibit 23.12, which is an excerpt from NFPA *101*.

The detailed installation and performance requirements for the sprinkler systems are contained in NFPA 13, *Standard for the Installation of Sprinkler Systems.* Included are requirements for waterflow alarms and a requirement for compliance with *NFPA 72* when alarm-initiating devices are connected as part of a fire alarm system. Refer to Exhibit 23.13, which is an excerpt from NFPA 13.

9.7.2.2 Alarm Signal Transmission. Where supervision of automatic sprinkler systems is provided in accordance with another provision of this *Code*, waterflow alarms shall be transmitted to an approved, proprietary alarm-receiving facility, a remote station, a central station, or the fire department. Such connection shall be in accordance with 9.6.1.3.

EXHIBIT 23.12 *Waterflow Alarm Signal Transmission. [Excerpt from NFPA 101, 2009 edition]*

6.9 Waterflow Alarm Devices.

6.9.1 General. Waterflow alarm devices shall be listed for the service and so constructed and installed that any flow of water from a sprinkler system equal to or greater than that from a single automatic sprinkler of the smallest orifice size installed on the system will result in an audible alarm on the premises within 5 minutes after such flow begins and until such flow stops.

6.9.2 Waterflow Detecting Devices.

6.9.2.1 Wet Pipe Systems. The alarm apparatus for a wet pipe system shall consist of a listed alarm check valve or other listed waterflow-detecting alarm device with the necessary attachments required to give an alarm.

6.9.2.2 Dry Pipe Systems.

6.9.2.2.1 The alarm apparatus for a dry pipe system shall consist of listed alarm attachments to the dry pipe valve.

6.9.2.2.2 Where a dry pipe valve is located on the system side of an alarm valve, connection of the actuating device of the alarms for the dry pipe valve to the alarms on the wet pipe system shall be permitted.

6.9.2.3 Preaction and Deluge Systems. The alarm apparatus for deluge and preaction systems shall consist of alarms actuated independently by the detection system and the flow of water.

6.9.2.3.1 Deluge and preaction systems operated by pilot sprinklers shall not require an independent detection system alarm.

6.9.2.4* Paddle-Type Waterflow Devices. Paddle-type waterflow alarm indicators shall be installed in wet systems only.

A.6.9.2.4 The surge of water that occurs when the valve trips can seriously damage the device. Paddle-type waterflow devices are also permitted to be installed on wet systems that supply auxiliary dry pipe and/or preaction systems.

6.9.3 Attachments — General.

6.9.3.1* An alarm unit shall include a listed mechanical alarm, horn, or siren or a listed electric gong, bell, speaker, horn, or siren.

A.6.9.3.1 Audible alarms are normally located on the outside of the building. Listed electric gongs, bells, horns, or sirens inside the building, or a combination of such used inside and outside, are sometimes advisable.

Outside alarms might not be necessary where the sprinkler system is used as part of a central station, auxiliary, remote station, or proprietary signaling fire alarm system, utillizing listed audible inside alarm devices.

6.9.3.2* Outdoor water motor-operated or electrically operated bells shall be weatherproofed and guarded.

A.6.9.3.2 All alarm apparatus should be so located and installed that all parts are accessible for inspection, removal, and repair, and such apparatus should be substantially supported. The water motor gong bell mechanism should be protected from weather-related elements such as rain, snow, or ice. To the extent practicable, it should also be protected from other influencing factors such as birds or other small animals that might attempt to nest in such a device.

6.9.3.3 All piping to water motor-operated devices shall be galvanized steel, brass, copper, or other approved metallic corrosion-resistant material of not less than ¾ in. (20 mm) nominal pipe size.

6.9.3.4 Piping between the sprinkler system and a pressure-actuated alarm-initiating device shall be galvanized steel, brass, copper, or other approved metallic corrosion-resistant material of not less than ⅜ in. (10 mm) nominal pipe size.

6.9.4* Attachments — Electrically Operated.

A.6.9.4 Switches that will silence electric alarm-sounding devices by interruption of electric current are not desirable; however, if such means are provided, then the electric alarm-sounding device circuit should be arranged so that, when the sounding device is electrically silenced, that fact should be indicated by means of a conspicuous light located in the vicinity of the riser or alarm control panel. This light should remain in operation during the entire period of the electric circuit interruption.

6.9.4.1 Electrically operated alarm attachments forming part of an auxiliary, central station, local protective, proprietary, or remote station signaling system shall be installed in accordance with *NFPA 72, National Fire Alarm and Signaling Code*.

6.9.4.2 Sprinkler waterflow alarm systems that are not part of a required protective signaling system shall not be required to be supervised and shall be installed in accordance with *NFPA 70, National Electrical Code*, Article 760.

6.9.4.3 Outdoor electric alarm devices shall be listed for outdoor use.

6.9.5 Alarm Device Drains. Drains from alarm devices shall be so arranged that there will be no overflowing at the alarm apparatus, at domestic connections, or elsewhere with the sprinkler drains wide open and under system pressure. *(See 8.16.2.6.)*

EXHIBIT 23.13 *Waterflow Alarms. [Excerpt from NFPA 13, 2010 edition]*

Again, the requirement for connection to a fire alarm system would be established from other sources such as NFPA *101* or the building code adopted by the jurisdiction and will depend on the type of occupancy involved. Even where not required by other codes or authorities, the design criteria used to meet the owner's goals may establish the need or desire for this input. Refer to Supplement 4 for a summary of the occupancy requirements from NFPA *101*.

Examples of typical waterflow switches are shown in Exhibits 23.14 and 23.15.

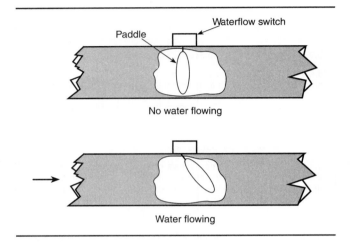

EXHIBIT 23.15 Waterflow Switch Operation. (Source: FIREPRO Incorporated, Andover, MA)

EXHIBIT 23.14 Vane-Type Waterflow Switch. (Source: Potter Electric Signal Company, LLC, St. Louis, MO)

23.8.5.5.1 Where required by other governing laws, codes, or standards to be electronically monitored, waterflow alarm-initiating devices shall be connected to a dedicated function fire alarm control unit designated as "sprinkler waterflow and supervisory system" and permanently identified on the control unit and record drawings.

Exception: Where waterflow alarm-initiating devices are connected to a building fire alarm system, a dedicated function fire alarm control unit shall not be required.

Where other codes, standards, or authorities having jurisdiction require the supervision of automatic sprinkler systems, a dedicated function FACU is used. This requirement assumes that there is no building fire alarm system. The exception explains that the dedicated function FACU is required only if there is no building fire alarm system. The installation of a dedicated function FACU does *not* trigger a requirement for a building fire alarm system if one does not already exist.

23.8.5.5.2* The number of waterflow alarm-initiating devices permitted to be connected to a single initiating device circuit shall not exceed five.

A.23.8.5.5.2 Circuits connected to a signaling line circuit interface are initiating device circuits and are subject to these limitations.

The Code permits a maximum of five waterflow switches on a single initiating device circuit. Limiting the number of switches minimizes the area emergency responders must search to find the fire location. It also limits loss of fire detection to a manageable area, since in some cases the sprinklers and waterflow switches also serve as the building fire detection system.

Even the limit of five waterflow switches on a single initiating device circuit may be too many based on design considerations and site-specific conditions. NFPA 13 permits a single sprinkler system to protect up to 52,000 ft² (4831 m²) per floor. Five waterflow switches on a single initiating device circuit would result in a common signal from an area of up to 260,000 ft² (24,155 m²). Locating fire and operating sprinklers in a large, open manufacturing building might be easy for emergency responders, but the task is much more difficult in an office building or educational facility that is divided into many small rooms.

The number of waterflow switches permitted on a signaling line circuit is not limited, other than the limits imposed by the design of the equipment, because each waterflow alarm can be annunciated individually. Refer to the definitions of *initiating device circuit* and *signaling line circuit* in 3.3.123 and 3.3.242 and the related commentary for an explanation of the differences between these two types of circuits.

Paragraph A.23.8.5.5.2 recognizes that a signaling line circuit interface may be used to connect waterflow–alarm initiating devices to a signaling line circuit and that the limit of five devices also applies to any waterflow alarm-initiating devices connected to the interface. Refer to the definition of *signaling line circuit interface* in 3.3.127.1.1.

23.8.5.6* Supervisory Signal Initiation — Sprinkler Systems.

A.23.8.5.6 This Code does not specifically require supervisory signal-initiating devices to be connected to the building fire alarm system. Connections to the building fire alarm system would be determined by the requirements established by the authority having jurisdiction. See A.1.2.4. Some systems utilize non-electrical methods to supervise conditions of the system such as chains on sprinkler control valves.

Supervisory signals are not intended to provide indication of design, installation, or functional defects in the supervised systems or system components and are not a substitute for regular testing of those systems in accordance with the applicable standard. Supervised conditions should include, but not be limited to, the following:

(1) Control valves $1\frac{1}{2}$ in. (38.1 mm) or larger
(2) Pressure, including dry-pipe system air, pressure tank air, preaction system supervisory air, steam for flooding systems, and public water
(3) Water tanks, including water level and temperature
(4) Building temperature, including areas such as valve closet and fire pump house
(5) Electric fire pumps, including running (alarm or supervisory), power failure, and phase reversal
(6) Engine-driven fire pumps, including running (alarm or supervisory), failure to start, controller off "automatic," and trouble (e.g., low oil, high temperature, overspeed)
(7) Steam turbine fire pumps, including running (alarm or supervisory), steam pressure, and steam control valves

The requirement for supervision of sprinkler system functions comes from other codes and standards, not directly from *NFPA 72*. For example, NFPA *101* requires that sprinkler systems in some occupancies be electrically supervised by the building fire alarm system. If there is no building fire alarm system, then a dedicated function fire alarm system would be installed to comply with the supervision and monitoring requirements. Refer to Exhibit 23.16, excerpted from NFPA *101*, which shows the general requirement for supervision and the minimum features to be monitored. Supplement 4 includes a summary of the occupancy requirements from NFPA *101*. Note that requirements of other codes and standards may be different.

◄ **FAQ**
Does *NFPA 72* require sprinkler system supervision?

Probably the most important fire suppression system feature monitored by the fire alarm system is the position of sprinkler and fire protection water supply control valves. NFPA 13 requires supervision of these control valves, but supervision by a fire alarm system is only one of the permitted choices. Exhibit 23.17, which is excerpted from NFPA 13, shows all the methods recognized by NFPA 13 for supervision of sprinkler control valves. Also refer to A.8.16.1.1.2 in NFPA 13 for extensive explanatory material addressing valve supervision. Although *NFPA 72* does not require the supervision of sprinkler control valves or other features essential for the operation of fire suppression systems, electrical supervision provides continuous information to facility management concerning the status of monitored fire protection and life safety systems.

9.7.2.1* Supervisory Signals. Where supervised automatic sprinkler systems are required by another section of this *Code*, supervisory attachments shall be installed and monitored for integrity in accordance with *NFPA 72, National Fire Alarm Code*, and a distinctive supervisory signal shall be provided to indicate a condition that would impair the satisfactory operation of the sprinkler system. System components and parameters that shall be monitored shall include, but shall not be limited to, control valves, fire pump power supplies and running conditions, water tank levels and temperatures, tank pressure, and air pressure on dry-pipe valves. Supervisory signals shall sound and shall be displayed either at a location within the protected building that is constantly attended by qualified personnel or at an approved, remotely located receiving facility.

A.9.7.2.1 *NFPA 72, National Fire Alarm Code*, provides details of standard practice in sprinkler supervision. Subject to the approval of the authority having jurisdiction, sprinkler supervision is also permitted to be provided by direct connection to municipal fire departments or, in the case of very large establishments, to a private headquarters providing similar functions. *NFPA 72* covers such matters.

Where municipal fire alarm systems are involved, reference should also be made to NFPA 1221, *Standard for the Installation, Maintenance, and Use of Emergency Services Communications Systems*.

EXHIBIT 23.16 *Supervisory Signals. [Excerpt from NFPA 101, 2009 edition]*

8.16.1.1.2* Supervision.

8.16.1.1.2.1 Valves on connections to water supplies, sectional control and isolation valves, and other valves in supply pipes to sprinklers and other fixed water-based fire suppression systems shall be supervised by one of the following methods:

(1) Central station, proprietary, or remote station signaling service
(2) Local signaling service that will cause the sounding of an audible signal at a constantly attended point
(3) Valves locked in the correct position
(4) Valves located within fenced enclosures under the control of the owner, sealed in the open position, and inspected weekly as part of an approved procedure

8.16.1.1.2.2 Floor control valves in high-rise buildings and valves controlling flow to sprinklers in circulating closed loop systems shall comply with 8.16.1.1.2.1(1) or 8.16.1.1.2.1(2).

8.16.1.1.2.3 The requirements of 8.16.1.1.2.1 shall not apply to underground gate valves with roadway boxes.

8.16.1.1.2.4 Where control valves are installed overhead, they shall be positioned so that the indicating feature is visible from the floor below.

EXHIBIT 23.17 *Supervision. [Excerpt from NFPA 13, 2010 edition]*

EXHIBIT 23.18 *Sprinkler and Water Supply Control Valves That Can Be Supervised. (Source: Potter Electric Signal Company, LLC, St. Louis, MO)*

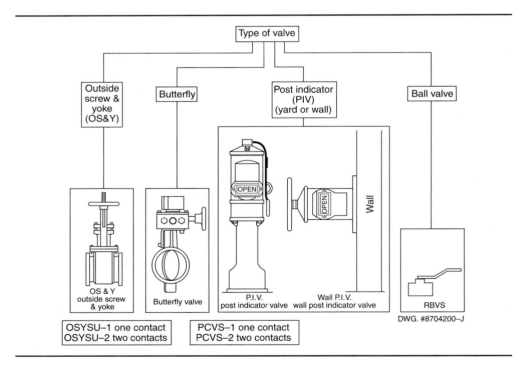

Exhibit 23.18 shows examples of control valves; Exhibit 23.19 is an example of a supervisory switch; and Exhibit 23.20 is an example of a pressure switch for supervising suppression system pressure.

23.8.5.6.1 Where required by other governing laws, codes, or standards to be electronically monitored, supervisory signal–initiating devices shall be connected to a dedicated function fire alarm control unit designated as "sprinkler waterflow and supervisory system" and permanently identified on the control unit and record drawings.

Exception: Where supervisory signal–initiating devices are connected to a building fire alarm system, a dedicated function fire alarm control unit shall not be required.

Where other codes, standards, or authorities having jurisdiction require the supervision of automatic sprinkler systems, a dedicated function FACU is used. This requirement assumes that there is no building fire alarm system. The exception explains that the dedicated function fire alarm panel is required only if there is no building fire alarm system. The installation of a dedicated function FACU does not trigger a requirement for a building fire alarm system.

23.8.5.6.2* The number of supervisory signal–initiating devices permitted to be connected to a single initiating device circuit shall not exceed 20.

A.23.8.5.6.2 Circuits connected to a signaling line circuit interface are initiating device circuits and are subject to these limitations.

The Code permits up to 20 supervisory signal-initiating devices on a single initiating device circuit because doing so does not degrade the reliability or operability of the fire alarm system. Site-specific needs and conditions might dictate that a circuit serves fewer devices. For example, if a facility has 20 sprinkler control valves each equipped with a supervisory switch, all the valve supervisory switches could be connected to the same initiating device circuit and still comply with the Code. However, if a supervisory signal were received, it would require that someone check every valve to find the one initiating the signal. Supervisory signal-initiating devices include valve supervisory switches, air pressure switches, building temperature switches, fire protection water tank level and temperature switches, and other devices that are designed to ensure that fire protection and life safety features are in service at the time of a fire. Refer to the definitions of *supervisory signal-initiating device* and *supervisory signal* in 3.3.122.5 and 3.3.240.6.

23.8.5.7 Alarm Signal Initiation — Fire Suppression Systems Other Than Sprinklers.

23.8.5.7.1 Where required by other governing laws, codes, or standards to be monitored and a building fire alarm system is installed, the actuation of a fire suppression system shall annunciate an alarm or supervisory condition at the building fire alarm control unit.

This paragraph no longer explicitly requires operation of an automatic fire suppression system (other than waterflow) to cause an alarm signal at the building fire alarm system control unit. Instead, 23.8.5.7.1 specifies that if the suppression system is required to be monitored and if a building fire alarm system is installed, the actuation of a fire suppression system is required to annunciate an alarm or supervisory condition at the building FACU. This requirement is a departure from previous editions of the Code, which required an alarm condition from any suppression system to be transmitted to the building FACU. The authority having jurisdiction now has the flexibility to permit either an alarm or a supervisory signal to be sent to the building FACU, depending on the fire safety objectives of the suppression system. For example, the actuation of a suppression system on an industrial process where fires are a routine part of the operation could provide a supervisory condition to be transmitted rather than an alarm. Some printing operations may experience frequent fires that are quickly extinguished by a carbon dioxide fire suppression system without ensuing damage and without sounding a general alarm throughout the facility. It should be noted that the actuation of most gaseous suppression systems is performed through a releasing system FACU, a control unit that is required by 23.8.2.1 and 23.8.2.2 to be monitored by the building fire alarm system, if present. The need to monitor the suppression system is generally established by the requirements of other codes or sources within the framework described in the general discussion

EXHIBIT 23.19 *Control Valve Supervisory Switch. (Source: Potter Electric Signal Company, LLC, St. Louis, MO)*

EXHIBIT 23.20 *High-Low-Pressure Supervisory Switch. (Source: Potter Electric Signal Company, LLC, St. Louis, MO)*

following 23.8.5. Documents such as NFPA *101* include requirements for these types of extinguishing systems to interface with the building fire alarm system. Refer to Exhibit 23.21, which is excerpted from NFPA *101*.

EXHIBIT 23.21 *Other Automatic Extinguishing Equipment. [Excerpt from NFPA 101, 2009 edition]*

9.7.3 Other Automatic Extinguishing Equipment.

9.7.3.1 In any occupancy where the character of the fuel for fire is such that extinguishment or control of fire is accomplished by a type of automatic extinguishing system in lieu of an automatic sprinkler system, such system shall be installed in accordance with the appropriate standard, as determined in accordance with Table 9.7.3.1.

Table 9.7.3.1 Fire Suppression System Installation Standards

Fire Suppression Systems	Installation Standard
Low-, medium-, and high-expansion foam systems	NFPA 11, *Standard for Low-, Medium-, and High-Expansion Foam*
Carbon dioxide systems	NFPA 12, *Standard on Carbon Dioxide Extinguishing Systems*
Halon 1301 systems	NFPA 12A, *Standard on Halon 1301 Fire Extinguishing Systems*
Water spray fixed systems	NFPA 15, *Standard for Water Spray Fixed Systems for Fire Protection*
Deluge foam-water sprinkler systems	NFPA 16, *Standard for the Installation of Foam-Water Sprinkler and Foam-Water Spray Systems*
Dry chemical systems	NFPA 17, *Standard for Dry Chemical Extinguishing Systems*
Wet chemical systems	NFPA 17A, *Standard for Wet Chemical Extinguishing Systems*
Water mist systems	NFPA 750, *Standard on Water Mist Fire Protection Systems*
Clean agent extinguishing systems	NFPA 2001, *Standard on Clean Agent Fire Extinguishing Systems*

9.7.3.2 If the extinguishing system is installed in lieu of a required, supervised automatic sprinkler system, the activation of the extinguishing system shall activate the building fire alarm system, where provided. The actuation of an extinguishing system that is not installed in lieu of a required, supervised automatic sprinkler system shall be indicated at the building fire alarm system, where provided.

Automatic fire suppression systems other than sprinklers include systems such as low-, medium-, and high-expansion foams, carbon dioxide, dry chemical, wet chemical, and clean agents. Each of these systems has an NFPA standard that covers the design, installation, testing, and maintenance of the system. For example, NFPA 17, *Standard for Dry Chemical Extinguishing Systems,* and NFPA 17A, *Standard for Wet Chemical Extinguishing Systems,* specifically require that each of these types of systems connect to a fire alarm system, if one is present.

23.8.5.7.2 The integrity of each fire suppression system actuating device and its circuit shall comply with 10.17.1.1, 10.17.1.2, and other applicable NFPA standards.

The actuation circuit for the fire suppression system must be monitored for integrity the same as any other fire alarm circuit. Any fault conditions on the releasing service FACU must initiate a trouble signal on the releasing service FACU but will initiate a supervisory signal on the building fire alarm system control unit if one is present. Also refer the requirements of 23.13.3 and 23.13.10.

23.8.5.8* Supervisory Signal Initiation — Fire Suppression Systems Other Than Sprinklers.

The requirement for fire alarm system inputs from supervisory signal–initiating devices is established by the requirements of other codes or sources within the framework described in the general discussion following 23.8.5. *NFPA 72* does not require this supervision.

◄ FAQ
Does *NFPA 72* require supervision of fire suppression systems other than sprinklers?

A.23.8.5.8 See A.23.8.5.6.

23.8.5.8.1 Where required to be monitored and a building fire alarm system is installed, an off-normal condition of a fire suppression system shall annunciate a supervisory condition at the building fire alarm control unit.

Paragraph 23.8.5.8.1 specifies that if the suppression system is required by another code or standard to be monitored and if a building fire alarm system is installed, any off-normal condition is required to be transmitted as a supervisory signal to the building FACU.

23.8.5.8.2 Supervisory signals that latch in the off-normal state and require manual reset of the system to restore them to normal shall be permitted.

Supervisory signals usually restore automatically when the off-normal condition is restored to a normal state. In some cases, having supervisory signals "latch" in the off-normal position can be beneficial. This requires manual reset of the system after restoration of the off-normal condition. Paragraph 23.8.5.8.2 permits this arrangement.

23.8.5.9 Signal Initiation — Fire Pump.

The requirement for fire pumps to be monitored comes from other codes and standards. For example, NFPA *101* includes the monitoring of fire pump power supplies and running conditions as a part of the supervision requirements for automatic sprinklers. Refer to Exhibit 23.16. Note that requirements of other codes and standards may be different.

The installation requirements for fire pumps are contained in NFPA 20, *Standard for the Installation of Stationary Pumps for Fire Protection*. This standard requires certain functions to be monitored and signals to be sent to a constantly attended location. Refer to Exhibit 23.22, which is excerpted from NFPA 20. Note that NFPA 20 does not specifically require these conditions to be monitored by a fire alarm system, but a dedicated function or building fire alarm system could be used to accomplish this monitoring.

23.8.5.9.1 Where fire pumps are required to be monitored and a building fire alarm system is installed, a pump running signal shall be permitted to be a supervisory or alarm signal.

Paragraph 23.8.5.9.1 makes it clear that a pump running signal monitored by a building fire alarm system can be either an alarm signal or a supervisory signal.

23.8.5.9.2 Where fire pumps are required to be monitored and a building fire alarm system is installed, signals other than pump running shall be supervisory signals.

In contrast to the pump running signal, 23.8.5.9.2 makes it clear any other fire pump signal monitored by a building fire alarm system must be a supervisory signal.

23.8.5.10 Fire Alarm and Supervisory Signal Initiation — Releasing Fire Alarm Systems.

23.8.5.10.1 Releasing service fire alarm control units shall be connected to the protected premises fire alarm system.

23.8.5.10.2 Fire alarm and supervisory signals generated at the releasing service fire alarm control unit shall be annunciated at a protected premises fire alarm unit.

23.8.5.10.3 Where required by other governing laws, codes, or standards, actuation of any suppression system connected to a releasing service fire alarm control unit shall be annunciated

EXHIBIT 23.22 *Fire Pump Alarm and Signal Devices Remote from Controller. [Excerpt from NFPA 20, 2010 edition]*

10.4.7* Fire Pump Alarm and Signal Devices Remote from Controller.

A.10.4.7 Where unusual conditions exist whereby pump operation is not certain, a "failed-to-operate" fire pump alarm is recommended. In order to supervise the power source for the fire pump alarm circuit, the controller can be arranged to start upon failure of the supervised alarm circuit power.

10.4.7.1 Where the pump room is not constantly attended, audible or visible signals powered by a source not exceeding 125 V shall be provided at a point of constant attendance.

10.4.7.2 These fire pump alarms and signals shall indicate the information in 10.4.7.2.1 through 10.4.7.2.4.

10.4.7.2.1 Pump or Motor Running. The signal shall actuate whenever the controller has operated into a motor-running condition. This signal circuit shall be energized by a separate reliable supervised power source or from the pump motor power, reduced to not more than 125 V.

10.4.7.2.2 Loss of Phase.

10.4.7.2.2.1 The fire pump alarm shall actuate whenever any phase at the line terminals of the motor contactor is lost.

10.4.7.2.2.2 All phases shall be monitored. Such monitoring shall detect loss of phase whether the motor is running or at rest.

10.4.7.2.2.3 When power is supplied from multiple power sources, monitoring of each power source for phase loss shall be permitted at any point electrically upstream of the line terminals of the contactor, provided all sources are monitored.

10.4.7.2.3 Phase Reversal. *(See 10.4.6.2.)* This fire pump alarm circuit shall be energized by a separate reliable supervised power source or from the pump motor power, reduced to not more than 125 V. The fire pump alarm shall actuate whenever the three-phase power at the line terminals of the motor contactor is reversed.

10.4.7.2.4 Controller Connected to Alternate Source. Where two sources of power are supplied to meet the requirements of 9.3.2, this signal shall indicate whenever the alternate source is the source supplying power to the controller. This signal circuit shall be energized by a separate, reliable, supervised power source, reduced to not more than 125 V.

at the protected premises fire alarm control unit, even where the system actuation is by manual means or otherwise accomplished without actuation of the releasing service fire alarm control unit.

Subsection 23.13.1 requires FACUs used for automatic or manual activation of a fire suppression system to be listed for releasing service. The Code defines the term *releasing service fire alarm control unit* as a subdefinition of protected premises (local) control unit. The requirements in 23.8.5.10.1, 23.8.5.10.2, and 23.8.5.10.3 correlate with the requirements in 23.8.2.1, 23.8.2.2, and 23.13.10. In addition, 23.8.5.10.3 includes a requirement to annunciate the actuation of the suppression system at the protected premises FACU even where the actuation is not accomplished through the connected releasing service control unit.

Each input to the fire alarm system corresponding to the operation of an automatic fire suppression system should be configured as a separate zone or discrete point to allow identification of the system involved. For example, if a building is equipped with a clean agent suppression system in a computer room and a wet-chemical system in the kitchen, there should be separate signals from each system.

23.8.5.10.4 If a valve is installed in the connection between a suppression system and an initiating device, the valve shall be supervised in accordance with Chapter 17.

Supervision of the valve in this case means monitoring the status of the valve and initiating a supervisory signal when the valve is moved to an off-normal (other than fully open) position. When the valve returns to its normal (fully open) position, the supervisory device initiates a restoration-to-normal signal.

Paragraph 23.8.5.10.4 requires supervision of any valve that if closed could prevent actuation of the alarm-initiating device. The alarm-initiating device is usually a pressure switch that actuates when the fire suppression system actuates. Exhibit 23.23 shows the proper method of providing an alarm-initiating device with no valves between the suppression system and the alarm-initiating device.

EXHIBIT 23.23 *Alarm-Initiating Device with No Valves Between Suppression System and Alarm-Initiating Device. (Source: Hughes Associates, Inc., Cincinnati, OH)*

23.8.5.10.5 In facilities that are not required to install a protected premises fire alarm system, the alarm and supervisory devices shall be connected to the releasing service fire alarm control unit, and their actuation shall be annunciated at the releasing service control unit.

This paragraph recognizes that suppression system alarm and supervisory devices need to be connected to an FACU. When a building FACU is not required, these devices need to be connected to the releasing service control unit.

23.8.5.11 Trouble Signal Initiation.

23.8.5.11.1 Automatic fire suppression system alarm–initiating devices and supervisory signal-initiating devices and their circuits shall be designed and installed so that they cannot be subject to tampering, opening, or removal without initiating a signal. This provision shall include junction boxes installed outside of buildings to facilitate access to the initiating device circuit.

Exception No. 1: Covers of junction boxes inside of buildings.

Exception No. 2: Tamper–resistant screws or other approved mechanical means shall be permitted for preventing access to junction boxes and device covers installed outside of buildings.

A junction box installed outside a building must be equipped with tamper-resistant screws or some other mechanical means preventing access to the junction box, or it must have a device to initiate a trouble signal when the box is opened, as required by 23.8.5.11.1. This precaution minimizes the possibility that unauthorized individuals can bypass the supervision of fire suppression systems by tampering with the wiring in junction boxes. Exception 1 exempts junction boxes within a building because this area should be under the general supervision of the building owner or occupant and not subject to tampering by outsiders. Exception 2 exempts junction boxes installed outside the building if they are equipped with special screws or other means specifically designed to prevent removal and tampering.

23.8.5.11.2 The integrity of each fire suppression system actuating device and its circuit shall be supervised in accordance with 10.17.1.1 and 10.17.1.2 and with other applicable NFPA standards.

23.8.6 Fire Alarm System Notification Outputs.

23.8.6.1 Occupant Notification. Fire alarm systems provided for evacuation or relocation of occupants shall have one or more notification appliances listed for the purpose on each floor of the building and be so located that they have the characteristics described in Chapter 18 for public mode or private mode, as required.

FAQ ►
Is occupant notification required for every fire alarm system?

Occupant notification is not a required output action of every fire alarm system installed in accordance with this chapter. The requirement in 23.8.6.1 applies only where a function of the fire alarm system is to provide notification to building occupants. The requirements for occupant notification and whether it is public mode, private mode, or coded notification come from the local building code, the *Life Safety Code*, or the system designer (where required to meet the performance goals of a nonrequired system). When a function of the protected premises fire alarm system is to notify the occupants, Chapter 18 requirements for public mode signaling must be followed.

23.8.6.2* Notification Appliances in Exit Stair Enclosures, Exit Passageways, and Elevator Cars. Notification appliances shall not be required in exit stair enclosures, exit passageways, and elevator cars in accordance with 23.8.6.2.1 through 23.8.6.2.4.

This paragraph was new to the 2007 edition of the Code. In 23.8.6.2, exit stairwells, exit passageways, and elevators are exempt from the requirements for installation of audible and visible notification appliances used to signal evacuation. Some of the allowances addressed here are not necessarily new and may already be provided to some extent by other codes and standards. For example, NFPA *101* already permits the exclusion of the general evacuation alarm in exit stair enclosures and in elevator cars.

The general purpose of a fire alarm system is to notify occupants of the need to evacuate and to get them to move to enclosed exits where they are protected and can exit the building. Once occupants have entered an exit stairwell enclosure or an exit passageway, there is no need to continue notification. If occupants are in an exit stairwell or exit passageway when the fire alarm system is actuated, they will hear and see the fire alarm notification appliances as soon as they open the stairwell door to a floor of the building. Likewise, occupants in an exit passageway are already in a protected enclosure that will lead them to the building exterior or to a horizontal exit to an adjacent building. Note that these requirements apply to evacuation signals. Speakers may still be required in stairwell enclosures in some buildings to facilitate communication by the fireground commander with those occupants in the stairwell enclosures.

A.23.8.6.2 The general purpose of the fire alarm audible and visual notification appliances is to alert occupants that there is a fire condition and for occupants to exit from the building.

Once the occupants are in the exit enclosures, high noise levels and light intensity from notification appliances could cause confusion and impede egress. There could be conditions that warrant the installation of notification appliances in exit passageways, but careful analysis is necessary to avoid impeding exiting from the building.

23.8.6.2.1 Visible signals shall not be required in exit stair enclosures and exit passageways.

Flashing strobe lights installed in stairwells could cause visual orientation as people are attempting to navigate the stairs during evacuation. Also, as explained in the commentary for 23.8.6.2, it is not generally necessary to continue notification for occupants who have already entered the exiting system.

23.8.6.2.2 Visible signals shall not be required in elevator cars.

A visible notification appliance installed in an elevator car does not serve to make the occupants safer. Once occupants are in the elevator car, they cannot take any action to exit the building until the car stops at an elevator lobby in the building. Once the elevator stops at a floor, the occupants will see the visual notification appliances operating on that floor and can take appropriate action.

23.8.6.2.3 The evacuation signal shall not be required to operate in exit stair enclosures and exit passageways.

Once occupants have entered an exit enclosure, they do not need to continually hear the audible alarm signal. The reverberation of the evacuation signal in a closed, masonry stairwell can create an environment in which the sound pressure level within the enclosure can be so uncomfortable as to cause the occupants to exit the enclosure to get away from the noise. This effect is exactly the opposite desired for a fire alarm system. The Code also recognizes that situations may occur in which notification appliances within exit enclosures might be desirable. Such situations include fire-rated corridors that serve as exit enclosures in a health care occupancy.

23.8.6.2.4 The evacuation signal shall not be required to operate in elevator cars.

An audible fire alarm signal in an elevator car does not make the occupants safer. Occupants are not in a position to take any action to evacuate the building until the elevator stops at a specific floor. When the doors open at a floor, the occupants will hear the alarm signal on that floor and can take appropriate action.

23.8.6.3 Notification Zones.

23.8.6.3.1 Notification zones shall be consistent with the emergency response or evacuation plan for the protected premises.

The best fire detection and alarm technology alone does not ensure an adequate level of fire safety in a building. A building evacuation or relocation plan is needed for every building to properly establish notification zones. This plan must be custom developed based on the site-specific needs of the facility, site-specific conditions, and the established fire safety objectives. The establishment of notification zones without a fully developed building evacuation or relocation plan is not possible. The *Life Safety Code* includes requirements for evacuation and relocation plans and fire drills for many occupancies. These requirements must be incorporated within the plan for the building.

23.8.6.3.2 The boundaries of notification zones shall be coincident with building outer walls, building fire or smoke compartment boundaries, floor separations, or other fire safety subdivisions.

FAQ ▶
What is a notification zone?

A *notification zone* is defined in 3.3.300.2 as "an area covered by notification appliances that are activated simultaneously." The boundaries described in 23.8.6.3.2 further define the term. A notification zone can contain multiple notification appliance circuits, but all notification appliances within a notification zone must actuate simultaneously.

23.8.6.4 Circuits for Addressable Notification Appliances.

23.8.6.4.1 Circuit configuration for addressable notification appliances shall comply with the applicable performance requirements for notification zones.

23.8.6.4.2 Where there are addressable notification appliances on a signaling line circuit that serves different notification zones, a single open, short–circuit, or ground on that signaling line circuit shall not affect operation of more than one notification zone.

Paragraph 23.8.6.4.2 requires that addressable signaling line circuits be arranged such that a single fault condition on the circuit does not disrupt the operation of notification appliances in more than one notification zone.

23.8.6.4.3 Riser conductors installed in accordance with 24.4.1.8.4.3 that are monitored for integrity shall not be required to operate in accordance with 23.8.6.4.2.

23.9 In-Building Fire Emergency Voice/Alarm Communications

23.9.1 In-building fire emergency voice/alarm communications shall meet the requirements of Chapter 24.

Beginning with the 2010 edition of the Code, the requirements for in-building fire emergency voice/alarm communications (formerly called just emergency voice/alarm communications) are covered in Chapter 24. Paragraph 23.9.1 refers users of the Code to Chapter 24 for the applicable requirements.

23.9.2 All live voice communications systems shall meet the requirements of Chapter 24.

23.10 Prerecorded (Digital) Voice and Tone Fire Alarm Systems

23.10.1 The requirements of Section 23.10 shall apply to both audible (tone and prerecorded voice) and visible notification appliance circuits.

23.10.2* Fire alarm systems used for partial evacuation and relocation shall be designed and installed such that attack by fire within an evacuation signaling zone shall not impair control and operation of the notification appliances outside the evacuation signaling zone. Performance features provided to ensure survivability shall be described and technical justification provided in the documentation submitted to the authority having jurisdiction with the evaluation required in 23.4.3.1.

A.23.10.2 One or more of the following means might be considered acceptable to provide a level of survivability consistent with the intent of this requirement:

(1) Installing a fire alarm system in a fully sprinklered building in accordance with NFPA 13, *Standard for the Installation of Sprinkler Systems*
(2) Routing notification appliance circuits separately
(3) Using short-circuit fault-tolerant signaling line circuits for controlling evacuation signals

The requirement for notification appliances to operate in those evacuation signaling zones that are not attacked by fire will also require that circuits and equipment that are common to more than one evacuation signaling zone be designed and installed such that the fire will not disable them. For instance, a signaling line circuit used to control notification appliances in multiple evacuation signaling zones should be properly designed and installed so that one fire would not impair the signaling line circuit, rendering the notification appliances serving more than one evacuation signaling zone inoperative. Power supply requirements of Chapter 10 apply to these systems. The secondary power supply requirements of that chapter meet the intent of these survivability requirements.

Paragraph 23.10.2 requires that the circuits, wiring, or communications paths to each evacuation signaling zone be arranged such that damage to those "paths" in one evacuation signaling zone will not impair communications to any other evacuation signaling zone. For example, assume that each floor in a high-rise building is an evacuation signaling zone. A circuit that feeds the notification appliances on the fifth floor of a building must be arranged such that damage to that circuit does not affect communications to any other floor above or below.

◄ **FAQ**
What is required for wiring or communications paths to ensure compliance with 23.10.2?

23.10.3 Speakers that transmit prerecorded voice and/or tone signals shall be permitted to be used as fire alarm notification appliances.

23.11 Two-Way Communication Service

Two-way communication service shall meet the requirements of Chapter 24.

Two-way communication service within a building provides a reliable method for fire fighters and other emergency response personnel to communicate with each other during the course of an emergency. The Code recognizes two means: two-way telephones and two-way in-building radio communications enhancement systems. The requirements for these systems are covered in Chapter 24.

23.12 Signal Annunciation

23.12.1 Protected premises fire alarm systems shall be arranged to annunciate alarm, supervisory, and trouble signals in accordance with Section 10.16.

The intent of 23.12.1 is that no confusion should exist in discerning whether a signal is alarm, supervisory, or trouble. Subsection 10.7.3 permits a common audible signal for alarm, supervisory, and trouble signals if the visible indicators are separate.

23.12.2* If a remote alarm indicator is provided for an automatic fire detector in a concealed location, the location of the detector and the area protected by the detector shall be prominently indicated at the remote alarm indicator by a permanently attached placard or by other approved means.

A.23.12.2 Embossed plastic tape, pencil, ink, or crayon should not be considered to be a permanently attached placard.

In a conventional fire alarm system (nonaddressable), a remote alarm indicator, usually a red light-emitting diode (LED) mounted on a single gang plate, is the most common method of indicating an alarm from a concealed detector. Locating and marking the remote alarm indicator is important so that the detector in alarm can be found easily. Engraved phenolic plates permanently attached to the remote alarm indicator are generally considered the most

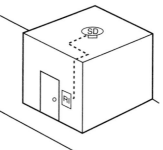

EXHIBIT 23.24 Concealed Smoke Detector (SD) in Locked Room with Remote Indicator (RI). (Source: FIREPRO Incorporated, Andover, MA)

EXHIBIT 23.25 Remote Indicator Used for Concealed Detectors. (Source: System Sensor Corp., St. Charles, IL)

appropriate way of complying with this requirement. See Exhibits 23.24 and 23.25 for examples of a concealed smoke detector and a remote indicator, respectively. In an addressable fire alarm system, the liquid crystal display (LCD) or video screen, located at the FACU or remote annunciator, provides detailed detector location information and is an acceptable alternative to meet the intent of 23.12.2 (see Exhibit 23.26).

EXHIBIT 23.26 FACU/LCD Display. (Source: Gamewell-FCI, Northford, CT)

23.13 Suppression System Actuation

See Exhibit 23.27 for an example of one type of suppression system, a wet chemical kitchen hood and duct cylinder with control head.

23.13.1 Releasing service fire alarm control units used for automatic or manual activation of a fire suppression system shall be listed for releasing service.

23.13.2 Releasing devices for suppression systems shall be listed for use with releasing service control units.

The requirement of 23.13.2 applies to releasing devices for any suppression system.

23.13.3 Each releasing device (e.g., solenoid, relay) shall be monitored for integrity (supervised) in accordance with applicable NFPA standards.

23.13.4 The installation wiring shall be monitored for integrity in accordance with the requirements of Section 10.17.

23.13.5 Releasing service fire alarm systems used for fire suppression–releasing service shall be provided with a disconnect switch to allow the system to be tested without actuating the fire suppression systems.

23.13.5.1 Operation of a disconnect switch or a disable function shall cause a supervisory signal at the releasing service fire alarm control unit.

23.13.5.2 The disconnect shall be a physical switch and not be accomplished by using software.

The requirements of 23.13.5 are extremely important. Very often, the contractor testing the fire alarm system is not an expert in the operation of fire suppression systems. The supervised disconnect switch allows the fire alarm system contractor to perform maintenance or tests on the fire alarm system without inadvertently actuating the suppression system. The Code now clarifies that the required disconnect switch must be a physical switch and cannot be simulated by software. Operation of the switch must provide a supervisory signal at the building fire alarm system control unit. This requirement minimizes the possibility of leaving the fire suppression system impaired after the testing of the fire alarm system is complete. Also refer to the testing requirements for releasing systems in 14.2.5.

23.13.6 Sequence of operation shall be consistent with the applicable suppression system standards.

The exact operating sequence of a fire suppression system depends on the type of system, the application, and site-specific conditions. The Code does not address the specific sequence of operation of any type of fire suppression system. The appropriate NFPA standard for the particular fire suppression system should be consulted.

23.13.7* Each space protected by an automatic fire suppression system actuated by the fire alarm system shall contain one or more automatic fire detectors installed in accordance with Chapter 17.

A.23.13.7 Automatic fire suppression systems referred to in 23.13.7 include, but are not limited to, preaction and deluge sprinkler systems, carbon dioxide systems, Halon systems, and dry chemical systems.

23.13.8 Suppression systems or groups of systems shall be controlled by a single releasing service fire alarm control unit that monitors the associated initiating device(s), actuates the associated releasing device(s), and controls the associated agent release notification appliances.

Unless the conditions of 23.13.9 have been met, a single control unit must be used to control suppression systems. This requirement prohibits an arrangement where the control unit used to actuate the suppression system is listed for releasing service, but it receives its signal to actuate from another FACU that is not listed for releasing service and that monitors the associated alarm-initiating devices. Several instances have occurred in which inadvertent system discharges resulted from multi-tier releasing arrangements. Inadvertent discharges occurred during normal system testing and maintenance and occasionally because of system wiring faults unrelated to the required operation of the releasing system.

Although the use of multiple control units is prohibited (unless 23.13.9 applies), the Code requires that the premises FACU monitor the suppression system control unit, if one is present. The interconnection of a fire suppression system control unit with a protected premises FACU must comply with the requirements of 23.8.2. The premises FACU must not affect the operation of the suppression system. Also refer to the requirements for releasing service control units in 23.8.5.10.

23.13.9 If the configuration of multiple control units is listed for releasing device service, and if a trouble condition or manual disconnect on either control unit causes a trouble or supervisory signal, the initiating device on one control unit shall be permitted to actuate releasing devices on another control unit in lieu of 23.13.8.

◄ **FAQ**
What means must be used to ensure that the suppression system will not be inadvertently actuated?

EXHIBIT 23.27 *Wet Chemical Kitchen Hood and Duct Cylinder with Control Head. (Source: Kidde Fire Systems, Ashland, MA)*

23.13.10 If the releasing service fire alarm control unit is located in a protected premises having a separate fire alarm system, it shall be monitored for alarm, supervisory, and trouble signals, but shall not be dependent on or affected by the operation or failure of the protected premises fire alarm system.

23.13.11 Releasing fire alarm systems performing suppression system releasing functions shall be installed in such a manner that they are effectively protected from damage caused by activation of the suppression system(s) they control.

The control unit must be sealed or enclosed in a cabinet designed to prevent entry of the extinguishing agent, or the control unit must be located outside the discharge area of the fire suppression system.

23.14 Off-Premises Signals

23.14.1 Systems requiring transmission of signals to continuously attended locations providing supervising station service (e.g., central station, proprietary supervising station, remote supervising station) shall also comply with the applicable requirements of Chapter 26.

23.14.2 Relays or modules providing transmission of trouble signals to a supervising station shall be arranged to provide fail-safe operation.

23.14.3 Means provided to transmit trouble signals to supervising stations shall be arranged so as to transmit a trouble signal to the supervising station for any trouble condition received at the protected premises control unit, including loss of primary or secondary power.

23.14.4* It shall be permitted to provide supplementary transmission of real-time data from the fire system to off-premises equipment.

A.23.14.4 Off-site logging of fire alarm data can be useful to preserve information in the face of fire or building failure to facilitate accurate reconstruction of the event. It can also be beneficial to send data off-premises to incident command personnel to enhance situational awareness and response decisions and to maintain safe and efficient operations.

23.14.4.1 Transmission of real-time data off-premises shall not affect the operation or response of the fire alarm control unit.

23.14.4.2 Any data transmitted shall be consistent with the data generated by the system.

23.15 Guard's Tour Supervisory Service

Guard's tour supervisory service may be used to provide fire protection and security surveillance during times when the building or portions of the building are unoccupied. Guard's tour supervisory services designed to continually report the performance of a guard may be found in connection with protected premises fire alarm systems using off-premises reporting to central or proprietary supervising stations. If a guard fails to complete a prescribed round, a runner is dispatched to the building. Failure of a guard to complete a round could be due to illness, injury, or other emergency condition. See NFPA 601, *Standard for Security Services in Fire Loss Prevention*, for additional information on guard patrol tours.

23.15.1 Guard's tour reporting stations shall be listed for the application.

23.15.2 The number of guard's tour reporting stations, their locations, and the route to be followed by the guard for operating the stations shall be approved for the particular installation in accordance with NFPA 601, *Standard for Security Services in Fire Loss Prevention.*

23.15.3 A permanent record indicating every time each signal-transmitting station is operated shall be made at a protected premises fire alarm control unit.

23.15.4 Where intermediate stations that do not transmit a signal are employed in conjunction with signal-transmitting stations, distinctive signals shall be transmitted at the beginning and end of each tour of a guard.

23.15.5 A signal-transmitting station shall be provided at intervals not exceeding 10 intermediate stations.

23.15.6 Intermediate stations that do not transmit a signal shall be capable of operation only in a fixed sequence.

23.16 Suppressed (Exception Reporting) Signal System

This guard's tour arrangement is somewhat more flexible than supervised tours. The advantages of this system are easier installation, because each station does not have to be connected to the circuit, and reduced signal traffic, because each station does not transmit a signal. The usual arrangement is to have the guard transmit a signal at the start of the tour and another signal at the completion of the tour. These signals must be received within a specific timeframe, or the system initiates a supervisory signal indicating that the guard is delinquent in completing the round.

23.16.1 The suppressed signal system shall comply with the provisions of 23.15.2.

23.16.2 The system shall transmit a start signal to the signal-receiving location.

23.16.3 The start signal shall be initiated by the guard at the start of continuous tour rounds.

23.16.4 The system shall automatically transmit a delinquency signal within 15 minutes after the predetermined actuation time if the guard fails to actuate a tour station as scheduled.

23.16.5 A finish signal shall be transmitted within a predetermined interval after the guard's completion of each tour of the premises.

23.16.6 For periods of over 24 hours during which tours are continuously conducted, a start signal shall be transmitted at least every 24 hours.

23.16.7 The start, delinquency, and finish signals shall be recorded at the signal-receiving location.

23.17 Protected Premises Fire Safety Functions

In the 2010 edition of the Code, all the requirements for protected premises fire safety functions have been relocated to Chapter 21. Chapter 23 refers users of the Code to the applicable sections in Chapter 21.

23.17.1 Emergency Elevator Operations. Emergency elevator operations shall meet the requirements of Sections 21.3, 21.4, 21.5, and 21.6.

23.17.2 HVAC Systems. HVAC systems shall meet the requirements of Section 21.7.

23.17.3 Door Release Service. Door release service shall meet the requirements of Section 21.8.

23.17.4 Electrically Locked Doors. Door-unlocking devices shall meet the requirements of Section 21.9.

23.17.5 Exit Marking Audible Notification Systems. Exit marking audible notification systems shall meet the requirements of Section 21.10.

23.18* Special Requirements for Low-Power Radio (Wireless) Systems

A.23.18 The term *wireless* has been replaced with the term *low-power radio* to eliminate potential confusion with other transmission media such as optical fiber cables.

Low-power radio devices are required to comply with the applicable *low-power* requirements of Title 47, Code of Federal Regulations, Part 15.

Listed low-power wireless fire alarm systems must meet the same basic requirements as any other fire alarm system. However, the special requirements provided in Section 23.18 modify the basic requirements of the Code.

Listed low-power wireless fire alarm systems have numerous applications. Historic buildings where wire or cable installation will damage the building or affect the historic significance of the property have used wireless fire alarm systems successfully. Industrial buildings that use corrosive materials that can affect the integrity of the wiring used to interconnect a fire alarm system may benefit from low-power wireless systems. Likewise, any buildings that are remote from the main facility can also be well served by a low-power wireless fire alarm system. See Exhibits 23.28, 23.29, and 23.30 for examples of low-power wireless fire alarm systems.

23.18.1* Listing Requirements. Compliance with Section 23.18 shall require the use of low-power radio equipment specifically listed for the purpose.

A.23.18.1 Equipment listed solely for dwelling unit use would not comply with this requirement.

23.18.2 Power Supplies. A primary battery (dry cell) shall be permitted to be used as the sole power source of a low-power radio transmitter where all of the following conditions are met:

(1) Each transmitter shall serve only one device and shall be individually identified at the receiver/fire alarm control unit.
(2) The battery shall be capable of operating the low-power radio transmitter for not less than 1 year before the battery depletion threshold is reached.
(3) A battery depletion signal shall be transmitted before the battery has been depleted to a level below that required to support alarm transmission after 7 additional days of nonalarm operation. This signal shall be distinctive from alarm, supervisory, tamper, and trouble signals; shall visibly identify the affected low-power radio transmitter; and, when silenced, shall automatically re-sound at least once every 4 hours.

EXHIBIT 23.28 *Low-Power Wireless System. (Source: Honeywell Security & Custom Electronics, Syosset, NY)*

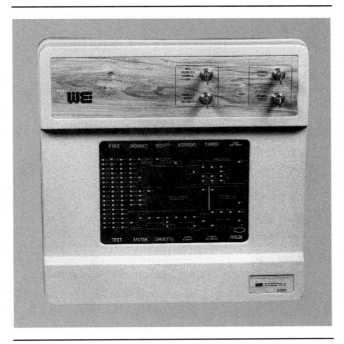

EXHIBIT 23.29 *Low-Power Wireless Combination System Control Unit. (Source: World Electronics, Inc., Sunrise, FL)*

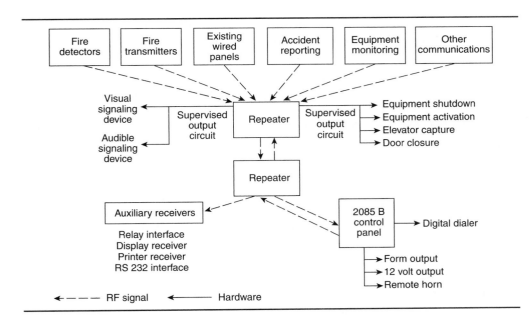

EXHIBIT 23.30 *Combination System Including a Low-Power Radio (Wireless) Fire Alarm System with Other Non-Fire Equipment. (Source: World Electronics, Inc., Sunrise, FL)*

(4) Catastrophic (open or short) battery failure shall cause a trouble signal identifying the affected low-power radio transmitter at its receiver/fire alarm control unit. When silenced, the trouble signal shall automatically re-sound at least once every 4 hours.

(5) Any mode of failure of a primary battery in a low-power radio transmitter shall not affect any other low-power radio transmitter.

23.18.3 Alarm Signals.

23.18.3.1* When actuated, each low-power radio transmitter shall automatically transmit an alarm signal.

A.23.18.3.1 This requirement is not intended to preclude verification and local test intervals prior to alarm transmission.

23.18.3.2 Each low-power radio transmitter shall automatically repeat alarm transmission at intervals not exceeding 60 seconds until the initiating device is returned to its nonalarm condition.

23.18.3.3 Fire alarm signals shall have priority over all other signals.

23.18.3.4 The maximum allowable response delay from activation of an initiating device to receipt and display by the receiver/fire alarm control unit shall be 10 seconds.

23.18.3.5 An alarm signal from a low-power radio transmitter shall latch at its receiver/fire alarm control unit until manually reset and shall identify the particular initiating device in alarm.

23.18.4 Monitoring for Integrity.

23.18.4.1 The low-power radio transmitter shall be specifically listed as using a transmission method that is highly resistant to misinterpretation of simultaneous transmissions and to interference (e.g., impulse noise and adjacent channel interference).

23.18.4.2 The occurrence of any single fault that disables transmission between any low-power radio transmitter and the receiver/fire alarm control unit shall cause a latching trouble signal within 200 seconds.

Exception: Until the expiration date for this exception of June 30, 2013, the time period for a low-power radio transmitter with only a single, connected alarm-initiating device shall be permitted to be increased to four times the minimum time interval permitted for a 1-second transmission up to the following:

(1) 4 hours maximum for a transmitter serving a single initiating device
(2) 4 hours maximum for a retransmission device (repeater), where disabling of the repeater or its transmission does not prevent the receipt of signals at the receiver/fire alarm control unit from any initiating device transmitter.

23.18.4.3 A single fault on the signaling channel shall not cause an alarm signal.

23.18.4.4 The periodic transmission required to comply with 23.18.4.2 from a low-power radio transmitter shall ensure successful alarm transmission capability.

23.18.4.5 Removal of a low-power radio transmitter from its installed location shall cause immediate transmission of a distinctive supervisory signal that indicates its removal and individually identifies the affected device.

23.18.4.6 Reception of any unwanted (interfering) transmission by a retransmission device (repeater) or by the main receiver/control unit, for a continuous period of 20 seconds or more, shall cause an audible and visible trouble indication at the main receiver/control unit. This indication shall identify the specific trouble condition as an interfering signal.

23.18.5 Output Signals from Receiver/Control.

When the receiver/control is used to actuate remote appliances, such as notification appliances and relays, by wireless means, the remote appliances shall meet the following requirements:

(1) Power supplies shall comply with Chapter 10 or the requirements of 23.18.2.
(2) All monitoring for integrity requirements of Chapter 10, Chapter 23, or 23.18.4 shall apply.
(3) The maximum allowable response delay from activation of an initiating device to activation of required alarm functions shall be 10 seconds.
(4) Each receiver/control shall automatically repeat alarm transmission at intervals not exceeding 60 seconds or until confirmation that the output appliance has received the alarm signal.
(5) The appliances shall continue to operate (latch-in) until manually reset at the receiver/control.

REFERENCES CITED IN COMMENTARY

Americans with Disabilities Act and Architectural Barriers Act Accessibility Guidelines, published in the *Federal Register,* U.S. Government Printing Office, Washington, DC, July 23, 2004, and amended August 5, 2005.

ANSI/UL 864, *Standard for Control Units and Accessories for Fire Alarm Systems,* Underwriters Laboratories Inc., Northbrook, IL, 2003, revised 2007.

NFPA 13, *Standard for the Installation of Sprinkler Systems*, 2010 edition, National Fire Protection Association, Quincy, MA.

NFPA 17, *Standard for Dry Chemical Extinguishing Systems*, 2009 edition, National Fire Protection Association, Quincy, MA.

NFPA 17A, *Standard for Wet Chemical Extinguishing Systems*, 2009 edition, National Fire Protection Association, Quincy, MA.

NFPA 20, *Standard for the Installation of Stationary Pumps for Fire Protection*, 2010 edition, National Fire Protection Association, Quincy, MA.

NFPA 70®, *National Electrical Code*®, 2008 edition, National Fire Protection Association, Quincy, MA.

NFPA *101*®, *Life Safety Code*®, 2009 edition, National Fire Protection Association, Quincy, MA.

NFPA 601, *Standard for Security Services in Fire Loss Prevention*, 2005 edition, National Fire Protection Association, Quincy, MA.

NFPA 720, *Standard for the Installation of Carbon Monoxide (CO) Detection and Warning Equipment*, 2009 edition, National Fire Protection Association, Quincy, MA.

Emergency Communications Systems (ECS)

CHAPTER 24

Chapter 24 is a new chapter in the 2010 edition of the Code. The requirements for the installation and performance of emergency communications systems (ECSs) for in-building fire emergency voice/alarm communications systems and other communications systems are covered in this chapter.

In the 2007 edition of the Code, the requirements for in-building fire emergency voice/alarm communications systems were located in Chapter 6. In the 2010 edition, these requirements have been moved to Chapter 24 and, in some cases, have been modified. Most of the requirements for other forms of ECSs in this chapter are new to the Code. The guidance for mass notification systems (MNSs) found in Annex G of the 2007 edition has been moved to this chapter and reworded as requirements or has been added to Annex A as explanatory information. Additionally, the requirements for MNSs have been correlated with the requirements established by the U.S. Department of Defense in the publication *Design and O&M: Mass Notification Systems* (UFC 4-021-01).

The arrangement of the sections containing the requirements for the ECSs presented in this chapter is shown in Figure A.24.3.6.

24.1 Application

24.1.1 The application, installation, and performance of emergency communications systems and their components shall comply with the requirements of this chapter.

24.1.2* The requirements of this chapter shall apply to emergency communications systems within buildings and outdoor areas.

As noted previously, parts of Chapter 6 in the 2007 edition of the Code have been moved to this chapter. Annex I provides a cross-reference of section and paragraph numbers from the 2007 edition to the 2010 edition. Users may find this table useful in determining the disposition of the 2007 requirements.

A.24.1.2 An emergency communications system could target the general building, area, space, campus, or region.

24.1.3 The requirements of Chapters 10, 12, 17, 18, 21, 23, 26 and 27 shall also apply, unless they are in conflict with this chapter.

24.1.4 The requirements of Chapter 14 shall apply.

24.1.5 The requirements of this chapter shall not apply to Chapter 29 unless specifically indicated.

Rarely, if ever, would a one- or two-family dwelling have a communications system as described in this chapter. However, should an owner decide to install some form of ECS in a dwelling, the designer should follow the requirements herein.

24.2 Purpose

24.2.1 The systems covered under Chapter 24 are for the protection of life by indicating the existence of an emergency situation and communicating information necessary to facilitate an appropriate response and action.

FAQ ▶
Do the requirements of Chapter 24 for ECSs apply only to in-building applications?

As can be seen from the types of systems described in Figure A.24.3.6, this chapter provides requirements for more than just in-building fire emergency voice/alarm communications systems. An event such as a terrorist attack, an on-campus shooter, or a natural disaster would necessitate clear and on-time communication from those in authority to the occupants of the building or outside areas during the emergency.

24.2.2 This chapter establishes minimum required levels of performance, reliability, and quality of installation for emergency communications systems but does not establish the only methods by which these requirements are to be achieved.

The Code and this chapter do not require an owner to install an ECS. However, once the decision has been made to install a system, all the applicable requirements of the Code must be followed for both the design and the installation.

24.2.3 An emergency communications system is intended to communicate information about emergencies including, but not limited to, fire, human-caused events (accidental and intentional), other dangerous situations, accidents, and natural disasters.

In order for the ECS to communicate information properly, it must reproduce the desired messages so that the intended listeners will both hear and understand the message. The information provided must be relevant and provide enough time for the occupants to take the correct action. An ECS should be more than just a technological solution — it should include a structured and rigorously tested procedural/management component to be effective. It should be recognized that simply providing information does not guarantee immediate and appropriate response from the target population.

FAQ ▶
What information should an effective emergency message contain?

Research shows that the message is one of the most important factors in determining the effectiveness of a warning system and that the message must provide the following content:

- Information on the hazard and danger
- Guidance on what people should do
- Description of the location of the risk or hazard
- An idea of when they need to act
- The name of the source of the warning (who is giving it)

Warning style is also crucial in that it must be specific, consistent, certain, clear, and accurate.

24.3 General

24.3.1* Intelligible Voice Messages. Emergency communications systems shall be capable of the reproduction of prerecorded, synthesized, or live (e.g., microphone, telephone handset, and radio) messages with voice intelligibility in accordance with Chapter 18.

Many designers, installers, and authorities having jurisdiction have struggled to meet the requirements concerning intelligible voice messages contained in earlier editions of the Code. Most sound system professionals agree that a majority of their sound and communication systems are designed as described in A.24.3.1. The important issue in meeting this requirement is to have a basic understanding of sound and communications principles. Designers and installers should understand the importance of a good distribution of speakers rather than a higher power output of a few speakers.

A.24.3.1 In certain situations, it is important to provide a distributed sound level with minimal sound intensity variations to achieve an intelligible voice message. This differs from past fire alarm design practice that used fewer notification appliances, but with each having greater sound pressure output levels. Non-emergency system design practice is to use more speakers and less sound intensity from each speaker. Besides improving intelligibility of the message, this approach minimizes annoyance to building occupants from the system and lessens the likelihood of tampering with the system by occupants because of speakers being too loud. In other applications, such as outdoor signaling where reverberation is not a problem, intelligibility can be achieved by using fewer appliances or clusters of appliances covering larger areas.

Intelligibility is a complex function of the source audio, the acoustic response of the architectural features and materials of the immediate vicinity, and the dynamics created by the room's occupants. Refer to Annex D for more information on speech intelligibility and how it is predicted. Spacing speakers closely can be an intelligibility-enhancing technique but can occasionally lead to opposite results when improperly designed. There are several techniques using directionality features that do not use closely spaced speakers but rather use the room/space acoustic response in their favor.

When actuated, recorded or live mass notification voice messages should take priority over fire alarm messages and signals. If the fire alarm system is in the alarm mode when recorded voice message or audible signals are sounding, and the mass notification system is actuated, it should temporarily cause deactivation of all fire alarm–initiated audible and visible notification appliances during the time period required to transmit the mass notification emergency message.

24.3.2* Required Emergency Communications Systems. An emergency communications system shall be installed in occupancies where required by the authority having jurisdiction or by other applicable governing laws, codes, or standards.

A.24.3.2 The requirements found in *NFPA 70, National Electrical Code*, Article 708, should be considered for emergency communications systems that are installed in vital infrastructure facilities classified as a designated critical operations area (DCOA). This includes facilities that, if destroyed or incapacitated, would disrupt national security, the economy, public health or safety and where enhanced electrical infrastructure for continuity of operation has been deemed necessary by governmental authority.

If the facility where the ECS is required per 24.3.2 is classified as a designated critical operations area (DCOA), then additional electrical requirements apply.

24.3.3* Nonrequired (Voluntary) Emergency Communications Systems.

An installation of an ECS is voluntary when the owner decides that a system is needed to meet the fire safety or emergency response plan for the occupancy. Although there is no building code or NFPA *101®, Life Safety Code®*, requirement for the system, the designer and the installer of an ECS must understand the owner's goals and objectives and the system's intended use.

◀ **FAQ**
When is an ECS installation considered nonrequired (voluntary)?

A.24.3.3 The features for a nonrequired system should be established by the system designer on the basis of the goals and objectives intended by the system owner.

24.3.3.1 Nonrequired emergency communications systems and components shall meet the requirements of this chapter.

With the exception of a standard public address system, the ECSs described in this chapter have an impact on the life safety of the occupants in the protected building. It is therefore imperative that regardless of whether an ECS is required by a building code or by the *Life Safety Code*, the design and installation of the ECS must be made in accordance with the requirements herein. Although the system may be installed voluntarily, the designer or installer does not have permission to install an unreliable or non-Code-compliant ECS.

24.3.3.2 Nonrequired emergency communications systems and components shall be identified on the record drawings required in 10.18.2.3(2).

Even though the ECS system may not be required by a code, if a system is designed and installed in a building, the record drawings (as-built drawings) must show the installation as if it were a required system.

24.3.4 Ancillary Functions.

24.3.4.1 Ancillary functions, including the use of a fire alarm system or mass notification system for general paging, background music, or other non-emergency functions are permitted and shall not interfere with the performance requirements of the fire alarm system or the mass notification system.

It is the intent of the Code to allow an ECS to be used on a regular basis for non-emergency purposes so that an owner is not required to install multiple systems. However, the Code requires that these non-emergency uses, such as paging or public address, do not interfere with the performance of any emergency function of the ECS.

24.3.4.2* Fire alarm system speakers providing ancillary functions shall meet the conditions of either 24.3.4.2(1) or (2):

Note the use of "either/or" in the requirement. An in-building fire emergency voice/alarm communications system may be used not only for other emergencies but also for non-emergency uses such as background music or public address. However, the intent of the Code is to ensure that the speakers and circuits are not compromised because of this non–fire alarm use.

(1) The fire command center shall be constantly attended by trained personnel, and selective paging is permitted by the authority having jurisdiction.
(2) All of the following conditions shall be met:
 (a) The speakers and associated audio equipment are installed or located with safeguards to resist tampering or misadjustment of those components essential for intended emergency notification.
 (b) The monitoring integrity requirements of Section 10.17 continue to be met while the system is used for non-emergency purposes.

Speaker systems are available that incorporate volume controls and components that allow occupants to lower or turn off the speakers in an area or office. These systems are also designed to allow the speakers to operate at their required power output when the fire alarm system is actuated. This is one of the safeguards now available to meet the requirements of 24.3.4.2(2)(a) and 24.4.2.18.2.

A.24.3.4.2 Dedicated in-building fire emergency voice/alarm communications systems are not required to monitor the integrity of the notification appliance circuits while active for emergency purposes. However, these circuits have to be monitored for integrity while active for non-emergency purposes. The building operator, system designer, and authority having jurisdiction should be aware that, in some situations, such a system could be subject to deliberate tampering. Tampering is usually attempted to reduce the output of a sound system that is in constant use, such as background music or a paging system, and that could be a source of annoyance to employees.

   The likelihood of tampering can be reduced through proper consideration of loudspeaker accessibility and system operation.

Access can be reduced through the use of hidden or nonadjustable transformer taps (which can reduce playback levels), use of vandal-resistant listed loudspeakers, and placement in areas that are difficult to access, such as high ceilings (any ceiling higher than could be reached by standing on a desk or chair). Non-emergency operation of the system should always consider that an audio system that annoys an employee potentially reduces employee productivity and can also annoy the public in a commercial environment. Most motivations for tampering can be eliminated through appropriate use of the system and employee discipline. Access to amplification equipment and controls should be limited to those authorized to make adjustments to such equipment. It is common practice to install such equipment in a manner that allows adjustment of non-emergency audio signal levels while defaulting to a fixed, preset level of playback when operating in emergency mode. Under extreme circumstances, certain zones of a protected area might require a dedicated in-building fire emergency voice/alarm communications zone.

24.3.4.3 Where ancillary functions are not monitored for integrity, they shall be inspected periodically in accordance with the frequency identified in Chapter 14.

24.3.5 Pathway Survivability.

24.3.5.1 Pathway survivability levels shall be as described in Section 12.4.

Pathway survivability levels are under the purview of the Technical Committee on Protected Premises Fire Alarm Systems. Chapter 12 requirements are referenced based on the need for the ECS to continue functioning during a fire.

24.3.5.2 Other component survivability shall comply with the provisions of 24.4.1.8.4.6.

24.3.5.3* The pathway survivability requirements in 24.3.5.4 through 24.3.5.12 shall apply to notification and communications circuits and other circuits necessary to ensure the continued operation of the emergency communications system.

A.24.3.5.3 This section is not meant to preclude a performance-based pathway survivability approach. As with most performance-based approaches, documentation should be provided by the designer and maintained with system documentation for the life of the system. Written documentation of the approval from the authority having jurisdiction should also be maintained. A performance-based approach to pathway survivability could be equivalent to, less stringent than, or more stringent than the prescriptive approach in 24.3.5. Often a performance-based approach will result from a risk analysis.

This section is also not meant to preclude less stringent pathway survivability requirements supported by a risk analysis for those unique occupancies that employ voice alarm/emergency communication systems for relocation or partial evacuation as part of their fire safety plan where relocation or partial evacuation could be readily superseded by total evacuation and where buildings are of a type other than Type I or Type II (222) construction where the pathway survivability performance requirement does not need to be for two hours. Examples include low rise education and day care occupancies, nursing homes, ambulatory health care occupancies, hotel and dormitory occupancies, and residential board and care occupancies.

24.3.5.4 In-building fire emergency voice/alarm communications systems shall comply with 24.3.5.4.1 or 24.3.5.4.2.

24.3.5.4.1 For systems employing relocation or partial evacuation, a Level 2 or Level 3 pathway survivability shall be required.

Each level of pathway survivability offers options for the designer and the installer to meet the survivability requirements. Some users of the Code have mistakenly assumed that if a circuit is in conduit, it is therefore survivable. Wire or cable in a raceway such as conduit is certainly mechanically protected, but it is not survivable from the impact of fire. Subsection 23.10.2 states in part that "fire alarm systems used for partial evacuation and relocation shall be designed and installed such that attack by fire within an evacuation signaling zone shall not impair control and operation of the notification appliances outside the evacuation signaling zone." This is the performance description of survivability. Designers, authorities having jurisdiction, and installers should also ensure that circuits controlling notification appliance circuits and equipment that are common to more than one evacuation signaling zone are designed and installed such that fire will not disable them. Paragraph 24.3.5.4.1 offers two options for survivability that are essentially equal, with the exception that survivability Level 3 has the additional requirement for complete sprinkler system protection in the building in accordance with NFPA 13, *Standard for the Installation of Sprinkler Systems.*

24.3.5.4.2 For systems that do not employ relocation or partial evacuation, a Level 0, Level 1, Level 2, or Level 3 pathway survivability shall be required.

The prudent designer or installer must understand the owner's goals and objectives for the ECS and perform a risk analysis as needed to determine the level of survivability that should be used.

24.3.5.4.3 Refer to Annex G for previous nomenclature and cross reference.

24.3.5.5 In-building mass notification systems shall be permitted to have a Level 0 pathway survivability or greater if determined by a risk analysis.

FAQ ▶
What are the survivability requirements where a system is also used as an in-building fire emergency voice/alarm communications system?

In-building MNSs may or may not be required to have pathway survivability depending on the results of the risk analysis. However, if the MNS is integrated with the in-building fire emergency voice/alarm communications system, then the survivability requirements must be as defined in 24.3.5.4.1.

24.3.5.6 All circuits for wide-area mass notification systems shall be permitted to have a pathway survivability of Level 0 or greater if determined by a risk analysis.

24.3.5.7 Two-way in-building wired emergency communications systems shall have a pathway survivability of Level 2 or Level 3.

Two-way in-building wired ECSs, formerly called fire fighter telephones or fire warden telephones, are generally used during fire conditions. Therefore, the circuits connecting the telephones to the main control must be survivable.

24.3.5.8 Two-way radio communications enhancement systems shall comply with 24.3.5.8.1 and 24.3.5.8.2.

24.3.5.8.1 Where a two-way radio communications enhancement system, exclusive of the antennae, is used in lieu of a two-way in-building wired emergency communications system, it shall have a pathway survivability of Level 2 or Level 3.

In order for a two-way radio communications enhancement system to be considered equal to and as reliable as the two-way in-building wired ECSs, the pathway survivability must be ensured. For example, a typical bi-directional amplified (BDA) system uses "leaky" coaxial cable to allow the fire fighter radios to operate anywhere in the building. If this cable cannot survive an attack by fire, there is no guarantee the fire department radio system will work throughout the building during the fire suppression and rescue efforts. Although 24.3.5.8.1 excludes the antennae from the Level 2 or Level 3 pathway survivability requirement, if the BDA system is located in a high-rise building and survivability is required, circuit integrity (CI) "leaky" coaxial cables are available.

24.3.5.8.2 Where a two-way radio communications enhancement system is used in lieu of a two-way in-building wired emergency communications system, the design of the system shall be approved by the authority having jurisdiction.

Some designers and installers assume that the authority having jurisdiction for the two-way radio communications enhancement system is the same as the authority having jurisdiction for the fire alarm system design review and approval. In fact, the authority having jurisdiction for the two-way radio communications enhancement system might be the fire department radio communications chief. The designer or installer must determine who the authority having jurisdiction is.

24.3.5.9* Area of refuge (area of rescue assistance) emergency communications systems shall comply with 24.3.5.9.1 and 24.3.5.9.2.

A.24.3.5.9 Although in some instances areas of refuge (areas of rescue assistance) might be installed in buildings that use general evacuation and not relocation/partial evacuation, it is still crucial that people awaiting assistance can communicate with emergency responders to facilitate their evacuation. Thus, their evacuation time might be prolonged, and therefore the emergency communications systems should be capable of operating reliably during a fire incident.

24.3.5.9.1 Area of refuge emergency communications systems shall have a pathway survivability of Level 2 or Level 3.

The area of refuge concept was established to provide a location for building occupants who cannot traverse the stairs without assistance to assemble and await assistance or instructions by the first responders. Therefore, the circuits connecting the area of refuge communications system to the fire command center must be designed to withstand the attack of fire during the time that the occupants await assistance.

24.3.5.9.2 Circuits intended to transmit off-premises shall have a pathway survivability of Level 0, Level 1, Level 2, or Level 3.

In almost every fire in the United States where there has been a large loss of life or property, one of the major factors leading to the large loss has been delayed notification to the fire department. Designers, installers, and authorities having jurisdiction should review the circuit and pathways connecting to the off-premises transmission component of the fire alarm system to determine what level of survivability is desired or needed for a reliable connection.

24.3.5.10 Elevator emergency communications systems shall have a pathway survivability of Level 0, Level 1, Level 2, or Level 3.

The prudent designer or installer must be sure to understand the owner's goals and objectives for the systems and circuits described in 24.3.5.9.2 and 24.3.5.10 and perform a risk analysis as needed to determine what level of survivability should be used.

24.3.5.11 Central command station emergency communications systems shall have pathway survivability as determined by the risk analysis.

24.3.5.12 All other emergency communications system circuits shall have pathway survivability as determined by the risk analysis.

24.3.6* System Classification.
Emergency communications systems (ECS) shall consist of two classifications of systems, one-way and two-way.

A.24.3.6 One-way emergency communications systems are intended to broadcast information, in an emergency, to personnel in one or more specified indoor or outdoor areas. It is intended that emergency messages be conveyed either by audible or visible textual means or both. This section does not apply to bells, horns, or other sounders and lights, except where used in conjunction with the desired operation of emergency messages and signaling.

Two-way emergency communications systems are divided into two categories, those systems that are anticipated to be used by building occupants and those systems that are to be used by fire fighters, police, and other emergency services personnel. Two-way emergency communications systems are used both to exchange information and to communicate information, such as, but not limited to, instructions, acknowledgement of receipt of messages, condition of local environment, and condition of persons, and to give assurance that help is on its way.

NFPA 72 contains requirements that can impact the application of emergency communications systems. For instance, coordination of the functions of an emergency communications system with other systems that communicate audibly and/or visibly [such as fire alarm systems, security systems, public address (PA) systems] is essential in order to provide effective communication in an emergency situation. Conflicting or competing signals or messages from different systems could be very confusing to occupants and have a negative impact on the intended occupant response. Where independent systems using audible and/or visible notification are present, the emergency communications system needs to interface with those systems to effect related control actions such as deactivating both audible and visible notification appliances. The use of a single integrated combination system might offer both economic and technical advantages. In any case, coordination between system functions is essential. The coordination of emergency communications systems with other systems should be considered part of the risk analysis for the emergency communications system. *(See Figure A.24.3.6.)*

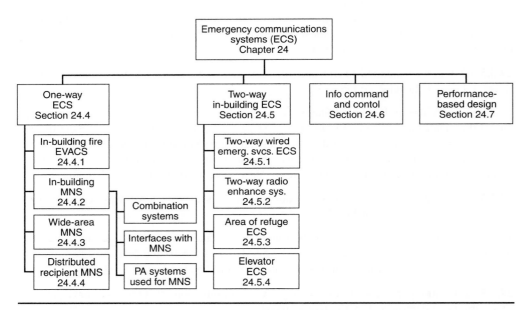

FIGURE A.24.3.6 *Emergency Communications Systems.*

Additional documents such as NEMA Standard SB 40, *Communications Systems for Life Safety in Schools*, can also be used as supplemental resources to provide help with risk assessment and application considerations.

Combining in-building fire emergency voice/alarm communications systems with other communications systems such as mass notification, public address, and paging is allowed by the Code. The technology is available to ensure that fire alarm or priority mass notification messages (as determined by the risk analysis) will take precedence over any other announcement, such as paging from a telephone system or other public address system. Using one speaker system with a combination of other communications systems that incorporates all the requirements of the Code is financially beneficial to the owner.

24.4 One-Way Emergency Communications Systems

24.4.1* In-Building Fire Emergency Voice/Alarm Communications Systems (EVACS).
Subsection 24.4.1 shall be used in the design and application of in-building fire emergency voice/alarm communications for fire alarm systems.

In-building fire emergency voice/alarm communications systems are usually found in high-rise and large area buildings, where evacuation of the entire building on every alarm is not practical or desirable. An in-building fire emergency voice/alarm communications system is more than a fire alarm system that uses a voice message to initiate evacuation of the building. The system is designed to assist emergency response personnel in managing the movement of both building occupants and fire fighters during a fire or other emergency.

The definition of *in-building fire emergency voice/alarm communications* provided in 3.3.79.1.2 reads: "Dedicated manual or automatic equipment for originating and distributing voice instructions, as well as alert and evacuation signals pertaining to a fire emergency, to the occupants of a building." This definition does not exclude systems used to automatically and simultaneously notify all occupants to evacuate the premises. Any system using voice messaging must meet the requirements of Section 24.4, although not all systems are required to have all the features described in Section 24.4. For example, the requirements of 24.4.1.8 are not intended to apply where voice messages are used to simultaneously notify all building occupants to evacuate. Exhibit 24.1 illustrates an in-building fire emergency voice/alarm communications system.

◀ **FAQ**
What systems must comply with the requirements of Section 24.4?

EXHIBIT 24.1 *In-Building Fire Emergency Voice/Alarm Communications System. (Source: SimplexGrinnell, Westminster, MA)*

A.24.4.1 Where used, recorded voice messages for fire emergency alarm systems should be prepared in accordance with this Code by persons who are experienced with the operation of building fire emergency alarm systems and are knowledgeable of the building's construction, layout, and fire protection plan, including evacuation procedures. The proposed voice messages should be approved by the authority having jurisdiction prior to being implemented. Persons who record the messages for fire emergency alarm systems should be able to read and speak the language used for the message clearly, concisely, and without an accent that would have an adverse affect on intelligibility.

It is not the intention that in-building fire emergency voice/alarm communications service be limited to English-speaking populations. Emergency messages should be provided in the language of the predominant building population. If there is a possibility of isolated groups that do not speak the predominant language, multilingual messages should be provided. It is expected that small groups of transients unfamiliar with the predominant language will be picked up in the traffic flow in the event of an emergency and are not likely to be in an isolated situation.

24.4.1.1 Automatic Response. The in-building fire emergency voice/alarm communications system shall be used to provide an automatic response to the receipt of a signal indicative of a fire alarm or other emergency.

The sequence of operation and actual voice messages will be different for each building, but the fire alarm system must automatically actuate the emergency voice/alarm sequence unless the conditions of either 24.4.1.1.1 or 24.4.1.1.2 apply.

24.4.1.1.1 When the monitoring location is constantly attended by trained operators, and operator acknowledgment of receipt of a fire alarm or other emergency signal is received within 30 seconds, automatic response shall not be required.

This paragraph exempts the system from the automatic actuation required in 24.4.1.1 if the system is continuously attended by trained operators. This arrangement is often the case for an in-building fire emergency voice/alarm communications system installed in a large building. The intent is that the operators be fully trained and competent and have the authority to initiate appropriate action based on the fire safety plan for the facility.

24.4.1.1.2 If acceptable to the authority having jurisdiction, the system shall permit the application of an automatic evacuation signal to one or more evacuation signaling zones and, at the same time, shall permit manual voice paging to the other evacuation signaling zones selectively or in any combination.

With the permission of the authority having jurisdiction, the system can be arranged to provide manual voice paging to some evacuation signaling zones while providing automatic evacuation signals to other zones. The arrangement(s) allowed will depend in large part on the building's evacuation plan.

24.4.1.2 Voice Evacuation Messages.

24.4.1.2.1 Evacuation messages shall be preceded and followed by a minimum of two cycles of the emergency evacuation signal specified in 18.4.2.

FAQ ▶
Is the standard evacuation signal required to precede an evacuation message?

The operating sequence for voice messages intended to initiate evacuation is two cycles of the standard evacuation signal (tone) followed by the voice message with evacuation instructions followed by two more cycles of the evacuation signal. The sequence is typically repeated three to five times followed by continuous sounding of the evacuation signal.

24.4.1.2.2 Voice messages shall comply with the requirements of 24.3.1.

24.4.1.2.2.1 The following requirements shall be met for layout and design:

(1) The speaker layout of the system shall be designed to ensure intelligibility and audibility.
(2) Intelligibility shall first be determined by ensuring that all areas in the building have the required level of audibility.

Speakers should not be located near the in-building fire emergency voice/alarm communications system control equipment. If they are located too near the microphone, audio feedback will distort the manual page message by the fire commander using the microphone. The same design concept applies to locations where fire fighters' telephones are located. Speakers required in these areas should be arranged to ensure that the sound pressure levels of the nearby speakers do not preclude the effective use of the fire fighters' telephones.

(3) The design shall incorporate speaker placement to provide intelligibility.

It is imperative that the designer understands the importance of ensuring that the correct number of speakers be located throughout the building. In the past, fire alarm system designers did not use enough speakers in their designs to ensure both audibility and intelligibility. In standard 10- to 12-foot ceiling height environments, a good rule of thumb is to install speakers in every occupied space and at intervals of twice the ceiling height. Of course, the ambient noise level of the areas served by the speakers must be considered to ensure that the sound pressure levels of the speakers are at the correct levels for both audibility and intelligibility of the speaker system. See also A.24.4.1.2.2.2 and Supplement 2.

24.4.1.2.2.2* System design shall incorporate designation of acoustically distinguishable spaces (ADS) within the occupied areas as required in Chapter 18.

A.24.4.1.2.2.2 Generally speaking, in a standard building configuration with normal ceiling height [8 ft to 12 ft (2.4 m to 3.7 m)], normal ceiling construction (e.g., drop acoustical ceiling tiles), standard wall configurations, and finishes and carpeted floors, ceiling-mounted speakers should be installed in all normally occupiable spaces and in corridors spaced at a maximum of twice the ceiling height or as determined by a commercially available computer acoustical/speaker modeling program. Where wall-mounted speakers are used, manufacturer recommendations should be reviewed and/or computer modeling should be employed. One of the goals of speaker placement is to provide the shortest practical distance from the source (speaker) to the recipient (person hearing the signal). In many applications, a combination of wall- and ceiling-mounted speakers might be required. The audibility and intelligibility of the speakers can be impacted by the tap/setting at which the speaker is connected and should meet the audibility requirements of the Code while still having the message intelligible. Connecting to a high setting to meet the audibility requirements of the code could distort the intelligibility of the signal.

In an ADS that is a non-acoustically challenging area, designing for audibility will typically result in an intelligible system provided minimum speaker guidelines are followed. Areas typically considered to be non-acoustically challenging include traditional office environments, hotel guest rooms, dwelling units, and spaces with carpeting and furnishings.

Special attention must be given to acoustically challenging ADSs. Such areas might incorporate appreciable hard surfaces (e.g., glass, marble, tile, metal, etc) or appreciably high ceilings (e.g., atriums, multiple ceiling heights). These conditions will require more stringent design guidelines to ensure intelligibility (e.g., a closer than normal speaker spacing with lower taps). This can help reduce the effect of excessive reverberation and result in better intelligibility. In extreme cases there could be areas where intelligibility is not attainable, but this can be acceptable if there is an ADS within 30 ft (9.1 m) where the intelligibility of the system is deemed adequate.

In an ADS where the ambient noise level exceeds 85 dB it is acknowledged that intelligibility might not be attainable and an alternate means of notification is required.

Design guidance is provided in the NEMA Standards Publication SB 50-2008, *Emergency Communications Audio Intelligibility Applications Guide*.

24.4.1.2.2.3 Audibility shall be required in all areas in accordance with Chapter 18.

24.4.1.2.2.4 Unless specifically required by the authority having jurisdiction, intelligibility shall not be required in the following locations:

(1) Private bathrooms, shower rooms, saunas and similar rooms/areas
(2) Mechanical/electrical/elevator equipment rooms
(3) Elevator cars
(4) Individual offices
(5) Kitchens
(6) Storage rooms
(7) Closets
(8) Rooms/areas where intelligibility cannot reasonably be predicted

FAQ ▶
Are all in-building fire emergency voice/alarm communications systems required to have voice intelligibility throughout?

Intelligibility is obviously important but equally important is to use common sense when applying the requirement. In some cases, the list in 24.4.1.2.2.4 represents areas where the ambient noise level is too high to attempt to achieve intelligibility. In other areas, the occupants are not in a position to do anything with the information. And in still other areas, the occupancy is either limited or considered to be of short duration.

24.4.1.3 Positive Alarm Sequence. In-building fire emergency voice/alarm communications systems shall be permitted to use positive alarm sequence complying with 23.8.1.3.

Positive alarm sequence essentially delays notification to the occupants, allowing time for security or authorized personnel to investigate and confirm the fire condition. The Code does not allow a delayed notification to the fire department. The use of positive alarm sequence also requires the permission of the authority having jurisdiction. For a more detailed discussion of this concept, refer to the commentary following 23.8.1.3.

24.4.1.4 Tones. The tone preceding any message shall be permitted to be a part of the voice message or to be transmitted automatically from a separate tone generator.

Depending on the goals and objectives of the owner and whether or not the in-building fire emergency alarm voice/communications system is to be used as a paging system or combined as an MNS, the tone may need to be separated from the voice message.

24.4.1.4.1 In occupancies where sleeping accommodations are provided, the pre-alert tone shall include a low frequency component of 520 Hz square wave range to accommodate the need of the hearing impaired for fire voice messages and emergency communication messages.

24.4.1.5 Controls.

FAQ ▶
What term is used in 24.4.1.5 instead of the term *fire command center*?

Previous editions of the Code included a subsection entitled Fire Command Center. In the 2010 edition of the Code, the technical committee has selected the term *controls* instead of *fire command center* to avoid implying the requirement for a separate room(s) and to avoid the use of terminology that might conflict with the usage of the term in other codes and standards. The building or life safety codes in force within a jurisdiction normally dictate the location of the fire command center where these controls will be located. Although Section 24.4 now uses the term *controls*, the term *fire command center* is still defined and used in other locations in the Code. Users should be aware that the committee's intent in the selection of a different term was not to change the concept of the functions historically associated with the term *fire command center*.

24.4.1.5.1* Controls for the in-building fire emergency voice/alarm communications system shall be at a location approved by the authority having jurisdiction.

A.24.4.1.5.1 The choice of the location(s) for the in-building fire emergency voice/alarm communications control equipment should also take into consideration the ability of the fire alarm system to operate and function during any probable single event. Although NFPA 72 does not regulate either building construction or contents, system designers should consider the potential for an event that could damage the equipment, including remotely located control devices, to disable the system or a portion thereof. Where practical, it is prudent to minimize unnecessary fire exposures of fire alarm control equipment through the use of fire-rated construction or enclosures, by limiting adjacent combustibles and ignition sources, or other appropriate means.

The controls for the system should be located where required by the authority having jurisdiction. Factors in selecting the location include ease of access during an emergency, adequate space for the incident command staff, and protection from the effects of smoke and fire during an incident. The system will likely be used for emergencies other than fires, so care should be exercised to ensure that the location of the controls is appropriate for dealing with other types of emergencies as well. For example, in a tornado-prone area, locating the controls in a room on an exterior wall with windows would not be wise.

24.4.1.5.2 Controls shall be located or secured to allow access only by trained and authorized personnel.

The intent of 24.4.1.5.2 is to prevent unauthorized individuals from accessing the controls. Only those personnel who are trained and authorized should be permitted access to the operating controls. This requirement does not preclude the provision of remote equipment with voice capability located in areas other than the main control equipment.

24.4.1.5.3 Operating controls shall be clearly identified.

The best way to ensure that the purpose of operating controls is clear to the fire department is to ask the fire department how they want the controls marked. A marking that may be perfectly clear to a designer who is intimate with every detail of the system may mean nothing to a fire officer responding to the building. Because the controls are for fire department use, they should be labeled as designated by the fire department. Also refer to the requirements of Section 18.11 and the guidance of Section A.18.11.

◄ **FAQ**
What is a good way to ensure that operating controls are clearly marked?

24.4.1.5.4 If there are multiple in-building fire emergency voice/alarm communications control locations, only one shall be in control at any given time.

24.4.1.5.5 The location having control of the system shall be identified by a visible indication at that location.

The intent of 24.4.1.5.4 and 24.4.1.5.5 is to control how many messages can be issued at one time. If there are multiple control locations and multiple people attempting to transmit an emergency message, confusion could result. These requirements are in place to avoid potentially confusing or conflicting message announcements.

24.4.1.5.6 Manual controls shall be arranged to provide visible indication of the on/off status for their associated evacuation signaling zone.

24.4.1.5.7 If live voice instructions are provided, they shall perform as follows:

(1) Override previously initiated signals to the selected notification zone(s).
(2) Have priority over any subsequent automatically initiated signals to the selected zone(s).

Once the fire department personnel arrive, they must have the capability to override all previously initiated recorded voice instructions and provide to the building occupants up-to-date information and instructions specific to the emergency and current conditions.

In-building fire emergency voice/alarm communications systems can be effective by calming occupants in areas remote from the fire and by directing others toward safety. Fire department and other emergency personnel who will be operating the in-building fire emergency voice/alarm communications system during an emergency must be thoroughly familiar with the system and its operation. This familiarity requires effective initial and follow-up training. Actual on-site drills may be required to fully understand the operation and use of the system.

24.4.1.6 Speakers.

24.4.1.6.1* Speakers and their enclosures shall be installed in accordance with Chapter 18.

A.24.4.1.6.1 Speakers located in the vicinity of the in-building fire emergency voice/alarm communications control equipment should be arranged so they do not cause audio feedback when the system microphone is used. Speakers installed in the area of two-way telephone stations should be arranged so that the sound pressure level emitted does not preclude the effective use of the two-way telephone system. Circuits for speakers and telephones should be separated, shielded, or otherwise arranged to prevent audio cross-talk between circuits.

Attention must be paid to the layout of the speakers to ensure that the proper number are installed to achieve both audibility and intelligibility. See the commentary following 24.4.1.2.2.1(3).

24.4.1.6.2 Speakers used as alarm notification appliances on fire alarm systems shall also be permitted to be used for mass notification.

24.4.1.7 Priority.

24.4.1.7.1* Notification appliances required to provide special suppression pre-discharge notification shall not be overridden by other systems.

A.24.4.1.7.1 Special suppression systems that are delivered through a total flooding or localized application include, but are not limited to, carbon dioxide, clean agents, halons, and other extinguishing agents. Special suppression systems require audible and visible warning alarms to provide personnel the opportunity to evacuate or to alert personnel not to enter the area of discharge that could be hazardous to life. A special suppression system discharge can be a life-threatening hazard for personnel who are not notified and, therefore, fail to react to the pre-discharge alarm. In such cases, pre-discharge and discharge alarms should be independent of the fire alarm speakers that are used as part of the mass notification system. A special suppression system discharge could pose a greater threat to personnel that are located in the protected area, or that could enter the protected area, if the local signals were to be overridden and they did not receive the appropriate warning.

24.4.1.7.2 When the fire alarm system has been activated, and mass notification has been given priority over the fire alarm system, a distinctive audible and visible indication shall be provided at the building fire alarm control unit.

Providing a distinctive audible and visible indication establishes clear requirements for indication of an MNS activation taking control over the fire alarm system.

24.4.1.7.3 It shall not be required to transmit this condition to a supervising station.

Transmitting a mass notification message over a fire alarm signal would, in all probability, confuse the operator located at a remote supervising station who will already be processing the original fire alarm condition.

24.4.1.7.4 The fire alarm system shall not automatically override emergency mass notification messages. Priority of mass notification messages over fire alarm evacuation shall be permitted when evaluated by the stakeholders through a risk analysis in accordance with 24.4.2.2.

24.4.1.8* Relocation and Partial Evacuation. The requirements of 24.4.1.8 shall apply only to systems used for relocation or partial evacuation during a fire condition.

Fire alarm systems designed for partial or selective evacuation and relocation of building occupants must have a degree of survivability to maintain communication with occupants who remain in the building during a fire. Total evacuation of a high-rise building or large area manufacturing facility may not be practical. An in-building fire emergency voice/alarm communications system can be used to provide instructions to specific areas of the building. In a high-rise building, the floor on which an alarm originates, the floor above, and the floor below may receive a message to evacuate the building. Other floors may be told to await further instructions. The system must be able to remain in service to maintain communication with the occupants remaining in the building.

A.24.4.1.8 When a fire or other emergency occurs in a building, the usual goal is to evacuate the occupants or relocate them so that they are not exposed to hazardous conditions. The exception occurs in occupancies using stay-in-place/defend-in-place (SIP/DIP)[1] strategies. It might also be necessary to alert and provide information to trained staff responsible for assisting evacuation or relocation. Figure A.24.4.1.8 shows several key steps in a person's reaction and decision-making process [2].

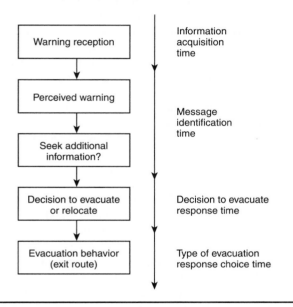

FIGURE A.24.4.1.8 *Key Steps in a Person's Reaction.*

Occupants rarely panic in fire situations [3,4]. The behavior that they adopt is based on the information they have, the perceived threat, and the decisions they make. The entire decision path is full of thought and decisions on the part of the occupant, all of which take time before leading to the development of adaptive behavior. In hindsight, the actions of many occupants in real fires are sometimes less than optimal. However, their decisions might have been the best choices given the information they had. Fire alarm systems that only use audible tones and/or flashing strobe lights impart only one bit of information: fire alarm. It has long been recognized that environments having complex egress situations or high hazard potentials require occupant notification systems that provide more than one bit of information [5]. To reduce the response time of the occupants and to effect the desired behavior, the message should contain several key elements [3,6].

The key elements include the following:

(1) Tell occupants what has happened and where.
(2) Tell occupants what they should do.
(3) Tell occupants why they should do it.

There does not seem to be any research that has tested actual message content to determine the best way to inform occupants. The problem is that each building and each fire is unique. Messaging is further complicated by the need to give different information to different people, depending on their location relative to the fire, their training, and their physical/mental capabilities.

Messages should use positive language and avoid negative instructions that could be misinterpreted due to unintelligible communications. For example, if you want people to leave an area, say so: "A fire has been reported in the area. For your safety, use the stairs to evacuate the area immediately." A bad example is: "The signal tone you have just heard indicated a report of an emergency. If your floor evacuation signal sounds after this message, do not use the elevator, walk to the nearest stairway and leave the floor. While the report is being verified, occupants on other floors should await further instructions." This message is too long, ambiguous, and subject to misunderstanding if not heard clearly. The word "not" might not be heard clearly, or it might be heard to apply to the entire remaining sentence. Similarly, care should be used in selecting and clearly enunciating words such as "fifth" and "sixth," which can sound the same if the system and environment lead to low intelligibility.

See A.24.4.2.17 for more information on methodology for improved message content, structure, and intelligibility. Refer to Annex D for more information on speech intelligibility and how it is predicted.

Content of the message should be predicated on the building fire safety plan, the nature of the building and its occupants, the design of the fire alarm system, and testing of the occupant reaction to the message. Caution is advised that the fire alarm system operation and message actuation might be initiated by a manual pull station or detector remote from the fire.

[1] Schifiliti, R. P., "To Leave or Not to Leave — That is the Question!", National Fire Protection Association, World Fire Safety Congress & Exposition, May 16, 2000, Denver, CO.

[2] Ramachandran, G., "Informative Fire Warning Systems," *Fire Technology*, vol. 47, no. 1, February 1991, National Fire Protection Association, 66–81.

[3] J., Bryan, "Psychological Variables That May Affect Fire Alarm Design," *Fire Protection Engineering*, Society of Fire Protection Engineers, Issue No. 11, Fall 2001.

[4] Proulx, G., "Cool Under Fire," *Fire Protection Engineering*, Society of Fire Protection Engineers, Issue No. 16, Fall 2002.

[5] General Services Administration, Proceedings of the Reconvened International Conference on Fire Safety in High Rise Buildings, Washington, D.C., October 1971.

[6] Proulx, G., "Strategies for Ensuring Appropriate Occupant Response to Fire Alarm Signals," National Research Council of Canada, Ottawa, Ontario, *Construction Technology Update*, No. 43, 1–6, December 2000.

24.4.1.8.1 Systems shall be provided with manual voice transmission capabilities selectively to one or more zones or on an all-call basis.

24.4.1.8.2 Under a fire condition, where the system is used to transmit relocation instructions or other fire emergency non-evacuation messages, a 1-second to 3-second alert tone followed by a message (or messages where multi-channel capability is used) shall be provided.

It is important that the alert tone not be used when transmitting non-fire messages to the building occupants. The intent of the Code is to allow the in-building fire emergency voice/alarm communications systems to be used with other communications systems, such as telephone paging and public address systems. There is no need for an alert tone when the in-building fire emergency voice/alarm communications systems are used to transmit non-fire and non-emergency messages.

24.4.1.8.2.1 The sequence [the alert tone followed by the message(s)] shall be repeated at least three times to inform and direct occupants in the evacuation signaling zone where the alarm initiation originated, as well as other evacuation signaling zones in accordance with the building fire safety plan.

The alert tone is required only for an in-building fire emergency voice/alarm communications system and only when the plan calls for evacuation.

24.4.1.8.2.2 Approved alternative fire alarm notification schemes shall be permitted so long as the occupants are effectively notified and are provided instructions in a timely and safe manner in accordance with the building fire safety plan.

24.4.1.8.3 Where provided, speakers in each enclosed stairway shall be connected to a separate notification zone for manual paging only.

Paragraph 24.4.1.8.3 requires speakers on a separate notification zone in stairwells only if speakers are required in stairwells by the local building code, *Life Safety Code*, or project specifications. A masonry stairwell is a difficult environment to get intelligible reproduction of a voice message. Usually, people who are in the stairwell when the system is actuated are already on their way out of the building and do not need additional instructions. If they exit the stairwell on a particular floor, they will hear the voice message with instructions for the occupants of that particular floor. Although it may be beneficial under certain circumstances, for example, in a high-rise building, where it might be necessary to provide voice instructions to occupants evacuating through the stairwells, only rarely is it necessary to provide speakers in stairwells. Emergency personnel may need to provide updated instructions to occupants who may be in the stairwell for an extended period of time during a prolonged emergency, particularly in very tall buildings where evacuation may take more than an hour. Refer to 23.8.6.2 for notification appliance allowances in stairwells.

24.4.1.8.4 The requirements of 24.4.1.8.4 shall apply to both audible (tone and voice) and visible notification appliance circuits.

24.4.1.8.4.1* Fire alarm systems used for partial evacuation and relocation shall be designed and installed such that attack by fire within an evacuation signaling zone does not impair control and operation of the notification appliances outside the evacuation signaling zone.

Paragraph 24.4.1.8.4.1 requires that the circuits, wiring, or communications paths to each evacuation signaling zone be arranged such that damage to those "paths" in one evacuation signaling zone will not impair communications to any other evacuation signaling zone. For example, assume that each floor in a high-rise building is an evacuation signaling zone. A circuit that feeds the notification appliances on the fifth floor of the building must be arranged such that damage to that circuit does not affect communications to any other floor above or below.

Survivability requirements are intended to minimize the possibility of a fire causing damage to the notification appliance riser cables within the fire area that would interrupt communications to areas outside the fire area. For example, circuits that serve individual floors in a multifloor building or individual areas in a large area building may be routed through areas where they could be exposed to fire before they reach another floor or area they serve. Fire-rated construction, a fire-rated circuit integrity cable, fire-rated cable system, or other approved protection minimizes the potential of early damage to circuits that serve areas outside the immediate fire area. Survivability is not intended to maintain every device, appliance, and circuit in service for the duration of the fire. However, if amplifiers are distributed in such a fashion as to serve multiple floors (speaker circuits), the amplifiers and their interconnection to the circuits supplied by those amplifiers must meet the survivability requirements. Alternating speaker circuits on each floor does not provide compliance with the survivability requirements of the Code. Specific fire alarm devices and components on the fire floor can be compromised by direct fire exposure. Fire alarm system components are not designed to withstand direct attack by fire. The intent of the survivability requirements is to prevent damage to notification appliance circuits and equipment serving other areas of the building, which might pass through or be located in the fire area.

Although 24.4.1.8.4.1 is contained as a subparagraph of 24.4.1, prudence would suggest that the requirements of 24.4.1.8.4.1 should be used for any system used for partial evacuation, selective evacuation, or relocation of occupants. Some facilities such as hospitals use coded signals to indicate the location of and response to a fire emergency. The intent is to have survivability requirements apply to both voice and non-voice systems used to partially or selectively evacuate or relocate the building occupants by floor or zone.

A.24.4.1.8.4.1 Along with the pathway survivability requirements, one or more of the following means could be considered acceptable to provide a level of survivability consistent with the intent of this requirement:

(1) Routing notification appliance circuits separately

Again, using what is popularly called "A – B" circuits — that is, alternately connecting speakers serving the same space or corridor on two separate circuits installed in the same space or raceway — does not make the circuits survivable.

(2) Using short-circuit, fault-tolerant signaling line circuits for controlling evacuation signals
    The requirement for notification appliances to operate in those evacuation signaling zones that are not attacked by fire will also require that circuits and equipment that are common to more than one evacuation signaling zone be designed and installed such that the fire will not disable them. For instance, a signaling line circuit used to control notification appliances in multiple evacuation signaling zones should be properly designed and installed so that one fire would not impair the signaling line circuit, rendering the notification appliances serving more than one evacuation signaling zone inoperative.

24.4.1.8.4.2 Performance features provided to ensure operational reliability under adverse conditions shall be described and technical justification provided in the documentation submitted to the authority having jurisdiction with the analysis required in 23.4.3.1.

Adverse conditions other than a fire could occur where it would be imperative for the communications system to continue to operate. These conditions are identified by consulting with the owner and performing a risk analysis. The results of the risk analysis are required to be documented and presented to the authority having jurisdiction.

24.4.1.8.4.3* All circuits necessary for the operation of the notification appliances shall be protected until they enter the evacuation signaling zone that they serve by the protection provided by the pathway survivability level required in 24.3.5.4.1 or by performance alternatives approved by the authority having jurisdiction.

Paragraph 24.4.1.8.4.3 reinforces the idea that the system must be designed and installed in a manner that minimizes the potential for fire exposure in a single evacuation zone from interrupting communications to other evacuation zones. Using one of the methods listed in Chapter 12, as required in 24.3.5.4.1, provides a minimum degree of protection for the circuit to meet the survivability requirements.

All fire alarm system wiring installations must conform to the requirements of *NFPA 70*®, *National Electrical Code*® (*NEC*®). The *NEC* provides general wiring methods and requirements in Chapter 1 through Chapter 4. Article 760, Fire Alarm Systems, contained in Chapter 7, supplements and modifies the requirements of Chapter 1 through Chapter 4 specifically for fire alarm systems. The wiring methods permitted in Article 760 include the use of Chapter 3 wiring methods as well as the use of specific types of non-power-limited and power-limited cables. The wiring method used must be installed in accordance with the manufacturer's instructions, any listing limitations, and the requirements of Article 760.

The authority having jurisdiction may approve other methods of providing the protection intended by 24.4.1.8.4.3. This might be a combination of installation methods and protection by the building structure. Technical justification must be provided by the designer to support the survivability design.

The intent of the Code is to ensure communications during a fire to occupants on the non-fire floors. Designers, installers, and authorities having jurisdiction should ensure that all circuits necessary for the operation of the notification appliances (including speakers and strobes) are survivable regardless of how the circuits are connected and installed.

A.24.4.1.8.4.3 Paragraph 24.4.1.8.4.3 requires the protection of circuits as they pass through fire areas other than the one served. The purpose of this is to delay possible damage to the circuits from fires in areas other than those served by the circuits and to increase the likelihood that circuits serving areas remote from the original fire will have the opportunity to be actuated and serve their purpose. Note that the protection requirement would also apply to a signaling line circuit that extends from a master fire alarm control unit to another remote fire alarm control unit where notification appliance circuits might originate.

24.4.1.8.4.4 Where the separation of in-building fire emergency voice/alarm control equipment locations results in the portions of the system controlled by one location being dependent upon the control equipment in other locations, the circuits between the dependent controls shall be protected against attack by fire by the protection provided by the pathway survivability level required in 24.3.5.4.1 or by performance alternatives approved by the authority having jurisdiction.

Where control equipment for in-building fire emergency voice/alarm communications is in multiple locations, damage to the interconnecting wiring can affect operability of the control equipment in one location or another. Protection of these circuits is required in a fashion similar to that specified for notification appliance circuits in 24.4.1.8.4.1 and 24.4.1.8.4.3.

Paragraph 24.4.1.8.4.4 in conjunction with 24.4.1.8.4.6 closes the loop on circuits and equipment that needs to be survivable against an attack by fire. The ultimate goal of the Code is to ensure that all circuits and equipment affecting the ability to communicate above and below the fire floor during the fire meet the survivability requirements.

24.4.1.8.4.5 Protection of circuits between redundant control equipment locations that are not mutually dependent shall not be required.

24.4.1.8.4.6 Where the separation of the in-building fire emergency voice/alarm control equipment occurs as in 24.4.1.8.4.4, and where the circuits are run through junction boxes, terminal cabinets or control equipment, such as system control units, power supplies and amplifiers, and where cable integrity is not maintained, these components shall, in addition to the pathway survivability required by 24.3.5.4.1, be protected by using one of the following methods:

(1) A 2-hour fire rated enclosure
(2) A 2-hour fire rated room
(3) Other equivalent means to provide a 2-hour fire resistance rating approved by the authority having jurisdiction

This paragraph, in conjunction with the requirement in 24.4.1.8.4.4, ensures that everything connecting the pathways and circuits or equipment necessary to operate the notification appliances will meet the requirements of survivability and maintain the communications system's operational capability as described in 24.4.1.8.4.1.

24.4.1.8.4.7 Paragraphs 24.4.1.8 through 24.4.1.8.4.6 shall not automatically apply when relocation or partial evacuation is of a non-fire emergency unless identified and required by a risk analysis.

24.4.1.9 Evacuation Signal Zoning.

24.4.1.9.1* Undivided fire or smoke areas shall not be divided into multiple evacuation signaling zones.

A.24.4.1.9.1 Paragraph 24.4.1.9.1 does not prohibit the provision of multiple notification appliance circuits within an evacuation signaling zone.

The division of a single fire or smoke area into more than one evacuation signaling zone is not practical. If a fire threatens one part of the zone, then the entire zone should be evacuated.

24.4.1.9.2 If multiple notification appliance circuits are provided within a single evacuation signaling zone, all of the notification appliances within the zone shall be arranged to activate or deactivate simultaneously, either automatically or by actuation of a common manual control.

24.4.1.9.3 Where there are different notification appliance circuits within an evacuation signaling zone that perform separate functions, such as presignal and general alarm signals, and pre-discharge and discharge signals, they shall not be required to activate or deactivate simultaneously.

An *evacuation signaling zone,* defined in 3.3.300.1, is "a discrete area of a building, bounded by smoke or fire barriers, from which the occupants are intended to relocate or evacuate." Signaling to a single evacuation signaling zone may need to be accomplished through the use of more than one notification appliance circuit. In this situation, all the notification appliance circuits serving the evacuation signaling zone must be arranged to act simultaneously, as required by 24.4.1.9.2.

The boundaries of the evacuation signaling zone are a function of the building fire safety subdivisions and the building emergency evacuation plan. The Code also uses other "zone" terminology, such as *notification zone,* which is defined in 3.3.300.2 as "an area covered by notification appliances that are activated simultaneously." Notification zones are addressed in 23.8.6.3 and associated commentary.

24.4.2* In-Building Mass Notification Systems. The requirements of 24.4.2 shall apply to mass notification systems installed in buildings or structures for the purpose of notifying and instructing occupants in an emergency.

There are essentially four tiers of MNSs:

- Tier 1
  - Immediate and intrusive alerting
    - Sirens, indoor/outdoor loudspeakers
    - Fire voice evacuation
    - Electronic signage
    - Code-compliant system
- Tier 2
  - Personal alerting
    - Short message service (SMS) text (cell phones)
    - Computer pop-ups
    - Tone alert radios
    - Email broadcast (Internet)
    - Automated voice dialing and text messaging
- Tier 3
  - Public alerting
    - Satellite/AM/FM radio broadcasts
    - Satellite/off-air TV broadcasts
    - Location-specific messages
    - Text messages
- Tier 4
  - Locally relevant alerting
    - Handheld bullhorns

- Radio cell phones
- Two-way radios

A.24.4.2 This section covers the application, installation, location, performance, and maintenance of mass notification systems used for emergency purposes.

An in-building mass notification system is considered to be a system used to provide information and instructions to people in a building(s) or other space using intelligible voice communications and including visible signals, text, graphics, tactile, or other communication methods.

Mass notification systems can consist of fully independent systems with minimal or no interface with the building fire alarm system, systems that report trouble and supervisory signals through the fire alarm system, systems that share audible and visible notification circuits and appliances with the fire alarm system, or combination mass notification and fire alarm systems.

Combining or integrating in-building fire emergency voice/alarm communications systems with other communications systems such as mass notification, public address, and paging is now allowed by the Code. A fire alarm interface is illustrated in Exhibit 24.2. The technology is available to ensure that fire alarm or priority mass notification messages (as determined by a risk analysis) will take precedence over any other announcement, such as paging from a telephone system or other public address system. Using one speaker system that is a combination of other communications systems and that incorporates all the requirements of the Code is financially beneficial to the owner. Not only could there be reduced design, installation, and ongoing life cycle costs, but regular use of the system for normal paging functions provides an end-to-end test of the audible notification components and circuits. Occupants familiar with use of the system for normal paging are also more likely to be comfortable and proficient using the system during an emergency.

EXHIBIT 24.2 *Fire Alarm Interface. (Source: Siemens Building Technologies, Inc., Florham Park, NJ)*

24.4.2.1* General Performance. The performance, selection, installation, operation, and use of a mass notification system shall comply with the requirements of 24.4.2.

A.24.4.2.1 Although some minimum criteria are outlined for a particular feature, the feature might not be applicable for every project.

The information and instructions delivered by a mass notification system could be initiated manually by an operator or automatically by sensors or other systems and might be delivered to the target audience using prerecorded messages or live messages, or both, tailored to the situation and the audience.

Each mass notification system could be different, depending on the anticipated threat and the level of protection intended. As an example, a particular project might not require secure radio transmissions. As such, criteria for such would not apply. However, if the authority having jurisdiction or design professional has specified secure radio transmissions, the minimum applicable criteria within this document would be required. Deviation from these minimum criteria would require approval of the stakeholders.

Mass notification systems can consist of fully independent systems with minimal or no interface with the building fire alarm system, systems that report trouble and supervisory signals through the fire alarm system, systems that share audible and visible notification circuits and appliances with the fire alarm system, or combination mass notification and fire alarm systems.

Combining or integrating in-building fire emergency voice/alarm communications systems with other communications systems such as mass notification, public address, and paging is now allowed by the Code. Fire alarm signals must take precedence except where mass notification messages as determined by a risk analysis are deemed to be a higher priority than fire. One example would be a terrorist event, another a shooter in the building.

24.4.2.1.1 Interconnection of protected premises emergency control functions with the mass notification systems shall comply with Chapter 21.

24.4.2.1.2 An in-building mass notification system shall include one or more of the following components:

(1) Autonomous control unit (ACU)
(2) Local operating console (LOC)
(3) Fire alarm control interface
(4) Notification appliance network
(5) Initiating devices
(6)* Interface to other systems and alerting sources

A.24.4.2.1.2(6) Other systems could include wide-area mass notification, distributed recipient mass notification, and regional and national alerting.

FAQ ▶
Which mass notification communication methods could be utilized effectively?

It is recommended that the MNS include two forms of communication, one from Tier 1 and a secondary method from one of the other tiers described in the commentary following 24.4.2. Relying on just one method in an emergency could result in a relatively large portion of the targeted population not receiving the message. The overall solution is to exploit a number of Tier 1 and secondary tier systems that combine to produce a reliable and robust design that meets the owner's goals and objectives. See 24.7.1.

24.4.2.1.3 Control units installed as part of a mass notification system shall be in compliance with this Code and applicable standards such as ANSI/UL 864, *Standard for Control Units and Accessories for Fire Alarm Systems,* or UL 2017, *Standard for General-Purpose Signaling Devices and Systems.*

24.4.2.1.4 Mass notification system components shall be installed, tested, and maintained in accordance with the manufacturer's published instructions and this Code.

24.4.2.1.5 In-building emergency mass notification operation shall be permitted to be initiated by manual or automatic means.

24.4.2.1.6 Mass notification system activation shall initiate recorded messages or live voice and visible notification.

24.4.2.1.7 The priority level of recorded messages shall be determined by the emergency response plan.

The priority levels will be based on an evaluation of a number of issues, including occupancy, impact on individual security, danger to life, danger to the community, or danger and impact on the nation. These priorities will also be used to determine if any mass notification message should take precedence over a fire alarm message, as stated in 24.4.2.1.8.

24.4.2.1.8 Only recorded messages determined by the emergency response plan to be of higher priority than fire alarm activation shall be permitted to override the fire alarm notification and initiate the mass notification priority indicator.

24.4.2.1.9 Activation of any other recorded message shall not interfere with the operation of fire alarm notification.

An example of this situation would be when a periodic timed general announcement is not allowed to override fire alarm messages and tones during a fire alarm condition.

24.4.2.1.10 Initiation of live voice announcements from microphones on the fire alarm system at an ACU, and at an LOC, shall not automatically place the fire alarm system in a mass notification priority mode.

24.4.2.1.11 Combination of mass notification with fire alarm systems shall be permitted and shall meet the requirements of 23.8.4.

Combining or integrating in-building fire emergency voice/alarm communications systems with other communications systems such as mass notification, public address, and paging is now allowed by the Code. Fire alarm signals must take precedence except where mass notification messages as determined by a risk analysis are deemed to be a higher priority than fire. In addition to reduced design, installation, and ongoing life cycle costs, regular use of the system for normal paging functions provides an end-to-end test of the audible notification components and circuits. Occupants familiar with use of the system for normal paging are also more likely to be comfortable and proficient in use of the system during an emergency.

24.4.2.2 Risk Analysis for Mass Notification Systems.

24.4.2.2.1* Each application of a mass notification system shall be specific to the nature and anticipated risks of each facility for which it is designed.

Emergency planning requires a detailed risk analysis (vulnerability and failure analysis), which includes an evaluation of the risk to the asset; probability of occurrence and frequency of loss; and the loss effect.

   Risk mitigation includes dissemination of information, which is the role an MNS plays in an emergency.

◄ **FAQ**
What are some of the basic issues that must be addressed by the MNS risk analysis?

A.24.4.2.2.1 Although this chapter outlines some specific criteria and/or limitations, each application should be based on recognized performance-based design practices and the emergency response plan developed for the specific facility. Refer also to the risk analysis information found in 24.7.7.

   Here are the general categories of questions that might be presented to the senior manager responsible for mass notification decisions. The actual questions for each project must be tailored to the area, the building, the campus, and the culture of the user organization. Following is a brief description of potential content within the mass notification event questions:

(1) What is the type of emergency event — that is, is it fire, security, safety, health, environmental, geological, meteorological, utility service disruption, or another type of event?
(2) What is the urgency of the emergency event — that is, does it represent immediate danger, has it already occurred, is it expected to occur soon, is it expected to occur in the future, or is its occurrence unknown?
(3) What is the anticipated or expected severity of the emergency event that is, how will it impact our facility and its functions, is it expected to be extreme, severe, etc.?
(4) What is the certainty of the emergency event that is, is it happening now, is it very likely to occur, is it likely to occur, is it possible that it will occur in the future, is it unlikely to occur, or is its occurrence unknown?
(5) What is the location of the event, or from what direction is the emergency event approaching, — that is, has it or will it be approaching from the north, south, east, or west?

(6) What zone or areas should receive the emergency message(s), — that is, is it a floor of a building, multiple floors of a building, the entire building, multiple buildings, a campus of buildings, an entire town or city, an entire state, an entire region of states, or an entire country?

Exhibit 24.3 illustrates the extent of an MNS.

EXHIBIT 24.3 *Extent of a Mass Notification System (MNS).*

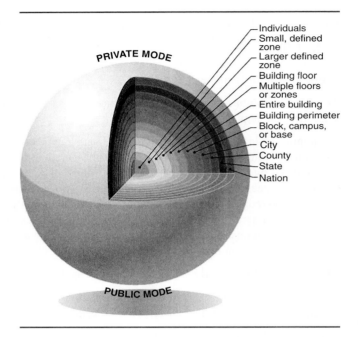

(7) What is the validity of the emergency event, — that is, has the emergency event been investigated and/or confirmed?
(8) What instructions should we send to our personnel — that is, should they evacuate the facility, should they shelter-in-place, should they shelter-in-place at a special location, should they proceed to a safe haven area, and other action oriented items?
(9) Are there any special instructions, procedures, or special tasks that we need to remind personnel about or to accomplish — that is, close your office door, open your office door, stay away from windows, do not use elevators, and other information relating to personnel actions?

The questions suggested in items (1) through (9) are offered for consideration, and not all of them might be appropriate for every mass notification system installation. It is important to remember that when an emergency event occurs, the response must be immediate and deliberate. Therefore, there is no time for indecision. So the questions selected to reside in the emergency messaging decision tree illustrated in items (1) through (9) must be straightforward and as simple as possible. They must also be tailored to the specific organization, culture, site, and unique requirements of each local environment.

24.4.2.2.2 The designer shall consider both fire and non-fire emergencies when determining risk tolerances for survivability for the mass notification system.

24.4.2.2.3 Performance-based design and the risk analysis shall be applied in accordance with Section 24.7.

24.4.2.2.4 The risk analysis shall be used as the basis for development of the emergency response plan.

24.4.2.3* Emergency Response Plan Elements. A well-defined emergency response plan shall be developed in accordance with *NFPA 1600, Standard on Disaster/Emergency Management and Business Continuity Programs*, and NFPA 1620, *Recommended Practice for Pre-Incident Planning*, as part of the design and implementation of a mass notification system.

A.24.4.2.3 The emergency response plan should include, but not be limited to, the following elements:

(1) Emergency response team structure
(2) Emergency response procedures, as follows:

   (a) Building system related emergencies
   (b) Human-related emergencies
   (c) Terrorism-related emergencies
   (d) Weather-related emergencies

(3) Emergency response equipment and operations
(4) Emergency response notification, as follows:

   (a) Emergency message content
   (b) Emergency notification approval process
   (c) Emergency notification initiation process

(5) Emergency response training and drills, as follows:

   (a) Classroom training
   (b) Table-top training
   (c) Live drills

24.4.2.4 System Operation.

24.4.2.4.1* Authorized personnel shall be permitted to control message initiation over the mass notification system.

A.24.4.2.4.1 Authorized personnel could include building occupants who can readily access and originate messages in emergency situations. Depending on the individual facility, use of the mass notification system to originate non-emergency messages could also be permitted. The selection of authorized personnel should be based on a risk assessment and the building emergency response plan.

24.4.2.4.2* Where identified by the risk analysis, the mass notification system shall provide the capability for authorized personnel to remotely activate live and prerecorded emergency messages.

A.24.4.2.4.2 Authorized personnel could effect message initiation over the mass notification system from either a central control station or a secondary (backup) control station(s). In cases where clusters of facilities within the same geographical region exist, one or more regional control stations could effect message initiation. The mass notification system could permit activation of messages originated by mobile sentries and roving patrols using wireless activation devices. Since it is common practice to allow mass notification systems to be utilized for "nonemergency" messages, the central control station should incorporate a clearly marked and easy to operate means to distinguish between emergency and non-emergency use. Comprehensive training and a fail-safe default to the emergency mode of operation should be employed to ensure that no actual emergency message gets transmitted as a non-emergency broadcast.

24.4.2.4.3* Operating controls shall be clearly identified.

A.24.4.2.4.3 As a general practice, the number of message selection switches included as part of the operating controls should be limited, so that authorized personnel can utilize the system with only minimal familiarity. This, of course, could be a different matter on an industrial or college campus where trained individuals are likely to be very familiar with the operation and use of the system. In that case, more selection switches could be beneficial.

24.4.2.4.4 If there are multiple control locations, only one shall be in control at any given time.

24.4.2.4.5 If there are multiple control locations, a visible indication shall be provided at all other control locations indicating that another control location is in use.

It is necessary to know if another location has been activated to avoid two locations attempting to transmit messages that may conflict or be confusing to the listeners.

24.4.2.4.6 Manual controls shall be arranged to provide visible indication of the on/off status for their associated notification zone.

24.4.2.4.7 If live voice instructions are provided, they shall perform as follows:

(1) Override previously initiated signals to the selected notification zone(s).
(2) Have priority over any subsequent automatically initiated signals to the selected zone(s).

24.4.2.4.8 A manual means shall be provided at each mass notification system control location to permit the mass notification system to relinquish control of the fire alarm system.

The purpose of this requirement is to not allow an intruder or terrorist who may be inside the building to actuate the fire alarm system and disable the MNS.

24.4.2.4.9* During the period after the mass notification system has seized control of the audible notification appliances, but before the mass notification system relinquishes control, an audible and visible signal shall be actuated by the notification appliances at least once every 30 seconds.

A.24.4.2.4.9 During emergencies, building occupants should periodically receive an audible clue that the emergency notification given by the mass notification system is still in effect. This also can help building occupants and emergency response personnel recognize that the mass notification system is overriding fire alarm notification appliances. The audible signal could consist of a simple signal such as a chirp of sufficient duration to be recognized by the usual building occupants and, typically, by occupants who are not hearing disabled.

24.4.2.5 Coverage.

24.4.2.5.1* The mass notification system shall provide for live voice and prerecorded localized messaging within a protected individual building, areas surrounding the building, and other outdoor designated areas.

A.24.4.2.5.1 The mass notification system could permit activation of messages originated by mobile sentries and roving patrols using wireless activation devices.

24.4.2.5.2 Notification zones shall be established on the basis of a risk analysis.

24.4.2.5.3* If the mass notification system serves more than one building, it shall be capable of providing separate messages to one individual building or to multiple buildings at any given time.

A.24.4.2.5.3 Generally, each separate building should be provided with a separate in-building mass notification system; however, some facilities (such as a campus-type high school with multiple separate buildings) might be more effectively served by a single in-building mass notification system. Alternately, a risk analysis could determine that a wide-area mass notification system provides the optimal capability for mass notification.

24.4.2.6 Speaker Circuits.

24.4.2.6.1* Speaker circuits used for mass notification that are not fire alarm circuits shall be exempt from the monitoring requirements of this Code, provided that alternate methods of achieving comparable reliability are accepted by the authority having jurisdiction.

A.24.4.2.6.1 Alternate methods that achieve the desired statistical availability could be deemed acceptable in lieu of monitoring the integrity of circuits, signaling channels, or communication pathways where consistent with the risk analysis and emergency response plan.

24.4.2.6.2 Survivability for speaker circuits used for mass notification shall be determined by the risk analysis for the building.

24.4.2.7 Documentation.

24.4.2.7.1 Security. Security for mass notification systems documentation shall be determined by the stakeholders.

24.4.2.7.2 Record of Completion.

24.4.2.7.2.1 A record of completion form, as shown in Figure 10.18.2.1.1, shall be required for documentation of the mass notification system.

24.4.2.7.2.2 All systems that are modified after the initial installation shall have the original record of completion revised to show all changes from the original information and shall be identified with a revision date.

24.4.2.7.3 Required Documentation. Every system shall include the following documentation, which shall be delivered to the owner or the owner's representative upon final acceptance of the system:

(1) An owner's manual including a complete set of operations and maintenance manuals, manufacturer's published instructions, and product data sheets covering all system equipment
(2) Record and as-built drawings
(3) One current copy of the record of completion form, updated to reflect all system additions or modifications
(4) For software-based systems, a record copy of the system-specific software
(5) Emergency response plan, with operational management procedures defined for management and activation of the system

24.4.2.7.4 Document Accessibility.

24.4.2.7.4.1 An as-built plans cabinet shall be provided to house the documentation required in 24.4.2.7.3.

24.4.2.7.4.2 The cabinet shall be sized so that it can neatly contain all necessary documentation, including future inspection and service reports.

24.4.2.7.4.3 The contents of the cabinet shall be accessible by authorized personnel only.

24.4.2.7.4.4 Mass notification system and fire alarm system as-built plans and other related documentation shall be permitted to be maintained together, including the appearance of both systems on the same drawings.

24.4.2.7.4.5 The requirements of 10.18.3 and Section 14.6 shall be applicable for mass notification system records and record keeping.

All the documentation required in 24.4.2.7 helps ensure long-term reliability by recording the information necessary for proper maintenance of the MNS.

24.4.2.8 Impairments. The requirements of Section 10.19 shall be applicable when a mass notification system is impaired.

FAQ ▶
How should an MNS
impairment be handled?

The impairment of an MNS should be treated with the same importance as impairments to a fire alarm system. Both systems affect life safety.

24.4.2.9 Inspection, Testing, and Maintenance Requirements. Mass notification systems shall be inspected, tested, and maintained in accordance with the manufacturer's requirements and the inspection, testing, and maintenance requirements of Chapter 14.

24.4.2.10* System Priorities. Priority levels shall be established on the basis of the risk analysis.

A.24.4.2.10 The risk analysis should identify what emergency situations will take priority over the fire alarm evacuation signal. Should a tornado warning for the area take priority over an active fire in the building? Should a breach of security at the campus entry gate take priority over an active fire in the building? If a manual fire alarm pull box has been activated, it might be a terrorist action to have people leave the building and walk into an exterior threat. In such a case, mass notification input is intended to override the fire alarm evacuation signals to redirect the occupants based on the conditions.

24.4.2.11 Initiation Indication. The source of system activation shall be visibly and audibly indicated at the central control station and at the building control unit, unless otherwise determined by the risk analysis.

24.4.2.12 Initiating Devices.

24.4.2.12.1 Devices connected to a mass notification system for the purpose of initiating an automatic response to an emergency shall be evaluated based on the risk analysis.

24.4.2.12.2* All mass notification initiating devices shall be listed for their intended purpose.

A.24.4.2.12.2 Devices such as gas or chemical sensors and detectors, weather alert signals, or other such signals can be desirable to connect to the mass notification system to provide a faster response to emergency conditions.

24.4.2.12.3 Where no listed device exists for the detection required by the emergency response plan, nonlisted devices shall be permitted to be used if their failure will not impair the operation of the mass notification system.

24.4.2.12.4 Non-fire emergency manual actuating stations (boxes) shall be listed with an applicable standard, such as ANSI/UL 2017, *Standard for General Purpose Signaling Devices and Systems.*

24.4.2.12.5 Non-fire emergency manual actuating boxes shall have tactile markings, be of a contrasting color to manual fire alarm boxes on the protected premises, and not be red.

24.4.2.12.6 Non-fire emergency manual actuating boxes shall be installed similarly to manual fire alarm boxes in accordance with the requirements of 17.14.3 through 17.14.5.

24.4.2.13* Secure Access of Fire Alarm/Mass Notification System Interface. Access to, and physical protection of, the fire alarm/mass notification system interface shall be determined by the risk analysis and as defined in the emergency response plan.

A.24.4.2.13 Refer to 24.4.2.4 for requirements related to operation of the system by authorized personnel. It is recognized that, based on the risk analysis, control equipment and circuits could need different levels of protection for different facilities. Access to the fire alarm/mass notification interface should be consistent with the action outlined in the emergency response plan. It could have been prior practice in some jurisdictions to locate the fire alarm control unit in the main lobby of a facility. However, it might not be appropriate to locate the mass notification system autonomous control unit within the lobby if the general public would have access to deactivate mass notification system components. Based on the risk analysis, it could be appropriate to locate the autonomous control unit within a secured room while providing local operating consoles for use by other authorized personnel.

24.4.2.14 Autonomous Control Unit (ACU).

24.4.2.14.1 Where provided, the building ACU shall monitor and control the notification appliance network.

24.4.2.14.2 Building occupants meeting the requirements of 24.4.2.4.1 shall be permitted to initiate communications from the ACU.

24.4.2.14.3 Unless otherwise identified through the risk analysis, actions taken at the building ACU shall take precedence over actions taken at any remote location, including the local operating console, or inputs from a wide-area mass notification system.

Authorized personnel located at the building will know better and faster what conditions are developing at the building and will be expected to provide more current and acute information through the MNS.

24.4.2.14.4 When there are multiple ACUs controlling the same notification appliance network, only one shall be in control at any given time.

24.4.2.14.5 When the ACU is integrated with the building fire alarm control unit to form one combined system that performs both functions, the system shall meet the standby power requirements of this chapter.

24.4.2.14.6 When a combined system is installed with an ACU and fire alarm control unit and placed in separate equipment enclosures, the ACU and fire alarm control unit shall be interfaced as required by this chapter.

24.4.2.14.7 When the ACU is part of a stand-alone mass notification system and no fire alarm system exists, the ACU shall meet the requirements of this chapter.

24.4.2.15 Local Operating Console (LOC).

24.4.2.15.1* Building occupants meeting the authorized personnel requirement of 24.4.2.4.1 shall be permitted to initiate communications from the LOC.

A.24.4.2.15.1 Mass notification systems can include a system local operating console(s) for authorized occupants to readily access and originate messages in emergency and non-emergency situations. The quantity and location(s) of an LOC(s) should be determined by the risk analysis and the facilities emergency response plan.

24.4.2.15.2 The use of lock wire seals or break-glass-type enclosures to house the operating consoles for the system, or equivalent protection against unauthorized use, shall be permitted.

24.4.2.15.3 Operating controls shall be clearly identified.

24.4.2.15.4 If there are multiple control locations, only one shall be in control at any given time.

24.4.2.15.5 The location having control of the system shall be identified by a visible indication at that location.

24.4.2.15.6 Manual controls shall be arranged to provide visible indication of the on/off status for their associated notification signaling zone.

24.4.2.15.7 If live voice instructions are provided, they shall override previously initiated signals to the selected notification zone(s) and shall have priority over any subsequent automatically initiated signals to the selected zone(s).

24.4.2.16 Voice Message Priority.

24.4.2.16.1* The priority of mass notification messages shall be established using risk analysis methods.

A.24.4.2.16.1 The following is an example scheme for message prioritization, from highest (1) to lowest (5), for consideration during the risk analysis:

(1) Live voice messages from personnel in the building should be the highest priority. If systems provide control locations that are usable by nonauthorized personnel, these controls should be disabled or overridden during emergency operations.
(2) Automatic fire alarm messages/other high priority messages as determined by risk analysis criteria.
(3) External messages originated by a wide-area mass notification system.
(4) Message priority for emergency conditions such as severe weather warnings, gas leaks, chemical spills, and other hazardous conditions should be determined by risk analysis criteria and defined in the emergency response plan.
(5) Non-emergency messages, such as general announcements and time function signaling (work breaks, class change, etc.), should have the lowest priority.

24.4.2.16.2 The local building mass notification system shall have the ability to override the fire alarm system with live voice or manual activation of a high priority message, but only where that message and operation are approved under the risk analysis criteria.

The risk analysis is required to be approved by the authority having jurisdiction, which will also be required to approve any message determined in the analysis to be a higher priority than the fire alarm signal.

24.4.2.16.3 All other messages shall also be prioritized by using the risk analysis method.

24.4.2.16.4 When identified by the risk analysis and emergency response plan, messages from the mass notification system shall take priority over fire alarm messages and signals.

24.4.2.16.5 If the fire alarm system is in the alarm mode and a recorded voice message or the audible signals are sounding, and the mass notification system is actuated, it shall cause deactivation of all fire alarm–initiated audible and visible notification appliances, unless they have also been designated for mass notification use.

24.4.2.16.6 After the mass notification system relinquishes control, the following shall occur:

(1) Without an active fire alarm signal, the fire alarm system shall automatically restore to normal operation.
(2)* With an active fire alarm signal, the fire alarm system shall operate based on the emergency response plan.

A.24.4.2.16.6(2) Unless the risk analysis determines otherwise, the fire alarm system should always be automatically returned to normal functionality. Specific instructions should be in place explaining how the fire alarm system notification appliances should be reactivated. This could vary and should be documented in the building emergency response plan.

24.4.2.16.7 Deactivation of fire alarm audible and visible notification signals shall cause an individually identified supervisory signal to be initiated at the building fire alarm control unit for each affected fire alarm control unit.

24.4.2.16.8 The fire alarm signal deactivation function shall be permitted to occur only when both the fire alarm system is in an alarm condition and a voice message is initiated by the mass notification system.

24.4.2.16.9 When the fire alarm notification is overridden as permitted in 24.4.2.16.8, all other features of the fire alarm system shall remain unaffected.

24.4.2.17* Message Content.

A.24.4.2.17 The fundamental structure of the prerecorded or live messages is critical for providing information and instructions that are intelligible. Prerecorded messages created in a controlled environment are considerably more intelligible than live messages and should be developed and provided to handle as many of the probable emergencies that a particular facility will encounter.

The voice instructions (live or prerecorded) should be preceded by a tone to get attention and prepare the target audience for voice instructions. This tone should be differentiated for specific emergencies, based on the standards for that facility. The actual voice message (live or pre-recorded) should be delivered in a well-enunciated, clear, calm, and deliberate manner, using respectful language. Focus the message on the action to be taken and minimize wasting words on the cause. For the voice itself, best results will vary, depending on the specific location — for example, in outdoor applications, it has been shown that a male voice will provide better intelligibility, as the naturally lower frequency of the male voice travels better. Inversely, in an interior application, where the background ambient noise is typically in the same lower frequencies, a female voice tends to penetrate better, as it is more distinct from the ambient. Messages should be constructed using 2-second to 3-second bursts of information and brief periods of quiet between the bursts of information. This methodology facilitates better processing of information by the brain and minimizes the negative effects of reverberation and echo.

Generally, the emergency message should consist of an alert tone of 1 second to 3 seconds, followed by a voice message that is repeated at least three times. The alert tone can be used in between repeats of the voice message.

For live instructions, it is critical that the message be delivered in a clear and calm manner. When possible, the following procedure is recommended:

(1) Think about what information must be delivered in the live announcement, keep it brief, and write down the message.
(2) Read the message out loud for a practice round in a clear and projecting voice.
(3) When you are ready to announce, key the microphone and read the message two to three times.
(4) When possible, use an alert tone, such as a Code 3, 1000 Hz signal preceding the message, and then announce over the live microphone.
(5) Repeat the message a few times more as the emergency warrants.

24.4.2.17.1 For an evacuation message, a tone in accordance with 18.4.2 shall be used with a minimum of two cycles preceding and following the voice message.

24.4.2.17.2 A test message that clearly states "this is a test" shall be provided.

24.4.2.18 Volume Control.

24.4.2.18.1 Local controls shall be permitted to adjust volume levels of non-emergency signals such as, but not limited to, background music and building paging.

24.4.2.18.2 Upon activation of an emergency signal, the system shall override any local volume setting to deliver at a preset volume setting that has been established through testing and acceptance of sound level and speech intelligibility as required by this Code.

Speaker systems are available that incorporate volume controls and components that allow occupants to lower or turn off the speakers in their area or office. These systems are also designed to allow the speakers to operate at their required power output when the fire alarm system is actuated. The volume control depicted in Exhibit 24.4 would be overridden by the fire

EXHIBIT 24.4 *Speaker Volume Control. (Source: Atlas Sound, Ennis, TX)*

◄ **FAQ**
Can a speaker be provided with a control that allows occupants to lower the volume?

alarm system actuation. This is one of the safeguards now available to meet the requirements of 24.3.4.2(2)(a) and 24.4.2.18.2.

24.4.2.19 Visible Notification.

24.4.2.19.1 Where audible notification is provided, mass notification systems shall also provide visible notification information to serve the hearing impaired and for high-noise areas.

24.4.2.19.2 The visible notification required by 24.4.2.19.1 shall be accomplished using strobes.

24.4.2.19.3 In addition to the strobes required by 24.4.2.19.1, textual, graphic, or video displays shall be permitted.

Unfortunately, strobe use in MNSs does not provide enough information for the hearing impaired to take appropriate action. Textual graphic or video displays can be used to serve this purpose. See the commentary following 24.4.2.21.5.

A visual notification appliance commands attention, but a textual visible appliance can provide more specific information. See Exhibit 24.5.

EXHIBIT 24.6 *Visible Notification Appliance with Amber Lens. (Source: SimplexGrinnell, Westminster, MA)*

EXHIBIT 24.5 *Textual Visible Appliance Directing Exit via Front Stairs Only.*

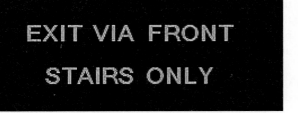

24.4.2.19.4 Transmission of visible notification and messages shall be simultaneous to audible notification and messages.

24.4.2.20 Visible Appliances.

24.4.2.20.1 Where strobes are used as visible appliances, they shall meet the requirements of Sections 18.5 or 18.6, as appropriate.

24.4.2.20.2 Visible notification appliances shall be of a sufficient quantity and intensity and located so as to meet the intent of the design and be in compliance with Section 18.5.

24.4.2.20.3 The word "ALERT" shall be stamped or imprinted on the appliance and be visible to the public.

Exhibit 24.6 shows a visible notification appliance with amber lens labeled "Alert."

The amber strobe is required by at least two Department of Defense organizations; however, the application of amber strobes may conflict with other strobe alerting appliances in some industrial settings. When a conflict arises, an analysis should be conducted, and a review of the options, with technical justification, should be made with the authority having jurisdiction. As an example, a designer might select a combination fire/alert visible notification appliance as shown in Exhibit 24.7.

24.4.2.20.4 Strobes used in combination systems where the same strobe is used for both mass notification and fire notification shall comply with the following:

(1) Be clear or nominal white, meeting the listing requirements of ANSI/UL 1971, *Standard for Signaling Devices for the Hearing Impaired*

(2) Have no marking or be marked with the word "ALERT" stamped or imprinted on the appliance

(3) Be visible to the public

24.4.2.20.5 In situations where existing notification appliances previously used exclusively for fire alarm applications, and are marked with the word "FIRE," and are to be used for other emergency notification purposes, field modification to the marking shall be permitted, provided that it is accomplished by one of the following methods:

(1) Replacement of the manufacturer's approved escutcheon or trim plate

(2) Covering of, or removal of, the word "FIRE" using a manufacturer's approved method

(3) Installation of a permanent sign directly adjacent or below the notification appliance indicating that it is multipurpose and will operate for fire and other emergency conditions

24.4.2.20.6 Strobes used in combination systems where the same strobe is used for both mass notification and fire notification shall be clear or nominal white, meeting the listing requirements of ANSI/UL 1971, *Standard for Signaling Devices for the Hearing Impaired.*

24.4.2.20.7 Strobes with colored lenses shall be marked with the listed effective intensity using the lens color installed.

24.4.2.20.8 The intensity of strobes shall meet the requirements of Chapter 18.

24.4.2.20.9 Strobes used for mass notification shall be listed to an applicable standard such as ANSI/UL 1971, *Standard for Signaling Devices for the Hearing Impaired.*

24.4.2.20.10 Strobes used for mass notification shall meet the synchronization requirements of Section 18.5.

24.4.2.21* Textual Visible Notification.

A.24.4.2.21 Care in location and placement is critical to the survivability of the textual visible appliance and maximizing its effectiveness. Locate the textual visible appliance away from direct sunlight or direct local area lighting. Avoid locating the textual visible appliance near heating and air-conditioning ducts.

24.4.2.21.1 Where textual visible appliances are provided, they shall meet the requirements of Section 18.9 and 24.4.2.21.

24.4.2.21.2 The intensity and readability of text, graphic, and video displays shall meet the requirements of 24.4.2.21.

The occupants of a building where text, graphic, and video displays are used for mass notification expect to get useful information from those displays so that they can act quickly and intelligently on the information provided. A textual visible appliance is depicted in Exhibit 24.8.

24.4.2.21.3 Textual visible appliances shall be listed for the purpose for which they are used.

24.4.2.21.4 Textual visible appliances shall be installed in accordance with the manufacturer's installation instructions.

24.4.2.21.5 Textual visible notification appliances shall be permitted to be used for primary or supplemental notification.

In many cases, textual visible appliances provide accurate and actionable crisis communication information. Using textual visible appliances in place of all strobes in a system would prove to be costly. Most owners and designers opt for a mix of both visible strobes and textual visible appliances as part of a comprehensive mass notification strategy. For example, using strobes with printed signs located next to them to instruct hearing-impaired occupants

EXHIBIT 24.7 *Combination Fire/Alert Visible Notification Appliance. (Source: SimplexGrinnell, Westminster, MA)*

EXHIBIT 24.8 *Textual Visible Appliance Directing Evacuation via North Exit. (Source: SimplexGrinnell, Westminster, MA)*

to move to a location where textual visible appliance have been installed could be a viable strategy for mass notification.

24.4.2.21.6 Textual visible notification shall be considered to be primary notification where it is the only method used to convey emergency mass notification information to the general public or to specific individuals.

24.4.2.21.7 Textual visible appliances within buildings shall meet the power supply requirements specific to protected premises fire alarm systems in 10.17.3.

24.4.2.21.8 If a textual visible appliance, other than the main control unit, is not on a dedicated branch circuit, it shall have a primary source of power and a secondary source of power and be monitored for power integrity in accordance with Section 10.5.

24.4.2.21.9 All mass notification system notification appliances that receive their power from a signaling line circuit of a mass notification system control unit shall be listed for use with the control unit.

24.4.2.21.10 Textual visible appliance messages shall be permitted to be static, flashing, or scrolling, depending on the message being delivered.

24.4.2.21.11 The message text shall be permitted to be any color, as long as it is clearly legible in the environment in which it is located.

24.4.2.21.12 Emergency textual messages shall override non-emergency textual messages.

24.4.2.21.13 Textual visible appliances that are not monitored for integrity or loss of communication by a control unit shall be provided with visual status indicators, including loss of communication or loss of power, that are clearly visible on the appliance.

24.4.2.21.14* Character Size and Viewing Distance.

A.24.4.2.21.14 The information in this section is based on the *NFPA Emergency Evacuation Planning Guide for People with Disabilities.*

24.4.2.21.14.1* Characters shall contrast with their background using either light characters on a dark background or dark characters on a light background.

A.24.4.2.21.14.1 Signs are more legible for persons with low vision when characters contrast as much as possible with their background. Additional factors affecting the ease with which the text can be distinguished from its background include shadows cast by lighting sources, surface glare, and the uniformity of the text and its background colors and textures.

24.4.2.21.14.2 Characters shall be permitted to be uppercase or lowercase, or a combination of both.

24.4.2.21.14.3 Characters shall be conventional in form and not italic, oblique, script, highly decorative, or of other unusual form.

24.4.2.21.14.4 Characters shall be selected from fonts where the width of the uppercase letter "O" is minimum 55 percent and maximum 110 percent of the height of the uppercase letter "I".

24.4.2.21.14.5 Character height shall meet the following criteria:

(1) Minimum character height shall comply with Table 24.4.2.21.14.5.
(2) Viewing distance shall be measured as the horizontal distance between the character and an obstruction preventing further approach towards the sign.
(3) Character height shall be based on the uppercase letter "I".

TABLE 24.4.2.21.14.5 *Visual Character Height*

Height to Finished Floor or Ground from Baseline of Character	Horizontal Viewing Distance	Minimum Character Height
>70 in. (1780 mm)−≤10 ft (3050 mm)	<15 ft (4570 mm)	2 in. (51 mm)
>70 in. (1780 mm)−≤10 ft (3050 mm)	≥15 ft (4570 mm)	2 in. (51 mm), + $\frac{1}{8}$ in. (3.2 mm)/12 in. (305 mm) of viewing distance above 15 ft (4570 mm)
>10 ft (3050 mm)	<21 ft (6400 mm)	3 in. (77 mm)
>10 ft (3050 mm)	≥21 ft (6400 mm)	3 in. (77 mm), + $\frac{1}{8}$ in. (3.2 mm)/ 12 in. (305 mm) of viewing distance above 21 ft (6400 mm)

24.4.2.21.14.6 Visual character height shall be greater than 70 in. (1780 mm) from finished floor in accordance with Table 24.4.2.21.14.5.

24.4.2.21.14.7 Stroke thickness of the uppercase letter "I" shall be minimum 10 percent and maximum 30 percent of the height of the character.

24.4.2.21.14.8 Character spacing shall be measured between the two closest points of adjacent characters, excluding word spaces. Spacing between individual characters shall be minimum 10 percent and maximum 35 percent of character height.

24.4.2.22 Tactile Notification Appliances. Where tactile notification appliances are provided for emergency notification, they shall meet the requirements of Section 18.10.

24.4.2.23* Video Alerting. Video display systems that provide alerts and messages to video appliances shall be permitted to be used to supplement mass notification.

Video information displays (VIDs) at an airport describing flight arrival and departure schedules can be used to supplement other visible and textual visible appliances.

A.24.4.2.23 The video display can be a video appliance used to facilitate mass notification. Information displayed could be video, graphic, text, or audio. Information can be transmitted over a video distribution network, MATV, or CATV system. These messages can be standardized or customized for specific applications or situations. Dynamic text elements can be derived from secure data or updated in real time, either locally or remotely. Messages can be controlled by authorities to update and alter content with manual overrides from authorized security, police, and so forth to ensure up-to-date and real-time information. The same can be accomplished with remote control from a central control station. Examples of interfaces used for real-time control include USB, Ethernet, RS-232, and GPI.

24.4.2.24 Supplemental Notification. Supplemental notification shall be permitted to provide additional information or more detailed instructions than those transmitted by the primary notification means.

24.4.2.25 Interfaces. Any system fault condition that would prevent reliable emergency operation of any interfaced system shall be annunciated both audibly and visibly at the affected control location.

24.4.2.25.1 Fire Alarm Control Interface (FACI).

24.4.2.25.1.1 Where a fire alarm system is installed covering all or part of the same building or other area as the mass notification system, an interface shall be provided between the systems for operational coordination purposes.

24.4.2.25.1.2 A listed barrier gateway in accordance with 10.3.1, integral with, or attached to, each control unit or group of control units, as appropriate, shall be provided to prevent the other systems from interfering with or controlling the fire alarm system.

24.4.2.25.1.3* The fire alarm control interface shall coordinate signals to and from each system to accomplish the following:

(1) Indicate the failure at the system control unit that will be impaired
(2) Provide indication to the fire alarm system that the mass notification system is active
(3) Cause the fire alarm system to deactivate all audible and visible notification appliances whose operation could interfere with the intelligibility of the mass notification message or that will deliver conflicting information to occupants
(4) Not permit the fire alarm system to turn off audible and visible notification appliances for special suppression pre-discharge notification required by 24.4.1.7.1
(5) Where required, provide for a signal to a supervising station in accordance with Chapter 26 that is indicative of the mass notification system overriding the fire alarm system notification appliances during simultaneous fire and mass notification events

According to 24.4.1.7.3, the transmission of a signal to the supervising station indicating that the MNS has overridden the fire alarm system is not required. Transmitting a mass notification message over a fire alarm signal, in all probability, would confuse the operator located at the remote supervising station, who will already be processing the original fire alarm condition. However, if the emergency response plan provides for appropriate action by the supervising station when the operator receives the override signal — and that plan has been approved by the authority having jurisdiction — then a variance to the Code requirement of 24.4.1.7.3 must be developed and recorded in the system documentation.

A.24.4.2.25.1.3 Where automatic transmission is required to a supervisory station, it should be performed in accordance with the emergency response plan. The purpose for disabling or overriding the fire alarm system notification appliances during simultaneous fire and mass notification events is so that occupants will not receive conflicting messages and fail to respond correctly. Fire alarm notification that should be overridden during a mass notification system activation could include audible notification appliances, visible notification appliances, textual notification appliances, and video notification appliances.

24.4.2.25.1.4 If the fire alarm control interface is used to broadcast non-emergency messages, music, or other signals over the fire alarm notification appliance circuits, the operation shall meet the requirements of 24.4.2.18.

Broadcasting of non-emergency messages, music, or other signals over the fire alarm notification appliance circuits might prompt occupants to attempt to disable the speakers. Paragraph 24.4.2.18 provides the requirements to allow this operation through speaker systems that incorporate volume controls and components that allow occupants to lower or turn off the speakers in their area or office. These controls are designed so that the speakers operate at their required power output when the fire alarm system is actuated. This is one of the safeguards now available to meet the requirements of 24.3.4.2(2)(a), 24.4.2.18.2, and 24.4.2.25.1.4.

24.4.2.25.2 Interfaces to Building Controls. The mass notification system shall be permitted to provide air-handling control, door control, elevator controls, and control of other building systems as determined by the risk analysis, and as permitted by the authority having jurisdiction.

24.4.2.25.3 Interfaces with Wide-Area Mass Notification Systems.

24.4.2.25.3.1* Individual building mass notification systems shall be permitted to interface with wide-area mass notification systems.

A.24.4.2.25.3.1 As part of the risk analysis and emergency response plan, consideration should be given to future interfacing in-building mass notification systems with a wide-area mass notification system if it does not presently exist. In-building mass notification systems should be designed to allow future interface with a wide-area mass notification system.

24.4.2.25.3.2 The in-building mass notification system shall not be activated or controlled by a wide-area mass notification system, unless the wide-area mass notification system also meets the design and performance requirements of this chapter or has been deemed to be acceptable by the risk analysis and the authority having jurisdiction.

24.4.2.26 Combination Emergency Communications Systems.

24.4.2.26.1* When the mass notification system is integrated with the building fire alarm control unit to form one combined system that performs both functions, the system shall comply with this chapter.

Combining or integrating in-building fire emergency voice/alarm communications systems with other communications systems such as mass notification, public address, and paging is now allowed by the Code. The technology is available to ensure that fire alarm and priority mass notification messages (as determined by a risk analysis) will take precedence over any other announcement, such as paging from a telephone system or other public address system. Using one speaker system that is a combination of other communications systems and that incorporates all the requirements of the Code is financially beneficial to the owner. Not only would there be reduced design, installation, and ongoing life cycle costs, but regular use of the system for normal paging functions provides an end-to-end test of the audible notification components and circuits. Occupants familiar with use of the system for normal paging are also more likely to be comfortable and proficient using the system during an emergency.

A.24.4.2.26.1 A combined system can include an autonomous control unit and fire alarm control unit supplied from different manufacturers or placed in separate equipment enclosures; however, the autonomous control unit and fire alarm control unit should be integrated in their controls and performance to meet the requirements of this Code.

24.4.2.26.2 All components that affect the operation of the fire alarm system shall be listed for fire alarm use and shall be in compliance with applicable standards such as ANSI/UL 864, *Standard for Control Units and Accessories for Fire Alarm Systems.*

24.4.2.27 Public Address (PA) Systems Used for Emergency Communications.

24.4.2.27.1 The voice communications or public address system that is to be used for mass notification shall be evaluated by the emergency communications system designer, as defined in Chapter 10, to determine applicability and compliance.

24.4.2.27.2 A document signed by the emergency communications system designer attesting to the fact that the public address system has been evaluated and meets the requirements determined by Chapter 24 and the risk analysis, and is therefore deemed reliable and acceptable to provide emergency communications for the particular facility, shall be maintained with the fire alarm record drawings.

24.4.2.28 Public Address (PA) System Interface with Facility Fire Alarm System.

24.4.2.28.1 When a public address system is used to deliver mass notification messages, the public address system shall provide (either internally as a design feature or with an approved or listed external controller) for a signal to control the facility's fire alarm system for the purpose of deactivating the fire alarm audible and visible notification appliances in accordance with 24.4.2.25.1.

The requirements contained in 24.4.2.27 and 24.4.2.28 ensure that if a public address system is planned for mass notification use, it is interfaced appropriately with the fire alarm system to cause deactivation of the fire alarm system notification appliances (assuming they are separate from the public address system speakers). This deactivation will occur only when the risk analysis has determined under what circumstances the mass notification message should override the fire alarm signal.

24.4.2.28.2 All of the following features shall be provided in, or added to, the public address system:

(1) Emergency messages must have priority over non-emergency messages.
(2) All individual or zone speaker volume controls must default to the emergency sound level when used for an emergency mass notification message.
(3) When monitoring of circuit integrity is provided by the public address system, monitoring must continue, even if local speaker volume controls are placed in the "off" position.
(4) The required visible notification appliance network (i.e., strobes and textual signs) must be provided where required.

24.4.3* Wide-Area Mass Notification Systems.

A.24.4.3 Wide-area mass notification systems are generally installed to provide real-time information to outdoor areas. These systems are normally provided with, and operated from, two or more central control stations. Communications between central control stations and in-building mass notification systems is provided. Communications between the central control stations and regional or national command systems could also be provided. Wide-area mass notification systems are often those such as campus giant voice systems, military base public address systems, civil defense warning systems, large outdoor visible displays, and so forth.

24.4.3.1 Voice Messages.

24.4.3.1.1 Voice messages shall comply with the requirements of 24.3.1.

24.4.3.1.2 Where identified by the risk analysis, multiple languages shall be permitted to be used.

24.4.3.1.3 Where required by the emergency response plan, specific warning tones shall be provided.

24.4.3.2* Wide-area mass notification systems shall have multiple levels of password protection access control, including levels for system operators, maintainers, supervisors, and executives, or other means to limit access to system controls shall be provided based on a risk analysis.

A.24.4.3.2 A commonly used method of protecting against unauthorized changes using multiple levels of password protection can be described as follows (in ascending levels of access):

(1) *Access Level 1.* Access by persons who have a general responsibility for safety supervision, and who might be expected to investigate and initially respond to an alarm or trouble signal.
(2) *Access Level 2.* Access by persons who have a specific responsibility for safety, and who are trained to operate the control unit.
(3) *Access Level 3.* Access by persons who are trained and authorized to take control over a given area of a site to allow local paging, which might be different from that of another area. Note: This might require a higher form of access to the local control.

EXHIBIT 24.9 *Wall-Mounted Message Display with Integral LEDs and Sounder. (Source: Alertus Technologies, LLC, Beltsville, MD)*

24.4.3.3* Wide-area mass notification systems shall be permitted to connect to regional mass notification systems, public emergency alarm reporting systems, as defined in this Code, and public reporting systems as defined in NFPA 1221, *Standard for the Installation, Maintenance, and Use of Emergency Services Communications Systems.*

A.24.4.3.3 A wide-area mass notification system could have the capability to communicate with other notification systems on the site, such as the telephone alerting system, paging system, cell phone, pager, PDA activation, e-Blast, message scrolling, reverse 911, fax transmission, and highway advisory radio and sign control system (used for dynamic control of radio information and traffic signs for emergency information and traffic management).

As indicated in A.24.4.3.3, a wide-area mass notification system may also have the capability to communicate with other notification systems. Exhibit 24.9 is an example of a message display that might be used as part of such a system.

24.4.3.4 Wide-Area Mass Notification System Components.

24.4.3.4.1 Central Control Station. Refer to Section 24.6 for requirements of a central control station.

24.4.3.4.2* High Power Speaker Array (HPSA). When required by the risk analysis, high power speaker arrays (HPSAs) shall be provided, installed, and maintained.

Exhibit 24.10 illustrates a high power speaker array.

A.24.4.3.4.2 High power speaker arrays should be designed with directional characteristics that will minimize the distortion of voice signals by interface from other zones and will minimize the transmission of voice or tone signals into environmentally sensitive areas or off the site.

24.4.3.4.2.1 The HPSA shall be arranged in such a manner to provide intelligible voice and audible tone communications.

(A) When multiple HPSAs are used, they shall be arranged in physical or virtual notification zones so that each notification zone can be individually controlled by the central control station.

(B)* HPSAs shall be designed to maintain the intelligibility of voice signals within the notification zone in accordance with the requirements of Chapter 18.

A.24.4.3.4.2.1(B) Refer to Annex D for more information on speech intelligibility and how it is predicted.

Normal weather conditions should be specified as appropriate for the geographic location. Intelligibility meters with internal compensation should be used to adjust STI measurements for other than normal weather conditions.

EXHIBIT 24.10 *High Power Speaker Array. (Source: Cooper Notification, Long Branch, NJ)*

In outdoor areas, such as in industrial areas with many multi-story buildings, the maximum distance of personnel from an outdoor speaker often has to be significantly reduced to retain acceptable intelligibility of the voice message. Speakers that provide directional capability should be used. These can be mounted on building exteriors if the speakers do not radiate unacceptable levels of sound into the building on which they are mounted.

At some sites, it could be necessary to control the amount of sound that propagates in undesirable directions, such as into civilian communities adjacent to the site boundaries or into wildlife areas with protected or endangered animal species. Additionally, in some areas, it might be necessary to mount wide-area mass notification speakers on the side of a building while simultaneously preventing an unacceptable increase in that building's interior noise levels.

24.4.3.4.2.2 Secondary power for HPSAs used for wide-area mass notification systems shall have sufficient capacity to operate the unit for a minimum of 7 days in standby, followed by 60 minutes of operation at full load.

24.4.3.4.2.3 An HPSA shall have the capability to provide voice and tone communications as determined by the emergency response plan.

24.4.3.4.2.4* An HPSA shall operate in the environment in which it is located, considering such factors as temperature, humidity, wind, dust, vibration, and other environmental factors.

A.24.4.3.4.2.4 At a minimum, the high power speaker array controller should be located above known high water level during historic floods. In northern states, the high power speaker array should be located above known snow levels. When selecting high power speaker arrays, care should be taken to ensure the equipment is rated to operate between the high and low temperature range and other anticipated environmental conditions for the geographical location of installation. The system designer should inquire about this information as part of the risk analysis.

24.4.3.4.3 High Power Speaker Array Enclosures.

24.4.3.4.3.1 Enclosures for HPSAs shall be of the NEMA 4 or 4X type.

24.4.3.4.3.2 HPSA enclosures shall have intrusion detection that signals the central control station.

(A) The signal shall be initiated whenever the door of the enclosure is in the open position.

(B) The transmitted signal shall be a latching supervisory signal.

24.4.3.4.4 High Power Speaker Array Mounting.

Exhibit 24.11 depicts a mounted high power speaker array.

24.4.3.4.4.1 HPSAs shall be mounted at a minimum mounting height that is based on the rated output of the array.

24.4.3.4.4.2* HPSAs shall be installed at a height and orientation to prevent hearing damage to anyone in the immediate vicinity of the speakers.

A.24.4.3.4.4.2 High power speaker arrays should be mounted not to exceed the OSHA occupational noise exposure limits to anyone in the immediate vicinity of the speakers.

24.4.3.4.4.3 All external conductors (conductors passing outside of the HPSA equipment cabinet) shall be provided with surge suppression to minimize potential equipment damage from lightning strikes.

24.4.3.4.5 High Power Speaker Array Noise Consideration. HPSA notification zones shall not be used to provide mass notification inside any structures.

EXHIBIT 24.11 *Mounted High Power Speaker Array. (Source: Cooper Notification, Long Branch, NJ)*

High power speaker arrays can use round or rectangular speakers. See Exhibit 24.12 for an example of round speakers installed on a column.

24.4.3.4.6* High Power Speaker Array Structural Loads, Wind, and Seismic Design. HPSAs and their supporting structures shall meet the structural, wind, and seismic loads as identified in the risk analysis.

A.24.4.3.4.6 High power speaker arrays and their supporting structures should have a minimum design wind speed of 100 miles/hr [161 km/hr (86.8 kn)]. The supporting structure should be sized to accommodate the static and dynamic loads produced by the sound systems and all attachments. Seismic loads are generally site specific.

24.4.3.4.7 Textual Visible Appliances. Textual visible appliances shall meet the requirements of Section 18.9 and 24.4.2.21.

24.4.3.4.7.1 After loss of primary power, textual visible appliances shall have sufficient secondary power to operate for a minimum of 2 hours of continuous display time during an emergency event.

24.4.3.4.7.2 Scrolling message boards shall be provided with means to control the scrolling rate.

EXHIBIT 24.12 *High Power Speaker Array with Round Speakers.*

24.4.3.4.8 In-Building Mass Notification Systems. The in-building mass notification system shall meet the requirements of 24.4.2.

This requirement reminds the user of the Code that all in-building MNSs must first comply with 24.4.2. When interfaced with wide area MNSs as described in the next requirement, they should seamlessly work together.

24.4.3.4.9 Interfaces with Wide-Area Mass Notification Systems. Interfaces between wide-area mass notification systems and in-building mass notification systems, other alert and notification systems, regional mass notification systems, and off-site interfaces shall have a standard interface method (such as an audio line-level output and multiple relay contacts) or supply the necessary communications protocols to provide interoperability and a secure communications link.

24.4.3.4.9.1 The interface shall be such that the primary function of both systems shall not be compromised.

24.4.3.4.9.2 The interface shall be monitored for integrity in accordance with Section 10.17, so that a fault that could prevent reliable system operation is audibly and visibly annunciated at both systems' control units.

24.4.3.4.10 Control Hierarchy. There shall be a predefined control hierarchy between the wide-area mass notification system, the in-building mass notification system, and the regional mass notification system for information flow from the remote control center, as well as information from specific locations.

This predefined control hierarchy should be developed through a review of the goals and objectives of the owner and a risk analysis approved by the authority having jurisdiction.

24.4.3.4.11 Communications Links.

24.4.3.4.11.1 The wide-area mass notification system, including communications links, shall minimize the potential for interference from jamming, spoofing, hacking, eavesdropping, or other malicious acts.

24.4.3.4.11.2 The wide-area mass notification system shall have a primary and redundant communications link with minimal functional and spatial interconnection with each other.

24.4.3.4.11.3 Wide-area and in-building mass notification systems equipment and interface methods connecting to, or utilizing, public emergency alarm reporting systems and associated communications infrastructure shall be electrically and operationally compatible so as not to interfere with the public emergency alarm reporting systems.

24.4.4* Distributed Recipient Mass Notification Systems (DRMNSs).

A.24.4.4 Distributed recipient mass notification systems are enterprise-class systems for the management of, and mass distribution of, emergency notification messages within buildings, throughout installations, across entire geographical regions, or throughout a worldwide military command. Using distributed recipient mass notification systems, designated system operators would be able to rapidly and reliably inform appropriate personnel of homeland security levels (including chemical, biological, radiological, and nuclear threats; hazardous weather conditions; and many other critical events), possibly with near real-time response capability.

A distributed recipient mass notification system is meant to communicate to a wide range of targeted individuals and groups. These systems might use mass dialing systems, including reverse 911, email, SMS, or other directed communications methods to broadcast information. They might also use wired or wireless networks for one- or two-way communications and/or control between a building or area and an emergency services organization (information, command, and control).

Distributed recipient mass notification systems could be capable of centrally tracking, in real time, all alerting activities for each individual recipient, including sending, receiving, and responding to alerts, and be able to generate reports based on tracked information.

Distributed recipient mass notification systems could incorporate a predefined library of signals and messaging appropriate for, but not limited to, the following:

(1) Presidential alert message
(2) Homeland security levels
(3) Terrorism threats, watches, or warnings
(4) Evacuation routes
(5) Emergency directives
(6) Personnel recall requirements
(7) Federal, DOD, police, fire, or locally/installation-specific warning and notification requirements
(8) Amber alerts

The distributed recipient mass notification system could be capable of monitoring emergency notifications from multiple data sources [Commercial Mobile Alert System (CMAS), National Weather Service, Emergency Managers Weather Information Network (EMWIN), Naval Meteorology and Oceanography (METOC), and others as determined locally] and automatically sending out notifications to designated facilities and personnel based on predefined rules.

A mass notification system could also be capable of reaching out to all online personnel by leveraging a highly secure, redundant, Web-based IP network architecture to manage the entire mass notification process. Agencies and organizations can create role-based uses such as operators, administrators, and recipients, based on their access rights across multiple facilities, campuses, and installations. System rules could be established to determine operator permissions and actions such as creating and activating scenarios, as well as the extent and geography of alerts and delivery systems and devices that should be used. Such a Web-based mass notification system would employ an open, standards-based architecture. The system could be integrated with existing user directories to support organizational hierarchy and emergency response groups. It could be structured to allow emergency criteria–based targeting of emergency alerts.

Additionally, this annex material provides information on ongoing development of system requirements for net-centric alerting systems (NCAS) that will be based on IP technologies. This annex is not mandatory, but is provided to stimulate development of suitable requirements and standards. Consequently, user suggestions and feedback on this annex are highly encouraged and requested. Methods to ensure reliability and robustness in off-normal or emergency conditions are of particular concern. The required amount of and method for isolating alerting functions from normal, non-alerting system functions needs development.

NCAS leverage the IP network infrastructure to instantly reach those personnel who have access to nearly any IP-connected devices [such as pop-up alerts on personal computers (PC), text messages to personal data assistants (PDA) and cellular telephones, electronic mail to IP-capable cellular telephones, and recorded voice messages to voiceover-IP (VoIP) telephones and PCs]. Additionally, NCAS could be used to activate, through a single interface, non-IP alerting systems, such as wide-area alerting systems and traditional dial-up telephone alerting systems.

NCAS can be installed independently or at a central location. In a centrally managed NCAS configuration, personnel and facilities in the regional operations center's particular area of coverage could be alerted instantly by events, either from any individual installation, or centrally from the regional operations center. Using management tools, designated operators from each installation in the region could log in via a web browser and have complete access to their own portion of the NCAS. The regional operations center would retain the ability to centrally monitor and manage all portions of the system.

The NCAS would incorporate a Web-based management and alert activation application through which all operators and administrators could gain access to the system's capabilities, based on the users' permissions and the defined access policy. Such a management application would incorporate management of the alert activation flow through all delivery methods, as well as end-user management, operators' permission and access, tracking and reporting, and all administrative aspects of the system.

Distributed recipient mass notification systems could interface and interoperate with other types of mass notification capabilities, including wide-area and in-building mass notification systems. During emergencies, systems operators should not need to send notifications using multiple alerting systems. The distributed recipient mass notification system, particularly NCAS, might be able to provide the capability to integrate user interfaces and consolidate access to multiple mass notification and alerting systems.

24.4.4.1* Overview. Distributed recipient mass notification system (DRMNS) alerting shall not be used in lieu of required audible and visible alerting mass notification systems but shall be integrated with mass notification systems whenever possible.

A.24.4.4.1 Distributed recipient mass notification systems could enable the management of the notification flow, including users' management, groups targeting, operators' permissions, access policies, predefined emergency scenarios, and response tracking and reporting.

24.4.4.2* Targeted Recipients. The DRMNS shall be capable of sending alert messages to target recipients.

A.24.4.4.2 Distributed recipient mass notification systems could be capable of sending alert messages in a prioritized method to target recipients according to the following:

(1) Hierarchical organizational structure (as would be imported from an active directory)
(2) Organizational roles
(3) Specific distribution lists [e.g., hazardous materials (HAZMAT) response teams]
(4) Specific distribution (e.g., hearing impaired or others with impairments that warrant prioritized notification)
(5) Dynamic groups created through on-the-fly queries of the user directory
(6) Geographical locations (e.g., entire bases, zones within bases)
(7) IP addresses (required for targeting devices in specific physical locations)

24.4.4.3* Network Security Compliance. DRMNSs shall be installed behind the appropriate internet system firewalls to protect the integrity of the network.

A.24.4.4.3 Distributed recipient mass notification systems could use a Web-based user interface, support locally designated standard network ports and protocols, and provide open interfaces to support interoperability, such as eXtensible markup language (XML) and common access protocol (CAP) based emergency messages.

24.4.4.4 Network Architecture. The network shall be provided with net-centric architecture that fully supports local designated standards and security requirements.

24.4.4.5* Delivery Methods. The DRMNS shall be capable of sending alert messages to end-users (recipients) via multiple delivery methods.

A.24.4.4.5 Distributed recipient mass notification systems would be capable of sending alert messages to end-users (recipients) via multiple delivery methods, including the following:

(1) Audio-visual network alerts to desktops and laptops via desktop pop-up
(2) Text alerts to mobile phones and pagers
(3) Text alerts to electronic mail (e-mail) clients
(4) Audio alerts to phones
(5) Audio alerts to existing wide-area or building voice and or mass notification systems
(6) Network alerts to any other IP-connected devices via standard XML and CAP protocols

The system could be extendable to support additional delivery methods in the future as this technology develops.

24.4.4.6* Backup Distributed Recipient Mass Notification Systems. A stand-alone DRMNS used to send emergency messages shall be provided with a backup configuration to facilitate distribution of messages.

A.24.4.4.6 A distributed recipient mass notification system could support multiple server configurations to achieve a "hot standby" failover configuration (i.e., no down time in case of failure in a single server), as well as to support higher load scenarios (e.g., more users). This could be accomplished with premises-based systems or hosted configurations.

24.5 Two-Way, In-Building Emergency Communications Systems

Two-way communications service within a building provides a reliable method for fire fighters and other emergency response personnel to communicate with each other during the course of an emergency. The Code recognizes two means: two-way telephones and two-way in-building radio communications enhancement systems.

EXHIBIT 24.13 *Fire Emergency Phone/Cabinet Assembly. (Source: SimplexGrinnell, Westminster, MA)*

24.5.1* Two-Way, In-Building Wired Emergency Services Communications Systems.

Two-way telephone communications service is normally provided because fire department handheld radios may be ineffective in buildings with a great deal of structural steel or when the amount of radio traffic is heavy. The authority having jurisdiction may waive this requirement if the handheld radios used by the fire department work effectively in the specific building in question. Refer to 24.5.2 for two-way in-building radio communications enhancement systems. See Exhibits 24.13 and 24.14 for examples of two-way telephone communications.

A.24.5.1 Two-way, in-building emergency services communications systems are used by fire fighters, police, and other emergency services personnel. This does not preclude equipment outside of the protected premises.

24.5.1.1 Two-way telephone communications equipment shall be listed for two-way telephone communications service and installed in accordance with 24.5.1.

24.5.1.2 Two-way telephone communications service, if provided, shall be for use by the fire service and collocated with the in-building fire emergency voice/alarm communications equipment.

24.5.1.3 Monitoring of the integrity of two-way telephone communications circuits shall be in accordance with 10.17.2.

24.5.1.4 Additional uses shall be permitted to include signaling and communications for a building fire warden organization and signaling and communications for reporting a fire and other emergencies (e.g., voice call box service, signaling, and communications for guard's tour service).

24.5.1.5 Variation of equipment and system operation provided to facilitate additional use of the two-way telephone communications service shall not adversely affect performance when used by the fire service.

24.5.1.6* Two-way telephone communications service shall be capable of permitting the simultaneous operation of any five telephone stations in a common talk mode.

EXHIBIT 24.14 *Two-Way Telephone Communications Service in Use.*

A.24.5.1.6 Consideration should be given to the type of telephone handset that fire fighters use in areas where high ambient noise levels exist or areas where high noise levels could exist during a fire condition. Push-to-talk handsets, handsets that contain directional microphones, or handsets that contain other suitable noise-canceling features, can be used.

Speakers required in the areas where fire fighters' telephones are located should be arranged to ensure that the sound pressure levels of the nearby speakers do not preclude the effective use of the fire fighters' telephones.

24.5.1.7 A notification signal at the control equipment, distinctive from any other alarm, supervisory, or trouble signal, shall indicate the off-hook condition of a calling telephone circuit. If a selective talk telephone communications service is supplied, a distinctive visible indicator shall be furnished for each selectable circuit, so that all circuits with telephones off-hook are continuously and visibly indicated.

24.5.1.8 A means for silencing the audible call-in signal sounding appliance shall be permitted, provided that it is key-operated or located in a locked cabinet, or provided with protection to prevent use by unauthorized persons. The means shall operate a visible indicator and sound a trouble signal whenever the means is in the silence position and no telephone circuits are in an off-hook condition.

Methods for silencing the audible call-in signal include switches, touch pads, and touch screens.

24.5.1.9 If a selective talk system is used, means as specified in 24.5.1.8 shall be permitted, provided that subsequent telephone circuits going off-hook operate the distinctive off-hook signal.

24.5.1.10 Two-way telephone systems shall be common talk (i.e., a conference or party line circuit).

24.5.1.11 In buildings provided with a two-way telephone communications system, at least one telephone station or jack shall be provided at the following locations:

(1) Each floor level
(2) Each notification zone
(3) Each elevator cab
(4) Elevator lobbies
(5) Elevator machine room(s)
(6) Emergency and standby power room(s)
(7) Fire pump room(s)

Fire pumps should be attended any time they run, particularly during a fire. The phone in the pump room or pump house allows continuous communication between the incident commander and the pump room in the event the fire pump experiences trouble or the pump room must be evacuated.

(8) Area(s) of refuge
(9) Each floor level inside an enclosed exit stair(s)
(10) Other room(s) or area(s) as required by the authority having jurisdiction

24.5.1.12 If the two-way telephone system is intended to be used by fire wardens in addition to the fire service, the minimum requirement shall be a selective talk system, where phones are selected from the control location.

24.5.1.13 Telephone circuits shall be selectable from the control location either individually or, if approved by the authority having jurisdiction, by floor or stairwell.

24.5.1.14 If the control equipment provided does not indicate the location of the caller (common talk systems), each telephone station or telephone jack shall be clearly and permanently labeled to allow the caller to identify his or her location to the control center by voice.

24.5.1.15 If telephone jacks are provided, two or more portable handsets, as determined by the authority having jurisdiction, shall be stored at each control center for use by emergency responders.

The number of portable handsets provided should be determined based on discussions with the authority having jurisdiction. The layout of the building, manual fire suppression strategy, rescue concerns, and other factors should be considered. The location of the portable handsets should also be given careful consideration. The portable handsets should be easily and quickly accessible to arriving fire fighters.

◀ **FAQ**
How many portable handsets should be provided?

24.5.1.16* All circuits necessary for the operation of two-way telephone communications systems shall be installed in accordance with the pathway survivability requirements in 24.3.5.7.

A.24.5.1.16 Two-way, in-building wired emergency services communications systems are intended to provide emergency service personnel and designated building occupants with a supervised, reliable communication system that is completely independent of other in-building communication systems. The survivability of two-way, in-building wired emergency services communications systems is paramount as they are intended for use during and throughout the duration of a fire or other emergency event. This kind of functionality requires that measures are taken to ensure that the system is designed, installed, and maintained in such a manner that they can survive and function under extreme conditions.

24.5.2* Two-Way Radio Communications Enhancement Systems.

Fire department radio systems may not operate properly where concrete and steel construction interfere with radio traffic. One means of enhancing fire department radio communications within a building is the installation of antennae and repeaters at strategic locations, typically called *bi-directional amplifier systems*. This method is often preferred by fire departments because it allows them to use their normal radio equipment and communications procedures within the building. See Exhibits 24.15 and 24.16 for examples of two-way in-building radio communications enhancement systems.

A.24.5.2 The use of radio communication enhancement systems has become prevalent throughout the country.
    Safety features and flexibilities of radio systems include:

(1) Allowing full building coverage to facilitate communications from any point within the building, in case access to the telephone jack is compromised.
(2) Allowing communications to be conducted between emergency responders in the field to allow quicker dissemination of safety and emergency information.
(3) Each emergency responder typically will carry an individual radio, allowing for each individual to provide information or request assistance individually, which can be important if members of crews separate from each other during an incident.
(4) Radio systems allow for "fire fighter down" emergency calls in case of injury, where, by pushing a single button, a call is placed to a central location to initiate a roll call in order to determine the emergency responder who has been injured and requires assistance.
(5) Radio systems can employ an emergency call where, by pushing a single button, an emergency responder call jump to the next radio given system access to allow wide-range communication of a superseding emergency, such as building structure failure, failure of a fire pump or standpipe system, or other emergency that could cause a change in operational strategies.

EXHIBIT 24.15 *Bi-Directional Amplifier System. (Source: Copyright © Jack Daniel Company, Victorville, CA)*

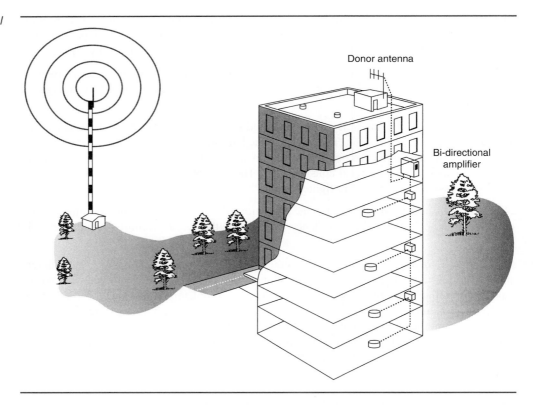

EXHIBIT 24.16 *Bi-Directional Amplifier System Floor Layout. (Source: Copyright © Jack Daniel Company, Victorville, CA)*

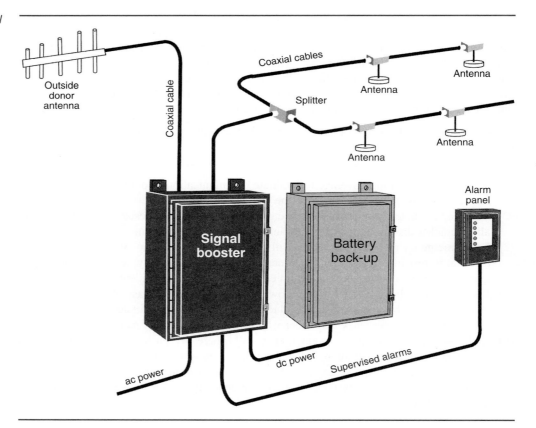

24.5.2.1 General.

24.5.2.1.1 Non-Interference. No amplification system capable of operating on frequencies or causing interference on frequencies assigned to the jurisdiction by the FCC shall be installed without prior coordination and approval of the authority having jurisdiction. The building manager/owner shall suspend and correct other equipment installations that degrade the performance of the public safety radio system or public safety radio enhancement system.

24.5.2.1.2 Approval and Permit. Plans shall be submitted for approval prior to installation. At the conclusion of successful acceptance testing, a renewable permit shall be issued for the public safety radio enhancement system where required by the authority having jurisdiction.

Some designers and installers assume that the authority having jurisdiction for the two-way radio communications enhancement system is the same as the authority having jurisdiction for the fire alarm system design review and approval. In fact, the authority having jurisdiction for the two-way radio communications enhancement system might be the fire department radio communications chief. The designer or installer must determine who the authority having jurisdiction is.

24.5.2.2 Radio Coverage. Radio coverage shall be provided throughout the building as a percentage of floor area as specified in 24.5.2.2.1 through 24.5.2.2.3.

24.5.2.2.1 Critical Areas. Critical areas, such as the emergency command center(s), the fire pump room(s), exit stairs, exit passageways, elevator lobbies, standpipe cabinets, sprinkler sectional valve locations, and other areas deemed critical by the authority having jurisdiction, shall be provided with 99 percent floor area radio coverage.

24.5.2.2.2 General Building Areas. General building areas shall be provided with 90 percent floor area radio coverage.

24.5.2.2.3 Amplification Components. Buildings and structures that cannot support the required level of radio coverage shall be equipped with a radiating cable system or a distributed antenna system (DAS) with FCC-certified signal boosters, or both, or with a system that is otherwise approved, in order to achieve the required adequate radio coverage.

24.5.2.3 Signal Strength.

24.5.2.3.1 Inbound. A minimum inbound signal strength of –95 dBm, or other signal strength as required by the authority having jurisdiction, shall be provided throughout the coverage area.

24.5.2.3.2 Outbound. A minimum outbound signal strength of –95 dBm at the donor site, or other signal strength as required by the authority having jurisdiction, shall be provided from the coverage area.

24.5.2.3.3 Isolation. If a donor antenna exists, isolation shall be maintained between the donor antenna and all inside antennas and shall be a minimum of 15 dB above the signal booster gain under all operating conditions.

24.5.2.4* System Radio Frequencies. The public safety radio enhancement system shall be capable of transmitting all public safety radio frequencies assigned to the jurisdiction and be capable of using any modulation technology.

A.24.5.2.4 Modulation technologies include analog and digital modulation.

It is important that interoperability be developed and maintained when implementing analog and digital two-way radio systems. The simplest means to gaining a measure of interoperability with analog two-way radio systems is programming into a radio existing, operational channels from agencies that are adjacent to each other geographically and that operate in the same public safety frequency band. To gain interoperability with digital two-way radio systems, systems and devices that are (APCO) Project 25 (P25) compatible can be used. Project 25 is a standard for the manufacturing of interpretable digital two-way wireless communications systems and devices. A P25 radio system provides interoperability, because it incorporates a common air interface and a multi-band excitation vocoder that converts speech into a digital bit stream. P25 defines standard modes of radio operation to enable multi-vendor interoperability such as trunking, encryption, over-the-air rekeying, and so forth. Formally, P25 specifications are defined in the ANSI/TIA/EIA 102 suite of standards. All homeland security funding promotes interoperable communications and recommends adherence to open architecture technologies and P25 standards.

24.5.2.4.1 List of Assigned Frequencies. The authority having jurisdiction shall maintain a list of all inbound/outbound frequency pairs for distribution to system designers.

24.5.2.4.2* Frequency Changes. Systems shall be capable of upgrade, to allow for instances where the jurisdiction changes or adds system frequencies, in order to maintain radio system coverage as originally designed.

A.24.5.2.4.2 There is currently an ongoing national effort to eliminate current interference issues between cellular carriers and public safety bands in the 800 MHz band. This effort could revise the actual frequencies for public agencies within this band. The public safety radio enhancement system design should be capable of being changed to accommodate updated frequencies in order to allow maintenance of the minimum system design criteria.

24.5.2.5 System Components.

24.5.2.5.1 Component Approval. Components utilized in the installation of the public safety radio enhancement system, such as repeaters, transmitters, receivers, signal boosters, cabling, and fiber-distributed antenna systems, shall be approved and shall be compatible with the public safety radio system.

24.5.2.5.2 Component Enclosures. All repeater, transmitter, receiver, and signal booster components shall be contained in a NEMA 4- or 4X- type enclosure(s).

24.5.2.5.3 External Filters. Permanent external filters and attachments shall not be permitted.

24.5.2.5.4 Signal Booster Components. If used, signal boosters shall meet the following requirements, as well as any other requirements determined by the authority having jurisdiction:

(1)* Signal boosters shall have FCC certification prior to installation.
(2) All signal boosters shall be compatible with both analog and digital communications simultaneously at the time of installation. The authority having jurisdiction shall provide the maximum acceptable propagation delay standard.

A.24.5.2.5.4(1) All repeaters, transmitters, receivers, and signal boosters should be installed and operated in a manner consistent with Title 47, CFR. Within these regulations is a mandatory requirement that repeaters, transmitters, and signal boosters have Federal Communications Commission (FCC) "certification." Receivers do not normally have a FCC certification requirement but must comply with other applicable FCC regulations. FCC certification is a formal procedure that verifies the equipment meets certain minimum FCC technical specifications. Each brand and model type is issued a distinct FCC certification number. Use of repeaters, transmitters, or signal boosters that do not have an existing FCC-issued certification is a violation of federal law, and users are subject to fine and/or imprisonment. A label displaying the exact FCC certification number must be placed in a visible place on the equipment itself.

FCC certification verification can be obtained from any FCC office or online (https://fjallfoss.fcc.gov/oetcf/eas/reports/genericsearch.cfm).

24.5.2.6 System Monitoring.

24.5.2.6.1 Fire Alarm System. The public safety radio communications enhancement system shall include automatic supervisory and trouble signals for malfunctions of the signal booster(s) and power supply(ies) that are annunciated by the fire alarm system and comply with the following:

(1) The integrity of the circuit monitoring signal booster(s) and power supply(ies) shall comply with 10.17.1.
(2) System and signal booster supervisory signals shall include the following:
　(a) Antenna malfunction
　(b) Signal booster failure
(3) Power supply supervisory signals shall include the following for each signal booster:
　(a) Loss of normal ac power
　(b) Failure of battery charger
　(c) Low-battery capacity, alarming at 70 percent of battery capacity

Because the Code allows two-way radio communications enhancement systems to replace the supervised two-way in-building wired emergency services communications systems, it is imperative that an equivalent level of supervision be used and that the owner know when this important system has a malfunction. For this reason, 24.5.2.6.1 requires the supervision and monitoring of the important operational components of the two-way radio communications enhancement system.

◀ **FAQ**
Is the two-way radio communications enhancement system required to be monitored and annunciated by the fire alarm system?

24.5.2.6.2* Dedicated Panel. A dedicated monitoring panel shall be provided within the emergency command center to annunciate the status of all signal booster locations. The monitoring panel shall provide visual and labeled indication of the following for each signal booster:

(1) Normal ac power
(2) Signal booster trouble
(3) Loss of normal ac power
(4) Failure of battery charger
(5) Low-battery capacity

A.24.5.2.6.2 Due to the longer backup battery requirement for the public safety radio communications enhancement system, it is recognized that the fire alarm system might not be available to provide monitoring of radio system signals, including low-battery signals. Therefore, redundant status annunciation is required to provide local signals to the incident commander or his/her designee at the emergency command center.

24.5.2.7 Technical Criteria. The authority having jurisdiction shall maintain a document of technical information specific to its requirements. This document shall contain, as a minimum, the following:

(1) Frequencies required
(2) Location and effective radiated power (ERP) of radio sites used by the public safety radio enhancement system
(3) Maximum propagation delay (in microseconds)
(4) List of specifically approved system components
(5) Other supporting technical information necessary to direct system design

24.5.2.8 Inspection and Testing. Inspection and testing shall be performed in accordance with testing frequencies and methods in Chapter 14.

24.5.3* Area of Refuge (Area of Rescue Assistance) Emergency Communications Systems.

A.24.5.3 "Areas of refuge" or "areas of rescue assistance" are areas that have direct access to an exit, where people who are unable to use stairs can remain temporarily in safety to await further instructions or assistance during emergency evacuation or other emergency situation. It is, therefore, important that a method to communicate between that location and a central control point where appropriate action for assistance be initiated.

24.5.3.1* Where required by the building code in force, an area of rescue assistance two-way emergency communications system shall be installed in accordance with 24.5.3.

A.24.5.3.1 Generally, the building code or engineer specification will provide the specifics on the required locations of the remote area of refuge (area of rescue assistance) stations, as well as the central control point.

24.5.3.2 The area of refuge (rescue assistance) emergency communications system shall be comprised of remotely located area of refuge stations and a central control point.

24.5.3.3 The remote area of refuge stations and the central control point shall communicate with each other.

Because of the obvious importance of the area of refuge, circuits connecting the area of refuge communications system to the fire command center must be designed to withstand the attack of fire during the time that the occupants await assistance. Refer to the requirements of 24.3.5.9.1. It is also important to ensure that speakers required in the areas where remote area of refuge stations are located should be arranged to ensure that the sound pressure levels of the nearby speakers do not preclude the effective use of the refuge stations.

24.5.3.4* If the central control point is not constantly attended, it shall have a timed automatic communications capability to connect with a constantly attended monitoring location acceptable to the authority having jurisdiction where responsible personnel can initiate the appropriate response.

A.24.5.3.4 In order to ensure a timely response to a call for assistance, the call is to be forwarded to a constantly attended approved location, such as a supervising station, 911 communications center, or other monitoring location where responsible personnel can initiate the appropriate response.

24.5.3.5 The physical location of the central control point shall be as designated by the building code in force or the authority having jurisdiction.

24.5.3.6 The area of refuge station shall provide for hands-free, two-way communication provide an audible and visible signal to indicate communication has occured and indicate to the receiver the location sending the signal.

24.5.3.7 Instructions for the use of the two-way communications system instructions for summoning assistance via the two-way communications system and written identification, including in braille, of the location shall be posted adjacent to the two-way communications system.

24.5.4 Elevator Emergency Communications Systems.
Elevator two-way emergency communications systems shall be installed in accordance with the requirements of ANSI/ASME A17.1a/CSA B44a, *Safety Code for Elevators and Escalators.*

24.6* Information, Command, and Control

The requirements of Section 24.6 shall apply to the communications methods and equipment used to receive and transmit information between premises sources or premises systems and the central control station(s).

A.24.6 An emergency communications system information, command, and control is intended to include wired or wireless networks for one- or two-way communications and/or control between a building or area and a central control station and could include an emergency services organization or public alarm reporting system. In a very basic configuration, a system and the receiving facility could be a supervising station system. However, there can be more complex systems that allow control of building systems and communication to building occupants from a remote location, including a municipal or other public alarm reporting command center or possibly even from a mobile command vehicle using secure communications.

24.6.1* Central Control Station for Emergency Communications Systems.

A.24.6.1 For the purposes of this chapter, a central control station is considered to be a mass notification system facility(s), with communications and control equipment serving more than one building, where responsible authorities receive information from premises sources or systems, or from (higher level) regional or national sources or systems, and then disseminate appropriate information to a building, multiple buildings, outside campus areas, municipalities, or a combination of these in accordance with the emergency response plan established for the premises. A mass notification system could include at least one central control station with optional secondary/alternate central control stations.

Exhibit 24.17 depicts a manned central control station.

EXHIBIT 24.17 *Manned Central Control Station. (Source: Cooper Notification, Long Branch, NJ)*

24.6.1.1* The location of the central control station shall be defined in the emergency response plan and as approved by the authority having jurisdiction.

A.24.6.1.1 The location of the central control station should be coordinated with the first responders. The primary central control station should be located at the command post, emergency operations center, or some such similar location. A redundant central control station, if required, should be located at a physically separate location, such as a police station, fire station, or similar facility.

Generally, the primary central control station should be housed in a building or portion of a building separated from the rest of the facility and having a 2-hour fire-resistive-rated separation.

The mass notification system might require activation of messages originated by mobile sentries and roving patrols using wireless activation devices. In cases where clusters of facilities within the same geographical region exist, one or more regional control stations might also exercise control.

24.6.1.2 The level of security at the central control station shall be defined in the emergency response plan.

24.6.1.3* Staffing.

A.24.6.1.3 The central control station should be staffed by qualified personnel who would monitor the system and take action appropriate to the emergency response plan established for the specific premises.

24.6.1.3.1 Central control station personnel requirements shall be defined in the documentation in the emergency response plan.

24.6.1.3.2* Individuals expected to operate an emergency communications system shall be properly trained in the purpose, functions, procedures, and anticipated actions of such systems.

A.24.6.1.3.2 It is imperative that individuals expected to initiate or deliver emergency messages be properly trained in the expected operations. Individuals must be familiar with the equipment, its location, and functions if they will be expected to react properly in an emergency. In an emergency situation. people only react according to instinct or habit. If the individual has not had proper and repeated training over the emergency expectations, they could lack the proper instinct or habit.

Reading an employee manual is generally not an effective means of training for an emergency. To be effective, training must be reinforced with multiple means such as text, audio, visual, and, most importantly, hands-on experience. Regular drills allowing for delivery of live messages indicating an emergency condition is important. Many people have a very difficult time communicating clearly and effectively in an emergency situation when they are excited or fearful. If live messages are to be effective, they must be short, to the point, and in a calm tone conveying exactly what is expected. Screaming into the microphone, for instance, would not be appropriate. Actual message content will depend on the emergency response plan in place for the respective business and the response to an unfolding event. Situations such as an intruder in a building have become more common today and, as such, should be considered and planned for.

24.6.1.4 The central control station shall be capable of receiving voice messages by telephone or radio and transmitting via equipment at the central control station.

24.6.1.5 The central control station operator shall have the ability to monitor inputs/sensors and control output devices automatically, manually, or automatically with operator override.

24.6.2 Emergency Communications Control Unit (ECCU).

24.6.2.1 An emergency communications control unit (ECCU), where identified by the risk analysis, and defined in the emergency response plan, shall be provided at each central control station.

24.6.2.2 The system operator shall be able to send live voice signals or activate prerecorded voice messages, tones, and other signals.

24.6.2.3 The signals shall be selectable to individual buildings; zones of buildings; individual outdoor speaker arrays; zones of outdoor speaker arrays; or a building, multiple buildings, outside areas, or a combination of these, in accordance with the emergency response plan established for the premises.

24.6.2.4 The central control emergency communications control unit shall automatically or manually assign priorities to all transmitted signals.

24.6.2.5 Multiple Emergency Communications Control Units.

24.6.2.5.1 In wide-area mass notification systems, the central control station shall have a primary emergency communications control unit.

24.6.2.5.2 Multiple emergency communications control units shall be permitted.

24.6.3* Signals. Where identified by the risk analysis and defined in the emergency response plan, the emergency communications control unit shall be permitted to automatically or manually send different messages or signals to different locations.

A.24.6.3 Different messages or signals could be prerecorded or live voice, tones, and so forth.

24.6.4 Power Supply.

24.6.4.1 At the central control station, the emergency communications control unit shall meet the requirements of Section 10.5.

24.6.4.2 The power supply for the central control station shall include an uninterrupted power source with capacity sufficient to support the emergency response plan established for the specific premises.

24.6.5 Transmission. Signals shall be capable of being automatically or manually transmitted to a regional or national emergency response center or to other nearby facilities that have a need to be alerted of the emergency.

24.6.6* Other Systems. The central control station shall be capable of interfacing with and controlling other notification systems, such as telephone dialers, tone alert systems, computer network alerting systems, pagers, facsimile machines, textual devices, and other visual control signs, as determined by the emergency response plan.

A.24.6.6 Text notification via wireless devices and desktop computer notification could be an effective means for delivering mass notification messages to multiple recipient groups. Supplementary wireless text messaging could be effective in reaching remote personnel. Desktop notification is particularly effective when more complex information must be conveyed, and it can be a cost-effective interim solution prior to, but not in lieu of, installing an in-building mass notification system.

24.6.7 Inspection, Testing, and Maintenance. Inspection, testing, and maintenance shall be performed on a periodic basis, as described in Chapter 14, to verify and ensure proper system operation and readiness.

24.7* Performance-Based Design of Mass Notification Systems

The requirements of Section 24.7 shall apply to mass notification systems designed to recognize performance-based practices.

A.24.7 Ensuring accurate information dissemination to the right people, at the right place, and at the right time is essential to the mitigation of threat actions and consequences. Trained personnel are charged with making such decisions in real time. Quite often, the instructions provided to personnel in affected areas pertain to acting in specific defensive ways so as not to expose them to danger. A typical example is the case of a chemical or biological agent attack wherein the right response is to relocate to secure areas within the building while sealing doors and windows and shutting down air intakes, rather than to leave the building and be exposed to the attacking agent.

In cases of bomb threats, where specific information is available, directions for evacuation are to be given; these directions require more specificity than simply the instruction "Evacuate the building." In most cases, the evacuation route might depend on threat intelligence and is likely to be different from that specified in an emergency response plan. Most people can tell where the fire comes from but do not always know where the bomb is. Automatic evacuation of a building, a common procedure in cases of a fire, is to be avoided, since it might expose personnel to even greater danger.

One of the reasons for implementing a mass notification system is the threat of terrorism. Terrorism attacks tend to be well organized and are often planned with details to inflict the widest degree of damage that is possible. The mass notification system must be designed to withstand various attack scenarios and survive even if some damage has already occurred.

Each design of a mass notification system should be specific to the nature and anticipated risks of each facility for which it is designed. Although this chapter outlines some specific criteria and/or limitations, each design should be based on recognized performance-based design practices.

The mass notification system should be evaluated (risk analysis) and take into account various considerations, such as those indicated in this chapter. The particular design might or might not incorporate these provisions.

Considerations for developing a mass notification system are as follows:

(1) Specific design for the facility
(2) Account for anticipated risks
(3) Use of live and/or prerecorded messaging
(4) Interfacing with other building emergency communications systems
(5) Interfacing with wide-area notification systems
(6) Ability to control the HVAC and access control systems
(7) Access to system components
(8) Survivability of the system
(9) Communication link redundancy and security
(10) Redundancy and security of the central control stations
(11) Ability to customize and add to prerecorded message library
(12) Messages should be tailored to the situation and audience
(13) Scripted messages for live voice messages
(14) Proper training of individuals that operate the system

24.7.1 Goals and Objectives. The performance-based design shall meet the following goals and objectives:

(1) The risk analysis, design criteria, design brief, system performance, and testing criteria are developed in the spirit of this chapter.
(2) The system disseminates information to the target audience in an accurate and timely manner.
(3) The design and performance criteria are specific to the nature and anticipated risks of each location.
(4) The system is capable of withstanding various scenarios and survives even if some damage has already occurred.

(5) Message initiation can be effected by all responding entities responsible for the safety and security of occupants.

24.7.2* Qualifications. The performance-based design and risk analysis shall be prepared by a design professional certified or approved by the authority having jurisdiction.

A.24.7.2 The design professional(s) as part of the design team should be experienced in multiple areas considered essential for conducting the risk analysis and performance design based on the scope and size of the project. Areas of experience can include, but are not limited to:

(1) Applying recognized performance-based design concepts,
(2) Conducting hazard and operability studies
(3) Technical aspects of fire alarm system design
(4) Technical aspects of emergency communication systems
(5) Security risks and/or terrorist threats
(6) Building code requirements and limitations with respect to egress
(7) Human response to emergency conditions
(8) Development of emergency response plans
(9) Other qualifications relative to the needs of the user/risk

The design professional(s) will often be a part of the engineering design team preparing project documents and specifications. However, the design professional can work for or be obtained by a qualified installation company. The design professional should be bound by professional licensing guidelines to ensure that the risk analysis is conducted in an objective manner based on user needs and not based on product or employment.

24.7.3 Independent Review. The authority having jurisdiction shall be permitted to require an approved, independent third party to review the proposed design brief and provide an evaluation of the design to the authority having jurisdiction.

24.7.4 Final Determination. The authority having jurisdiction shall make the final determination as to whether the performance objectives have been met.

24.7.5 Maintenance of Design Features. The design features required for the system to continue to meet the performance goals and objectives of this Code shall be maintained for the life of the building.

24.7.6 Performance Criteria.

24.7.6.1 General. All designs shall meet the goals and objectives specified in 24.7.1 and shall be considered equivalent, provided that the performance criterion in 24.7.6.2 is met, the design team concurs with the design, and the risk analysis considers the following factors:

(1) Number of persons to be notified
(2) Occupancy characteristics
(3) Anticipated threat
(4) Staff capabilities
(5) Coordination with the emergency response plan

24.7.6.2 Performance Criterion. The performance criterion shall include timely and accurate notification of all persons within the boundaries of the mass notification system in a medium to which they can respond when given directions by responding entities.

24.7.6.3* Design Team. The design team shall be comprised of the design professional, the owner or owner's representative, representatives of the authority having jurisdiction, and representatives of the responding entities.

A.24.7.6.3 Communication and coordination between and among the various members of the design team is an important element to achieving the goals for performance of the system.

24.7.7* Risk Analysis.

A.24.7.7 The risk analysis forms the basis for the emergency response plan.

24.7.7.1 General.

24.7.7.1.1 The design of the mass notification system shall be specific to the nature and anticipated risks of each facility for which it is designed.

24.7.7.1.2 The design of the mass notification system shall include the preparation of a design brief that is prepared utilizing recognized performance-based design practices.

24.7.7.1.3 The risk analysis shall consider the number of persons, type of occupancy, and perceived peril to occupants.

24.7.7.2 Number of Persons. The analysis shall be based on the maximum number of people that every occupied room, building, area, space, campus, or region is expected to contain.

24.7.7.3 Occupancy Characteristics.

24.7.7.3.1 The risk analysis shall consider characteristics of the buildings, areas, spaces, campuses or regions, equipment, and operations that are not inherent in the design specifications.

24.7.7.3.2 Those elements that are not inherent in the design specifications, but that affect occupant behavior or the rate of hazard development, shall be explicitly identified and included in the risk analysis.

24.7.7.4 Anticipated Threat. The risk analysis shall consider hazards from natural disasters, accidental hazards, and human-caused events (accidental and intentional).

24.7.7.5 Extent of Notification. The risk analysis shall include a review of the extent to which occupants and personnel are notified, based on the incident (potential hazard).

24.7.7.6 Operational Status and System Effectiveness. The performance of the system shall reflect the documented performance and reliability of the components of those systems or features, unless design specifications are incorporated to modify the expected performance.

24.7.7.6.1 Staff Assistance. The inclusion of trained employees as part of the mass notification system shall be identified and documented.

24.7.7.6.2 Emergency Response Personnel. The design shall consider the characteristics or other conditions related to the availability, speed of response, effectiveness, roles, and other characteristics of emergency response personnel.

24.7.8* Design Brief.

A.24.7.8 The *Guide to Performance Based Design*, published by the Society of Fire Protection Engineers, provides guidance on the elements of a design brief.

24.7.8.1 Clear Statement. Design specifications and briefs used in the performance-based design shall be clearly stated and shown to be realistic and sustainable.

24.7.8.2 Testing. Specific testing requirements that are necessary to maintain reliable performance shall be stated in the design brief.

REFERENCES CITED IN COMMENTARY

NFPA 13, *Standard for the Installation of Sprinkler Systems*, 2010 edition, National Fire Protection Association, Quincy MA.

NFPA 70®, *National Electrical Code®*, 2008 edition, National Fire Protection Association, Quincy, MA.

NFPA *101®*, *Life Safety Code®*, 2009 edition, National Fire Protection Association, Quincy, MA.

United Facilities Criteria (UFC) 4-021-01, *Design and O&M: Mass Notification Systems,* 9 April 2008, U.S. Department of Defense, Washington, DC.

Reserved

In this 2010 edition of *NFPA 72®*, *National Fire Alarm and Signaling Code*, Chapter 25 is reserved for future use.

Supervising Station Alarm Systems

Chapter 26 (Chapter 8 in previous editions of the Code) presents the requirements for three supervising station services: central station, proprietary station, and remote station. It also presents the requirements for various transmission technologies.

The Technical Committee on Supervising Station Fire Alarm Systems has made several minor editorial changes to the text of Chapter 26. These changes amplify, clarify, or simplify the text without substantially modifying the intent of the requirements. Throughout the text, in keeping with the broader scope of the overall Code, the technical committee has removed the word *fire* from many phrases to make the wording more suitably generic.

In addition to those minor changes, the technical committee has made a few significant changes. The following list is a summary of significant changes to the chapter on supervising station alarm systems in the 2010 edition:

- New 26.2.4 requiring the operator of a supervising station to meet qualifications in accordance with the requirements of 10.4.4
- New 26.5.2 requiring owners who utilize remote supervising station alarm systems to provide annual documentation to the authority having jurisdiction that identifies the party responsible for the inspection, testing, and maintenance of the system
- New 26.6.3.1 and related subsections describing the general requirements for communications methods used for supervising station service.
- Deleted sections from the 2007 edition of the Code that contained requirements for active multiplex systems, McCulloh systems, directly connected noncoded systems, and private microwave radio systems
- New annex material addressing the continued recognition of the deleted "legacy" system technologies

26.1* Application

The performance, installation, and operation of alarm systems at a continuously attended supervising station and between the protected premises and the continuously attended supervising station shall comply with the requirements of this chapter.

Chapter 26 of the Code covers the requirements for the connection of a protected premises fire alarm system to and monitoring by a continuously attended supervising station. The chapter also covers the installation of supervising station transmitters at the protected premises where those transmitters connect to alarm and supervisory initiating devices. Such an installation often occurs where the particular protected premises does not require notification appliances but does require that initiating devices transmit signals to a supervising station. This supervising station may be either a central station, a proprietary supervising station, or a remote supervising station. See Exhibit 26.1 for an illustration of the organization of Chapter 26.

A.26.1 Table A.26.1 provides a tool for users of the Code to easily and systematically look up requirements for protected premises, central station service, remote supervising station, and proprietary supervising station alarm systems.

EXHIBIT 26.1 *Organization of Chapter 26, Supervising Station Alarm Systems. (Source: Dean K. Wilson, P.E., Erie, PA)*

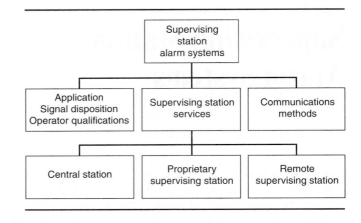

TABLE A.26.1 *Alarm System Performance Criteria*

Attribute	Protected Premises Fire Alarm System	Central Station Service Alarm System	Remote Supervising Station Alarm System	Proprietary Supervising Station Alarm System
Applicability	All fire alarm systems	Supervising station service provided by a prime contractor. There is a subscriber *(26.3.2, 26.3.3, and 26.3.4)*.	Where central station service is neither required nor elected, properties under various ownership monitored by a remote supervising station *(26.5.1.1 and 26.5.1.2)*	Supervising station monitoring contiguous or non-contiguous properties under one ownership and responsible to the owner of the protected property *(26.4.2.1 and 26.4.2.2)*
Listing	Equipment listed for the use intended *(10.3)*	Equipment listed for the use intended *(10.3)*. Compliance documentation *(26.3.4)*.	Equipment listed for use intended *(10.3)*	Equipment listed for use intended *(10.3)*
Design	According to Code by experienced persons *(10.4.1)*	According to Code by experienced persons *(10.4.1)*	According to Code by experienced persons *(10.4.1)*	According to Code by experienced persons *(10.4.1)*
Compatibility	Detector devices pulling power from initiating or signaling circuits listed for control unit *(10.3.3)*	Detector devices pulling power from initiating or signaling circuits listed for control unit *(10.3.3)*	Detector devices pulling power from initiating or signaling circuits listed for control unit *(10.3.3)*	Detector devices pulling power from initiating or signaling circuits listed for control unit *(10.3.3)*
Performance and limitations	85% and 110% of the nameplate rated input voltage, 32°F (0°C) and 120°F (49°C) ambient temperature, 85% relative humidity at 85°F (29.4°C) *(10.14.1)*	85% and 110% of the nameplate rated input voltage, 32°F (0°C) and 120°F (49°C) ambient temperature, 85% relative humidity at 85°F (29.4°C) *(10.14.1)*	85% and 110% of the nameplate rated input voltage, 32°F (0°C) and 120°F (49°C) ambient temperature, 85% relative humidity at 85°F (29.4°C) *(10.14.1)*	85% and 110% of the nameplate rated input voltage, 32°F (0°C) and 120°F (49°C) ambient temperature, 85% relative humidity at 85°F (29.4°C) *(10.14.1)*
Documentation	Authority having jurisdiction notified of new or changed specifications, wiring diagrams, battery calculations, floor plans.	Authority having jurisdiction notified of new or changed specifications, wiring diagrams, battery calculations, floor plans.	Authority having jurisdiction notified of new or changed specifications, wiring diagrams, battery calculations, floor plans.	Authority having jurisdiction notified of new or changed specifications, wiring diagrams, battery calculations, floor plans. Statement from contractor

TABLE A.26.1 *Continued*

Attribute	*Protected Premises Fire Alarm System*	*Central Station Service Alarm System*	*Remote Supervising Station Alarm System*	*Proprietary Supervising Station Alarm System*
	Statement from contractor that system meets manufacturer's published instructions and NFPA requirements *(10.18.1)*. Record of completion *(10.18.2)*. Results of evaluation required in 23.4.3.3.	Statement from contractor that system meets manufacturer's published instructions and NFPA requirements *(10.18.1)*. Record of completion *(10.18.2)*. Results of evaluation required in 23.4.3.3.	Statement from contractor that system meets manufacturer's published instructions and NFPA requirements *(10.18.1)*. Record of completion *(10.18.2)*. Results of evaluation required in 23.4.3.3.	that system meets manufacturer's published instructions and NFPA requirements *(10.18.1)*. Record of completion *(10.18.2)*. Results of evaluation required in 23.4.3.3.
Supervising station facilities	None	UL 827-compliant for the supervising station and any subsidiary station *(26.3.5.1 and 26.3.5.2)*	Communications centers or other location acceptable to the authority having jurisdiction *(26.5.3)*	Fire-resistive, detached building or cut-off room not near or exposed to hazards. Access restricted, NFPA 10, 26-hour emergency lighting *(26.4.3)*.
Testing and maintenance	Chapter 14	Chapter 14. Pass code must be provided to place system into test mode *(26.3.7.5.6)*.	Chapter 14	Chapter 14
Runner service	No	Yes Alarm — arrive at the protected premises within 2 hours where equipment needs to be reset. Guard's tour — 30 minutes. Supervisory — 2 hours. Trouble — 4 hours. *(26.3.7)*	No	Yes Alarm — arrive at the protected premises within 2 hours where equipment needs to be reset. Guard's tour — 30 minutes. Supervisory — 2 hours. Trouble — 4 hours. *(26.4.5.6)*
Operations and management requirements	None	Prime contractor provides all elements of central station service under a variety of contractual arrangements *(26.3.2)*	None	Supervising station is under same ownership and management responsibility as premises being supervised
Staff	None	Minimum of two persons on duty at supervising station. Operation and supervision primary task *(26.3.6.2)*.	Minimum of two persons on duty at supervising station at all times. Other duties permitted per the authority having jurisdiction *(26.5.4.5)*.	Two operators of which one may be the runner. When runner is not in attendance at station, time between contact not to exceed 15 minutes. Primary duties are monitoring alarms and operations of station *(26.4.4.6)*.

(continues)

TABLE A.26.1 *Continued*

Attribute	*Protected Premises Fire Alarm System*	*Central Station Service Alarm System*	*Remote Supervising Station Alarm System*	*Proprietary Supervising Station Alarm System*
Monitor supervisory signals	Control unit and command center *(10.11.3 and 10.11.4)*	Control unit, command center, and central station *(10.11.3 and 10.11.4)*	Control unit, command center, and remote supervising station *(10.11.3 and 10.11.4)*	Control unit, command center, and proprietary supervising station *(10.11.3 and 10.11.4)*
Retransmission of signals	None	Alarm to public service communications center and subscriber. Supervisory, trouble, and guard service to designated personnel *(26.3.7).*	Alarm to public service communications center when monitored privately. Supervisory and trouble signals to owner's designated representative *(26.5.5).*	Alarm to public service communications center and plant brigade. Supervisory, trouble, and guard service to designated personnel *(26.4.5.6).*
Retransmission time	None	Alarm — immediate. Supervisory — immediate. Guard's tour supervisory — without unreasonable delay. Trouble — immediate. *(26.3.7)*	Alarm — immediate. Supervisory — immediate. Trouble — immediate. *(26.5.5)*	Alarm — immediate. Supervisory — immediate. Guard's tour supervisory — at once. Trouble — immediate. *(26.4.5.6)*
Records	Current year and 1 year after *(10.18.3)*	Complete records of all signals received must be retained for at least 1 year. Reports provided of signals received to authority having jurisdiction in a form it finds acceptable *(10.3.8).*	At least 1 year *(26.5.6.1).*	Complete records of all signals received shall be retained for at least 1 year. Reports provided of signals received to authority having jurisdiction in a form it finds acceptable *(26.4.6).*

Table A.26.1 compares the various performance characteristics of different types of facility alarm systems.

26.1.1* Where a protected premises fire alarm system has its signals sent to a supervising station, the entire system shall become a supervising station alarm system.

FAQ ►
When an alarm system at a protected premises transmits a signal to a supervising station, what designation does the system take?

Once an alarm system connects to a supervising station, the entire alarm system becomes a supervising station alarm system. Prior to the combination of all NFPA signaling standards into the *National Fire Alarm Code* in 1993, users and authorities having jurisdiction could classify each type of system by virtue of a separate and distinct signaling standard. After the combination, the defining of system types installed in a protected building became somewhat less clear. Some users and some authorities having jurisdiction thought that only the part of the system that actually connected to or interfaced with the supervising station comprised the supervising station alarm system. Subsection 26.1.1 clarifies that once an alarm system connects to a supervising station, the *entire system* becomes a supervising station alarm system.

A.26.1.1 Supervising station alarm systems include the equipment at the protected premises as well as the equipment at the supervising station itself. While the operational requirements relating to the signals sent off-premises fall under the scope of Chapter 26, the requirements of Chapter 23 also apply. Refer to Figure A.26.1.1.

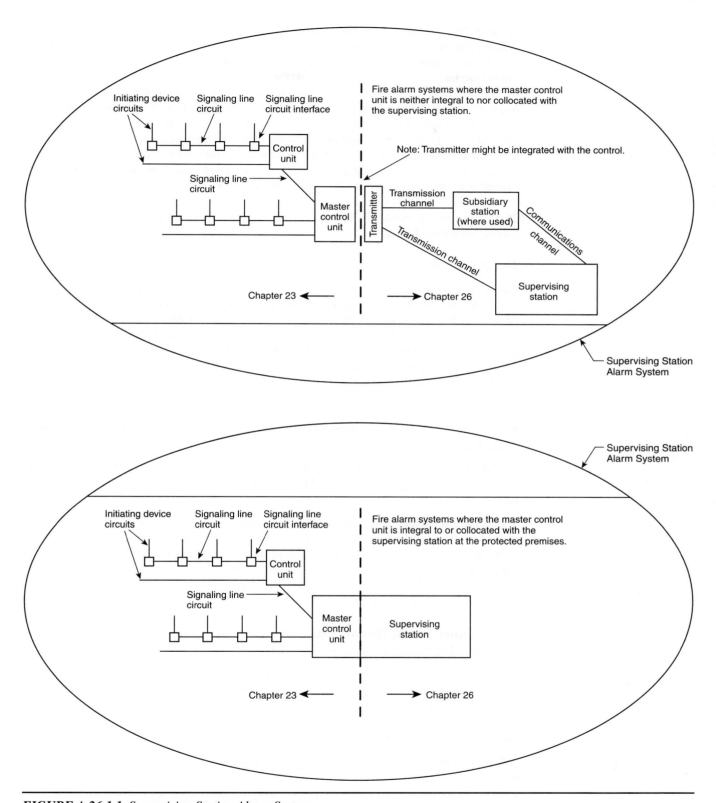

FIGURE A.26.1.1 *Supervising Station Alarm System.*

Figure A.26.1.1 correlates requirements between the chapter on protected premises fire alarm systems and the chapter on supervising station alarm systems. The figure clearly illustrates that all the components and subsystems in either arrangement constitute a supervising station alarm system.

Figure A.26.1.1 specifically shows the responsibility of each of the two chapters for the two common arrangements of fire alarm systems transmitting from a protected premises to a supervising station. In the first arrangement, the fire alarm system master control unit connects to a supervising station transmitter at the protected premises that, in turn, transmits either to an off-site supervising station or to a supervising station located at some other location on the same site. In the second arrangement, the fire alarm system master control unit is co-located with the supervising station at the protected premises.

26.1.2 The requirements of Chapters 10, 12, 14, and 23 shall also apply unless they are in conflict with this chapter.

26.1.3 The requirements of this chapter shall not apply to Chapter 29 unless otherwise noted.

Subsections 26.1.2 and 26.1.3 set the parameters for the other portions of the Code that apply to supervising station alarm systems. In 26.1.2, the requirements of Chapters 10, 12, 14, and 23 apply unless they conflict with the requirements of Chapter 26. In 26.1.3, the requirements of Chapter 26 apply only to household fire alarm systems as directed by Chapter 29. The requirements of Chapter 26 apply to commercial and industrial facilities where an owner or authority having jurisdiction requires a significantly higher level of service than would be necessary for a dwelling unit.

26.2 General

26.2.1 Alarm Signal Disposition. Except as permitted by 29.7.8.2, all fire alarm signals received by a supervising station shall be immediately retransmitted to the communications center.

This subsection, added in the 2007 edition, emphasizes the importance of the action a supervising station must take upon receipt of signals from a protected building. In the case of fire alarm signals, the supervising station must immediately retransmit the fire alarm signals to the communications center serving the area in which the protected building is located. This subsection recognizes that a specific exception exists in 29.7.8.2 to the requirement to immediately retransmit alarm signals.

26.2.2 Other Signal Disposition. Signals received at a supervising station, other than fire alarm, shall be handled as required by Section 26.3, 26.4, or 26.5.

As indicated in 26.2.2, when the supervising station receives other signals — such as supervisory or trouble signals — from a protected building, the supervising station must follow the specific requirements found in Section 26.3, 26.4, or 26.5.

26.2.3* Change of Service.

A.26.2.3 Changing where signals go from an existing to a new or different supervising station facility is sometimes done simply by changing a call-forward phone number. Or, within a supervising station, a new receiving computer and software can be constructed and lines changed over. Often, the account data are manually entered into the new system. Sometimes the data are transferred electronically. Errors can be made, causing the supervising station to get undefined alarms or incorrect account data, resulting in incorrect response by the supervising station. When such changes are made, the only visible way to ensure correct operation is to conduct an end-to-end test.

26.2.3.1 Supervising station customers or clients shall be notified in writing within 30 days of any scheduled change in service that results in signals from their property being handled by a different supervising station facility.

26.2.3.2 Where the supervising station provides the required testing and where service changes covered by 26.2.3.1 occur, the supervising station shall test all zones, points, and signals from each affected property in accordance with the requirements of Chapter 14.

26.2.3.3 Where the supervising station does not provide the required testing and where service changes covered by 26.2.3.1 occur, the supervising station shall notify the prime contractor of the need to test all zones, points, and signals from each affected property in accordance with the requirements of Chapter 14.

These requirements emphasize the importance of notifying the customer of changes to the service provided by a supervising station. Such changes often occur when one supervising station buys the client accounts of another supervising station. Commonly, instead of visiting each customer's protected building to reprogram the supervising station transmitter, the supervising station will call-forward the receiving telephone line (number) to a new receiving telephone line (number). This action may make the change in receiving location completely transparent to the customer. To maintain the effective integrity of the quality of the service provided, the customer must know whenever changes occur.

◀ **FAQ**
Why is the notification of changes in service for supervising station customers important?

26.2.4 Qualification of Supervising Station Operators.
Supervising station operators shall be qualified in accordance with the requirements of 10.4.4.

This new requirement in the 2010 edition of the Code seeks to ensure the qualifications and competence of the operators at the supervising station. It makes specific reference to the requirements in 10.4.4, which include the following:

- All operators in the supervising station must demonstrate competence in all tasks required of them by means of one or more of the following:
  - Be certified by the manufacturer of the receiving system or equipment or the alarm-monitoring automation system
  - Be certified by an organization acceptable to the authority having jurisdiction
  - Be licensed or certified by a state or local authority
  - Have other training or certification approved by the authority having jurisdiction
- All operators in the supervising station must present evidence of qualifications and/or certification when requested by the authority having jurisdiction.
- A license or qualification listing must be current in accordance with the requirements of the issuing authority or organization.
- Operator trainees must be under the direct supervision of a qualified operator until each becomes personally qualified.

26.3 Alarm Systems for Central Station Service

Alarm systems used to provide central station service shall comply with the general requirements and the use requirements of Section 26.3.

26.3.1 System Scope.
Alarm systems for central station service shall include the central station physical plant, exterior communications channels, subsidiary stations, and alarm and signaling equipment located at the protected premises.

Central station alarm systems offer service that integrates the overall protection design of a facility.

Protection, at both the most complex and the simplest facilities, must include a carefully developed strategy. A holistic approach usually proves best. This approach emphasizes the organic or functional relationship between parts and the whole. In other words, a holistic approach to protection asserts that the effectiveness of the strategy depends on a series of interconnected and interrelated protection features. These features must function as a complete entity. They cannot work effectively when applied only as individual components.

Some of these features, such as automatic sprinkler systems, fire extinguishers, and special hazard fire extinguishing or suppression systems, provide active physical protection. Other features, such as fire walls, fire barriers, fire doors, and other construction features, provide passive protection. Still other features, such as the central station alarm system, provide supervision and feedback by sensing conditions and reporting those conditions. Last, some features provide management control of the human response to fire or other emergency conditions. Every element is critical. Leaving out an element significantly reduces the overall effectiveness of the protection for the facility.

When selecting the elements to include, the design professional must begin by conducting a needs assessment to determine the overall site-specific protection goals for the facility. The designer must analyze and define goals for life safety, property protection, mission continuity, heritage preservation, and environmental protection.

Once the designer, working with the property owner and other stakeholders, has defined the goals, he or she must determine the objectives of each element of the overall protection system. For example, if the occupants of a building cannot move freely on their own to escape a fire or other emergency condition, a central station alarm system can summon aid. This aid could come from the public fire department, from a private emergency response team, or from some other appropriately trained and equipped emergency responders.

At a facility with complex property protection issues, the protection must provide a means of preserving the value that the physical property represents. The overall system must meet objectives that provide the necessary level of protection.

Finally, the design professional must choose some way to oversee or manage the interrelationship between the individual elements of protection for the facility. The design professional must choose the tool that management will use to help ensure that the protection systems will work as intended.

A fire alarm system installed throughout a facility and connected to a supervising station operated by a listed central station operating company provides one of the most effective tools for managing the protection at a facility. For example, property insurance companies have long required high-value industrial and commercial facilities to have at least one of the following: continuous occupancy in all areas of the facility, recorded guard patrol tours in all unoccupied areas, or a complete central station alarm system.

See Exhibit 26.2 for an example of a central station and Exhibit 26.3 for methods of contracting central station service.

26.3.2* Service Scope. Section 26.3 shall apply to central station service, which consists of the following elements:

(1) Installation of alarm transmitters
(2) Alarm, guard, supervisory, and trouble signal monitoring
(3) Retransmission
(4) Associated record keeping and reporting
(5) Testing and maintenance
(6) Runner service

A.26.3.2 There are related types of contract service that often are provided from, or controlled by, a central station but that are neither anticipated by, nor consistent with, the provi-

EXHIBIT 26.2 *A Central Station. Notice that the display in the background indicates the signal traffic and availability to process incoming signals. (Source: SimplexGrinnell, Westminster, MA)*

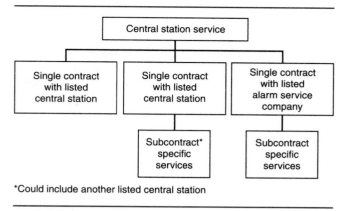

*Could include another listed central station

EXHIBIT 26.3 *Subscriber Contracts for Central Station Services. (Source: R. P. Schifiliti Associates, Inc., Reading, MA)*

sions of 26.3.2. Although 26.3.2 does not preclude such arrangements, a central station company is expected to recognize, provide for, and preserve the reliability, adequacy, and integrity of those supervisory and alarm services intended to be in accordance with the provisions of 26.3.2.

26.3.3 Contract Requirements. The central station service elements shall be provided under contract to a subscriber by one of the following:

(1) A listed central station that provides all of the elements of central station service with its own facilities and personnel.
(2) A listed central station that provides, as a minimum, the signal monitoring, retransmission, and associated record keeping and reporting with its own facilities and personnel and shall be permitted to subcontract all or any part of the installation, testing, and maintenance and runner service.
(3) A listed alarm service–local company that provides the installation, testing, and maintenance with its own facilities and personnel and that subcontracts the monitoring, retransmission, and associated record keeping and reporting to a listed central station. The required runner service shall be provided by the listed alarm service–local company with its own personnel or the listed central station with its own personnel.
(4) A listed central station that provides the installation, testing, and maintenance with its own facilities and personnel and that subcontracts the monitoring, retransmission, and associated record keeping and reporting to another listed central station. The required runner service shall be provided by either central station.

Central station service consists of six distinct elements: (1) installation, (2) testing and maintenance, and (3) runner service, all at the protected premises; and, at the supervising station,

(4) monitoring of signals from the protected premises, (5) retransmission of signals, and (6) record keeping. Chapter 26 recognizes the following four ways of providing central station service:

1. A listed central station can provide all six elements.
2. A listed central station can provide the three elements at the supervising station and subcontract one or more of the three elements at the protected premises.
3. A listed alarm service–local company can provide the installation, testing, and maintenance at the protected premises and subcontract the supervising station duties to a listed central station. Either the listed alarm service–local company or the listed central station would provide the runner service.
4. A central station can provide the three elements at the protected premises and subcontract the three elements at the supervising station to another listed central station. Either listed central station would provide the runner service.

Typically, the listed central station provides the three elements at the supervising station and subcontracts one or more of the elements at the protected premises. Most commonly, the central station subcontracts part of the installation. A typical situation where subcontracting might occur includes those facilities where a sprinkler system installer, acting as a subcontractor of the listed central station operating company, installs the fire alarm and supervisory initiating devices on the sprinkler system at a protected premises.

FAQ ▶

What important distinctions are involved when true central station service is provided?

Many fire alarm system installers connect protected premises fire alarm systems to a location remote from the protected premises that monitors signals. Relatively few such arrangements meet the requirements of 26.3.3 and should not be called a *central station service*. Only service that incorporates all six elements of central station service provided by listed alarm service providers that design, specify, install, test, maintain, and use the system in accordance with the requirements of 26.3.3 should be called *central station service*.

Because of unique requirements, central station alarm systems that comply with the Code offer seven important advantages over other types of alarm systems:

1. The Code requires the central station operating company to obtain listing by a testing laboratory acceptable to the authority having jurisdiction. The Code, in order to meet the requirements of the *Manual of Style for NFPA Technical Committee Documents,* makes a significant effort to use generic language when making reference to the work done by a testing laboratory. The Code strives to avoid any appearance of recommending or preferring any particular testing laboratory over any other testing laboratory. Conducting laboratory tests of alarm systems and providing the results to a wide range of authorities having jurisdiction has inherent complexity. From a practical standpoint of usage, the marketplace considerations in each country have effectively limited the testing laboratories to a very small number of principal national laboratories. For example, in the United States, the vast majority of the authorities having jurisdiction accept the alarm system laboratory testing and listing of either Underwriters Laboratories Inc. (UL) or FM Approvals (FM).
2. The Code requires tight control over the manner in which a central station operating company provides service.
3. The Code requires the central station operating company to conspicuously indicate that the installation complies with the Code.
4. The Code requires the central station operating company to automatically record signals received from a protected premises.
5. The Code carefully states the procedures for handling the various types of signals.
6. The Code spells out the manner in which central station operating companies may use the various transmission technologies to receive signals from a protected premises.
7. The Code requires tight control over who conducts the testing and maintenance of the system.

In examining each of these advantages, the design professional will recognize that the significant challenge to life safety, the high value of the property, the critical nature of the mission, the importance of preserving heritage, or the crucial necessity of protecting the environment drives these requirements. Although every protected property could benefit from having central station service, not every property can justify the additional cost. Thus, owners normally purchase central station service only when the protection goals or the specific requirements of an authority having jurisdiction demand it.

To ensure the baseline level of quality for a central station alarm system, the Code requires a testing laboratory acceptable to the authority having jurisdiction to list both the equipment and the operating company providing the service. (See the definition of *listed* in 3.2.5.)

From the outset, in 10.3.1, the Code requires that alarm system service providers use only listed equipment. The listing process involves not only testing the equipment to make certain it performs properly but also inspecting the production of listed equipment to make certain the manufacturer has not changed the product after the laboratory tested it.

Listing can apply to a material or a service, which is important to note when considering the third distinct advantage of central station service. As previously stated, most authorities having jurisdiction accept the services of one or both of the UL and FM testing laboratories. Both laboratories rely on the requirements of the Code to guide their testing requirements. In addition, each laboratory has developed a performance standard for central station service: ANSI/UL 827, *Standard for Central-Station Alarm Services*, and FM Approval Standard 3011, *Central Station Service for Fire Alarms and Protective Equipment Supervision*. Representatives of the laboratory visit each central station operating company to review records of signals and to audit the personnel performing operations and service. The representatives verify the construction of the physical central station and check the equipment and the power supplies.

Both UL and FM also provide for the listing of alarm service–local companies. UL does so under the category "Protective Signaling Services-Local, Auxiliary, Remote Station, and Proprietary (UUJS)." FM offers listing under the category "Fire Alarm Service Local Company (FIRE)."

UL publishes the results of the listing process annually in the *UL Fire Protection Equipment Directory*. FM publishes the results of its listing process annually in the FM Global *Approval Guide*. Public and private authorities having jurisdiction can use these publications to determine whether a central station operating company has obtained listing.

26.3.4* Indication of Central Station Service.
The prime contractor shall conspicuously indicate that the alarm system providing service at a protected premises complies with all the requirements of this Code through the use of a systematic follow-up program under the control of the organization that has listed the prime contractor.

A.26.3.4 The terms *certificated* and *placarded*, which appeared in previous editions of *NFPA 72*, were considered by some to be too specific to two listing organizations and were replaced with more generic wording. The concept of providing documentation to indicate ongoing compliance of an installed system continues to be reflected by the current language.

To help ensure the inherent higher level of protection that a central station alarm system provides, 26.3.4 requires the prime contractor to indicate that the entire alarm system meets the requirements of the Code through the use of a systematic follow-up program under the control of the organization that has listed the prime contractor.

This requirement does not intend that the organization providing the systematic follow-up service will actually inspect every central station alarm system. Nor does it mean that when the organization providing the systematic follow-up service does inspect a central station alarm system it will inspect every aspect of that system. However, by providing a systematic follow-up program under the control of the organization that has listed the prime

Does having a systematic follow-up program mean that every central station alarm system will be inspected under the program provisions?
◀ FAQ

contractor, the prime contractor makes provision for a potential additional level of oversight.

The requirement in 26.3.4 tends to promote and encourage installation, testing, and maintenance procedures that will help ensure the overall quality of the central station alarm system. Further, the conspicuous indication that the installation complies with all the requirements of the Code helps promote a much more determined effort to implement the requirements of the Code than might otherwise occur.

The prime contractor must conspicuously post within a stated distance of the main control unit documentation issued by the organization that has listed the prime contractor.

By intent, the Code does not provide details of the process by which the listing organization provides follow-up service or issues the required documentation to the listed prime contractor. Rather, the Code leaves these details up to the procedures and practices of the listing organization.

Exhibits 26.4 through 26.6 illustrate typical documentation as issued by two organizations that list prime contractors providing central station service.

26.3.4.1 Documentation indicating Code compliance of the alarm system shall be issued by the organization that has listed the prime contractor.

26.3.4.2 The documentation shall include, at a minimum, the following information:

(1) Name of the prime contractor involved with the ongoing Code compliance of the central station service
(2)* Full description of the alarm system as installed
(3) Issue and expiration dates of the documentation
(4) Name, address, and contact information of the organization issuing the document
(5) Identification of the authority(ies) having jurisdiction for the central station service installation

A.26.3.4.2(2) The record of completion *(see Chapter 10)* can be used to fulfill this requirement.

26.3.4.3 The documentation shall be physically posted within 3 ft (1 m) of the control unit, and copies of the documentation shall be made available to the authority(ies) having jurisdiction upon request.

26.3.4.4 A central repository of issued documentation, accessible to the authority having jurisdiction, shall be maintained by the organization that has listed the prime contractor.

26.3.4.5* Alarm system service that does not comply with all the requirements of Section 26.3 shall not be designated as central station service.

A.26.3.4.5 It is the prime contractor's responsibility to remove all compliance markings (certification markings or placards) when a service contract goes into effect that conflicts in any way with the requirements of 26.3.4.

26.3.4.6* For the purpose of Section 26.3, the subscriber shall notify the prime contractor, in writing, of the identity of the authority(ies) having jurisdiction.

A.26.3.4.6 The prime contractor should be aware of statutes, public agency regulations, or certifications regarding alarm systems that might be binding on the subscriber. The prime contractor should identify for the subscriber which agencies could be an authority having jurisdiction and, if possible, advise the subscriber of any requirements or approvals being mandated by these agencies.

The subscriber has the responsibility for notifying the prime contractor of those private organizations that are being designated as an authority having jurisdiction. The subscriber also has the responsibility to notify the prime contractor of changes in the authority having jurisdiction, such as where there is a change in insurance companies. Although the responsibility is primarily the subscriber's, the prime contractor should also take responsibility for

EXHIBIT 26.4
Documentation for Central Station Systems: Fire Alarm System Certificate. (Source: Underwriters Laboratories Inc., Northbrook, IL)

Underwriters Laboratories Inc. ®

Northbrook, IL   Santa Clara, CA
Melville, NY   Research Triangle Park, NC
A not-for-profit organization dedicated to public safety
and committed to quality service

File No **S1234**   CCN: **UUFX**
Service Center No: **1**
Expires: **01/01/2011**
Issued: **01/01/2006**

CENTRAL STATION - FIRE
FIRE ALARM SYSTEM CERTIFICATE
(NFPA 72)

THIS CERTIFIES that the Alarm Service Company is included by Underwriters Laboratories Inc. (UL) in its Directory as qualified to use the UL Listing Mark in connection with the certificated Alarm System. This Certificate is the Alarm Service Company's representation that the Alarm System including all connecting wiring and equipment has been installed and will be maintained in compliance with requirements established by UL. This Certificate does not apply in any way to the installation of any additional signaling systems, such as fire, smoke, waterflow, burglary, holdup, medical emergency, or otherwise, that may be connected to or installed along with the Certificated Alarm System.

LIMITATION OF LIABILITY: Underwriters Laboratories Inc. makes no representations or warranties, express or implied, that the Alarm System will prevent any loss by fire, smoke, water damage, burglary, hold-up or otherwise, or that the Alarm System will in all cases provide the protection for which it is installed or intended. UL may at times conduct inspections of the Alarm Service Company including inspections of representative installations made by it. UL does not assume or undertake to discharge any liability of the Alarm Service Company or any other party. UL is not an insurer and assumes no liability which may result directly or indirectly from inspection of the equipment, failure of the equipment, failure to conduct inspections, incorrect certification, nonconformity with requirements, failure to discover nonconformity with requirements, cancellation of the Certificate or withdrawal of the Alarm Service Company from inclusion in UL's Directory prior to the expiration date appearing on this Certificate.

OPERATIONAL REQUIREMENTS: The Alarm Service Company bears the responsibility for the correctness of the installation; maintenance of the system documentation; periodic system inspection and testing; maintaining and providing any necessary repairs. All operations and maintenance shall be conducted in the manner prescribed by the NFPA standard referenced. All required service is to be provided for in an appropriate contract. System documentation is defined to include any "As Built Drawings"; the records of any "Acceptance Testing"; and the records of all periodic system testing and maintenance.

SYSTEM DESCRIPTION: This system is installed and operated in accordance with standard NFPA 72, 2002 edition.

Area Covered: BUILDING
Authority Having Jurisdiction: ANY CITY FD
Responding Fire Department: ANY CITY FD
SYSTEM DEVIATIONS FROM REFERENCED NFPA STANDARDS
2 PULL STATIONS ARE MORE THAN 5 FEET FROM DOOR DUE TO GLASS WALL

Protected Property:
ANY BUILDING
123 OAK STREET
ANY CITY, IL 01234

SN : FC12345678

Alarm Service Company:
AN ALARM COMPANY
912 MAIN STREET
ANY CITY IL 01234

Alarm Service Company's Representative

Date

© 1998 UL

seeking out these private authority(ies) having jurisdiction through the subscriber. The prime contractor is responsible for maintaining current records on the authority(ies) having jurisdiction for each protected premises.

The most prevalent public agency involved as an authority having jurisdiction with regard to alarm systems is the local fire department or fire prevention bureau. These are normally city or county agencies with statutory authority, and their approval of alarm system installations might be required. At the state level, the fire marshal's office is most likely to serve as the public regulatory agency.

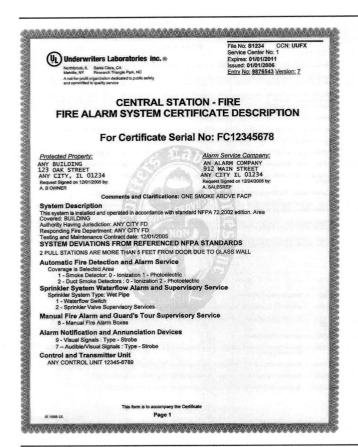

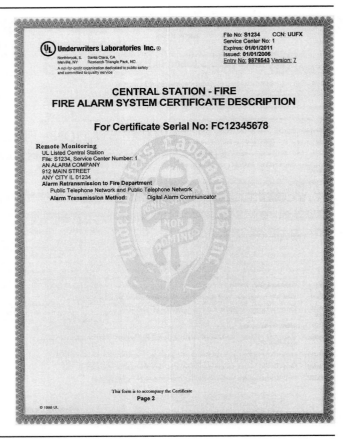

EXHIBIT 26.5 *Documentation for Central Station Systems: Fire Alarm System Certificate Description. (Source: Underwriters Laboratories Inc., Northbrook, IL)*

The most prevalent private organizations involved as authorities having jurisdiction are insurance companies. Others include insurance rating bureaus, insurance brokers and agents, and private consultants. It is important to note that these organizations have no statutory authority and become authorities having jurisdiction only when designated by the subscriber.

With both public and private concerns to satisfy, it is not uncommon to find multiple authorities having jurisdiction involved with a particular protected premises. It is necessary to identify all authorities having jurisdiction in order to obtain all the necessary approvals for a central station alarm system installation.

The subscriber and the prime contractor must identify all the authorities having jurisdiction involved at the protected premises. Although this responsibility rests primarily with the subscriber, the subscriber would normally know only the private authorities having jurisdiction. From experience gained by working in a particular jurisdiction, the prime contractor would most often know any additional public authorities having jurisdiction. Thus, a joint effort most effectively resolves this important requirement.

26.3.4.7 The authority(ies) having jurisdiction identified in 26.3.4.2(5) shall be notified of expiration or cancellation by the organization that has listed the prime contractor.

26.3.4.8 The subscriber shall surrender expired or canceled documentation to the prime contractor within 30 days of the termination date.

FIRE DEPARTMENT WILL RESPOND

TO ALARM SIGNALS UNLESS TELEPHONE NUMBER

_____

CALLED BEFORE TESTS OF THIS SYSTEM ARE MADE

ALARM SERVICE BY: _____

TELEPHONE NUMBER: _____

SUPERVISING (CENTRAL) STATION: _____

TELEPHONE NUMBER: _____

CENTRAL STATION SERVICE PLACARD
This fire protection signaling system installation, all
equipment and wiring plus the maintenance,
testing and supervision thereof are in accordance
with the central station Approval requirements of
FM Approval Standard No. 3011.

◇ **FM** ◇
APPROVED

PLACARD IDENTIFICATION: _____
EXPIRATION DATE: _____

PRIME CONTRACTOR:

EXHIBIT 26.6 *Documentation for Central Station Systems: Placard. (Source: FM Global Property Loss Prevention Data Sheet 5-40, Fire Alarm Systems. © 2006 FM Global. Reprinted with permission. All rights reserved.)*

Over the life of a central station system, someone might make a change that results in the expiration or cancellation of contracted service. In turn, that expiration or cancellation would invalidate the designation "central station service." In such a case, the organization that has listed the prime contractor must notify the authority having jurisdiction, as required in 26.3.4.7. Further, the subscriber must return the expired or cancelled documentation to the prime contractor within 30 days of the termination date.

The authority having jurisdiction should rigorously enforce this requirement, which will ensure that only those systems meeting and maintaining all the Code requirements for central station service will have this designation.

26.3.5 Facilities.

26.3.5.1 The central station building or that portion of a building occupied by a central station shall conform to the construction, fire protection, restricted access, emergency lighting, and power facilities requirements of the latest edition of ANSI/UL 827, *Standard for Central-Station Alarm Services*.

ANSI/UL 827 details protection features that help to maintain the integrity and continuity of the physical central station. In 26.3.3, the Code requires that a qualified testing laboratory acceptable to the authority having jurisdiction must list the central station and examine the protection features required by ANSI/UL 827 for compliance.

26.3.5.2 Subsidiary station buildings or those portions of buildings occupied by subsidiary stations shall conform to the construction, fire protection, restricted access, emergency lighting, and power facilities requirements of the latest edition of ANSI/UL 827, *Standard for Central-Station Alarm Services.*

A *subsidiary station* is defined in 3.3.265 as a normally unattended facility located remotely from the central station and linked to the central station by a communications channel. A central station may receive signals from many subscribers in a particular geographic area through one or more subsidiary stations.

FAQ ▶
What do the requirements in 26.3.5.2 serve to ensure?

The requirement detailed in 26.3.5.2 and those that follow in 26.3.5.2.1 through 26.3.5.2.8 reflect the fact that, under normal operating conditions, no one staffs a subsidiary station. Usually, a subsidiary station serves a particular geographic area. The subsidiary station concentrates signals from many protected premises and transmits those concentrated signals to a supervising station. A malfunction at a subsidiary station can substantially impair the successful transmission of signals from the properties it serves. Thus, these requirements help ensure the overall operational reliability of the subsidiary station. They also help ensure the integrity of the transmission path between the subsidiary station and the supervising station.

26.3.5.2.1 All intrusion, fire, power, and environmental control systems for subsidiary station buildings shall be monitored by the central station in accordance with 26.3.5.

One way the central station staff manages the integrity of the subsidiary station is by monitoring certain critical building systems of the subsidiary station at the central station. This action helps to ensure the operational continuity of the subsidiary station.

26.3.5.2.2 The subsidiary facility shall be inspected at least monthly by central station personnel for the purpose of verifying the operation of all supervised equipment, all telephones, all battery conditions, and all fluid levels of batteries and generators.

The central station staff also manages the integrity of the subsidiary station by inspecting it monthly. Not simply a stop-by visit, this thorough inspection verifies the continuity of the equipment, systems, and communications channels installed at the subsidiary station.

26.3.5.2.3 In the event of the failure of equipment at the subsidiary station or the communications channel to the central station, a backup shall be operational within 90 seconds.

26.3.5.2.4 With respect to 26.3.5.2.3, restoration of a failed unit shall be accomplished within 5 days.

The subsidiary station must have backup equipment, which in the event of a failure the central station must be able to place into operation within 90 seconds. A technician must repair or replace defective equipment within 5 days.

26.3.5.2.5 Each communications channel shall be continuously supervised between the subsidiary station and the central station.

The equipment connected to each communications channel between the subsidiary station and the central station must continuously monitor for channel integrity. In most cases, the equipment uses some form of continuous multiplex transmission technology. Today, many central stations communicate with their subsidiary stations using high speed, large bandwidth data transmission equipment, such as T1 or T3 network technology.

26.3.5.2.6 When the communications channel between the subsidiary station and the supervising station fails, the communications shall be switched to an alternate path. Public switched telephone network facilities shall be used only as an alternate path.

In addition to a highly reliable, primary communications channel, an alternate communications channel must provide redundancy in case of a failure to the primary channel. The central station may use "dial up, make good" service provided by the public telephone utility for the alternate communications channel. If the dedicated primary communications channel between the central station and the subsidiary station fails, "dial up, make good" service allows the central station to access a substitute communications channel using the normal voice telephone network. Use of this substitute communications channel provides an emergency communications path until technicians can restore the primary communications channel. The central station initiates the "dial up, make good" service to re-establish the data communications between the subsidiary station and the central station.

26.3.5.2.7 In the subsidiary station, there shall be a communications path, such as a cellular telephone, that is independent of the telephone cable between the subsidiary station and the serving wire center.

This requirement ensures that service personnel can establish communication with the central station upon arrival at a totally impaired subsidiary station.

26.3.5.2.8 A plan of action to provide for restoration of services specified by this Code shall exist for each subsidiary station.

26.3.5.2.8.1 This plan shall provide for restoration of services within 4 hours of any impairment that causes loss of signals from the subsidiary station to the central station.

26.3.5.2.8.2 An exercise to demonstrate the adequacy of the plan shall be conducted at least annually.

The central station must formulate a written plan for restoring service from a subsidiary station. This plan must encompass all services not already covered by 26.3.5.2.3. Such restoration must occur within 4 hours as required by 26.3.5.2.8.1. Commonly, the organization listing a central station that uses one or more subsidiary stations will review such a plan as a part of the listing process.

   As with all emergency plans, the central station must test the plan's accuracy and validity. By performing the annual exercise as required by 26.3.5.2.8.2, the implementing personnel have an opportunity to become thoroughly familiar with the procedure. Such an exercise also helps keep the plan up-to-date and discloses changes at either the subsidiary station or the central station that may affect the integrity of the plan.

26.3.6 Equipment and Personnel.

26.3.6.1 Equipment.

26.3.6.1.1 The central station and all subsidiary stations shall be equipped so as to receive and record all signals in accordance with 26.6.4.

26.3.6.1.2 Circuit-adjusting means for emergency operation shall be permitted to be automatic or to be provided through manual operation upon receipt of a trouble signal.

Paragraph 26.3.6.1.2 permits specially trained central station operators (see 26.2.4 and 26.3.6.2 for personnel requirements) to manually operate circuit-adjusting means. Central station equipment may also automatically operate circuit-adjusting means.

26.3.6.1.3 Computer-aided alarm and supervisory signal–processing hardware and software shall be listed for the purpose.

The organization listing the central station must also specifically list any computer-aided alarm and supervisory signal–processing hardware and software for central station service. This requirement helps ensure the operational integrity of the signal handling at the central station.

   Virtually all modern central stations use software to process signals. Typically, a series of listed digital alarm communicator receivers (DACRs) connect to incoming telephone lines from the public switched telephone network. In some cases, specially designed DACRs might also connect to incoming data links to the Internet. These DACRs initially receive all signals from subscriber premises. A terminal data connection from each receiver using standard computer protocols transfers information concerning each incoming signal to redundant PC-based servers listed for central station service. Special listed software within the servers processes the information and displays it on computer workstations at each operator's desk. The software provides display priority for various types of signals. The software also provides detailed subscriber information, including the telephone numbers of the appropriate fire and police departments and the subscriber's representatives.

This arrangement of listed hardware and software significantly automates the processing of signals. It allows a smaller number of operators to handle a larger volume of signal traffic with a great deal of efficiency and effectiveness.

Some central stations that handle a very large volume of signal traffic have invested in data management architecture that includes off-site redundant servers. This level of redundancy helps ensure the continuity of operations during times of hardware or software failure or routine hardware or software maintenance.

26.3.6.1.4 Power supplies shall comply with the requirements of Chapter 10.

26.3.6.1.5 Transmission means shall comply with the requirements of Section 26.6.

26.3.6.1.6* Two independent means shall be provided to retransmit an alarm signal to the designated communications center.

A.26.3.6.1.6 Two telephone lines (numbers) at the central station connected to the public switched telephone network, each having its own telephone instrument connected, and two telephone lines (numbers) available at the communications center to which a central station operator can retransmit an alarm meet the intent of this requirement.

26.3.6.1.6.1 The use of a universal emergency number, such as the 911 public safety answering point, shall not meet the intent of this Code for the principal means of retransmission.

26.3.6.1.6.2 If the principal means of retransmission is not equipped to allow the communications center to acknowledge receipt of each alarm report, both means shall be used to retransmit.

26.3.6.1.6.3 The retransmission means shall be tested in accordance with Chapter 14.

26.3.6.1.6.4 The retransmission signal and the time and date of retransmission shall be recorded at the central station.

In 26.3.2, the Code states that the third of the six elements of central station service includes retransmitting emergency signals to the appropriate communications center. The central station must have a reasonably secure means to retransmit signals.

FAQ ▶
What is the most common means of retransmitting emergency signals?

In most cases, the central station will use the public switched telephone network to dial the 7-digit or 10-digit reporting number assigned to the communications center. The Code states in 26.3.6.1.6.1 that the central station may not use 9-1-1 as the principal means of retransmission. This requirement exists because (1) the central station may not be located in the same community as the protected premises and will have no way to dial 9-1-1 for a location in a different geographical area; (2) a public service answering point (PSAP) staffed with civilian personnel who are not a part of the public emergency responders answer most 9-1-1 and enhanced 9-1-1 emergency telephone calls; and (3) the vast majority of 9-1-1 calls concern non-fire emergencies. Complying with this requirement helps to avoid the bottleneck that sometimes occurs at the PSAP.

The provision of 26.3.6.1.6.4 requires the central station to record the actual telephone call to the communications center. This recording, along with records of signals received at the central station, often helps investigators reconstruct the sequence of events that occurred during a major fire. Paragraph 26.3.6.1.6.4 does not mandate the central station to record the time and date automatically. However, when computer-based automation systems manage the receipt and processing of signals, including the retransmission signal, the central station can and should automatically record the time and date of the retransmission.

Previous editions of the Code gave the authority having jurisdiction the option to require a supervised means of retransmission. This requirement would have been used in certain cases where the authority having jurisdiction did not accept the inherent reliability of the public switched telephone network. The requirement permitted the authority having jurisdiction to require the central station to have a retransmission channel that was monitored for integrity for each communications center that served the central station's customers. However, due to the consistently high reliability of the public switched telephone network, this permissive requirement was seldom used. For that reason, the provision was deleted from the 2002 edition of the Code.

26.3.6.2 Personnel.

26.3.6.2.1 The central station shall have not less than two qualified operators on duty at the central station at all times to ensure disposition of signals in accordance with the requirements of 26.3.7.

26.3.6.2.2 Operation and supervision shall be the primary functions of the operators, and no other interest or activity shall take precedence over the protective service.

The central station must have two qualified operators on duty at all times (see 26.3.6.2.1). By mandating the presence of two operators, the Code maximizes the likelihood that at all times at least one operator will be fully alert to receive and process incoming signals. The Code also requires that the operators have no other duties that would distract them from the prompt, effective handling of signals.

Realistically, the volume of signal traffic determines the number of operators on duty. Over the past 20 years, central station operating companies of all sizes have consistently consolidated the number of central station locations. Various innovations in communications technology have eliminated the need for the location of the central station to closely match the proximity of the subscribers. Today, a single central can serve thousands, even tens of thousands, of subscribers. The organizations that list the central station must keep a careful watch on the ratio of operators to signal traffic to ensure the prompt handling of emergency signals.

26.3.7 Disposition of Signals.

26.3.7.1 Alarm Signals.

26.3.7.1.1 Alarm signals initiated by manual fire alarm boxes, automatic fire detectors, waterflow from the automatic sprinkler system, or actuation of other fire suppression system(s) or equipment shall be treated as fire alarms.

26.3.7.1.2 The central station shall perform the following actions:

(1)* Immediately retransmit the alarm to the communications center.
(2) Dispatch a runner or technician to the protected premises to arrive within 2 hours after receipt of a signal if equipment needs to be manually reset by the prime contractor. Except where prohibited by the authority having jurisdiction, the runner or technician shall be permitted to be recalled prior to arrival at the premises if a qualified representative of the subscriber at the premises can provide the necessary resetting of the equipment and is able to place the system back in operating condition.
(3) Immediately notify the subscriber.
(4) Provide notice to the subscriber or authority having jurisdiction, or both, if required.

Exception: If the alarm signal results from a prearranged test, the actions specified by 26.3.7.1.2(1) and (3) shall not be required.

A.26.3.7.1.2(1) The term *immediately* in this context is intended to mean "without unreasonable delay." Routine handling should take a maximum of 90 seconds from receipt of an alarm signal by the central station until the initiation of retransmission to the communications center.

The central station operators should perform the actions required in 26.3.7.1.2 in the order in which they appear in the Code. This order reflects intended levels of urgency and the priority of activities.

A central station must give highest priority to the prompt handling and retransmission of fire alarm signals. Under the most adverse circumstances — for example, where a digital alarm communicator transmitter (DACT) takes the maximum number of permitted attempts before it connects with the central station — it may have already taken up to 15 minutes to complete the transmission of a signal from the protected premises to the central station. [See 26.6.3.2.1.3(B) and 26.6.3.2.1.3(C).]

Note that the Code does not permit the operator to verify whether the alarm signal comes from the scene of a real emergency. The operator must immediately retransmit the signal.

FAQ ▶
Does *NFPA 72* allow the central station operator to verify the alarm signal prior to retransmitting the signal?

An exception to this requirement to immediately retransmit does exist (see 29.7.8.2). Upon receipt of an alarm signal from a household fire alarm system, the supervising station must immediately (within 90 seconds) retransmit the alarm to the communications center. However, the supervising station may contact the residence for verification of an alarm condition. If, within 90 seconds, the operator receives acceptable indication that the fire department does not need to respond, the operator may withhold the retransmission to the communications center.

Some proponents of quick-fix solutions to the problem of false fire alarm signals urge that central station operating companies verify *all* signals, including alarm signals. As noted previously, the Code does not permit this verification for other than household fire alarm systems.

Therefore, when a central station receives alarm signals from alarm systems other than household fire alarm systems, the central station must immediately retransmit the alarm signal to the communications center as required by 26.2.1 and 26.3.7.1.2(1).

The runner or technician in 26.3.7.1.2(2) needs to respond only when the prime contractor must manually reset equipment at the protected premises. For some central station alarm systems, the authority having jurisdiction may permit the subscriber or some other trained individual to reset the equipment. In such a case, the prime contractor would not need to reset the system, and a runner would not need to respond.

To comply with 26.3.7.1.2(3), the central station will usually notify the subscriber by means of a telephone call. In most cases, this constitutes the quickest available method of notification.

The word *notice,* in the context of 26.3.7.1.2(4), means "written notice." Written notice to the subscriber and the authority having jurisdiction should follow a format useful to each recipient. The subscriber can use such notice to document system operations, as required by 10.18.3. The authority having jurisdiction can use the notice to help document response to system operations at the location.

26.3.7.2 Guard's Tour Supervisory Signal.

26.3.7.2.1 Upon failure to receive a guard's tour supervisory signal within a 15-minute maximum grace period, the central station shall perform the following actions:

(1) Communicate without unreasonable delay with personnel at the protected premises
(2) Dispatch a runner to the protected premises to arrive within 30 minutes of the delinquency if communications cannot be established

(3) Report all delinquencies to the subscriber or authority having jurisdiction, or both, if required

In 26.3.7.2.1(2), if the central station cannot promptly contact personnel at the protected premises, then it should dispatch a runner to investigate why the guard missed a signal. Once dispatched, the runner must arrive at the protected premises within 30 minutes. This time frame means the runner may actually arrive 45 minutes after the guard missed the signal. Even so, in actual cases, a responding runner has found the guard injured or ill and, by summoning medical assistance, has saved the guard's life.

26.3.7.2.2 Failure of the guard to follow a prescribed route in transmitting signals shall be handled as a delinquency.

Guard's tour supervision by a central station mandates a compulsory tour arrangement. The central station can provide this service in a number of ways. The central station could monitor every reporting station along a route. Alternatively, the central station could monitor only a few of the stations along a route. In this case, the guard would have to sequentially operate each station in the route, including those that do not transmit signals. Typically the stations will not operate unless the guard has first operated the previous station in the route. But in either case, the guard must follow a prescribed route, proceeding from station to station in a fixed sequence. A delinquency is incurred if the guard fails to follow the prescribed route, as stated in 26.3.7.2.2.

Central station operating companies report that very few contracts to provide guard's tour service remain in effect. In those cases where a heightened level of oversight of guard's tours seems prudent, central station guard's tour supervision provides such a heightened level.

26.3.7.3* Supervisory Signals. Upon receipt of a supervisory signal from a sprinkler system, other fire suppression system(s), or other equipment, the central station shall perform the following actions:

(1)*Communicate immediately with the persons designated by the subscriber and notify the fire department or law enforcement agency, or both, when required by the authority having jurisdiction
(2) Dispatch a runner or maintenance person to arrive within 2 hours to investigate

Exception: Where the supervisory signal is cleared in accordance with a scheduled procedure determined by 26.3.7.3(1).

(3) Notify the authority having jurisdiction when sprinkler systems or other fire suppression systems or equipment have been wholly or partially out of service for 8 hours
(4) When service has been restored, provide notice, if required, to the subscriber or the authority having jurisdiction, or both, as to the nature of the signal, the time of occurrence, and the restoration of service when equipment has been out of service for 8 hours or more

Exception: If the supervisory signal results from a prearranged test, the actions specified by 26.3.7.3(1), (3), and (4) shall not be required.

A.26.3.7.3 It is anticipated that the central station will first attempt to notify designated personnel at the protected premises. When such notification cannot be made, it might be appropriate to notify law enforcement or the fire department, or both. For example, if a valve supervisory signal is received where protected premises are not occupied, it is appropriate to notify the police.

A.26.3.7.3(1) The term *immediately* in this context is intended to mean "without unreasonable delay." Routine handling should take a maximum of 4 minutes from receipt of a supervisory signal by the central station until the initiation of communications with a person(s) designated by the subscriber.

Supervisory signals may indicate that something or someone has impaired a vital protection system, so the central station must handle supervisory signals promptly and accurately. Central station supervisory service can materially assist the owner, occupants, or management of a facility in overseeing the operational readiness of automatic fire extinguishing or suppression systems. The service can also help oversee the operation of critical premises emergency control (fire safety) functions.

FAQ ▶
What is the typical course of action upon receipt of a supervisory signal?

A runner or a technician needs to respond only when the central station operator cannot resolve restoration of the supervisory signal to normal by contacting designated personnel as required by 26.3.7.3(1). Typically, upon receipt of a supervisory signal, a central station operator will telephone the premises. If there is no answer, then the operator will telephone the individuals on a calling list provided by the subscriber. If the operator cannot reach someone on the calling list who will promptly respond to investigate and resolve the supervisory off-normal signal, then the operator must dispatch a runner. When dispatched, the runner must arrive at the protected premises within 2 hours.

26.3.7.4 Trouble Signals. Upon receipt of trouble signals or other signals pertaining solely to matters of equipment maintenance of the alarm systems, the central station shall perform the following actions:

(1)* Communicate immediately with persons designated by the subscriber
(2) Dispatch personnel to arrive within 4 hours to initiate maintenance, if necessary
(3) When the interruption is more than 8 hours, provide notice to the subscriber and the fire department if so required by the authority having jurisdiction as to the nature of the interruption, the time of occurrence, and the restoration of service

The central station must handle trouble signals promptly and accurately. Trouble signals indicate that the alarm system, the transmitter, or the communications path is wholly or partly out of service. The central station operator plays a key role in the initial troubleshooting of a system outage. The degree to which the operator has received training to properly interpret the exact nature of the trouble signal can materially assist in getting the system back in service as quickly as possible.

The personnel, dispatched to arrive within 4 hours, must initiate repairs. This requirement generally means that a technician, rather than a runner, must respond. The Code anticipates that the responding technician will have the necessary tools, test equipment, and spare parts to make the needed repairs as quickly as possible. Those training the technicians must place emphasis on the time-critical nature of this type of troubleshooting and repair activity. The Code anticipates that the technician will make every effort to minimize the length of the impairment to the fire alarm system.

A.26.3.7.4(1) The term *immediately* in this context is intended to mean "without unreasonable delay." Routine handling should take a maximum of 4 minutes from receipt of a trouble signal by the central station until initiation of the investigation by telephone.

26.3.7.5 Test Signals.

26.3.7.5.1 All test signals received shall be recorded to indicate date, time, and type.

26.3.7.5.2 Test signals initiated by the subscriber, including those for the benefit of an authority having jurisdiction, shall be acknowledged by central station personnel whenever the subscriber or authority inquires.

26.3.7.5.3* Any test signal not received by the central station shall be investigated immediately, and action shall be taken to reestablish system integrity.

A.26.3.7.5.3 The term *immediately* in this context is intended to mean "without unreasonable delay." Routine handling should take a maximum of 4 minutes from receipt of a trouble signal by the central station until initiation of the investigation by telephone.

The central station must handle test signals immediately; the Code recommends doing so within 4 minutes. Test signals help to ensure that the alarm system continues to function properly. The central station must cooperate with any authority having jurisdiction that inquires regarding test signals. If a subscriber initiates a test signal, then calls the central station and determines that the central station did not receive the signal, the central station should treat this occurrence as a trouble signal and follow the procedures outlined in 26.3.7.4. The central station should dispatch a service technician to arrive within 4 hours to begin repairs.

26.3.7.5.4 The central station shall dispatch personnel to arrive within 2 hours if protected premises equipment needs to be manually reset after testing.

26.3.7.5.5 The prime contractor shall provide each of its representatives and each alarm system user with a unique personal identification code.

26.3.7.5.6 In order to authorize the placing of an alarm system into test status, a representative of the prime contractor or an alarm system user shall first provide the central station with his or her personal identification code.

The prime contractor issues each of its representatives and each alarm system user with a unique personal identification code (see 26.3.7.5.5) and requires its use (see 26.3.7.5.6) in order to carefully control those who may place the system into a test mode.

Some systems permit the central station representative at the protected premises or alarm system user to enter the personal identification code on a key pad at the protected premises. Other systems require the individual provide the personal identification code by using a telephone to dial a special number and then entering the code on the telephone's touch-tone key pad. Still other systems require that the code be given verbally to a central station operator in a telephone call to the central station.

This requirement helps to maintain the security and operational integrity of the alarm system. Without this precaution, the central station has no way of verifying that the person placing the alarm system into test status has authorization to do so.

26.3.8 Record Keeping and Reporting.

26.3.8.1 Complete records of all signals received shall be retained for at least 1 year.

26.3.8.2 Testing and maintenance records shall be retained as required by 14.6.3.

26.3.8.3 The central station shall make arrangements to furnish reports of signals received to the authority having jurisdiction in a manner approved by the authority having jurisdiction.

It is important for the central station to keep accurate and complete records of signals received. See the requirements of 10.18.3, Section 14.6, and especially 14.6.3 for information on retaining testing and maintenance records.

When an authority having jurisdiction requests reports from a central station, the central station must provide the reports in a useful and usable form. In many cases, authorities having jurisdiction can use information from central station records to reconstruct events leading up to and following an emergency or other incident.

When a fire does occur, the record of signals received at the central station assists investigators tremendously. The date-stamped and time-stamped automatic record of signals received at the central station helps investigators develop a step-by-step sequence of events for the fire. Investigators can piece together the direction of fire and smoke travel based on patterns described by which initiating devices operated at which particular points in the fire development timeline. Sometimes the control unit at the protected premises has a memory that records system functions and operations in an accessible log. A technician can access this log by means of a laptop computer. Comparing the record from the control unit at the protected premises with the record of signals received at the central station can further clarify details regarding the fire development.

◀ **FAQ**
How are the reports of signals received commonly used?

An authority having jurisdiction may also want to receive a report from the central station in order to verify the frequency and duration of impairments to supervised fire extinguishing or fire suppression systems at a protected premises. In addition, an authority having jurisdiction may want to receive a report simply to verify various operational aspects of the central station service at a specific protected premises.

A central station must respond to the request for a report from an authority having jurisdiction. Failure to provide such a report in a timely fashion can result in an authority having jurisdiction withdrawing the approval of the service provided by the delinquent central station.

26.3.9 Testing and Maintenance. Testing and maintenance for central station service shall be performed in accordance with Chapter 14.

26.4 Proprietary Supervising Station Systems

26.4.1 Application. Supervising facilities of proprietary alarm systems shall comply with the operating procedures of Section 26.4. The facilities, equipment, personnel, operation, testing, and maintenance of the proprietary supervising station shall also comply with Section 26.4.

The management of a facility protected by a proprietary supervising station alarm system often uses that system to oversee the built-in fire extinguishing or fire suppression systems at that facility. The proprietary supervising station alarm system may also oversee certain facility emergency control (fire safety) functions. Used as a management tool, the proprietary alarm system can help ensure that these fire protection systems and functions remain in service.

26.4.2 General.

26.4.2.1 Proprietary supervising stations shall be operated by trained, competent personnel in constant attendance who are responsible to the owner of the protected property.

26.4.2.2 The protected property shall be either a contiguous property or noncontiguous properties under one ownership.

From a single proprietary supervising station, an owner can oversee the protection features at one or more properties. These properties might contiguously occupy a single piece of land or might occupy noncontiguous portions of land (see 3.3.191 for the definitions of *contiguous property* and *noncontiguous property*). The Code does not limit the geographic distance that might exist between noncontiguous properties. This permits an owner to oversee protection features at geographically diverse locations from a single proprietary supervising station.

26.4.2.3 If a protected premises control unit is integral to or co-located with the supervising station equipment, the requirements of Section 26.6 shall not apply.

Paragraph 26.4.2.3 recognizes that in some cases the proprietary alarm system may have a *master fire alarm control unit,* as defined in 3.3.92.1, co-located in the proprietary supervising station. (See Figure A.26.1.1.) Where this situation occurs, the transmission technology requirements described in Section 26.6 do not apply. Rather, the system would use initiating device circuits and signaling line circuits, as described in Chapter 23, to transmit signals to the master fire alarm control unit co-located in the proprietary supervising station. Section 26.4 provides the requirements for all other aspects of such a proprietary alarm system.

26.4.2.4* The systems of Section 26.4 shall be permitted to be interconnected to other systems intended to make the premises safer in the event of fire or other emergencies indicative of hazards to life or property.

A.26.4.2.4 The following functions are included in Annex A to provide guidelines for utilizing building systems and equipment in addition to proprietary fire alarm equipment in order to provide life safety and property protection.

Building functions that should be initiated or controlled during a fire alarm condition include, but should not be limited to, the following:

(1) Elevator operation consistent with ANSI/ASME A17.1a/CSA B44a, *Safety Code for Elevators and Escalators*

(2) Unlocking of stairwell and exit doors *(see* NFPA 80, *Standard for Fire Doors and Other Opening Protectives, and* NFPA *101, Life Safety Code)*

(3) Release of fire and smoke dampers *(see* NFPA 90A, *Standard for the Installation of Air-Conditioning and Ventilating Systems,* and NFPA 90B, *Standard for the Installation of Warm Air Heating and Air-Conditioning Systems)*

(4) Monitoring and initiating of self-contained automatic fire extinguishing system(s) or suppression system(s) and equipment *(see* NFPA 11, *Standard for Low-, Medium-, and High-Expansion Foam*; NFPA 12, *Standard on Carbon Dioxide Extinguishing Systems*; NFPA 12A, *Standard on Halon 1301 Fire Extinguishing Systems;* NFPA 13, *Standard for the Installation of Sprinkler Systems;* NFPA 14, *Standard for the Installation of Standpipe and Hose Systems;* NFPA 15, *Standard for Water Spray Fixed Systems for Fire Protection;* NFPA 17, *Standard for Dry Chemical Extinguishing Systems; and* NFPA 17A, *Standard for Wet Chemical Extinguishing Systems)*

(5) Lighting control necessary to provide essential illumination during alarm conditions *(see* NFPA 70, *National Electrical Code,* and NFPA *101, Life Safety Code)*

(6) Emergency shutoff of hazardous gas

(7) Control of building environmental heating, ventilating, and air-conditioning equipment to provide smoke control *(see* NFPA 90A, *Standard for the Installation of Air-Conditioning and Ventilating Systems)*

(8) Control of process, data processing, and similar equipment as necessary during alarm conditions

The permissive requirement of 26.4.2.4 allows a proprietary supervising station alarm system to provide building emergency control (fire safety) functions. This provision correlates with the permissive requirement in 21.2.1. For details on building emergency control (fire safety) functions, see Chapter 21.

26.4.3 Facilities.

26.4.3.1* The proprietary supervising station shall be located in either of the following:

(1) Fire-resistive, detached building

(2) A fire-resistive room protected from the hazardous parts of the building

A.26.4.3.1 Consideration should be given to providing the following features for a proprietary supervising station location:

(1) Fire resistive construction meeting the requirements of adopted building codes

The requirements of 26.4.3.1 help to maintain a high degree of physical integrity for the proprietary supervising station. The Code intends a "fire-resistive, detached building" to describe a building constructed of materials that meet the adopted building code's designation for "fire-resistive construction." This construction, in conjunction with sufficient detachment, should protect the building from any hazardous processes or hazardous areas of the facility. In some cases, locating the proprietary supervising station in a segregated area within a fire-resistive guard house at the entrance to the property would provide a location sufficiently detached from facility hazards. In selecting this location, the owner of the facility would have to provide protection against any damage that a runaway vehicle might cause. Surrounding

◄ **FAQ**
What does the Code intend by the description "fire-resistive, detached building" and "fire-resistive room"?

the guard house with strong concrete barriers in the direction of vehicle traffic would provide appropriate protection.

Similarly, the owner could house the proprietary supervision station in a "fire-resistive room" protected by the nature of its construction from any hazardous processes or hazardous areas of the facility.

In addition, A.26.4.3.1 recommends that the building or room housing the proprietary supervising station have a separate air handling system isolated from common building systems. This will help protect the proprietary supervising station from the incursion of smoke and heat during a fire in the other portions of the facility.

(2) Air handling systems isolated from common building systems

26.4.3.2 Access to the proprietary supervising station shall be restricted to those persons directly concerned with the implementation and direction of emergency action and procedure.

The proprietary supervising station must not become a congregating place for guards, emergency response team members, or other facility personnel. The presence of such persons could interfere with the operators and distract them from giving proper attention to signal traffic. If management locates the proprietary supervising station within a guard house where guards admit vehicles and personnel to the premises, management should provide some means of segregation to separate the operators of the proprietary supervising station from other incidental employees. Such segregation will help to ensure that operators can effectively and efficiently handle the signal traffic without distraction.

26.4.3.3 The proprietary supervising station, as well as remotely located power rooms for batteries or engine-driven generators, shall be provided with portable fire extinguishers that comply with the requirements of NFPA 10, *Standard for Portable Fire Extinguishers.*

Personnel in a proprietary supervising station must have the means to handle a small fire in the supervising station or in the power rooms for batteries or engine-driven generators. Management should refer to the requirements of NFPA 600, *Standard on Industrial Fire Brigades.* These requirements ensure that management properly organizes and trains personnel to safely use the fire extinguishers provided.

26.4.3.4 The emergency lighting system shall comply with the requirements of 26.4.3.4.1 through 26.4.3.4.3.

26.4.3.4.1 The proprietary supervising station shall be provided with an automatic emergency lighting system.

26.4.3.4.2 The emergency source shall be independent of the primary lighting source.

26.4.3.4.3 In the event of a loss of the primary lighting for the supervising station, the emergency lighting system shall provide illumination for a period of not less than 26 hours to permit the operators to carry on operations and shall be tested in accordance with the requirements of Chapter 14.

26.4.3.5 If 25 or more protected buildings or premises are connected to a subsidiary station, both of the following shall be provided at the subsidiary station:

(1) Automatic means for receiving and recording signals under emergency staffing conditions
(2) A telephone

A *subsidiary station* is defined in 3.3.265 as a normally unattended facility located remotely from the proprietary supervising station and linked to the proprietary supervising station by a communications channel. A proprietary supervising station may receive signals from many buildings on a very large premises or from several noncontiguous premises through one or more subsidiary stations. Where 25 or more protected buildings or protected premises transmit through a subsidiary station, management must equip that subsidiary station so that it can be staffed by operators in an emergency. For example, if the signaling path between the subsidiary station and the proprietary supervising station fails, operators will travel to the subsidiary station, staff it, and operate it independently of the proprietary supervising station. See Exhibit 26.7 for an illustration of a proprietary supervisory station that uses subsidiary stations.

26.4.4 Equipment and Personnel.

26.4.4.1 Signal-Receiving Equipment.

26.4.4.1.1 Signal-receiving equipment in a proprietary supervising station shall comply with 26.4.4.

26.4.4.1.2 Provision shall be made to designate the building in which a signal originates.

26.4.4.1.3 The floor, section, or other subdivision of the building in which a signal originates shall be designated at the proprietary supervising station or at the building that is protected.

Exception: Where the area, height, or special conditions of occupancy make detailed designation unessential as approved by the authority having jurisdiction.

To effectively manage the built-in fire protection features of the protected premises, the Code requires that the signals received by the proprietary supervising station contain sufficient detail to allow operators to quickly and accurately locate the source of the signals. Graphic annunciators, video displays, and addressable systems installed at the protected building will

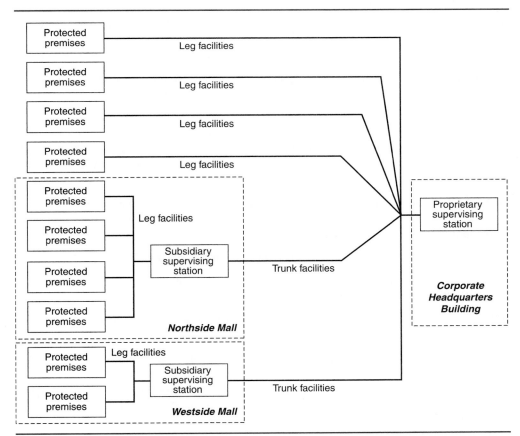

EXHIBIT 26.7 *Proprietary Supervising Station Facilities. Noncontiguous properties are under a single ownership with some properties connecting through subsidiary supervising stations. (Source: Dean K. Wilson, P.E., Erie, PA)*

meet this requirement. If the nature of the protected property eliminates the need for such detail, the authority having jurisdiction may waive the requirement.

26.4.4.1.4 Designation, as required by 26.4.4.1.2 and 26.4.4.1.3, shall use private-mode notification appliances approved by the authority having jurisdiction.

26.4.4.2 Signal-Alerting Equipment.

26.4.4.2.1 The proprietary supervising station shall have, in addition to a recording device, two different means for alerting the operator when each signal is received that indicates a change of state of any connected initiating device circuit.

Paragraph 26.4.4.2.1 requires two means of notifying the operators of the receipt of a signal. This requirement relates to the one in 26.4.4.6.4 that requires operators to have no other duties that would impair their ability to process signals from the proprietary supervising station alarm system. By implication, the Code, in 26.4.4.6.3, accepts that the operators in the supervising station may attend to other duties, as long as those duties do not interfere with the operation of the protective service. The two means of notification required by 26.4.4.2.1 help make certain the operators properly attend to the incoming signals.

26.4.4.2.1.1 One of these means shall be an audible signal, which shall persist until manually acknowledged.

26.4.4.2.1.2 Means shall include the receipt of alarm, supervisory, and trouble signals, including signals indicating restoration.

26.4.4.2.1.3 If means is provided in the proprietary supervising station to identify the type of signal received, a common audible indicating appliance shall be permitted to be used for alarm, supervisory, and trouble indication.

Section 10.7 and 26.6.4 require distinctive signals for alarm, supervisory, and trouble signals. Paragraph 26.4.4.2.1.3 correlates with 10.7.3 to permit a common audible notification appliance in the supervising station, as long as other means readily identify the type of signal.

26.4.4.2.1.4 At a proprietary supervising station, an audible trouble signal shall be permitted to be silenced, provided that the act of silencing does not prevent the signal from operating immediately upon receipt of a subsequent trouble signal.

26.4.4.2.2 All signals required to be received by the proprietary supervising station that show a change in status shall be automatically and permanently recorded, including time and date of occurrence, in a form that expedites operator interpretation in accordance with any one of the means detailed in 26.4.4.2.2.1 through 26.4.4.2.2.4.

26.4.4.2.2.1 If a visual display is used that automatically provides change of status information for each required signal, including type and location of occurrence, any form of automatic permanent visual record shall be permitted.

(A) The recorded information shall include the content described in 26.4.4.2.2.

(B) The visual display shall show status information content at all times and be distinctly different after the operator has manually acknowledged each signal.

(C) Acknowledgment shall produce recorded information indicating the time and date of acknowledgment.

Paragraph 26.4.4.2.2.1 describes an annunciator that continuously shows the status of every point in the system that generates a signal. At a glance, the operator can literally see the status of every point. With this type of visual display, the proprietary supervising station system may use any type of permanent visual record. Such systems most often use a logging-type printer, which keeps a running list of signals received as a back-up to the visual display. The printed information will not necessarily have a format that would allow an operator to easily locate information, but it does provide a running summary of signals as they occur with respect to the date and time each signal was received.

26.4.4.2.2.2 If a visual display is not provided, required signal content information shall be automatically recorded on duplicate, permanent visual recording instruments.

When the proprietary supervising station system does not provide a visual display, such a system must use two printers. Where a proprietary supervising station receives signals from systems other than an alarm system, these printers will assist the operators in giving priority to signals from the alarm system. One printer will record all signals that the system receives. The other printer will record only alarm, supervisory, and trouble signals. Both printers must format the output to allow the operator to easily read, interpret, and act upon the information provided.

◄ **FAQ**
What is required when a visual display is not provided?

26.4.4.2.2.3 One recording instrument shall be used for recording all incoming signals, while the other shall be used for required alarm, supervisory, and trouble signals only.

(A) Failure to acknowledge a signal shall not prevent subsequent signals from recording.

(B) Restoration of the signal to its prior condition shall be recorded.

26.4.4.2.2.4 In the event that a system combines the use of a sequential visual display and recorded permanent visual presentation, the required signal content information shall be displayed and recorded.

(A) The visual information component shall be retained either on the display until manually acknowledged or repeated at intervals not greater than 5 seconds, for durations of 2 seconds each, until manually acknowledged.

(B) Each new displayed status change shall be accompanied by an audible indication that persists until manual acknowledgment of the signal is performed.

26.4.4.3* Redisplay of Status. A means shall be provided for the operator to redisplay the status of required signal-initiating inputs that have been acknowledged but not yet restored.

A.26.4.4.3 Proprietary station procedures should include periodic review of nonrestored signals. One method for such a review could be by the use of equipment that would automatically redisplay the information.

The requirements in 26.4.4.3 apply to a visual display unit that presents one or more lines of information at a time but does not simultaneously display the status of all points covered by the proprietary supervising station system. The operator must scroll through the display after having acknowledged each signal. To help the operator give proper precedence to alarm signals, either the signals must appear on a separate display or the system must give them priority status on a common display. The system must still provide a permanent visual record, but the Code does not specify the type of printer. Such a system most often uses a logging-type printer, as described in the commentary following 26.4.4.2.2.1(C).

When operators use a system that visually displays a limited number of signals at one time, they must not forget about signals that await restoration. In the flurry of activity surrounding subsequent incoming signals, an operator could easily lose track of previously received signals that indicated an off-normal status change. Such signals must restore to normal in order to indicate that the off-normal condition has been resolved. As suggested in A.26.4.4.3, an operational procedure can prompt operators to periodically scroll through the list of signals, or the system itself can cause the redisplay of nonrestored signals.

26.4.4.3.1 If the system retains the signal on the visual display until manually acknowledged, subsequent recorded presentations shall not be inhibited upon failure to acknowledge.

26.4.4.3.2 Alarm signals shall be segregated on a separate visual display in this configuration.

Exception: Alarm signals shall not be required to be segregated on a separate display if given priority status on the common visual display.

26.4.4.4 Display Rate. To facilitate the prompt receipt of alarm signals from systems handling other types of signals that are able to produce multiple simultaneous status changes, the requirements of either of the following shall be met:

(1) The system shall record simultaneous status changes at a rate not slower than either a quantity of 50 or 10 percent of the total number of initiating device circuits connected, within 90 seconds, whichever number is smaller, without loss of any signal.

(2) The system shall either display or record alarm signals at a rate not slower than one every 10 seconds, regardless of the rate or number of status changes occurring, without loss of any signals.

The requirements of 26.4.4.4 help to ensure the prompt receipt of alarm signals when a proprietary supervising station system receives other types of signals and uses technology that permits the processing and display of multiple status changes at the same time. Paragraph 26.4.4.4 substitutes for and takes precedence over the general requirements for all communications methods contained in 26.6.3.1.9. Paragraph 26.4.4.4 applies similar requirements to other transmission technologies where a proprietary supervising station alarm system uses those technologies.

26.4.4.5 Trouble Signals. Trouble signals and their restoration shall be automatically indicated and recorded at the proprietary supervising station.

The requirements of 10.12.1 and 10.12.7 also directly relate to the requirement in 26.4.4.5. The proprietary supervising station alarm system must indicate trouble signals and their restoration to normal both visibly and audibly at the proprietary supervising station within 200 seconds.

26.4.4.5.1 The recorded information for the occurrence of any trouble condition of signaling line circuit, leg facility, or trunk facility that prevents receipt of alarm signals at the proprietary supervising station shall be such that the operator is able to determine the presence of the trouble condition.

26.4.4.5.2 Trouble conditions in a leg facility shall not affect or delay receipt of signals at the proprietary supervising station from other leg facilities on the same trunk facility.

The requirement of 26.4.4.5.2 in effect mandates that the transmission technology preserve the signals from other leg facilities when one leg facility experiences trouble. Management of a facility proposing to install a proprietary supervising station alarm system would have to analyze each proposed transmission technology to determine if it could meet the requirements of 26.4.4.5.2. For example, in the past if management had chosen to use an active multiplex transmission technology — now considered a "legacy" technology — compliance with the requirement of 26.4.4.5.2 would have dictated that the system meet the requirements for what was then called a Type 1 or Type 2 active multiplex system. Both of these technologies used a "closed window bridge" that effectively isolated each leg facility on a trunk from each other. A Type 3 active multiplex system could not have met this requirement because it used an "open window bridge," in which all the leg facilities on a trunk were subject to potential failure from a fault on a single leg.

26.4.4.6 Personnel.

26.4.4.6.1 The proprietary supervising station shall have at least two qualified operators on duty at all times. One of the two operators shall be permitted to be a runner.

Exception: If the means for transmitting alarms to the fire department is automatic, at least one operator shall be on duty at all times.

The allowance provided by the exception to 26.4.4.6.1 does not relieve other requirements of the Code, such as those of 26.4.5.6 concerning the dispatch of personnel to the premises.

26.4.4.6.2 When the runner is not in attendance at the proprietary supervising station, the runner shall establish two-way communications with the station at intervals not exceeding 15 minutes.

Exception: Where two or more operators are on duty in the supervising station, a runner physically in attendance at a noncontiguous protected premises and immediately available via telephone or other approved means of communication shall not be required to maintain two-way communications at 15-minute intervals if that runner is not responsible for another protected premises.

The exception to 26.4.4.6.2 recognizes that management of a facility may have stationed a trained runner at a noncontiguous protected premises. For example, management may have stationed a runner at the reception desk at another facility it owns where that facility is not located on the same physical property as the one implied in 26.4.4.6.2. Where the runner has principal responsibility only for the noncontiguous premises to which he or she is assigned and remains immediately available by some reliable means of communications, the requirement to establish two-way communications at 15-minute intervals serves no real purpose. In addition, where a facility consists of multiple noncontiguous properties, the frequent communications between each stationed runner and the operators at the proprietary supervising station could hinder either the runner or the operators from performing more important duties.

26.4.4.6.3 The primary duties of the operator(s) shall be to monitor signals, operate the system, and take such action as shall be required by the authority having jurisdiction.

26.4.4.6.4 The operator(s) shall not be assigned any additional duties that would take precedence over the primary duties.

Although the operators are not prohibited from performing other duties, as noted in 26.4.4.6.4, the Code expects the operators to have no duties that would distract them from the prompt, effective handling of signals.

◄ **FAQ**
Does 26.4.4.6.4 prohibit operators from performing other duties?

26.4.5 Operations.

26.4.5.1 Communications and Transmission Channels.

26.4.5.1.1 All communications and transmission channels between the proprietary supervising station and the protected premises control unit shall be operated manually or automatically once every 24 hours to verify operation.

26.4.5.1.2 If a communications or transmission channel fails to operate, the operator shall immediately notify the person(s) identified by the owner or authority having jurisdiction.

26.4.5.2 Operator Controls.

26.4.5.2.1 All operator controls at the proprietary supervising station(s) designated by the authority having jurisdiction shall be operated at each change of shift.

26.4.5.2.2 If operator controls fail, the operator shall immediately notify the person(s) identified by the owner or authority having jurisdiction.

The requirements of 26.4.5.1 through 26.4.5.2.2 help to ensure the proper and continued operational readiness of the proprietary supervising station.

26.4.5.3 Retransmission. Indication of a fire shall be promptly retransmitted to the communications center or other locations accepted by the authority having jurisdiction, indicating the building or group of buildings from which the alarm has been received.

26.4.5.4* Retransmission Means. The means of retransmission shall be accepted by the authority having jurisdiction and shall be in accordance with 26.3.6.1.6, 26.5.4.4, or Chapter 27.

Exception: Secondary power supply capacity shall be as required in Chapter 10.

A.26.4.5.4 It is the intent of this Code that the operator within the proprietary supervising station should have a secure means of immediately retransmitting any signal indicative of a fire to the public fire department communications center. Automatic retransmission using an approved method installed in accordance with Sections 26.3 through 26.5, and Chapter 27 is the best method for proper retransmission. However, a manual means can be permitted to be used, consisting of either a manual connection following the requirements of Section 26.3, Section 26.5, and Chapter 27, or, for proprietary supervising stations serving only contiguous properties, a means in the form of a municipal fire alarm box installed within 50 ft (15 m) of the proprietary supervising station in accordance with Chapter 27 can be permitted.

26.4.5.5* Coded Retransmission. Retransmission by coded signals shall be confirmed by two-way voice communications indicating the nature of the alarm.

A.26.4.5.5 Regardless of the type of retransmission facility used, telephone communications between the proprietary supervising station and the fire department should be available at all times and should not depend on a switchboard operator.

Paragraph 26.4.5.4 requires that the proprietary supervising station retransmit signals to the communications center by means of one of the following:

1. An automatic or manual connection using a connection to a central station alarm system
2. An automatic or manual connection using a connection to a remote supervising station alarm system
3. A manual or automatic connection to a public emergency alarm reporting system

In the third case, the retransmission from a proprietary supervising station system serving a contiguous property could consist of the operator manually actuating a municipal alarm box. The retransmission could also consist of an auxiliary alarm system that meets the requirements of 27.6.3.2.

Paragraph 26.4.5.5 requires two-way voice confirmation of a coded retransmission signal. This confirmation would most likely occur when an operator at the supervising station contacts the communications center by telephone.

Paragraph 26.4.5.4 does not contain a specific provision that would allow an operator at the proprietary supervising station to use a telephone as the sole means to report an alarm signal to the communications center. However, 26.4.5.5 requires the availability of a telephone. It seems reasonable that if an authority having jurisdiction is willing to permit the use of a telephone call as the sole means of retransmission, the authority having jurisdiction could make an exception to the explicit requirements of 26.4.5.4.

Management should provide the proprietary supervising station with a connection to the public switched telephone network that does not require the operator of a private branch exchange (PBX) switchboard to manually intervene to obtain access to the network. In fact, management should provide a direct connection to the network that completely bypasses any PBX, whether that PBX uses manual or automatic switching. This direct connection to the public switched telephone network will allow operators in the proprietary supervising station to make a telephone call, even if the PBX fails.

26.4.5.6 Dispositions of Signals.

26.4.5.6.1 Alarms. Upon receipt of an alarm signal, the proprietary supervising station operator shall initiate action to perform the following:

(1) Immediately notify the fire department, the emergency response team, and such other parties as the authority having jurisdiction requires

(2) Dispatch a runner or technician to the alarm location to arrive within 2 hours after receipt of a signal

(3) Restore the system as soon as possible after disposition of the cause of the alarm signal

26.4.5.6.2 Guard's Tour Supervisory Signal. If a guard's tour supervisory signal is not received from a guard within a 15-minute maximum grace period, or if a guard fails to follow a prescribed route in transmitting the signals (where a prescribed route has been established), the proprietary supervising station operator shall initiate action to perform the following:

(1) Communicate at once with the protected areas or premises by telephone, radio, calling back over the system circuit, or other means accepted by the authority having jurisdiction

(2) Dispatch a runner to arrive within 30 minutes to investigate the delinquency if communications with the guard cannot be promptly established

26.4.5.6.3 Supervisory Signals. Upon receipt of sprinkler system and other supervisory signals, the proprietary supervising station operator shall initiate action to perform the following, if required:

(1) Communicate immediately with the designated person(s) to ascertain the reason for the signal

(2) Dispatch personnel to arrive within 2 hours to investigate, unless supervisory conditions are promptly restored

(3) Notify the fire department if required by the authority having jurisdiction

(4) Notify the authority having jurisdiction when sprinkler systems are wholly or partially out of service for 8 hours or more

(5) Provide written notice to the authority having jurisdiction as to the nature of the signal, time of occurrence, and restoration of service when equipment has been out of service for 8 hours or more

26.4.5.6.4 Trouble Signals. Upon receipt of trouble signals or other signals pertaining solely to matters of equipment maintenance of the alarm system, the proprietary supervising station operator shall initiate action to perform the following, if required:

(1) Communicate immediately with the designated person(s) to ascertain reason for the signal

(2) Dispatch personnel to arrive within 4 hours to initiate maintenance, if necessary

(3) Notify the fire department if required by the authority having jurisdiction

(4) Notify the authority having jurisdiction when interruption of service exists for 4 hours or more

(5) When equipment has been out of service for 8 hours or more, provide written notice to the authority having jurisdiction as to the nature of the signal, time of occurrence, and restoration of service

The requirements in 26.4.5.6.1 through 26.4.5.6.4 almost match those in 26.3.7 for central station alarm systems with the following notable differences:

◄ FAQ
What are the notable differences in the requirements for the disposition of signals between a central station and a proprietary station?

1. The term *immediately* has no specific definition.

2. Upon receipt of an alarm signal, the proprietary supervising station must always dispatch a runner.

3. If required by the authority having jurisdiction, the proprietary supervising station must notify the fire department upon receipt of a supervisory signal or a trouble signal. This notification will alert the fire department to impaired protection.

4. The proprietary supervising station must notify the authority having jurisdiction if an interruption to service producing a trouble signal persists for 4 hours.

26.4.6 Record Keeping and Reporting.

26.4.6.1 Complete records of all signals received shall be retained for at least 1 year.

26.4.6.2 Testing and maintenance records shall be retained as required by 14.6.3.

26.4.6.3 The proprietary supervising station shall make arrangements to furnish reports of signals received to the authority having jurisdiction in a form the authority will accept.

Whenever an authority having jurisdiction requests reports from a proprietary supervising station, the supervising station must provide the reports in a useful and usable form. Paragraph 26.4.6.3 gives the authority having jurisdiction a requirement in the Code to cite should a property owner refuse to disclose information regarding signals received at the proprietary supervising station.

26.4.7 Testing and Maintenance. Testing and maintenance of proprietary alarm systems shall be performed in accordance with Chapter 14.

26.5 Remote Supervising Station Alarm Systems

26.5.1 Application and General.

26.5.1.1 Section 26.5 shall apply where central station service is neither required nor elected.

An authority having jurisdiction may require a remote supervising station alarm system where the desired level of protection does not warrant the level of protection offered by a central station alarm system. Similarly, the management of a facility may choose to provide a remote supervising station alarm system when management does not believe it needs the level of protection offered by a central station alarm system or a proprietary supervising station alarm system.

When the requirements for a remote supervising station alarm system first appeared in the Code in 1961, they provided a means of transmitting alarm, supervisory, and trouble signals from a somewhat remotely located protected premises to the nearest communications center. In most of those cases, the municipality did not have a public emergency alarm reporting system. And, due to the limitations of the transmission technologies employed at that time, no vendor could provide central station service to such a remotely located facility.

Sometimes the municipality did not even have a constantly attended communications center. Rather, officials relied on a multiple-location emergency telephone system. When an individual placed a telephone call to the seven-digit emergency reporting number, telephones in several locations throughout the community rang. These locations included local businesses, as well as the homes of the fire chief and other fire officers. A switch at each telephone could actuate sirens throughout the community or transmit signals to radio receivers or pagers that would summon volunteer fire fighters. (Even today, some less built-up areas use this method to handle public reports of an emergency.)

In such communities, officials had to find an alternative location to receive signals from remote supervising station alarm systems. Often, officials chose a local 24-hour telephone answering service — normally used by doctors, dentists, and people from other trades — to receive the remote supervising station alarm signals. In some cases, the officials chose a gasoline service station or local restaurant that remained open around the clock to receive the signals.

In more recent times, some alarm system installers who chose not to provide listed central station service set up monitoring centers to receive remote supervising station alarm signals. In turn, some listed central station operating companies began to provide equipment in their central stations that would meet the requirements for remote supervising station alarm systems in order to legitimately receive such signals. Some municipalities have partnered to create regional emergency communications centers to dispatch fire, police, and emergency medical services. These centers may have equipment to receive signals from remote supervising station alarm systems.

26.5.1.2 The installation, maintenance, testing, and use of a remote supervising station alarm system that serves properties under various ownership from a remote supervising station shall comply with the requirements of Section 26.5.

Some authorities having jurisdiction have interpreted 26.5.1.2 to mean that the requirements of Section 26.5 apply only to those cases where a remote supervising station system serves properties under various ownerships. In so doing, those authorities having jurisdiction have refused to accept the use of hardware and software listed for use in providing a remote station supervising station system at a single facility under one ownership. Instead, those authorities having jurisdiction have required the facility to use hardware and software listed for a proprietary supervising station system.

The intent of 26.5.1.2, however, does not specifically forbid the application of the requirements in Section 26.5 to a remote station supervising station alarm system serving single or multiple facilities under one ownership. At the same time, the requirements in 26.5.1.4 make it clear that alarm, supervisory, and trouble signals must transmit to a location remote from the protected premises.

In analyzing whether a particular type of supervising station system will appropriately serve a facility, the authorities having jurisdiction should carefully examine the protection goals of the owner, as well as the protection goals for the jurisdictions they represent. Obviously, an authority having jurisdiction should not encourage an owner to choose one particular supervising station system simply to avoid having to meet the more stringent requirements of another, more appropriate system.

Exhibit 26.8 illustrates a communications center equipped to receive signals as a remote supervising station in accordance with 26.5.3.1.1.

EXHIBIT 26.8 *A Public Emergency Services Communications Center Equipped to Receive Signals as a Remote Station Supervising Station. (Source: James A. Spear, P.E., LeRoy, NY)*

26.5.1.3 Remote supervising station physical facilities, equipment, operating personnel, response, retransmission, signals, reports, and testing shall comply with the minimum requirements of Section 26.5.

26.5.1.4 Remote supervising station alarm systems shall provide an automatic audible and visible indication of alarm, supervisory, and trouble conditions at a location remote from the protected premises.

Without the requirement of 26.5.1.4, trouble conditions involving the primary power supply for the alarm system at a protected premises that connects to a remote supervising station might go unrecognized for periods that could extend beyond the 24-hour capacity of the secondary power supply at the protected premises.

26.5.1.5 Section 26.5 shall not require the use of audible or visible notification appliances other than those required at the remote supervising station. If it is desired to provide alarm evacuation signals in the protected premises, the alarm signals, circuits, and controls shall comply with the provisions of Chapters 18 and 23 in addition to the provisions of Section 26.5.

Paragraph 26.5.1.5 emphasizes that Chapter 26 does not address specific requirements for evacuation notification at the protected premises. Chapters 18 and 23 address these requirements.

When property protection, mission continuity, heritage preservation, or environmental protection has been chosen as the predominant protection goal for a facility, the owner of the protected premises might purchase an alarm system that does not itself provide evacuation notification to the occupants. In such a case, the owner likely will rely on some other system to notify the occupants of the need to evacuate the premises. Historically, many such systems are connected to various remote station supervising stations in order to summon emergency responders at the time of an emergency. On occasion, some authorities having jurisdiction would insist that the Code required audible and visible notification appliances at the protected premises for such systems. Paragraph 26.5.1.5 clarifies that this portion of the Code does not mandate notification appliances at a protected premises. Refer to Section 23.3 for the requirement to document the features required for a protected premises fire alarm system.

26.5.1.6 The loading capacities of the remote supervising station equipment for any approved method of transmission shall be as designated in Section 26.6.

Remote station fire alarm systems have the full range of transmission technologies available. However, those technologies must meet the requirements of Section 26.6.

26.5.2 Indication of Remote Station Service. Owners utilizing remote station alarm systems shall provide annual documentation to the authority having jurisdiction identifying the party responsible for the inspection, testing, and maintenance requirements of Chapter 14. This documentation shall take one of the following forms:

(1)* An affidavit attesting to the responsibilities and qualifications of the parties performing the inspection, testing, and maintenance and accepting responsibility of compliance with Chapter 14. This document shall be signed by a representative of the service provider.
(2) Documentation indicating code compliance of the remote station alarm system issued by the organization that listed the service provider.
(3) Other documentation acceptable to the authority having jurisdiction.

New in the 2010 edition, the requirements in 26.5.2 help ensure the integrity of the remote supervising station system throughout its life cycle. Every year, the owner of the protected premises must provide written documentation to the authorities having jurisdiction that identifies the person or organization responsible for the inspection, testing, and maintenance of the remote supervising station system. The requirements in this subsection offer three alternatives: (1) an affidavit attesting to the competency of the person or organization performing the services and signed by a representative of the service provider; (2) a document from the testing laboratory that has listed the service provider; or (3) some other form of documentation acceptable to the authorities having jurisdiction.

The second option permissively supports the listing of protective signaling service companies by the testing laboratories. Such listing includes specific follow-up procedures by the laboratories similar to those described in 26.3.4 for central station service.

A.26.5.2(1) Chapter 14 permits the building owner or his designated representative to perform these services if they are qualified. In this situation, the documentation could be a declaration of qualification signed by the building owner. Multiple service providers are permitted.

26.5.3* Facilities.

A.26.5.3 As a minimum, the room or rooms containing the remote supervising station equipment should have a 1-hour fire rating, and the entire structure should be protected by an alarm system complying with Chapter 23.

26.5.3.1 Alarm systems utilizing remote supervising station connections shall transmit alarm and supervisory signals to a facility meeting the requirements of either 26.5.3.1.1, 26.5.3.1.2 or 26.5.3.1.3.

Some authorities having jurisdiction have interpreted 26.5.3.1 as requiring that both alarm and supervisory signals must transmit to a *single* facility that meets the requirements of 26.5.3.1.1, 26.5.3.1.2, or 26.5.3.1.3. Whether the technical committee intended the phrase "a facility" to mean "a single facility" remains unclear. Paragraph 26.5.1.4 requires the transmission of alarm, supervisory, and trouble signals to a location remote from the protected premises. In addition, 26.5.3.2 seems to imply that alarm and supervisory signals normally transmit to the same location.

The argument could be made that having all the signals transmit to the same remote supervising station gives the operators a better understanding of what may be occurring at a facility. However, some remote supervising stations may refuse to accept supervisory or trouble signals from a particular protected premises. In such a case, the facility should seek approval from the authority having jurisdiction to transmit those signals to another suitable remote supervising station.

Paragraphs 26.5.3.1.1, 26.5.3.1.2, and 26.5.3.1.3 offer three general categories of suitable locations for the remote supervising station.

26.5.3.1.1 Alarm, supervisory, and trouble signals shall be permitted to be received at a communications center that complies with the requirements of NFPA 1221, *Standard for the Installation, Maintenance, and Use of Emergency Services Communications Systems.*

26.5.3.1.2 Alarm, supervisory, and trouble signals shall be permitted to be received at the fire station or at the governmental agency that has public responsibility for taking prescribed action to ensure response upon receipt of a alarm signal.

26.5.3.1.3* Where permitted by the authority having jurisdiction, alarm, supervisory, and trouble signals shall be permitted to be received at an alternate location approved by the authority having jurisdiction.

A.26.5.3.1.3 A listed central station might be considered an acceptable alternate location for receipt of fire alarm, supervisory, and trouble signals.

The authority having jurisdiction may accept any suitable location as the remote supervising station. For example, an authority having jurisdiction could permit a listed central station to receive these signals. Accepting the use of a listed central station to receive such signals would constitute "remote supervising station service," but not "central station service." In such a case, the equipment at the protected premises and at the central station must meet the requirements for remote supervising station alarm systems. According to the requirements of 10.3.1, the equipment must be specifically listed for use as part of a remote supervising station alarm system.

◄ FAQ
Can a listed central station also provide remote supervising station service?

26.5.3.2* Trouble signals shall be permitted to be received at an approved location that has personnel on duty who are trained to recognize the type of signal received and to take prescribed action. The location shall be permitted to be other than that at which alarm and supervisory signals are received.

A.26.5.3.2 A listed central station might be considered an acceptable alternate location for receipt of trouble signals.

Paragraph 26.5.1.4 requires the transmission of trouble signals to a constantly attended location. This location may be the same location that receives alarm and supervisory signals, or it may be a separate location. This paragraph tends to support the claim by some authorities having jurisdiction that alarm and supervisory signals must transmit to the same location. See the commentary following 26.5.3.1.

26.5.3.3 If locations other than the communications center are used for the receipt of signals, access to receiving equipment shall be restricted in accordance with the requirements of the authority having jurisdiction.

NFPA 1221, *Standard for the Installation, Maintenance, and Use of Emergency Services Communications Systems,* covers the requirements for access to and security of the communications center. Refer to the definition of *communications center* in 3.3.49. The requirement of 26.5.3.3 helps to ensure the security and operational integrity of the remote supervising station receiving equipment installed at locations other than the public communications center.

26.5.4 Equipment and Personnel.

26.5.4.1 Signal-receiving equipment shall indicate receipt of each signal both audibly and visibly.

26.5.4.1.1 Audible signals shall meet the requirements of Chapter 18 for the private operating mode.

The requirements for private mode audible signaling are in 18.4.4.

26.5.4.1.2 Means for silencing alarm, supervisory, and trouble signals shall be provided and shall be arranged so that subsequent signals shall re-sound.

Silencing one signal must not prevent a subsequent signal from causing the audible notification appliance to sound. This reinforces the requirements contained in Section 10.10, 10.11.5, and 10.12.8.

26.5.4.1.3 A trouble signal shall be received when the system or any portion of the system at the protected premises is placed in a bypass or test mode.

The requirement in 26.5.4.1.3 prevents the use of any type of a so-called "silent disconnect switch" at the protected premises. A facility might use such a switch to prevent the transmission of signals to the remote supervising station during maintenance on the alarm system or on a fire protection system connected to the alarm system. However, operation of any disconnect switch must produce a trouble signal at the remote supervising station.

26.5.4.1.4 An audible and visible indication shall be provided upon restoration of the system after receipt of any signal.

The Code does not permit the indication of the remote supervising station system restoration to normal by the mere extinguishing of a lamp. The audible notification appliance at the remote supervising station must also sound. The extinguishing of a lamp or other visible indicator, such as a light-emitting diode (LED), could still give the visible indication.

Some larger remote supervising station systems make provision for the operators to manually mark the illuminated visible indicators, usually with a circular plastic "donut." When the audible appliance signals a change in status, the operator can look at all the marked visible indicators and quickly determine which one has been extinguished, thus indicating a restoration to normal.

Note that the requirements of 26.6.4.3(2) still apply and require each change of state to be recorded. Refer also to 26.5.6.3 and the associated commentary.

26.5.4.1.5 If visible means are provided in the remote supervising station to identify the type of signal received, a common audible notification appliance shall be permitted to be used.

26.5.4.2 Power supplies shall comply with the requirements of Chapter 10.

A major change took place in the 2002 edition of the Code that included a revision to the duration of the secondary power. In previous editions, remote supervising station fire alarm systems had to have 60 hours of secondary power. Paragraphs 10.5.1, 10.5.6.2, and 10.5.6.3.1(3) specify 24 hours of secondary power under quiescent load (nonalarm condition).

26.5.4.3 Transmission means shall comply with the requirements of Section 26.6.

Remote supervising station fire alarm systems have the full range of transmission technologies given in Section 26.6, as long as they also meet any special requirements of Section 26.5.

26.5.4.4 Retransmission of an alarm signal, if required, shall be by one of the following methods, which appear in descending order of preference as follows:

(1) A dedicated circuit that is independent of any switched telephone network. This circuit shall be permitted to be used for voice or data communications.
(2) A one-way (outgoing only) telephone at the remote supervising station that utilizes the public switched telephone network. This telephone shall be used primarily for voice transmission of alarms to a telephone at the communications center that cannot be used for outgoing calls.
(3) A private radio system using the fire department frequency, where permitted by the fire department.
(4) Other methods accepted by the authority having jurisdiction.

The requirements of 26.5.4.4 must correlate with the requirements of 26.5.5.1. If the remote supervising station alarm system signals transmit from the protected premises to the communications center and that center serves as the remote supervising station, then obviously retransmission of the alarm signals will not be necessary. Retransmission of alarm signals will become necessary only when a location other than the communications center serves as the remote supervising station.

◄ FAQ
When is retransmission of an alarm signal not required?

When retransmission becomes necessary, the vast majority of remote supervising stations will use a retransmission method that complies with the requirements of 26.5.4.4(2). Special programming at the public telephone utility switch will block incoming telephone calls to the number assigned to the retransmission telephone. This arrangement allows operators at the remote supervising station to make outgoing calls on this telephone line (number), but not to receive incoming calls. This prevents the line (number) from being tied up by incoming calls.

26.5.4.5 Personnel staffing and duties shall comply with 26.5.4.5.1 and 26.5.4.5.2.

26.5.4.5.1 The remote supervising station shall have not less than two qualified operators on duty at the remote supervising station at all times to ensure disposition of signals in accordance with the requirements of 26.5.5.

26.5.4.5.2 Duties pertaining to other than operation of the remote supervising station receiving and transmitting equipment shall be permitted, subject to the approval of the authority having jurisdiction.

The authority having jurisdiction may permit operators at the remote supervising station to perform duties not related to the operation of the system. However, the Code limits the extent to which those other duties may interfere with the proper handling of signals.

26.5.5 Operations.

26.5.5.1 If the remote supervising station is at a location other than the communications center, alarm signals shall be immediately retransmitted to the communications center.

26.5.5.2 Upon receipt of an alarm, a supervisory, or a trouble signal by the remote supervising station other than the communications center, the operator on duty shall be responsible for notifying the owner or the owner's designated representative immediately.

The Code limits the requirements of 26.5.5.2 to those cases where the signals transmit to a location other than the communications center. However, an owner can make arrangements with the communications center to notify a list of designated representatives when the communications center receives supervisory and trouble signals from a protected premises. Such notification will facilitate proper action by the owner to resolve the source of such signals.

When a remote supervising station other than the communications center receives a signal, the Code requires the operator to promptly contact designated representatives to help ensure that the owner of the protected premises will take appropriate action as soon as possible.

26.5.5.3 All operator controls at the remote supervising station shall be operated at the beginning of each shift or change in personnel, and the status of all alarm, supervisory, and trouble signals shall be noted and recorded.

The requirements of 26.5.5.3 provide for the operational continuity of the remote supervising station. By exercising operating controls at shift change or when the on-duty personnel changes, operators can more quickly identify potential failures of equipment and initiate action to summon a technician to make necessary repairs.

This paragraph also requires operators to note and record the status of alarm, supervisory, and trouble signals. The record helps ensure continuity of handling of those signals, which is particularly important when a signal that indicates a supervisory off-normal condition or a trouble condition persists across a change in personnel. Operators going off-shift can brief incoming operators as to what action has been taken and what responding actions they anticipate as a result of the action taken.

26.5.6 Record Keeping and Reporting.

26.5.6.1 A permanent record of the time, date, and location of all signals and restorations received and the action taken shall be maintained for at least 1 year and shall be able to be provided to the authority having jurisdiction.

26.5.6.2 Testing and maintenance records shall be retained as required in 14.6.3.

26.5.6.3 Records shall be permitted to be created by manual means.

Unlike central station and proprietary alarm systems that keep records automatically, the Code does not require remote supervising station alarm systems to provide an automatic permanent visible record of signals received. Most often, as permitted by 26.5.6.3, operators in the remote supervising station maintain a manual log book that contains the required records. In some cases, operators maintain the log book by making manual data entries into a computer database. Paragraph 26.5.6.3 effectively serves as an exception to the requirements contained in 26.6.4.3(2).

26.5.7 Inspection, Testing, and Maintenance.

26.5.7.1 Inspection, testing, and maintenance for remote supervising stations shall be performed in accordance with Chapter 14.

26.6 Communications Methods for Supervising Station Alarm Systems

Exhibit 26.9 illustrates the communications methods addressed by the Code. The first communications method shown is a digital alarm communicator system (DACS), addressed in

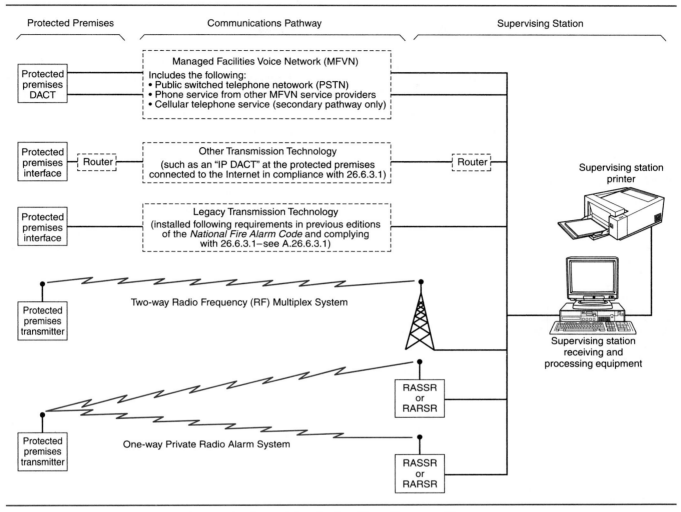

EXHIBIT 26.9 *Communications Methods for Supervising Station Alarm Systems. (Source: Dean K. Wilson, P.E., Erie, PA)*

26.6.3.2, which uses a DACT at the protected premises. The second method shown depicts a more general category of current communications methods, addressed in 26.6.3.1, which uses "other technology" such as an "IP DACT" at the protected premises. The third method shown depicts the category known as legacy transmission technologies, which are no longer being installed, addressed conceptually in 26.6.3.1 and in specific sections of previous editions of the Code that have been deleted in the 2010 edition. The last two communications methods depict two types of radio systems, addressed in 26.6.3.3, that use radio transmitters at the protected premises. All these communications methods are addressed in more detail in subsequent commentary.

26.6.1* Application. The methods of communications between the protected premises and the supervising station shall comply with the requirements in Section 26.6. These requirements shall include the following:

(1) The transmitter located at the protected premises
(2) The transmission channel between the protected premises and the supervising station or subsidiary station

(3) If used, any subsidiary station and its communications channel

(4) The signal receiving, processing, display, and recording equipment at the supervising station

Exception: Transmission channels owned by, and under the control of, the protected premises owner that are not facilities leased from a supplier of communications service capabilities, such as video cable, telephone, or other communications services that are also offered to other customers.

A.26.6.1 Refer to Table A.26.6.1 for communications methods.

TABLE A.26.6.1 *Communications Methods for Supervising Stations*

Criteria	*General 26.6.3.1*	*Digital Alarm Communicator Systems 26.6.3.2*	*Two-Way Radio Frequency (RF) Multiplex Systems 26.6.3.3.1*	*One-Way Private Radio Alarm Systems 26.6.3.3.2*
FCC approval when applicable	Yes	Yes	Yes	Yes
Conform to *NFPA 70, National Electrical Code*	Yes	Yes	Yes	Yes
Monitoring for integrity of the transmission and communications channel	Monitor for integrity or provide backup channel tested as below	Both the premises unit and the system unit monitor for integrity in a manner approved for the means of transmission employed. A single signal received on each incoming DACR line once every 24 hours.	Systems are periodically polled for end-to-end communications integrity.	Test signal from every transmitter once every 24 hours
Annunciate, at the supervising station, the degradation and restoration of the transmission or communications channel	Within 5 minutes (can use a second separate path to report failure)	Within 4 minutes using alternate phone line to report the trouble	Not exceed 90 seconds from the time of the actual failure	Only monitor the quality of signal received and indicate if the signal falls below minimum signal quality specified in Code
Redundant communication path where a portion of the transmission or communications channel cannot be monitored for integrity	Provide a redundant path if communication failure not annunciated at supervising station	Employ a combination of two separate transmission channels alternately tested at intervals not exceeding 24 hours.	Redundant path not required — supervising station always indicates a communications failure	Minimum of two independent RF paths must be simultaneously employed
Interval testing of the backup path(s)	If backup path required, test path once every 24 hours on alternating channels, testing each channel every 48 hours	When two phone lines are used, test alternately every 24 hours. Testing for other back-up technologies, see 26.6.3.2.1.4(B).	Backup path not required	No requirement, because the quality of the signal is continuously monitored
Annunciation of communication failure or ability to communicate at the protected premises	Systems where the transmitter at the local premises unit detects a communication failure before the supervising station, the premises unit will annunciate the failure within 5 minutes of detecting the failure	Indication of failure at premises due to line failure or failure to communicate after from 5 to 10 dialing attempts	Not required — always annunciated at the supervising station that initiates corrective action	Monitor the interconnection of the premises unit elements of transmitting equipment, and indicate a failure at the premises or transmit a trouble signal to the supervising station.

TABLE A.26.6.1 *Continued*

Criteria	General 26.6.3.1	Digital Alarm Communicator Systems 26.6.3.2	Two-Way Radio Frequency (RF) Multiplex Systems 26.6.3.3.1	One-Way Private Radio Alarm Systems 26.6.3.3.2
Time to restore signal-receiving, processing, display, and recording equipment	Where duplicate equipment not provided, spare hardware required so a repair can be effected within 30 minutes. Complete set of critical spare parts on a 1 to 5 ratio of parts to system units or a duplicate functionally equivalent system unit for every five system units.	Spare digital alarm communicator receivers required for switchover to backup receiver in 30 seconds. One backup system unit for every five system units.	Where duplicate equipment not provided, spare hardware required so a repair can be effected within 30 minutes	Where duplicate equipment not provided, spare hardware required so a repair can be effected within 30 minutes
Loading capacities for system units and transmission and communications channels	512 independent alarm systems on a system unit with no backup. Unlimited if you can switch to a backup in 30 seconds. The system must be designed such that a failure of a transmission channel serving a system unit must not result in the loss in the ability to monitor more than 3000 transmitters.	See Table 26.6.3.2.2.2(C) for the maximum number of transmitters on a hunt group in a system unit	512 buildings and premises on a system unit with no backup. Unlimited if you can switch to a backup in 30 seconds.	512 buildings and premises on a system unit with no backup. Unlimited if you can switch to a backup in 30 seconds.
End-to-end communication time for an alarm	90 seconds from initiation of alarm until displayed to the operator and recorded on a medium from which the information can be retrieved	Off-hook to on-hook not to exceed 90 seconds per attempt. 10 attempts maximum. 900 seconds maximum for all attempts.	90 seconds from initiation until it is recorded	90% probability to receive an alarm in 90 seconds, 99% probability in 180 seconds, 99.999% probability in 450 seconds
Record and display rate of subsequent alarms at supervising station	Not slower than one every 10 additional seconds	Not addressed	When any number of subsequent alarms come in, record at a rate not slower than one every additional 10 seconds	When any number of subsequent alarms come in, record at a rate not slower than one every additional 10 seconds
Signal error detection and correction	Signal repetition, parity check, or some equivalent means of error detection and correction must be used.	Signal repetition, digital parity check, or some equivalent means of signal verification must be used.	Not addressed	Not addressed
Path sequence priority	No need for prioritization of paths. The requirement is that both paths are equivalent.	The first transmission attempt uses the primary channel.	Not addressed	Not addressed

(continues)

TABLE A.26.6.1 *Continued*

Criteria	General 26.6.3.1	Digital Alarm Communicator Systems 26.6.3.2	Two-Way Radio Frequency (RF) Multiplex Systems 26.6.3.3.1	One-Way Private Radio Alarm Systems 26.6.3.3.2
Carrier diversity	When a redundant path is required, the alternate path must be provided by a public communication service provider different from the primary path where available.	Where long distance service (including WATS) is used, the second telephone number must be provided by a different long distance service provider where there are multiple providers.	Not addressed	Not addressed
Throughput probability	When the supervising station does not regularly communicate with the transmitter at least once every 200 seconds, then the throughput probability of the alarm transmission must be at least 90% in 90 seconds, 99% in 180 seconds, 99.999% in 450 seconds.	Demonstrate 90% probability of a system unit immediately answering a call or follow the loading Table 8.6.3.2.2.2(c). One-way radio backup demonstrates 90% probability of transmission.	Not addressed	90% probability to receive an alarm in 90 seconds, 99% probability in 180 seconds, 99.999% in probability 450 seconds
Unique premises identifier	If a transmitter shares a transmission or communication channel with other transmitters, it must have a unique transmitter identifier.	Yes	Yes	Yes
Unique flaws	From time to time, there may be unique flaws in a communication system. Unique requirements must be written for these unique flaws.	If call forwarding is used to communicate to the supervising station, verify the integrity of this feature every 4 hours.	None addressed	None addressed
Signal priority	If the communication methodology is shared with any other usage, all alarm transmissions must preempt and take precedence over any other usage. Alarm signals take precedence over supervisory signals.	Chapter 1 on fundamentals requires that alarm signals take priority over supervisory signals unless there is sufficient repetition of the alarm signal to prevent the loss of an alarm signal.	Chapter 1 on fundamentals requires that alarm signals take priority over supervisory signals unless there is sufficient repetition of the alarm signal to prevent the loss of an alarm signal.	Chapter 1 on fundamentals requires that alarm signals take priority over supervisory signals unless there is sufficient repetition of the alarm signal to prevent the loss of an alarm signal.
Sharing communications equipment on premises	If the transmitter is sharing on-premises communications equipment, the shared equipment must be listed for the purpose (otherwise the transmitter must be installed ahead of the unlisted equipment).	Disconnect outgoing or incoming telephone call and prevent its use for outgoing telephone calls until signal transmission has been completed.	Not addressed	Not addressed

The Code makes a full range of listed transmission technologies available to all the supervising station services (see 26.6.2.2). This range of transmission technologies gives designers maximum flexibility in choosing the transmission technology most appropriate for a particular application.

In the 2010 edition, the Code has removed specific reference to certain long-standing technologies in recognition of the significant reduction in their actual use. The Code has noted these technologies and refers to them as "legacy" technologies in A.26.6.3.1. These legacy technologies include the following:

1. Active multiplex system, including systems using derived local channel
2. McCulloh systems
3. Directly connected, noncoded systems
4. Private microwave radio systems

Where existing systems continue to use these legacy technologies, their use remains acceptable, because these systems still meet the requirements of 26.6.3.1.

In addition to general requirements found in 26.6.3.1, the Code provides specific requirements for the following technologies:

1. Digital alarm communication systems (see 26.6.3.2)
2. Radio systems (see 26.6.3.3)

    a. Two-way radio frequency (RF) multiplex systems (see 26.6.3.3.1)
    b. One-way private radio alarm systems (see 26.6.3.3.2)

The Code has no direct jurisdiction over public utilities such as telephone service provided by public telephone utility companies over the public switched telephone network.

In 1964, a "signaling summit" meeting was held to determine which organizations would take on the responsibility for ensuring the life-cycle quality assurance of central station systems. Representatives from Underwriters Laboratories Inc., the National Board of Fire Underwriters, and major insurance companies, including Factory Insurance Association and Factory Mutual Engineering Corporation, attended this meeting. Many of those representatives also served on the NFPA Signaling Correlating Committee responsible for the NFPA alarm and signaling systems standards. Among the decisions made at that meeting was acceptance of the inherent reliability of the private line (PL) circuits provided by the public switched telephone network. Most central station operating companies leased PL circuits from the public telephone company utility to provide a signal pathway between various protected premises and the central station.

Representatives of the Bell Laboratories division of the American Telephone & Telegraph Company (AT&T) had earlier submitted detailed documentation in the form of standards known as "tariffs" that described the methods of ensuring operational integrity of the public switched telephone network and the PL circuits that used the cable plant of that system. These tariffs included requirements that provided for extensive standby (backup) power supplies at the telephone company wire centers to ensure the availability of independent power to operate all circuits and equipment for a period of at least 72 hours.

Based on this extensive documentation, the representatives at the signaling summit agreed that the NFPA standards did not need to address any requirements for the signaling pathways inside the public switched telephone network, provided that the various telephone companies adhered to the current tariffs and provided that the listed signaling equipment would electrically supervise the integrity of the signaling connection (pathway). AT&T further agreed to apply to the NFPA for admission as a member of the appropriate signaling systems standards technical committee.

In the late 1970s, manufacturers first proposed that the Technical Committee of Signaling Systems for Central Station Service recognize and write requirements for the inclusion of the use of DACSs in NFPA 71, *Standard for the Installation, Maintenance, and Use of*

Signaling Systems for Central Station Service. The technical committee received documentation and heard testimony from the AT&T representative on the technical committee. The representative outlined the current scope of the applicable tariffs and described in detail the statistical analysis methods that Bell Laboratories used to determine the operational reliability of the public switched telephone network. Based on that testimony, the technical committee voted in favor of requirements to permit the use of DACSs, providing that the equipment monitored the voltage on the circuit extending from the nearest telephone company wire center to the protected premises.

This technology required the use of so-called "loop start" telephone pairs. The public telephone utility company typically provided loop start pairs for use in single line service drops to residences or businesses using only one or two telephone lines (numbers). When a business needed multiple telephone lines (numbers), the public telephone utility company typically provided "ground start" pairs to conserve standby battery power at their wire centers. (See the commentary following A.26.6.3.2.1.1.)

The Committee further determined that a test of the DACS from each protected premises every 24 hours would give a level of transmission integrity equivalent to that used by radio master fire alarm boxes as then stated in NFPA 1221.

In 1982, Judge Harold Greene of the U.S. District Court in Washington, DC, issued a momentous decision [552 F.Supp. 131 (DDC 1982)] in *United States v. AT&T.* The consent decree filed in this case resulted in the breakup of the telephone "empire" of AT&T into seven Regional Bell Holding Companies. Many changes in operations and technology grew out of this decision, including a change in the rigorous enforcement of the implementation standards behind various operational tariffs.

Over time, various public telephone utility companies began to implement technology to provide service using the public switch telephone network without regard for a consistently long period of standby power. In some cases, the provision of voltage on loop start telephone pairs no long originated from a telephone company wire center. Instead, localized concentrator units placed in the field provided power to the loop start telephone pairs. Initially, some of these field-located concentrators had no standby power whatsoever. When some authorities having jurisdiction discovered this fact, they began to refuse to accept supervising station alarm systems using such telephone pairs. In response, the public telephone utility companies began to provide some standby power for field-located equipment. Most of the time, the standby power consisted of only 8 hours of continuous power following the loss of primary power.

Today, customers can purchase telephone service from a variety of service providers; however, a state's public utility authority might not regulate all these providers. For example, some companies that provide cable television services now also provide telephone service. In many locales, the cable television provider has a local contract to do business with a local governmental agency. It is not treated as a utility company and is not regulated by the state public utility authority.

The Code continues to require 24 hours of standby power for fire alarm systems. Owners and authorities having jurisdiction should keep this requirement in mind when selecting a particular transmission technology. The careful addition of an alternate signaling pathway may offer a prudent solution.

26.6.2 General.

26.6.2.1 Master Control Unit. If the protected premises master control unit is neither integral to nor co-located with the supervising station, the communications methods of Section 26.6 shall be used to connect the protected premises to either a subsidiary station, if used, or a supervising station for central station service in accordance with Section 26.3, proprietary station in accordance with Section 26.4, or remote station in accordance with Section 26.5.

26.6.2.2* Alternate Methods. Nothing in Chapter 26 shall be interpreted as prohibiting the use of listed equipment using alternate communications methods that provide a level of reliability and supervision consistent with the requirements of Chapter 10 and the intended level of protection.

A.26.6.2.2 It is not the intent of Section 26.6 to limit the use of listed equipment using alternate communications methods, provided these methods demonstrate performance characteristics that are equal to or superior to those technologies described in Section 26.6. Such demonstration of equivalency is to be evidenced by the equipment using the alternate communications methods meeting all the requirements of Chapter 10, including those that deal with such factors as reliability, monitoring for integrity, and listing. It is further expected that suitable proposals stating the requirements for such technology will be submitted for inclusion in subsequent editions of this Code.

Over the years, as it encompassed new transmission technologies, the Code most often compared new technologies to the performance capabilities of the McCulloh system, which was the first transmission technology used by supervising station systems. This comparison allowed an intermixing of certain operational requirements among the various technologies. Therefore, 26.6.2.2 becomes a caveat to make certain that when applying a particular transmission technology, authorities having jurisdiction, system designers, installers, and users do not ignore critical operational requirements that appear in Chapter 10, as well as those that appear in Section 26.6.

◄ FAQ
What was the first transmission technology used by supervising station systems?

In the 1999 edition of the Code, the technical committee introduced a separate section of Chapter 26 titled "Other Transmission Technologies." This section provided a generic set of requirements that would allow the use of any new transmission technology that demonstrated it could meet certain critical operational requirements. The technical committee intended this section to address the advent of different new technologies, such as packet switched networks.

In the 2010 edition of the Code, the technical committee moved the vast majority of the requirements from the section on other transmission technologies to 26.6.3.1.

The last sentence of A.26.6.2.2 contains important guidance: "It is further expected that suitable proposals for stating the requirements for such technology will be submitted for inclusion in subsequent editions of this Code." The Code recognizes that from time to time manufacturers will introduce new transmission technologies. Paragraphs 26.6.2.2 and 26.6.3.1 through 26.6.3.1.13 include provisions that manufacturers should consider in developing new technology to meet the intent of the Code. However, as manufacturers develop new technologies, they should take advantage of the NFPA standards-making process and submit appropriate new requirements for consideration by the technical committee.

26.6.2.3 Multiple Buildings. For multiple building premises, the requirements of 10.16.6.3 shall apply to the alarm, supervisory, and trouble signals transmitted to the supervising station.

26.6.2.4 Equipment.

26.6.2.4.1 Alarm system equipment and installations shall comply with Federal Communications Commission (FCC) rules and regulations, as applicable, concerning the following:

(1) Electromagnetic radiation
(2) Use of radio frequencies
(3) Connection to the public switched telephone network of telephone equipment, systems, and protection apparatus

Paragraph 26.6.2.4.1 recognizes that the Federal Communications Commission (FCC) has jurisdiction over the installation requirements for certain communications equipment used to transmit signals from a protected premises to a supervising station. Circumstances can occur in which the FCC requirements supersede a requirement of this Code. For example, in certain portions of the regulated radio spectrum, FCC regulations may limit the amount of time a transmitter may operate continuously. Likewise, FCC regulations may limit the number of times within a prescribed time period that a radio transmitter may operate, such as a certain number of times per hour. These requirements can limit the way in which such technologies are used for transmitting signals from a protected premises.

The FCC also has jurisdiction over the engineering practices and services offered by providers of telephone service to subscribers using managed facilities-based voice networks (MFVNs). Refer to the definitions of *managed facilities-based voice network* and *public switched telephone network* in 3.3.141 and 3.3.273.2, respectively.

26.6.2.4.2 Radio receiving equipment shall be installed in compliance with *NFPA 70, National Electrical Code*, Article 810.

When a particular supervising station transmission technology uses equipment that transmits an RF signal, that equipment, in particular its antenna, must be installed in compliance with the appropriate articles of *NFPA 70®, National Electrical Code®*. As stated, in part, in Section 810.1 of *NFPA 70*: "This article covers antenna systems for radio and television receiving equipment, amateur radio transmitting and receiving equipment, and certain features of transmitter safety. This article covers antennas such as multi-element, vertical rod, and dish, and also covers the wiring and cabling that connects them to equipment."

26.6.2.4.3 The external antennas of all radio transmitting and receiving equipment shall be protected in order to minimize the possibility of damage by static discharge or lightning.

26.6.2.5 Adverse Conditions.

26.6.2.5.1 For active and two-way RF multiplex systems, the occurrence of an adverse condition on the transmission channel between a protected premises and the supervising station that prevents the transmission of any status change signal shall be automatically indicated and recorded at the supervising station. This indication and record shall identify the affected portions of the system so that the supervising station operator will be able to determine the location of the adverse condition by trunk or leg facility, or both.

Interrogation and response transmission, back and forth along the communication path, monitors the integrity of two-way RF multiplex transmission technology, as well as the legacy technology of active multiplex transmission. The satisfactory exchange of data ensures that all trunks and legs remain operational. If the system does not successfully complete an interrogation and response sequence, an unsuccessful sequence can indicate the possible failure of a trunk or a leg. In such a case, 26.6.2.5.1 requires the system to notify the supervising station and provide sufficient detail to allow prompt troubleshooting and repair of the trunk or leg. This adverse condition must be indicated as a trouble signal as required by 10.12.1.

26.6.2.5.2 For a one-way radio alarm system, the system shall be supervised to ensure that at least two independent radio alarm repeater station receivers (RARSRs) are receiving signals for each radio alarm transmitter (RAT) during each 24-hour period.

26.6.2.5.2.1 The occurrence of a failure to receive a signal by either RARSR shall be automatically indicated and recorded at the supervising station.

26.6.2.5.2.2 The indication shall identify which RARSR failed to receive such supervisory signals.

26.6.2.5.2.3 Received test signals shall not be required to be indicated at the supervising station.

The satisfactory receipt of at least one transmission every 24 hours by at least two independent radio alarm repeater station receivers (RARSRs) monitors the integrity of one-way radio transmission technology. If receivers do not receive such a signal, then 26.6.2.5.2.1 requires the system to notify the supervising station. This adverse condition must be indicated as a trouble signal as required by 10.12.1.

26.6.2.5.3 For active and two-way RF multiplex systems that are part of a central station alarm system, restoration of service to the affected portions of the system shall be automatically recorded. When service is restored, the first status change of any initiating device circuit, any initiating device directly connected to a signaling line circuit, or any combination thereof that occurred at any of the affected premises during the service interruption also shall be recorded.

Two-way RF multiplex systems and legacy active multiplex systems that serve a central station fire alarm system not only must automatically record restoration of interrupted service but must also report the first status change on any connected initiating device circuit or any connected initiating device. This reporting requirement means that for each connected initiating device circuit or any connected initiating device, the equipment at the protected premises must retain the signal during a transmission interruption and, upon restoration of the transmission path, report the first status change that occurred during the transmission interruption.

26.6.2.6 Dual Control.

26.6.2.6.1 Dual control, if required, shall provide for redundancy in the form of a standby circuit or other alternate means of transmitting signals over the primary trunk portion of a transmission channel.

26.6.2.6.1.1 The same method of signal transmission shall be permitted to be used over separate routes, or alternate methods of signal transmission shall be permitted to be used.

26.6.2.6.1.2 Public switched telephone network facilities shall be used only as an alternate method of transmitting signals.

Dual control, though retained in the 2010 edition of the Code, actually applies only to legacy systems using active multiplex transmission technology. Paragraph 26.6.2.6 describes a feature provided for a Class I active multiplex system. An authority having jurisdiction or a fire alarm system designer could also specify this feature as an option for other active multiplex systems.

◄ **FAQ**
"Dual control" applies to what communications method?

    Although dual control does not provide full redundancy for every trunk and leg, it does offer an option that an authority having jurisdiction or a system designer can choose to help ensure the receipt of signals during interruptions to each primary trunk extending from the supervising station. Most often, technology called "DataPhone Select-A-Station (DSAS)," offered by the public telephone utility company, provides this redundancy. When the primary trunk fails, this technology allows the supervising station to establish an alternate transmission path by automatically or manually dialing into the PSTN and establishing an alternate path for the signals that would normally transmit over the primary trunk. Telephone technicians sometimes refer to this arrangement as "dial up, make good."

26.6.2.6.2 If using facilities leased from a telephone company, that portion of the primary trunk facility between the supervising station and its serving wire center shall not be required to comply with the separate routing requirement of the primary trunk facility. Dual control, if used, shall require supervision as follows:

(1) Dedicated facilities that are able to be used on a full-time basis, and whose use is limited to signaling purposes as defined in this Code, shall be exercised at least once every hour.
(2) Public switched telephone network facilities shall be exercised at least once every 24 hours.

To ensure that the dual control system can use the alternate path when needed, operators must exercise the alternate path for each primary trunk. Operators must exercise each dedicated alternate path once each hour. They must exercise each alternate path provided as part of the PSTN at least once each day.

26.6.3 Communications Methods.

26.6.3.1* General.

A.26.6.3.1 Certain legacy technologies (active multiplex, McCulloh, directly connected non-coded and private microwave) have been removed from the text of the document. Existing systems utilizing these technologies are acceptable, because all these technologies also comply with the general provisions of 26.6.3.1.

The technical committee relocated almost all the requirements that are in 26.6.3.1 from 8.6.4, Other Transmission Technologies, in the 2007 edition of the Code. Paragraphs 26.6.3.1.1 through 26.6.3.1.13 provide general requirements for transmission methods used by supervising station systems. Specific requirements to be followed for digital alarm communicator systems and for radio systems are provided in 26.6.3.2 and 26.6.3.3, respectively.

As explained in A.26.6.3.1, the technical committee has removed certain legacy technologies from the Code:

1. Active multiplex system, including systems using derived local channel
2. McCulloh systems
3. Directly connected, noncoded systems
4. Private microwave radio systems

Where existing systems continue to use these legacy technologies, their use remains acceptable since these systems still meet the requirements of 26.6.3.1.

In addition, as new technologies develop, the requirements of 26.6.3.1.1 through 26.6.3.1.13 will provide users of the Code a way to assess the acceptability and equivalency of those new technologies.

Exhibit 26.10 shows the circuit board for an internet protocol (IP) DACT. This equipment transmits data across a packet switched network using IP. The term *IP DACT* should not be confused with the more traditional DACT, which is addressed in 26.6.3.2.

EXHIBIT 26.10 *A Listed IP DACT That Connects a Protected Premises to a Supervising Station via the Internet. It concentrates signals from two loop start telephone circuits into a packet switched network in compliance with 26.6.3.1. (Source: NOTIFIER, Northfield, CT)*

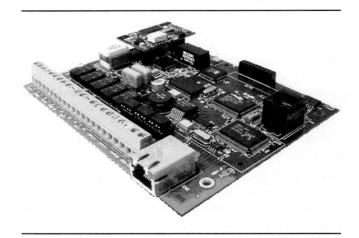

26.6.3.1.1 Conformance. Communications methods operating on principles different from specific methods covered by this chapter shall be permitted to be installed if they conform to the performance requirements of this section and to all other applicable requirements of this Code.

26.6.3.1.2 Federal Communications Commission. Alarm system equipment and installations shall comply with the Federal Communications Commission (FCC) rules and regulations, as applicable, concerning electromagnetic radiation, use of radio frequencies, and connections to the public switched telephone network of telephone equipment, systems, and protection apparatus.

The Code recognizes that the FCC has jurisdiction over certain aspects of communications technology. While 26.6.3.1.2 specifically mentions the PSTN, in fact the FCC has some jurisdiction over all providers of telephone service, including, but not limited to, broadband service providers, cable service providers, and other service providers.

26.6.3.1.3 NFPA 70, National Electrical Code. Equipment shall be installed in compliance with *NFPA 70, National Electrical Code.*

26.6.3.1.4 Communications Integrity. Provision shall be made to monitor the integrity of the transmission technology and its communications path.

26.6.3.1.4.1 Single Communications Technology. Where only one communications technology is used, any failure of the communications path shall be annunciated at the supervising station within 5 minutes of the failure.

26.6.3.1.4.2 Multiple Communications Technologies. Where two or more different technologies are used, the following requirements shall be met:

(1) Provision shall be made to monitor the integrity of each communications path.
(2) Failure of any communications path shall be annunciated at the supervising station and at the protected premises within not more than 24 hours of the failure.

Exception: Where technologies used are described elsewhere in this Code, monitoring for integrity shall be permitted to comply with those requirements.

Monitoring of communications pathways is important. In fact, it is at the heart of the requirements that determine the operational reliability of the various transmission technologies.

Paragraph 26.6.3.1.4.1 requires notification of failure of a single transmission technology within 5 minutes (300 seconds). It is important to note that this provision extends the requirement of 10.12.1 by 100 seconds.

In contrast, a DACT using a single telephone line with derived local channel or a single integrated services digital network telephone line must send a trouble signal upon loss of the transmission pathway within 200 seconds.

Paragraph 26.6.3.3.1.1(2) requires a two-way RF multiplex system to transmit, process, and record a trouble signal upon adverse conditions affecting the transmission pathway within 200 seconds.

Paragraph 26.6.3.1.4.2 requires systems using two or more communications technologies to annunciate the failure of any communications path at the supervising station and at the protected premises within not more than 24 hours. In contrast, 26.6.3.2.1.4(B)(3) requires a DACT using one telephone line (number) and one of the secondary transmission means stated in 26.6.3.2.1.4(A)(1) through 26.6.3.2.1.4(A)(7) to send a trouble signal upon loss of either transmission pathway within 4 minutes (240 seconds). Of course, the catastrophic loss of both transmission means would be annunciated only at the supervising station following failure to receive the 24-hour test signal.

26.6.3.1.5 Spare System Unit Equipment. An inventory of spare equipment shall be maintained at the supervising station such that any failed piece of equipment can be replaced and the systems unit restored to full operation within 30 minutes of failure.

Not only must the supervising station maintain spare equipment, operators at the supervising station must be able to place the spare equipment into service within 30 minutes of unit failure. This requirement dictates a careful design of the supervising station to allow a relatively quick change out of failed equipment.

26.6.3.1.6 Loading Capacity of a System Unit.

26.6.3.1.6.1 The maximum number of independent fire alarm systems connected to a single system unit shall be limited to 512.

26.6.3.1.6.2 If duplicate spare system units are maintained at the supervising station and switchover can be achieved in 30 seconds, then the system capacity shall be permitted to be unlimited.

The loading capacity of a system unit directly relates to the ability of that system to process and display signal traffic on a timely basis. The requirements of 26.6.3.1.6.1 and 26.6.3.1.6.2 set a baseline level of loading to ensure the system's ability to perform in an emergency with high signal traffic.

26.6.3.1.7 End-to-End Communication Time for an Alarm. The maximum duration between the initiation of an alarm signal at the protected premises, transmission of the signal, and subsequent display and recording of the alarm signal at the supervising station shall not exceed 90 seconds.

The 90-second time limit was introduced into the Code in the late 1960s, when active multiplex technology was first recognized. At the time the operational details of the first multiplex system were presented to the technical committee, the particular unit scanned all connected transponders every 90 seconds. After a great deal of discussion as to whether a 90-second interrogation and response cycle presented a suitable substitute for continuous electrical supervision of the communications pathway, the technical committee adopted the 90-second value and placed that value into various relevant requirements. Thus, the 90-second requirement became the standard end-to-end alarm communications time for all subsequent communications technologies.

During the early 1970s, a manufacturer submitted a proposal to the technical committee to modify the requirements to permit a time-division multiplex system that actually took 300 seconds to scan all connected transponders. The system operated by sending a reset pulse to the transponders. The system then "listened" for a status change report from each transponder during a specifically assigned time frame consisting of either the first second or the second second of each 3-second time interval. During the third second of each 3-second time interval, the system "listened" for an alarm status change report from any connected transponder. Thus, an alarm signal could reach the multiplex receiving unit in either of two ways: during its assigned reporting second or during the third "all-alarm-status-change-reporting" second.

The technical committee eventually accepted this arrangement as meeting the intent of alarm receipt in 90 seconds. However, after considerable discussion, the technical committee decided not to accept the 300-second scan time for nonalarm status changes. Rather, the technical committee set the limit on receipt of a trouble signal as 200 seconds.

26.6.3.1.8 Unique Identifier. If a transmitter shares a transmission or communications channel with other transmitters, it shall have a unique transmitter identifier.

26.6.3.1.9 Recording and Display Rate of Subsequent Alarms. Recording and display of alarms at the supervising station shall be at a rate no slower than one complete signal every 10 seconds.

The time limit of 10 seconds sets a baseline level for the recording and display of incoming signals. This time frame has its roots not only in the processing speed of the equipment but also takes into account the ability of an operator to perceive the nature of the signal and mentally filter the information contained in the incoming signal and what it intends to convey. However, the time frame does not take into consideration the time it may take the operator to decide what to do about the signal nor the time it would take the operator to take the prescribed action.

26.6.3.1.10 Signal Error Detection and Correction.

26.6.3.1.10.1 Communication of alarm, supervisory, and trouble signals shall be in accordance with this section to prevent degradation of the signal in transit, which in turn would result in either of the following:

(1) Failure of the signal to be displayed and recorded at the supervising station
(2) An incorrect corrupted signal displayed and recorded at the supervising station

26.6.3.1.10.2 Reliability of the signal shall be achieved by any of the following:

(1) Signal repetition — multiple transmissions repeating the same signal
(2) Parity check — a mathematically check sum algorithm of a digital message that verifies correlation between transmitted and received message
(3) An equivalent means to 26.6.3.1.10.2(1) or 26.6.3.1.10.2(2) that provides a certainty of 99.99 percent that the received message is identical to the transmitted message

The requirements in 26.6.3.1.10.1 and 26.6.3.1.10.2 provide a baseline level of performance to help ensure that the transmission technology delivers clear and consistent signal information from the protected premises. The intent of the requirements is to offer guidance to the manufacturer using a new technology by explaining how existing technologies have achieved the objective. At the same time, 26.6.3.1.10.2(3) carefully permits alternative means of achieving the objective within a critical level of statistical certainty (99.99 percent).

26.6.3.1.11* Sharing Communications Equipment On-Premises. If the fire alarm transmitter is sharing on-premises communications equipment, the shared equipment shall be listed.

A.26.6.3.1.11 Most communications equipment is not specifically listed for fire alarm applications, but is listed in accordance with applicable product standard for general communications equipment.

The requirement for listing in 26.6.3.1.11 intends to support the requirement of 10.3.1. The Annex A material helps clarify that the technical committee recognizes that, in most cases, shared communications equipment will not bear a specific listing for alarm service. Rather, the shared equipment will bear a listing for communications equipment. An example of this would be a router, switch, or other piece of data communications equipment through which alarm system data might pass.

In general, to determine whether a piece of equipment should have a specific listing for alarm service, ask the question: "Does this equipment translate or change the alarm system data in any way, or does it merely pass the alarm system data through and onto other parts of the communications pathway?" If the equipment changes or translates the data in some way, then the nature of the change or translation should be investigated to determine whether the equipment could adversely affect the transmission of the alarm data. Such investigation should help determine whether the particular piece of equipment should bear a specific listing for alarm service use.

26.6.3.1.12* Secondary Power. Secondary power capacity in accordance with 10.5.6 shall be provided for all equipment necessary for the transmission and reception of alarm, supervisory, trouble, and other signals located at the protected premises and at the supervising station.

A.26.6.3.1.12 This requirement is to ensure that communications equipment will operate for the same period of time on secondary power as the alarm control unit.

It is important to note that the requirement in 26.6.3.1.12 for standby power applies to the equipment at the protected premises and the equipment at the supervising station. It does not specifically apply to equipment in the communications pathway supplied by the provider of the communications pathway, including equipment installed at the protected premises by the provider of the communications pathway. Recognition of this limitation becomes important in light of recent information that MFVN service providers typically install only 8 hours of standby power for field-located units.

The fact that a particular communications pathway might have only 8 hours of standby power does not in any way alter the requirement for 24 hours of standby power for the fire alarm system equipment located at the protected premises and the supervising station. The potential for longer power outages at specific locations, such as a protected premises or supervising station to a lesser extent, statistically exceeds the likelihood of longer power outages over a wider area that might affect field-located communications pathway equipment. The standby power to the signaling pathway should be robust enough to permit the prompt transmission of a loss of power trouble signal. Then, with the longer (24 hours) standby power for the fire alarm equipment, that equipment will continue to provide a level of fire alarm protective service.

26.6.3.1.13 Unique Flaws Not Covered by This Code. If a communications technology has a unique flaw that could result in the failure to communicate a signal, the implementation of that technology for alarm signaling shall compensate for that flaw so as to eliminate the risk of missing an alarm signal.

This requirement reminds manufacturers to carefully investigate any new technology they may be considering. They must identify any unique flaws and compensate for those flaws accordingly.

26.6.3.2 Digital Alarm Communicator Systems.

26.6.3.2.1 Digital Alarm Communicator Transmitter (DACT).

26.6.3.2.1.1* Public Switched Network. A DACT shall be connected to the public switched telephone network upstream of any private telephone system at the protected premises.

(A) The connections to the public switched telephone network shall be under the control of the subscriber for whom service is being provided by the supervising station alarm system.

(B) Special attention shall be required to ensure that this connection is made only to a loop start telephone circuit and not to a ground start telephone circuit.

Exception: If public cellular telephone service is used as a secondary means of transmission, the requirements of 26.6.3.2.1.1 shall not apply to the cellular telephone service.

A.26.6.3.2.1.1 Special care should be used when connecting a DACT to a digital service such as DSL or ADSL. Filters or other special equipment might be needed to communicate reliably.

Throughout this section, the Code makes reference to the PSTN. See 3.3.273.2 for the definition of *public switched telephone network*. It is important to recognize that the 2010 edition of the Code revised the definition of PSTN to take a broader view of what has traditionally constituted a PSTN and to embrace the service provided through the use of managed facilities-based voice networks, as defined in 3.3.141.

The Code has long presumed a level of reliability of the PSTN that may no longer exist. For example, 40 years ago, nearly 100 percent of all telephone circuits extended from a telephone utility company wire center directly to a subscribers' premises. The telephone company wire center typically had standby power supplies that would supply power for at least 72 hours upon loss of primary power. Today, the PSTN serves many locales through field-located equipment that may typically have only 8 hours of standby power. Thus, the anticipated level of reliability of the traditional PSTN has devolved as the telephone utility companies have introduced new "pair sharing" technologies.

A number of other service providers, including, but not limited to, broadband service providers, cable service providers, and other service providers, have joined the public telephone company utility in providing telephone service to subscribers. The majority of these service providers use MFVNs to provide a subscriber with a telephone circuit that has the operational equivalency of the traditional PSTN. In many areas of the United States, the public telephone utility company itself provides the PSTN using an MFVN.

Not all alternative telephone service providers use MFVNs. Some providers use methods that might not have the same rigorous standards and practices as the methods employed by an MFVN. For example, it has been reported that some deployments of voice over internet protocol (VOIP) systems might not consistently provide a level of service reliability equivalent to that of the traditional PSTN or an MFVN.

Any time a facility changes telephone service providers, best practice would dictate that a qualified person test the alarm system to make certain it can successfully transmit signals to the supervising station.

The DACT connects to the PSTN, so that it can seize the line to which it is connected. This seizure disconnects any private telephone equipment beyond the DACT's point of connection and gives the DACT control over the line at all times. Connection to a dedicated telephone line is not required, but the connection must be to a loop start telephone line (circuit). This permits the DACT to monitor the continuity of the line from the protected premises to the first piece of telephone utility equipment.

On a loop start telephone line, the public telephone utility continuously supplies voltage, normally 48 vdc from the telephone utility wire center or from field-located pair-sharing terminal equipment where the individual line originates. A connected DACT can monitor the integrity of the connected line by reading this constant voltage. The vast majority of residential telephone connections use loop start lines.

In contrast, almost all business telephone connections, particularly those employing PBX connections, use ground start lines. To obtain dial tone and operating power on a ground start line, the user equipment momentarily connects one side of the line to earth ground. Because the public telephone utility does not supply voltage to an idle ground start line, the DACT cannot use the presence of voltage to monitor the integrity of the ground start line, as it can with a loop start line.

Functionally, a DACT can signal over a ground start line and frequently does so when used as part of a burglar alarm system. However, the DACT can only monitor a loop start line for integrity.

Each DACT must connect to its own set of two loop start telephone lines or the accepted equivalent in accordance with 26.6.3.2.1.4(A). Use of the same two telephone lines for several DACTs in a campus-style arrangement is not acceptable.

The exception to 26.6.3.2.1.1 is necessary because public cellular telephone systems do not use telephone lines. Thus, when the public cellular telephone system is used as a secondary means of signal transmission, the requirements of 26.6.3.2.1.1 do not apply to the cellular portion of the system.

26.6.3.2.1.2 Signal Verification. All information exchanged between the DACT at the protected premises and the digital alarm communicator receiver (DACR) at the supervising or subsidiary station shall be by digital code or some other approved means. Signal repetition, digital parity check, or some other approved means of signal verification shall be used.

The functional requirements of 26.6.3.2.1.2 rule out the use of an analog voice tape dialer or digital voice dialer to transmit fire alarm signals. Such a device dials a predetermined telephone number and then plays a voice message such as, "There is a fire at 402 Spruce Street." Over the years, officials have reported many cases where a voice tape dialer has malfunctioned and endlessly repeated its message, tying up a vital emergency telephone line in a communications center. The Code strictly forbids the use of analog or digital voice tape dialers.

The Code also requires the DACT and the digital alarm communicator receiver (DACR) to use some method to verify the transmission of digital data.

26.6.3.2.1.3* Requirements for DACTs.

(A) A DACT shall be configured so that, when it is required to transmit a signal to the supervising station, it shall seize the telephone line (going off-hook) at the protected premises and disconnect an outgoing or incoming telephone call and prevent use of the telephone line for outgoing telephone calls until signal transmission has been completed. A DACT shall not be connected to a party line telephone facility.

(B) A DACT shall have the means to satisfactorily obtain a dial tone, dial the number(s) of the DACR, obtain verification that the DACR is able to receive signals, transmit the signal, and receive acknowledgment that the DACR has accepted that signal. In no event shall the time from going off-hook to on-hook exceed 90 seconds per attempt.

Paragraph 26.6.3.2.1.3(B) describes the normal sequence of operation for a DACT. Upon initiation of an alarm, supervisory, or trouble signal, the DACT seizes the line, obtains a dial tone, dials the number of the DACR, receives a "handshake" signal from the DACR, transmits its data, receives an acknowledgment signal — sometimes called the *kiss-off signal* — from the DACR, and hangs up. Each attempt of this calling and verification sequence must take no longer than 90 seconds to complete.

Under typical circumstances, the successful transmission of a signal should occur on the first attempt well within the 90-second period allowed. Note that the test methods of Table 14.4.2.2, item 18(a), allow a maximum of 90 seconds during testing of the system. However, under the most adverse conditions, more than one attempt may be needed for a successful transmission. See 26.6.3.2.1.3(C), its related annex material, and commentary.

(C)* A DACT shall have means to reset and retry if the first attempt to complete a signal transmission sequence is unsuccessful. A failure to complete connection shall not prevent subsequent attempts to transmit an alarm where such alarm is generated from any other initiating device circuit or signaling line circuit, or both. Additional attempts shall be made until the signal transmission sequence has been completed, up to a minimum of 5 and a maximum of 10 attempts.

FAQ ▶
What is the reason that the Code limits the number of attempts to 10?

The DACT, as described in 26.6.3.2.1.3(C), must make at least 5 attempts to complete the sequence. However, the DACT must not make more than 10 attempts, so that a malfunctioning DACT does not tie up one of the lines connected to the DACR by making an unlimited number of repeated calls.

Under the most adverse circumstances, in which the DACT finally completes a transmission on the last, or tenth, attempt, at a maximum of 90 seconds per attempt [see 26.6.3.2.1.3(B)], nearly 900 seconds, or 15 minutes, could have elapsed.

(D) If the maximum number of attempts to complete the sequence is reached, an indication of the failure shall be made at the premises.

A.26.6.3.2.1.3 To give the DACT the ability to disconnect an incoming call to the protected premises, telephone service should be of the type that provides for timed-release disconnect. In some telephone systems (step-by-step offices), timed-release disconnect is not provided.

To ensure reliability for transmission of fire alarm, supervisory, and trouble signals, 26.6.3.2.1.3 and its related annex recommendation give the DACT exclusive control over the telephone line to which it is connected.

A.26.6.3.2.1.3(C) A DACT can be programmed to originate calls to the DACR telephone lines (numbers) in any alternating sequence. The sequence can consist of single or multiple calls to one DACR telephone line (number), followed by single or multiple calls to a second

DACR telephone line (number), or any combination thereof that is consistent with the minimum/maximum attempt requirements in 26.6.3.2.1.3(C).

26.6.3.2.1.4 Transmission Channels.

(A)* A system employing a DACT shall employ one telephone line (number). In addition, one of the following transmission means shall be employed:

(1) A second telephone line (number)
(2) A cellular telephone connection
(3) A one-way radio system
(4) A one-way private radio alarm system
(5) A private microwave radio system
(6) A two-way RF multiplex system
(7) A transmission means complying with 26.6.3.1

Exception: One telephone line (number) equipped with a derived local channel or a single integrated services digital network (ISDN) telephone line using a terminal adapter specifically listed for supervising station alarm service, where the path between the transmitter and the switched telephone network serving central office is monitored for integrity so that the occurrence of an adverse condition in the path shall be annunciated at the supervising station within 200 seconds.

(B) The following requirements shall apply to all combinations listed in 26.6.3.2.1.4(A):

(1) Both channels shall be supervised in a manner approved for the means of transmission employed.
(2) Both channels shall be tested at intervals not exceeding 24 hours.

Exception No. 1: For public cellular telephone service, a verification (test) signal shall be transmitted at least monthly.

Exception No. 2: Where two telephone lines (numbers) are used, it shall be permitted to test each telephone line (number) at alternating 24-hour intervals.

Note the additional testing and reporting requirements for call-forwarded lines in 26.6.3.2.1.5(7).

(3) The failure of either channel shall send a trouble signal on the other channel within 4 minutes.

As important as monitoring the integrity of the transmission means is, avoiding nuisance trouble signals is equally important. The permissible 4-minute delay in transmitting a trouble signal in 26.6.3.2.1.4(B)(3) allows for momentary, or even somewhat longer, interruptions in the transmission path, such as might occur during a storm.

(4) When one transmission channel has failed, all status change signals shall be sent over the other channel.

Exception: Where used in combination with a DACT, a derived local channel shall not be required to send status change signals other than those indicating that adverse conditions exist on the telephone line (number).

(5) The primary channel shall be capable of delivering an indication to the DACT that the message has been received by the supervising station.

Because a one-way radio alarm system transmits only from a protected premises to a supervising station and has no means of receiving a signal at the protected premises from the supervising station, it would not be able to meet the requirement in 26.6.3.2.1.4(B)(5). Thus, the one-way radio alarm system cannot serve as the primary transmission means.

(6)* The first attempt to send a status change signal shall use the primary channel.

Exception: Where the primary channel is known to have failed.

(7) Simultaneous transmission over both channels shall be permitted.
(8) Failure of telephone lines (numbers) or cellular service shall be annunciated locally.

The purpose of 26.6.3.2.1.4 is to provide the DACT with two reasonably reliable means of connecting to the DACR. Note that the Code has no jurisdiction over utility-provided services such as telephone services. Thus, the Code must rely on the traditionally accepted inherent reliability of all such utility-provided services. [See commentary following A.26.6.3.2.1.1.]

Of all the transmission means permitted in 26.6.3.2.1.4, currently only a few are actually used. The most common transmission method consists of two loop start telephone lines. The next most popular transmission method consists of one loop start telephone line and a cellular telephone connection. The third most popular transmission method uses one loop start telephone line provided with either a derived local channel or an integrated services digital network (ISDN) for cut line supervision.

In this last method, the derived local channel or ISDN only provides notification that the telephone line has become impaired. The actual transmission of signals uses the PSTN. However, should the telephone line become disconnected or otherwise impaired, the derived local channel or ISDN connection will signal that loss of service.

It is particularly important for authorities having jurisdiction to understand the distinction between a DACS that meets the requirements of 26.6.3.2 and a system using an "Other Transmission Technology" that meets the requirements of 26.6.3.1. This second system employs a listed DACT connecting to a listed module that transmits as a packet switched network through a Transmission Control Protocol/Internet Protocol (TCP/IP) broadband data connection to the Internet. Both systems appear to use DACTs, but each must comply with distinct requirements of the applicable section of the Code.

Since the introduction of provisions for "Other Technologies" in the 1999 edition of the Code, a significant migration to this type of a system began. (The "Other Technologies" requirements have been moved to 26.6.3.1 in the 2010 edition of the Code.) Industry spokespeople have estimated that this migration will continue until the vast majority of DACTs use TCP/IP broadband data communications technology or a yet-to-be-developed equivalent.

A.26.6.3.2.1.4(A) With respect to the exception, a two-number ISDN line is not a substitute for the requirement to monitor the integrity of the path.

Some public telephone utilities offer so-called *cut line supervision* to supervising station alarm system providers. This service uses either derived local channel or ISDN equipment to detect adverse conditions on a telephone line. When a supervising station uses cut line supervision, it may operate its DACS with each DACT connected to a single telephone line.

A.26.6.3.2.1.4(B)(6) Where two telephone lines (numbers) are used, care should be taken to assign the primary DACT telephone line (number) to a nonessential telephone line (number) at the protected premises so that the primary line used in the premises is not unnecessarily interrupted.

26.6.3.2.1.5 DACT Transmission Means. The following requirements shall apply to all digital alarm communications transmitters:

(1) A DACT shall be connected to two separate means of transmission at the protected premises.
(2) The DACT shall be capable of selecting the operable means of transmission in the event of failure of the other means.

If the DACT detects that one of the two transmission means has failed (loss of voltage on a wire line, loss of one-way radio alarm service, or loss of cellular telephone service), the DACT must switch to the other operable means. The DACT must also transmit a trouble signal over the other communications means. See Exhibits 26.11 and 26.12 for typical connection methods to a DACT.

(3) The primary means of transmission shall be a telephone line (number) connected to the public switched network.

(4)* The first transmission attempt shall utilize the primary means of transmission.

(5) Each DACT shall be programmed to call a second DACR line (number) when the signal transmission sequence to the first called line (number) is unsuccessful.

To help avoid a possible disarrangement of the transmission path on the receiving end of the DACS, the requirement in 26.6.3.2.1.5(5) specifies that the DACT must call a second number if calling the first number does not result in completion of the transmission.

(6) Each DACT shall automatically initiate and complete a test signal transmission sequence to its associated DACR at least once every 24 hours. A successful signal transmission sequence of any other type, within the same 24-hour period, shall fulfill the requirement to verify the integrity of the reporting system, provided that signal processing is automated so that 24-hour delinquencies are individually acknowledged by supervising station personnel.

Each DACT must initiate a signal at least once every 24 hours to verify the end-to-end integrity of the DACS [see 26.6.3.2.1.5(6)]. If the receiving or processing equipment at the supervising station has sufficient intelligence to automatically keep track of signal traffic, any incoming signal from a particular DACT may serve to satisfy this requirement, as long as the receiver receives one signal during every 24-hour period.

◄ **FAQ**
How often must each DACT initiate a signal?

Note the additional requirements in 26.6.3.2.1.4(B)(1) and 26.6.3.2.1.4(B)(2), including Exception Nos. 1 and 2. Particularly note the requirement that the daily test may alternate between telephone lines. Also, please refer to the commentary after 26.6.3.2.1.5(5).

(7)* If a DACT is programmed to call a telephone line (number) that is call forwarded to the line (number) of the DACR, a means shall be implemented to verify the integrity of the call forwarding feature every 4 hours.

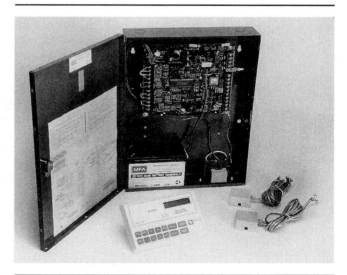

EXHIBIT 26.12 *Control Unit and DACT Showing Two Phone Line Connections. (Source: Silent Knight by Honeywell, Maple Grove, MN; photo courtesy of Mammoth Fire Alarms, Inc., Lowell, MA)*

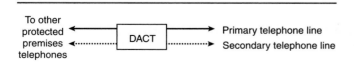

EXHIBIT 26.11 *Connections to a DACT. (Source: R.P. Schifiliti Associates, Inc., Reading, MA)*

A.26.6.3.2.1.5(4) Where two telephone lines (numbers) are used, care should be taken to assign the primary DACT telephone line (number) to a nonessential telephone line (number) at the protected premises so that the primary line used in the premises is not unnecessarily interrupted.

The term *nonessential* in A.26.6.3.2.1.5(4) does not mean "seldom used." Rather, it means a telephone line that likely would not be used during an emergency. When a DACT must transmit a signal, it seizes the telephone line and disconnects any telephone subsets downstream of the DACT. Thus, a telephone line that would be needed during an emergency should not be connected to a DACT as the primary means of transmission.

On the other hand, it is preferable to connect a DACT to a telephone line that has some usage during a normal day. That way, a user of the telephone line likely would detect and then report any trouble on that line. If a telephone line is assigned exclusively to a DACT, detection and reporting of trouble on the line would occur only during an attempted transmission of the daily test signal. If the DACT alternates between the primary and the secondary telephone lines, it could take up to 47 hours and 59 minutes to detect a failure of a line where the loop start voltage remained intact but the line could not obtain dial tone. [See Exception No. 2 to 26.6.3.2.1.4(B).]

A.26.6.3.2.1.5(7) Because call forwarding requires equipment at a telephone company central office that could occasionally interrupt the call forwarding feature, a signal should be initiated whereby the integrity of the forwarded telephone line (number) that is being called by DACTs is verified every 4 hours. This can be accomplished by a single DACT, either in service or used solely for verification, that automatically initiates and completes a transmission sequence to its associated DACR every 4 hours. A successful signal transmission sequence of any other type within the same 4-hour period should be considered sufficient to fulfill this requirement.

Call forwarding should not be confused with WATS or 800 service. The latter, differentiated from the former by dialing the 800 prefix, is a dedicated service used mainly for its toll-free feature; all calls are preprogrammed to terminate at a fixed telephone line (number) or to a dedicated line.

Occasionally, a supervising station will maintain one or more telephone numbers in a local calling area that the telephone equipment will call-forward to another number connected to the DACR. When the supervising station employs this practice, the station must verify the integrity of the call-forward instruction every 4 hours to satisfy the requirement of 26.6.3.2.1.5(7). Most often, the supervising station does this by having the service technicians coordinate the programming of the automatic daily test signal from six of the DACTs in the service area that uses the call-forwarded number. This arrangement allows one of the six DACTs to initiate its test signal every 4 hours during a 24-hour period.

When one supervising station takes over the subscribers from another supervising station, common practice uses call-forwarding to prevent having to reprogram new telephone numbers into the DACT at each protected premises. A series of acquisitions can create the situation in which a subscriber's DACT dials a telephone number that may be call-forwarded several times before reaching the current supervising station. The requirement to verify the call-forwarding every 4 hours helps ensure continuity of service.

26.6.3.2.2 Digital Alarm Communicator Receiver (DACR).

26.6.3.2.2.1 Equipment.

(A) Spare DACRs shall be provided in the supervising or subsidiary station. The spare DACRs shall be on line or able to be switched into the place of a failed unit within 30 seconds after detection of failure.

The mere presence of a spare DACR does not by itself satisfy the requirements of 26.6.3.2.2.1(A). The spare unit must either be continuously on-line or be capable of being switched into place within 30 seconds of the failure. To meet the switching requirement in 26.6.3.2.2.1(A), someone must provide adequate written instructions and train the personnel on duty in the supervising station to accomplish the switchover. Preferably, the connections to the unit should terminate in a manner that permits rapid, error-free reconnection to the spare unit. For example, multiple telephone line connections could terminate in a single plug and jack assembly that would permit rapid disconnection and rapid reconnection to the second unit.

(B) One spare DACR shall be permitted to serve as a backup for up to five DACRs in use.

(C) The number of incoming telephone lines to a DACR shall be limited to eight lines, unless the signal-receiving, processing, display, and recording equipment at the supervising or subsidiary station is duplicated and a switchover is able to be accomplished in less than 30 seconds with no loss of signal during this period, in which case the number of incoming lines to the unit shall be permitted to be unlimited.

Under most circumstances, the Code allows a maximum of eight incoming lines to connect to a single DACR. This limit helps to prevent overloading a DACR's ability to receive and process signals promptly. However, some fully automated supervising station facilities may provide completely duplicate equipment arranged to complete a switchover within 30 seconds of detection of a failure with no loss of signals. In most cases, to accomplish this switchover, the supervising station provides a "hot" standby. A hot standby simultaneously receives all of the same signals received by the primary unit for which it provides standby coverage. If the primary unit fails, the standby unit simply takes over in place of the primary.

In a few cases in which a supervising station receives thousands of signals from a wide geographic area, the supervising station operating company has provided fully operational duplicate receiving and processing equipment at two remote locations. All signals are received at both locations. Failure of the equipment at either location is totally transparent to the receipt and processing of incoming signals. No signals are ever lost. The economics of this level of redundancy depends significantly on a very large number of subscribers being served by the supervising station.

26.6.3.2.2.2 Transmission Channels.

(A)* The DACR equipment at the supervising or subsidiary station shall be connected to a minimum of two separate incoming telephone lines (numbers). The lines (numbers) shall have the following characteristics:

(1) If the lines (numbers) are in a single hunt group, they shall be individually accessible; otherwise, separate hunt groups shall be required.
(2) The lines (numbers) shall be used for no other purpose than receiving signals from a DACT.
(3) The lines (numbers) shall be unlisted.

(B) The failure of any telephone line (number) connected to a DACR due to loss of line voltage shall be annunciated visually and audibly in the supervising station.

The DACR must connect to loop start telephone lines with voltage normally present. The DACR will monitor this voltage to ensure an operable line, extending from the supervising station to the first public telephone utility wire center or first public telephone utility field-located pair gain equipment.

On a loop start telephone line, the public telephone utility continuously supplies voltage from the telephone utility wire center where the line originates. A connected DACR can monitor the integrity of the connected line by reading this constant voltage. The vast majority of residential telephone connections use loop start lines.

In contrast, almost all business telephone connections, particularly those employing PBX connections, use ground start lines. To obtain dial tone and operating power on a ground start

◄ FAQ
How is monitoring for integrity accomplished for telephone lines connected to a DACR?

line, the user equipment momentarily connects one side of the line to earth ground. Because the public telephone utility does not supply voltage to an idle ground start line, the DACR cannot use the presence of voltage to monitor the integrity of the ground start line, as it can with a loop start line.

Functionally, a DACR can receive signals over a ground start line. However, the DACR can only monitor a loop start line for integrity. See 26.6.3.2.1.1(B).

The same issues discussed in the commentary following Table A.26.6.1 and following A.26.6.3.2.1.1, relating to the provider of telephone service, apply to the supervising station.

(C)* The loading capacity for a hunt group shall be in accordance with Table 26.6.3.2.2.2(C) or be capable of demonstrating a 90 percent probability of immediately answering an incoming call.

(1) Table 26.6.3.2.2.2(C) shall be based on an average distribution of calls and an average connected time of 30 seconds for a message.
(2) The loading figures in Table 26.6.3.2.2.2(C) shall presume that the lines are in a hunt group (i.e., DACT is able to access any line not in use).
(3) A single-line DACR shall not be allowed for any of the configurations shown in Table 26.6.3.2.2.2(C).

TABLE 26.6.3.2.2.2(C) Loading Capacities for Hunt Groups

System Loading at the Supervising Station	Number of Lines in Hunt Group				
	1	**2**	**3**	**4**	**5–8**
With DACR lines processed in parallel					
Number of initiating circuits	NA	5,000	10,000	20,000	20,000
Number of DACTs	NA	500	1,500	3,000	3,000
With DACR lines processed serially (put on hold, then answered one at a time)					
Number of initiating circuits	NA	3,000	5,000	6,000	6,000
Number of DACTs	NA	300	800	1,000	1,000

NA: Not allowed.

(D) Each supervised burglar alarm (open/close) or each suppressed guard's tour transmitter shall reduce the allowable DACTs as follows:

(1) Up to a four-line hunt group, by 10
(2) Up to a five-line hunt group, by 7
(3) Up to a six-line hunt group, by 6
(4) Up to a seven-line hunt group, by 5
(5) Up to an eight-line hunt group, by 4

(E) Each guard's tour transmitter shall reduce the allowable DACTs as follows:

(1) Up to a four-line hunt group, by 30
(2) Up to a five-line hunt group, by 21
(3) Up to a six-line hunt group, by 18
(4) Up to a seven-line hunt group, by 15
(5) Up to an eight-line hunt group, by 12

(F)* A signal shall be received on each individual incoming DACR line at least once every 24 hours.

(G) The failure to receive a test signal from the protected premises shall be treated as a trouble signal.

The requirements of 26.6.3.2.2.2(G) relate to those contained in 26.6.3.2.1.5(6). At least once every 24 hours, each DACT must initiate a signal to verify the end-to-end integrity of the DACS. If the receiving or processing equipment at the supervising station has sufficient intelligence to automatically keep track of signal traffic, any incoming signal from a particular DACT may serve to satisfy this requirement, as long as the receiver receives one signal during every 24-hour period. In addition, the manufacturer of the particular DACT must have designed this feature into the unit so that the unit knows it has successfully transmitted a signal within the 24-hour period following the previous test signal.

Also note the additional requirements in 26.6.3.2.1.4(B)(1) and 26.6.3.2.1.4(B)(2), including Exception Nos. 1 and 2. Particularly note the requirement that the daily test can alternate between telephone lines.

The daily test signal serves to verify the end-to-end functioning of the system. The daily test signal monitors the integrity of the system and guards against the loss of both telephone lines connected to the DACT. The signal may also detect the malfunctioning of an entire hunt group at the DACR. In large supervising stations, the computer-based automation system often oversees the test signals. Small supervising stations might use a manual logging system to keep track of the test signals.

◄ **FAQ**
What is the purpose of the daily test signal?

A.26.6.3.2.2.2(A) The timed-release disconnect considerations as outlined in A.26.6.3.2.1.3 apply to the telephone lines (numbers) connected to a DACR at the supervising station.

It might be necessary to consult with appropriate telephone service personnel to ensure that numbers assigned to the DACR can be individually accessed even where they are connected in rotary (a hunt group).

The hunt groups provided by some older public telephone utility central office equipment may have the potential for locking onto a defective line, an action that would disable all lines in the hunt group. The requirements contained in 26.6.3.2.2.2(A) help to ensure that the design of the DACS receiving network has as high a degree of reliability as practically possible.

A.26.6.3.2.2.2(C) In determining system loading, Table 26.6.3.2.2.2(C) can be used, or it should be demonstrated that there is a 90 percent probability of incoming line availability. Table 26.6.3.2.2.2(C) is based on an average distribution of calls and an average connected time of 30 seconds per message. Therefore, where it is proposed to use Table 26.6.3.2.2.2(C) to determine system loading, if any factors are disclosed that could extend DACR connect time so as to increase the average connect time, the alternate method of determining system loading should be used. Higher (or possibly lower) loadings might be appropriate in some applications.

(1) Some factors that could increase (or decrease) the capacity of a hunt group follow:

   (a) Shorter (or longer) average message transmission time can influence hunt group capacity.
   (b) The use of audio monitoring (listen-in) slow-scan video or other similar equipment can significantly increase the connected time for a signal and reduce effective hunt group capacity.
   (c) The clustering of active burglar alarm signals can generate high peak loads at certain hours.
   (d) Inappropriate scheduling of 24-hour test signals can generate excessive peak loads.

(2) Demonstration of a 90 percent probability of incoming line availability can be accomplished by the following in-service monitoring of line activity:

   (a) Incoming lines are assigned to telephone hunt groups. When a DACT calls the main number of a hunt group, it can connect to any currently available line in that hunt group.

(b) The receiver continuously monitors the "available" status of each line. A line is available when it is waiting for an incoming call. A line is unavailable for any of the following reasons:

    i. Currently processing a call

    ii. Line in trouble

    iii. Audio monitoring (listen-in) in progress

    iv. Any other condition that makes the line input unable to accept calls

(c) The receiver monitors the "available" status of the hunt group. A hunt group is available when any line in it is available.

(d) A message is emitted by the receiver when a hunt group is unavailable for more than 1 minute out of 10 minutes. This message references the hunt group and the degree of overload.

The loading of a DACR helps to determine the overall reliability of a DACS. System designers have two options to determine loading capacity: (1) using Table 26.6.3.2.2.2(C) or (2) ensuring 90 percent probability of a call being immediately answered. Larger capacity supervising stations that employ a computer-based automation system to oversee the handling of signals normally use the second option. Such a system can monitor traffic and report the probability of a call being immediately answered by means of an automatic and real-time–generated report.

As loading increases with the addition of new customers, management of the supervising station may refer to the statistical analysis contained in that automatic report. They can use the details to determine when they must add equipment or take other action to maintain the necessary immediate answering capability.

A.26.6.3.2.2.2(F) The verification of the 24-hour DACR line test should be done early enough in the day to allow repairs to be made by the telephone company.

Depending on the number of lines involved and the design and complexity of the particular hunt group arrangements, the supervising station automation system may perform these required tests automatically. Alternatively, the supervising station operators may initiate the test signals manually while sequentially creating a busy signal on each line in a hunt group.

26.6.3.2.3 Digital Alarm Radio System (DARS).

The digital alarm radio system (DARS) described in 26.6.3.2.3 functionally combines within one listed system a DACT connected to a single telephone line and a digital alarm radio transmitter (DART), which uses radio frequency technology to transmit signals to a digital alarm radio receiver (DARR) at the supervising station.

The requirements in 26.6.3.2.3 were introduced into the Code simultaneously with the requirements in 26.6.3.3.2. The original intent was to describe a DACS that used a DACT connected to a single telephone line with an alternative means of transmission provided by a one-way private radio alarm system transmitter. Over the ensuing 20 years, alarm service providers have deployed relatively few such systems compared with the total number of subscribers using more traditional DACS. This is not a reflection on the efficacy of the technology. Rather, it relates more to market issues.

26.6.3.2.3.1 General Requirements.

(A) If any DACT signal transmission is unsuccessful, the information shall be transmitted by means of the digital alarm radio transmitter (DART).

(B) The DACT shall continue its transmission sequence as required by 26.6.3.2.3.1(C).

When a DARS provides the secondary transmission path for a DACT, the DACT must continue to attempt to complete the call to the DACR. Paragraph 26.6.3.2.1.4(B)(7) permits simultaneous transmission by both the DACT and the DART.

(C) The DARS shall be capable of demonstrating a minimum of 90 percent probability of successfully completing each transmission sequence.

To fulfill the requirement in 26.6.3.2.3.1(C), engineers must complete radio propagation studies that satisfy the specified 90 percent reliability factor. The Code has similar requirements for a one-way radio alarm system in 26.6.3.3.2.2, with additional explanatory text in A.26.6.3.3.2.2.

(D) Transmission sequences shall be repeated a minimum of five times. The DART transmission shall be permitted to be terminated in less than five sequences if the DACT successfully communicates to the DACR.

To provide overall system reliability, the system must make a sufficient number of attempts to complete the signal transmission.

(E) Each DART shall automatically initiate and complete a test signal transmission sequence to its associated digital alarm radio receiver (DARR) at least once every 24 hours. A successful DART signal transmission sequence of any other type within the same 24-hour period shall fulfill the requirement to test the integrity of the reporting system, provided that signal processing is automated so that 24-hour delinquencies are individually acknowledged by supervising station personnel.

The requirements of 26.6.3.2.3.1(E) correlate with the requirements of 26.6.3.2.1.4(B)(2). When a DACT connects to a single telephone line as the primary transmission path and through a DARS as the secondary transmission path, the system must conduct a test at least once every 24 hours for each transmission path.

26.6.3.2.3.2 Digital Alarm Radio Transmitter (DART). A DART shall transmit a digital code or another approved signal by use of radio transmission to its associated digital alarm radio receiver (DARR).

(A) Signal repetition, digital parity check, or another approved means of signal verification shall be used.

(B) The DART shall comply with applicable FCC rules consistent with its operating frequency.

The requirements of 26.6.3.2.3.2(A) and 26.6.3.2.3.2(B) ensure that a DART uses digital information or other coded signal radio transmission to communicate the status of the fire alarm system at the protected premises. These requirements preclude the use of voice information transmission.

26.6.3.2.3.3 Digital Alarm Radio Receiver (DARR) Equipment.

(A) A spare DARR shall be provided in the supervising station and shall be able to be switched into the place of a failed unit within 30 seconds after detection of failure.

(B) Facilities shall be provided at the supervising station for supervisory and control functions of subsidiary and repeater station radio-receiving equipment. This shall be accomplished via a supervised circuit where the radio equipment is remotely located from the supervising or subsidiary station. The following conditions shall be supervised at the supervising station:

(1) Failure of ac power supplying the radio equipment
(2) Malfunction of receiver
(3) Malfunction of antenna and interconnecting cable
(4) Indication of automatic switchover of the DARR
(5) Malfunction of data transmission line between the DARR and the supervising or subsidiary station

Monitoring the integrity of the functions included in 26.6.3.2.3.3(B) helps to ensure overall system reliability. A large supervising station equipped with a computer-based automation system likely will use that automation system to perform most or all of these functions.

26.6.3.3 Radio Systems.

26.6.3.3.1 Two-Way Radio Frequency (RF) Multiplex Systems.

A two-way RF multiplex system in 26.6.3.3.1 consists of a traditional multiplex fire alarm system that uses a licensed two-way radio system to receive interrogation signals from the supervising station to the protected premises and to transmit signals from the protected premises to the supervising station. Essentially, the multiplex-based interrogation and response fire alarm system operates transparently over the radio portion of the system.

These systems must use licensed two-way radio because of the restrictions that current FCC regulations place on the number of times in a 1-hour period that an unlicensed radio transmitter may transmit information. In addition, the FCC has set aside a portion of the radio spectrum for use by radio telemetry applications. The use of licensed radio to transmit fire alarm, supervisory, and trouble signals falls within the definition of radio telemetry.

The Code states requirements for two-way RF multiplex systems that are essentially identical to those requirements that the Code stated for legacy active multiplex systems in previous editions.

26.6.3.3.1.1 Maximum Operating Time. The maximum end-to-end operating time parameters allowed for a two-way RF multiplex system shall be as follows:

(1) The maximum allowable time lapse from the initiation of a single alarm signal until it is recorded at the supervising station shall not exceed 90 seconds. When any number of subsequent alarm signals occur at any rate, they shall be recorded at a rate no slower than one every additional 10 seconds.

The requirements of 26.6.3.3.1.1(1) ensure that two-way RF multiplex systems will complete an interrogation and response sequence for each protected premises interface transceiver (transmitter/receiver) at least every 90 seconds. Any change of status that would indicate a fire alarm condition would transmit within this time frame.

As an alternative, the system may provide some other means to ensure alarm receipt within the specified time period. For example, a designer could devise equipment that immediately transmits alarm signals from any two-way RF multiplex interface transceiver at the protected premises, regardless of what point the system has reached in its normal 90-second interrogation and response sequence.

(2) The maximum allowable time lapse from the occurrence of an adverse condition in any transmission channel until recording of the adverse condition is started shall not exceed 200 seconds for Type 4 and Type 5 systems. The requirements of 26.6.3.3.1.4 shall apply.

Paragraph 26.6.3.3.1.1(2) also ensures that, as a part of the interrogation and response sequence for each protected premises, any change of status that would indicate an adverse condition would transmit within a time frame of at least every 200 seconds for both Type 4 and Type 5 two-way RF multiplex systems.

(3) In addition to the maximum operating time allowed for alarm signals, the requirements of one of the following shall be met:

   (a) A system unit that has more than 500 initiating device circuits shall be able to record not less than 50 simultaneous status changes within 90 seconds.
   (b) A system unit that has fewer than 500 initiating device circuits shall be able to record not less than 10 percent of the total number of simultaneous status changes within 90 seconds.

The requirements in 26.6.3.3.1.1 ensure that the portion of the two-way RF multiplex system that processes and records status changes can do so with sufficient speed to handle a reasonable volume of signal traffic, based on the system's signal capacity.

26.6.3.3.1.2 Supervisory and Control Functions. Facilities shall be provided at the supervising station for the following supervisory and control functions of the supervising or subsidiary station and the repeater station radio transmitting and receiving equipment, which shall be accomplished via a supervised circuit where the radio equipment is remotely located from the system unit:

(1) RF transmitter in use (radiating).
(2) Failure of ac power supplying the radio equipment.
(3) RF receiver malfunction.
(4) Indication of automatic switchover.
(5) Independent deactivation of either RF transmitter shall be controlled from the supervising station.

The supervisory functions described in 26.6.3.3.1.2 help to ensure continuity of signal transmission between the protected premises and the supervising station.

26.6.3.3.1.3 Transmission Channel.

(A) The RF multiplex transmission channel shall terminate in an RF transmitter/receiver at the protected premises and in a system unit at the supervising or subsidiary station.

(B) Operation of the transmission channel shall conform to the requirements of this Code whether channels are private facilities, such as microwave, or leased facilities furnished by a communications utility company. If private signal transmission facilities are used, the equipment necessary to transmit signals shall also comply with requirements for duplicate equipment or replacement of critical components, as described in 26.6.4.2.

The requirements in 26.6.3.3.1.3(B) help ensure that the system complies with the requirements of the Code, even if the facilities are leased from a communications utility company. The paragraph further ensures continuity of operations by requiring either redundant critical assemblies or replacement with on-premises spares. Either action must restore service within 30 minutes. (See 26.6.3.1.5 and 26.6.4.2.)

◀ **FAQ**
What is the purpose of the requirements of 26.6.3.3.1.3(B)?

26.6.3.3.1.4* Categories. Two-way RF multiplex systems shall be divided into Type 4 or Type 5 classifications based on their ability to perform under adverse conditions.

(A) A Type 4 system shall have two or more control sites configured as follows:

(1) Each site shall have an RF receiver interconnected to the supervising or subsidiary station by a separate channel.
(2) The RF transmitter/receiver located at the protected premises shall be within transmission range of at least two RF receiving sites.
(3) The system shall contain two RF transmitters that are one of the following:

    (a) Located at one site with the capability of interrogating all of the RF transmitters/receivers on the premises
    (b) Dispersed with all of the RF transmitters/receivers on the premises having the capability to be interrogated by two different RF transmitters

(4) Each RF transmitter shall maintain a status that allows immediate use at all times. Facilities shall be provided in the supervising or subsidiary station to operate any off-line RF transmitter at least once every 8 hours.
(5) Any failure of one of the RF receivers shall in no way interfere with the operation of the system from the other RF receiver. Failure of any receiver shall be annunciated at the supervising station.

(6) A physically separate channel shall be required between each RF transmitter or RF receiver site, or both, and the system unit.

(B) A Type 5 system shall have a single control site configured as follows:

(1) A minimum of one RF receiving site
(2) A minimum of one RF transmitting site

A.26.6.3.3.1.4 The intent of the plurality of control sites is to safeguard against damage caused by lightning and to minimize the effect of interference on the receipt of signals. The control sites can be co-located.

With a two-way RF multiplex system, each protected premises has its own RF transceiver (transmitter/receiver) unit. The requirements for a Type 4 system essentially create a two-way RF multiplex system that has redundancy of critical components. A Type 4 two-way RF multiplex system must have a plurality of control sites. Each site contains an RF transceiver (transmitter/receiver) unit. An authority having jurisdiction or a system designer, expecting a high volume of traffic or unusual transient radio frequency propagation problems, would use such a system.

The requirements for a Type 5 system provide for a minimum level of system integrity that would offer adequate service for most normal applications.

26.6.3.3.1.5 Loading Capacities.

(A) The loading capacities of two-way RF multiplex systems shall be based on the overall reliability of the signal receiving, processing, display, and recording equipment at the supervising or subsidiary station and the capability to transmit signals during adverse conditions of the transmission channels.

(B) Allowable loading capacities shall comply with Table 26.6.3.3.1.5(B).

TABLE 26.6.3.3.1.5(B) *Loading Capacities for Two-Way RF Multiplex Systems*

	System Type	
Trunks	*Type 4*	*Type 5*
Maximum number of alarm service initiating device circuits per primary trunk facility	5,120	1,280
Maximum number of leg facilities for alarm service per primary trunk facility	512	128
Maximum number of leg facilities for all types of alarm service per secondary trunk facility*	128	128
Maximum number of all types of initiating device circuits per primary trunk facility in any combination	10,240	2,560
Maximum number of leg facilities for types of alarm service per primary trunk facility in any combination*	1,024	256
System Units at the Supervising Station		
Maximum number of all types of initiating device circuits per system unit*	10,240	10,240
Maximum number of protected buildings and premises per system unit	512	512
Maximum number of alarm service initiating device circuits per system	5,120	5,120
Systems Emitting from Subsidiary Station†	—	—

*Includes every initiating device circuit (e.g., waterflow, alarm, supervisory, guard, burglary, hold-up).
†Same as system units at the supervising station.

The loading of a two-way RF multiplex system depends on the capability of the type of system. Because a Type 4 system has a redundant transceiver (transmitter/receiver) exerting control over the interrogation and response sequence between the protected premises and the supervising station, it has the greatest permitted system loading. A Type 5 system does not have redundant transceivers in control of the system, so it has a more limited trunk capacity.

(C) The capacity of a system unit shall be permitted to be unlimited if the signal-receiving, processing, display, and recording equipment are duplicated at the supervising station and a switchover is able to be accomplished in not more than 30 seconds, with no loss of signals during this period.

The requirements of 26.6.3.3.1.5(C) modify the lower half of Table 26.6.3.3.1.5(B). However, to meet these requirements, a two-way RF multiplex system would have to employ complete redundancy of all critical components and complete a switchover in 30 seconds with no loss of signals.

Systems that meet these requirements generally process all incoming signals in tandem, that is, both the main unit and the standby unit process incoming signals at all times. When the main unit fails, the standby unit continues to function normally. Operators would actually change over only those incidental peripheral devices that have no required redundancy.

26.6.3.3.2 One-Way Private Radio Alarm Systems.

One-way private radio alarm systems in 26.6.3.3.2 contemplate the use of a single radio alarm transmitter (RAT) at a protected premises that transmits fire alarm, supervisory, and trouble signals from the protected premises to at least two radio alarm repeater station receivers (RARSRs). These RARSRs likely would be located in different geographic locations. Usually, they would be part of a network of multiple RARSRs located at widely diverse geographic locations throughout a city, county, or other political subdivision. This network of RARSRs would connect through a suitable transmission path to the radio alarm supervising station receiver (RASSR).

Because this one-way radio system does not have interrogation and response capability, the use of either multiple RARSRs or multiple RASSRs would increase the likelihood that the single transmitter would successfully transmit a signal that could be received by the supervising station. In creating the network of RARSRs or RASSRs, engineers probably would conduct radio propagation studies to determine factors likely to influence the reception of signals from transmitters at various protected premises.

To create the requirements for an RF transmission system that does not have an interrogation and response sequence to monitor the integrity of the transmission of signals between the protected premises and the supervising station, the Technical Committee on Supervising Station Fire Alarm Systems borrowed heavily from the requirements for DACSs.

26.6.3.3.2.1 Independent Receivers.

The requirements in 26.6.3.3.2.1 for a one-way private radio alarm system allow the use of either a private system operated by a single alarm service provider or a multi-user system operated by a one-way radio network provider. Most systems communicate through a multi-user network.

◄ **FAQ**
What type of network is most commonly used for a one-way private radio alarm system?

Paragraph 26.6.3.3.2.1(C) also permits a RAT to transmit directly to a single RASSR as long as the RAT has the capability of receiving an acknowledgement that the RASSR has received the transmitted signal. Such an arrangement, of course, belies the title "one-way," since communication would in fact take place in two directions, or "two-way."

(A) The requirements of 26.6.3.3.2 for a radio alarm repeater station receiver (RARSR) shall be satisfied if the signals from each radio alarm transmitter (RAT) are received and supervised, in accordance with Chapter 26, by at least two independently powered, independently operating, and separately located RARSRs or radio alarm supervising station receivers (RASSRs), or by one of each.

(B) At least two separate paths shall be provided from a RAT to the ultimate RASSR.

(C) Only one path to the RASSR shall be required to be utilized in the event alarms can be transmitted from a RAT to the RASSR and the RAT has the ability to receive a positive acknowledgment that the RASSR has received the signal.

26.6.3.3.2.2* Maximum Operating Time. The end-to-end operating time parameters allowed for a one-way radio alarm system shall be as follows:

(1) There shall be a 90 percent probability that the time between the initiation of a single alarm signal until it is recorded at the supervising station will not exceed 90 seconds.
(2) There shall be a 99 percent probability that the time between the initiation of a single alarm signal until it is recorded at the supervising station will not exceed 180 seconds.
(3) There shall be a 99.999 percent probability that the time between the initiation of a single alarm signal until it is recorded at the supervising station will not exceed 7.5 minutes (450 seconds), at which time the RAT shall cease transmitting. When any number of subsequent alarm signals occurs at any rate, they shall be recorded at an average rate no slower than one every additional 10 seconds.
(4) In addition to the maximum operating time allowed for alarm signals, the system shall be able to record not less than 12 simultaneous status changes within 90 seconds at the supervising station.

A.26.6.3.3.2.2 It is intended that each RAT communicate with two or more independently located RARSRs. The location of such RARSRs should be such that they do not share common facilities.

NOTE: All probability calculations required for the purposes of Chapter 17 should be made in accordance with established communications procedures, should assume the maximum channel loading parameters specified, and should further assume that 25 RATs are actively in alarm and are being received by each RARSR.

Because one-way private radio alarm systems do not have an interrogation and response sequence to verify the operating capability of the communications channel and all equipment associated with it, the system must rely on other means to achieve an acceptable level of operational integrity. The probabilities specified in 26.6.3.3.2.2(1), 26.6.3.3.2.2(2), and 26.6.3.3.2.2(3) help to ensure that level of integrity.

To achieve the required probabilities, the RAT functions similarly to a DACT. The RAT makes a given number of attempts to transmit to one or both of the two receivers. After a number of attempts, the RAT stops transmitting so it will not tie up the receiver.

26.6.3.3.2.3 Supervision. Equipment shall be provided at the supervising station for the supervisory and control functions of the supervising or subsidiary station and for the repeater station radio transmitting and receiving equipment. This shall be accomplished via a supervised circuit where the radio equipment is remotely located from the system unit and the conditions of 26.6.3.3.2.3(A) through 26.6.3.3.2.3(D) are met.

(A) The following conditions shall be supervised at the supervising station:

(1) Failure of ac power supplying the radio equipment
(2) Malfunction of RF receiver
(3) Indication of automatic switchover, if applicable

(B) Interconnections between elements of transmitting equipment, including any antennas, shall be supervised either to cause an indication of failure at the protected premises or to transmit a trouble signal to the supervising station.

(C) If elements of transmitting equipment are physically separated, the wiring or cabling between them shall be protected by conduit.

(D) Personnel shall be dispatched to arrive within 12 hours to initiate maintenance after detection of primary power failure.

The specified supervisory functions of 26.6.3.3.2.3(A), the requirements of 26.6.3.3.2.3(B), and the installation requirements of 26.6.3.3.2.3(C) help to ensure the continuity of signal transmission between the protected premises and the supervising station. Paragraphs 26.6.3.3.2.3(B) and 26.6.3.3.2.3(C) address two serious points of potential failure. Either the loss of the antenna or the loss of connection between the transmitter and the antenna would impair transmission.

In some systems, the transmitter connects directly to the antenna. In others, the installer locates the antenna at a point in the building more advantageous for successful transmission of a signal. The requirement in 26.6.3.3.2.3(B) helps ensure that a trouble signal resulting from the loss of the antenna or its connection will annunciate at least locally. The installation requirement in 26.6.3.3.2.3(C) further requires mechanical protection. An installer would achieve this protection by installing the conductors between the transmitter and the remote antenna in conduit.

26.6.3.3.2.4 Transmission Channels. Transmission channels shall comply with 26.6.3.3.2.4(A) through 26.6.3.3.2.4(F).

(A) The one-way RF transmission channel shall originate with a RAT at the protected premises and shall terminate at the RF receiving system of an RARSR or RASSR capable of receiving transmissions from such transmitting devices.

(B) A receiving network transmission channel shall terminate at an RARSR at one end and with either another RARSR or an RASSR at the other end.

The requirements in 26.6.3.3.2.4(B) permit the overall system architecture necessary to develop a network suitably robust to handle a large number of RATs. The network interconnections can use multiple RARSRs that, in turn, repeat the received signals to other RARSRs until the signals ultimately reach a RASSR.

Along each segment of the transmission path, at least two RARSRs must always receive the signal.

(C) Operation of receiving network transmission channels shall conform to the requirements of this Code whether channels are private facilities, such as microwave, or leased facilities furnished by a communications utility company.

The requirement in 26.6.3.3.2.4(C) intends to ensure that the system will comply with the Code, even if the installer leases facilities from a communications utility company or some other one-way radio network service provider.

(D) If private signal transmission facilities are used, the equipment necessary to transmit signals shall also comply with requirements for duplicate equipment or replacement of critical components as described in 26.6.4.2.

The requirements in 26.6.3.3.2.4(D) intend to further ensure continuity of operations by requiring either redundant critical assemblies or an arrangement such that technicians can replace critical assemblies with on-premises spares and restore service within 30 minutes.

(E) The system shall provide information that indicates the quality of the received signal for each RARSR supervising each RAT in accordance with 26.6.3.3.2 and shall provide information at the supervising station when such signal quality falls below the minimum signal quality levels set forth in 26.6.3.3.2.

The system must monitor the quality of the transmitted signal, including the various operating time parameters specified in 26.6.3.3.2.2.

FAQ ▶
**What is one method used to
achieve compliance with
26.6.3.3.2.4(E)?**

To accomplish the requirement of 26.6.3.3.2.4(E), one design provides each RAT with an internal clock. Each transmitted signal includes the time of first transmission and the current time, along with the alarm, supervisory, or trouble data. A software program connected to the RASSR can use the time information from each received signal to calculate a statistical analysis that verifies compliance with the time probability parameters of 26.6.3.3.2.2.

(F) Each RAT shall be installed in such a manner so as to provide a signal quality over at least two independent one-way RF transmission channels, of the minimum quality level specified, that satisfies the performance requirements in 26.6.2.4 and 26.6.4.

26.6.3.3.2.5 System Categories. One-way radio alarm systems shall be divided into two categories on the basis of the following number of RASSRs present in the system:

(1) A Type 6 system shall have one RASSR and at least two RARSRs.
(2) A Type 7 system shall have more than one RASSR and at least two RARSRs.
(3) In a Type 7 system, when more than one RARSR is out of service and, as a result, any RATs are no longer being supervised, the affected supervising station shall be notified.
(4) In a Type 6 system, when any RARSR is out of service, a trouble signal shall be annunciated at the supervising station.

A Type 6 one-way private radio alarm system serves a single supervising station. A Type 7 one-way private radio alarm system serves more than one supervising station. A multi-user one-way radio network used to connect one or more protected premises to a supervising station most closely fits the Type 7 system description.

26.6.3.3.2.6 Loading Capacities. The loading capacities of one-way radio alarm systems shall be based on the overall reliability of the signal-receiving, processing, display, and recording equipment at the supervising or subsidiary station and the capability to transmit signals during adverse conditions of the transmission channels. Loading capacities shall comply with 26.6.3.3.2.6(A) and 26.6.3.3.2.6(B).

(A) Allowable loading capacities shall be in accordance with Table 26.6.3.3.2.6(A), except as modified by the following:

(1) Each guard's tour transmitter shall reduce the allowable RATs by 15.
(2) Each two-way protected premises radio transmitter shall reduce the allowable RATs by two.
(3) Each supervised burglar alarm (open/close) or each suppressed guard's tour transmitter shall reduce the allowable RATs by five.

(B) If the signal-receiving, processing, display, and recording equipment is duplicated at the supervising station and a switchover is able to be accomplished in not more than 30 seconds, with no loss of signals during this period, the capacity of a system unit shall be permitted to be unlimited.

Paragraph 26.6.3.3.2.6(B) modifies the requirements for system units at the supervising station given in Table 26.6.3.3.2.6(A). However, to meet this requirement, a one-way private radio alarm system would have to employ complete redundancy of all critical components and complete a switchover in 30 seconds with no loss of signals. Those systems that meet this requirement generally process all incoming signals in tandem; that is, both the main unit and the standby unit process incoming signals at all times. When the main unit fails, the standby unit continues to function normally. Operators would actually change over only those incidental peripheral devices that have no required redundancy.

TABLE 26.6.3.3.2.6(A) *Loading Capacities of One-Way Radio Alarm Systems*

Radio Alarm Repeater Station Receiver (RARSR)	System Type	
	Type 6	Type 7
Maximum number of fire alarm service initiating device circuits per RARSR	5,120	5,120
Maximum number of RATs for fire	512	512
Maximum number of all types of initiating device circuits per RARSR in any combination*	10,240	10,240
Maximum number of RATs for all types of fire alarm service per RARSR in any combination*	1,024	1,024
System Units at the Supervising Station		
Maximum number of all types of initiating device circuits per system unit*	10,240	10,240
Maximum number of fire-protected buildings and premises per system unit	512	512
Maximum number of fire alarm service initiating device circuits per system unit	5,120	5,120

*Includes every initiating device circuit (e.g., waterflow, fire alarm, supervisory, guard, burglary, hold-up).

26.6.4 Display and Recording Requirements for All Transmission Technologies.

Subsection 26.6.4 specifies the content and nature of the display and recording of signals received at a supervising station. The requirements take into account a reasonable quantity of signal traffic. They also consider certain ergonomic necessities for interfacing electronically reproduced signals with one or more human operators.

◄ **FAQ**
What does 26.6.4 specify?

26.6.4.1* Any status changes, including the initiation or restoration to normal of a trouble condition, that occur in an initiating device or in any interconnecting circuits or equipment, including the local protected premises controls from the location of the initiating device(s) to the supervising station, shall be presented in a form to expedite prompt operator interpretation. Status change signals shall provide the following information:

(1) Identification of the type of signal to show whether it is an alarm, supervisory, delinquency, or trouble signal
(2) Identification of the signal to differentiate between an initiation of an alarm, a supervisory, a delinquency, or a trouble signal and a clearing from one or more of these conditions
(3) Identification of the site of origin of each status change signal
(4)* Identification of specific types of signals that dictate a different response

A.26.6.4.1 The signal information can be permitted to be provided in coded form. Records can be permitted to be used to interpret these codes.

A.26.6.4.1(4) Any signal that would dictate a different response, such as carbon monoxide alarms or mass notification alarms, should be individually identifiable so the appropriate response to the event can be initiated. There are more types of alarms and other signals that are being received at supervising stations and that require different responses by supervising station operators. These signals could be other than fire, but still life safety in nature, and must be uniquely identified because their signal is indicative of a different response.

26.6.4.2* If duplicate equipment for signal receiving, processing, display, and recording is not provided, the installed equipment shall be designed so that any critical assembly is able to be replaced from on-premises spares and the system is able to be restored to service within

30 minutes. A critical assembly shall be an assembly in which a malfunction prevents the receipt and interpretation of signals by the supervising station operator.

Exception: Proprietary station systems.

A.26.6.4.2 In order to expedite repairs, it is recommended that spare modules, such as printed circuit boards, CRT displays, or printers, be stocked at the supervising station.

The requirements in 26.6.4.2 ensure that a technician will promptly repair any malfunction in a critical assembly, as defined in this paragraph. The technician may repair the defective assembly or, more often, replace the defective assembly with an on-premises spare. Any assembly too complex for a technician to readily repair requires a duplicate. Note that the exception limits the application of 26.6.4.2 to central station and remote supervising station alarm systems.

26.6.4.3* Any method of recording and display or indication of change of status signals shall be permitted, provided that all of the following conditions are met:

(1) Each change of status signal requiring action to be taken by the operator shall result in an audible signal and not less than two independent methods of identifying the type, condition, and location of the status change.
(2) Each change of status signal shall be automatically recorded. The record shall provide the type of signal, condition, and location, as required by 26.6.4.1, in addition to the time and date the signal was received.
(3) Failure of an operator to acknowledge or act upon a change of status signal shall not prevent subsequent alarm signals from being received, indicated or displayed, and recorded.
(4) Change of status signals requiring action to be taken by the operator shall be displayed or indicated in a manner that clearly differentiates them from those that have been acted upon and acknowledged.
(5) Each incoming signal to a DACR or DARR shall cause an audible signal that persists until manually acknowledged.

Exception: Test signals required by 26.6.3.2.1.5(6) received at a DACR or a DARR.

A.26.6.4.3 For all forms of transmission, the maximum time to process an alarm signal should be 90 seconds. The maximum time to process a supervisory signal should be 4 minutes. The time to process an alarm or supervisory signal is defined as that time measured from receipt of a signal until retransmission or subscriber contact is initiated.

When the level of traffic in a supervising station system reaches a magnitude such that delayed response is possible, even if the loading tables or loading formulas of this Code are not exceeded, it is envisioned that it will be necessary to employ an enhanced method of processing.

For example, in a system where a single DACR instrument provided with fire and burglar alarm service is connected to multiple telephone lines, it is conceivable that, during certain periods of the day, fire alarm signals could be delayed by the security signaling traffic, such as opening and closing signals. Such an enhanced system would perform as follows, upon receipt of a signal:

(1) Automatically process the signals, differentiating between those that require immediate response by supervising station personnel and those that need only be logged
(2) Automatically provide relevant subscriber information to assist supervising station personnel in their response
(3) Maintain a timed, unalterable log of the signals received and the response of supervising station personnel to such signals

26.6.5 Testing and Maintenance Requirements for All Transmission Technologies. Testing and maintenance of communications methods shall be in accordance with the requirements of Chapter 14.

REFERENCES CITED IN COMMENTARY

ANSI/UL 827, *Standard for Central-Station Alarm Services*, 2008 edition, revised June 11, 2008, American National Standards Institute, Inc. New York, NY.

Approval Guide, FM Global, Norwood, MA, published annually.

FM Approval Standard 3011, *Central Station Service for Fire Alarms and Protective Equipment Supervision*, April 1999, FM Global, Norwood, MA. *Manual of Style for NFPA Technical Committee Documents*, 2004 edition, National Fire Protection Association, Quincy, MA.

NFPA 70®, National Electrical Code®, 2008 edition, National Fire Protection Association, Quincy, MA.

NFPA 71, *Standard for the Installation, Maintenance, and Use of Signaling Systems for Central Station Service* (incorporated into NFPA 70 in 1993), National Fire Protection Association, Quincy, MA.

NFPA 600, *Standard on Industrial Fire Brigades*, 2005 edition, National Fire Protection Association, Quincy, MA.

NFPA 1221, *Standard for the Installation, Maintenance, and Use of Emergency Services Communications Systems*, 2010 edition, National Fire Protection Association, Quincy, MA.

UL Fire Protection Equipment Directory, Underwriters Laboratories Inc., Northbrook, IL, published annually.

Public Emergency Alarm Reporting Systems

CHAPTER 27

Chapter 27 (Chapter 9 in previous editions of the Code) covers the configuration, performance, installation, and operation of all public emergency alarm reporting systems and auxiliary alarm systems. Throughout the text, in keeping with the broader scope of the overall Code, the technical committee has deleted the word *fire* from many phrases to make the wording more suitably generic, including in the chapter title, which was formerly Public Fire Alarm Reporting Systems.

The following list is a summary of significant changes to the chapter on public emergency alarm reporting systems in the 2010 edition:

- Revised 27.1.1 clarifying the way users should apply this chapter
- New 27.1.7 stating that when a protected premises transmits signals to a communications center via a public emergency alarm reporting system, the entire alarm system becomes classified as an auxiliary alarm system
- New 27.4.1.1 describing the types of communications pathways that a public emergency alarm reporting system may use
- New 27.4.1.2 granting permission to use a public emergency alarm reporting system with emergency communications systems covered by Chapter 24
- New Section 27.8 providing requirements for emergency communications systems

Exhibit 27.1 shows the typical installation of a public emergency alarm reporting system located at a major office building complex.

EXHIBIT 27.1 Public Emergency Alarm Reporting System Box 1896.

27.1 Application

27.1.1 The provisions of this chapter apply to the proper configuration, performance, installation, and operation of public emergency alarm reporting systems and auxiliary alarm systems. Public emergency alarm reporting systems shall consist of alarm boxes and alarm processing equipment that communicate on a wired or wireless network(s), one-way or two-way, meeting the requirements of this chapter. This shall include systems that use a communications infrastructure that is publicly owned, operated, and controlled.

The key to understanding this chapter rests with the last sentence in 27.1.1. The systems described in this chapter use a communications infrastructure owned, operated, and controlled by a public agency.

Originally, the contents of this chapter, along with the requirements that now reside in NFPA 1221, *Standard for the Installation, Maintenance, and Use of Emergency Services Communications Systems*, appeared first as part of a general NFPA signaling standard. Later, the NFPA Standards Council divided the requirements into a public fire communications standard under the designation of NFPA 73 (not to be confused with the current NFPA 73, which has nothing to do with alarm systems). In the early 1970s, NFPA began to consolidate all fire service–related standards using standard numbers 1000 and above. At that time, NFPA 73 became NFPA 1221.

In July of 1990, the NFPA Standards Council disbanded all the then-existing signaling systems technical committees and reconstituted the NFPA signaling systems project to create a single, unified national fire alarm code. At that time, the Standards Council directed that the municipal emergency reporting boxes, their related communications pathways, and the auxiliary alarm systems portions of NFPA 1221 be transferred to the new signaling project and become a chapter in the new *NFPA 72, National Fire Alarm Code*.

Chapter 27 provides requirements for publicly accessible alarm boxes installed throughout a community that connect to a receiving location that meets the requirements of NFPA 1221 using communications pathways owned, operated, and controlled by a public authority, such as a municipal government. Such boxes permit members of the public to transmit a request for emergency response from the public authority. In the simplest arrangement, these boxes transmit a signal indicating the need for response to a fire. In other, more complex arrangements, alarm boxes transmit distinct signals indicating the need for a variety of different types of emergency response, such as fire, police, emergency medical, or even vehicle repair services on limited access highways.

This chapter also provides requirements for special alarm boxes, known as *master boxes*, that provide an interface between a protected premises alarm system and the public emergency alarm reporting system. Signals from the protected premises transmit to the communications center through the public emergency alarm reporting system. When such a connection is made, the entire alarm system becomes designated as an auxiliary alarm system. (See 27.1.7.)

27.1.2 The installation and use of public emergency alarm reporting systems and auxiliary alarm systems shall comply with the requirements of this chapter.

Chapter 27 addresses public emergency alarm reporting systems and auxiliary alarm systems that connect an alarm system at a protected premises to a public emergency alarm reporting system. (See Exhibit 27.2.) Public emergency alarm reporting systems are also known as *municipal emergency (fire) alarm systems*. Paragraph 3.3.199 defines a *public emergency alarm reporting system* as "a system of alarm-initiating devices, transmitting and receiving equipment, and communication infrastructure (other than a public telephone network) used to communicate with the communications center to provide any combination of manual or auxiliary alarm service." The *communications center,* defined in 3.3.49, houses the central operating part of the public emergency alarm reporting system. Larger municipalities usually locate the communications center at a facility specially designed for the purpose.

Smaller communities often locate the communications center at the fire station, police station, sheriff's office, or even a private agency that has contracted with one or more municipalities to provide public emergency communications services. Some rural communities even locate the communications center at a local business, such as a gasoline service station or restaurant, that has personnel on duty 24 hours each day.

EXHIBIT 27.2 *Communications Center. (Source: Lakes Region Mutual Fire Aid, Laconia, NH; photo by Debbie Kardaseski)*

In most cases, smaller municipalities will not have public emergency alarm reporting systems as described by this chapter. Rarely, a small community that has a high-value property, such as a large hospital complex or college campus, may provide a public emergency alarm reporting system in order to hasten the dispatch of emergency responders to alarm signals from the buildings at the high-value property.

NFPA 1221 addresses the facilities and operations of communications centers, while *NFPA 72* addresses the alarm systems used for signaling to the communications center.

An *auxiliary alarm system* is defined in 3.3.199.1 as "a protected premises fire alarm system or other emergency system at the protected premises and the system used to connect the protected premises system to a public emergency alarm reporting system for transmitting an alarm to the communications center." Where permitted by the authority having jurisdiction, fire alarm systems at a protected premises can connect to the public emergency alarm reporting system as a means of transmitting alarm signals to the communications center. The method of connecting the building alarm system to a public emergency alarm reporting system will depend on the type of public reporting system.

Where the public emergency alarm reporting system uses alarm boxes connected to a wired network, the Code offers two methods to connect a building fire alarm system: a *local energy type auxiliary alarm system*, defined in 3.3.199.1.1, and a *shunt-type auxiliary alarm system*, defined in 3.3.199.1.2.

Boxes using a wireless network or boxes using a telephone (series) wired network require a local energy auxiliary connection.

◀ **FAQ**
What two methods does the Code offer for connecting a building alarm system to a communications center that uses a wired network?

27.1.3 The requirements of this chapter shall apply to systems and equipment for the transmission and reception of alarm and other emergency signals, including those from auxiliary alarm systems, connected to the public emergency alarm reporting system.

27.1.4 The requirements of Chapters 10 and 14 shall also apply unless they are in conflict with this chapter.

27.1.5 The requirements of this chapter shall not apply to Chapter 29 unless otherwise noted.

27.1.6 The application of public emergency alarm reporting systems and auxiliary alarm systems to provide defined reporting functions from or within private premises shall be permitted where approved by the authority having jurisdiction.

Historically, the requirements of Chapter 27 have permitted the transmission of only fire alarm signals or trouble signals relating to the reporting system itself to the communications center. An exception exists in the permissive requirements of 27.2.2.

However, these requirements typically do not consider the transmission of supervisory signals or trouble signals from a protected premises. In rare cases, a municipality or other governmental entity may exercise its right as an authority having jurisdiction and permit the transmission of supervisory or trouble signals from buildings the entity owns. In most cases in this situation, the municipality uses wireless network municipal boxes that provide for the transmission of multiple data points from each box.

27.1.7* Where a protected premises fire alarm system or other emergency system at the protected premises has its signals sent to a communications center via public emergency alarm reporting system, the protected premises system shall become an auxiliary alarm system.

A.27.1.7 Auxiliary alarm systems include the equipment at the protected premises as well as the equipment connecting it to the public emergency alarm reporting system. While the operational requirements relating to the signals sent off-premises fall under the scope of Chapter 27, the requirements of Chapter 23 also apply.

27.2 General Fundamentals

27.2.1* Public emergency alarm reporting systems shall be designed, installed, operated, and maintained in accordance with this chapter to provide reliable transmission and receipt of alarms in a manner acceptable to the authority having jurisdiction.

A.27.2.1 When choosing from available options to implement a public emergency alarm reporting system, the operating agency should consider which of the choices would facilitate the maximum reliability of the system, where such a choice is not cost prohibitive.

27.2.2 A public emergency alarm reporting system, as described herein, shall be permitted to be used for the transmission of other signals or calls of a public emergency nature, provided that such transmission does not interfere with the transmission and receipt of fire alarms.

Subsection 27.2.2 permits a public emergency alarm reporting system to transmit other signals of a public emergency nature, such as a request for emergency medical response or police response. The Code permits these transmissions as long as they do not interfere with the transmission of fire alarm signals. In most cases where a system will transmit multiple signals from a municipal box, it will use either a wireless network or a telephone (series) type wired network.

Wireless network systems frequently offer the option of transmitting several distinct data points from a single box. The system operator may assign these data points to other emergency response functions. Governmental agencies sometimes provide such systems on limited-access highways to allow travelers to summon aid in the case of various emergencies.

A telephone (series) reporting system allows a person using the telephone handset to request various kinds of assistance from the operator at the communications center.

27.2.3* All devices shall be designed to function satisfactorily under the climatic and environmental conditions to which they could be exposed.

A.27.2.3 Consideration should be given to the fact that devices could be installed in areas that are exposed to higher or lower temperatures, moisture, or other environmental conditions that could be more severe than ambient conditions found in a typical building. As an example, equipment could be installed inside a building in a boiler room, basement, attic, and so forth, where temperatures actually exceed ambient conditions outside the building. It is recommended that the authority having jurisdiction consider all possible installation locations and environmental conditions and that the equipment selected be designed to operate within the most extreme conditions to which it could be exposed.

27.2.3.1 All devices shall be identified as suitable for the location and conditions for which they are installed.

27.3 Management and Maintenance

27.3.1 All systems shall be under the control of a designated jurisdictional employee.

27.3.2 Maintenance by an organization or person other than from the jurisdiction or an employee of the jurisdiction shall be by written contract, guaranteeing performance acceptable to the authority having jurisdiction.

27.3.3 Where maintenance is provided by an organization or person(s) other than the jurisdiction or its employees, complete written records of the installation, maintenance, test, and extension of the system shall be forwarded to the designated employee in a time period and manner approved by the authority having jurisdiction.

Subsection 27.1.4 and 27.3.6.1 require those operating public emergency alarm reporting systems to test and maintain the systems in accordance with the requirements of Chapter 14. Subsection 27.3.1 indicates that a single employee must have responsibility for controlling the system. In many communities, this individual has the title Fire Alarm Superintendent, Superintendent of Fire Alarms, Deputy Chief of Communications, Director of Signals, or other similar title. Sometimes, this individual has responsibility for both the public emergency alarm reporting system and the traffic signals in a community.

The International Municipal Signal Association (IMSA) serves as the professional membership association for those individuals responsible for overseeing and operating pubic emergency alarm reporting systems. IMSA provides certification programs, technical literature, and other professional services to assist in the continuing education and professional development of such individuals. IMSA can be reached at P.O. Box 539, Newark, NY 14513, or at *www.imsasafety.org.*

Where the jurisdiction does not have adequate staff or knowledge of the system to perform testing and maintenance, 27.3.2 and 27.3.3 permit a written contract with a maintenance organization. The organization performing these services must provide written records to the designated employee in a time and manner approved by the authority having jurisdiction.

◄ FAQ
What is required when maintenance is performed by an organization outside the jurisdiction responsible for the system?

27.3.4 All equipment shall be installed in locations accessible to the authority having jurisdiction for the purpose of maintenance and inspection.

27.3.5 Records of wired public emergency alarm reporting system circuits shall include the following:

(1) Outline plans showing terminals and box sequence
(2) Diagrams of applicable office wiring
(3) List of materials used, including trade name, manufacturer, and year of purchase or installation

Proper plans, material specification sheets, and diagrams allow for ease of repair, maintenance, and testing of the system. The requirements of 27.3.5 supplement the requirements of 10.18.3 and Section 14.6.

27.3.6 Public emergency alarm reporting systems as defined in this chapter shall, in their entirety, be subject to a complete operational acceptance test upon completion of system installation.

27.3.6.1 The test(s) required by 27.3.6 shall be made in accordance with the requirements of the authority having jurisdiction; however, in no case shall the operational functions tested be less than those stipulated in Chapter 14.

27.3.6.2 Operational acceptance tests shall be performed on any alarm-reporting devices, as covered in this chapter, that are installed or modified subsequent to the test required by 27.3.6.

Chapter 14 contains the requirements for testing and maintaining public emergency alarm reporting systems. Chapter 27 requires a complete acceptance test for all public emergency alarm reporting systems, as is required for any other fire alarm system.

27.3.7 Personnel Qualification.

27.3.7.1 System Designer.

27.3.7.1.1 Public emergency alarm reporting system plans and specifications shall be developed in accordance with this Code by persons who are qualified in the proper design, application, installation, and testing of public emergency alarm reporting systems.

27.3.7.1.2 The system design documents shall include the name and contact information of the system designer.

27.3.7.2 System Installer. Installation personnel shall be qualified in the installation, inspection, and testing of public emergency alarm reporting systems.

27.3.7.3 Service Personnel. Service personnel shall be qualified in the service, inspection, maintenance, and testing of public emergency alarm reporting systems.

27.3.7.4 Qualification.

27.3.7.4.1 Personnel shall demonstrate qualification by being trained and certified in public emergency alarm reporting system design, installation, or service (as appropriate) by one or more of the following:

(1) Certified by the manufacturer of the system or equipment
(2)* Certified by an organization acceptable to the authority having jurisdiction
(3) Licensed or certified by a state or local authority

A.27.3.7.4.1(2) An example of an organization providing public emergency alarm reporting system certification is the International Municipal Signal Association. Note that this reference is for information purposes only. Information concerning the product or service has been provided by the manufacturer or other outside sources, and the information concerning the product or service has not been independently verified, nor has the product or service been endorsed or certified by NFPA or any of its technical committees.

27.3.7.4.2 Evidence of qualifications and/or certification shall be provided when requested by the authority having jurisdiction. A license or qualification listing shall be current in accordance with the requirements of the issuing authority or organization.

Subsection 27.3.7 provides a list of qualifications for persons designing, installing, and servicing public emergency alarm reporting systems. The paragraphs in 27.3.7 emphasize the importance of individuals having qualifications specific to public emergency alarm reporting systems. Since these systems have become increasingly rare, such specialized knowledge has become all the more important.

27.4 Communications Methods

In the 2010 edition of the Code, the technical committee has added new text in Section 27.4 to consolidate the general requirements for wired and wireless networks used for public emergency alarm reporting systems. Fundamentally, this section acts somewhat like a road map — it points the user of the Code to other relevant sections that contain more detailed requirements for the various components that make up a public emergency alarm reporting system.

27.4.1 Application.

27.4.1.1 A public emergency alarm reporting system shall include wired or wireless network(s), for one-way signaling or two-way command and control communications between alarm boxes, alarm processing equipment, and the communications center.

27.4.1.2 A public emergency alarm reporting system shall be permitted to be used with emergency communications systems covered under Chapter 24.

27.4.2 Wired Network(s). The terms *wired network* and *public cable plant* shall be considered the same and interchangeable throughout this chapter.

The permissive requirements in 27.4.2 allow the provider of a public emergency alarm reporting system to use the system in conjunction with an emergency communications system covered under Chapter 24, allowing the smooth integration of both systems.

27.4.2.1 All wired networks or public cable plants shall meet the requirements of Section 27.7.

27.4.2.1.1 Fiber-optic cabling shall be considered an acceptable transmission medium, provided that the cabling and installation comply with the requirements of Section 27.7 and the conversion equipment used to interface to the fiber-optic signal complies with all applicable requirements of Chapter 27.

27.4.2.2 Alarm processing equipment at the communications center shall meet the requirements of 27.5.2 and 27.5.4.

27.4.2.3 Alarm processing equipment at a remote communications center shall meet the requirements of 27.4.2.2 and 27.5.3.

Exhibit 27.3 shows an example of alarm processing equipment.

EXHIBIT 27.3 *Wired Network Receiving Equipment. (Source: Lakes Region Mutual Fire Aid, Laconia, NH; photo by Debbie Kardaseski)*

27.4.2.4 Alarm boxes shall meet the following requirements:

(1) Publicly accessible boxes shall meet the requirements of 27.6.1 through 27.6.2 and 27.6.5.
(2) Auxiliary boxes shall meet the requirements of 27.6.1, 27.6.3, and 27.6.5.
(3) Master boxes shall meet the requirements of 27.6.1 through 27.6.3 and 27.6.5.

27.4.3 Wireless Network(s). The terms *wireless network* and *radio system* shall be considered the same and interchangeable throughout this chapter.

27.4.3.1 All wireless networks shall meet the requirements of 27.4.3.2 through 27.4.3.3.

27.4.3.2 In addition to the requirements of this Code, all wireless equipment shall be designed and operated in compliance with all applicable rules and regulations of the Federal Communications Commission (FCC) or, where required, the National Telecommunications and Information Administration (NTIA).

Publicly accessible wireless network boxes operate on a designated frequency assigned by the Federal Communications Commission (FCC). When actuated, wireless network boxes send a data burst that contains information on the status of the specific box. This data burst may contain one or more signals and permits wireless network boxes to transmit signals relating to more than simply fire alarm signals. (See the commentary following 27.1.6 and 27.2.2.)

27.4.3.3 Radio Channel (Frequency). The number of alarm boxes permitted on a single frequency shall be governed by the following:

(1) For systems that use one-way transmission in which the individual alarm box automatically initiates the required message *(see 27.5.5.3.3)* using circuitry integral to the alarm boxes, not more than 500 boxes shall be permitted on a single frequency.
(2) For systems that use a two-way concept in which interrogation signals *(see 27.5.5.3.3)* are transmitted to the individual alarm boxes from the communications center on the same frequency used for receipt of alarms, not more than 250 alarm boxes shall be permitted on a single frequency. Where interrogation signals are transmitted on a frequency that differs from that used for receipt of alarms, not more than 500 alarm boxes shall be permitted on a single frequency.
(3) A specific frequency shall be designated for both fire and other fire-related or public safety alarm signals and for monitoring for integrity signals.

Paragraph 27.4.3.3(3) requires the assignment of a specific frequency for the wireless network boxes. This assignment prevents the communications center from using the radio frequency assigned to the boxes for other normal two-way or one-way radio communications. Such use might inadvertently interfere with receipt of signals from the boxes.

27.4.3.4 Alarm processing equipment at the communications center shall meet the requirements of 27.5.2 and 27.5.5.

27.4.3.5 Alarm processing equipment at a remote communications center shall meet the requirements of 27.4.3.4 and 27.5.3.

27.4.3.6 Alarm boxes shall meet the following requirements:

(1) Publicly accessible boxes shall meet the requirements of 27.6.1 through 27.6.2 and 27.6.6.
(2) Auxiliary boxes shall meet the requirements of 27.6.1, 27.6.3, and 27.6.6.
(3) Master boxes shall meet the requirements of 27.6.1 through 27.6.3 and 27.6.6.

27.5 Alarm Processing Equipment

The alarm processing equipment required to receive and control the public emergency alarm reporting system shall be installed in the communications center or remote communications center used by emergency response agencies as defined in NFPA 1221, *Standard for the Installation, Maintenance, and Use of Emergency Services Communications Systems.*

27.5.1 General. The requirements of 27.5.2 shall apply to all processing equipment, wired or wireless, for a public emergency alarm reporting network.

27.5.2 Alarm Processing Equipment at a Communications Center.

Meeting the requirements of Section 27.5 ensures that the communications center will receive the signals transmitted over the public emergency alarm reporting system and will automatically record them in a manner that provides a permanent visual record of the signals. At the same time, an audible notification appliance will alert the operators to incoming signals.

The signal received in the communications center indicates the exact location of its origin. This indication comes from a unique number assigned to each public emergency alarm reporting box. An operator reads a manual chart or an interface to a computer-aided dispatching system and then translates the box number to an exact location. NFPA 1221 covers the requirements for computer-aided dispatching systems.

27.5.2.1 Type A and Type B Systems.

27.5.2.1.1 Alarm systems shall be Type A or Type B.

27.5.2.1.2 A Type A system shall be provided where the number of all alarms required to be retransmitted exceeds 2500 per year.

27.5.2.1.3 Where a Type A system is required, the automatic electronic retransmission of incoming alarms shall be permitted, provided that both of the following conditions are met:

(1) Approved facilities are provided for the automatic receipt, storage, retrieval, and retransmission of alarms in the order received.
(2) The operator(s) of the dispatch facility has the capability to immediately override the automatic retransmission and revert to manual retransmission.

In a Type A system, the operator(s) at the communications center receives signals from the public emergency alarm reporting system. The operator(s) then manually and selectively retransmits these signals to only the emergency response stations designated to respond to the location of each particular signal.

In a Type B system, equipment at the communications center automatically retransmits the received signals to all emergency response stations and other locations connected to the system.

Where signaling traffic exceeds 2500 alarms per year, 27.5.2.1.2 requires the use of a Type A system. The intent of this requirement is to limit the number of signals retransmitted to each emergency response station, particularly where an individual emergency response station would not need to respond to a specific alarm signal.

27.5.2.2 Visual Recording Devices.

27.5.2.2.1 Alarms from alarm boxes shall be automatically received and recorded at the communications center.

27.5.2.2.2 A device for producing a permanent graphic recording of all alarm, supervisory, trouble, and test signals received or retransmitted, or both, shall be provided at each communications center for each alarm circuit and tie circuit.

27.5.2.2.3 Reserve recording devices shall be provided in accordance with 27.5.2.2.3.1 and 27.5.2.2.3.2.

27.5.2.2.3.1 Where each circuit is served by a dedicated recording device, the number of reserve recording devices required on-site shall be equal to at least 5 percent of the circuits in service and in no case less than one device.

27.5.2.2.3.2 Where two or more circuits are served by a common recording device, a reserve recording device shall be provided on-site for each circuit connected to a common recorder.

FAQ ▶
What two cases does the Code address for reserve recording devices?

The subject of reserve recording devices often causes some confusion. The Code deals with two specific cases. In the first case, covered by the requirements of 27.5.2.2.3.1, each circuit has a dedicated recording device. The receiving location must have an additional number of reserve recording devices equal to at least 5 percent of the total number of receiving circuits or no less than one reserve recording device.

In the second case, covered by the requirements of 27.5.2.2.3.2, a common recording device serves multiple receiving circuits. Each recording device has multiple "channels," one for each circuit. Paragraph 27.5.2.2.3.2 requires a reserve recording device on-site for each circuit connected to a common recorder.

For example, a large northeastern city has over 120 circuits serving 2500 boxes. These circuits connect to 7 recording devices, each of which can handle up to 20 circuits. The city maintains 20 reserve individual circuit recording devices, or one reserve device for each circuit connected to a common recorder. The switchboard in the communications center allows the 20 circuits from any single failed common recording device to connect to those 20 reserve individual circuit recording devices.

27.5.2.2.4 In a Type B wired system, one such recording device shall be installed in each fire station, and at least one shall be installed in the communications center.

27.5.2.2.5 A permanent visual record and an audible signal shall be required to indicate the receipt of an alarm. The permanent record shall indicate the exact location from which the alarm is being transmitted.

27.5.2.2.6 The audible signal device shall be permitted to be common to two or more box circuits and arranged so that the emergency alarm operator is able to manually silence the signal temporarily by a self-restoring switch.

27.5.2.2.7 Facilities shall be provided that automatically record the date and time of receipt of each alarm.

Exception: Only the time shall be required to be automatically recorded for voice recordings.

27.5.2.3 System Integrity.

27.5.2.3.1 Wired circuits upon which transmission and receipt of alarms depend shall be constantly monitored for integrity to provide prompt warning of conditions adversely affecting reliability.

27.5.2.3.2 The power supplied to all required circuits and devices of the system shall be constantly monitored for integrity.

Paragraphs 27.5.2.3.1 and 27.5.2.3.2 provide requirements for monitoring the integrity of system wiring and power supplies. Rather than detailing the specific kinds of faults that might impair the operation of the system, these requirements cover all conditions that would adversely affect reliability. Similar requirements exist in 10.17.1 and 10.17.3.

27.5.2.4 Trouble Signals.

27.5.2.4.1 Trouble signals shall be indicated where there is a trained and competent person on duty at all times.

27.5.2.4.2 Trouble signals shall be distinct from alarm signals and shall be indicated by a visual and audible signal.

27.5.2.4.3 The audible signal shall be permitted to be common to more than one circuit that is monitored for integrity.

27.5.2.4.4 A switch for silencing the audible trouble signal shall be permitted, provided that the visual signal remains operating until the silencing switch is restored to its normal position.

27.5.2.4.5 The audible signal shall be responsive to faults on any other circuits that occur prior to restoration of the silencing switch to its normal position.

The paragraphs under 27.5.2.4 provide requirements for trouble signals and trouble signal appliance silencing. Similar requirements exist in Section 10.12. Trouble signals must alert the operator to problems with the circuits or power supplies. An operator may silence an audible trouble signal appliance only if a visible indication remains. Once silenced, the audible trouble signal must resound if faults occur on other circuits.

27.5.2.5 Power Supply. The forms and arrangements for public emergency alarm reporting systems power supplies shall comply with 27.5.2.5.1 through 27.5.2.5.8.

27.5.2.5.1 Each box circuit or wireless receiving system shall be served by the following:

(1)* Form 4A, which is an inverter, powered from a common rectifier, receiving power by a single source of alternating current with a floating storage battery having a 24-hour standby capacity
(2)* Form 4B, which is an inverter, powered from a common rectifier, receiving power from two sources of alternating current with a floating storage battery having a 4-hour standby capacity
(3)* Form 4C, which is a rectifier, converter, or motor generator receiving power from two sources of alternating current with transfer facilities to apply power from the secondary source to the system within 30 seconds

For convenience, the Code identifies three specific types of power supplies for public emergency alarm reporting systems: Form 4A, Form 4B, and Form 4C. Figures A.27.5.2.5.1(1), A.27.5.2.5.1(2), and A.27.5.2.5.1(3) provide graphic descriptions of these supplies. Technically, the Form 4C power supply does not require two generators. However, NFPA 1221 permits the use of two generators. This allowance may explain the origin of the graphic shown in Figure A.27.5.2.5.1(3). The equipment must accomplish a transfer between the primary source and the other source of alternating current within 30 seconds.

A.27.5.2.5.1(1) Figure A.27.5.2.5.1(1) illustrates a Form 4A arrangement.

A.27.5.2.5.1(2) Figure A.27.5.2.5.1(2) illustrates a Form 4B arrangement.

A.27.5.2.5.1(3) Figure A.27.5.2.5.1(3) illustrates a Form 4C arrangement. Refer to NFPA 1221, *Standard for the Installation, Maintenance, and Use of Emergency Services Communications Systems.*

27.5.2.5.2 Form 4A and Form 4B shall be permitted to distribute the system load between two or more common rectifiers and batteries.

27.5.2.5.3 The capacity of batteries, motor generators, rectifiers, or other permitted power supplies shall exceed the calculated load of all connected circuits, so that circuits developing grounds or crosses with other circuits each shall be able to be supplied by an independent source to the extent required by 27.5.2.5.1.

27.5.2.5.4 Provision shall be made to connect any circuit to any battery, generator, or rectifier, or other permitted power supply.

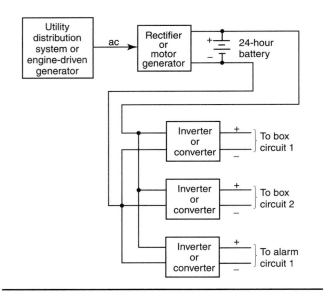

FIGURE A.27.5.2.5.1(1) Form 4A.

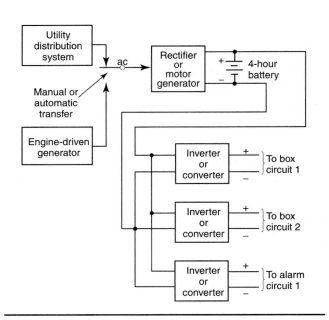

FIGURE A.27.5.2.5.1(2) Form 4B.

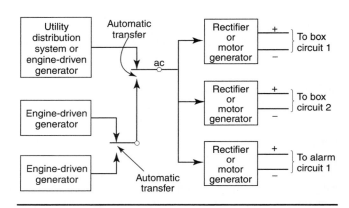

FIGURE A.27.5.2.5.1(3) Form 4C.

The requirements in 27.5.2.5.4 ensure maximum reliability for the public emergency alarm reporting system. When one power supply fails, the circuits it normally serves must receive power from other power supplies until technicians repair the failed power supply.

27.5.2.5.5 Individual circuits supplied from common leads shall be protected by the installation of enclosed fuses located at the point where the circuit conductors receive their supply.

27.5.2.5.6 Local circuits at communications centers shall be supplied in accordance with 27.5.2.5.6.1 and 27.5.2.5.6.2.

27.5.2.5.6.1 The source of power for local circuits required to operate the essential features of the system shall be monitored for integrity.

The system must monitor the integrity of the power for circuits and equipment within the communications center. The loss of this power must cause a trouble signal. See 27.5.2.3.1, 27.5.2.3.2, and the commentary following 27.5.2.3.2 for additional requirements and information related to system integrity.

27.5.2.5.6.2 Local circuits at communications centers shall be permitted to be connected to the same power source as box circuits, wireless receiving system circuits, or a separate power source.

27.5.2.5.7 Visual and audible means to indicate a 15 percent or greater reduction of normal power supply (rated voltage) shall be provided.

When power for the public emergency alarm reporting system or for local circuits at the communications center drops 15 percent or more below the normal rated voltage, such a reduction must initiate a trouble signal.

27.5.2.5.8 Where the electrical service/capacity of the equipment required under Section 4.7 of NFPA 1221, *Standard for the Installation, Maintenance, and Use of Emergency Services Communications Systems*, satisfies the needs of equipment in this chapter, such equipment shall not be required to be duplicated.

NFPA 1221 has specific power supply requirements. The design of the system must supply two sources of power: one a connection to a utility distribution system, the other a connection to an engine-driven generator. As an alternative, the design of the system may rely upon power supplied by two engine-driven generators. One unit supplies normal power, and the other unit serves as a standby. If these required sources meet the requirements of 27.5.2.5.1, then 27.5.2.5.8 permits the use of such a source without the need for duplication.

◀ **FAQ**
What are the power supply requirements of NFPA 1221?

27.5.2.6 Rectifiers, Converters, Inverters, and Motor Generators.

27.5.2.6.1 Rectifiers shall be supplied from the secondary of an isolating transformer.

27.5.2.6.1.1 The primary of the isolating transformer shall be connected to a circuit not exceeding 250 volts.

27.5.2.6.2 Complete spare units or spare parts shall be in reserve.

27.5.2.6.3 One spare rectifier shall be provided for every 10 operating rectifiers on a system. No system shall have less than one spare.

27.5.2.6.4 Leads from rectifiers or motor generators, with a float-charged battery, shall be protected by fuses rated at a minimum of 1 ampere and a maximum of 200 percent of connected load at nominal circuit voltage. Where not provided with a float-charged battery, the fuses shall be rated at a minimum of 3 amperes.

The requirements in 27.5.2.6.4 provide for the sizing of fuse-type overcurrent protection devices. The intent of these requirements is to provide circuits with sufficient protection without making the protective fuses overly sensitive. Too frequent operation of the fuses would tend to reduce the overall reliability of the public emergency alarm reporting system.

27.5.2.7 Engine-Driven Generators. The installation of engine-driven generator sets shall conform to the provisions of NFPA 37, *Standard for the Installation and Use of Stationary Combustion Engines and Gas Turbines*; NFPA 110, *Standard for Emergency and Standby Power Systems*; and NFPA 1221, *Standard for the Installation, Maintenance, and Use of Emergency Services Communications Systems*.

To maintain reliability, the system must ensure the continuity of supplied power. Compliance with the requirements of the NFPA standards identified in 27.5.2.7 helps ensure such continuity.

27.5.2.8 Float-Charged Batteries.

To maintain reliability, the system must ensure the continuity of supplied power. The requirements in 27.5.2.8 help ensure such continuity.

27.5.2.8.1 Float-charged batteries shall be of the storage type. Primary batteries (dry cells) shall not be used. Lead-acid batteries shall be in jars of glass or other identified or approved transparent materials; other types of batteries shall be in containers identified or approved for the purpose.

27.5.2.8.2 Float-charged batteries shall be above building grade level.

27.5.2.8.3 Float-charged batteries shall be located on the same floor of the building as the operating equipment.

Paragraph 27.5.2.8.3 requires the municipality or government agency to locate storage batteries on the same floor or level as the operating equipment for the public emergency alarm reporting system.

27.5.2.8.4 Float-charged batteries shall be accessible for maintenance and inspection.

27.5.2.8.5 Float-charged batteries shall be installed in accordance with Article 480 of *NFPA 70, National Electrical Code*.

27.5.2.8.6 Batteries shall be mounted to provide effective insulation from the ground or working platform and from other batteries. Mounting equipment shall be listed and identified for the location. It shall be permissible for the authority having jurisdiction to waive this requirement to allow the use of alternative mounting equipment where it is assured that equivalent objectives can be achieved.

27.5.2.8.7 Battery mounting shall be protected against deterioration and shall provide stability, especially in geographic areas subject to seismic disturbance.

27.5.2.9 Equipment Fire Protection. Where applicable, electronic computer/data processing equipment shall be protected in accordance with NFPA 75, *Standard for the Protection of Information Technology Equipment*.

The requirement of 27.5.2.9 recognizes that modern communications centers use equipment quite similar to that found at any computer or data processing facility. Logic, therefore, requires the same level of fire protection for this critical equipment as industrial or commercial facilities provide for other such computer or data processing equipment. NFPA 75, *Standard for the Protection of Information Technology Equipment*, provides requirements for such protection.

27.5.3 Alarm Processing Equipment at a Remote Communications Center. Where the alarm-receiving equipment is located at a location other than where the box circuit protection, controls, and power supplies are located, the requirements of 27.5.3.1 through 27.5.3.8, in addition to all of the requirements of Section 27.5, shall apply.

FAQ ▶
What is one reason why a municipality might establish a remote communications center?

Subsection 27.5.3 provides requirements for those circumstances where the municipality or government agency has located the communications center at a location remote from the location of the control equipment for the public emergency alarm reporting system. This circumstance might occur when the municipality or government agency has moved the communications center to combine its service with other emergency dispatching, such as police or emergency medical services. In such a case, the high cost of completely relocating the public emergency alarm reporting system terminal equipment might prohibit moving it. Leaving the equipment at its original location and connecting it remotely to the new communications center location offers a much more cost-effective solution.

27.5.3.1 All equipment used to provide the primary and remote receiving facilities shall be listed for its intended use and shall be installed in accordance with *NFPA 70, National Electrical Code*.

27.5.3.2 The monitoring for integrity of all box circuits shall be provided with a visual and audible means to indicate a 20 percent or greater reduction or increase in the normal current in any box alarm circuit. The visual means shall identify the exact circuit affected.

27.5.3.3 Monitoring for integrity of all power supplies shall be provided with visual and audible means to indicate a loss of primary or standby power supplies at both the communications center and remote communications center.

27.5.3.4 A minimum of two separate means of interconnection shall be provided between the communications center and remote communications center receiving equipment. This interconnection shall be dedicated and shall not be used for any other purpose.

27.5.3.5 Where data transmission or multiplexing equipment is used that is not an integral part of the alarm-receiving equipment, a visual and audible means shall be provided to monitor the integrity of the external equipment. This shall include monitoring all primary and standby power supplies as well as the transmission of data.

A particular system design may employ data transmission technology, using either time division or frequency division multiplexing, to connect remote receiving locations to the communications center. Paragraph 27.5.3.5 requires the monitoring of the integrity of this transmission method.

27.5.3.6 Power shall be provided in accordance with 27.5.2.5.

27.5.3.7 The use of an uninterruptible power supply (UPS) to comply with standby power requirements shall not be permitted.

27.5.3.8 Tie circuits shall be provided in accordance with 27.5.3.8.1 through 27.5.3.8.3.

27.5.3.8.1 A separate tie circuit shall be provided from the communications center to each subsidiary communications center.

27.5.3.8.2 The tie circuit between the communications center and the subsidiary communications center shall not be used for any other purpose.

27.5.3.8.3 In a Type B wired system, where all boxes in the system are of the succession type, it shall be permitted to use the tie circuit as a dispatch circuit to the extent permitted by NFPA 1221, *Standard for the Installation, Maintenance, and Use of Emergency Services Communications Systems.*

Remote receiving locations use tie circuits, which connect the communications center with the original terminal location of the public emergency alarm reporting system.

Tie circuits can also connect the communications center with a subsidiary communications center. For example, in a large municipality, a subsidiary communications center concentrates signals from a particular neighborhood or geographic area before transmitting them to the communications center.

In some cities where several political subdivisions have their own communications center (e.g., New York City), the system might use tie circuits to interconnect the centers. This interconnection allows the centers to handle signals from all the boroughs, even if one of the communications centers suffers a temporary impairment.

27.5.4 Wired Network Systems.

Subsection 27.5.4 establishes requirements for public emergency alarm reporting systems using a wired network.

27.5.4.1 System Arrangement and Operation.

27.5.4.1.1 For a Type B system, the effectiveness of noninterference and succession functions between box circuits shall be no less than between boxes in any one circuit.

In a Type B (coded) wired system, the system repeats signals from one box circuit or alarm circuit onto the other box and alarm circuits. The repetition of these signals causes other boxes connected to the system to sense a busy circuit and wait for a clear circuit before transmitting. This approach provides for the proper functioning of the noninterfering and successive features of the "three-fold" (coded) wired alarm boxes.

27.5.4.1.2 A metallic box open circuit condition shall cause a warning signal in all other circuits, and, thereafter, the circuit(s) not in the open circuit condition shall be automatically restored to operative condition.

With regard to 27.5.4.1.2, when an open fault occurs on a box or alarm circuit, the repeater equipment must repeat only one tap or blow onto all other circuits. The equipment must then restore the circuits to a closed circuit condition, so that boxes on the circuits do not see the open on one circuit as an open circuit condition on all other circuits. The single tap or blow repeated to all circuits of a Type B system provides a warning or trouble signal. This signal indicates that one of the circuits in the system has an open fault.

27.5.4.1.3 Box circuits shall be sufficient in number and laid out so that the areas that would be left without box protection in case of disruption of a circuit do not exceed those covered by 20 properly spaced boxes where all or any part of the circuit is of aerial open-wire, or by 30 properly spaced boxes where the circuit is entirely in underground or messenger-supported cable.

The requirements of 27.5.4.1.3 are intended to limit the extent of the loss of service to any given area of a municipality should an outage occur in a box circuit. This provision effectively limits the "number of eggs in one basket."

The actual area covered by any box circuit will depend on the topography of the particular municipality. It will also depend on whether the box circuit covers a residential area or a nonresidential area.

Paragraph 27.6.2.1.6 leaves the decision regarding box locations up to the authority having jurisdiction. Guidance in A.27.6.2.1.6 suggests that a person should not have to travel more than one block or 500 ft (150 m) to reach a box in a nonresidential area or two blocks or 800 ft (240 m) in a residential area.

27.5.4.1.4 Where all boxes on any individual circuit and associated equipment are designed and installed to provide for receipt of alarms through the ground in the event of a break in the circuit, the circuit shall be permitted to serve twice the number of aerial open-wire and cable circuits, respectively, as are specified in 27.5.4.1.3.

In most (coded) wired systems, when an actuated alarm box senses that the circuit has an open fault, it idles for one round, connects the box to earth ground, and then transmits four rounds of its identifying signal. Sensing an open circuit, the receiving equipment at the communications center also connects itself to earth ground. This conditioning of the circuit allows the box to transmit its signal through earth ground.

FAQ ▶
What number of boxes does the Code permit if all boxes have the ability to transmit through earth ground?

If two open faults occur on the circuit, the boxes isolated between the faults cannot transmit a signal. When all boxes have this ability to transmit through earth ground in the case of an open fault on the circuit, the circuit can serve double the number of boxes that it might serve where the boxes do not have this capability. With this feature provided, an aerial open-wire circuit can serve an area equal to that covered by up to 40 properly spaced boxes, and an underground or messenger-supported circuit can serve an area equal to that covered by up to 60 properly spaced boxes.

27.5.4.1.5 The installation of additional boxes in an area served by the number of boxes spaced as indicated in 27.5.4.1.1 through 27.5.4.1.4 shall not constitute geographical overloading of a circuit.

The key phrase to understanding the requirement in 27.5.4.1.5 is "shall not constitute." The intent of this requirement is that, if technicians install additional boxes in a particular geographical area and connect them to a circuit that already serves properly spaced boxes installed in that geographical area, these additional boxes do not constitute an overload on the circuit. This provision allows the addition of boxes to serve particular hazards within a geographical area without the need to add any additional circuits.

27.5.4.1.6 Sounding devices for signals shall be provided for box circuits.

27.5.4.1.6.1 A common sounding device for more than one circuit shall be permitted to be used in a Type A system and shall be installed at the communications center.

27.5.4.1.6.2 In a Type B system, a sounding device shall be installed in each fire station at the same location as the recording device for that circuit, unless installed at the communications center, where a common sounding device shall be permitted.

27.5.4.2 Constant-Current (100 milliampere) Systems. Constant-current systems shall comply with the requirements of 27.5.4.2.1 through 27.5.4.2.6.

27.5.4.2.1 Means shall be provided for manually regulating the current in box circuits so that the operating current is maintained within 10 percent of normal throughout changes in external circuit resistance from 20 percent above normal to 50 percent below normal.

27.5.4.2.2 The voltage supplied to maintain normal line current on box circuits shall not exceed 150 volts, measured under no-load conditions, and shall be such that the line current cannot be reduced below the approved operating value by the simultaneous operation of four boxes.

27.5.4.2.3 Visual and audible means to indicate a 20 percent or greater reduction in the normal current in any alarm circuit shall be provided.

27.5.4.2.4 All devices connected in series with any alarm circuit shall function when the alarm circuit current is reduced to 70 percent of normal.

27.5.4.2.5 Meters shall be provided to indicate the current in any box circuit and the voltage of any power source. Meters used in common for two or more circuits shall be provided with cut-in devices designed to reduce the probability of cross-connecting circuits.

27.5.4.2.6 Necessary switches, testing, and signal transmitting and receiving devices shall be provided to allow the isolation, control, and test of each circuit up to at least 10 percent of the total number of box and dispatch circuits, but never less than two circuits.

The (coded) wired public emergency alarm reporting system operates at a constant current of nominally 100 mA. The requirements of 27.5.4.2 and its subparagraphs regulate and maintain the current, limit the voltage, provide a visual indication of current reduction, and provide meters to allow operators to measure current. These features all ensure that such a system maintains a high level of operational integrity.

Paragraph 27.5.4.2.6 provides a "spare parts on hand" requirement. The communications center must maintain sufficient spare parts — necessary switches and testing, signal transmitting, and signal receiving devices — to properly isolate, control, or test up to 10 percent of the total number of box and dispatch circuits. For example, if a system has 40 box and 8 dispatch circuits, the communications center would need to maintain at least 5 sets of spare parts. For systems with a smaller number of box and dispatch circuits, in no case should the communications center maintain fewer spare parts than those needed to properly isolate, control, or test at least two circuits.

27.5.4.3 Grounded Common-Current Systems. Where common-current source systems are grounded, the requirements of 27.5.4.3.1 and 27.5.4.3.2 shall apply.

27.5.4.3.1 Where common-current source systems are grounded, the resistance of the ground shall not exceed 10 percent of resistance of any connected circuit and shall be located at one side of the battery.

27.5.4.3.2 Visual and audible indicating devices shall be provided for each box and dispatch circuit to give immediate warning of ground leakage current that will have a detrimental effect on circuit operation.

The requirements of 27.5.4.3 and its subparagraphs apply only to older constant-current systems that used Form 2 power supplies. The Code no longer recognizes this type of power supply. Some of these Form 2 power supplies had one side of the battery connected to earth ground to facilitate ground return signaling in the case of an open fault on a box circuit. The more modern Form 4 power supply operates above ground under normal operating conditions. The Form 4 power supply connects to earth ground to permit ground return signaling only when the equipment at the communications center detects an open fault on a box circuit.

Table 14.4.2.2 describes tests essential to ensuring the integrity of the constant-current (coded) wired public emergency alarm reporting system. Foreign grounds on a metallic box or dispatch circuit can render a portion of the circuit inoperable. For that reason, operators at the communications center must give attention to testing procedures that will result in the prompt discovery of excess voltage or current to ground.

27.5.4.4 Telephone (Series) Reporting Systems.

Sometimes installers for a municipality add components to all or a portion of an existing (coded) wired reporting system to give that system the capability of transmitting and receiving voice alarm signals. In these cases, the telephone (series) reporting system uses the same cable plant as the (coded) wired system. In other cases, a municipality may choose to install a new telephone (series) reporting system or completely replace a (coded) wired system with a new telephone (series) reporting system. These systems follow the same installation requirements in Section 27.7 as do (coded) wired systems. See 27.6.5.1 regarding the requirement to comply with Section 27.7.

27.5.4.4.1 Recording devices shall be provided in accordance with 27.5.4.4.1.1 and 27.5.4.4.1.2.

27.5.4.4.1.1 A permanent visual recording device installed in the communications center shall be provided to record all incoming box signals.

FAQ ▶
What does the permanent visual recording device record?

The permanent visual recording device noted in 27.5.4.4.1.1 records the date, time, and box number but not the content of the voice message. See 27.5.4.4.4 and associated commentary regarding voice transmissions.

27.5.4.4.1.2 A spare recording device shall be provided for five or more box circuits.

27.5.4.4.2 A second visual means of identifying the calling box shall be provided.

27.5.4.4.3 Audible signals shall indicate all incoming calls from box circuits.

27.5.4.4.4 All voice transmissions from boxes for emergencies shall be recorded with the capability of instant playback.

Specially designed audio recording equipment not only provides an audio log of signal content from the boxes but also allows an operator to instantly recycle to the beginning of each message. In this way, operators at the communications center can review unclear messages.

Many communications centers use a common recording system to record all incoming emergency voice communications. This system may include messages from telephone (series) reporting systems, 9-1-1 emergency telephone calls, other public telephone calls, and two-way radio traffic. Modern multi-channel computer-controlled digital recording systems can easily handle many channels of recorded information and give the operators instant access to play back all or any portion of a recorded conversation.

27.5.4.4.5 A voice-recording facility shall be provided for each operator handling incoming alarms to eliminate the possibility of interference.

27.5.4.4.6 Box circuits shall be sufficient in number and laid out so that the areas that would be left without box protection in case of disruption of a circuit do not exceed those covered by 20 properly spaced boxes where all or any part of the circuit is of aerial open-wire, or 30 properly spaced boxes where the circuit is entirely in underground or messenger-supported cable.

The requirements of 27.5.4.4.6 intend to limit the extent of the loss of service to any given area of a municipality should an outage occur in a box circuit. This requirement effectively limits the "number of eggs in one basket."

The actual area covered by any box circuit will depend on the topography of the particular municipality. It will also depend on whether the box circuit covers a residential area or a nonresidential area.

Paragraph 27.6.2.1.6 leaves the decision regarding box locations up to the authority having jurisdiction. Guidance in A.27.6.2.1.6 suggests that a person should not have to travel more than one block or 500 ft (150 m) to reach a box in a nonresidential area or two blocks or 800 ft (240 m) in a residential area.

27.5.4.4.7 Where all boxes on any individual circuit and associated equipment are designed and installed to provide for receipt of alarms through the ground in the event of a break in the circuit, the circuit shall be permitted to serve twice the number of aerial open-wire and cable circuits, respectively, as is specified in 27.5.4.4.6.

In some telephone (series) reporting systems, when an actuated alarm box senses that the circuit has an open fault, the system connects the box to earth ground to establish a voice transmission path. Sensing an open circuit, the receiving equipment at the communications center also connects itself to earth ground. This conditioning of the circuit allows the box to transmit its voice signal through earth ground.

If two open faults occur on the circuit, the boxes isolated between the faults cannot transmit a signal. When all telephone (series) boxes have this ability to transmit through earth ground in the case of an open fault on the circuit, the circuit can serve double the number of boxes that it might serve where the boxes do not have this capability. With this feature provided, an aerial open-wire circuit can serve an area equal to that covered by up to 40 properly spaced boxes, and an underground or messenger-supported circuit can serve an area equal to that covered by up to 60 properly spaced boxes.

27.5.4.4.8 The installation of additional boxes in an area served by the number of boxes spaced as indicated in 27.5.4.4.6 shall not constitute geographical overloading of a circuit.

As with 27.5.4.1.5, "shall not constitute" is the key phrase to understanding the requirement in 27.5.4.4.8. The intent of this requirement is that if technicians install additional boxes in a particular geographical area and connect them to a circuit that already serves properly spaced boxes installed in that geographical area, these additional boxes do not constitute an overload on the circuit. This provision allows the addition of boxes to serve particular hazards within a geographical area without the need to add additional circuits.

27.5.5 Wireless Network.

27.5.5.1 System Arrangement and Operation.

27.5.5.1.1 Type A systems shall comply with 27.5.5.1.1.1 through 27.5.5.1.1.6.

27.5.5.1.1.1* Two separate receiving networks shall be required for each frequency. Each network shall include the following:

(1) Antenna
(2) RF receiver
(3) Signaling processing equipment
(4) Time/date alarm printer
(5) Audible alerting device
(6) Power supply

A.27.5.5.1.1.1 Figure A.27.5.5.1.1.1 illustrates a Type A receiving network.

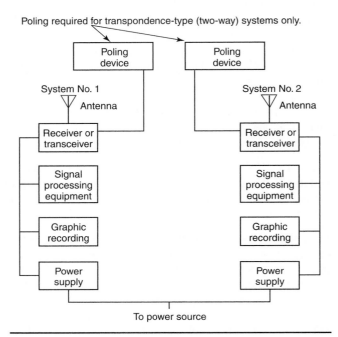

FIGURE A.27.5.5.1.1.1 *Type A System Receiving Networks.*

Redundant equipment increases the overall reliability of the wireless network public emergency alarm reporting system. Due to the heavier signaling traffic anticipated with a Type A system, 27.5.5.1.1.1 requires redundant receiving equipment. Most wireless network reporting systems operate as one-way radio systems. However, if a public emergency alarm reporting system employs a two-way system, then the polling device shown in Figure A.27.5.5.1.1.1 would request a test signal from each radio box at least once every 24 hours.

27.5.5.1.1.2 Both receiving networks shall be installed at the communications center.

27.5.5.1.1.3 The failure of one receiving network shall not interfere with the other receiving network's ability to receive messages from boxes.

27.5.5.1.1.4 Where the system configuration is such that a polling device is incorporated into the receiving network to allow remote or selective initiation of box tests, a separate device shall be included in each of the two required receiving networks.

How often do the polling devices typically request a test signal from each two-way radio box?

FAQ ▶

Most wireless network reporting systems operate as one-way radio systems. However, some wireless network systems provide for an interrogation and response sequence initiated from the communications center. This interrogation and response sequence monitors the integrity of the radio channel signaling pathway. Typically, the polling device would request a test signal from each two-way radio box at least once every 24 hours.

27.5.5.1.1.5 The polling devices shall be configured for automatic cycle initiation in their primary operating mode, shall be capable of continuous self-monitoring, and shall be integrated into the network(s) to provide automatic switchover and operational continuity in the event of failure of either device.

27.5.5.1.1.6 Test signals from boxes shall not be required to include the date as part of their permanent recording, provided that the date is automatically printed on the recording tape at the beginning of each calendar day.

27.5.5.1.2 Type B systems shall comply with 27.5.5.1.2.1 and 27.5.5.1.2.2.

27.5.5.1.2.1 For each frequency used, a single, complete receiving network shall be permitted in each fire station, provided that the communications center conforms to 27.5.5.1.1.1 through 27.5.5.1.1.3. Where the jurisdiction maintains two or more alarm reception points in operation, one receiving network shall be permitted to be at each alarm reception point.

27.5.5.1.2.2 Where alarm signals are transmitted to a fire station from the communications center using the wireless-type receiving equipment in the fire station to receive and record the alarm message, a second receiving network conforming to 27.5.5.1.2.1 shall be provided at each fire station, and that receiving network shall employ a frequency other than that used for the receipt of box messages.

Paragraphs 27.5.5.1.2.1 and 27.5.5.1.2.2 contain requirements for various configurations of Type B wireless network public emergency alarm reporting systems. Some configurations have each emergency response station simultaneously receive the transmission from any box in the system. Others receive the box signals at the communications center and automatically repeat the signals to the fire stations.

27.5.5.1.3 A device for producing a permanent graphic recording of all alarm, supervisory, trouble, and test signals received or retransmitted, or both, shall be provided at the communications center.

27.5.5.1.4 Where box message signals to the communications center or acknowledgment of message receipt signals from the communications center to the box are repeated, associated repeating facilities shall conform to the requirements indicated in 7.1.1.4(d) of NFPA 1221, *Standard for the Installation, Maintenance, and Use of Emergency Services Communications Systems.*

27.5.5.2 Power. Power shall be provided in accordance with 27.5.2.5.

27.5.5.3 Monitoring for Integrity.

27.5.5.3.1 All wireless box systems shall provide constant monitoring of the frequency in use. Both an audible and a visual indication of any sustained carrier signal, where in excess of a 15-second duration, shall be provided for each receiving system at the communications center.

An open fault or ground fault on a (coded) wired public emergency alarm reporting system interferes with the transmission of signals. Similarly, the sustained transmission of a radio carrier signal can interfere with the transmission of signals from the boxes on a wireless network public emergency alarm reporting system. Paragraph 27.5.5.3.1 requires the detection of such a sustained carrier signal and the audible and visible annunciation of such an occurrence.

27.5.5.3.2 The power supplied to all required circuits and devices of the system shall be monitored for integrity.

27.5.5.3.3* Each wireless box shall automatically transmit a test message at least once in each 24-hour period.

A.27.5.5.3.3 See A.27.6.6.2.

The 24-hour test signal safeguards against the catastrophic failure of any single alarm box and its antenna.

27.5.5.3.4 Receiving equipment associated with wireless-type systems, including any related repeater(s), shall be tested at least hourly. The receipt of test messages that do not exceed 60-minute intervals shall meet this requirement.

The hourly test signal safeguards against the catastrophic failure of the wireless network receiving equipment and its antenna.

27.5.5.3.5 Radio repeaters upon which receipt of alarms depend shall be provided with dual receivers, transmitters, and power supplies. Failure of the primary receiver, transmitter, or power supply shall cause an automatic switchover to the secondary receiver, transmitter, or power supply.

Exception: Manual switchover shall be permitted, provided that it is completed within 30 seconds.

Wireless network public emergency alarm reporting systems serving areas where radio propagation requires the use of repeaters make the integrity of the repeaters an important issue. Paragraph 27.5.5.3.5 requires redundant equipment to help ensure the continued operation of this critical equipment. The requirement prefers the automatic switchover from primary equipment to secondary equipment. The exception permits manual switchover when accomplished within 30 seconds of the failure of the primary equipment.

27.5.5.3.6 Trouble signals shall actuate a sounding device located where there is always a trained, competent person on duty.

27.5.5.3.7 Trouble signals shall be distinct from alarm signals and shall be indicated by a visual and audible signal.

27.5.5.3.7.1 The audible signal shall be permitted to be common to two or more monitored circuits.

27.5.5.3.7.2 A switch for silencing the audible trouble signal shall be permitted where the visual signal remains operating until the silencing switch is restored to its normal position.

27.5.5.3.8 The audible signal shall be responsive to subsequent faults in other monitored functions prior to restoration of the silencing switch.

27.5.5.4 Physical Protection of Transmission Line. The antenna transmission line between the transmitter and the antenna shall be installed in rigid metal, intermediate metal conduit, or electrical metallic tubing in accordance with *NFPA 70, National Electrical Code.*

Paragraph 27.5.5.4 requires physical protection for the cable connecting the wireless network public emergency alarm reporting system boxes (transmitters) to their respective antennas. Section 810, Part II Receiving Equipment — Antenna Systems, of *NFPA 70®, National Electrical Code®*, covers the requirements for the installation of such antennas.

27.6 Alarm Boxes

27.6.1* General. The requirements of 27.6.1.1 through 27.6.1.6 shall apply to all alarm boxes.

A.27.6.1 There are three types of alarm boxes covered under Chapter 27. They are the publicly accessible box, auxiliary box, and master box.

(1) The publicly accessible box has a manual control that can be operated by the public. This type of alarm box is typically located outside on a pole or building and was previously called a street box. The box type was renamed because it is not necessarily located on or near a street.

(2) An auxiliary box is part of an auxiliary alarm system and can be automatically activated either by initiating devices in limited applications or by a protected premises alarm system (Chapter 23). An auxiliary box can be located inside or outside a building.

(3) The master box is a combination box that can be manually operated (publicly accessible) and automatically activated by the auxiliary alarm system (auxiliary box). The master box is typically located outside on a pole or building.

27.6.1.1 Concurrent operation of at least four boxes shall not result in the loss of an alarm.

To meet the requirement of 27.6.1.1, each box installed on a wired network circuit must sense that another box has begun to transmit a signal over the common box circuit. The first box withholds transmitting its signal until it senses a clear circuit, and then it transmits the signal. Manufacturers describe this box design as noninterfering and successive.

Boxes installed on a wireless network meet the requirements of 27.6.1.1 by the fact that the transmission from each box is accomplished in a very short period of time and repeated sufficiently to ensure that signals from four concurrently operated boxes will be received without interference.

Telephone (series) boxes installed on a wired network rely on the operator receiving the calls to manage those cases where multiple users attempt to talk to the operator at the same time.

27.6.1.2 Boxes and associated equipment, when in an abnormal condition, shall not disable the public emergency alarm reporting system circuit.

Locating publicly accessible alarm boxes along public streets and thoroughfares subjects them to possible damage from a variety of sources, including vandals, vehicular accidents, and street repair and maintenance operations. When a box is damaged, the remainder of the system must continue to operate normally.

27.6.1.3 Boxes shall be designed so that recycling does not occur when a box-actuating device is held in the actuating position and shall be ready to accept a new signal as soon as the actuating device is released.

The requirement in 27.6.1.3 ensures that if a person in the panic of an emergency continues to hold the box actuating lever in the actuated position, the box will not recycle. This feature prevents a box from tying up the circuit. Exhibit 27.4 shows a typical publicly accessible alarm box.

27.6.1.4* Boxes, when actuated, shall give a visible or audible indication to the user that the box is operating or that the signal has been transmitted to the communications center.

A.27.6.1.4 If the operating mechanism of a box creates sufficient sound to be heard by the user, the requirements are satisfied.

Most wired network boxes provide an audible indication of actuation from the noise created by the mechanism that drives the mechanical code wheel. Telephone (series) boxes indicate actuation by means of a sound generated in the handset or speaker. Publicly accessible wireless network boxes usually provide a visible means to indicate actuation.

27.6.1.5 Box cases and parts that are accessible to the public shall be permitted to be of nonconductive material.

27.6.1.6 Box cases and parts that are accessible to the public and that are constructed of conductive materials shall be installed in accordance with the requirements of *NFPA 70, National Electrical Code,* Articles 250 and 760.

EXHIBIT 27.4 *Publicly Accessible Alarm Box. (Source: Gamewell-FCI, Northford, CT)*

◄ **FAQ**
How is the requirement of 27.6.1.4 typically accomplished?

27.6.2* Publicly Accessible Alarm Boxes.

A.27.6.2 Publicly accessible alarm boxes were commonly referred to as "street boxes" in previous editions of the Code. Applications of these boxes are no longer limited to street locations.

27.6.2.1 Fundamental Requirements. The requirements of 27.6.2.1.1 through 27.6.2.1.11 shall apply to all publicly accessible alarm boxes.

27.6.2.1.1 Means for actuation of alarms by the public shall be located where they are visible, unobstructed, and readily accessible.

27.6.2.1.2 The box housing shall protect the internal components and shall be identified for the location installed.

27.6.2.1.3 Doors on boxes shall remain operable under adverse climatic conditions, including icing and salt spray.

27.6.2.1.4 Boxes shall be recognizable as such and shall have instructions for use plainly marked on their exterior surfaces.

27.6.2.1.5 Boxes shall be securely mounted on poles, pedestals, or structural surfaces as directed by the authority having jurisdiction.

27.6.2.1.6* The location of publicly accessible boxes shall be designated by the authority having jurisdiction.

A.27.6.2.1.6 Where the intent is for complete coverage, it should not be necessary to travel in excess of one block or 500 ft (150 m) to reach a box. In residential areas, it should not be necessary to travel in excess of two blocks or 800 ft (240 m) to reach a box.

In most cases, the municipal fire officials or the emergency management officials serve as the authority having jurisdiction.

27.6.2.1.7 Schools, hospitals, nursing homes, and places of public assembly shall have a box located at the main entrance, as directed by the authority having jurisdiction.

27.6.2.1.8 Boxes shall be conspicuously visible and be highlighted with a distinctive color.

27.6.2.1.9 All publicly accessible boxes mounted on support poles shall be identified by a wide band of distinctive colors or signs placed 8 ft (2.44 m) above the ground and visible from all directions wherever possible.

27.6.2.1.10* Location-designating lights of distinctive color, visible for at least 1500 ft (460 m) in all directions, shall be installed over boxes. The street light nearest the box, where equipped with a distinctively colored light, shall meet this requirement.

The requirements of 27.6.2.1.8, 27.6.2.1.9, and 27.6.2.1.10 provide for a means of identifying the location of publicly accessible alarm boxes. The use of a distinctive color for the box itself in conjunction with the banding of support poles and the provision of identifying lamps all help ensure that citizens seeking emergency aid can promptly locate a box.

A.27.6.2.1.10 The current supply for designating lights at boxes should be secured at lamp locations from the local electric utility company.

Alternating-current power can be permitted to be superimposed on metallic fire alarm circuits for supplying designating lamps or for control or actuation of equipment devices for fire alarm or other emergency signals, provided that the following conditions exist:

(1) Voltage between any wire and ground or between one wire and any other wire of the system does not exceed 150 volts, and the total resultant current in any line circuit does not exceed $\frac{1}{4}$ ampere.

(2) Components such as coupling capacitors, transformers, chokes, or coils are rated for 600-volt working voltage and have a breakdown voltage of at least twice the working voltage plus 1000 volts.

(3) There is no interference with fire alarm service under any conditions.

27.6.2.1.11 Where boxes are installed inside a structure, the installation shall comply with 27.6.2.1.11.1 and 27.6.2.1.11.2.

27.6.2.1.11.1 The box shall be placed as close as is practicable to the point of entrance of the circuit.

27.6.2.1.11.2 The exterior wire shall be installed in rigid metal conduit or intermediate metal conduit in accordance with Chapter 3 of *NFPA 70, National Electrical Code*.

Exception: Schedule 80 rigid nonmetallic conduit shall be permitted for underground installations, provided that all elbows used are rigid or intermediate metal conduit.

Paragraph 27.6.2.1.11.2 includes specific installation details drawn from *NFPA 70*. The requirements of this paragraph are intended to help maintain the integrity of any exterior wire connecting to a box installed inside a structure.

27.6.3 Auxiliary Alarm Box.

See definitions for *auxiliary box* in 3.3.8.1, *master box* in 3.3.8.4, and *publicly accessible alarm box* in 3.3.8.5. Exhibits 27.5 and 27.6 show different views of master boxes.

27.6.3.1 Fundamental Requirements. The requirements of 27.6.3.1.1 through 27.6.3.1.5 shall apply to all auxiliary alarm boxes.

EXHIBIT 27.5 *Building Fire Alarm System Connected to a Master Box.*

EXHIBIT 27.6 *Inside View of a Master Box. (Source: Lakes Region Mutual Fire Aid, Laconia, NH; photo by Debbie Kardaseski)*

27.6.3.1.1 The authority having jurisdiction shall designate the location of the auxiliary box.

27.6.3.1.2 All exterior wire and cable shall be installed in rigid metal conduit or intermediate metal conduit in accordance with Chapter 3 of *NFPA 70, National Electrical Code.*

Exception: Schedule 80 rigid nonmetallic conduit shall be permitted for underground installations, provided that all elbows used are rigid or intermediate metal conduit.

27.6.3.1.3 Where installed outside a structure, the requirements of 27.6.2.1.2 and 27.6.2.1.5 shall apply.

27.6.3.1.4 Where the auxiliary box is a wired box, the requirements of Section 27.7 shall apply.

27.6.3.1.5 Where the auxiliary box is a wireless box, the requirements of 27.6.6 shall apply.

27.6.3.2 Auxiliary Alarm Systems.

FAQ ▶
What is the function of an
auxiliary alarm system?

For a definition of an *auxiliary alarm system,* see 3.3.199.1. Auxiliary alarm systems connect a building alarm system to the communications center using the public emergency alarm reporting system. If a community does not have a public emergency alarm reporting system, it obviously cannot have an auxiliary alarm system connection. (See commentary following 27.6.3.2.3.9.)

Due to the continued reduction of the number of municipalities and government agencies that have a public emergency alarm reporting system, the number of auxiliary alarm systems has also decreased.

27.6.3.2.1 Application. The equipment and circuits necessary to connect a protected premises to a public emergency alarm reporting system shall comply with the requirements of 27.6.3.2.

27.6.3.2.1.1 The requirements of Chapter 10, in addition to those of Chapters 14 and 17, shall apply to auxiliary alarm systems unless they conflict with the requirements of 27.6.3.2.

27.6.3.2.1.2 Where permitted by the authority having jurisdiction, the use of systems described in Chapter 27 shall be permitted to provide defined reporting functions from or within private premises.

27.6.3.2.1.3 The requirements of Section 27.7 shall also apply to wired auxiliary alarm systems.

27.6.3.2.2 Types of Systems.

The detailed requirements of 27.6.3.2.2.1(1) and 27.6.3.2.2.1(2) describe the two types of auxiliary systems: local energy and shunt. (See definitions and commentary for each type of system in 3.3.199.1.1 and 3.3.199.1.2.) Most authorities having jurisdiction consider the shunt system less desirable.

In the local energy system, power from the fire alarm control unit at the protected premises energizes an actuating mechanism inside the auxiliary box to cause the auxiliary box to transmit a fire alarm signal. The fire alarm control unit at the protected premises monitors the integrity of the interconnecting wiring between the fire alarm control unit and the auxiliary box.

In the shunt-type system, a coil winding of the auxiliary box actuating mechanism diverts operating power from the municipal emergency (fire) alarm circuit and causes it to flow current into the protected building through a closed electrical loop. Manual fire alarm boxes or sprinkler waterflow initiating devices, with normally closed contacts, connect in series to this shunt loop. Actuation of the manual fire alarm box or waterflow switch will open the shunt loop. This opening causes the municipal emergency alarm circuit power to actuate the mechanism that trips the auxiliary box.

Throughout the requirements in 27.6.3, the additional items for shunt-type systems are intended to overcome some of the potential problems associated with their use. For example, an open fault on the shunt circuit due to a broken wire will cause the auxiliary box to actuate. A foreign ground on the shunt circuit will appear as a ground on the municipal emergency alarm circuit. Because multiple grounds on the municipal circuit can cause the system to malfunction, and because the municipal authorities may not always have easy access to the shunt circuit within a building, detection and clearing of foreign grounds on the shunt circuit become vital but usually are difficult.

Further, an open fault on the municipal emergency alarm circuit will prevent the shunt circuit from actuating the auxiliary box because the open fault has effectively disconnected the operating power. With an open circuit, even though someone may manually pull the auxiliary box and the box will transmit using the "three-fold" arrangement through earth ground, the shunt loop in the building will have no operating power to actuate the auxiliary box. This condition will remain until technicians locate and repair the open fault on the municipal circuit.

27.6.3.2.2.1 Auxiliary alarm systems shall be of the following two types:

(1)* Local energy type

    (a) Local energy systems shall be permitted to be of the coded or noncoded type.

    (b) Power supply sources for local energy systems shall conform to Chapter 10.

    (c) Transmitter trouble signals shall be indicated at the control unit and the building fire command center in accordance with 10.12.6.

(2)* Shunt type

    (a) Shunt systems shall be noncoded with respect to any remote electrical tripping or actuating devices.

    (b) All conductors of the shunt circuit shall be installed in accordance with *NFPA 70, National Electrical Code*, Article 344, for rigid metal conduit, or Article 358, for electrical metallic tubing.

    (c) Both sides of the shunt circuit shall be in the same conduit.

    (d) Where a shunt loop is used, it shall not exceed a length of 750 ft (230 m) and shall be in conduit.

    (e) Conductors of the shunt circuits shall not be smaller than 14 AWG and shall be insulated as prescribed in *NFPA 70, National Electrical Code*, Article 310.

    (f) The power for shunt-type systems shall be provided by the public emergency alarm reporting system.

    (g)* A local system made to an auxiliary alarm system by the addition of a relay whose coil is energized by a local power supply and whose normally closed contacts trip a shunt-type master box shall not be permitted.

A.27.6.3.2.2.1(1) The local energy-type system *[see Figure A.27.6.3.2.2.1(1)(a) and Figure A.27.6.3.2.2.1(1)(b)]* is electrically isolated from the public emergency alarm reporting system and has its own power supply. The tripping of the transmitting device does not depend on the current in the system. In a wired circuit, receipt of the alarm by the communications center when the circuit is accidentally opened depends on the design of the transmitting device and the associated communications center equipment (i.e., whether or not the system is designed to receive alarms through manual or automatic ground operational facilities). In a radio box–type system, receipt of the alarm by the communications center depends on the proper operation of the radio transmitting and receiving equipment.

A.27.6.3.2.2.1(2) The shunt-type system *[see Figure A.27.6.3.2.2.1(2)(a) and Figure A.27.6.3.2.2.1(2)(b)]* is electrically connected to, and is an integral part of, the public emergency alarm reporting system. A ground fault on the auxiliary circuit is a fault on the public emergency alarm reporting system circuit, and an accidental opening of the auxiliary circuit

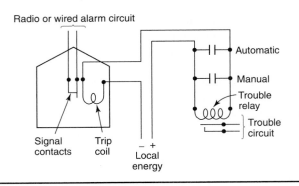

FIGURE A.27.6.3.2.2.1(1)(a) *Local Energy-Type Auxiliary Alarm System — Radio or Wired.*

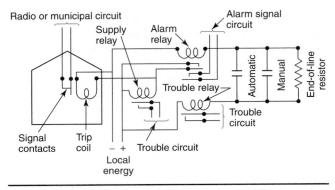

FIGURE A.27.6.3.2.2.1(1)(b) *Local Energy-Type Auxiliary Alarm System with Supply and Alarm Relay — Radio or Wired.*

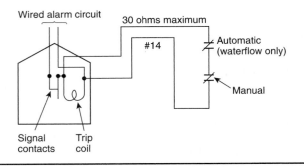

FIGURE A.27.6.3.2.2.1(2)(a) *Shunt-Type Auxiliary Alarm System (Permitted).*

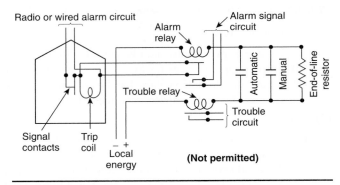

FIGURE A.27.6.3.2.2.1(2)(b) *Shunt-Type Auxiliary Alarm System (Not Permitted).*

sends a needless (or false) alarm to the communications center. An open circuit in the transmitting device trip coil is not indicated either at the protected property or at the communications center. Also, if an initiating device is operated, an alarm is not transmitted, but an open circuit indication is given at the communications center. If a public emergency alarm reporting system circuit is open when a connected shunt-type system is operated, the transmitting device does not trip until the public emergency alarm reporting system circuit returns to normal, at which time the alarm is transmitted, unless the auxiliary circuit is first returned to a normal condition.

Additional design restrictions for shunt-type systems are found in laws or ordinances.

A.27.6.3.2.2.1(2)(g) See Figure A.27.6.3.2.2.1(2)(b).

27.6.3.2.2.2 The interface of the two types of auxiliary alarm systems with the three types of public emergency alarm reporting systems shall be in accordance with Table 27.6.3.2.2.2.

27.6.3.2.2.3 The application of the two types of auxiliary alarm systems shall be limited to the initiating devices specified in Table 27.6.3.2.2.3.

27.6.3.2.3 System Arrangement and Operation.

27.6.3.2.3.1 Shunt-type auxiliary alarm systems shall be arranged so that one auxiliary transmitter does not serve more than 100,000 ft² (9290 m²) total area.

Exception: Where otherwise permitted by the authority having jurisdiction.

TABLE 27.6.3.2.2.2 *Application of Public Emergency Alarm Reporting Systems with Auxiliary Alarm Systems*

Reporting Systems	Local Energy Type	Shunt Type
Wired	Yes	Yes
Wireless	Yes	No
Telephone series	Yes	No

TABLE 27.6.3.2.2.3 *Application of Initiating Devices with Auxiliary Alarm Systems*

Initiating Devices	Local Energy Type	Shunt Type
Manual fire alarm	Yes	Yes
Waterflow or actuation of the fire extinguishing system(s) or suppression system(s)	Yes	Yes
Automatic detection devices	Yes	No

27.6.3.2.3.2 A separate auxiliary transmitter shall be provided for each building, or where permitted by the authority having jurisdiction, for each group of buildings of single ownership or occupancy.

27.6.3.2.3.3 The same box shall be permitted to be used as a public emergency alarm reporting system box and as a transmitting device for an auxiliary alarm system where permitted by the authority having jurisdiction, provided that the box is located at the outside of the entrance to the protected property.

27.6.3.2.3.4 Where 27.6.3.2.3.3 is applied, the fire department shall be permitted to require the box to be equipped with a signal light to differentiate between automatic and manual operation, unless local outside alarms at the protected property serve the same purpose.

27.6.3.2.3.5 The transmitting device shall be located as required by the authority having jurisdiction.

27.6.3.2.3.6 The system shall be designed and arranged so that a single fault on the auxiliary alarm system shall not jeopardize operation of the public emergency alarm reporting system and shall not, in case of a single fault on either the auxiliary or public emergency alarm reporting system, transmit a false alarm on either system.

Exception: Shunt systems complying with 27.6.3.2.2.1(2).

27.6.3.2.3.7 A means that is available only to the agency responsible for maintaining the public emergency alarm reporting system shall be provided for disconnecting the auxiliary loop to the connected property.

If an installer makes a connection to the public emergency alarm reporting system in accordance with the requirements of 27.6.3, 27.6.3.2.3.7 requires that the installer provide a means to disconnect the protected premises connection. Only the authority having jurisdiction over the public emergency alarm reporting system can have access to this disconnecting means. Locating the disconnecting means inside a locked auxiliary box will satisfy this requirement.

Some large municipalities do issue a special license or permit for contractors that allows them to have keys that will access the auxiliary boxes. This permit allows the contractor to disconnect the protected premises connection during testing and maintenance of the fire alarm system at the protected premises.

◀ **FAQ**
What method is often used to satisfy the requirements of 27.6.3.2.3.7?

27.6.3.2.3.8 Notification shall be given to the designated representative of the property when the auxiliary box is not in service.

27.6.3.2.3.9 An auxiliary alarm system shall be used only in connection with a public emergency alarm reporting system that is approved for the service. A system approved by the authority having jurisdiction shall meet this requirement.

In reference to 27.6.3.2.3.9, if a community has not provided a public emergency alarm reporting system, no auxiliary alarm system can exist. An auxiliary alarm system depends on the public emergency alarm reporting system to transmit signals from the protected premises to the communications center.

27.6.3.2.3.10 Permission for the connection of an auxiliary alarm system to a public emergency alarm reporting system, and acceptance of the type of auxiliary transmitter and its actuating mechanism, circuits, and components connected thereto, shall be obtained from the authority having jurisdiction.

27.6.3.2.3.11 Paragraph 27.6.3.2 shall not require the use of audible alarm signals other than those necessary to operate the auxiliary alarm system. Where it is desired to provide fire alarm evacuation signals in the protected property, the alarms, circuits, and controls shall comply with the provisions of Chapter 23 in addition to the provisions of 27.6.3.2.

By itself, an auxiliary alarm system does not include the components necessary to notify occupants in a building of the need to evacuate or relocate to areas of refuge within the building. If the authority having jurisdiction requires such notification, then the authority having jurisdiction will need to require the building owner to install a protected premises alarm system with initiating devices and notification appliances in accordance with Chapters 1, 10, 12, 14, 17, 18, and 23.

At one time, some manufacturers of auxiliary alarm systems offered a means for building evacuation notification. They did so by imposing an alternating current to operate audible alarm notification appliances on the direct current manual fire alarm–initiating device circuit of a shunt-type master alarm box. This arrangement no longer meets the requirements of the Code.

27.6.3.2.3.12 Where an auxiliary alarm system is in an alarm condition that has been acknowledged, deactivated, or bypassed, subsequent actuation of initiating devices on other initiating device circuits or subsequent actuation of addressable initiating devices on signaling line circuits shall cause an alarm signal to be transmitted to the communications center.

27.6.3.2.3.13 Where an auxiliary transmitter is located within a private premises, it shall be installed in accordance with 27.6.2.1.11 and 27.7.2.

27.6.3.2.3.14 Where data communications between a microprocessor-based control unit and an auxiliary alarm system are utilized, they shall comply with the requirements of 27.6.3.2.3.14(A) through 27.6.3.2.3.14(C).

(A) The monitoring for integrity shall include communications test messages transmitted between the control unit and the auxiliary alarm system.

(B) The communications test message shall be initiated by either the control unit or the auxiliary alarm system and shall require a response from the corresponding unit, and the following shall apply:

(1) An invalid response or no response from the control unit or the auxiliary alarm system shall be recognized as a communications failure.
(2) A communications failure shall initiate a specific communications failure trouble message, which shall be transmitted from the auxiliary alarm system and shall be automatically indicated within 200 seconds at the communications center.
(3) A trouble condition in 27.6.3.2.3.14(B)(2) shall activate an audible and distinctive visual signal at the auxiliary box indicating a communications failure.
(4) A trouble condition shall be indicated at the control unit and the building fire command center in accordance with 10.12.6.

(C) Where a separate device is required to interface the control unit to the auxiliary alarm system, all communication paths shall be monitored for integrity and shall comply with 27.6.3.2.3.14.

Paragraph 27.6.3.2.3.14 provides additional requirements for the use of data communications between a computer microprocessor–based building fire alarm control unit and an auxiliary alarm system. The intent of these requirements is to maintain the integrity of the communications pathway, to provide a means of monitoring the interconnecting communications pathway for integrity, and to ensure the overall reliability of the arrangement.

27.6.4 Master Alarm Boxes. Master alarm boxes shall comply with the requirements of 27.6.2 and 27.6.3.

27.6.5 Wired Network Boxes. The requirements of Section 27.7 shall apply to wired network boxes.

Publicly accessible wired network boxes initiate a coded signal from an actuated box by interrupting the current flow through a metallic circuit with telegraphic impulses. Most wired network boxes operate by means of a spring-wound mechanical clock-like movement that drives a code wheel. Teeth on the code wheel break the circuit in accordance with a predetermined pattern. The mechanism drives the code wheel to make at least four revolutions, sending the coded signal four times.

27.6.5.1 Telephone Boxes. The requirements of Section 27.7 shall also apply to telephone boxes.

Over the years, public emergency alarm reporting systems have employed two types of publicly accessible telephone boxes. The first type uses an existing (coded) wired system cable plant to connect telephone boxes to the communications center. This connection permits the municipality or government agency to retrofit some or all of the wired network boxes for two-way voice communications. Some of these units used telephone handsets. Other designs of this same type use a hands-free-type speaker installed under a heavy protective grill. This first type of telephone box, commonly referred to as a telephone (series) reporting system, connects the boxes to the cable plant electrically in series, in the same fashion as wired network boxes. One manufacturer also produces a wired network box with a telephone handset in the bottom portion of the box.

The second type of telephone box, which is no longer available, was provided by the public telephone utility company and leased to the municipality or government agency. This system included special equipment that would print out a box numerical designation at the communications center. This printout gave the operator at the communications center the location of the box, even if no one spoke to the operator through the handset. This system, commonly referred to as a telephone (parallel) system, connected the boxes in parallel circuits extending between each box and the communications center.

The 1999 edition of the Code removed the references to the telephone (parallel) system because the public telephone utility companies no longer offer new installations of these systems. However, some municipalities continue to use these telephone (parallel) systems. Obviously, these municipalities will do so only as long as their public telephone utility continues to maintain this legacy service.

27.6.5.1.1 Where a handset is used, the caps on the transmitter and receiver shall be secured to reduce the probability of the telephone box being disabled due to vandalism.

27.6.5.1.2 Telephone boxes shall be designed to allow the communications center operator to determine whether or not the telephone box has been restored to normal condition after use.

27.6.6 Wireless Network Boxes.

Publicly accessible wireless network boxes operate on a designated frequency assigned by the FCC. When actuated, wireless network boxes send a data burst that contains information on the status of the specific box. This data burst can contain one or more signals and permits wireless network boxes to transmit signals relating to more than simply fire alarm signals. (See the commentary following 27.1.6 and 27.2.2.)

27.6.6.1 In addition to the requirements of this Code, wireless boxes shall be designed and operated in compliance with all applicable rules and regulations of the Federal Communications Commission (FCC) or, where required by other governing laws, the National Telecommunications and Information Administration (NTIA).

27.6.6.2* Each wireless box shall automatically transmit a test message at least once in each 24-hour period.

A.27.6.6.2 The transmission of an actual emergency-related message, initiated at the same time it is preselected for a test message, and, in turn, preempts said test message, must satisfy the intent of 27.6.6.2.

With regard to 27.6.6.2, a daily test timer initiates a signal from the box at least once each day. This signal ensures that the box remains in an operable condition and serves as a means of monitoring the integrity of the box, its antenna, and its transmission channel.

When the technical committee first developed requirements for digital alarm communicator systems, the existence of this means of monitoring the integrity of the communications pathway for wireless boxes formed the basis of the requirement in 26.6.3.2.1.4(B)(2). Thus the concept of a test signal transmitted once during each 24-hour time period originated with the requirement in 27.6.6.2.

27.6.6.3 Wireless boxes shall provide no less than three specific and individually identifiable functions to the communications center, in addition to the box number, as follows:

(1) Test
(2) Tamper
(3) Fire

27.6.6.4 Wireless boxes shall transmit to the communications center as follows:

(1) No less than one repetition for "test"
(2) No less than one repetition for "tamper"
(3) No less than two repetitions for "fire"

27.6.6.5 Where multifunction-wireless boxes are used to transmit signals in addition to those in 27.6.6.3, each such additional signal shall be individually identifiable.

27.6.6.6 Multifunction-wireless boxes shall be designed so as to prevent the loss of supplemental or concurrently actuated messages.

27.6.6.7 An actuating device held or locked in the activating position shall not prevent the activation and transmission of other messages.

27.6.6.8 The primary power source for wireless boxes shall be permitted to be from one or more of the following, as approved by the authority having jurisdiction:

(1) A utility distribution system
(2) A solar photovoltaic power system
(3) User power
(4) Self-powered, using either an integral battery or other stored energy source

FAQ ▶
How many options are available for primary power?

Paragraph 27.6.6.8 makes provision for four discrete power sources for wireless network boxes. The requirements in 27.6.6.9 through 27.6.6.12 provide details for each power source. None of the requirements would prevent a designer of wireless network boxes from using these sources in combination to provide enhanced operability of the system.

27.6.6.9 Boxes powered by a utility distribution system shall comply with 27.6.6.9.1 through 27.6.6.9.6.

27.6.6.9.1 Boxes shall have an integral standby, sealed, rechargeable battery that is capable of powering box functions for at least 60 hours in the event of primary power failure. Transfer to standby battery power shall be automatic and without interruption to box operation.

27.6.6.9.2 A local trouble indication shall activate upon primary power failure.

27.6.6.9.3 Boxes operating from primary power shall be capable of operation with a dead or disconnected battery.

27.6.6.9.4 A battery charger shall be provided in compliance with 10.5.9.3, except as modified in 27.6.6.9.

27.6.6.9.5 When the primary power has failed, boxes shall transmit a power failure message to the communications center as part of subsequent test messages until primary power is restored.

27.6.6.9.6 A low-battery message shall be transmitted to the communications center where the remaining battery standby time is less than 54 hours.

27.6.6.10 Boxes powered by a solar photovoltaic system shall comply with 27.6.6.10.1 through 27.6.6.10.5.

27.6.6.10.1 Solar photovoltaic power systems shall provide box operation for not less than 6 months.

27.6.6.10.2 Solar photovoltaic power systems shall be monitored for integrity.

27.6.6.10.3 The battery shall have power to sustain operation for a minimum period of 15 days without recharging.

27.6.6.10.4 The box shall transmit a trouble message to the communications center when the charger has failed for more than 24 hours. This message shall be part of all subsequent transmissions.

27.6.6.10.5 Where the remaining battery standby duration is less than 10 days, a low-battery message shall be transmitted to the communications center.

27.6.6.11 User-powered boxes shall have an automatic self-test feature.

User-powered boxes can store additional power each time a user actuates the box beyond that needed to transmit the immediate signal. This stored power can then operate the daily test feature. In other cases, a user-powered box may have one of the other power sources to supply power for the daily test feature.

27.6.6.12 Self-powered boxes shall comply with 27.6.6.12.1 through 27.6.6.12.3.

27.6.6.12.1 Self-powered boxes shall operate for a period of not less than 6 months.

27.6.6.12.2 Self-powered boxes shall transmit a low-power warning message to the communications center for at least 15 days prior to the time the power source will fail to operate the box. This message shall be part of all subsequent transmissions.

27.6.6.12.3 Use of a charger to extend the life of a self-powered box shall be permitted where the charger does not interfere with box operation. The box shall be capable of operation for not less than 6 months with the charger disconnected.

27.7 Public Cable Plant

Metallic and fiber-optic cabling systems and interconnections between alarm transmission equipment and alarm-receiving equipment shall comply with the requirements of Section 27.7.

27.7.1 Requirements for Metallic and Fiber-Optic Systems — Metallic and Fiber-Optic Interconnections.

27.7.1.1 Circuit Conductors and Fiber-Optic Strands.

27.7.1.1.1 Exterior metallic, fiber-optic cable and wire shall conform to International Municipal Signal Association (IMSA) specifications or an approved equivalent.

Exception: Where circuit conductors or fiber-optic strands are provided by a public utility on a lease basis, IMSA specifications shall not apply.

IMSA publishes wire and cable specifications for use in the installation of public emergency alarm reporting systems. IMSA can be reached at P.O. Box 539, Newark, NY 14513, or at *www.imsasafety.org.*

Some jurisdictions lease conductors for their (coded) wired or telephone (series) public emergency alarm reporting systems from utilities, such as a local telephone company or local television cable company, rather than install their own conductors. When conductors are leased, the provider determines the specifications for the conductors in the same fashion they determine the specifications for their normal communications conductors. The exception indicates that in such a case the requirements of 27.7.1.1.1 will not apply.

27.7.1.1.2 Where a public box is installed inside a building, the circuit from the point of entrance to the public box shall be installed in rigid metal conduit, intermediate metal conduit, or electrical metallic tubing in accordance with *NFPA 70, National Electrical Code.*

Exception: This requirement shall not apply to wireless box systems.

FAQ ►
What is the purpose of the requirement in 27.7.1.1.2?

The intent of 27.7.1.1.2 is to limit the exposure of the public emergency alarm reporting system circuit to mechanical damage within a building. If an installer runs the emergency alarm reporting circuit extensively throughout the building, mechanical damage might occur to the circuit concurrent with the transmission of an alarm signal and defeat the protection afforded by the alarm system.

Although not specifically covered by 27.7.1.1.2, a fire might also burn through a portion of the public emergency alarm reporting system circuit before the system transmits an alarm signal. The installation of the circuit in conduit or raceway alone would not prevent a fire from damaging the circuit. Though not required by 27.7.1.1.2, an installer could use a cable type listed for fire survivability to protect a circuit against possible fire damage. See Section 12.4 for the requirements for pathway survivability. Also see 27.7.2.1.2 for other physical protection requirements.

27.7.1.1.3 Wires and fiber-optic strands shall be terminated so as to prevent breaking from vibration or stress.

27.7.1.1.4 Circuit conductors and fiber-optic cables on terminal racks shall be identified and isolated from conductors of other systems wherever possible and shall be protected from mechanical injury.

27.7.1.2 Cables. The requirements of 27.7.1.2 shall apply to 27.7.1.3 through 27.7.1.6.

27.7.1.2.1 Exterior metallic and fiber-optic cable and wire shall conform to IMSA specifications or an approved equivalent.

27.7.1.2.2 Overhead, underground, or direct burial cables shall be specifically approved for the purpose.

One way of obtaining the approval required by 27.7.1.2.2 involves using specifically listed cables. For example, cables installed underground inside mechanical protection should have conductors listed for wet locations. Cables installed underground without other mechanical protection could have conductors listed for direct burial.

27.7.1.2.3 Metallic and fiber-optic cables used in interior installations shall comply with *NFPA 70, National Electrical Code*, and shall be installed in accordance with the manufacturer's installation instructions and practices.

27.7.1.2.4 The combination of other signal wires or fiber-optic strands in the same cable with fire alarm wires shall comply with 27.7.1.2.4.1 and 27.7.1.2.4.2.

27.7.1.2.4.1 Other municipally controlled signal wires and fiber-optic strands shall be permitted to be installed in the same cable with fire alarm wires.

Occasionally, municipalities that maintain their own governmental service telephone system, centralized traffic control, or monitoring systems run the wiring or optical fiber strands for those services in the same cable as the public emergency alarm reporting system.

27.7.1.2.4.2 Cables controlled by, or containing wires or fiber-optic strands of, private signaling organizations shall be permitted to be used for fire alarm purposes only by permission of the authority having jurisdiction.

On rare occasions, public emergency alarm reporting systems consist of signaling wiring leased from the public telephone utility or even from a private organization. The requirements of 27.7.1.2.4.2 apply to such cases.

27.7.1.2.5 Signaling wire and fiber-optic cables containing metallic protection or strength members shall comply with 27.7.1.2.5.1 and 27.7.1.2.5.2.

27.7.1.2.5.1 Signaling wires supplied by a power source having a voltage and/or current rating sufficient to introduce a hazard shall be installed in accordance with *NFPA 70, National Electrical Code*, Article 760, Part II.

See *NFPA 70*, Articles 760 and 800, for protection requirements.

27.7.1.2.5.2 Fiber-optic cables containing metallic protection or strength members shall be grounded and protected in accordance with *NFPA 70, National Electrical Code*.

See *NFPA 70*, Article 770, for protection requirements.

27.7.1.2.6 All metallic cables, with all taps and splices made, shall be tested for insulation resistance when installed but before connection to terminals. Such tests shall indicate an insulation resistance of at least 200 megohms per mile between any one conductor and all other conductors, the sheath, and the ground.

Paragraph 27.7.1.2.6 requires installers to test cables and splices with a megohm meter to ensure the dielectric strength of the insulation (see Exhibit 27.7). Installers must conduct this test before they connect any devices or appliances to the cable plant.

27.7.1.3 Underground Cables.

To maintain the overall operational integrity of a public emergency alarm reporting system, the requirements of 27.7.1.3 are intended to protect underground metallic and optical fiber cables from exposure to potential mechanical injury.

27.7.1.3.1 Underground metallic and fiber-optic cables in duct or direct burial shall be permitted to be brought aboveground only at locations approved by the authority having jurisdiction.

27.7.1.3.1.1 Protection from physical damage or heat incidental to fires in adjacent buildings shall be provided.

27.7.1.3.2 Metallic and fiber-optic cables shall be permitted to be located in duct systems and manholes containing power-limited fire alarm system conductors only, except power-limited secondary power cables shall be permitted.

EXHIBIT 27.7 Megohm Meter Used for Insulation Testing of Installed Wiring. (Source: Megger®, Dallas, TX)

27.7.1.3.3 Where located in duct systems or manholes that contain power circuit conductors over 250 volts to ground, metallic and fiber-optic emergency alarm cables shall be located as far as possible from such power cables and shall be separated from them by a noncombustible barrier or other means approved by the authority having jurisdiction to protect the emergency alarm cables from physical damage.

27.7.1.3.4 All cables installed in manholes shall be racked and marked for identification.

27.7.1.3.5 Raceways or ducts entering buildings from underground duct systems shall be effectively sealed with an identified sealing compound or other means acceptable to the authority having jurisdiction to prevent the entrance of moisture or gases from the underground duct system.

27.7.1.3.6 All cable joints shall be located only in manholes, fire stations, and other locations where accessibility is provided and where there is little liability of injury to the cable due to either falling walls or operations in the buildings.

27.7.1.3.6.1 Cable joints shall be made to provide and maintain conductivity, optical continuity for fiber-optic cable, insulation, and protection at least equal to that afforded by the cables that are joined.

27.7.1.3.6.2 Open cable ends shall be sealed against moisture.

27.7.1.3.7 Direct-burial cable, without enclosure in ducts, shall be laid in grass plots, under sidewalks, or in other places where the ground is not likely to be opened for other underground construction.

27.7.1.3.7.1 Where splices are made, such splices shall be accessible for inspection and tests.

27.7.1.3.7.2 Such cables shall be buried at least 18 in. (500 mm) deep and, where crossing streets or other areas likely to be opened for other underground construction, shall be in duct or conduit.

27.7.1.4 Aerial Construction.

FAQ ▶
What is the primary purpose of 27.7.1.4 and 27.7.1.5?

To maintain the overall operational integrity of a public emergency alarm reporting system, the requirements of 27.7.1.4 and 27.7.1.5 are intended to protect aerial cables and leads down poles to reduce the risk of mechanical injury and electrical failure.

27.7.1.4.1 Fire alarm wires and cables shall be located under all other wires except communications wires.

ANSI/IEEE C2, *National Electrical Safety Code* (*NESC*), contains requirements for the relative position of public emergency alarm reporting system wiring with respect to other aerial supported wiring on utility poles. (See 27.7.2.1.1 for specific reference to the requirements of ANSI/IEEE C2.)

27.7.1.4.1.1 Precautions shall be provided where passing through trees, under bridges, over railroads, and at other places where subject to physical damage.

27.7.1.4.1.2 Conductors and cables for public emergency alarm reporting system use shall not be attached to a crossarm that carries electric light and power conductors.

Exception: Power conductors for public emergency alarm reporting system use, operating at 250 volts or less, shall be permitted to share the crossarm with the conductors and cables and shall be tagged.

27.7.1.4.2 Aerial cable shall be supported by messenger wire of approved tensile strength or shall conform to one of the following:

(1) IMSA specifications as a self-supporting cable assembly or an approved equivalent
(2) Fiber-optic cable with integral supporting means or all-dielectric self-supporting (ADSS) type

27.7.1.4.3 Single wire shall meet IMSA specifications and shall not be smaller than No. 10 Roebling gauge if of galvanized iron or steel; 10 AWG if of hard-drawn copper; 12 AWG if of approved copper-covered steel; or 6 AWG if of aluminum. Span lengths shall not exceed the manufacturer's recommendations.

27.7.1.4.4 Wires to buildings shall contact only intended supports and shall enter through an approved weatherhead or sleeves slanting upward and inward. Drip loops shall be formed on wires outside of buildings.

27.7.1.5 Leads Down Poles.

27.7.1.5.1 Leads down poles shall be protected from physical damage. Any metallic covering shall form a continuous conducting path to ground. Installation, in all cases, shall prevent water from entering the conduit or box.

27.7.1.5.2 Leads to boxes shall have 600-volt insulation listed or approved for wet locations, as defined in *NFPA 70, National Electrical Code.*

27.7.1.6 Wiring Inside Buildings.

To maintain the overall operational integrity of a public emergency alarm reporting system, the intent of the requirements of 27.7.1.6 is to protect wiring inside a building. This protection limits the risk of mechanical injury or electrical failure. The requirements also make certain that the wiring does not contribute to the spread of a fire in a building.

27.7.1.6.1 At the communications center, all conductors, cables, and fiber-optic cables shall extend as directly as possible to the operations center in conduits, ducts, shafts, raceways, or overhead racks and troughs listed or identified as suitable to provide protection against physical damage.

27.7.1.6.2* Where installed in buildings, conductors and fiber-optic cables shall be installed in any of the following wiring methods:

(1) Electrical metallic tubing
(2) Intermediate metal conduit
(3) Rigid metal conduit

Exception: Rigid nonmetallic conduit shall be permitted where approved by the authority having jurisdiction.

A.27.7.1.6.2 There could be environmental conditions that necessitate the use of rigid nonmetallic conduit.

27.7.1.6.3 Conductors and fiber-optic cables shall have an approved insulation. The insulation or other outer covering shall be flame-retardant and moisture resistant.

27.7.1.6.4 Conductors and fiber-optic cables shall be installed as far as possible without splices or joints. Splices or joints shall be permitted only in listed junction or terminal boxes.

27.7.1.6.4.1 Fire alarm circuits shall be identified by the use of red covers or doors. The words "public fire alarm circuit" shall be clearly marked on all terminal and junction locations to prevent unintentional interference.

27.7.1.6.4.2 Wire and fiber-optic terminals, terminal boxes, splices, and joints shall conform to *NFPA 70, National Electrical Code.*

27.7.1.6.5 Metallic and fiber-optic cables and wiring exposed to a fire hazard shall be protected in an approved manner.

27.7.1.6.6 Metallic and fiber-optic cable terminals and cross-connecting facilities shall be located in or adjacent to the operations room.

27.7.1.6.7 Where signal conductors, non-dielectric fiber-optic cables, and electric light and power wires are run in the same shaft, they shall be separated by at least 2 in. (51 mm), or either system shall be encased in a noncombustible enclosure.

27.7.2 Signal Transmission and Receiving Circuits. Signal transmission and receiving circuits shall comply with the requirements of 27.7.2.1 and 27.7.2.2.

27.7.2.1 General.

27.7.2.1.1 ANSI/IEEE C2, *National Electrical Safety Code*, shall be used as a guide for the installation of outdoor circuitry.

Public and private electric company utilities, public and private telephone utilities, and public and private community antenna television company utilities use ANSI/IEEE C2. A committee from the IEEE (Institute of Electrical and Electronics Engineers) developed the *NESC* to describe the placement and spacing of outdoor aerial cable installations. The *NESC* ensures the safe operation of the associated systems.

27.7.2.1.2 Installation shall provide for the following:

(1) Continuity of service
(2) Protection from mechanical damage
(3) Disablement from heat that is incidental to fire
(4) Protection from falling walls
(5) Damage by floods, corrosive vapors, or other causes

27.7.2.1.3 Open local circuits within single buildings shall be permitted in accordance with Chapter 23.

The requirements of Chapter 23 apply to protected premises fire alarm system circuits that do not serve as a part of the public emergency alarm reporting system.

27.7.2.1.4 All circuits shall be routed so as to allow tracing of circuits for trouble.

27.7.2.1.5 Circuits shall not pass over, under, through, or be attached to buildings or property not owned by or under the control of the authority having jurisdiction or the agency responsible for maintaining the system.

Exception: Where the circuit is terminated at a public emergency alarm reporting system initiating device on the premises and where a means, approved by the authority having jurisdiction, is provided to disconnect the circuit from the building or property.

Paragraph 27.7.2.1.5 requires installers to discontinue a previous practice. At one time, installers strung the circuits for many of the original public emergency alarm reporting systems in various East Coast municipalities throughout a city from building to building. Engineers soon learned that fires in those buildings would damage the circuits, thereby placing the operational integrity of the public emergency alarm reporting system in jeopardy.

The exception to 27.7.2.1.5 permits the circuit to terminate at a public emergency alarm reporting system initiating device on the protected premises. However, a means must exist to disconnect the circuit from the building. This disconnecting means allows isolation of the device inside the protected premises in the event of a fault on the conductors that run through the protected premises. See 27.6.3.2.3.7 regarding the disconnecting means for auxiliary alarm systems.

27.7.2.2 Box Circuits. Interior box circuits shall comply with 27.7.2.2.1 and 27.7.2.2.2.

27.7.2.2.1 A means accessible only to the authority having jurisdiction or the agency responsible for maintaining the public emergency alarm reporting systems shall be provided to disconnect all circuit conductors inside a building or other structure.

If an installer makes a connection to the public emergency alarm reporting system in accordance with the requirements of 27.6.3, 27.7.2.2.1 requires — similar to the requirements of 27.6.3.2.3.7 — that the installer provide a means to disconnect the protected premises connection. Only the authority having jurisdiction over the public emergency alarm reporting system can have access to this disconnecting means. Locating the disconnecting means inside a locked auxiliary box will satisfy this requirement.

Some large municipalities do issue a special license or permit for contractors that allows them to have keys that will access the auxiliary boxes. This permit allows the contractor to disconnect the protected premises connection during testing and maintenance of the alarm system at the protected premises.

27.7.2.2.2 Definite notification shall be given to the designated building representative when the interior box(es) is out of service.

◄ **FAQ**
Who is permitted to have access to the disconnecting means for an auxiliary circuit?

27.7.3* Circuit Protection. Circuit protection shall be provided in accordance with 27.7.3.1 through 27.7.3.12.

A.27.7.3 All requirements for circuit protection do not apply to coded radio reporting systems. These systems do not use metallic circuits.

Circuit protection, addressed in 27.7.3, limits equipment damage caused when an incident applies transient currents to the circuits of the public emergency alarm reporting system. Lightning is one source of such transient currents.

Article 800 of *NFPA 70* covers protection of communications circuits, including the installation of surge suppressors and lightning arresters.

27.7.3.1 The protective devices shall be located close to or be combined with the cable terminals.

27.7.3.2 Surge arresters designed and approved for the purpose shall be installed at a location accessible to qualified persons and shall be marked with the name of the manufacturer and model designation.

27.7.3.3 All surge arresters shall be connected to a ground in accordance with *NFPA 70, National Electrical Code.*

27.7.3.4 All fuses, fuseholders, and adapters shall be plainly marked with their ampere rating. All fuses rated over 2 amperes shall be of the enclosed type.

27.7.3.5 Circuit protection required at the communications center shall be provided in every building that houses communications center equipment.

27.7.3.6 Each metallic conductor entering a fire station from partially or entirely aerial lines shall be protected by a lightning arrester.

27.7.3.7 All metallic conductors entering the communications center shall be protected by the following devices, in the order named, starting from the exterior circuit:

(1) A fuse rated at 3 amperes minimum to 7 amperes maximum and not less than 2000 volts
(2) A surge arrester(s)
(3) A fuse or circuit breaker rated at $\frac{1}{2}$ ampere

27.7.3.8 In regard to 27.7.3.7, the $\frac{1}{2}$-ampere protection on the tie circuits shall be omitted at subsidiary communications centers.

27.7.3.9 At junction points of open aerial metallic conductors and metallic cable, each conductor shall be protected by a surge arrester(s) of the weatherproof type. A connection shall also be between the surge arrester ground, any metallic sheath, and the messenger wire.

27.7.3.10 Aerial open-wire and nonmessenger-supported, two-conductor cable circuits shall be protected by a surge arrester(s) at intervals not to exceed 2000 ft (610 m).

27.7.3.11 Where used for aerial construction, surge arresters, other than of the air-gap or self-restoring type, shall not be installed in fire alarm circuits.

27.7.3.12 All protective devices used for aerial construction shall be accessible for maintenance and inspection.

27.8 Emergency Communications Systems (ECS)

27.8.1* ECS shall be permitted to be connected to public emergency alarm reporting systems.

A.27.8.1 The public emergency alarm reporting system infrastructure could be used to facilitate the operation of wide area signaling, as is currently being done for emergency notification to the public in some communities and as has been done in the past for civil defense notification.

27.8.2 ECS equipment and interface methods connecting to or utilizing public emergency alarm reporting systems shall be electrically and operationally compatible so as not to interfere with the public emergency alarm reporting systems.

REFERENCES CITED IN COMMENTARY

ANSI/IEEE C2, *National Electrical Safety Code*, 2007 edition as amended, Institute of Electrical and Electronics Engineers, New York, NY.

NFPA 70®, National Electrical Code®, 2008 edition, National Fire Protection Association, Quincy, MA.

NFPA 75, *Standard for the Protection of Information Technology Equipment*, 2009 edition, National Fire Protection Association, Quincy, MA.

NFPA 1221, *Standard for the Installation, Maintenance, and Use of Emergency Services Communications Systems*, 2010 edition, National Fire Protection Association, Quincy, MA.

Reserved

In this 2010 edition of *NFPA 72®*, *National Fire Alarm and Signaling Code*, Chapter 28 is reserved for future use.

Single- and Multiple-Station Alarms and Household Fire Alarm Systems

Chapter 29 (Chapter 11 in previous editions of the Code) covers the performance, installation, and use of all single- and multiple-station alarms and household fire alarm systems — in essence, all fire-warning equipment. The definition of *fire warning equipment* in 3.3.100, which was added in the 2002 edition, is "any detector, alarm, device, or material related to single- and multiple-station alarms or household fire alarm systems." This definition helps to clarify the intent of the requirements in Chapter 29.

In the 2002 edition, the scope of this chapter was changed from one limited to fire-warning equipment specifically in dwelling units to one that covers fire-warning equipment independent of the occupancy. This new scope is reflected in the chapter title and in 29.1.1. Historically, reference to the requirements for smoke alarms in *NFPA 72®* from building codes and from NFPA *101®, Life Safety Code®*, has not been limited to dwelling unit applications; the "household" chapter has been used as a source for the installation of smoke alarms, regardless of occupancy.

The definition of *household fire alarm system* in 3.3.95.2, which was revised in 2002, is intended to clarify that the term refers to equipment that uses a fire alarm control unit to process signals and produce alarm (warning) signals to occupants. As a part of this clarification, it is important to understand the difference between a smoke detector and a smoke alarm: A *smoke detector* is part of a fire alarm system, whereas a *smoke alarm* includes the detection and warning components all in one unit and does not require a control unit for power and supervision. Also refer to the commentary following 14.1.2 for more information on the difference between smoke alarms and smoke detectors.

The format and content of Chapter 29 in this edition generally follow the 2002 and 2007 editions of the Code. A complete cross-reference from the 2007 Code is provided in Annex I.

The following list is a summary of significant changes to the chapter on single- and multiple-station alarms and household fire alarm systems in the 2010 edition:

- New guidance in A.29.1.1 concerning currently available smoke alarm technology
- New 29.3.8 identifying different levels of hearing loss and the notification requirements in sleeping areas for those with these conditions, including a requirement for a low frequency alarm signal for those with mild to severe hearing loss and a requirement for tactile notification appliances in addition to high intensity strobes for those with profound hearing loss
- New 29.7.7.2 requiring wireless interconnected alarms to meet specific performance requirements to ensure adequate transmission and reception capability within a structure
- New 29.7.8.3 requiring household fire alarm systems to be manufactured to automatically generate at least a monthly test of the communication or transmission means
- Revised 29.8.3 eliminating the requirement that smoke alarms be at least 4 in. (100 mm) from an adjoining wall or ceiling when mounted on flat ceilings or walls
- Revised 29.8.3.4(4) providing new requirements and supporting Annex A material for the type and location of smoke alarms relative to cooking appliances
- New 29.8.3.4(11) and 29.8.3.4(12) requiring smoke and heat alarms installed in rooms with joists or beams to comply with the requirements in Chapter 17

29.1 Application

29.1.1* The performance, selection, installation, operation, and use of single- and multiple-station alarms and household fire alarm systems shall comply with the requirements of this chapter.

A.29.1.1 Chapter 29 does not attempt to cover all equipment, methods, and requirements that might be necessary or advantageous for the protection of lives and property from fire.

NFPA 72 is a "minimum code." This chapter provides a number of requirements related to single- and multiple-station alarms and household fire alarm systems that are deemed to be the practical and necessary minimum for average conditions at the present state of the art.

Currently Available Smoke Alarm Technology. The technologies used in currently available smoke alarms include ionization smoke detection and photoelectric detection. These detection types are defined in 3.3.252.2 and 3.3.252.4 and are further explained in A.3.3.252.2 and A.3.3.252.4. Ionization smoke detection is more responsive to invisible particles produced by most flaming fires. Photoelectric smoke detection is more responsive to the visible particles produced by most smoldering fire. Residential smoke alarms and commercial smoke detectors are currently available with either ionization technology or photoelectric technology or a combination of both technologies. The use of both technologies generally offers the advantage of providing a faster response to both flaming and smoldering fires, and is recommended for those who desire a higher level of protection than the minimum requirements of this Code.

Fatal home fires involving smoldering fires and flaming fires occur at night and during the day. It is not possible to reliably predict what type of fire will occur or at what hour of the day it will occur. Therefore, the preference of one technology over the other on the basis of the expectation of a particular type of fire (predominately smoldering or flaming) is not a sound basis for selection. While the current consensus of experts suggests that neither technology offers an advantage when the fire type is not known, there is a consensus that there would be a benefit to having both technologies since the type of fire cannot be predicted.

Based on recent analysis of the full scale fire tests documented by the National Institute of Standards and Technology in Report TN 1455-1_2-2008, the minimum provisions of the Code using either technology are considered to provide an adequate level of protection for most individuals who are not intimate with the fire and are capable of self rescue. This would include occupants in the room of fire origin for both flaming and smoldering fires who escape through the normal path of egress. Protection beyond the minimum provisions of the Code using both technologies should be considered for situations involving individuals who are not capable of self rescue or who might need additional time for escape. These situations might include families where extra time is needed to awaken or assist others.

While it is true that ionization detection technology is more susceptible to nuisance alarms due to cooking, the use of this technology should not be dismissed, particularly where the additional protection of both technologies is suggested. In addition, there is no substantial evidence that suggests that either technology is more susceptible to nuisance alarms from bathroom steam. Provisions and guidance have been added to 29.8.3.4 to help minimize nuisance alarms from both sources. This is important since smoke alarms that are disabled due to frequent nuisance alarms offer no protection whatsoever. A higher level of protection would be afforded by using both technologies in all locations required by this Code with additional locations in other rooms of the dwelling. In considering this, pending the availability of smoke alarms specifically designed for nuisance alarm immunity, additional locations within 20 ft of a cooking appliance should be minimized, especially for smoke alarms using ionization technology.

While these considerations reflect the consensus of experts based on currently available test data that allows analysis of tenability along with alarm response, full scale fire testing and nuisance alarm testing of current technologies has continued and analysis of this data will also continue. In addition, new technologies are being considered with the prospect of enhanced detection response along with a higher immunity to nuisance activations. The work of the industry and the NFPA technical committee responsible for smoke alarm provisions will be ongoing.

Except for installations near cooking appliances, the requirements of *NFPA 72, National Fire Alarm and Signaling Code,* do not specify the type — ionization or photoelectric — of smoke alarm to be used. An ionization smoke alarm is generally more responsive to flaming fires, and a photoelectric smoke alarm is generally more responsive to smoldering fires. Both types of alarms have improved home fire safety.

The requirements in *NFPA 72* for smoke alarms assume average conditions and are considered adequate for most individuals who are not intimate with the fire and who are capable of self-rescue. It is assumed that a full complement of smoke alarms is installed in accordance with the requirements of Section 29.5. Additional protection, using both ionization and photoelectric smoke alarms (separately or in combination), should be considered for situations in which individuals either are not capable of self-rescue or might need additional time for escape (including families for whom extra time is needed to awaken or assist others). For those not capable of self-rescue and who cannot rely on immediate assistance, additional protection (potentially including the use of automatic sprinklers) should be considered. Refer to A.29.3.3 for additional guidance.

When additional smoke alarms are being installed, the impact of additional nuisance alarms needs to be considered. Refer to 29.8.3.4(4) for restrictions on the installation of smoke alarms relative to cooking appliances.

29.1.2* Smoke and heat alarms shall be installed in all occupancies where required by other governing laws, codes, or standards.

A.29.1.2 An example of the applicable code within the NFPA set of codes and standards is NFPA *101, Life Safety Code.* Other codes such as local building codes are other examples to be considered.

The requirements of Chapter 29 are intended to apply to installations in the following new and existing locations:

(1) One- and two-family dwelling units
(2) Sleeping rooms of lodging and rooming houses
(3) Individual dwelling units of apartment buildings
(4) Guest rooms, sleeping rooms, and living areas within guest suites of hotels and dormitories
(5) Day-care homes
(6) Residential board and care facilities
(7) Other locations where applicable laws codes or standards specify a requirement for the installation of smoke alarms

As noted earlier, Chapter 29 deals specifically with single- and multiple-station alarms and household fire alarm systems, regardless of the occupancy. Generally, this equipment will be used in residential occupancies as required by applicable laws, codes, or standards. Although the list in A.29.1.2 identifies applications commonly addressed by applicable laws, codes, or standards, it is recognized that these sources may identify other applications for which the rules of Chapter 29 would be appropriate. The applications and locations addressed in this chapter are not intended to cover requirements for common or tenantless areas, such as apartment building lobbies or hallways. Requirements for those other applications and locations are contained in the balance of this Code.

29.1.3 The requirements of Chapters 10, 12, 14, 17, 18, 21, 23, 24, 26 and 27 shall not apply unless otherwise noted.

The requirements of Chapter 1, the references in Chapter 2, and the definitions in Chapter 3 apply throughout the Code, including Chapter 29.

Since the 2002 edition, all testing and maintenance requirements are located in the inspection, testing, and maintenance chapter, currently Chapter 14.

29.1.4* The requirements of this chapter shall not apply to installations in manufactured homes.

A.29.1.4 Installations in manufactured homes are under the jurisdiction of The Department of Housing and Urban Development (HUD). The rules for installation are addressed in the Federal Manufactured Housing Construction Safety Standards (available at http://www.hud.gov/offices/hsg/sfh/mhs/mhshome.cfm).

29.1.5 This chapter shall apply to the life safety of occupants and not to the protection of property.

In the United States, residential occupancies lead all other types of occupancies as the site of fire-related deaths. As indicated in 29.1.5 and Section 29.2, the fire-warning equipment addressed by this chapter is intended to provide warning to occupants but is not intended to provide property protection or to extinguish the fire. The occupants are responsible for following their emergency exit plan when the alarm signal sounds. Paragraphs A.29.1.1, A.29.2, A.29.4.1, and A.29.4.2 describe fire-warning equipment capabilities, home fire statistics, recommendations for fire safety and life safety, a more detailed explanation of an escape plan, and special provisions for people with disabilities.

Additional safety equipment such as residential fire sprinklers can provide additional escape time and can limit damage to the premises.

29.2* Purpose

Fire-warning equipment for residential occupancies shall provide a reliable means to notify the occupants of the presence of a threatening fire and the need to escape to a place of safety before such escape might be impeded by untenable conditions in the normal path of egress.

An effective fire-warning system depends on the proper installation, use, and maintenance of equipment. The locations and requirements specified in Chapter 29 reflect a level of protection determined by consensus agreement. In many cases, additional protection may be desirable to provide a higher degree of protection. Recommendations for additional equipment and other guidance can be found in A.29.1.1, A.29.3.3, A.29.5.1, A.29.7.3.2, and A.29.8.3.

A.29.2 *Fire Danger in the Home.* In 2005, fire was the third leading cause of unintentional injury deaths in the home, and the sixth leading cause of unintentional injury deaths overall (*Injury Facts*, 2007 edition, National Safety Council).

Eighty-four (84.4) percent of the fire fatalities in 2007 resulted from residential fires — 68.5 percent resulted from fires in one- and two-family dwellings, including manufactured homes, 15.0 percent were caused by apartment fires, and 0.9 percent resulted from fires in other residential occupancies ("Fire Loss in the United States during 2007," Michael J. Karter, NFPA Fire Analysis and Research Division).

Approximately half (53 percent) of the home (dwellings and apartments) fire fatalities resulted from fires reported between 11:00 p.m. and 7:00 a.m., the common sleeping hours ("Home Structure Fires," Marty Ahrens, NFPA Fire Analysis and Research Division, February 2007).

Over three-quarters (76.9 percent) of all reported fire injuries occurred in the home, with more than one-half (54.6 percent) in one- and two-family dwellings (including manufactured housing), and more than one-fifth (22.3 percent) in apartments ("Fire Loss in the United States during 2007," Michael J. Karter, NFPA Fire Analysis and Research Division).

It is estimated that each household will experience three (usually unreported) fires per decade and two fires serious enough to report to a fire department per lifetime ("A Few Fire Facts at the Household Level," NFPA Fire Analysis Division, *Fire Journal*, May 1986).

Fire Safety in the Home. NFPA 72 is intended to provide reasonable fire safety for persons in family living units. Reasonable fire safety can be produced through the following three-point program:

(1) Minimizing fire hazards
(2) Providing fire-warning equipment
(3) Having and practicing an escape plan

Minimizing Fire Hazards. This Code cannot protect all persons at all times. For instance, the application of this Code might not provide protection against the following three traditional fatal fire scenarios:

(1) Smoking in bed
(2) Leaving children home alone
(3) Cleaning with flammable liquids, such as gasoline

However, Chapter 29 can lead to reasonable safety from fire when the three-point program is observed.

Fire-Warning Equipment. There are two types of fire to which household fire-warning equipment needs to respond. One is a rapidly developing, high-heat fire. The other is a slow, smoldering fire. Either can produce smoke and toxic gases.

Family Escape Plan. There often is very little time between the detection of a fire and the time it becomes deadly. This interval can be as little as 1 or 2 minutes. Thus, this Code requires detection means to give a family some advance warning of the development of conditions that become dangerous to life within a short period of time. Such warning, however, could be wasted unless the family has planned in advance for rapid exit from their residence. Therefore, in addition to the fire-warning equipment, this Code assumes that the residents have developed and practiced an exit plan.

Planning and practicing for fire conditions with a focus on rapid exit from the residence are important. Drills should be held so that all family members know the action to be taken. Each person should plan for the possibility that exit out of a bedroom window could be necessary. An exit out of the residence without the need to open a bedroom door is essential.

Household fires are especially dangerous at night when the occupants are asleep. Fires produce smoke and deadly gases that can overcome occupants while they are asleep. Furthermore, dense smoke reduces visibility. Most fire casualties are victims of smoke and gas inhalation rather than burns. To warn against a fire, Chapter 29 provides smoke detector (alarm) requirements in accordance with 29.5.1, and the associated annex recommends heat or smoke detectors (alarms) in all other major areas.

29.3 Basic Requirements

29.3.1 All devices, combinations of devices, and equipment to be installed in conformity with this chapter shall be approved or listed for the purposes for which they are intended.

The term *approved* means acceptable to the authority having jurisdiction. Further explanation can be found in A.3.2.1. The term *listed* is defined in 3.2.5 and refers to products or services that have been evaluated by an organization acceptable to the authority having jurisdiction. The listing organization does not approve equipment or services — only the authority having jurisdiction can approve equipment or services. Subsection 29.3.1 requires equipment to be either approved or listed. If equipment is not labeled or listed, the authority having jurisdiction can still approve the equipment if it is shown that the requirements of the Code have been met. Also refer to Section 1.5 for the rules governing equivalence.

29.3.2 Fire-warning equipment shall be installed in accordance with the listing and manufacturer's published instructions.

29.3.3* The installation of smoke alarms or fire alarm systems, or combinations of these, shall comply with the requirements of this chapter and shall satisfy the minimum requirements for number and location of smoke alarms or smoke detectors by one of the following arrangements:

(1) The required minimum number and location of smoke detection devices shall be satisfied (independently) through the installation of smoke alarms. The installation of additional smoke alarms shall be permitted. The installation of additional system-based smoke detectors, including partial or complete duplication of the smoke alarms satisfying the required minimum, shall be permitted.
(2) The required minimum number and location of smoke detection devices shall be satisfied (independently) through the installation of system smoke detectors. The installation of additional smoke detectors shall be permitted. The installation of additional smoke alarms, including partial or complete duplication of the smoke detectors satisfying the required minimum, shall be permitted.

A.29.3.3 This Code establishes minimum standards for the use of fire-warning equipment. The use of additional alarms or detectors over and above the minimum standard is encouraged. The use of additional devices can result in a combination of equipment (e.g., a combination of single- and multiple-station alarms or a combination of smoke alarms or smoke detectors that are part of a security/fire system and existing multiple-station alarms). Though a combination is allowed, one type of equipment must independently meet the requirements of the Code. Compliance with the requirements of the Code cannot rely on the combination of the following fire-warning equipment:

(1) Single-station alarms
(2) Multiple-station alarms
(3) Household fire alarm system (includes a security/fire system with smoke alarms or smoke detectors)

It is encouraged that the highest level of protection be used where possible. For example, if multiple-station alarms are added to an occupancy with compliant single-station alarms, the multiple-station alarms should be installed to replace all of the single-station alarms. Similarly, if a monitored household fire alarm system is added to a house that has compliant multiple-station alarms, monitored smoke alarms or smoke detectors should be installed to replace the multiple-station alarms or be installed to provide the same required coverage.

The responsiveness of ionization- and photoelectric-type smoke alarms depends on a number of factors, including the type of fire (smoldering, flaming), the chemistry of materials involved in the fire, and the properties of the resulting smoke. Several fire safety organizations recommend that a consumer utilize both ionization and photoelectric technologies in their home smoke alarm systems to permit the longest potential escape times for nonspecific fire situations. This will not preclude the development of new technology with equivalent performance.

FAQ ▶
Does the Code permit the use of both smoke alarms and smoke detectors?

The text of 29.3.3 and A.29.3.3 clarifies the acceptable use of combinations of equipment (i.e., single-station alarms, multiple-station alarms, and system detectors). The minimum siting requirements must be met independently either by smoke alarms or by a household fire alarm system. As an example, if multiple-station smoke alarms exist in a dwelling unit and

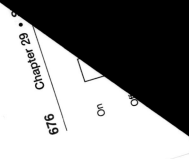

fully satisfy the number, location, and installation requirements of the Code, and the homeowner then has a combination fire and burglar alarm system installed, system smoke detectors can be added to the home in new locations without duplication of the smoke alarm locations. The system detectors would be required to meet the installation rules of the Code in all other respects. Although this arrangement is permitted by the Code, the homeowner should be made aware of the importance of the role of the existing smoke alarms and of maintaining both the new system and the existing smoke alarms. In addition, where off-site monitoring is provided, the homeowner should be made aware that the smoke alarms will not transmit the alarm to the monitoring station. Smoke alarm replacement is required for one- and two-family dwellings every 10 years, in accordance with 14.4.8. Therefore, in this scenario, replacement of existing smoke alarms with new system smoke detectors may be an advantage in the long term.

29.3.4 Supplementary functions, including the extension of an alarm beyond the residential occupancy, shall be permitted and shall not interfere with the performance requirements of this chapter.

The supplementary functions described in 29.3.4 can include connection to a remote supervising station, to a central station, or to another remote monitoring location. See 29.7.8 and Chapter 26 for information regarding supervising station connection requirements. Also refer to Section 29.9 for other optional functions permitted by the Code and to 29.7.6 for requirements for combination systems.

29.3.5* Fire-warning equipment to be installed in residential occupancies shall produce the audible emergency evacuation signal described in ANSI S3.41, *American National Standard Emergency Evacuation Signal*, whenever the intended response is to evacuate the building.

A.29.3.5 The use of the distinctive three-pulse temporal pattern fire alarm evacuation signal has been recommended by this Code since 1979. It has since been adopted as both an American National Standard (ANSI S3.41, *American National Standard Audible Emergency Evacuation Signal*) and an International Standard (ISO 8201, *Audible Emergency Evacuation Signal*).

Copies of both of these standards are available from either of the following:

(1) The web at asastore.aip.org
(2) Standards Publication Fulfillment, P.O., Box 1020, Sewickly, PA 15143-9998, Tel. 412-741-1979

For information about the Acoustical Society of America, or for how and why the three-pulse temporal pattern signal was chosen as the international standard evacuation signal, contact Standards Secretariat, Acoustical Society of America, 35 Pinelawn Road, Suite 114E, Melville, NY 11747, Tel. 531-490-0215, Email: asastds@aip.org.

The standard fire alarm evacuation signal is a three-pulse temporal pattern using any appropriate sound. The pattern consists of the following in this order:

(1) An "on" phase lasting 0.5 second ±10 percent.
(2) An "off" phase lasting 0.5 second ±10 percent for three successive "on" periods.
(3) An "off" phase lasting 1.5 seconds ±10 percent *[see Figure A.29.3.5(a) and Figure A.29.3.5(b)]*. The signal should be repeated for a period appropriate for the purposes of evacuation of the building, but for not less than 180 seconds. A single-stroke bell or chime sounded at "on" intervals lasting 1 second ±10 percent, with a 2-second ±10 percent "off" interval after each third "on" stroke, is permitted *[see Figure A.29.3.5(c)]*.

The minimum repetition time is permitted to be manually interrupted.

29.3.5.1 The audible emergency evacuation signal shall be permitted to be used for other devices as long as the desired response is immediate evacuation.

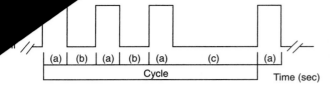

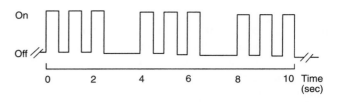

Key:
Phase (a) signal is on for 0.5 sec ±10%
Phase (b) signal is off for 0.5 sec ±10%
Phase (c) signal is off for 1.5 sec ±10% [(c) = (a) + 2(b)]
Total cycle lasts for 4 sec ±10%

FIGURE A.29.3.5(a) *Temporal Pattern Parameters.*

FIGURE A.29.3.5(b) *Temporal Pattern Imposed on Signaling Appliances That Emit a Continuous Signal While Energized.*

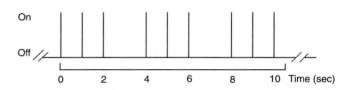

FIGURE A.29.3.5(c) *Temporal Pattern Imposed on a Single-Stroke Bell or Chime.*

29.3.5.2* Fire-warning equipment producing the audible emergency evacuation signal shall be permitted to incorporate voice notification under either or both of the following conditions:

(1) Where the voice message is contained completely within the 1.5-second pause period of the audible emergency evacuation signal
(2) Where the voice message complies with 29.3.5.2(2)(a) and (b) as follows:

    (a) The voice message is first preceded by a minimum of eight cycles of the audible emergency evacuation signal.
    (b) The voice message periodically interrupts the signal for no longer than 10 seconds, followed by a minimum of two cycles of the audible emergency evacuation signal between each voice message. The initial eight-cycle period shall not be required to be repeated.

A.29.3.5.2 It is recommended that the voice notification message be intelligible, audible, and appropriate for the hazard. Care should be taken to avoid excessive silence during the message. Figure A.29.3.5.2(a) through Figure A.29.3.5.2(c) provide examples of acceptable combinations of the emergency evacuation signal and voice messages.

Upon review of technical literature and research, the Technical Committee on Single- and Multiple-Station Alarms and Household Fire Alarm Systems concluded that the use of voice notification may provide benefit to certain portions of the population, particularly children. However, the limited studies are not fully clear as to what characteristics of the voice signal result in improved waking effectiveness; the same effect might be achieved with non-voice signals, such as multi-frequency signals (see the commentary following 29.3.8). Therefore, the Code was revised in the 2007 edition to allow the limited use of voice notification in con-

Alarm initiation — eight T3 cycles minimum.								Two T3 cycles minimum — repeat as desired.		
T3 cycle	T3 cycle	T3 cycle	T3 cycle	T3 cycle	T3 cycle	T3 cycle	T3 cycle	Voice — 10-sec maximum	T3 cycle	T3 cycle
(1)	(2)	(3)	(4)	(5)	(6)	(7)	(8)		(1)	(2)

FIGURE A.29.3.5.2(a) *Temporal Pattern Parameters with 10-Second Voice Allowance.*

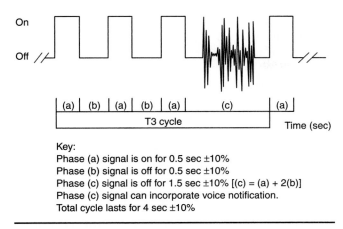

Key:
Phase (a) signal is on for 0.5 sec ±10%
Phase (b) signal is off for 0.5 sec ±10%
Phase (c) signal is off for 1.5 sec ±10% [(c) = (a) + 2(b)]
Phase (c) signal can incorporate voice notification.
Total cycle lasts for 4 sec ±10%

FIGURE A.29.3.5.2(b) *Temporal Pattern Parameters with 1.5-Second Voice Allowance.*

Alarm initiation — eight T3 cycles minimum. Optional voice allowed in any T3 cycle.								Two T3 cycles minimum — repeat as desired.		
T3 cycle with voice	T3 cycle with voice	T3 cycle with voice	T3 cycle with voice	T3 cycle with voice	T3 cycle with voice	T3 cycle with voice	T3 cycle with voice	Voice — 10-sec maximum	T3 cycle with voice	T3 cycle with voice
(1)	(2)	(3)	(4)	(5)	(6)	(7)	(8)		(1)	(2)

FIGURE A.29.3.5.2(c) *Temporal Pattern Parameters with 10-Second Voice Allowance.*

junction with the audible emergency evacuation signal. The limiting conditions ensure that the majority of the population will be effectively awakened by the audible emergency evacuation signal before the voice message begins [Bruck, 2001; Bruck, 2005; Duncan, 1999]. The specified conditions allow for both 1.5- and 10-second voice messages in accordance with ANSI S3.41, *American National Standard Audible Emergency Evacuation Signal.*

29.3.6 Audible fire alarm signals shall meet the performance requirements of 18.4.3 and 18.4.5.

To ensure that smoke alarms or notification appliances can be heard by occupants inside closed sleeping areas, the sound pressure level (SPL) must be measured with bedroom doors shut and in conditions as similar as possible to those conditions normally occurring in the home at night. For example, if air conditioning units or humidifiers are used routinely in a home, those appliances should be operating when the measurements are made. Chapter 18 requires the warning signal to have a minimum level that satisfies the greatest of the following three conditions:

◄ FAQ
What performance requirements for audibility must be met when smoke alarms or notification appliances are installed?

1. At least 15 decibels (dB) above the average ambient SPL
2. At least 5 dB above the maximum SPL that lasts 1 minute or longer
3. A level of at least 75 dBA

   All measurements must be made in the bedroom at pillow level using the A-weighted scale (dBA) of an SPL meter adjusted to the time-weighted characteristic F (FAST) scale as described in Table 14.4.2.2, item 15. Refer to the definition of *average ambient sound level* in 3.3.25.

   Listed smoke alarms are tested to meet a minimum SPL of 85 dBA at 10 ft (3.0 m). Many devices will produce levels of 90 dBA or higher. Because not all actual environmental conditions can be anticipated in standardized testing, on-site testing of installed smoke or heat alarms is recommended, particularly for applications with high ambient noise levels or a room construction that may adversely affect the alarm signal. Because the smoke alarm is installed in rooms and areas that can have an effect on audibility, the audibility requirements of Chapter 18 are recommended for review in addition to the requirements in this chapter.

A study recently published by the Consumer Product Safety Commission (CPSC) examined sound levels from smoke alarms in several residential dwellings [Lee, 2005]. The results indicate that smoke alarms located within bedrooms would provide the required sound levels. Smoke alarms located outside bedrooms, however, may not provide the required sound level of 75 dBA within the bedroom at pillow level, particularly if the door is closed. For this reason, the Code now requires interconnected alarms throughout the dwelling, including bedrooms (see 29.5.2.1.1 and associated commentary).

Note that 18.4.5.3 includes a new requirement that all notification appliances provided for sleeping areas produce a low frequency alarm signal. While that requirement is not effective until January 1, 2014, the requirements provided in 29.3.8 are effective without delay.

29.3.7 When visible appliances are provided, they shall meet the requirements of Section 18.5. Since hearing deficits are often not apparent, the responsibility for advising the appropriate person(s) of the existence of this deficit shall be that of the party with hearing loss.

Subsection 29.3.7 directs users to Section 18.5 for requirements to be followed when visible appliances are used. It also states that it is the responsibility of those with hearing loss to advise the appropriate people, such as hotel personnel or landlords, of the hearing deficit so that appropriate notification equipment can be provided. Subsection 29.3.8 provides further details of the required equipment for people with different levels of hearing loss.

29.3.8 Notification appliances provided in sleeping rooms and guest rooms for those with hearing loss shall comply with 29.3.8.1 and 29.3.8.2, as applicable.

Subsection 29.3.8 addresses the notification requirements in sleeping rooms and guest rooms for people with different levels of hearing loss. Based on the testing to date regarding waking effectiveness of alarm signals, two degrees of hearing loss are denoted as needing different types of alarm signals. Paragraph 29.3.8.1 discusses the requirements for those with mild to severe hearing loss (sometimes described as "hard of hearing"), and 29.3.8.2 discusses the requirements for those with profound hearing loss (sometimes described as "deaf"). The term *hearing loss* is defined in 3.3.113 and further explained in A.3.3.113. The terms *mild to severe* and *profound* refer to the minimum decibel level at which a person will perceive sound. The material in A.3.3.113 includes a listing of the decibel thresholds corresponding to mild, moderate, moderately severe, severe, and profound hearing loss. As noted in 29.3.7, it is the responsibility of persons with hearing loss to inform the appropriate person(s) of the existence and type of their hearing loss.

29.3.8.1 Mild to Severe Hearing Loss. Notification appliances provided for those with mild to severe hearing loss shall comply with the following:

(1) An audible notification appliance producing a low frequency alarm signal shall be installed in the following situations:

   (a)*Where required by governing laws, codes or standards for people with hearing loss
   (b) Where provided voluntarily for those with hearing loss

(2)*The low frequency alarm signal output shall comply with the following:

   (a) The alarm signal shall be a square wave or provide equivalent awakening ability.
   (b)*The wave shall have a fundamental frequency of 520 Hz +/ −10 percent.
   (c) The minimum sound level at the pillow shall be 75 dBA, or 15 dB above the average ambient sound level, or 5 dB above the maximum sound level having a duration of at least 60 seconds, whichever is greater.

Based on recent sleep studies to assess the waking effectiveness of different types of alarm signals, it has been shown that a low frequency square wave alarm signal with a fundamental frequency of 520 Hz provides improved awakening for people with mild to severe hearing loss [Bruck and Thomas, 2008] compared to typical alarms from high frequency piezoelectric sounders used in most smoke alarms. It has also been shown that visible alarm signals, such as strobes, are not very effective at waking people with mild to severe hearing loss [Thomas and Bruck, 2008; Ashley and Du Bois, 2004]. As for all alarm signals, the effectiveness of the installed notification for the specific occupants should be tested by the occupants, if possible.

The low frequency square wave alarm signal can be provided by the sounder within a smoke alarm or by a separate notification appliance. Exhibit 29.1 shows an example of a notification appliance that uses a low frequency square wave to alert those with hearing loss; the appliance is activated by the sound from a traditional smoke alarm. This particular appliance also includes a supplementary bed shaker.

EXHIBIT 29.1 *Low Frequency Notification Appliance. (Source: Lifetone Technology, Oklahoma City, OK)*

A.29.3.8.1(1)(a) As an example, governing laws, codes, or standards might require a certain number of accommodations be equipped for those with hearing loss or other disability.

A.29.3.8.1(2) It is not the intent of this section to preclude devices that have been demonstrated through peer reviewed research to awaken occupants with hearing loss as effectively as those using the frequency and amplitude specified in this section.

A.29.3.8.1(2)(b) Fundamental frequency: 520 Hz $\pm$ 10 percent. Odd harmonic frequency components 3, 5, 7, and 9 times the fundamental frequency should be present in appropriate magnitude defined by the Fourier transform of a square wave (see below) $\pm$ 20 percent.

On a linear scale where X is the peak magnitude of the fundamental frequency component, the harmonic frequencies should have the following peak magnitudes with the tolerance defined above:

(1) 520 Hz X
(2) 1560 Hz $\frac{1}{3}$ X
(3) 2600 Hz $\frac{1}{5}$ X
(4) 3640 Hz $\frac{1}{7}$ X
(5) 4680 Hz $\frac{1}{9}$ X

A square wave contains only the odd integer harmonics. In general, a square wave can be expressed using the Fourier series. As presented by Wolfram MathWorld, the general mathematical expression for the function of an ideal square wave as an infinite series is

$$\chi_{square}(t) = \frac{4}{\pi} \sum_{n=1,3,5,...}^{\infty} \frac{1}{n} \sin(2n\pi ft)$$

where $\chi_{square}(t)$ is the square wave as a function of time, t, $sin(\ )$ is the sine wave function, f is the frequency, π is pi, the relationship between the circumference and the diameter of a circle, and n is the odd harmonics. An expanded expression for the 1st, 3rd, 5th, 7th, and 9th harmonics is

$$\chi_{square}(t) = \frac{4}{\pi} \left[\frac{1}{1} \sin(2\pi ft) + \frac{1}{3} \sin(6\pi ft) + \frac{1}{5} \sin(10\pi ft) + \frac{1}{7} \sin(14\pi ft) + \frac{1}{9} \sin(18\pi ft) \right]$$

An example of a 520 Hz square wave audio signal is presented as a spectrograph in Figure A.29.3.8.1(2)(b). Note the dBA scale and weighting.

Additional harmonics for the square wave can be present in the signal, but should not contribute more than 10 percent of the integrated-averaged sound level.

29.3.8.2* Profound Hearing Loss. Visible notification appliances in accordance with the requirements of 18.5.4.6 and tactile notification appliances in accordance with the requirements of 18.10 shall be required for those with profound hearing loss in the following situations:

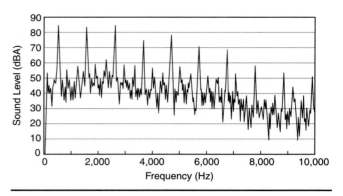

FIGURE A.29.3.8.1(2)(b) *Spectrograph of a 520 Hz Square Wave Audio Signal.*

(1)* Where required by governing laws, codes, or standards for people with hearing loss

(2) Where provided voluntarily for those with hearing loss

The use of visible notification appliances (strobes) has been shown to be more effective for the deaf population than for those with mild to severe hearing loss. In addition, the low frequency signals specified in 29.3.8.1 are not adequate for those with profound hearing loss. Therefore, 29.3.8.2 requires the use of both visible notification appliances and tactile notification appliances per the requirements of Chapter 18. Tactile appliances can be effective for waking sleeping occupants. However, visible appliances also are needed because people might not always be in contact with the signal from tactile notification appliances. (Refer to A.29.3.8.2 for further insight into the performance of tactile appliances.) For those who are awake, visible appliances enhance the ability of the system or equipment to alert them of a fire condition. Section 18.5 addresses requirements for visible signaling. The minimum illumination levels required for rooms in general are based on achieving a level of 0.0375 lumens/ft^2 (0.4036 lumens/m^2). However, Chapter 18 requires a higher intensity for sleeping areas. See Section 18.5 for requirements on visible notification appliances and 18.5.4.6 for requirements specific to sleeping areas.

Early studies of persons who are deaf indicated that a 110 cd visible notification appliance, installed at least 24 in. (610 mm) below the ceiling, generally provides sufficient light intensity to awaken a sleeping deaf person. A 177 cd appliance is required where mounted within 24 in. (610 mm) of the ceiling because during a fire the light signal may be attenuated by the smoke layer. See Exhibit 29.2 and Exhibit 29.3 for examples of smoke alarms with integral and remote notification appliances.

A.29.3.8.2 Tactile notification appliances such as bed shakers have been shown to be effective in waking those with profound hearing loss [Ashley et al., 2005, UL 1971, 1991]. Tactile signaling has been studied and found to be an effective way to alert and notify sleeping persons. However, there are many variables that have not been tested that might affect the reliability of their performance. Some of the appliance variables include the mass of the appliance, frequency of vibration and the throw or displacement of the vibrating mass. Occupant variables that might affect the reporting of test results and the effectiveness of the appliance include the person's age, how long a person has lived with their hearing loss, and what sleep stage the person is experiencing when the appliance operates. The type of mattress might also have an effect of the performance of certain tactile appliances. Mattress variables can include thickness, firmness, memory foam, pillow tops, water beds, air beds, and motion isolation mattresses. Users of tactile appliances should be cautioned to test how well they might sense the effect of the appliance.

EXHIBIT 29.2 *Smoke Alarm with Integral Notification Appliance for the Hearing Impaired. (Source: BRK Brands, Inc., Aurora, IL — Makers of First Alert Brand Products)*

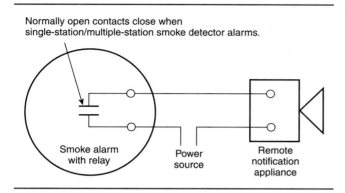

Normally open contacts close when
single-station/multiple-station smoke detector alarms.

Smoke alarm
with relay

Power
source

Remote
notification
appliance

EXHIBIT 29.3 *Single-Station Smoke Alarm with Remote Notification Appliance. (Source: Hughes Associates, Inc., Warwick, RI)*

The Code requires both strobes and tactile appliances. Strobes can awaken sleeping persons, provide verification that there is a fire alarm condition, and serve to alert persons when they are not in contact with a tactile appliance.

A.29.3.8.2(1) As an example, governing laws, codes, or standards might require a certain number of accommodations be equipped for those with hearing loss or other disability.

29.3.9 Signals from notification appliances shall not be required to be synchronized.

29.4 Assumptions

29.4.1* Occupants. The requirements of this chapter shall assume that occupants are not intimate with the ignition and are capable of self-rescue.

A.29.4.1 Working smoke alarms cut the risk of dying in reported home structure fires in half. Victims who are intimate with the fire or are incapable of taking action to escape might not benefit from the early warning. For these people, other strategies such as protection in-place or assisted escape or rescue would be necessary.

29.4.2* Escape Route.

A.29.4.2 *Family Escape Plan.* There often is very little time between the detection of a fire and the time it becomes deadly. This interval can be as little as 1 or 2 minutes. Thus, this Code requires detection means to give a family some advance warning of the development of conditions that become dangerous to life within a short period of time. Such warning, however, could be wasted unless the family has planned in advance for rapid exit from their residence. Therefore, in addition to the fire-warning equipment, this Code requires exit plan information to be furnished.

Planning and practicing for fire conditions with a focus on rapid exit from the residence are important. Drills should be held so that all family members know the action to be taken. Each person should plan for the possibility that exit out of a bedroom window could be necessary. An exit out of the residence without the need to open a bedroom door is essential.

Special Provisions for the Disabled. For special circumstances where the life safety of an occupant(s) depends on prompt rescue by others, the fire-warning equipment should include means of prompt automatic notification to those who are to be depended on for rescue.

As noted in A.29.4.1, some occupants will not be able to self-rescue even when they are warned early enough. These people may not be able to respond appropriately because they are too old, too young, or physically or mentally impaired. Therefore, it is important for occupants to have an understanding of what actions to take and a plan for able-bodied occupants to assist those who require help to escape. Such a plan is particularly true for very young children, who likely will not awaken to a traditional alarm. Sleep studies have shown that the majority of children, particularly those under the age of 10, will not awaken to a traditional alarm signal even at a sound level of 89 dBA at the pillow [Bruck, 1999; Bruck and Bliss, 2000]. This sound level is approximately the peak expected for smoke alarms either in the bedroom or outside the room if the door is open. A recent study by the Consumer Products Safety Commission found sound levels in bedrooms from a smoke alarm operating in an adjacent hallway ranged from 85 to 96 dBA with the door open [Lee, 2005]. One smoke alarm operating in one of the bedrooms produced sound levels at the pillow of approximately 90 dBA. Besides the very young, others may be at risk due to physical or mental disabilities or from being impaired by medication, alcohol, or drugs. Recent research programs suggest that low frequency alarm signals as required in 29.3.8.1 also may have some benefit for children and individuals impaired by alcohol.

Where additional time is needed to assist others who require help to escape, consideration should be given to the use of both ionization and photoelectric smoke alarms as well as to the installation of smoke alarms in locations in addition to those required by 29.5.1. Refer to A.29.1.1 and A.29.3.3 for further discussion on the performance of current smoke alarm technology.

29.4.2.1 The requirements of this chapter shall assume that the occupants have an escape plan.

29.4.2.2 An escape route shall be assumed to be available to occupants and to be unobstructed prior to the event of the fire.

29.4.2.3* The escape route shall be along the normal path of egress for the occupancy.

A.29.4.2.3 The normal path of egress does not include windows or other means of escape.

29.4.3* **Equipment.** The performance of fire-warning equipment discussed in this chapter shall depend on such equipment being properly selected, installed, operated, tested, and maintained in accordance with the provisions of this Code and with the manufacturer's published instructions provided with the equipment.

A.29.4.3 Assumptions — Equipment is as follows:

(1) Maintenance. Good fire protection requires that the equipment be maintained periodically. If the system owner or responsible party is unable to perform the required maintenance, a maintenance agreement should be considered.
(2) Reliability of fire alarm systems. Fire alarm systems located in dwelling units and having all of the following features are considered to have a functional reliability of 95 percent:

   (a) Utilizes a control unit
   (b) Has at least two independent sources of operating power
   (c) Monitors all initiating and notification circuits for integrity
   (d) Transmits alarm signals to a constantly attended, remote monitoring location
   (e) Is tested regularly by the homeowner and at least every 3 years by a qualified service technician

(3) Reliability of fire alarm systems without remote monitoring or with wireless transmission. Fire alarm systems for dwelling units with all of the preceding features except (d) or systems that use low-power wireless transmission from initiating devices within the dwelling units are considered to have a functional reliability of 90 percent.
(4) Reliability of other systems. Fire alarm systems for dwelling units comprised of interconnected smoke alarms where the interconnecting means is monitored for integrity are

considered to have a functional reliability of 88 percent. If the interconnecting means is not supervised or the alarms are not interconnected, such systems are considered to have a functional reliability of 85 percent.

Periodic testing of equipment is vital to ensure that it is functioning properly. Chapter 14 covers the testing and maintenance of all fire-warning equipment and requires service personnel to be qualified and experienced in the inspection, testing, and maintenance of fire alarm systems. The Code specifically requires that household fire alarm systems be tested at least annually by a qualified service technician. System owners need to arrange for a maintenance contract with a qualified service organization to ensure that testing and maintenance are performed properly. The Code requires homeowners in one- and two-family dwellings to inspect and test smoke alarms in accordance with manufacturer's published instructions at least monthly. If homeowners are unable to perform proper smoke alarm maintenance, they should consider an appropriate maintenance contract. All the manufacturer's published instructions need to be retained by the owner for reference during testing and maintenance. Smoke alarms in occupancies other than one- and two-family dwellings must be functionally tested annually (including smoke entry and alarm response) and be sensitivity tested per 14.4.5.3. Additional testing provisions are specified in Table 14.4.2.2, item 14(g).

◀ **FAQ**
What are the periodic testing requirements for household fire alarm systems and smoke alarms?

29.5 Detection and Notification

The use of fire alarm system smoke detectors and notification appliances shall be permitted to meet the fire-warning requirements for smoke alarms specified in 29.5.1.

The siting requirements of Section 29.5 are generally specified in terms of smoke alarms. However, the Code allows the use of a complete household fire alarm system that contains system-type smoke detectors connected to a listed fire alarm system control unit along with other devices, such as heat detectors and alarm notification appliances. Refer to the introductory commentary for this chapter regarding the difference between smoke alarms and smoke detectors. Whether smoke alarms or a household fire alarm system is used, the installation must comply with the requirements of 29.3.3. Accordingly, the minimum siting requirements (number and location) of 29.5.1 must be independently satisfied either by the use of smoke alarms or by the use of fire alarm system–connected smoke detectors. The mixing of smoke alarms and smoke detectors to satisfy the minimum siting requirements is not permitted. Thus, a fire alarm system could be used in place of the single- and multiple-station smoke alarms specified throughout Section 29.5. Or, if single-station or multiple-station alarms are intended to independently satisfy the minimum siting requirements in Section 29.5, then a household fire alarm/security system could be used to provide additional detectors and a higher level of protection. See also the related commentary following 29.3.3.

In addition, a listed commercial (not household) fire alarm system installed in accordance with the requirements of Chapter 29 would be an acceptable alternative to a system of single- and multiple-station alarms or a household fire alarm system as described in this chapter.

29.5.1* Required Detection.

A.29.5.1 All hostile fires in dwelling units generate smoke and heat. However, the results of full-scale experiments conducted over the last several decades in the United States, using typical fires in dwelling units, indicate that detectable quantities of smoke precede detectable levels of heat in nearly all cases (NBS GCR 75-51, *Detector Sensitivity and Siting Requirements for Dwellings*, 1975; NBS GCR 77-82, *Detector Sensitivity and Siting Requirements for Dwellings Phase 2*, 1977; and NIST Technical Note 1455-1, *Performance of Home Smoke Detectors Analysis of the Response of Several Available Technologies in a Residential Setting*, 2007). In addition, slowly developing, smoldering fires can produce smoke and toxic gases without a significant increase in the room's temperature. Again, the results of experiments indicate that detectable quantities of smoke precede the development of hazardous thermal atmospheres in nearly all cases.

For the preceding reasons, the required protection in this Code utilizes smoke alarms as the primary life safety equipment for providing a reasonable level of protection against fire.

The installation of additional alarms of either the smoke or heat type should result in a higher degree of protection. Adding alarms to rooms that are normally closed off from the required alarms increases the escape time because the fire does not need to build to the higher level necessary to force smoke out of the closed room to the required alarms. As a consequence, it is recommended that the householder consider the installation of additional fire protection devices. However, it should be understood that Chapter 29 does not require additional smoke alarms over and above those called for in 29.5.1. Refer to Figure A.29.5.1(a) through Figure A.29.5.1(d) where required smoke alarms are shown.

Where to Locate the Required Smoke Alarms. Fifty-three percent of home fire deaths were reported between 11:00 p.m. and 7:00 a.m. Persons in sleeping areas can be threatened by fires in the remainder of the unit; therefore, smoke alarms are best located in each bedroom and between the bedroom areas and the rest of the unit as shown in Figure A.29.5.1(b). In dwelling units with more than one bedroom area or with bedrooms on more than one floor, more than one smoke alarm is required, as shown in Figure A.29.5.1(c).

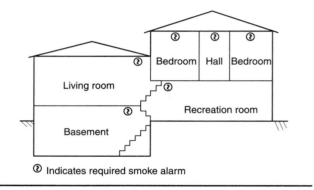

Indicates required smoke alarm

FIGURE A.29.5.1(a) *Split Level Arrangement.*

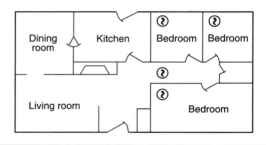

FIGURE A.29.5.1(b) *A Smoke Alarm Should Be Located Between the Sleeping Area and the Rest of the Dwelling Unit, as Well as in Each Bedroom.*

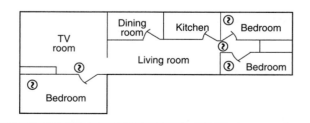

FIGURE A.29.5.1(c) *In Dwelling Units with More Than One Sleeping Area, a Smoke Alarm Should Be Provided to Protect Each Sleeping Area in Addition to Smoke Alarms Required in Bedrooms.*

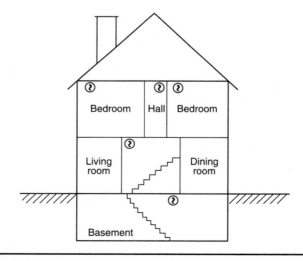

FIGURE A.29.5.1(d) *A Smoke Alarm Should Be Located on Each Level in Addition to Each Bedroom.*

In addition to smoke alarms outside of the sleeping areas and in each bedroom, Chapter 29 requires the installation of a smoke alarm on each additional level of the dwelling unit, including the basement. These installations are shown in Figure A.29.5.1(d). The living area smoke alarm should be installed in the living room or near the stairway to the upper level, or in both locations. The basement smoke alarm should be installed in close proximity to the stairway leading to the floor above. Where installed on an open-joisted ceiling, the smoke alarm should be placed on the bottom of the joists. The smoke alarm should be positioned relative to the stairway so as to intercept smoke coming from a fire in the basement before the smoke enters the stairway.

Are More Smoke Alarms Desirable? The required number of smoke alarms might not provide reliable early warning protection for those areas separated by a door from the areas protected by the required smoke alarms. For this reason, the use of additional smoke alarms for those areas for increased protection is recommended. The additional areas include dining room, furnace room, utility room, and hallways not protected by the required smoke alarms. The installation of smoke alarms in kitchens, attics (finished or unfinished), or garages is not normally recommended, because these locations occasionally experience conditions that can result in improper operation.

29.5.1.1* Where required by other governing laws, codes, or standards for a specific type of occupancy, approved single- and multiple-station smoke alarms shall be installed as follows:

(1)* In all sleeping rooms and guest rooms
(2)* Outside of each separate dwelling unit sleeping area, within 21 ft (6.4 m) of any door to a sleeping room, with the distance measured along a path of travel
(3) On every level of a dwelling unit, including basements
(4) On every level of a residential board and care occupancy (small facility), including basements and excluding crawl spaces and unfinished attics
(5)* In the living area(s) of a guest suite

The detection requirements noted in 29.5.1.1 begin with the phrase "where required by other governing laws, codes, or standards for a specific type of occupancy." The statutory requirement to have smoke detection within a specified occupancy usually is contained within a building or occupancy code that is adopted by the enforcing jurisdiction. The rules specified by these codes may vary from those specified in 29.5.1. The enforcing jurisdiction should be consulted to determine if any differences exist and to determine the specific requirements for the application. If the specified code requires that smoke alarms be installed per *NFPA 72*, the requirements of 29.5.1 apply unless specifically exempted.

◄ FAQ
Where is the requirement to have smoke detection established?

The 2007 Code included a number of changes to promote the use of additional interconnected smoke alarms throughout dwellings and to address new technology issues. In past editions, the requirement for the installation of smoke alarms in bedrooms was restricted to new construction. The Code was changed to require a uniform set of installation requirements regardless of occupancy age. The recommendation for all construction has always been that smoke alarms be located in bedrooms as well as outside each separate sleeping area and on each level of a dwelling unit. Recent studies have further reinforced the benefit of having smoke alarms in bedrooms. The anticipation is that model building and life safety codes as well as local ordinances will eventually mandate that existing construction structures meet the new requirements when a property is sold or when significant renovations are made.

(6) In the living area(s) of a residential board and care occupancy (small facility)

A.29.5.1.1 Occupancies where smoke alarms are typically required include residential, residential board and care, or day-care home. The term *residential occupancy* is defined in 3.3.227 and includes one- and two-family dwellings; lodging or rooming houses; hotels, motels, and dormitories; and apartment buildings. The term *residential board and care occupancy* is defined in 3.3.226 and includes both small and large facilities. NFPA *101, Life Safety*

Code, specifies a small facility to be one with sleeping accommodations for not more than 16 residents. The term *day-care home*, defined in 3.3.54, is a specific category of day-care occupancy. It should be noted that applicable laws, codes, or standards might include conditions that could impact the applicability of these requirements. The local authority should be consulted for specific details.

A.29.5.1.1(1) The term *sleeping room* applies to several occupancies including: one- and two-family dwellings; lodging or rooming houses; hotels, motels, and dormitories; apartment buildings; residential board and care facilities; and day-care homes. The term *guest room*, defined in 3.3.111, is an accommodation that includes sleeping facilities. It applies in the context of hotel and dormitory occupancies.

A.29.5.1.1(2) The term *dwelling unit* is defined in 3.3.74 and applies to one- and two-family dwellings and dwelling units of apartment buildings (including condominiums).

A.29.5.1.1(5) The term *guest suite* is defined in 3.3.112, and the term *living area* is defined in 3.3.133.

29.5.1.2 Where the area addressed in 29.5.1.1(2) is separated from the adjacent living areas by a door, a smoke alarm shall be installed in the area between the door and the sleeping rooms, and additional alarms shall be installed on the living area side of the door as specified by 29.5.1.1 and 29.5.1.3.

This requirement addresses circumstances in which a door separates the area outside the sleeping rooms from the rest of the living area, as may occur if there is a door to a hallway leading to the bedrooms. In such a case, a smoke alarm must be on both sides of the door, consistent with the other siting requirements, so that people in rooms on both sides of the door will be warned in a timely manner of a fire developing on the opposing side.

29.5.1.3 In addition to the requirements of 29.5.1.1(1) through (3), where the interior floor area for a given level of a dwelling unit, excluding garage areas, is greater than 1000 ft² (93 m²), smoke alarms shall be installed per 29.5.1.3.1 and 29.5.1.3.2.

29.5.1.3.1* All points on the ceiling shall have a smoke alarm within a distance of 30 ft (9.1 m) travel distance or shall have an equivalent of one smoke alarm per 500 ft² (46 m²) of floor area. One smoke alarm per 500 ft² (46 m²) is evaluated by dividing the total interior square footage of floor area per level by 500 ft² (46 m²).

A.29.5.1.3.1 The requirements do not preclude the installation of smoke alarms on walls in accordance with 29.8.3.3. Some building configurations, such as division of rooms and open foyers or great rooms, dictate that alarms be located so that they do not cover distinctly separate 500 ft² (46 m²) areas but rather provide overlapping coverage relative to this spacing requirement.

29.5.1.3.2 Where dwelling units include great rooms or vaulted/cathedral ceilings extending over multiple floors, smoke alarms located on the upper floor that are intended to protect the aforementioned area shall be permitted to be considered as part of the lower floor(s) protection scheme used to meet the requirements of 29.5.1.3.1.

The requirement introduced in 29.5.1.3 addresses the need for additional smoke alarms in larger dwellings. The average home size in the United States has increased considerably over the last 30 years, particularly in the last 13 years. For example, the average floor area of a new one-family house was 1695 ft² (158 m²) in 1974, 2100 ft² (195 m²) in 1994, and 2349 ft² (218 m²) in 2004. Homes greater than 3000 and 4000 ft² (279 and 372 m²) are not uncommon in many areas of the country. The new requirement generally does not change the number of smoke alarms for floors with bedrooms beyond those already required in the Code. However, for large dwellings, the requirements tend to lead to the use of additional smoke alarms on floors that are required to have only one alarm per the current Code.

On any level of a dwelling with an interior floor area that exceeds 1000 ft^2 (93 m^2), excluding garage areas, the new spacing requirements dictate the placement of smoke alarms to meet either of two criteria: (1) All points on a ceiling (or vertical wall locations) have a smoke alarm within a distance of 30 ft (9 m) in travel distance, or (2) there is at least one smoke alarm for every 500 ft^2 (46 m^2) of floor area. Exhibit 29.4 shows an example of the first criterion. For an example of the second criterion, if the floor area shown in Exhibit 29.5 is 1400 ft^2 (130 m^2), then three smoke alarms would be required [1400 ft^2 (130 m^2) divided by 500 ft^2 (46 m^2) is 2.8, which rounded up is 3]. Two alarms would not be sufficient, since 2 times 500 ft^2 (46 m^2) is less than the 1400 ft^2 (130 m^2) floor area. Exhibit 29.5 shows possible locations for meeting the 500 ft^2 (46 m^2) requirement. Although the Code allows the coverage areas for the smoke alarms to overlap, consideration should be given to strategically positioning smoke alarms in separate areas and rooms on the floor to maximize the early warning potential of the smoke alarms to detect fire anywhere on that level of the dwelling.

As shown in Exhibit 29.6, 29.5.1.3.2 specifically allows a smoke alarm to satisfy the required number of smoke alarms for more than one floor if that smoke alarm is located to protect the ceiling area over a multi-floor space, such as a two-floor great room. For example, the house shown in Exhibit 29.6 has a first floor with 1852 ft^2 (172 m^2) and a second floor with 1300 ft^2 (121 m^2). Based on the criterion of one or more smoke alarms for every 500 ft^2 (46 m^2), four smoke alarms would be required on the first floor and three would be required on the second floor. However, for the second floor, the requirements in 29.5.1.1 require a smoke alarm in every bedroom and one outside each sleeping area within 21 ft (6.4 m) of any bedroom door. These requirements result in six smoke alarms being required on the second floor, as shown in Exhibit 29.6. Per 29.5.1.3.2, the second floor smoke alarm that is positioned over the open walkway to the master bedroom also satisfies one of the four smoke alarms required on the first floor since the family room is open to the second floor with a vaulted ceiling.

29.5.2 Required Occupant Notification.

29.5.2.1 Fire-warning equipment used to provide required or optional detection shall produce audible fire alarm signals that comply with 29.5.2.1.1 or 29.5.2.1.2.

29.5.2.1.1* Smoke and Heat Alarms. Unless exempted by applicable laws, codes, or standards, smoke or heat alarms used to provide a fire-warning function, and when two or more

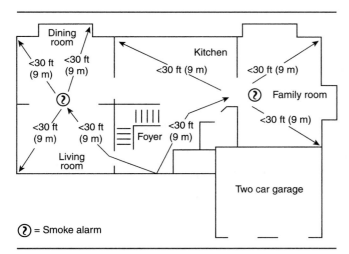

EXHIBIT 29.4 *Example of the 30 ft (9 m) Spacing Criterion for Dwellings with Interior Floor Areas Greater Than 1000 ft^2 (93 m^2). (Source: Hughes Associates, Inc., Baltimore, MD)*

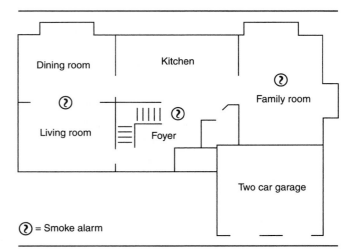

EXHIBIT 29.5 *Example of the Spacing Criterion of One or More Smoke Alarms for Every 500 ft^2 (46 m^2) of Interior Floor Area on Every Floor Greater Than 1000 ft^2 (93 m^2). (Source: Hughes Associates, Inc., Baltimore, MD)*

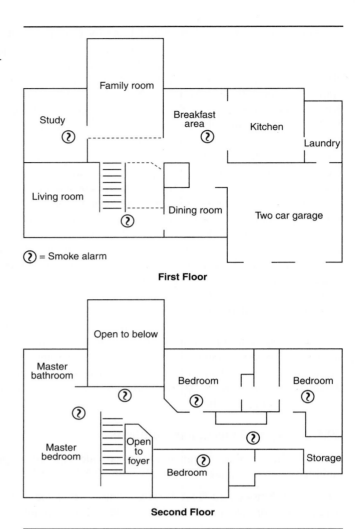

EXHIBIT 29.6 *Example of Smoke Alarm Requirements for a Large House with Multi-Floor Spaces as Addressed in 29.5.1.3.2. (Source: Hughes Associates, Inc., Baltimore, MD)*

alarms are installed within a dwelling unit, suite of rooms, or similar area, shall be arranged so that the operation of any smoke or heat alarm causes all alarms within these locations to sound.

Exception: The arrangement for all alarms to sound shall not be required for mechanically powered single-station heat alarms.

A.29.5.2.1.1 Fire-warning performance is improved when all alarms are interconnected so that alarm notification is achieved throughout the occupiable areas. In some cases for existing construction, interconnection of alarms is specifically exempted by jurisdictional requirements. This allowance takes into consideration the cost of hard-wired interconnection.

The use of the hard-wired interconnect feature with multiple-station alarms satisfies the requirements of 29.5.2.1.1. See Exhibit 29.7 for a typical arrangement of interconnected multiple-station smoke alarms. Additional notification appliances connected to and powered through the dry contacts of a single- or multiple-station smoke alarm relay can be used to provide an audible signal to meet the requirements in 29.3.6. Smoke alarms and notification appliances should not be interconnected between separate dwelling units, such as duplex arrangements or apartments. Exhibit 29.8 and Exhibit 29.9 show equipment that could be used for remote notification.

690

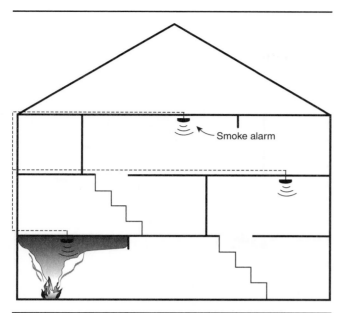

EXHIBIT 29.7 *Hard-Wired Multiple-Station (Interconnected) Smoke Alarms. (Source: Hughes Associates, Inc., Baltimore, MD)*

Smoke alarm

EXHIBIT 29.8 *Multiple-Station Smoke Alarm Auxiliary Relay Module for Remote Notification Appliance. (Source: Kidde, Mebane, NC)*

EXHIBIT 29.9 *Notification Appliances. Left: Bell; Right: Mini-Horn. (Source: GE Security, Bradenton, FL)*

The 2007 Code included a number of changes to promote the use of additional interconnected smoke alarms throughout dwellings and to address new technology issues. In editions prior to 2007, requirements for the installation of smoke alarms in bedrooms and for the interconnection of smoke alarms (so that when one sounds, they all sound) were restricted to new construction. The Code was changed to require a uniform set of installation requirements regardless of occupancy age. The recommendation for all construction has always been that smoke alarms be located in bedrooms as well as outside each separate sleeping area and on each level of a dwelling unit. The interconnection of all smoke alarms in the dwelling also ensures that an alarm signal meeting the Code will be provided in the bedrooms regardless of the location of the first sounding smoke alarm, which may be two floors away from the sleeping area. Recent studies have further reinforced the benefit that smoke alarms sounding in bedrooms provide the most effective waking potential, particularly for children and older adults, and thus maximize escape time. These Code changes are partly enabled by several new wireless technologies that permit battery-operated smoke alarms to be interconnected (see Exhibits 29.10 and 29.11); therefore, costly alternating current (ac) wiring renovation is not required to provide interconnection in existing construction. The anticipation is that model building and life safety codes as well as local ordinances will eventually mandate that

◄ **FAQ**
What important changes have been made in the Code regarding requirements for interconnection of smoke alarms?

EXHIBIT 29.10 *Wireless Interconnected Multiple-Station Smoke Alarm Device. (Source: Kidde, Mebane, NC)*

EXHIBIT 29.11 *Wireless Interconnected Multiple-Station Smoke Alarms. (Source: Hughes Associates, Inc., Baltimore, MD)*

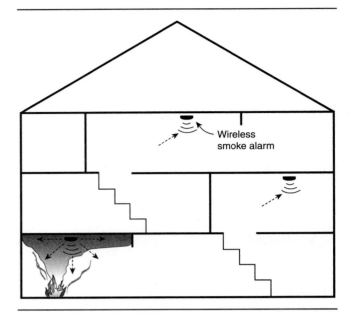

existing construction structures meet the new requirements when a property is sold or when significant renovations are made.

The 2010 Code includes new requirements in 29.7.7.2 for wireless interconnected alarms to meet specific performance requirements to ensure adequate transmission and reception capability within a structure.

29.5.2.1.2 Household Fire Alarm System. Where a household fire alarm system is used to provide a fire-warning function, notification appliances shall be installed to meet the performance requirements of 18.4.3 and 18.4.5.

29.5.2.2* Unless otherwise permitted by the authority having jurisdiction, audible fire alarm signals shall sound only in an individual dwelling unit, suite of rooms, or similar area and shall not be arranged to operate fire-warning equipment or fire alarm systems outside these locations. Remote annunciation shall be permitted.

A.29.5.2.2 One of the common problems associated with smoke alarms and detectors is the nuisance alarms that are usually triggered by products of combustion from cooking, smoking, or other household particulates. While an alarm for such a condition is anticipated and tolerated by the occupant of a dwelling unit through routine living experience, the alarm is not permitted where it also sounds alarms in other dwelling units or in common use spaces. Nuisance alarms caused by cooking are a very common occurrence, and inspection authorities should be aware of the possible ramifications where the coverage is extended beyond the limits of the dwelling unit.

29.6 Power Supplies

29.6.1 Smoke and Heat Alarms. Smoke and heat alarms shall be powered by one of the following means:

(1) A commercial light and power source along with a secondary power source that is capable of operating the device for at least 24 hours in the normal condition, followed by 4 minutes of alarm.

The requirement in 29.6.1(1) for an ac-powered alarm with backup power supply (see Exhibit 29.12) addresses the need to have a functioning smoke alarm during a power outage. The 2007 Code changed the term *secondary battery source* to *secondary power source* to be more generic and to allow for future technological innovation in power supplies. Batteries, however, are the principal backup source in current smoke and heat alarms. Periodic testing of smoke alarms as well as annual replacement of batteries or replacement after a prolonged power outage are vital to ensure that this secondary power supply to the smoke alarm will function. During a power outage, occupants often greatly increase the risk of fire by using candles, lanterns, space heaters, and other equipment not usually in operation in the home environment. For that reason, the smoke alarm plays an even more important role in warning residents of a fire during a power outage. A national advertising campaign recommends changing the batteries every fall when daylight savings time ends.

EXHIBIT 29.12 *AC-Powered Ionization Smoke Alarm with Battery Backup. (Source: Kidde, Mebane, NC)*

(2) If a commercial light and power source is not normally available, a noncommercial ac power source along with a secondary power source that is capable of operating the device for at least 7 days in the normal condition, followed by 4 minutes of alarm.

The power source options listed in 29.6.1(1) and 29.6.1(2) both require an ac power source in combination with a secondary power source. Note that some model building and life safety codes allow the exclusion of the secondary power source in specific occupancies, and for some occupancies they require that smoke alarms be supplied by a commercial power source. Where the exclusion of secondary power is permitted, consideration must be given to the requirement in 29.6.3(5) regarding smoke alarms powered by arc-fault circuit interrupter (AFCI)–protected circuits and the requirement for secondary power.

(3) A nonrechargeable, nonreplaceable primary battery that is capable of operating the device for at least 10 years in the normal condition, followed by 4 minutes of alarm, followed by 7 days of trouble.

Smoke alarms powered by a primary 10-year battery identified in 29.6.1(3) must also be of the multiple-station type so that they can meet the interconnection requirements of 29.5.2.1.1 unless otherwise exempted. The 4 minutes of alarm requirement applies to battery-powered smoke alarms as well as to smoke alarms powered by 120 VAC or by a control unit power supply. Four minutes is considered sufficient time to warn occupants that a fire condition exists. Note that some building and life safety codes require primary power to be from a commercial power source.

◄ **FAQ**
Do the interconnection requirements of 29.5.2.1.1 still apply to smoke alarms that use a primary 10-year battery?

(4) If a battery primary power supply is specifically permitted, a battery meeting the requirements of 29.6.6 (nonrechargeable primary battery) or the requirements of 29.6.7 (rechargeable primary battery) shall be used.

Some model building and life safety codes specifically permit the use of smoke alarms with batteries as the primary power source in specific occupancies. For example, NFPA *101* permits the use of battery-only smoke alarms in existing one- and two-family dwelling units. The use of existing battery-only smoke alarms in occupancies such as existing day-care homes or an existing residential board and care large facility is conditional on the authority having jurisdiction ensuring that proper testing, maintenance, and battery replacement programs are in place. Though battery primary power is allowed in some cases, smoke and heat alarms are recommended to be powered by ac with battery backup, where practical.

In many instances, battery-operated smoke and heat alarms are rendered inoperable because the batteries have been removed or dead batteries have not been replaced. The use of rechargeable batteries that meet the requirements of 29.6.7 is intended to result in fewer instances of non-powered smoke alarms. New battery technologies allow for a 10-year life, which is longer than the 1-year minimum required in 29.6.7(1).

(5) A suitable spring-wound mechanism for the nonelectrical portion of a listed single-station alarm. A visible indication shall be provided to show that sufficient operating power is not available.

29.6.2 Household Fire Alarm Systems. Power for household fire alarm systems shall comply with the following requirements:

(1) Household fire alarm systems shall have two independent power sources consisting of a primary source that uses commercial light and power and a secondary source that consists of a rechargeable battery.

The authority having jurisdiction should require the submission of battery calculations for household fire alarm systems. These calculations are used to determine the capacity required for standby and alarm time requirements for the household fire alarm system when the standby power is supplied by rechargeable batteries. See Exhibit 29.13 for a schematic of a typical household fire alarm system.

EXHIBIT 29.13 *Household Fire Alarm System with Separate Control Unit.*

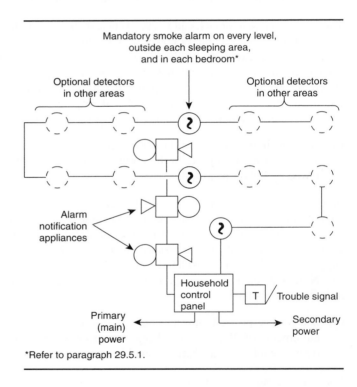

Mandatory smoke alarm on every level, outside each sleeping area, and in each bedroom*

Optional detectors in other areas

Optional detectors in other areas

Alarm notification appliances

Household control panel

T / Trouble signal

Primary (main) power

Secondary power

*Refer to paragraph 29.5.1.

(2) The secondary source shall be capable of operating the system for at least 24 hours in the normal condition, followed by 4 minutes of alarm.
(3) The secondary power source shall be supervised and shall cause a distinctive audible and visible trouble signal upon removal or disconnection of a battery or a low-battery condition.
(4) A rechargeable battery used as a secondary power source shall meet the following criteria:

(a) Be automatically recharged by an ac circuit of the commercial light and power source.
(b) Be recharged within 48 hours.
(c) Provide a distinctive audible trouble signal before the battery is incapable of operating the device(s) for alarm purposes.

(5) Low-power wireless systems shall comply with the performance criteria of Section 23.18.

29.6.3 AC Primary Power Source. The ac power source shall comply with the following conditions:

(1) A visible "power on" indicator shall be provided.

The "power on" indicator in 29.6.3(1) is required on single- and multiple-station smoke alarms as well as smoke detectors that are part of a fire alarm system with a control unit.

(2) All electrical systems designed to be installed by other than a qualified electrician shall be powered from a source not in excess of 30 volts that meets the requirements for power-limited fire alarm circuits as defined in *NFPA 70, National Electrical Code*, Article 760.

The voltage limit regulation in 29.6.3(2) is included in the Code to reduce the shock and fire hazards associated with the 120 VAC wiring. Most jurisdictions require licensed electricians to install all 120 VAC outlets and connections. Some jurisdictions permit a licensed fire alarm technician to install any 120 VAC connection that is associated with the fire alarm system. It is imperative that the authority having jurisdiction be consulted as to the installation requirements of the fire alarm system being installed.

(3) A restraining means shall be used at the plug-in of any cord-connected installation.

Cord-connected smoke and heat alarms are effective only when the power supply is not interrupted. In most residential situations, accidental bumping of the plug or inadvertent removal is a real possibility. The requirement in 29.6.3(3) is intended to reduce the risk of unplugging the equipment and applies to the plug-in of any cord-connected smoke or heat alarm or notification appliance as well as control unit powered household systems with plug-in-type connections to ac power (e.g., a plug-in-type transformer).

(4) AC primary (main) power shall be supplied either from a dedicated branch circuit or the unswitched portion of a branch circuit also used for power and lighting.

When single- or multiple-station smoke alarms are installed, a good practice is to connect the power to a branch circuit serving lighting outlets in a habitable area, such as a hallway, living room, or family room. This practice ensures that if for any reason the circuit breaker is tripped or in the "off" position, the condition will be noticed more quickly because lights and other loads used frequently in the dwelling unit will not operate. The power connection to a household fire alarm control unit can be connected in the same way. When connecting to a branch circuit that serves lighting and other loads, the installer must ensure that the circuit is not overloaded, which would cause the circuit breaker to trip frequently. Some state and local codes require this power connection to be made to a dedicated branch circuit. Consult with the authority having jurisdiction to determine if local codes or regulations differ from the requirements in this section of the Code.

For standard (compared to those addressed in 29.6.7) single- and multiple-station alarms, the power must not be connected to the switched portion of a branch circuit. Connection to a switched portion of a circuit will likely lead to the smoke alarms being disabled without the occupants' knowledge.

(5) Operation of a switch (other than a circuit breaker) or a ground-fault circuit-interrupter shall not cause loss of primary (main) power. Smoke alarms powered by AFCI-protected circuits shall have a secondary power source.

Recent editions of *NFPA 70®, National Electrical Code® (NEC®)*, have required that all 120 volt outlets in bedrooms, which includes 120 volt–powered smoke alarms, be protected by an AFCI.

FAQ ▶
What is required when a smoke
alarm is powered by an AFCI
circuit?

This requirement initially generated concern as to whether smoke alarms would be functional if the AFCI activated and prevented the smoke alarm from being powered. In response to that concern, a new requirement was added to the 2007 Code as specified in 29.6.3(5) to mandate that any smoke alarm powered by an AFCI circuit must have a secondary power source. The *NEC* was also modified with a note to refer readers to *NFPA 72* relative to secondary power source requirements.

(6) Neither loss nor restoration of primary (main) power shall cause an alarm signal.

Exception: An alarm signal shall be permitted but shall not exceed 2 seconds.

Generally, a loss or restoration of power is not permitted to cause any alarm signal. However, the exception to 29.6.3(6) permits a 120 VAC single- and multiple-station smoke alarm and system-based notification appliances to sound briefly (2 seconds or less) to alert the occupant that the power has been interrupted.

(7) Where a secondary (standby) battery is provided, the primary (main) power supply shall be of sufficient capacity to operate the system under all conditions of loading with any secondary (standby) battery disconnected or fully discharged.

29.6.4 Secondary (Standby) Power Source. Where alarms include a battery that is used as a secondary power source, the following conditions shall be met:

In the 2007 Code, changes were made to what is now 29.6.4 in the preamble and 29.6.4(3)(a). In the preamble, the wording was changed for clarity to specifically tie the requirements in 29.6.4(1) through 29.6.4(3) to batteries used as the secondary power source. In 29.6.4(3)(a), the wording was changed to more generically specify that recharging must be automatic from the primary power source; the 2002 Code identified the primary power source as an ac circuit of the commercial light and power source.

(1) The secondary power source shall be supervised and shall cause a distinctive audible or visible trouble signal upon removal or disconnection of a battery or a low-battery condition.

Paragraph 29.6.4(1) requires that an obvious indicator be provided to indicate that the battery is not properly connected or charged. Besides audible trouble signals, some smoke or heat alarms have physical indicators to show that a battery is missing or installed incorrectly. Such indicators include battery covers that do not close unless the battery is installed and mechanisms that prevent the alarm from being mounted to its base.

(2) Acceptable replacement batteries shall be clearly identified by the manufacturer's name and model number on the unit near the battery compartment.

(3) A rechargeable battery used as a secondary power source shall meet the following criteria:

(a) Be automatically recharged by the primary power source

(b) Be recharged within 4 hours where power is provided from a circuit that can be switched on or off by means other than a circuit breaker, or within 48 hours where power is provided from a circuit that cannot be switched on or off by means other than a circuit breaker

(c) Provide a distinctive audible trouble signal before the battery is incapable of operating the device(s) for alarm purposes

(d) At the battery condition at which a trouble signal is obtained, be capable of producing an alarm signal for at least 4 minutes, followed by not less than 7 days of trouble signal operation

(e) Produce an audible trouble signal at least once every minute for 7 consecutive days

29.6.5 Notification Appliance (with Smoke or Heat Alarm). If a visible notification appliance is used in conjunction with a smoke or heat alarm application for compliance with 29.3.7, the notification appliance shall not be required to be supplied with a secondary power source.

29.6.6 Primary Power Source (Nonrechargeable Battery). If smoke alarms are powered by a primary battery, the battery shall be monitored to ensure the following conditions are met:

(1) All power requirements are met for at least 1 year of battery life, including weekly testing.
(2) A distinctive audible trouble signal before the battery is incapable of operating (from causes such as aging or terminal corrosion) the device(s) for alarm purposes.
(3) For a unit employing a lock-in alarm feature, automatic transfer is provided from alarm to a trouble condition.
(4) At the battery voltage at which a trouble signal is obtained, the unit is capable of producing an alarm signal for at least 4 minutes, followed by not less than 7 days of trouble signal operation.
(5) The audible trouble signal is produced at least once every minute for 7 consecutive days.
(6) Acceptable replacement batteries are clearly identified by the manufacturer's name and model number on the unit near the battery compartment.
(7) A noticeable, visible indication is displayed when a primary battery is removed from the unit.

Battery-powered smoke alarms, once installed, often are not maintained by household occupants. NFPA studies [Ahrens, 2007] indicate that in nearly 20 percent of households that had at least one smoke alarm, none were working. This was primarily because of dead or missing batteries. The requirements of 29.6.6 address features designed to ensure a minimum level of safe operation and features that promote proper use and maintenance of the smoke alarm. The trouble signal requirement allows occupants to be alerted to an imminent battery failure. However, many homeowners or tenants do not recognize the trouble signal and may think it is a nuisance alarm. Establishing a routine battery replacement program is important to keep smoke alarms functioning. A popular program sponsored by the International Association of Fire Chiefs in conjunction with a battery manufacturer is the "Change Your Clocks, Change Your Batteries" campaign. This program reminds people living where the time changes to and from daylight savings time to also change the batteries in their smoke alarms. In those few areas where time changes are not observed, some other means of public awareness should be devised.

The requirement for a minimum of 7 days of trouble signals and weekly testing of battery-powered smoke alarms is based on the need to warn occupants of low-power conditions after reasonable vacancies of the dwelling unit. Dwellings are commonly empty for periods of up to 7 days while occupants are on vacation. Occupants should test an alarm upon returning from an extended absence to ensure the unit is still properly powered. Many smoke alarms actually provide trouble signals beyond the 7-day minimum requirement.

29.6.7 Primary Power Source (Rechargeable Battery). If smoke alarms are powered by a rechargeable battery, the following conditions shall be met:

(1) The battery shall, with proper charging, be able to power the alarm for a life of 1 year.
(2) The battery shall be automatically recharged by an circuit of the commercial light and power source.
(3) The battery shall be recharged within 4 hours where power is provided from a circuit that can be switched on or off by means other than a circuit breaker, or within 48 hours where

power is provided from a circuit that cannot be switched on or off by means other than a circuit breaker.

(4) A distinctive audible trouble signal shall sound before the battery is incapable of operating the device(s) for alarm purposes.

(5) For a unit employing a lock-in alarm feature, automatic transfer shall be provided from alarm to a trouble condition.

(6) At the battery condition at which a trouble signal is obtained, the unit shall be capable of producing an alarm signal for at least 4 minutes, followed by not less than 7 days of trouble signal operation.

(7) The audible trouble signal shall be produced at least once every minute for 7 consecutive days.

FAQ ▶
Smoke alarms powered by primary rechargeable batteries are permitted to be connected to what types of circuits?

The requirements for rechargeable battery-powered smoke alarms allow devices that are automatically charged by an ac circuit (switched or unswitched). Rechargeable battery–powered smoke alarms connected to a switched ac light source have been designed to offer various test and use features, such as switch-controlled silence and functional test capabilities that are not available with standard battery-powered smoke alarms. The use of automatically rechargeable batteries meeting the requirements of 29.6.7 should reduce the number of occurrences of nonfunctioning smoke alarms caused by people forgetting to replace batteries. Current technologies are designed to provide batteries with functional lives of 10 years, which is longer than the minimum required in 29.6.7(1). As noted in the commentary following 29.6.1(4), battery-powered smoke alarms (primary power) are permitted only in certain existing occupancies. They are not allowed in new construction by model building codes, which typically require unswitched ac primary power with battery back-up.

29.6.8 Secondary (Standby) Non-Battery Power Source. Where alarms include a secondary power source (non-battery), the following conditions shall be met:

(1) The secondary power source shall be supervised and shall cause a distinctive audible or visible trouble signal upon depletion or failure.

(2) A distinctive audible trouble signal shall be provided before the power source is incapable of operating the device(s) for alarm purposes.

(3) At a power source condition at which a trouble signal is obtained, the power source shall be capable of producing an alarm signal for at least 4 minutes, followed by not less than 7 days of trouble signal operation.

(4) The audible trouble signal shall be produced at least once every minute for 7 consecutive days.

(5) A rechargeable secondary power source shall meet the following criteria:

 (a) Be automatically recharged.
 (b) Be recharged within 4 hours where power is provided from a circuit that can be switched on or off by means other than a circuit breaker, or within 48 hours where power is provided from a circuit that cannot be switched on or off by means other than a circuit breaker.

29.7 Equipment Performance

29.7.1 Self-Diagnostic. Any failure of any nonreliable or short-life component that renders the detector inoperable shall result in a trouble signal or otherwise be apparent to the occupant of the living unit without the need for test.

Subsection 29.7.1 requires the supervision of the sensor electronics and all circuitry in the alarm and some form of audible or visible indication of detector component failure, such as indicator lights or a distinctive audible trouble signal.

29.7.2* Smoke Alarms, System Smoke Detectors, and Other Non-Heat Fire Detectors.
Each device shall detect abnormal quantities of smoke or applicable fire signature, shall operate in the normal environmental conditions, and shall be in compliance with applicable standards such as ANSI/UL 268, *Standard for Smoke Detectors for Fire Alarm Systems,* or ANSI/UL 217, *Standard for Single and Multiple Station Smoke Alarms.*

A.29.7.2 The UL listing for smoke alarms addresses two categories of these devices: one for applications where sensitivity testing is not required [UTGT], and one for applications where sensitivity testing is required [UTHA]. Refer to the testing requirements for these devices in Chapter 14.

ANSI/UL 268, *Standard for Smoke Detectors for Fire Alarm Systems,* is the standard for "system" smoke detectors. These detectors are connected to and powered by a control unit and may also have integral notification appliances, depending on the model and manufacturer. All ac-powered, battery-powered, or combination ac- and battery-powered single- and multiple-station smoke alarms must comply with ANSI/UL 217, *Standard for Single and Multiple Station Smoke Alarms,* in order to be listed. Both the ionization-type and the photoelectric-type smoke detectors/smoke alarms are available under ANSI/UL 268 or ANSI/UL 217.

The wording in 29.7.2 was changed in the 2010 edition to clarify the intent to be applicable to any device or system that responds to smoke or other fire signatures (except for heat-only detectors). In all cases, the equipment must be in compliance with applicable standards. The technical committee recognizes that research and advancements in technology are demonstrating that multi-sensor detection can provide improved detection performance. The applicable standards for these newer technologies will have to demonstrate equivalent or better performance to current detectors and smoke alarms tested per ANSI/UL 268 or ANSI/UL 217.

EXHIBIT 29.14 *Fixed-Temperature Combination Smoke Alarm and Heat Alarm. (Source: Gentex Corp., Zeeland, MI)*

29.7.3* Heat Detectors and Heat Alarms.

A.29.7.3 The linear space rating is the maximum allowable distance between heat detectors. The linear space rating is also a measure of detector response time to a standard test fire when tested at the same distance. A higher rating corresponds to a faster response time. This Code recognizes only those heat detectors with ratings of 50 ft (15.2 m) or more.

29.7.3.1 Each heat detector and heat alarm, including a heat detector or heat alarm integrally mounted on a smoke detector or smoke alarm, shall detect abnormally high temperature or rate-of-temperature rise, and all such detectors shall be listed for not less than 50 ft (15 m) spacing.

The heat detector types that are allowed by the requirements within 29.7.3 are either fixed-temperature (see Exhibit 29.14) or rate-of-rise (see Exhibit 29.15) detectors.

Rate-of-rise heat detectors respond to rapid temperature increases. The designer should consider the environment in which rate-of-rise heat detectors are to be installed. Areas near dishwashers, hot air vents, and ovens are examples of areas to be avoided.

29.7.3.2* Fixed-temperature detectors or alarms shall have a temperature rating at least 25°F (14°C) above the normal ambient temperature and shall not be rated 50°F (28°C) higher than the maximum anticipated ambient temperature in the room or space where installed.

A.29.7.3.2 A heat detector with a temperature rating somewhat in excess of the highest normally expected ambient temperature is specified in order to avoid the possibility of premature response of the heat detector to non-fire conditions.

Some areas or rooms of the dwelling unit can experience ambient temperatures considerably higher than those in the normally occupied living spaces. Examples are unfinished attics, the space near hot air registers, and some furnace rooms. This fact should be considered

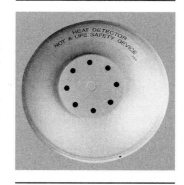

EXHIBIT 29.15 *Low-Profile Rate-of-Rise Heat Detector. (Source: GE Security, Bradenton, FL)*

in the selection of the appropriate temperature rating for fixed-temperature heat detectors to be installed in these areas or rooms.

29.7.4 Operability. Single- and multiple-station alarms, including heat alarms, shall be provided with a convenient means for testing its operability by the occupant, system owner, or other responsible parties.

FAQ ▶
In one- and two-family dwellings, what is required to perform a functional test?

Requirements for testing of smoke and heat alarms are in Chapter 10. The required functional testing of smoke alarms for one- and two-family dwellings can be accomplished by pushing a test button. Listed test aerosol can be used, provided that the smoke alarm manufacturer does not prohibit its use. Refer to the commentary following Section 29.10 for additional information on maintenance and testing.

Restorable-type heat alarms should be tested per the manufacturer's instructions in accordance with Table 14.4.2.2, item 14(d)(6). Open flames should never be used to test smoke or heat alarms because of the obvious fire hazard. Homeowners who are unable to perform these tests should consider a service contract.

29.7.5 System Control Equipment.

29.7.5.1 The system control equipment shall be automatically restoring upon restoration of electrical power.

29.7.5.2 The system control equipment shall be of a type that "locks in" on an alarm condition. Smoke detection circuits shall not be required to lock in.

The control unit must have the "lock-in" feature, as required by 29.7.5.2. System-connected smoke detectors utilizing a control unit are required by ANSI/UL 268 to provide a lamp or equivalent on a spot-type detector head or base to identify it as the unit from which the alarm was initiated. ANSI/UL 268 requires that the means incorporated to identify the initiation of an alarm remain activated after the smoke has dissipated from within the detector. The lock-in feature is, therefore, required on all spot-type smoke detectors connected to a control unit.

29.7.5.3 If a reset switch is provided, it shall be of a self-restoring (momentary operation) type.

29.7.5.4 A means for silencing the trouble notification appliance(s) shall be permitted only if the following conditions are satisfied:

(1) The means is key-operated or located within a locked enclosure, or arranged to provide equivalent protection against unauthorized use.
(2) The means transfers the trouble indication to an identified lamp or other acceptable visible indicator, and the visible indication persists until the trouble condition has been corrected.

EXHIBIT 29.16 *Keypad Display Arrangement. (Source: NAPCO Security Systems, Inc.–Gemini, Amityville, NY)*

The requirements in 29.7.5.4 can be met with a password-protected interface, such as a fire alarm/security system keypad, that visibly displays the trouble condition. See Exhibit 29.16 for a keypad display arrangement that might satisfy this requirement.

29.7.5.5 A means for turning off activated alarm notification appliances shall be permitted only if the following conditions are satisfied:

(1) The means is key-operated or located within a locked cabinet, or arranged to provide equivalent protection against unauthorized use.
(2) The means includes the provision of a visible alarm silence indication.

29.7.5.6 Household fire alarm system smoke detectors, initiating devices, and notification appliances shall be monitored for integrity so that the occurrence of a single open or single ground fault in the interconnection, which prevents normal operation of the interconnected devices, is indicated by a distinctive trouble signal.

29.7.5.7 System control equipment shall be in compliance with applicable standards such as ANSI/UL 985, *Standard for Household Fire Warning System Units*; ANSI/UL 1730, *Standard for Smoke Detector Monitors and Accessories for Individual Living Units of Multifamily Residences and Hotel/Motel Rooms*; or ANSI/UL 864, *Standard for Control Units and Accessories for Fire Signaling Systems*.

The requirement in 29.7.5.7 establishes appropriate standards for system control equipment and indicates that either household fire alarm systems or commercial systems can be used as equivalent in residential applications.

29.7.6 Combination System.

29.7.6.1 If designed and installed to perform additional functions, fire-warning equipment shall operate reliably and without compromise to its primary functions.

29.7.6.2 Fire signals shall take precedence over any other signal or functions, even if a non-fire signal is activated first.

The emergency evacuation signal, as required in 29.3.5, must override all other notification signals if a fire alarm occurs.

29.7.6.3 Signals shall be distinctive so that a fire signal can be distinguished from signals that require different actions by the occupants.

29.7.6.4 Faults in other systems or components shall not affect the operation of the fire alarm system.

29.7.6.5 Where common wiring is employed for a combination system, the equipment for other than the fire alarm system shall be connected to the common wiring of the system so that short circuits, open circuits, grounds, or any fault in this equipment or interconnection between this equipment and the fire alarm system wiring does not interfere with the supervision of the fire alarm system or prevent alarm or trouble signal operation.

Fire-warning systems in dwellings are permitted to be combination systems. Refer to the definition of a *combination system* in 3.3.95.1. Equipment not required for the operation of the fire alarm system that is modified, removed, or malfunctioning in any way must not impair the operation of the fire alarm system.

See Exhibit 29.17 for a typical listed combination fire/burglar alarm control unit.

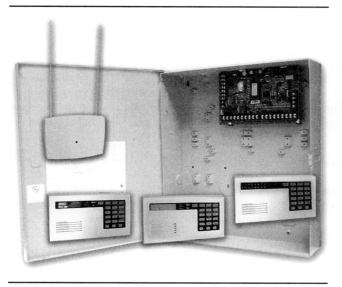

EXHIBIT 29.17 *Combination Household Fire/Burglar Alarm System. (Source: Bosch Security Systems, Fairport, NY)*

29.7.6.6 In a fire/burglar system, the operation shall be as follows:

(1) A fire alarm signal shall take precedence or be clearly recognizable over any other signal, even when the non-fire alarm signal is initiated first.
(2) Distinctive alarm signals shall be used so that fire alarms can be distinguished from other functions, such as burglar alarms. The use of a common-sounding appliance for fire and burglar alarms shall be permitted where distinctive signals are used.

Unless the fire alarm signals are unique, they could be confused with security, carbon monoxide alarms, or other signals in the home. Where the intended response is to evacuate, 29.3.5 requires new systems to produce the audible emergency evacuation signal described in ANSI S3.41, *American National Standard Audible Emergency Evacuation Signal*. The requirement for a unique signal does not mean that two separate notification appliances must be used. A single notification appliance may be used provided that it can supply different, distinctive signals. For example, a fully integrated system might sound the National Standard Audible Emergency Evacuation Signal for a fire alarm, sound a different signal for a security alarm, and sound a third signal to indicate detection of excessive levels of carbon monoxide.

29.7.6.7* Installations that include the connection of single- or multiple-station alarms with other input or output devices shall be permitted. An open, ground fault or short circuit of the wiring connecting input or output devices to the single- or multiple-station alarms shall not prevent operation of each individual alarm.

A.29.7.6.7 Such input and output devices include, but are not limited to, relay modules, notification appliances, phone dialers, security control units, heat detectors, and manual fire alarm boxes.

Paragraph 29.7.6.7 was modified for the 2010 edition to clarify that the intent is to permit the interconnection of smoke alarms with other input or output devices. The examples of input and output devices were moved to Annex A. Furthermore, the revised paragraph requires that a failure of the multiple-station interconnecting means not prevent single-station operation of the multiple-station alarms. This coincides with ANSI/UL 217, which requires a fault to allow alarms to operate as single-station alarms.

29.7.7 Wireless Devices.

A new heading has been added to address wireless devices in general. Paragraph 29.7.7.1 is specific to wireless household fire alarm systems and requires these systems to meet the same requirements as commercial wireless fire alarm systems. Note that household systems are no longer exempt from the requirement in 23.18.4.5 regarding the need to cause a supervisory signal when the radio transmitter is removed from its installed location. Wireless fire alarm systems should not be confused with wireless interconnected smoke alarms, which are addressed separately in 29.7.7.2.

29.7.7.1 Wireless Systems. Household fire alarm systems utilizing low-power wireless transmission of signals within the protected dwelling unit shall comply with the requirements of Section 23.18.

29.7.7.2 Nonsupervised Wireless Interconnected Alarms.

Multiple-station smoke alarms that are capable of being "interconnected" through wireless radio signals rather than hard-wired connections have been on the market since mid-2005. Paragraph 29.7.7.2 was added in the 2010 edition to provide clear performance requirements for the wireless interconnection of these alarms. Interconnection of smoke alarms can provide earlier warning, ensure proper sound levels, and increase the available escape time in home fire scenarios. Because of these capabilities, *NFPA 72* now requires all homes to have interconnected alarms (see 29.5.2.1.1 and related commentary). Prior to the 2010 edition, neither

NFPA 72 nor ANSI/UL 217 had specifications for the distance that wireless alarms must communicate. Therefore, detailed methods and requirements were developed to ensure that devices will properly respond when spaced up to 100 ft (30.5 m) apart within a dwelling. Additional background for the development of these requirements is provided in A.29.7.7.2.1.

29.7.7.2.1* To ensure adequate transmission and reception capability, nonsupervised, low-power wireless alarms shall be capable of reliably communicating at a distance of 100 ft (30.5 m) indoors as tested to an equivalent open area test distance, D_{EOAT} between two devices in accordance with the following equations:

$$D_{EOAT} = 30.5 \times \left(10^{\frac{L_b}{40}}\right)$$

where L_b is the building attenuation factor, a value dependent on the frequency of the wireless transmission. The building attenuation factor, L_b, represents the maximum attenuation value of typical floors and walls within a majority of structures the factor. L_b shall assume four walls and two floors and be calculated as follows:

$$L_b = 4 \times L_w + 2 \times L_f$$

where:

L_w = attenuation value of a wall

    = $2 \times L_1 + L_2$

L_f = attenuation value of a floor

    = $L_1 + L_2 + L_3 + L_4$

L_1 = frequency-dependent attenuation value for $\frac{1}{2}$ in. (13 mm) drywall

L_2 = frequency-dependent attenuation value for $1\frac{1}{2}$ in. (38 mm) structural lumber

L_3 = frequency-dependent attenuation value for $\frac{3}{4}$ in. (19 mm) plywood

L_4 = frequency-dependent attenuation value for $\frac{1}{2}$ in. (13 mm) glass/tile floor

A.29.7.7.2.1 For RF waves traveling along the earth surface, the signal power loss (in dB), L_p, can be calculated using the following plane-earth propagation loss model:

$$L_p = 10 \log\left[\frac{D_p^4}{h_{TX}^2 h_{RX}^2}\right] \qquad (A.29.7.7.2.1a)$$

where D_p represents the distance between the transmitter and receiver and h_{TX} and h_{RX} are the heights of the transmitter and receiver, respectively, above the earth.

The plane earth propagation model is a practical simplification and requires that h_{TX}, h_{RX} $<< D_p$. It reflects the average expected attenuation due to distance of the RF carrier for a stationary set of radios with an essentially clear line of sight. It predicts maximum communications range only in the UHF band (300 MHz to 3 GHz) and is not dependent on frequency.

Inside a building, the model can be expanded to determine the total path loss, L_T, which includes the plane earth loss, L_p (equation A.29.7.7.2.1a), and the loss due to the building materials in the propagation path, L_b, as follows:

$$L_T = 10 \log\left[\frac{D_p^4}{(h_{TX} h_{RX})^2}\right] + L_b \qquad (A.29.7.7.2.1b)$$

If an equivalent open area test distance D_{EOAT} is defined as follows:

$$L_T = 10 \log\left[\frac{D_{EOAT}^4}{(h_{TX} h_{RX})^2}\right] \qquad (A.29.7.7.2.1c)$$

then D_{EOAT} can be shown to be:

$$D_{EOAT} = 10^{\frac{-L_T}{40}} \sqrt{h_{TX}} \sqrt{h_{RX}} = D_p \cdot 10^{\frac{L_b}{40}} \qquad (A.29.7.7.2.1d)$$

The D_{EOAT} function is used to calculate a test distance required to verify the functional range of wireless alarm products. As noted above in the right side of equation A.29.7.7.2.1d, the function represents two factors — one that describes the attenuation of a radio frequency signal due to plane earth propagation path loss (D_p), and one that describes the dwelling material losses (L_b) in the signal's propagation path. It is the combination of dwelling loss and propagation path loss that is used in the calculation of the test distance D_{EOAT}. The losses are expressed in dB, and the unit for distances is meter.

In reviewing average home sizes, a reliable (indoor) communication of 100 ft (30.5 m) is adequate for a majority of dwellings, based on an average house size of 2200 ft^2 (204 m^2) [National Association of Home Builders]. Construction materials of a home (walls and floors) can attenuate an RF signal, with the RF signal being attenuated more at higher frequencies [Stone, 1997]. Communication specifications for devices of this type are typically specified as open field (no obstructions) test distances, and not in terms of attenuation. Therefore, the standard specifies a minimum open area test distance, D_{EOAT}, that the RF products must communicate. This distance is equal to 100 ft (30.5 m) (the longest straight line distance within a majority of homes) plus an additional distance that is equivalent to the attenuation of four walls and two floors (the most straight line obstructions in a majority of homes). The additional distance varies depending on the operating frequency of the product. Formulas for calculating D_{EOAT} are included below, along with examples for a number of different frequencies. These criteria are expected to yield reliable indoor communications at 100 ft (30.5 m) when used inside a majority of dwellings.

The building attenuation factor, L_b, represents the maximum attenuation value of typical floors and walls within a majority of structures. L_b is calculated using attenuation values of different materials. The following method is used to calculate L_b. The building materials attenuation coefficients specified in this application are taken from Stone, 1977. Other sources of appropriate building material attenuation coefficients may be used; however, testing organizations should apply values consistently for all products tested.

L_1 = Frequency dependent attenuation value for $\frac{1}{2}$ in. (13 mm) drywall
L_2 = Frequency dependent attenuation value for $1\frac{1}{2}$ in. (38 mm) structural lumber
L_3 = Frequency dependent attenuation value for $\frac{3}{4}$ in. (19 mm) plywood
L_4 = Frequency dependent attenuation value for $\frac{1}{2}$ in. (13 mm) glass/tile floor
L_w = Attenuation value of a wall = $2 \times L_1 + L_2$
L_f = Attenuation value of a floor = $L_1 + L_2 + L_3 + L_4$
Assuming four walls and two floors,

$$L_b = 4 \times L_w + 2 \times L_f$$

The source for the equation in 29.7.7.2.1 is Stone, W. *"Electromagnetic Attenuation in Construction Materials,"* National Institute of Standards and Technology, NISTIR 6055, 1997.

29.7.7.2.2 Fire alarm signals shall have priority over all other signals.

29.7.7.2.3 The maximum allowable response delay from activation of an initiating device to receipt and alarm/display by the receiver/control unit shall be 20 seconds.

29.7.7.2.4* Wireless interconnected smoke alarms (in receive mode) shall remain in alarm as long as the originating unit (transmitter) remains in alarm.

The requirement in 29.7.7.2.4 ensures that remote smoke alarms will continue to be in alarm at least as long as the initiating smoke alarm is in alarm. The requirement does not prohibit remote smoke alarms from continuing to be in alarm after the initiating smoke alarm stops under conditions in which the initiating device has been damaged by a growing fire. However, this function would need to be balanced with the need to silence all alarms when activated by a nuisance source.

A.29.7.7.2.4 Receiving units that stay in alarm for 30 seconds or 1 minute longer than the transmitting alarm would provide additional protection if the first alarm is damaged due to a very fast growing fire. The persisting alarm signal would provide additional notification to occupants. This option needs to be considered in light of the potential for the longer alarm signals on receiving smoke alarms being a potential nuisance to occupants during test and other nuisance alarm events.

29.7.7.2.5 The occurrence of any single fault that disables a transceiver shall not prevent other transceivers in the system from operating.

The requirement in 29.7.7.2.5 ensures that the interconnection of wireless alarms throughout the occupancy will not be compromised by the failure of one unit to perform correctly.

29.7.8 Supervising Stations.

29.7.8.1 Means to transmit alarm signals to a constantly attended, remote monitoring location shall perform as described in Chapter 26, except as modified by 29.7.8.1.1 through 29.7.8.1.4.

29.7.8.1.1 Where a digital alarm communicator transmitter (DACT) is used, the DACT serving the protected premises shall only require a single telephone line and shall only require a call to a single digital alarm communicator transmitter (DACR) number.

29.7.8.1.2 Where a DACT is used, the DACT test signals shall be transmitted at least monthly.

29.7.8.1.3 Supervising station systems shall not be required to comply with requirements for indication of central station service in 26.3.4.

Paragraph 29.7.8.1 addresses the transmission of fire alarm system signals to a supervising station. The means to transmit must comply with the requirements of Chapter 26 except as noted in 29.7.8.1.1 through 29.7.8.1.4. Where the means involves the use of a DACT, as defined in 3.3.62 of the Code, a single telephone line may be used. Also, the frequency of the daily test signal required by 26.6.3.2.1.5(6) for a DACT may be extended to monthly. However, these allowances do not prevent a homeowner from installing and using a system that meets the full requirements of Chapter 26.

◀ **FAQ**
Where a digital alarm communicator transmitter (DACT) is used as the means of transmitting an alarm signal, how many telephone lines are required?

29.7.8.1.4 A dedicated cellular telephone connection shall be permitted to be used as a single means to transmit alarms to a constantly attended remote monitoring location.

Subsection 29.7.8.1.5 was deleted by a tentative interim amendment (TIA).

29.7.8.2* Remote monitoring stations shall be permitted to verify alarm signals prior to reporting them to the fire service, provided that the verification process does not delay the reporting by more than 90 seconds.

A.29.7.8.2 Where 29.7.8.2, which provides for screening alarm signals to minimize response to false alarms, is to be implemented, the following should be considered:

(1) Was the verification call answered at the protected premises?
(2) Did the respondent provide proper identification?
(3) Is it necessary for the respondent to identify the cause of the alarm signal?
(4) Should the public service fire communications center be notified and advised that an alarm signal was received, including the response to the verification call, when an authorized respondent states that fire service response is not desired?
(5) Should the public service fire communications center be notified and advised that an alarm signal was received, including the response to the verification call, for all other situations, including both a hostile fire and no answer to the verification call?
(6) What other actions should be required by a standard operating procedure?

Paragraph 29.7.8.2 permits supervising station personnel to place a verification call before re-transmitting the alarm signal. The homeowner should use a preassigned personal identification code or password to verify that the source of an alarm signal does not require emergency response by the fire department. Although a verification call is allowed, it is highly preferable to have the alarm reported immediately unless the call is required by the owner.

29.7.8.3 Household fire alarm systems shall be programmed by the manufacturer to generate at least a monthly test of the communication or transmission means.

Paragraph 29.7.8.3 is new. It improves reliability by requiring that a mandatory, automatic test for at least a monthly communication check be built into the system.

29.8 Installation

29.8.1 General.

29.8.1.1 All equipment shall be installed in accordance with the manufacturer's published instructions and applicable electrical standards.

Equipment must be installed in a workmanlike manner that is neat, safe, and easily maintained and that complies with all appropriate codes and standards.

29.8.1.2 All devices shall be so located and mounted that accidental operation is not caused by jarring or vibration.

29.8.1.3 All fire-warning equipment shall be mounted so as to be supported independently of its attachment to wires.

29.8.1.4 The supplier or installing contractor shall provide the system owner or other responsible parties with the following:

(1) An instruction booklet illustrating typical installation layouts
(2) Instruction charts describing the operation, method, and frequency of testing and maintenance of fire-warning equipment
(3) Printed information for establishing an emergency evacuation plan
(4) Printed information to inform system owners where they can obtain repair or replacement service, and where and how parts requiring regular replacement, such as batteries or bulbs, can be obtained within 2 weeks
(5) Information noting both of the following:

  (a) Unless otherwise recommended by the manufacturer's published instructions, smoke alarms shall be replaced when they fail to respond to tests.
  (b) Smoke alarms installed in one- and two-family dwellings shall not remain in service longer than 10 years from the date of manufacture.

29.8.2 Interconnection of Detectors or Multiple-Station Alarms.

29.8.2.1 Smoke detectors shall be connected to central controls for power, signal processing, and activation of notification appliances.

29.8.2.2* The interconnection of smoke or heat alarms shall comply with the following:

(1) Smoke or heat alarms shall not be interconnected in numbers that exceed the manufacturer's published instructions.
(2) In no case shall more than 18 initiating devices be interconnected (of which 12 can be smoke alarms) where the interconnecting means is not supervised.
(3) In no case shall more than 64 initiating devices be interconnected (of which 42 can be smoke alarms) where the interconnecting means is supervised.

(4) Smoke or heat alarms shall not be interconnected with alarms from other manufacturers unless listed as being compatible with the specific model.

(5) When alarms of different types are interconnected, all interconnected alarms shall produce the appropriate audible response for the phenomena being detected or remain silent.

A.29.8.2.2 Once these limits have been exceeded, a fire alarm system should be installed.

The intent of the requirements in 29.8.2.2 is to recognize that systems designed for use in large residences differ from those intended for use in smaller residences. It is important to remember that the configuration allowed in 29.8.2.2(2) incorporates heat alarms that may be connected to multiple-station smoke alarms. The number of multiple-station smoke alarms used to protect a residence is limited to 12 because the wiring that interconnects hard-wired smoke alarms is not monitored for integrity.

For applications that require more than 12 smoke alarms, a fire alarm system with a control unit must be used.

◄ FAQ
What course of action is needed when the number of smoke alarms exceeds 12?

For large residences that require many smoke alarms and the interconnection of different types of smoke alarms or sensors (such as carbon monoxide or waterflow switches on a sprinkler system), the use of a household fire alarm system should be considered instead of smoke alarms. If multiple-station smoke alarms are to be interconnected with other types of smoke alarms, the equipment must be listed as compatible. The manufacturers' published instructions provide guidance on the compatibility of equipment.

Paragraph 29.8.2.2(4) specifically requires that smoke alarms of different manufacturers are not to be interconnected unless they have been tested to be compatible. Interconnection of equipment from different manufacturers can lead to devices not operating as intended.

Paragraph 29.8.2.2(5) was added in the 2010 edition based on the requirements in ANSI/UL 2034, *Standard for Single and Multiple Station Carbon Monoxide Alarms*, for carbon monoxide (CO) alarms and ANSI/UL 217 for smoke alarms to provide consistent notification from all interconnected alarms. For example, additional notification throughout a dwelling via smoke alarms interconnected with CO alarms can be beneficial when a CO alarm sounds. However, to avoid confusion, the alarm signal should be appropriate for the initiating device and should be the same from all sounding devices.

29.8.2.3 A single fault on the interconnecting means between multiple-station alarms shall not prevent single-station operation of any of the interconnected alarms.

29.8.2.4 Remote notification appliance circuits of multiple-station alarms shall be capable of being tested for integrity by activation of the test feature on any interconnected alarm. Activation of the test feature shall result in the operation of all interconnected notification appliances.

The activation of remote notification appliances, which are part of a group of interconnected multiple-station smoke alarms, should sound at all locations as well as at all multiple-station smoke alarms. Testing at any smoke alarm should sound all smoke alarms and appliances. Proper distribution of the alarm signal throughout the dwelling unit (or other required area) can be checked during routine testing of the smoke alarms.

29.8.3* Smoke Alarms and Smoke Detectors. Smoke alarms, smoke detectors, devices, combination of devices, and equipment shall be installed in accordance with the manufacturer's listing and published instructions, and, unless specifically listed for the application, shall comply with requirements in 29.8.3.1 through 29.8.3.4.

Compliance with the requirements in 29.8.3 is essential to provide an effective installation. In some cases, manufacturers have designed equipment that can be effective in applications that exceed the Code-specified limits, such as those for temperature or humidity. In such cases, the equipment must be listed for the special conditions and be installed within the listed limits. Also refer to the commentary following 29.8.3.4.

The requirement to maintain at least a 4 in. (100 mm) spacing between a ceiling-mounted detector or alarm and the adjoining wall has been deleted from the 2010 edition of the Code. Similarly, the 4 in. (100 mm) spacing requirement (between device and the ceiling) for wall mounting also has been deleted. As noted in A.29.8.3, current research and testing have shown that there is no reduction in performance if detectors are positioned closer than 4 in. (100 mm) from the adjoining wall or ceiling surface.

It should be noted that this change is applicable only to smoke alarms. Heat alarms are still required to comply with the 4 in. (100 mm) area of exclusion. Refer to 29.8.4.3.

A.29.8.3 One of the most critical factors of any fire alarm system is the location of the fire detecting devices. This annex is not a technical study. It is an attempt to provide some fundamentals on fire-warning equipment location. For simplicity, only those types of alarms or detectors recognized by Chapter 29 (e.g., smoke and heat alarms or smoke and heat detectors) are discussed. Specific mounting locations of fire-warning equipment in unoccupied or architecturally unique areas (e.g., as in attics or in rooms with high ceilings) should be evaluated by a qualified professional.

The conclusions of the Kemano Study and FPRF Smoke Detector Spacing Requirements Report (2008) have determined revisions to smoke alarm and smoke detector mounting within 4 in. (100 mm) of a flat ceiling/wall corner are now acceptable. The studies have shown that acceptable detection performance does not depend on the 4 in. (100 mm) separation. Figure A.29.8.3 illustrates acceptable smoke alarm and smoke detector mounting locations.

29.8.3.1* Peaked Ceilings. Smoke alarms or smoke detectors mounted on a peaked ceiling shall be located within 36 in. (910 mm) horizontally of the peak, but not closer than 4 in. (100 mm) vertically to the peak.

A.29.8.3.1 Figure A.29.8.3.1 illustrates acceptable smoke alarm or smoke detector mounting locations for a peaked ceiling.

29.8.3.2* Sloped Ceilings. Smoke alarms or smoke detectors mounted on a sloped ceiling having a rise greater than 1 ft in 8 ft (1 m in 8 m) horizontally shall be located within 36 in. (910 mm) of the high side of the ceiling, but not closer than 4 in. (100 mm) from the adjoining wall surface.

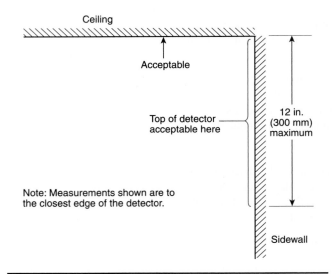

FIGURE A.29.8.3 *Example of Proper Mounting for Smoke Alarms and Smoke Detectors.*

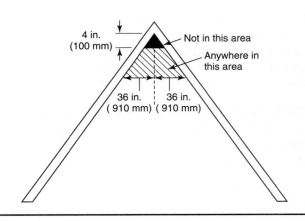

FIGURE A.29.8.3.1 *Example of Proper Mounting for Alarms and Detectors with Peaked Ceilings.*

A.29.8.3.2 Figure A.29.8.3.2 illustrates acceptable smoke alarm or smoke detector mounting locations for a sloped ceiling.

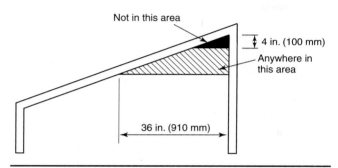

FIGURE A.29.8.3.2 *Example of Proper Mounting for Alarms and Detectors with Sloped Ceilings.*

29.8.3.3* Wall Mounting. Smoke alarms or smoke detectors mounted on walls shall be located not farther than 12 in. (300 mm) from the adjoining ceiling surface.

A.29.8.3.3 Figure A.29.8.3 illustrates acceptable smoke alarm or smoke detector mounting locations.

In those dwelling units employing radiant heating in the ceiling, the wall location is the recommended location. Radiant heating in the ceiling can create a hot air boundary layer along the ceiling surface, which can seriously restrict the movement of smoke and heat to a ceiling-mounted detector.

29.8.3.4 Specific Location Requirements. The installation of smoke alarms and smoke detectors shall comply with the following requirements:

(1) Smoke alarms and smoke detectors shall not be located where ambient conditions, including humidity and temperature, are outside the limits specified by the manufacturer's published instructions.

Garages and attic spaces often experience ambient conditions that exceed the operating limits of smoke alarms. Smoke alarms listed to ANSI/UL 217 are tested to operate at temperatures from 32°F to 120°F (0°C to 49°C). However, some manufacturers design and list devices beyond the standard temperature range. The use of heat alarms may be more appropriate in locations such as garages if conditions are not suitable for smoke alarms.

(2) Smoke alarms and smoke detectors shall not be located within unfinished attics or garages or in other spaces where temperatures can fall below 40°F (4°C) or exceed 100°F (38°C).

(3)* Where the mounting surface could become considerably warmer or cooler than the room, such as a poorly insulated ceiling below an unfinished attic or an exterior wall, smoke alarms and smoke detectors shall be mounted on an inside wall.

(4)* Smoke alarms and smoke detectors shall not be installed within an area of exclusion determined by a 10 ft (3.0 m) radial distance along a horizontal flow path from a stationary or fixed cooking appliance, unless listed for installation in close proximity to cooking appliances. Smoke alarms and smoke detectors installed between 10 ft (3.0 m) and 20 ft (6.1 m) along a horizontal flow path from a stationary or fixed cooking appliance shall be equipped with an alarm-silencing means or use photoelectric detection.

Exception: Smoke alarms or smoke detectors that use photoelectric detection shall be permitted for installation at a radial distance greater than 6 ft (1.8 m) from any stationary or fixed cooking appliance when the following conditions are met:

(a) *The kitchen or cooking area and adjacent spaces have no clear interior partitions or headers and*

(b) *The 10 ft (3.0 m) area of exclusion would prohibit the placement of a smoke alarm or smoke detector required by other sections of this code.*

The minimization of nuisance alarms is essential to help reduce the number of disabled smoke alarms. The technical committee reviewed the available information on the occurrence of nuisance alarms and concluded that the primary source of nuisance alarms was cooking activities. Steam from bathroom activities was also a source but to a much more limited extent. Nuisance alarms caused by cooking activities occur far more frequently with ionization smoke alarms than with photoelectric smoke alarms. However, nuisance alarms from either type of smoke alarm are likely if the smoke alarm is placed too close to a cooking appliance. For that reason, 29.8.3.4(4) was revised to exclude the installation of any smoke alarm within 10 ft (3.0 m) of a stationary or fixed cooking appliance. The exclusion area can be reduced to 6 ft (1.8 m) under the circumstance specified in the exception. A further exclusion area between 10 ft (3.0 m) and 20 ft (6.1 m) is specified similar to that in previous editions of the Code. No exclusion is specified beyond 20 ft (6.1 m). Exhibit 29.18 shows an example of a photoelectric smoke detector located between 10 ft (3.0 m) and 20 ft (6.1 m) from a cooking appliance.

EXHIBIT 29.18 *Photoelectric Smoke Detector Located Between 10 ft (3.0 m) and 20 ft (6.1 m) from a Cooking Appliance. (Source: R. P. Schifiliti Associates, Inc., Reading, MA)*

Nuisance alarms caused by steam from bathroom activities occurred in both types of smoke alarms. (Refer to A.29.8.3.4(4) for additional guidance on location of smoke alarms near bathrooms.)

(5)* Smoke alarms and smoke detectors shall not be installed within a 36 in. (910 mm) horizontal path from a door to a bathroom containing a shower or tub.

(6) Smoke alarms and smoke detectors shall not be installed within a 36 in. (910 mm) horizontal path from the supply registers of a forced air heating or cooling system and shall be installed outside of the direct airflow from those registers.

(7) Smoke alarms and smoke detectors shall not be installed within a 36 in. (910 mm) horizontal path from the tip of the blade of a ceiling-suspended (paddle) fan.

(8) Where stairs lead to other occupied levels, a smoke alarm or smoke detector shall be located so that smoke rising in the stairway cannot be prevented from reaching the smoke alarm or smoke detector by an intervening door or obstruction.

(9) For stairways leading up from a basement, smoke alarms or smoke detectors shall be located on the basement ceiling near the entry to the stairs.

Doors at the tops of stairwells prevent smoke flow in the upward direction. The stairwell acts as a dead air space and traps smoke below, which can prevent smoke from reaching a smoke alarm located in the stairwell. Therefore, smoke alarms should be mounted on the basement ceiling near the stairwell, as required by 29.8.3.4(9). Common practice is to mount smoke alarms on the bottom of floor joists in basements with unfinished construction.

(10)*For tray-shaped ceilings (coffered ceilings), smoke alarms and smoke detectors shall be installed on the highest portion of the ceiling or on the sloped portion of the ceiling within 12 in. (300 mm) vertically down from the highest point.

(11) Smoke alarms and detectors installed in rooms with joists or beams shall comply with the requirements of 17.7.3.2.4.

Per 17.7.3.2.4.2(5), if a room with a level ceiling is smaller than 900 ft^2 (84 m^2), only one smoke alarm or detector is required for the room, regardless of whether there are beams. Since most spaces that utilize smoke warning equipment per Chapter 29 are less than 900 ft^2 (84 m^2), no special attention is needed. However, if the space is larger or the ceiling is sloped, additional spacing requirements apply. These requirements are dependent on the height of the beams relative to the ceiling height and the orientation of beams relative to the ceiling slope.

(12) Heat alarms and detectors installed in rooms with joists or beams shall comply with the requirements of 17.6.3.

The siting of heat detectors on ceilings with beams or joists shall follow the requirements of Chapter 17, which takes into account beam depths and construction.

A.29.8.3.4(3) Smoke detectors and smoke alarms should be installed in those locations recommended by the manufacturer's published instructions, except in those cases where the space above the ceiling is open to the outside and little or no insulation is present over the ceiling. Such cases result in the ceiling being excessively cold in the winter or excessively hot in the summer. Where the ceiling is significantly different in temperature from the air space below, smoke and heat have difficulty reaching the ceiling and a detector that is located on that ceiling.

A.29.8.3.4(4) As per annex material located in A.29.5.1, it is not normally recommended that smoke alarms or smoke detectors be placed in kitchen spaces. This section of the code provides guidelines for safe installation if a need exists to install a smoke alarm or smoke detector in a residential kitchen space or cooking area.

Within this Code section, a fixed cooking appliance is any appliance that is intended to be permanently connected electrically to the wiring system or the fuel source. A stationary cooking appliance is any appliance that is intended to be fastened in place or located in a dedicated space, and is connected to the supply circuit or fuel source.

Smoke alarms and smoke detectors that are currently available to consumers are susceptible to particles released into the air during normal cooking procedures. If smoke alarms and smoke detectors are placed too close to the area where the cooking source originates, a high level of nuisance alarms can occur. Frequent nuisance alarms can result in an occupant disabling the smoke alarm or smoke detector.

Nuisance alarm studies show that commercially available residential smoke alarms and smoke detectors are susceptible to nuisance alarms when installed too close to cooking appliances. As the horizontal distance between the smoke alarm or smoke detectors and the cooking appliance increases, the frequency of nuisance alarms decreases. Smoke alarms or smoke detectors that use ionization smoke detection have been shown to be more susceptible to cooking nuisance alarms than those that use photoelectric smoke detection when the alarms or detectors are installed within 10 ft (3.0 m) along a horizontal smoke travel path from a cooking appliance. Smoke alarms or smoke detectors that use photoelectric smoke detection produce nuisance alarms when installed less than 10 ft (3.0 m) from a cooking appliance, though to a lesser degree.

The occurrence of the higher frequency of nuisance alarms observed in smoke alarms or smoke detectors that use ionization detection have been documented in the fire research data. Due to the differences in technology between ionization detection and photoelectric detection, the sensitivity typically used for ionization detection is much higher than that used for photoelectric detection. This sensitivity difference is a result of each type of the detection being required to satisfy UL 217 performance tests. Removing detection technology from consideration, the frequency of nuisance alarms is solely due to the sensitivity of the detection method used. Thus, both ionization and photoelectric detector technologies will produce nuisance alarms due to cooking, but currently available smoke alarms and smoke detectors that use ionization detection typically produce more cooking-related nuisance alarms.

The higher sensitivities of currently available smoke alarms and smoke detectors that use ionization detection do provide a benefit at the expense of a potentially higher rate of cooking-related nuisance alarms. Research has demonstrated that ionization detection will typically respond faster than photoelectric detection to flaming fires, providing earlier warning to occupants that might allow for quicker intervention or faster egress. In general, the installation of smoke alarms or smoke detectors that use ionization detection will result in increased fire safety at the risk of a higher frequency of nuisance alarms. The installation of smoke alarms or smoke detectors that use photoelectric detection will result in reduced fire safety for flaming fires and a reduced risk of nuisance alarms. Based on the trade-off between faster response to fires and the frequency of nuisance alarms, detectors that utilize both technologies (i.e., ionization, photoelectric, and a combination) are allowed to be installed between 10 ft (3.0 m) and 20 ft (6.1 m) along a horizontal flow path from a standard or fixed cooking appliance if the specific detector is equipped with an alarm silencing means or is of the photoelectric-type.

Nuisance alarm studies provide data on cooking nuisances that emanate from both fixed cooking appliances and stationary cooking appliances (e.g., stove, oven) as well as portable cooking appliances (e.g., toaster). Based on these studies, which demonstrate the potential of all cooking appliances to generate nuisance sources, a zone of exclusion has been specified surrounding each stationary or fixed cooking appliance. The purpose of this zone is to limit the installation of smoke alarms and detectors in areas where stationary, fixed, or portable cooking appliances will be located within the residential kitchen space such that potential nuisance alarms are minimized. The size of the zone of exclusion is specified to attempt to take into account the unknown and transitory locations of portable cooking appliances. This zone of exclusion is determined by measuring a 10 ft (3.0 m) radial distance from the closest edge of a stationary or fixed cooking appliance. The zone of exclusion is not intended to pass through walls or doorways. Figure A.29.8.3.4(4)(a) provides an example of the zone of exclusion in a generalized residential kitchen.

If other areas of this code require that a smoke alarm or smoke detector be placed within a horizontal flow path distance between 10 ft (3.0 m) and 20 ft (6.1 m) from a stationary or fixed cooking appliance, the following method should be used to determine the distance, and only photoelectric detection or smoke alarms/detectors with alarm silencing means can be installed in this area.

To install a smoke alarm or detector between 10 ft (3.0 m) and 20 ft (6.1 m) from the cooking appliance, an installer must first determine the 10 ft (3.0 m) area of exclusion. Once the area of exclusion is determined, an installer must then determine the horizontal flow distance. This is the horizontal distance along the ceiling from the closest edge of the cooking appliance to the smoke alarm or detector. The horizontal distance can consist of line segments due to impediments, such as interior partitions. Once an impediment is met, the measurement of the distance will then continue along the new horizontal path segment until the distance requirement is met or another impediment is encountered. Figure A.29.8.3.4(4)(b) provides an example for placement outside a kitchen in a nearby hallway. Figure A.29.8.3.4(4)(c) provides another example of appropriate placement outside of a kitchen in an adjacent room.

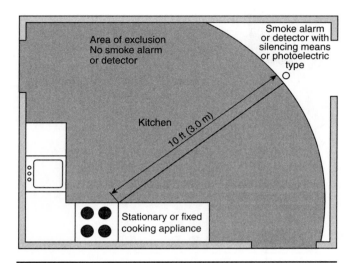

FIGURE A.29.8.3.4(4)(a) *Example of the Zone of Exclusion (gray area) Within a Typical Residential Kitchen.*

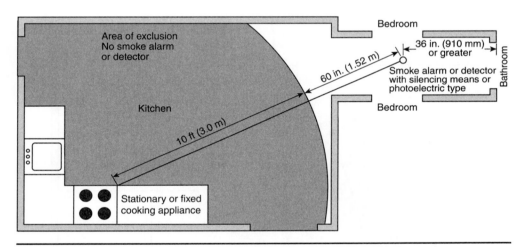

FIGURE A.29.8.3.4(4)(b) *Example of Smoke Alarm or Smoke Detector Placement Between 10 ft (3.0 m) and 20 ft (6.1 m) Away in a Hallway from the Center of a Stationary or Fixed Cooking Appliance.*

At a horizontal flow path distance of greater than 20 ft (6.1 m), any type of smoke alarm or smoke detector can be installed.

In rare cases, a residential dwelling can be of such size and configuration that an area of exclusion of 10 ft (3.0 m) from a stationary or fixed cooking appliance excludes the placement of a smoke alarm or smoke detector required by other areas of this Code. In these cases, a smoke alarm or smoke detector using photoelectric detection can be installed at least 72 in. (1.83 m) from the fixed or stationary cooking appliance. Figure A.29.8.3.4(4)(d) provides an example of this situation in practice where a smoke alarm or smoke detector is required outside of the sleeping area, but the space is in close proximity to the kitchen space.

A.29.8.3.4(5) Studies indicate that smoke alarms and smoke detectors that use ionization detection, photoelectric detection, or a combination of ionization and photoelectric detection, are susceptible to nuisance alarms caused by steam. Little research has been done on the

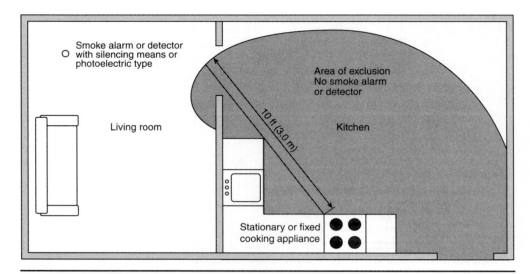

FIGURE A.29.8.3.4(4)(c) *Example of Smoke Alarm or Smoke Detector Placement Between 10 ft (3.0 m) and 20 ft (6.1 m) Away in a Hallway from the Center of a Stationary or Fixed Cooking Appliance.*

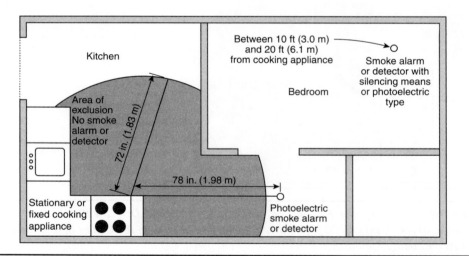

FIGURE A.29.8.3.4(4)(d) *Example of the Exception Placement of a Photoelectric Smoke Alarm or Smoke Detector at 72 in. (1.83 m) from a Stationary or Fixed Cooking Appliance.*

comparative response of these types of detection to steam. Steam particles, in general, are visible, reflect light easily, and are typically produced in a size range that would be more likely to activate a photoelectric sensor. Thus, it is required that smoke alarms and smoke detectors be installed greater than 36 in. (910 mm) from the bathroom door where possible. Increasing the distance between the smoke alarm or smoke detector and the bathroom door can reduce the frequency of nuisance alarms from bathroom steam. Frequent nuisance alarms can result in the occupant disabling the smoke alarm. Each incremental increase in separation, up to 10 ft (3.0 m), between the bathroom door and the smoke alarm or smoke detector is expected to reduce the frequency of nuisance alarms.

A.29.8.3.4(10) Figure A.29.8.3.4(10) illustrates acceptable smoke alarm or smoke detector mounting locations for tray-shaped ceilings.

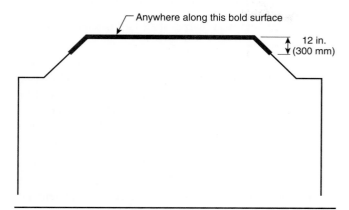

FIGURE A.29.8.3.4(10) *Locations Permitted for Smoke Alarms and Smoke Detectors on Tray-Shaped Ceilings.*

For tray-shaped ceilings that are level at the top, smoke and heat alarms must be mounted on the high ceiling or on the sloped rise between levels within 12 in. (300 mm) vertically from the adjoining high ceiling, as required in 29.8.3.4(10). The other location requirements in 29.8.3.4 also apply. Exhibit 29.19 shows an example of a smoke detector located on the sloped portion of a tray-shaped ceiling and at least 3 ft (910 mm) from the tip of the blade of the ceiling fan.

EXHIBIT 29.19 *Smoke Detector Located on a Tray-Shaped Ceiling. (Source: R. P. Schifiliti Associates, Inc., Reading, MA)*

29.8.4* Heat Detectors and Heat Alarms.

A.29.8.4 While Chapter 29 does not require heat alarms or heat detectors as part of the basic protection scheme, it is recommended that the householder consider the use and placement of additional heat detectors for the same reasons presented under A.29.8.3. For example, additional heat alarms or heat detectors could be considered, but not limited to, the following areas: kitchen, dining room, attic (finished or unfinished), furnace room, utility room, basement, and integral or attached garage.

The placement of the heat alarm or heat detector is critical where maximum speed of fire detection is desired. Thus, a logical location for a heat alarm or heat detector is the center of the ceiling. At this location, the heat alarm or heat detector is closest to all areas of the room.

29.8.4.1* On smooth ceilings, heat detectors and heat alarms shall be installed within the strict limitations of their listed spacing.

A.29.8.4.1 *Heat Alarm or Heat Detector Mounting — Dead Air Space.* Heat from a fire rises to the ceiling, spreads out across the ceiling surface, and begins to bank down from the ceiling. The corner where the ceiling and the wall meet is an air space into which heat has difficulty penetrating. In most fires, this dead air space measures about 4 in. (100 mm) along the ceiling from the corner and about 4 in. (100 mm) down the wall as shown in Figure A.17.6.3.1.3.1. Heat alarm or heat detectors should not be placed in this dead air space.

29.8.4.2* For sloped ceilings having a rise greater than 1 ft in 8 ft (1 m in 8 m) horizontally, the detector or alarm shall be located within 36 in. (910 mm) of the peak. The spacing of additional detectors or alarms, if any, shall be based on a horizontal distance measurement, not on a measurement along the slope of the ceiling.

A.29.8.4.2 Figure A.29.8.3.2 illustrates acceptable heat alarm or heat detector mounting locations for sloped ceilings.

29.8.4.3* Heat detectors or alarms shall be mounted on the ceiling at least 4 in. (100 mm) from a wall or on a wall with the top of the detector or alarm not less than 4 in. (100 mm), nor more than 12 in. (300 mm), below the ceiling.

Exception: Where the mounting surface could become considerably warmer or cooler than the room, such as a poorly insulated ceiling below an unfinished attic or an exterior wall, the detectors or alarms shall be mounted on an inside wall.

A.29.8.4.3 *Spacing of Detectors.* Where a room is too large for protection by a single heat alarm or heat detector, multiple alarms or detectors should be used. It is important that they be properly located so all parts of the room are covered. *(For further information on the spacing of detectors, see Chapter 17.)*

Where the Distance Between Detectors Should Be Further Reduced. The distance between detectors is based on data obtained from the spread of heat across a smooth ceiling. Where the ceiling is not smooth, the placement of the heat alarm or heat detector should be tailored to the situation.

Figure A.17.6.3.1.3.1 illustrates acceptable heat alarms or heat detector mounting locations for smooth ceilings and sidewalls.

29.8.4.4 In rooms with open joists or beams, all ceiling-mounted detectors or alarms shall be located on the bottom of such joists or beams.

29.8.4.5* Detectors or alarms installed on an open-joisted ceiling shall have their smooth ceiling spacing reduced where this spacing is measured at right angles to solid joists; in the case of heat detectors or heat alarms, this spacing shall not exceed one-half of the listed spacing.

A.29.8.4.5 Refer to Figure A.29.8.4.5, where the distance between heat alarms or heat detectors should be further reduced.

For instance, with open wood joists, heat travels freely down the joist channels so that the maximum distance between the heat alarm or heat detectors [(50 ft) 15.2 m] can be used. However, heat has trouble spreading across the joists, so the distance in this direction should be one-half the distance allowed between detectors, as shown in Figure A.29.8.4.5, and the distance to the wall is reduced to 12.5 ft (3.8 m). Since one-half of 50 ft (15.2 m) is 25 ft (7.6 m), the distance between heat alarms or detectors across open wood joists should not exceed 25 ft (7.6 m), as shown in Figure A.29.8.4.5, and the distance to the wall is reduced [one-half

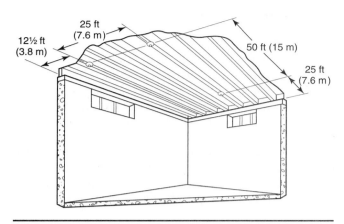

FIGURE A.29.8.4.5 *Open Joists, Attics, and Extra-High Ceilings are Some of the Areas that Require Special Knowledge for Installation.*

of 25 ft (7.6 m)] to 12.5 ft (3.8 m). Paragraph 29.8.4.4 requires that a heat alarm or heat detectors be mounted on the bottom of the joists and not up in joist channels.

Walls, partitions, doorways, ceiling beams, and open joists interrupt the normal flow of heat, thus creating new areas to be protected.

In addition to the special requirements for heat detectors installed on ceilings with exposed joists, reduced spacing also might be required due to other structural characteristics of the protected area, possible drafts, or other conditions that could affect heat alarm or detector operation.

29.8.5 Wiring and Equipment. The installation of wiring and equipment shall be in accordance with the requirements of *NFPA 70, National Electrical Code*, Article 760.

The installation of all fire alarm system wiring should take into account the fire alarm system manufacturer's published installation instructions and the limitations of the applicable product listings or approvals.

29.9 Optional Functions

The following optional functions of fire-warning equipment shall be permitted:

(1) Notification of the fire department, either directly or through an alarm-monitoring service

(2) Monitoring of other safety systems, such as fire sprinklers for alarm or proper operating conditions

Connection of an automatic sprinkler system waterflow alarm–initiating device to the dwelling fire alarm system should be approved by the authority having jurisdiction. Where used, such a connection must use fire alarm equipment that has been specifically listed for this purpose. A listed fire alarm control unit or combination burglar/fire alarm control unit already serving the residence could be used to accept a connection from the waterflow alarm–initiating device. Additionally, a waterflow alarm–initiating device could be connected to a separate fire alarm system control unit to sound separate notification appliances throughout the dwelling unit. Although this function is included in Section 29.9 as an optional function, it still must comply with the requirements of Chapter 29 as part of the fire alarm system.

(3) Notification of occupants or others of potentially dangerous conditions, such as the presence of fuel gases or toxic gases such as carbon monoxide

Carbon monoxide (CO) warning systems are covered by NFPA 720, *Standard for the Installation of Carbon Monoxide (CO) Detection and Warning Equipment.* NFPA 720 has recently undergone a major revision and includes several significant changes with regard to household applications. It includes requirements for the location and quantity of CO alarms and the means of interconnection with fire-warning equipment.

Previous editions of NFPA 720 required signals from CO detectors to be either a supervisory signal or other non–fire alarm signal. The 2009 edition of NFPA 720 makes it clear that CO alarm signals must be treated as unique "carbon monoxide alarm signals," not as supervisory signals. It is important that alarm signals be identified properly so that appropriate action is taken in a timely manner. CO alarm signals must never be connected to produce a fire alarm signal.

(4) Notification of occupants or others of the activation of intrusion (burglar alarm) sensors

Burglar alarm systems should be installed in accordance with NFPA 731, *Standard for the Installation of Electronic Premises Security Systems.* See 29.7.6.2, 29.7.6.6, and the associated commentary for more information on signal priorities.

(5) Any other function, safety related or not, that could share components or wiring

---

29.10 Maintenance and Tests

Fire-warning equipment shall be maintained and tested in accordance with the manufacturer's published instructions and per the requirements of Chapter 14.

As of the 2002 Code, the testing and maintenance requirements for single- and multiple-station smoke and heat alarms and household fire alarm systems are located in the inspection, testing, and maintenance chapter, currently Chapter 14. Table 14.4.2.2, Test Methods, and Table 14.4.5, Testing Frequencies, as well as 14.4.5.3 and 14.4.6 through 14.4.9, have been specifically modified to address this equipment. Note that Chapter 14 requires all fire alarm equipment to be tested to the manufacturer's published instructions to verify correct operation.

In accordance with Table 14.4.2.2, item 14(g)(4), and Table 14.4.5, item 15(j), single- and multiple-station smoke alarms in one- and two-family dwellings must be functionally tested at least monthly and in accordance with the manufacturer's published instructions. While many manufacturers require monthly functional testing, some manufacturers require weekly testing, which would then be the required frequency.

In accordance with Table 14.4.2.2, item 14(g)(1), and Table 14.4.5, items 15(h), 15(i), and 15(j), single- and multiple-station smoke alarms and system smoke detectors in other than one- and two-family dwellings must be functionally tested at least annually to ensure smoke entry into the sensing chamber and an alarm response. Manufacturer's published instructions for smoke alarms may require more frequent functional testing using the means specified by the manufacturer. In addition to the required functional testing, smoke alarms and system smoke detectors in other than one- and two-family dwellings must also be tested for sensitivity per the requirements of Table 14.4.2.2, Table 14.4.5, and 14.4.5.3.

Subsection 14.4.7 requires that household fire alarm systems be tested at least annually by a qualified service technician in accordance with Table 14.4.2.2.

FAQ ▶
Does the 10-year replacement requirement apply to all smoke alarms?

In accordance with 14.4.8.1, smoke alarms in one- and two-family dwellings must be replaced when they fail to respond to operability tests or after 10 years from the date of manufacture. The 10-year replacement requirement does not apply to smoke alarms used in other occupancies, based on the assumption that all other periodic testing and maintenance requirements are met. In accordance with 14.4.8.2, combination smoke/carbon monoxide alarms must be replaced when the end-of-life signal activates or 10 years after the date of manufacture, whichever occurs first.

29.11 Markings and Instructions

29.11.1 Alarms. All alarms shall be plainly marked with the following information on the unit:

(1) Manufacturer's or listee's name, address, and model number
(2) A mark or certification that the unit has been approved or listed by a testing laboratory
(3) Electrical rating (where applicable)
(4) Manufacturer's published operating and maintenance instructions
(5) Test instructions
(6) Replacement and service instructions
(7) Identification of lights, switches, meters, and similar devices regarding their function, unless their function is obvious
(8) Distinction between alarm and trouble signals on units employing both
(9) The sensitivity setting for an alarm having a fixed setting (For an alarm that is intended to be adjusted in the field, the range of sensitivity shall be indicated. The marked sensitivity shall be indicated as a percent per foot obscuration level. The marking shall include a nominal value plus tolerance.)
(10) Reference to an installation diagram and system owner's manual
(11) Date of manufacture in the format YEAR (in four digits), MONTH (in letters), and DAY (in two digits) located on the outside of the alarm

Exception: Where space limitations prohibit inclusion of 29.11.1(4) and (6), it is not prohibited for this information to be in the installation instructions instead.

29.11.2 Fire Alarm Control Unit. All household fire-warning equipment or systems shall be plainly marked with the following information on the unit:

(1) Manufacturer's or listee's name, address, and model number
(2) A mark or certification that the unit has been approved or listed by a testing laboratory
(3) Electrical rating (where applicable)
(4) Identification of all user interface components and their functions (such as, but not limited to, lights, switches, and meters) located adjacent to the component
(5) Manufacturer's published operating and maintenance instructions
(6) Test instructions
(7) Replacement and service instructions
(8) Reference to an installation wiring diagram and homeowner's manual, if not attached to control unit, by drawing number and issue number and/or date

Exception: Where space limitations prohibit inclusion of 29.11.2(5) and (7), it is not prohibited for this information to be in the installation instructions instead.

REFERENCES CITED IN COMMENTARY

Ahrens, M., "U.S. Experience with Smoke Alarms and Other Fire Alarms," National Fire Protection Association, Quincy, MA, 2007.
ANSI S3.41, *American National Standard Audible Emergency Evacuation Signal,* 1990 (R2008), American National Standards Institute, Inc., New York, NY.
ANSI/UL 217, *Standard for Single and Multiple Station Smoke Alarms,* 2006, revised 2008, American National Standards Institute, Inc., New York, NY.

ANSI/UL 268, *Standard for Smoke Detectors for Fire Alarm Systems*, 2006 edition, American National Standards Institute, Inc., New York, NY.

ANSI/UL 2034, *Standard for Single and Multiple Station Carbon Monoxide Alarms*, 2008 edition, American National Standards Institute, Inc., New York, NY.

Ashley, E. M. and Du Bois, J., "Waking Effectiveness of Audible, Visual, and Vibratory Emergency Alarms Across All Hearing Levels," 9th Fire Suppression and Detection Research Application Symposium, Fire Protection Research Foundation, Orlando, FL, January 21–23, 2004.

Bruck, D., "Non-Awakening in Children in Response to a Smoke Detector Alarm," *Fire Safety Journal*, 32, 1999, pp. 369–376.

Bruck, D., "The Who, What, Where and Why of Waking to Fire Alarms: A Review," *Fire Safety Journal*, 36, 2001, pp. 623–639.

Bruck, D., "Sleep and Fire: Who Is at Risk and Can the Risk Be Reduced?" *Fire Safety Science — Proceedings of the Eighth International Symposium*, D. T. Gottuk and B. Y. Lattimer, eds., International Association for Fire Safety Science, Worcester, MA, September 18–23, 2005, pp. 37–51.

Bruck, D., and Bliss, R. A., "Sleeping Children and Smoke Alarms," *Proceedings of the Fourth Asia-Oceania Symposium on Fire Science and Technology,* T. Yamada, ed., co-organized by Asia-Oceania Association for Fire Science and Technology (AOAFST) and Japan Association for Fire Science and Engineering (JAFSE), May 24–26, 2000, pp. 603–611.

Bruck, D. and Thomas, I., "Towards a Better Smoke Alarm Signal — An Evidence Based Approach," *Fire Safety Science — Proceedings of the Ninth International Symposium*, International Association of Fire Safety Science, 2008.

Duncan, C., "The Effectiveness of the Domestic Smoke Alarm Signal," Fire Engineering Research Report 99/5, University of Canterbury, Christchurch, New Zealand, March 1999.

Lee, A., "The Audibility of Smoke Alarms in Residential Homes," CPSC-ES-0503, U.S. Consumer Product Safety Commission, Washington, DC, 2005. Available online at http://www.cpsc.gov/library/foia/foia05/os/audibility.pdf.

NFPA 70®, National Electrical Code®, 2008 edition, National Fire Protection Association, Quincy, MA.

NFPA *101®, Life Safety Code®*, 2009 edition, National Fire Protection Association, Quincy, MA.

NFPA 720, *Standard for the Installation of Carbon Monoxide (CO) Detection and Warning Equipment*, 2009 edition, National Fire Protection Association, Quincy, MA.

NFPA 731, *Standard for the Installation of Electronic Premises Security Systems*, 2008 edition, National Fire Protection Association, Quincy, MA.

Thomas, I. and Bruck, D,, "Strobe Lights, Pillow Shakers and Bed Shakers as Smoke Alarm Signals," *Fire Safety Science — Proceedings of the Ninth International Symposium*, International Association of Fire Safety Science, 2008.

Explanatory Material

Annex A is not a part of the requirements of this NFPA document but is included for informational purposes only. This annex contains explanatory material, numbered to correspond with the applicable text paragraphs.

The material contained in Annex A of *NFPA 72*® is included within the text of this handbook and, therefore, is not repeated here.

Engineering Guide for Automatic Fire Detector Spacing

ANNEX B

This annex is not a part of the requirements of this NFPA document but is included for informational purposes only.

Users of Annex B should refer back to the text of NFPA 72 to familiarize themselves with the limitations of the design methods summarized herein.

Section B.2, and particularly B.2.2 and B.2.3, are largely based on the work of Custer and Meacham as found in "Performance-Based Fire Safety Engineering: An Introduction of Basic Concepts" (Meacham and Custer 1995) and Introduction to Performance-Based Fire Safety (Custer and Meacham 1997). [25]

The National Fire Protection Association and the Technical Committee on Initiating Devices for Fire Alarm Systems gratefully acknowledge the technical contributions of the Society of Fire Protection Engineers, Richard Custer, and Brian Meacham to performance-based design and this annex.

B.1 Introduction

B.1.1 Scope. Annex B provides information intended to supplement Chapter 17. It includes a procedure for determining detector spacing based on the objectives set for the system, size, and rate of growth of fire to be detected, various ceiling heights, ambient temperatures, and response characteristics of the detectors. In addition to providing an engineering method for the design of detection systems using plume-dependent detectors, heat detectors, and smoke detectors, this annex also provides guidance on the use of radiant energy–sensing detectors.

Most jurisdictions deem the design of fire alarm systems to be "engineering work" and require licensed engineers to perform such work. Some jurisdictions, however, permit technologists to lay out fire alarm systems as long as they follow the prescriptive requirements found in the Code. Designers using a performance-based approach must review the relevant engineering licensure laws in the jurisdictions in which they practice. Performance-based designs of fire alarm systems very likely will be deemed engineering of the type that requires licensure as a professional engineer. The designer should also be knowledgeable in the principles of fire protection engineering and apply those principles judiciously.

B.1.2 General.

B.1.2.1 In the 1999 edition Annex B was revised in its entirety from previous editions. The correlations originally used to develop the tables and graphs for heat and smoke detector spacings in the earlier editions have been updated to be consistent with current research. These revisions correct the errors in the original correlations. In earlier editions, the tables and graphs were based on an assumed heat of combustion of 20,900 kJ/kg (8986 Btu/lb). The effective heat of combustion for common cellulosic materials is usually taken to be approximately 12,500 kJ/kg (5374 Btu/lb). The equations in this annex were produced using test data and data correlations for cellulosic (wood) fuels that have a total heat of combustion of about 12,500 kJ/kg (5374 Btu/lb).

For the technical basis for the changes described in B.1.2.1, see Reference 11 in B.6.5.

B.1.2.2 In addition to the revisions undertaken in 1999, the concept of performance-based design was further expanded on. This included, to a large extent, additional material taken from the work of Custer and Meacham. Since this time, the industry continues to develop additional codes, standards, and guides to further assist in undertaking a performance-based assessment. This includes the work of SFPE [40, 49], NFPA [50, 51, 52], and ICC [53].

New B.1.2.2 provides additional information and a broader background on performance-based approaches and references documents that have been produced in the past few years to assist the designer in undertaking a performance-based assessment.

B.1.2.3 For the purposes of this annex, the heat produced by a fire is manifested either as convective heat or radiant heat. It is assumed that conductive heat transfer is of little consequence during the early stages of the development of a fire, where this annex is relevant. A convective heat release rate fraction equal to 75 percent of the total heat release rate has been used in this annex. Users should refer to references 12 and 13 in H.1.2.15 for fuels or burning conditions that are substantially different from these conditions.

B.1.2.4 The design methods for plume-dependent fire detectors provided in this annex are based on full-scale fire tests funded by the Fire Detection Institute in which all fires were geometrically growing flaming fires. *(See Environments of Fire Detectors — Phase 1: Effect of Fire Size, Ceiling Height and Material; Measurements Vol. I and Analysis Vol. II [10].)*

B.1.2.5 The guidance applicable to smoke detectors is limited to a theoretical analysis based on the flaming fire test data and is not intended to address the detection of smoldering fires.

The design methods in Annex B rely on the presence of a buoyant plume. The relatively large heat release rate from a flaming fire produces the plume. A smoldering fire essentially has no buoyant plume. The pre-existing ambient air currents provide the dominant smoke transport mechanism. Unfortunately, a designer cannot use the design methods in Annex B to analyze the ambient air currents. Consequently, the designer can use the design methods outlined in Annex B only for cases in which a flaming fire produces a buoyant plume.

B.1.2.6 The design methods for plume-dependent fire detectors do not address the detection of steady-state fires.

B.1.2.7 The design methods for plume-dependent fire detectors used in this annex are only applicable when employed in the context of applications where the ceiling is smooth and level. They cannot be used for ceilings where there are beams, joists, or bays formed by beams and purlins. The research upon which the following methods have been based did not consider the effect of beams, joists, and bays in sufficient detail to justify the use of this annex to those applications.

B.1.3 Purpose.

B.1.3.1 The purpose of Annex B is to provide a performance basis for the location and spacing of fire detection–initiating devices. The sections for heat and smoke detectors provide an alternative design method to the prescriptive approach presented in Chapter 17 (i.e., based on their listed spacings). The section on radiant energy–sensing detectors elaborates on the performance-based criteria already existing in Chapter 17. A performance-based approach allows one to consider potential fire growth rates and fire signatures, the individual compartment characteristics, and damageability characteristics of the targets (e.g., occupants, equipment, contents, structures, and so on) in order to determine the location of a specific type of detector to meet the objectives established for the system.

B.1.3.2 Under the prescriptive approach, heat detectors are installed according to their listed spacing. The listed spacing is determined in a full-scale fire test room. The fire test room used for the determination of listed spacing for heat detectors has a ceiling height of 4.8 m

(15 ft 9 in.). A steady-state, flammable liquid fire with a heat release rate of approximately 1137 kW (1200 Btu/sec), located 0.9 m (3 ft) above the floor, is used as the test fire. Special 71°C (160°F) test sprinklers are installed on a 3 m × 3 m (10 ft × 10 ft) spacing array such that the fire is in the center of the sprinkler array. The heat detectors being tested are installed in a square array with increasing spacing centered about the fire location. The elevation of the test fire is adjusted during the test to produce the temperature versus time curve at the test sprinkler heads to yield actuation of the heads in 2.0 minutes ±10 seconds. The largest heat detector spacing that achieves alarm before the actuation of the sprinkler heads in the test becomes the listed spacing for the heat detector. See Figure A.17.6.3.1.1(c). If the room dimensions, ambient conditions, and fire and response characteristics of the detector are different from above, the response of the heat detector must be expected to be different as well. Therefore, the use of an installed detector spacing that is different from the listed spacing might be warranted through the use of a performance-based approach if the conditions are as follows:

(1) The design objectives are different from designing a system that operates at the same time as a sprinkler in the approval test.
(2) Faster response of the device is desired.
(3) A response of the device to a smaller fire than used in the approved test is required.
(4) Accommodation to room geometry that is different from that used in the listing process.
(5) Other special considerations, such as ambient temperature, air movement, ceiling height, or other obstruction, are different from or are not considered in the approval tests.
(6) A fire other than a steady state 1137 kW (1200 Btu/sec) fire is contemplated.

B.1.3.3 The designer of fire alarm systems needs to be knowledgeable in the applicable areas associated with undertaking a performance-based design, including fire dynamics, performance-based design, detector response, and so forth, and apply these principles judiciously. In addition, the majority of jurisdictions consider the design of fire alarm systems as "engineering work." They therefore require licensed engineers to perform such work. Other jurisdictions allow technologists to lay out fire alarm systems as long as they follow the appropriate prescriptive requirements. Designers who are using a performance-based design approach need to review the relevant engineering licensure laws in the jurisdictions in which they are practicing, as performance-based designs might very likely be deemed engineering and of the type that requires licensure of a professional engineer.

B.2 Performance-Based Approach to Designing and Analyzing Fire Detection Systems

Section B.2, particularly B.2.2 and B.2.3, are largely based on the work of Richard Custer and Brian Meacham as found in "Performance-Based Fire Safety Engineering: An Introduction of Basic Concepts" [Meacham and Custer, 1995] and *Introduction to Performance-Based Fire Safety* [Custer and Meacham, 1997]. The National Fire Protection Association and the Technical Committee on Initiating Devices for Fire Alarm Systems gratefully acknowledge the technical contributions of the Society of Fire Protection Engineers, Richard Custer, and Brian Meacham to performance-based design and to this annex.

This annex is intended to be used in the context of the performance-based design process. The process provides an environment in which the designer can develop solutions that differ from the prescriptive approaches in the body of the Code. The process provides checks and balances and a document trail so the genesis of any given decision can be traced back to its source. If the computational methods outlined in this annex are used outside the environment of the performance-based design process, the designer loses those checks, balances, and decision trails and can go astray. Designers should carefully review the references before undertaking a design project using this annex.

B.2.1 Overview. Subsection B.2.1 provides an overview of a systematic approach to conducting a performance-based design or analysis of a fire detection system. The approach has been outlined by Custer and Meacham and the SFPE *Engineering Guide to Performance Based Fire Protection Analysis and Design* [40] and is summarized below in the context of design and analysis of fire detection systems. *(Refer to Figure B.2.1.)* This approach has been divided into two phases: defining goals and objectives and system design and evaluation.

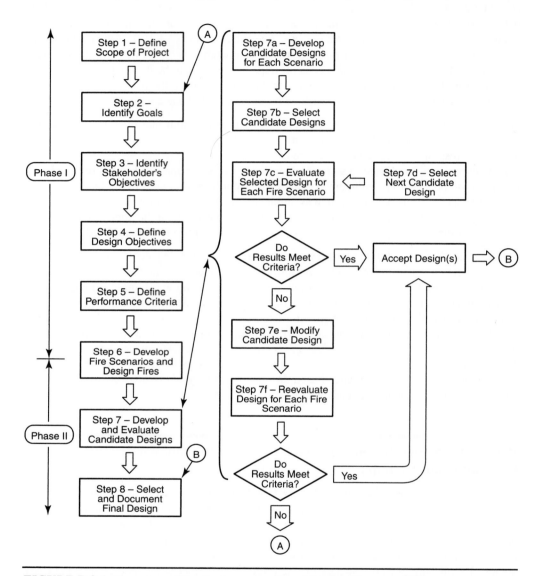

FIGURE B.2.1 *Overview of the Performance-Based Design Process. [25]*

B.2.2 Phase 1 — Defining Goals and Objectives.

B.2.2.1 Define Scope of Project.

B.2.2.1.1 The initial step of this approach is to identify information relative to the overall scope of work on the project, including characteristics of the building, design intent, design and construction team organization, constraints on design and project schedule, proposed building construction and features, relevant hazards, how the building functions, occupant characteristics, and so forth. Additional information that one might want to consider could also include characteristics of the fire departments, historic preservation, building management, and applicable regulations.

At this point in the design process, the designer should also consider the following factors:

1. Design limitations
2. Fire service capabilities
3. Historical preservation
4. Building management
5. Applicable regulations

B.2.2.1.2 While defining the project's scope, the designer will identify which of the three situations in Table B.2.2.1.2 best describes the project at hand (i.e., a performance-based analysis of an existing detection system in an existing building).

TABLE B.2.2.1.2 *Design/Analysis Situation*

Building Type	System Type	Design/Analysis
New	New	Design
Existing	New	Design
Existing	Existing	Analysis

B.2.2.2 Identify Goals.

B.2.2.2.1 Fire protection assets are acquired in order to attain one or more of the following four goals:

(1) To provide life safety (occupants, employees, fire fighters, and so forth)
(2) To protect property and heritage (structure, contents, and so forth)
(3) To provide for continuity of operations (protect stakeholder's mission, operating capability, and so forth)
(4) To limit the environmental impact of fire (toxic products, fire-fighting water run-off, and so forth)

B.2.2.2.2 Fire protection goals are like other goals in that they are generally easy to agree on, are qualitative, and are noncontroversial in nature. They express the desired overall outcome to be achieved, that is, to provide life safety to the building occupants.

The design team might also identify other goals that do not relate directly to fire safety. Often design goals reflect the use of the space and are characterized as mission continuity, property protection, environmental protection, and so on. These goals might include specific design objectives such as having a large open space that has no compartmentation, minimizing damage to the building's historic fabric, and reducing costs. The design team must consider those design parameters at the start of a project. See also Custer and Meacham [1997].

B.2.2.2.3 When starting the performance-based process, the various parties — including the stakeholders (i.e., the architect, building owner, insurance carrier, building or fire officials, and so forth), the authority having jurisdiction, and the design engineer — work together to prioritize the basic fire protection goals. Prioritizing is based on the stakeholder's objective and the building and occupancy involved. For example, life safety is a high priority in a hospital or stadium, while property protection might have an equally high priority in a large warehouse or historic building.

The performance-based design process creates a design environment in which all parties that have an interest in the finished system have a say in the decision-making process. Such individuals or entities are called *stakeholders*. The list of stakeholders varies from project to project. Sometimes the stakeholders are few, and other times they are many. Potential stakeholders include the following:

1. Building managers
2. Design team members
3. Authorities having jurisdiction
4. Tenants
5. Neighbors
6. Accreditation agencies
7. Construction team members
8. Fire service

See also Meacham and Custer [1995].

B.2.2.3 Identify Stakeholder's Objectives.

B.2.2.3.1 Each stakeholder must explicitly state her or his objectives in terms of acceptable loss for the various goals previously stated.

B.2.2.3.2 Stakeholder objectives specify how much safety the stakeholder wants, needs, or can afford. "No loss of life within the room of origin" is a sample stakeholder objective or statement of the stakeholder's maximum acceptable loss.

Designers should note that most buildings contain ignition sources and some type of fuel. The chance that a fire could occur always exists. Similarly, some probability always exists that a fire in an occupied building may result in injury or death, some degree of property damage, or interruption to business (or all three). Therefore, the designer should ensure that the stakeholders understand that creating an entirely hazard-free or risk-free environment is impossible [Custer and Meacham, 1997]. Prescriptive building codes and construction standards do *not* produce a risk-free built environment. Usually, the performance-based design process is used to achieve a level of fire safety equivalent to that achieved by the prescriptive codes or to achieve some elected design objective such as those derived from mission continuity, property protection, and so forth.

B.2.2.3.3 The stakeholder's objectives are generally not stated in fire protection engineering terms.

See Table B.2.2.4.1(a) through Table B.2.2.4.1(c) for additional examples of stakeholders' objectives.

B.2.2.3.4 Note that in a performance-based code environment, the Code will most likely define a performance objective or stakeholder objective.

Stakeholders should define their objectives as clearly as possible. The objectives derived from the prescriptive criteria in a building code are generally considered to be the objectives of the populace — the code writers are acting as fiduciaries for the public. At the beginning of the design process, the designer must orchestrate a meeting of the stakeholders to develop a consensus on the objectives for the system. Some stakeholders will have more stringent, difficult-to-achieve objectives. As consensus is developed, each party or stakeholder must agree to the consensus objectives for the system. The sooner consensus is attained, the better. Without the stakeholders reaching early consensus on the objectives, the designer will have a far more difficult task developing quantitative engineering criteria with which to evaluate trial designs.

Furthermore, cost is always a factor. Some objectives are laudable but prohibitively expensive. Stakeholders must recognize that the owner has an alternative: to locate the building in another jurisdiction where the environment is more conducive. The stakeholders must be willing to address the cost issue as they are developing objectives. The design professional becomes a mediator and discussion facilitator in the performance-based design environment. Ideally, the process is one of give and take among the stakeholders as they reach consensus.

B.2.2.4 Define Design Objectives.

B.2.2.4.1 The stakeholder's objective must then be explicitly stated and quantified in fire protection engineering terms that describe how the objective will be achieved. This demands that the design objectives be expressed quantitatively. See Table B.2.2.4.1(a) through Table B.2.2.4.1(c).

TABLE B.2.2.4.1(a) *Defining Goals and Objectives — Life Safety*

Fire protection goal	Provide life safety
Stakeholder's objective	No loss of life within compartment of origin
Design objective	Maintain tenable conditions within the compartment of origin
Performance criteria	Maintain:
	Temperatures below xx°C (°F)
	Visibility above yy m (ft)
	CO concentration below zz ppm for tt minutes

TABLE B.2.2.4.1(b) *Defining Goals and Objectives — Property Protection*

Fire protection goal	Provide protection of property
Stakeholder's objective	No fire damage outside compartment of origin
Design objective	Limit the spread of flame to the compartment of origin
Performance criteria	Maintain upper layer temperature below xx°C (°F) and radiation level to the floor below yy kW/m^2 (Btu/sec·ft^2) to prevent flashover

TABLE B.2.2.4.1(c) *Defining Goals and Objectives — Continuity of Operations*

Fire protection goal	Provide continuity of operations
Stakeholder's objective	Prevent any interruption to business operations in excess of 2 hours
Design objective	Limit the temperature and the concentration of HCl to within acceptable levels for continued operation of the equipment
Performance criteria	Provide detection such that operation of a gaseous suppression system will maintain temperatures below xx°C (°F) and HCl levels below yy ppm

The designer uses the design objectives as a benchmark against which the predicted performance of a trial design is measured. The designer will use performance criteria expressed in engineering terms. See also Custer and Meacham [1997].

B.2.2.4.2 The design objective provides a description of how the stakeholder's objective will be achieved in general fire protection engineering terms prior to this description being quantified. The general objective is then reduced to explicit and quantitative fire protection engineering terms. The explicit fire protection engineering objectives provide a performance benchmark against which the predicted performance of a candidate design is evaluated.

The designer quantifies the design objectives in either deterministic or probabilistic terms. Deterministic methods consider any and all possible incident scenarios equally, regardless of how likely or unlikely a scenario might be. For example, the designer can translate the stakeholder objective of "no fire damage outside the compartment of origin" to "limiting the spread of flame to the compartment of origin." This translation of the stakeholder objective is a deterministic statement of the design objective. Probabilistic methods assign probabilities to incident scenarios, weighing the more likely ones higher than the less likely ones. The designer restates the stakeholder objective of "no fire damage outside the compartment of origin" as "limiting the probability of flame spreading to an adjacent compartment to a value that does not exceed a threshold value" [Custer and Meacham, 1997].

B.2.2.5 Define Performance Criteria.

A performance criterion is a measurement that will be used as a go/no-go decision value. For example, if the objective is to achieve occupant evacuation before the loss of tenability, the designer must come up with a quantitative measure of what constitutes *tenability*. Some practitioners have used the elevation of the upper smoke layer as a determinant of tenability and deemed a space untenable when the smoke layer descends to a level equal to or less than 1.5 m (5 ft). That measurement can be used to assess performance. A fire model can be developed for the space and the time at which the upper layer reaches a 1.5 m (5 ft) elevation. An egress model can be used to determine how long it takes to evacuate all the occupants. The evacuation time is then compared to the smoke layer descent time to determine if all the occupants have been able to leave before the smoke layer produced the *untenable* condition. The identification and selection of performance criteria are, therefore, a critical part of the design process.

B.2.2.5.1 Once the design objective has been established, specific, quantitatively expressed criteria that indicate attainment of the performance objective are developed.

B.2.2.5.2 Performance criteria provide a yardstick or threshold values that can measure a potential design's success in meeting stakeholder objectives and their associated design objectives. [25]

When defining performance criteria, a designer cannot achieve an environment totally free of risk or hazard. Also, the cost associated with an incremental reduction in risk typically increases as the intended risk or hazard level decreases.

B.2.2.5.3 Quantification of the design objectives into performance criteria involves determination of the various fire-induced stresses that are a reflection of the stated loss objectives. Performance criteria can be expressed in various terms, including temperature, radiant flux, a rate of heat release, or concentration of a toxic or corrosive species that must not be exceeded.

Other performance criteria relating to occupants include visibility, clear layer height, smoke concentration, ignition levels of adjacent fuel packages, and smoke product and toxic product damage. However, there are often objectives that are derived from mission continuity, property preservation, cultural preservation, or environmental protection that will yield different performance criteria. For example, a hotel might have a maximum area contaminated with smoke as a mission continuity performance criterion. Rooms cannot be rented if they smell of smoke. The performance criterion would then relate to the number of rooms that cannot be rented because of smoke contamination. See also Meacham and Custer [1995].

B.2.2.5.4 Once the design performance criteria are established, appropriate safety factors are applied to obtain the working design criteria. The working design criteria reflect the performance that must be achieved by the detection system. This performance level must allow appropriate actions to be undertaken (e.g., activate suppression systems, occupants' egress, notify fire department, and so forth) to meet the objectives. An acceptable fire detection system design provides the detection of the fire sufficiently early in its development to permit the other fire protection systems to meet or exceed the relevant performance criteria established for those systems.

B.2.2.5.5 Throughout the process identified as Phase I and II, communication should be maintained with the authorities having jurisdiction (AHJs) to review and develop consensus on the approach being taken. It is recommended that this communication commence as early in the design process as possible. The AHJ should also be involved in the development of performance criteria. Often the acceptance of a performance-based design in lieu of a design based on a prescriptive approach relies on demonstrating equivalence. This is called the comparative method, where the designer demonstrates that the performance-based design responds at least as well as, if not better than, a system designed using a prescriptive approach.

Table B.2.2.4.1(a) through Table B.2.2.4.1(c) present sample goals, objectives, and performance criteria. See also Custer and Meacham [1997].

B.2.3 Phase II — System Design and Evaluation.

B.2.3.1 Develop Fire Scenarios.

B.2.3.1.1 General.

B.2.3.1.1.1 A fire scenario defines the development of a fire and the spread of combustion products throughout a compartment or building. A fire scenario represents a set of fire conditions that are deemed a threat to a building and its occupants and/or contents, and, therefore, should be addressed in the design of the fire protection features of the structure. [25]

Fire scenarios are used to evaluate the performance of proposed designs. Consequently, it is critical that all the stakeholders agree, up front, on how a proposed design will be evaluated. This decision prevents the performance evaluation from changing as the design process moves forward. The fire scenario will be used to produce a model of the effects of fire in the building or compartment to be protected. The time at which the fire alarm system is predicted to respond to those fire effects is compared to the time needed to execute the planned response. Thus the performance of the fire alarm system is evaluated in the context of a set of scenarios, which should be chosen and agreed upon by the stakeholders as representing reasonable worst-case situations.

B.2.3.1.1.2 The process of developing a fire scenario is a combination of hazard analysis and risk analysis. The hazard analysis identifies potential ignition sources, fuels, and fire development. Risk is the probability of occurrence multiplied by the consequences of that occurrence. The risk analysis looks at the impact of the fire to the surroundings or target items.

B.2.3.1.1.3 The fire scenario should include a description of various conditions, including building characteristics, occupant characteristics, and fire characteristics. [25, 40]

B.2.3.1.2 Building Characteristics. Building characteristics include the following:

(1) Configuration (area; ceiling height; ceiling configuration, such as flat, sloped beams; windows and doors, and thermodynamic properties)
(2) Environment (ambient temperature, humidity, background noise, and so forth)
(3) Equipment (heat-producing equipment, HVAC, manufacturing equipment, and so forth)
(4) Functioning characteristics (occupied, during times, days, and so forth)
(5) Target locations
(6) Potential ignition sources
(7) Aesthetic or historic preservation considerations

(Note target items — that is, areas associated with stakeholder objectives — along the expected route of spread for flame, heat, or other combustion products.)

Annex B uses the term *building characteristics*, in B.2.3.1.2, to encompass the physical layout, ambient environment, structural features, fire hazards, and target locations within a compartment. Each of these characteristics affects fire initiation and growth, the spread of the products of combustion, and occupant evacuation. The designer must address these building characteristics when developing a design fire scenario.

The designer should also consider additional building characteristics:

1. Potential ignition sources
2. Architectural details to be designed around (i.e., ornate ceilings)
3. Concealed, enclosed spaces or voids

B.2.3.1.3 Occupant Characteristics. Occupant characteristics include the following:

(1) Alertness (sleeping, awake, and so forth)
(2) Age
(3) Mobility
(4) Quantity and location within the building
(5) Sex
(6) Responsiveness
(7) Familiarity with the building
(8) Mental challenges

Human behavior plays a key role in life safety, as well as with the other fire safety goals. *(See SFPE Engineering Guide to Human Behavior in Fire.)* The possible actions that could be taken upon detecting a fire as well as how one reacts once they hear an alarm need to be considered. These actions can include alerting and rescuing other family members, gathering belongings, interpreting or verifying the message, shutting down processes. They should also include a look at how individuals respond on their own as well as in group situations.

Once these occupant characteristics and their behavior have been analyzed, one might also want to determine evacuation times. Numerous factors again need to be considered, including number of occupants, distribution throughout the building, pre-movement times, motivation, state of wakefulness, familiarity, capacity, and layout of the means of egress.

Due to the nature of human behavior, it is difficult to accurately quantify the movements and evacuation times of occupants from a building. Thus, particular attention should be given to assumptions and uncertainties assigned to these occupant characteristics.

B.2.3.1.4 Fire Characteristics.

B.2.3.1.4.1 Fire characteristics include the following:

(1) Ignition sources — temperature, energy, time, and area of contact with potential fuels
(2) Initial fuels

    (a) *State.* Fuels can come in various states (i.e., solid, liquid, or gas). Each state can have very different combustion characteristics (i.e., a solid block of wood versus wood shavings versus wood dust)

    (b) *Type and quantity of fuel.* A fire's development and duration depends also on what is burning. Cellulosic-based materials burn quite differently compared to plastics, or flammable liquids, in terms of producing different fire growth rates, heat release rates, and products of combustion.

    (c) *Fuel configuration.* The geometrical arrangement of the fuel can also influence the fire growth rate and heat release rate. A wood block will burn very differently from a wood crib, as there is more surface area and ventilation, and radiation feedback between the combustible materials is increased.

    (d) *Fuel location.* The location of the fuel (i.e., against wall, in corner, in open, against the ceiling) will influence the development of the fire. Fires in the corner of a room or against a wall will typically grow faster than a fire located in the center of a room.

    (e) *Heat release rate.* The rate at which heat is released depends on the fuel's heat of combustion, the mass loss rate, the combustion efficiency, and the amount of incident heat flux. The mass loss rate also directly relates to the production rate of smoke, toxic gases, and other products of combustion.

(f) *Fire growth rate.* Fires grow at various rates that are dependent on type of fuel, configuration, and amount of ventilation. Some fires such as confined flammable liquid fires might not be growing fires as their burning area is fixed. These are referred to as steady state fires. The faster a fire develops, the faster the temperature rises, and the faster the products of combustion are produced.

(g) *Production rate of combustion products (smoke, CO, CO$_2$, etc.).* As the characteristics of various fuels vary, so will the type of quantity of materials generated during combustion. Species production rates can be estimated with species yields, which are representative of the mass of species produced per mass of fuel loss.

(3) Secondary fuels — proximity to initial fuels; amount; distribution, ease of ignitibility *(see initial fuels)*; and extension potential (beyond compartment, structure, area, if outside)

Conduction, convection, radiation, or a combination of these can ignite secondary fuels. The designer must consider the issues itemized in B.2.3.1.4.1(2) when considering the participation of secondary fuels in a fire scenario. See also Custer and Meacham [1997].

B.2.3.1.4.2 An example of a fire scenario in a computer room might be as follows.

The computer room is 9.1 m × 6 m (30 ft × 20 ft) and 2.8 m (8 ft) high. It is occupied 12 hours a day, 5 days a week. The occupants are mobile and familiar with the building. There are no fixed fire suppression systems protecting this location. The fire department is capable of responding to the scene in 6 minutes, and an additional 15 minutes for fire ground evolution is needed.

Overheating of a resistor leads to the ignition of a printed circuit board and interconnecting cabling. This leads to a fire that quickly extends up into the above ceiling space containing power and communications cabling. The burning of this cabling produces large quantities of dense, acrid smoke and corrosive products of combustion that spread throughout the computer suite. This causes the loss of essential computer and telecommunications services for 2 months.

B.2.3.2 Develop Design Fires.

B.2.3.2.1 General.

B.2.3.2.1.1 The design fire is the fire the system is intended to detect. When specifying a design fire, the specifics regarding the ignition, growth, steady-state output (if appropriate), and decay of the fire are expressed quantitatively.

There are numerous analysis techniques available to identify fire scenarios. These can typically fall into one of two categories: probabilistic or deterministic.

Probabilistic approaches typically relate to the statistical likelihood that ignition will occur, and the resultant outcome if a fire does occur. Probabilistic approaches could use the following as sources of data:

(1) Fire statistics (ignition, first items ignited, and so on)
(2) Past history
(3) Hazard/failure analysis
(4) Failure modes and effects analysis (FMEA)
(5) Event trees
(6) Fault trees
(7) HAZOP studies
(8) Cause-consequence analysis

Deterministic approaches use analysis or engineering judgment that is based on chemistry, physics, or correlations based on experimental data.

The selection of the design fire scenario and the supporting analysis techniques should be appropriate to the premise or processes. Inappropriate scenario selection or analysis can result in conservative designs that are not economical or designs with unacceptably high risks.

B.2.3.2.1.2 Fire development varies depending on the combustion characteristics of the fuel or fuels involved, the physical configuration of the fuels, the availability of combustion air, and the influences due to the compartment. Once a stable flame is attained, most fires grow in an accelerating pattern *(see Figure B.2.3.2.3.5)*, reach a steady state characterized by a maximum heat release rate, and then enter into a decay period as the availability of either fuel or combustion air becomes limited. Fire growth and development are limited by factors such as quantity of fuel, arrangement of fuel, quantity of oxygen, and the effect of manual and automatic suppression systems.

For design fires with a smoldering period, very little data are available. The design engineer should, therefore, be careful in specifying the duration of this period. The fire growth rate of flaming fires is determined by a variety of factors, including the following:

(1) Type of fuel and ease of ignition
(2) Fuel configuration and orientation
(3) Location of secondary fuel packages
(4) Proximity of fire to walls and corners
(5) Ceiling height
(6) Ventilation

It is important to note when using heat release data that the fuel burning as well as the compartment in which it is burning need to be considered together. A couch can produce sufficient heat to cause flashover in a small compartment, whereas this same couch placed in a large compartment with high ceilings can cause a limited fire and never reach flashover.

Several sources for developing design fires should be reviewed, including *SFPE Handbook of Fire Protection Engineering* [41]; NFPA *101, Life Safety Code*; *NFPA 5000, Building Construction and Safety Code*; and *SFPE Engineering Guide to Performance Based Fire Protection Analysis and Design of Buildings* [40].

The text in B.2.3.2.1.2 highlights the need to consider fires associated with extreme events.

B.2.3.2.1.3 Designers might also need to consider fires that might be related to extreme events. These can either be fires used to trigger extreme events, or post-extreme-event-induced fires. If these are deemed credible, then designers should take these into consideration as design fires and also with respect to the overall reliability, redundancy, and robustness of the detection system to function during these types of events. (54)

B.2.3.2.2 Heat Release Rates.

B.2.3.2.2.1 Fires can be characterized by their rate of heat release, measured in terms of the number of kW (Btu/sec) of heat liberated. Typical maximum heat release rates (Q_m) for a number of different fuels and fuel configurations are provided in Table B.2.3.2.6.2(a) and Table B.2.3.2.6.2(c). The heat release rate of a fire can be described as a product of a heat release density and fire area using the following equation:

$$Q_m = qA \qquad \text{(B.1)}$$

where:

Q_m = maximum or peak heat release rate [kW (Btu/sec)]

q = heat release rate density per unit floor area [kW/m^2 (Btu/sec·ft^2)]

A = floor area of the fuel [m^2 (ft^2)]

B.2.3.2.2.2 The following example is provided: A particular hazard analysis is to be based on a fire scenario involving a 3.05 m × 3.05 m (10 ft × 10 ft) stack of wood pallets stored 1.5 m (5 ft) high. Approximately what peak heat release rate can be expected?

From Table B.2.3.2.6.2(a), the heat release rate density (q) for 1.5 m (5 ft) high wood pallets is approximately 3745 kW/m^2 (330 Btu/sec·ft^2).

The area is 3.05 m $\times$ 3.05 m (10 ft $\times$ 10 ft), or 9.29 m^2 (100 ft^2). Using equation B.1 to determine the heat release rate yields the following:

$$3745 \times 9.29 = 34{,}791 \text{ kW } (330 \times 100 = 33{,}000 \text{ Btu/sec})$$

As indicated in the Table B.2.3.2.6.2(a), this fire generally produces a medium to fast fire growth rate, reaching 1055 kW (1000 Btu/sec) in approximately 90 to 190 seconds.

B.2.3.2.3 Fire Growth Rate.

B.2.3.2.3.1 Fires can also be defined by their growth rate or the time (t_g) it takes for the fire to reach a given heat release rate. Previous research [16] has shown that most fires grow exponentially and can be expressed by what is termed the "power law fire growth model":

$$Q \cong t^p \tag{B.2}$$

where:

Q = heat release rate (kW or Btu/sec)

t = time (seconds)

p = 2

This relation is known as the "t-square" fire. As the length of time that the fire burns doubles, the heat release rate quadruples.

Since Q is a heat release rate, it is by definition dH/dt. Thus, the relation can be written as

$$\frac{dH}{dt} = kt^2$$

where:

k = a constant

p = 2

This relation can be integrated from t_1 to t_2.

$$\int_{t_1}^{t_2} \frac{dH}{dt} = \left[\frac{1}{3} kt^3 \right]_{t_1}^{t_2}$$

This allows calculation of the total quantity of heat released and then, using the net heat of combustion, the total quantity of fuel consumed.

B.2.3.2.3.2 In fire protection, fuel packages are often described as having a growth time (t_g). This is the time necessary after the ignition with a stable flame for the fuel package to attain a heat release rate of 1055 kW (1000 Btu/sec). The following equations describe the growth of design fires:

$$Q = \frac{1055}{t_g^2} t^2 \text{ (for SI units)} \tag{B.3a}$$

or

$$Q = \frac{1000}{t_g^2} t^2 \text{ (for inch-pound units)} \tag{B.3b}$$

and thus

$$Q = \alpha t^2 \tag{B.4}$$

where:

Q = heat release rate [kW or (Btu/sec)]

α = fire growth rate [$1055/t_g^2$ (kW/sec^2) or $1000/t_g^2$ (Btu/sec^3)]

t_g = fire growth time to reach 1055 kW (1000 Btu/sec) after established burning

t = time after established burning occurs (seconds)

Here, the variable α has been substituted for the more general parameter k above.

B.2.3.2.3.3 Table B.2.3.2.6.2(a) and Table B.2.3.2.6.2(e) provide values for t_g, the time necessary to reach a heat release rate of 1055 kW (1000 Btu/sec), for a variety of materials in various configurations.

B.2.3.2.3.4 Test data from 40 furniture calorimeter tests, as indicated in Table B.2.3.2.6.2(e), have been used to independently verify the power law fire growth model, $Q = \alpha t^2$. [14] For reference, the table contains the test numbers used in the original NIST reports.

The virtual time of origin (t_v) is the time at which a stable flame had appeared and the fires began to obey the power law fire growth model. Prior to t_v, the fuels might have smoldered but did not burn vigorously with an open flame. The model curves are then predicted by the following equations:

$$Q = \alpha(t - t_v)^2 \tag{B.5}$$

and

$$Q = \left(\frac{1055}{t_g^2}\right)(t - t_v)^2 \text{ (for SI units)} \tag{B.6a}$$

or

$$Q = \left(\frac{1000}{t_g^2}\right)(t - t_v)^2 \text{ (for inch-pound units)} \tag{B.6b}$$

where:

Q = heat release rate [kW or (Btu/sec)]

α = fire growth rate [$1055/t_g^2$ (kW/sec^2) or $1000/t_g^2$ (Btu/sec^3)]

t_g = fire growth time to reach 1055 kW (1000 Btu/sec)

t = time after established burning occurs (seconds)

t_v = virtual time of origin (seconds)

B.2.3.2.3.5 Figure B.2.3.2.3.5 is an example of actual test data with a power law curve superimposed.

B.2.3.2.3.6 For purposes of this annex, fires are classified as being either slow-, medium-, or fast-developing from the time that established burning occurs until the fire reaches a heat release rate of 1055 kW (1000 Btu/sec). Table B.2.3.2.3.6 results from using the relationships discussed earlier. *[See also Table B.2.3.2.6.2(a).]*

B.2.3.2.4 Flame Height.

B.2.3.2.4.1 There are a number of flame height to heat release rate correlations available that can be used to determine an appropriate design fire. The differences in the various correlations arise from the different data sets and curve-fitting methods used by the researchers. One such correlation is shown in Figure B.2.3.2.4.1. It indicates that flame height and fire heat release rate are directly related. [2] The lines in Figure B.2.3.2.4.1 were derived from the following equation:

$$h_f = 0.182(kQ)^{2/5} \text{ (for SI units)} \tag{B.7a}$$

or

$$h_f = 0.584(kQ)^{2/5} \text{ (for inch-pound units)} \qquad\qquad \text{(B.7b)}$$

where:

h_f = flame height (m or ft)

k = wall effect factor

Q = heat release rate (kW or Btu/sec)

Where there are no nearby walls, use $k = 1$.
Where the fuel package is near a wall, use $k = 2$.
Where the fuel package is in a corner, use $k = 4$.

Other flame height correlations are published in the literature. Each correlation will give the user slightly different results. However, the calculated flame height is an average height for diffusion flames. Typically, diffusion flames exhibit a great deal of variability in flame height due to flow turbulence.

The flame height correlation in B.2.3.2.4.1 is used extensively later in this annex for the design of flame detection systems.

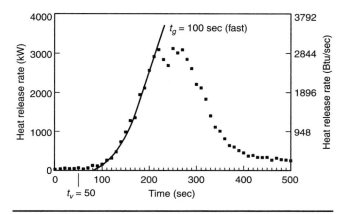

FIGURE B.2.3.2.3.5 *Test 38, Foam Sofa. (Courtesy of R. P. Schifiliti Associates, Inc.)*

TABLE B.2.3.2.3.6 *Power Law Heat Release Rates*

Fire Growth Rate	Growth Time (t_g)	α (kW/sec^2)	α (Btu/sec^3)
Slow	$t_g \geq 400$ sec	$\alpha \leq 0.0066$	$\alpha \leq 0.0063$
Medium	$150 \leq t_g < 400$ sec	$0.0066 < \alpha \leq 0.0469$	$0.0063 < \alpha \leq 0.0445$
Fast	$t_g < 150$ sec	$\alpha > 0.0469$	$\alpha > 0.0445$

B.2.3.2.4.2 The following example is provided: What is the average flame height of a fire with a heat release rate of 1055 kW (1000 Btu/sec) located in the middle of a compartment?

From Figure B.2.3.2.4.1, find the heat release rate on the abscissa and read estimated flame height from the ordinate, or use equation B.7a or B.7b:

$h_f = 0.182(kQ)^{2/5}$ (for SI units) or
$h_f = 0.584(kQ)^{2/5}$ (for inch-pound units)
$h_f = 0.182(1 \times 1055 \text{ kW})^{2/5}$ or
$h_f = 0.584(1 \times 1000 \text{ Btu/sec})^{2/5}$
$h_f = 2.8$ m (9.25 ft)

Another correlation has been derived by Drysdale [42]:

$$I = 0.235\, Q_c^{2/5} - 1.02D$$

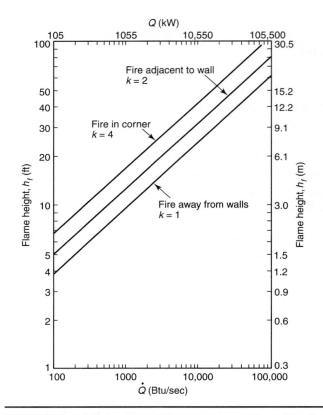

FIGURE B.2.3.2.4.1 Heat Release Rate vs. Flame Height.

where:

I = the flame height (m)

Q_c = the convective heat release rate (kW)

D = the diameter of the fuel bed

These correlations will not produce the same prediction when used for exactly the same input data. There is inherent uncertainty in the calculated flame height due to the fact that the flaming combustion in the diffusion regime is a dynamic phenomenon. The designer should run multiple predictions with bounding values to address the inherent uncertainty of the correlations.

The reader should note that the relation developed by Drysdale does not have an equivalent relation using U.S. customary units. With the growing international influence in fire protection engineering, much of the current research is published only with the International System (SI) of units. In general, most practitioners of performance-based design perform the calculations using SI units. Often there are no U.S. customary unit equivalents due to the combination of a number of variables into a single parameter for design correlations.

B.2.3.2.5 Selection of Critical Fire Size. Because all fire control means require a finite operation time, there is a critical difference between the time at which the fire must be detected and the time at which it achieves the magnitude of the design fire. Even though a fire has been detected, this does not mean that it stops growing. Fires typically grow exponentially until they become ventilation controlled, and limited by the availability of fuel, or until some type of fire suppression or extinguishment is commenced. Figure B.2.3.2.5 shows that there can be a significant increase in the heat release rate with only a small change in time due to the exponential growth rate of fire.

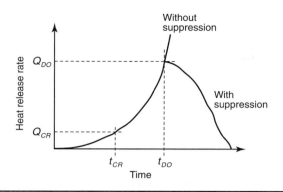

FIGURE B.2.3.2.5 *Critical and Design Objective Heat Release Rates vs. Time.*

B.2.3.2.5.1 Once the design objectives and the design fire have been established, the designer will need to establish two points on the design fire curve: Q_{DO} and Q_{CR}.

B.2.3.2.5.2 Q_{DO} represents the heat release rate, or product release rate, which produces conditions representative of the design objective. This is the "design fire." However, Q_{DO} does not represent the point in time at which detection is needed. Detection must occur sufficiently early in the development of the fire to allow for any intrinsic reaction time of the detection as well as the operation time for fire suppression or extinguishing systems. There will be delays in both detection of the fire as well as the response of equipment, or persons, to the alarm.

B.2.3.2.5.3 A critical fire size (Q_{CR}) is identified on the curve that accounts for the delays in detection and response. This point represents the maximum permissible fire size at which detection must occur that allows appropriate actions to be taken to keep the fire from exceeding the design objective (Q_{DO}).

B.2.3.2.5.4 Delays are inherent in both the detection system as well as in the response of the equipment or people that need to react once a fire is detected. Delays associated with the detection system include a lag in the transport of combustion products from the fire to the detector and response time lag of the detector, alarm verification time, processing time of the detector, and processing time of the control unit. Delays are also possible with an automatic fire extinguishing system(s) or suppression system(s). Delay can be introduced by alarm verification or crossed zone detection systems, filling and discharge times of preaction systems, delays in agent release required for occupant evacuation (e.g., CO_2 systems), and the time required to achieve extinguishment.

B.2.3.2.5.5 Occupants do not always respond immediately to a fire alarm. The following must be accounted for when evaluating occupant safety issues:

(1) Time expected for occupants to hear the alarm (due to sleeping or manufacturing equipment noise)
(2) Time to decipher the message (e.g., voice alarm system)
(3) Time to decide whether to leave (get dressed, gather belongings, call security)
(4) Time to travel to an exit

B.2.3.2.5.6 Response of the fire department or fire brigade to a fire incident involves several different actions that need to occur sequentially before containment and extinguishment efforts of the fire can even begin. These actions should also be taken into account to properly design detection systems that meet the design objectives. These actions typically include the following:

(1) Detection (detector delays, control unit delays, and so forth)
(2) Notification to the monitoring station (remote, central station, proprietary, and so forth)

(3) Notification of the fire department
(4) Alarm handling time at the fire department
(5) Turnout time at the station
(6) Travel time to the incident
(7) Access to the site
(8) Set-up time on site
(9) Access to building
(10) Access to fire floor
(11) Access to area of involvement
(12) Application of extinguishant on the fire

B.2.3.2.5.7 Unless conditions that limit the availability of combustion air or fuel exist, neither the growth of the fire nor the resultant damage stop until fire suppression begins. The time needed to execute each step of the fire response sequence of actions must be quantified and documented. When designing a detection system, the sum of the time needed for each step in the response sequence (t_{delay}) must be subtracted from the time at which the fire attains the design objective (t_{DO}) in order to determine the latest time and fire size (Q_{CR}) in the fire development at which detection can occur and still achieve the system design objective.

B.2.3.2.5.8 The fire scenarios and design fires selected should include analysis of best and worst-case conditions and their likelihood of occurring. It is important to look at different conditions and situations and their effects on response.

B.2.3.2.6 Data Sources.

B.2.3.2.6.1 To produce a design fire curve, information is needed regarding the burning characteristics of the object(s) involved. Data can be obtained from either technical literature or by conducting small or large scale calorimeter tests.

B.2.3.2.6.2 Some information is contained in Figure B.2.3.2.6.2 and Table B.2.3.2.6.2(a) through Table B.2.3.2.6.2(e).

B.2.3.2.6.3 Graphs of heat release data from the 40 furniture calorimeter tests can be found in *Investigation of a New Sprinkler Sensitivity Approval Test: The Plunge Test*. Best fit power law fire growth curves have been superimposed on the graphs. Data from these curves can be used with this guide to design or analyze fire detection systems that are intended to respond to similar items burning under a flat ceiling. Table B.2.3.2.6.2(e) is a summary of the data.

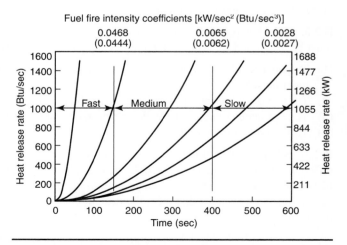

FIGURE B.2.3.2.6.2 *Power Law Heat Release Rates.*

Additional sources of information for developing design fire curves include the following:

1. Heat release rate data determined from experimental work (i.e., using a furniture calorimeter)
2. Full-scale tests of actual contents
3. Generic curves
4. Fire growth model that automatically generates heat release rate data

TABLE B.2.3.2.6.2(a) *Maximum Heat Release Rates — Warehouse Materials*

Warehouse Materials	Growth Time (t_g) (sec)	Heat Release Density (q) kW/m²	Btu/sec·ft²	Classification
1. Wood pallets, stack, 0.46 m (1½ ft) high (6%–12% moisture)	150–310	1,248	110	fast–medium
2. Wood pallets, stack, 1.52 m (5 ft) high (6%–12% moisture)	90–190	3,745	330	fast
3. Wood pallets, stack, 3.05 m (10 ft) high (6%–12% moisture)	80–110	6,810	600	fast
4. Wood pallets, stack, 4.88 m (16 ft) high (6%–12% moisture)	75–105	10,214	900	fast
5. Mail bags, filled, stored 1.52 m (5 ft) high	190	397	35	medium
6. Cartons, compartmented, stacked 4.57 m (15 ft) high	60	2,270	200	fast
7. Paper, vertical rolls, stacked 6.10 m (20 ft) high	15–28	—	—	*
8. Cotton (also PE, PE/cot, acrylic/nylon/PE), garments in 3.66 m (12 ft) high racks	20–42	—	—	*
9. Cartons on pallets, rack storage, 4.57 m–9.14 m (15 ft–30 ft) high	40–280	—	—	fast–medium
10. Paper products, densely packed in cartons, rack storage, 6.10 m (20 ft) high	470	—	—	slow
11. PE letter trays, filled, stacked 1.52 m (5 ft) high on cart	190	8,512	750	medium
12. PE trash barrels in cartons, stacked 4.57 m (15 ft) high	55	2,837	250	fast
13. FRP shower stalls in cartons, stacked 4.57 m (15 ft) high	85	1,248	110	fast
14. PE bottles, packed in item 6	85	6,242	550	fast
15. PE bottles in cartons, stacked 4.57 m (15 ft) high	75	1,929	170	fast
16. PE pallets, stacked 0.91 m (3 ft) high	130	—	—	fast
17. PE pallets, stacked 1.83 m–2.44 m (6 ft–8 ft) high	30–55	—	—	fast
18. PU mattress, single, horizontal	110	—	—	fast
19. PE insulation board, rigid foam, stacked 4.57 m (15 ft) high	8	1,929	170	*
20. PS jars, packed in item 6	55	13,619	1,200	fast
21. PS tubs nested in cartons, stacked 4.27 m (14 ft) high	105	5,107	450	fast
22. PS toy parts in cartons, stacked 4.57 m (15 ft) high	110	2,042	180	fast
23. PS insulation board, rigid, stacked 4.27 m (14 ft) high	7	3,291	290	*
24. PVC bottles, packed in item 6	9	3,405	300	*
25. PP tubs, packed in item 6	10	4,426	390	*
26. PP and PE film in rolls, stacked 4.27 m (14 ft) high	40	3,972	350	*
27. Distilled spirits in barrels, stacked 6.10 m (20 ft) high	23–40	—	—	*
28. Methyl alcohol	—	738	65	—
29. Gasoline	—	2,270	200	—
30. Kerosene	—	2,270	200	—
31. Diesel oil	—	2,043	180	—

PE: Polyethylene. PS: Polystyrene. PVC: Polyvinyl chloride. PP: Polypropylene. PU: Polyurethane. FRP: Fiberglass-reinforced polyester.

Note: The heat release rates per unit floor area are for fully involved combustibles, assuming 100 percent combustion efficiency. The growth times shown are those required to exceed 1000 Btu/sec heat release rate for developing fires, assuming 100 percent combustion efficiency.

*Fire growth rate exceeds design data.

TABLE B.2.3.2.6.2(b) *Maximum Heat Release Rates from Fire Detection Institute Analysis*

	Approximate Values	
Materials	*kW*	*Btu/sec*
Medium wastebasket with milk cartons	105	100
Large barrel with milk cartons	148	140
Upholstered chair with polyurethane foam	369	350
Latex foam mattress (heat at room door)	1265	1200
Furnished living room (heat at open door)	4217–8435	4000–8000

TABLE B.2.3.2.6.2(c) *Unit Heat Release Rates for Fuels Burning in the Open*

	Heat Release Rate	
Commodity	*kW*	*Btu/sec*
Flammable liquid pool	$3291/m^2$	$290/ft^2$ of surface
Flammable liquid spray	557/Lpm	2000/gpm of flow
Pallet stack	3459/m	1000/ft of height
Wood or PMMA* (vertical)		
0.6 m (2 ft) height	104/m	30/ft of width
1.8 m (6 ft) height	242/m	70/ft of width
2.4 m (8 ft) height	623/m	180/ft of width
3.7 m (12 ft) height	1038/m	300/ft of width
Wood or PMMA*		
Top of horizontal surface	$715/m^2$	$63/ft^2$ of surface
Solid polystyrene (vertical)		
0.6 m (2 ft) height	218/m	63/ft of width
1.8 m (6 ft) height	450/m	130/ft of width
2.4 m (8 ft) height	1384/m	400/ft of width
3.7 m (12 ft) height	2352/m	680/ft of width
Solid polystyrene (horizontal)	$1362/m^2$	$120/ft^2$ of surface
Solid polypropylene (vertical)		
0.6 m (2 ft) height	218/m	63/ft of width
1.8 m (6 ft) height	346/m	100/ft of width
2.4 m (8 ft) height	969/m	280/ft of width
3.7 m (12 ft) height	1626/m	470/ft of width
Solid polypropylene (horizontal)	$795/m^2$	$70/ft^2$ of surface

*Polymethyl methacrylate (Plexiglas™, Lucite™, Acrylic).
[**92B:** Table B.1, 1995.]

B.2.3.2.6.4 In addition to heat release rate data, the original NIST reports [8] contain data on particulate conversion and radiation from the test specimens. These data can be used to determine the threshold fire size (heat release rate) at which tenability becomes endangered or the point at which additional fuel packages might become involved in the fire.

B.2.3.2.6.5 The *NFPA Fire Protection Handbook* [22], SFPE *Handbook of Fire Protection Engineering*, and *Upholstered Furniture Heat Release Rates Measured with a Furniture Calorimeter* contain further information on heat release rates and fire growth rates.

B.2.3.2.6.6 Technical literature searches can be performed using a number of resources including FIREDOC, a document base of fire literature that is maintained by NIST.

TABLE B.2.3.2.6.2(d) *Characteristics of Ignition Sources*

	Typical Heat Output		Burn Time[a]	Maximum Flame Height		Flame Width		Maximum Heat Flux	
	W	Btu/sec	(sec)	mm	in.	mm	in.	kW/m²	Btu/sec · ft²
Cigarette 1.1 g (not puffed, laid on solid surface)									
Bone dry	5	0.0047	1200	—	—	—	—	42	3 . 7
Conditioned to 50% relative humidity	5	0.0047	1200	—	—	—	—	35	3.1
Methenamine pill, 0.15 g (0.0053 oz)	45	0.043	90	—	—	—	—	4	0.35
Match, wooden, laid on solid surface	80	0.076	20–30	30	1.18	14	0.092	18–20	1.59–1.76
Wood cribs, BS 5852 Part 2									
No. 4 crib, 8.5 g (0.3 oz)	1,000	0.95	190	—	—	—	—	15[d]	1.32
No. 5 crib, 17 g (0.6 oz)	1,900	1.80	200	—	—	—	—	17[d]	1.50
No. 6 crib, 60 g (2.1 oz)	2,600	2.46	190	—	—	—	—	20[d]	1.76
No. 7 crib, 126 g (4.4 oz)	6,400	6.07	350	—	—	—	—	25[d]	2.20
Crumpled brown lunch bag, 6 g (0.21 oz)	1,200	1.14	80	—	—	—	—	—	—
Crumpled wax paper, 4.5 g (0.16 oz) (tight)	1,800	1.71	25	—	—	—	—	—	—
Crumpled wax paper, 4.5 g (0.16 oz) (loose)	5,300	5.03	20	—	—	—	—	—	—
Folded double-sheet newspaper, 22 g (0.78 oz) (bottom ignition)	4,000	3.79	100	—	—	—	—	—	—
Crumpled double-sheet newspaper, 22 g (0.78 oz) (top ignition)	7,400	7.02	40	—	—	—	—	—	—
Crumpled double-sheet newspaper, 22 g (0.78 oz) (bottom ignition)	17,000	16.12	20	—	—	—	—	—	—
Polyethylene wastebasket, 285 g (10.0 oz), filled with 12 milk cartons [390 g (13.8 oz)]	50,000	47.42	200[b]	550	21.7	200	7.9	35[c]	3.08
Plastic trash bags, filled with cellulosic trash [1.2–14 kg (42.3–493 oz)][e]	120,000– 350,000	113.81– 331.96	200[b]	—	—	—	—	—	—

Note: Based on Table B.5.3(b) of NFPA 92B, 2009 edition.

[a]Time duration of significant flaming.

[b]Total burn time in excess of 1800 seconds.

[c]As measured on simulation burner.

[d]Measured from 25 mm away.

[e]Results vary greatly with packing density.

[**92B:** Table B.5.3(b)]

TABLE B.2.3.2.6.2(e) *Furniture Heat Release Rates [3, 14, 16]*

Test No.	Item/Description/Mass	Growth Time (t_g) (sec)	Classification	Fuel Fire Intensity Coefficient (α)		Virtual Time (t_v) (sec)	Maximum Heat Release Rates	
				kW/sec²	Btu/sec³		kW	Btu/sec
15	Metal wardrobe, 41.4 kg (91.3 lb) (total)	50	fast	0.4220	0.4002	10	750	711
18	Chair F33 (trial love seat), 29.2 kg (64.4 lb)	400	slow	0.0066	0.0063	140	950	901
19	Chair F21, 28.15 kg (62.01 lb) (initial)	175	medium	0.0344	0.0326	110	350	332
19	Chair F21, 28.15 kg (62.01 lb) (later)	50	fast	0.4220	0.4002	190	2000	1897
21	Metal wardrobe, 40.8 kg (90.0 lb) (total) (initial)	250	medium	0.0169	0.0160	10	250	237
21	Metal wardrobe, 40.8 kg (90.0 lb) (total) (average)	120	fast	0.0733	0.0695	60	250	237
21	Metal wardrobe, 40.8 kg (90.0 lb) (total) (later)	100	fast	0.1055	0.1001	30	140	133
22	Chair F24, 28.3 kg (62.4 lb)	350	medium	0.0086	0.0082	400	700	664
23	Chair F23, 31.2 kg (68.8 lb)	400	slow	0.0066	0.0063	100	700	664
24	Chair F22, 31.2 kg (68.8 lb)	2000	slow	0.0003	0.0003	150	300	285
25	Chair F26, 19.2 kg (42.3 lb)	200	medium	0.0264	0.0250	90	800	759

(continues)

TABLE B.2.3.2.6.2(e) *Continued*

Test No.	Item/Description/Mass	Growth Time (t_g) (sec)	Classification	Fuel Fire Intensity Coefficient (α) kW/sec²	Btu/sec³	Virtual Time (t_v) (sec)	Maximum Heat Release Rates kW	Btu/sec
26	Chair F27, 29.0 kg (63.9 lb)	200	medium	0.0264	0.0250	360	900	854
27	Chair F29, 14.0 kg (30.9 lb)	100	fast	0.1055	0.1001	70	1850	1755
28	Chair F28, 29.2 kg (64.4 lb)	425	slow	0.0058	0.0055	90	700	664
29	Chair F25, 27.8 kg (61.3 lb) (later)	60	fast	0.2931	0.2780	175	700	664
29	Chair F25, 27.8 kg (61.3 lb) (initial)	100	fast	0.1055	0.1001	100	2000	1897
30	Chair F30, 25.2 kg (55.6 lb)	60	fast	0.2931	0.2780	70	950	901
31	Chair F31 (love seat), 39.6 kg (87.3 lb)	60	fast	0.2931	0.2780	145	2600	2466
37	Chair F31 (love seat), 40.4 kg (89.1 lb)	80	fast	0.1648	0.1563	100	2750	2608
38	Chair F32 (sofa), 51.5 kg (113.5 lb)	100	fast	0.1055	0.1001	50	3000	2845
39	$^1\!/_2$ in. plywood wardrobe with fabrics, 68.5 kg (151.0 lb)	35	*	0.8612	0.8168	20	3250	3083
40	$^1\!/_2$ in. plywood wardrobe with fabrics, 68.32 kg (150.6 lb)	35	*	0.8612	0.8168	40	3500	3320
41	$^1\!/_8$ in. plywood wardrobe with fabrics, 36.0 kg (79.4 lb)	40	*	0.6594	0.6254	40	6000	5691
42	$^1\!/_8$ in. plywood wardrobe with fire-retardant interior finish (initial growth)	70	fast	0.2153	0.2042	50	2000	1897
42	$^1\!/_8$ in. plywood wardrobe with fire-retardant interior finish (later growth)	30	*	1.1722	1.1118	100	5000	4742
43	Repeat of $^1\!/_2$ in. plywood wardrobe, 67.62 kg (149.08 lb)	30	*	1.1722	1.1118	50	3000	2845
44	$^1\!/_8$ in. plywood wardrobe with fire-retardant latex paint, 37.26 kg (82.14 lb)	90	fast	0.1302	0.1235	30	2900	2751
45	Chair F21, 28.34 kg (62.48 lb)	100	*	0.1055	0.1001	120	2100	1992
46	Chair F21, 28.34 kg (62.48 lb)	45	*	0.5210	0.4941	130	2600	2466
47	Chair, adj. back metal frame, foam cushions, 20.82 kg (45.90 lb)	170	medium	0.0365	0.0346	30	250	237
48	Easy chair CO7, 11.52 kg (25.40 lb)	175	medium	0.0344	0.0326	90	950	901
49	Easy chair F34, 15.68 kg (34.57 lb)	200	medium	0.0264	0.0250	50	200	190
50	Chair, metal frame, minimum cushion, 16.52 kg (36.42 lb)	200	medium	0.0264	0.0250	120	3000	2845
51	Chair, molded fiberglass, no cushion, 5.28 kg (11.64 lb)	120	fast	0.0733	0.0695	20	35	33
52	Molded plastic patient chair, 11.26 kg (24.82 lb)	275	medium	0.0140	0.0133	2090	700	664
53	Chair, metal frame, padded seat and back, 15.54 kg (34.26 lb)	350	medium	0.0086	0.0082	50	280	266
54	Love seat, metal frame, foam cushions, 27.26 kg (60.10 lb)	500	slow	0.0042	0.0040	210	300	285
56	Chair, wood frame, latex foam cushions, 11.2 kg (24.69 lb)	500	slow	0.0042	0.0040	50	85	81
57	Love seat, wood frame, foam cushions, 54.6 kg (120.37 lb)	350	medium	0.0086	0.0082	500	1000	949
61	Wardrobe, $^3\!/_4$ in. particleboard, 120.33 kg (265.28 lb)	150	medium	0.0469	0.0445	0	1200	1138
62	Bookcase, plywood with aluminum frame, 30.39 kg (67.00 lb)	65	fast	0.2497	0.2368	40	25	24
64	Easy chair, molded flexible urethane frame, 15.98 kg (35.23 lb)	1000	slow	0.0011	0.0010	750	450	427
66	Easy chair, 23.02 kg (50.75 lb)	76	fast	0.1827	0.1733	3700	600	569
67	Mattress and box spring, 62.36 kg (137.48 lb) (later)	350	medium	0.0086	0.0082	400	500	474
67	Mattress and box spring, 62.36 kg (137.48 lb) (initial)	1100	slow	0.0009	0.0009	90	400	379

Note: For tests 19, 21, 29, 42, and 67, different power law curves were used to model the initial and the latter realms of burning. In examples such as these, engineers should choose the fire growth parameter that best describes the realm of burning to which the detection system is being designed to respond.

*Fire growth exceeds design data.

B.2.3.2.6.7 A series of design fire curves are included as part of the "Fastlite" computer program available from NIST.

B.2.3.2.6.8 In addition, there are various organizations conducting tests and posting results of various test data on their websites, including the UK's British Research Establishment (BRE), Worcester Polytechnic Institute, and NIST's FASTData Fire Test Database.

Designers should be aware of additional resources regarding information on design fires that would assist in the development of design fire scenarios.

B.2.3.3 Develop and Evaluate Candidate Fire Detection Systems.

B.2.3.3.1 Once the design objectives, the potential fire scenarios, and the room characteristics are well understood, the designer can select an appropriate detection strategy to detect the fire before its critical fire size (Q_{CR}) is reached. Important factors to consider include the type of detector, its sensitivity to expected fire signatures, its alarm threshold level and required duration at that threshold, expected installed location (e.g., distance from fire, or below ceiling), and freedom from nuisance response to expected ambient conditions. *(See Chapter 17 and Annex A.)*

Candidate designs usually differ from the design outlined in the prescriptive code or standard. Usually a designer compares the response of the detection system designed using a performance-based approach to the response of a system designed following prescriptive requirements. A designer also evaluates candidate designs against acceptance criteria previously established by a consensus of the relevant stakeholders.

In addition to the operational and response characteristics, stakeholders often set limits on the amount of disruption, visibility, or other ways the fire alarm system will affect the intended use of the protected space. For example, in historic structures, the intended use must preserve the history and heritage by preserving the appearance of the structure. In such cases, the visibility of the fire protection system must be limited; the less visible the fire alarm system, the better.

B.2.3.3.2 Reliability of the detection system and individual components should be computed and included in the selection and evaluation of the candidate fire detection system. A performance-based alternative design cannot be deemed performance-equivalent unless the alternative design provides comparable reliability to the prescriptive design it is intended to replace.

Reliability studies can be part of RAMS studies (i.e., reliability, availability, maintainability, and safety). RAMS is a tool that is used to manage dependability in "mission critical" systems. These are all factors that should be considered to ensure the system will continue to operate as designed, as well as ensure ease of and safety during maintenance.

The basis of RAMS is a systematic process, based on the system life cycle and tasks within it, that does the following:

(1) Assists the client to specify system requirements, in terms of dependability, from a general mission statement to availability targets for systems and subsystems, components (including software)
(2) Assesses proposed designs, using formal RAMS techniques, to see how targets are met and where objectives are not achieved
(3) Provides a means to make recommendations to designers and a system of hazard logging, to record and eventually "check off" identified necessary actions

The technical concepts of availability and reliability are based on a knowledge of and means to assess the following:

(1) All possible system failure modes in the specified application environment
(2) The probability (or rate) of occurrence of a system failure mode
(3) The cause and effect of each failure mode on the functionality of the system
(4) Efficient failure detection and location
(5) The efficient restorability of the failed system
(6) Economic maintenance over the required life cycle of the system
(7) Human factors issues regarding safety during inspection, testing, and maintenance

Fire alarm systems typically have high levels of supervision and fault-tolerance. Consequently, designers usually use mission effectiveness to evaluate fire alarm systems rather than strict reliability. The equipment, the system design, the installation, and the maintenance all contribute to the inherent mission effectiveness of a fire alarm system.

B.2.3.3.3 Various methods are available to evaluate whether a candidate design will achieve the previously established performance criteria. Some methods are presented in Section B.3.

Section B.6 discusses additional modeling methods.

B.2.3.3.4 Candidate designs developed in the context of comparison evaluation might require comparing the response of the detection system designed using a performance-based approach to that of a prescriptive-based design. It could also be evaluated against acceptance criteria previously established with applicable stakeholders.

In addition to the preceding operational and response characteristics that need to be considered, there might be limitations set on the amount of disruption, visibility, or the impact the system will have on the space in which it is to be installed. This is particularly important in heritage-type buildings where one would want these to be as unobtrusive as possible, yet not require ripping down ornate ceilings to install.

B.2.3.4 Select and Document Final Design.

B.2.3.4.1 The last step in the process is the preparation of design documentation and equipment and installation specifications.

The designer must be sure to properly document each design decision. Proper documentation establishes the reasoning behind the design decisions, minimizing the opportunity for error. Proper documentation also ensures that all involved parties understand the steps needed to implement the design. Such steps include the selection of equipment, the methods of installation, and the maintenance program.

B.2.3.4.2 These documents should encompass the following information [25]:

(1) Participants in the process — persons involved, their qualifications, function, responsibility, interest, and contributions.
(2) Scope of work — purpose of conducting the analysis or design, part of the building evaluated, assumptions, and so forth.
(3) Design approach — approach taken, where and why assumptions were made, and engineering tools and methodologies applied.
(4) Project information — hazards, risks, construction type, materials, building use, layout, existing systems, occupant characteristics, and so forth.
(5) Goals and objectives — agreed upon goals and objectives, how they were developed, who agreed to them and when.
(6) Performance criteria — clearly identify performance criteria and related objective(s), including any safety, reliability, or uncertainty factors applied, and support for these factors where necessary.
(7) Fire scenarios and design fires — description of fire scenarios used, bases for selecting and rejecting fire scenarios, assumptions, and restrictions.
(8) Design alternative(s) — describe design alternative(s) chosen, basis for selecting and rejecting design alternative(s), heat release rate, assumptions, and limitations. [This step should include the specific design objective (Q_{DO}) and the critical heat release rate (Q_{CR}) used, comparison of results with the performance criteria and design objectives, and a discussion of the sensitivity of the selected design alternative to changes in the building use, contents, fire characteristics, occupants, and so forth.]
(9) Engineering tools and methods used — description of engineering tools and methods used in the analysis or design, including appropriate references (literature, date, software version, and so forth), assumptions, limitations, engineering judgments, input data, validation data or procedures, and sensitivity analyses.

(10) Drawings and specifications — detailed design and installation drawings and specification.

(11) Test, inspection, and maintenance requirements *(see Chapter 14)*.

(12) Fire safety management concerns — allowed contents and materials in the space in order for the design to function properly, training, education, and so forth.

(13) References — software documentation, technical literature, reports, technical data sheets, fire test results, and so forth.

(14) Critical design assumptions — should include all assumptions that need to be maintained throughout the life cycle of the building so that the design functions as intended. Critical design features — should include the design features and parameters that need to be maintained throughout the life of the building so that the design functions as intended.

(15) Operations and maintenance manual — an operation and maintenance manual should be developed that clearly states the requirements for ensuring that the components of the performance-based design are correctly in place and functioning as designed. All subsystems should be identified, as well as their operation and interaction with the fire detection system. It should also include maintenance and testing frequencies, methods, and forms. The importance of testing interconnected systems should be detailed (i.e., elevator recall, suppression systems, HVAC shutdown, and so on).

(16) Inspection, testing, maintenance, and commissioning — requirements for commissioning of systems and any special procedures or test methods — should be documented as well as inspection, testing, and maintenance procedures to address the design as well as any pertinent features or systems that need to be assessed.

B.2.3.5 Management. It is important to ensure that the systems are designed, installed, commissioned, maintained, and tested on regular intervals as indicated in Chapter 14. In addition, the person conducting the testing and inspections should be aware of the background of the design and the need to evaluate not only the detector and whether it operates but also be aware of changing conditions including the following:

(1) Changes in hazard being protected
(2) Location of the hazard changes
(3) Other hazards introduced into the area
(4) Ambient environment
(5) Invalidity of any of the design assumptions

B.3 Evaluation of Heat Detection System Performance

With the issuance of the 2002 edition of the Code, the performance-based design process for fire alarm systems was formally recognized as an alternative to designs developed using the prescriptive rules of the Code. Calculations, such as those outlined in Section B.3, represent an integral part of performance-based design. However, performance-based design is a process, and the computational tools outlined here are intended to be used only in the context of that process.

Users should review Section 17.3 carefully before undertaking a design based upon these computational methods. When undertaking a performance-based design, designers assume responsibility for the propriety of the design assumptions offered to the other stakeholders as well as an assessment of the implications of adopting such assumptions or criteria. This approach puts a greater burden of responsibility on the designers than when they are implementing the requirements of a prescriptive code.

B.3.1 General. Section B.3 provides a method for determining the application spacing for both fixed-temperature heat detectors (including sprinklers) and rate-of-rise heat detectors.

This method is valid only for use when detectors are to be placed on a large, flat ceiling. It predicts detector response to a geometrically growing flaming fire at a specific fire size. This method takes into account the effects of ceiling height, radial distance between the detector and the fire, threshold fire size [critical heat release rate (Q_{CR})], rate of fire development, and detector response time index. For fixed-temperature detectors, the ambient temperature and the temperature rating of the detector are also considered. This method also allows for the adjustment of the application spacing for fixed-temperature heat detectors to account for variations in ambient temperature (T_a) from standard test conditions.

B.3.1.1 This method can also be used to estimate the fire size at which detection will occur, given an existing array of listed heat detectors installed at a known spacing, ceiling height, and ambient conditions.

To analyze the response of an existing fire detection system, the designer must also quantify the fire growth rate and detector temperature rating.

B.3.1.2 The effect of rate of fire growth and fire size of a flaming fire, as well as the effect of ceiling height on the spacing and response of smoke detectors, can also be determined using this method.

A designer can predict the response of a smoke detector by modeling the smoke detector as a very sensitive heat detector. Engineers have used this model for many years. The model relies on the premise that the ceiling jet, formed by the buoyant plume as it collides with the ceiling, provides the force to move smoke horizontally beneath the ceiling from the fire to the detector. Consequently, the smoke and the heat are conveyed together. This model supports the notion that a correlation exists between temperature rise and smoke density. However, the prudent designer exercises caution, knowing that this correlation is loose at best.

B.3.1.3 The methodology contained herein uses theories of fire development, fire plume dynamics, and detector performance. These are considered the major factors influencing detector response. This methodology does not address several lesser phenomena that, in general, are considered unlikely to have a significant influence. A discussion of ceiling drag, heat loss to the ceiling, radiation to the detector from a fire, re-radiation of heat from a detector to its surroundings, and the heat of fusion of eutectic materials in fusible elements of heat detectors and their possible limitations on the design method are provided in References 4, 11, 16, and 18 in H.1.2.15.

B.3.1.4 The methodology in Section B.3 does not address the effects of ceiling projections, such as beams and joists, on detector response. While it has been shown that these components of a ceiling have a significant effect on the response of heat detectors, research has not yet resulted in a simplified method for quantifying this effect. The prescriptive adjustments to detector spacing in Chapter 17 should be applied to application spacings derived from this methodology. Computational fluid dynamics (CFD) programs are available and can assist in analyzing the fire and development and spread of heat and smoke, as well as the potential effects of varying ceiling configurations and characteristics including sloped and beamed ceilings.

Ceiling slope and surface obstructions affect the flow of a ceiling jet and hence cause changes in the computed detector response. One method for adjusting spacings to deal with sloped or obstructed ceilings is to apply the spacing adjustments outlined in Chapter 17.

Plume and ceiling jet dynamics can be used to qualitatively estimate the effect of sloped and obstructed ceilings on the response of heat detectors. However, no algebraic computational method has become sufficiently well accepted in the fire protection engineering community to warrant inclusion in Annex B. The use of the Fire Dynamics Simulator Computational Fluid Dynamics (CFD) program developed and supported by the National Institute of Standards and Technology (NIST) has the capability to model buoyant plume and ceiling jet flows across sloped ceilings and can be used for estimated detector response.

B.3.2 Considerations Regarding Input Data.

B.3.2.1 Required Data. The following data are necessary in order to use the methods in this annex for either design or analysis.

The computational method shown in Annex B can be implemented with either SI or U.S. customary units of measure. Most engineers use SI units for the calculations. All parameters must be expressed in the same measurement environment, SI or U.S. customary.

The following are the units for the variables listed in B.3.2.1:

T = °C or °F

H = m or ft

RTI = $m^{1/2}sec^{1/2}$ or $ft^{1/2}sec^{1/2}$

α = kW/sec^2 or Btu/sec^3

t_g = sec

S = m or ft

Q = kW or Btu/sec

B.3.2.1.1 Design. Data required to determine design include the following:

(1) Ceiling height or clearance above fuel (H)
(2) Threshold fire size at which response must occur (Q_d) or the time to detector response (t_d)
(3) Response time index (RTI) for the detector (heat detectors only) or its listed spacing
(4) Ambient temperature (T_a)
(5) Detector operating temperature (T_s) (heat detectors only)
(6) Rate of temperature change set point for rate-of-rise heat detectors (T_s/min)
(7) Fuel fire intensity coefficient (α) or the fire growth time (t_g)

B.3.2.1.2 Analysis. Data required to determine analysis include the following:

(1) Ceiling height or clearance above fuel (H)
(2) Response time index (RTI) for the detector (heat detectors only) or its listed spacing
(3) Actual installed spacing (S) of the existing detectors
(4) Ambient temperature (T_a)
(5) Detector operating temperature (T_s) (heat detectors only)
(6) Rate of temperature change set point for rate-of-rise heat detectors (T_s/min)
(7) Fuel fire intensity coefficient (α) or the fire growth time (t_g)

B.3.2.2 Ambient Temperature Considerations.

B.3.2.2.1 The maximum ambient temperature expected to occur at the ceiling will directly affect the choice of temperature rating for a fixed-temperature heat detector application. However, the minimum ambient temperature likely to be present at the ceiling is also very important. When ambient temperature at the ceiling decreases, more heat from a fire is needed to bring the air surrounding the detector's sensing element up to its rated (operating) temperature. This results in slower response when the ambient temperature is lower. In the case of a fire that is growing over time, lower ambient temperatures result in a larger fire size at the time of detection.

B.3.2.2.2 Therefore, selection of the minimum ambient temperature has a significant effect on the calculations. The designer should decide what temperature to use for these calculations and document why that temperature was chosen. Because the response time of a given detector to a given fire is dependent only on the detector's time constant and the temperature difference between ambient and the detector rating, the use of the lowest anticipated ambient temperature for the space results in the most conservative design. For unheated spaces, a review of historical weather data would be appropriate. However, such data might show extremely low temperatures that occur relatively infrequently, such as every 100 years. Depending on actual design considerations, it might be more appropriate to use an average minimum ambient temperature. In any case, a sensitivity analysis should be performed to determine the effect of changing the ambient temperature on the design results.

In reference to B.3.2.2.2, the National Oceanic and Atmospheric Administration (NOAA) is a frequently used source for weather data in the United States (*www.noaa.gov*).

B.3.2.2.3 In a room or work area that has central heating, the minimum ambient temperature would usually be about 20°C (68°F). On the other hand, certain warehouse occupancies might be heated only enough to prevent water pipes from freezing and, in this case, the minimum ambient temperature can be considered to be 2°C (35°F), even though, during many months of the year, the actual ambient temperature can be much higher.

B.3.2.3 Ceiling Height Considerations.

B.3.2.3.1 A detector ordinarily operates sooner if it is nearer to the fire. Where ceiling heights exceed 4.9 m (16 ft), ceiling height is the dominant factor in the detection system response.

When the calculations show that the fire size at the time of response exceeds the design objective (design fire), the designer can try reducing the spacing of detectors. This action has the effect of moving detectors closer to the fire plume centerline. In some circumstances, particularly with high ceilings and small design fires, the designer must understand that further reductions in the detector spacing cannot improve the system response. When the detector spacing is reduced to less than 0.4 the ceiling height, a detector is in the plume regardless of the fire location. Because the temperature and velocity gradients across the plume are not large, further spacing reductions likely will not enhance system performance. The design goals for the hazard area can conceivably require a faster response than that attainable from heat detectors. Under this set of circumstances, the designer will have little alternative but to consider other types of detection.

B.3.2.3.2 As flaming combustion commences, a buoyant plume forms. The plume is comprised of the heated gases and smoke rising from the fire. The plume assumes the general shape of an inverted cone. The smoke concentration and temperature within the cone varies inversely as a variable exponential function of the distance from the source. This effect is very significant in the early stages of a fire, because the angle of the cone is wide. As a fire intensifies, the angle of the cone narrows and the significance of the effect of height is lessened.

B.3.2.3.3 As the ceiling height increases, a larger-size fire is necessary to actuate the same detector in the same length of time. In view of this, it is very important that the designer consider the size of the fire and rate of heat release that might develop before detection is ultimately obtained.

B.3.2.3.4 The procedures presented in this section are based on analysis of data for ceiling heights up to 9.1 m (30 ft). No data were analyzed for ceiling heights greater than 9.1 m (30 ft). In spaces where the ceiling heights exceed this limit, this section offers no guidance. [40]

B.3.2.3.5 The relationships presented here are based on the difference between the ceiling height and the height of the fuel item involved in the fire. It is recommended that the designer assume the fire is at floor level and use the actual distance from floor to ceiling for the calculations. This will yield a design that is conservative, and actual detector response can be expected to exceed the needed speed of response in those cases where the fire begins above floor level.

When analyzing an existing detection system, if the designer assigns a value for H that represents the distance from the floor to the ceiling, this ceiling height assignment will lead to a maximum predicted detection time. In such a case, the predicted detection time will exceed the actual detection time during a fire. Often, systems exceed the calculated detection time because the ignited fuel is located a significant distance above the floor. Some structures are constructed and used in a manner that precludes a credible fuel load at the floor level. In such cases, the designer can produce a more accurate analysis by selecting a value for H that represents a reasonable worst case. The fuel load location assumed for the purposes of design or analysis must be thoroughly documented.

B.3.2.3.6 Where the designer desires to consider the height of the potential fuel in the room, the distance between the base of the fuel and the ceiling should be used in place of the ceiling height. This design option is appropriate only if the minimum height of the potential fuel is always constant and the concept is approved by the authority having jurisdiction.

B.3.2.4 Operating Temperature.

B.3.2.4.1 The operating temperature, or rate of temperature change, of the detector required for response is obtained from the manufacturer's data and is determined during the listing process.

B.3.2.4.2 The difference between the rated temperature of a fixed-temperature detector (T_s) and the maximum ambient-temperature (T_a) at the ceiling should be as small as possible. However, to reduce unwanted alarms, the difference between operating temperature and the maximum ambient temperature should be not less than 11°C (20°F). *(See Chapter 17.)*

The designer should thoroughly analyze the location of each heat detector to make certain that no non-fire heat sources, including but not limited to machinery and equipment, vehicles, space heaters, steam lines, reactor vessels, or compressors, are in the vicinity of a heat detector. These types of heat sources can cause local or intermittent hot spots and lead to unwanted alarms.

B.3.2.4.3 If using combination detectors incorporating both fixed temperature and rate-of-rise heat detection principles to detect a geometrically growing fire, the data contained herein for rate-of-rise detectors should be used in selecting an installed spacing, because the rate-of-rise principle controls the response. The fixed-temperature set point is determined from the maximum anticipated ambient temperature.

A prudent designer will calculate the response of the detector for both rate-of-rise and fixed-temperature operation. When the fires and compartment dimensions are similar to those used in the listing investigation, the detector usually responds with the rate-of-rise principle first.

B.3.2.5 Time Constant and Response Time Index (RTI). The flow of heat from the ceiling jet into a heat detector sensing element is not instantaneous. It occurs over a period of time. A measure of the speed with which heat transfer occurs, the thermal response coefficient is needed to accurately predict heat detector response. This is currently called the detector time constant (τ_0). The time constant is a measure of the detector's sensitivity. The sensitivity of a heat detector, τ_0 or RTI, should be determined by validated test. Research by FM Global [43,44,45] has shown that such a correlation exists and has resulted in a test method to determine RTI. This test method is documented in FM Approval Standard 3210, *Heat Detectors for Automatic Fire Alarm Signaling*. Heat detectors should be listed with their RTI so that heat detector spacing can be appropriately determined for various objectives and applications. For older or existing detectors, given the detector's listed spacing and the detector's rated temperature (T_s), Table B.3.2.5, developed in part by Heskestad and Delichatsios [10], can be used to find the detector time constant.

Additional research material relevant to this section will assist designers in their work and in understanding the response time index (RTI).

TABLE B.3.2.5 *Time Constants (τ_0) for Any Listed Heat Detector [at a reference velocity of 1.5 m/sec (5 ft/sec)]*

Listed Spacing		Underwriters Laboratories Inc.						Factory Mutual Research Corporation (All Temperatures)
m	*ft*	*53.3°C (128°F)*	*57.2°C (135°F)*	*62.8°C (145°F)*	*71.1°C (160°F)*	*76.7°C (170°F)*	*91.1°C (196°F)*	
3.05	10	400	330	262	195	160	97	196
4.57	15	250	190	156	110	89	45	110
6.10	20	165	135	105	70	52	17	70
7.62	25	124	100	78	48	32	—	48
9.14	30	95	80	61	36	22	—	36
12.19	40	71	57	41	18	—	—	—
15.24	50	59	44	30	—	—	—	—
21.34	70	36	24	9	—	—	—	—

Notes:

(1) These time constants are based on an analysis [10] of the Underwriters Laboratories Inc. and Factory Mutual listing test procedures.

(2) These time constants can be converted to response time index (RTI) values by using the equation RTI = τ_0 (5.0 ft/sec)$^{1/2}$. *(See also B.3.3.)*

The RTI is a measure of the speed with which heat can flow into the detector and raise the temperature of the heat-sensing component. The RTI can be thought of as a measure of the sensitivity of the heat-sensing element responding to rising temperature. Commercially available heat detectors generally exhibit RTIs with values less than 100, with 10 indicating a more rapid response than 100. The response time of a heat detector to a given fire in a given compartment can be predicted if and only if both the operating temperature and the RTI are known. The computational method for predicting heat detector response is outlined in B.3.3. RTI has units of $m^{1/2}sec^{1/2}$, and the computational method that uses RTI requires that only metric units be employed. The only method for determining RTI is the "plunge test" as outlined in FM Approval Standard 3210, *Thermal Fire Detectors for Automatic Fire Alarm Signaling*.

Note that small differences in the numerical value of RTI will suggest only small differences in response time. The conclusion that a heat detector with an RTI of 15 is significantly faster than one with a published RTI of 16 has no basis. However, a heat detector with an RTI of 5 will respond substantially faster than one with an RTI of 50, if all other factors affecting response are held constant.

While other testing laboratories are free to perform the test to quantify the RTI for a heat detector, they must correlate the test procedure and instrumentation to produce a numerical value consistent with that obtained by FM Approvals using FM Approval Standard 3210. At this time, the only recognized test method that has been validated is the method outlined in and performed in accordance with FM Approval Standard 3210.

The designer should obtain the value of RTI, as determined through testing in accordance with FM Standard 3210, for the heat detector to be used from the detector manufacturer. The 2007 edition of *NFPA 72*® incorporated a requirement that the RTI be marked on the detector or its installation bulletin. This requirement has been retained in the 2010 edition. See 17.6.2.2.2.3.

For existing systems using heat detectors for which no value of RTI has been determined, the only available means to obtain a measure of heat detector thermal response is to calculate an approximate value for RTI.

To calculate RTI, obtain the value for τ_0 from Table B.3.2.5 and use it in the following relations:

$$\text{RTI} = \tau_0 \, (1.5 \text{ m/sec})^{1/2}$$
$$\text{RTI} = \tau_0 \, (5.0 \text{ ft/sec})^{1/2}$$

See B.3.3.3 for additional information regarding time constants.

If a value for RTI has been calculated, prudent designers will perform a sensitivity analysis to verify that their design will remain valid over a range of values of RTI.

B.3.2.6 Fire Growth Rate.

B.3.2.6.1 Fire growth varies depending on the combustion characteristics and the physical configuration of the fuels involved. After ignition, most fires grow in an accelerating pattern. Information regarding the fire growth rate for various fuels has been provided previously in this annex.

Information on fire growth rates can be found in B.2.3.2.3.

B.3.2.6.2 If the heat release history for a particular fire is known, the α or t_g can be calculated using curve fitting techniques for implementation into the method detailed herein. [16]

B.3.2.6.3 In most cases, the exact fuel(s) and growth rates will not be known. Engineering judgment should therefore be used to select α or t_g that is expected to approximate the fire. Sensitivity analysis should also be performed to determine the effect on response from changes in the expected fire growth rate. In some analyses the effect on response will be negligible. Other cases might show that a more thorough analysis of potential fuels and fire scenarios is necessary.

B.3.2.7 Threshold Fire Size. The user should refer to previous sections regarding discussions on determining threshold fire sizes (Q_{DO} and Q_{CR}) to meet the design objectives.

Designers should select threshold fire sizes carefully and should perform a sensitivity analysis to quantify the effect that variations in threshold fire size have on the system response.

B.3.3 Heat Detector Spacing.

B.3.3.1 Fixed-Temperature Heat Detector Spacing. The following method can be used to determine the response of fixed-temperature heat detectors for designing or analyzing heat detection systems.

B.3.3.1.1 The objective of designing a detection system is to determine the spacing of detectors required to respond to a given set of conditions and goals. To achieve the objectives, detector response must occur when the fire reaches a critical heat release rate, or in a specified time.

B.3.3.1.2 When analyzing an existing detection system, the designer is looking to determine the size of the fire at the time that the detector responds.

B.3.3.2 Theoretical Background. [26, 28] The design and analysis methods contained in Annex B are the joint result of extensive experimental work and of mathematical modeling of the heat and mass transfer processes involved. The original method was developed by Heskestad and Delichatsios [9, 10], Beyler [4], and Schifiliti [16]. It was recently updated by Marrion [28] to reflect changes in the original correlations as discussed in work by Heskestad and Delichatsios [11] and Marrion [27]. Additional research has been conducted by FM Global [43, 44, 45]. Paragraph B.3.3.2 outlines methods and data correlations used to model the heat transfer to a heat detector, as well as velocity and temperature correlations for growing fires at the location of the detector. Only the general principles are described here. More detailed information is available in References 4, 9, 10, 16, and 28 in H.1.2.15.

B.3.3.3 Heat Detector Correlations. The heat transfer to a detector can be described by the following equation:

$$Q_{total} = Q_{cond} + Q_{conv} + Q_{rad} \tag{B.8}$$

where:

Q_{total} = total heat transfer to a detector (kW or Btu/sec)
Q_{cond} = conductive heat transfer
Q_{conv} = convective heat transfer
Q_{rad} = radiative heat transfer

B.3.3.3.1 Because detection typically occurs during the initial stages of a fire, the radiant heat transfer component (Q_{rad}) can be considered negligible. In addition, because the heat-sensing elements of most of the heat detectors are thermally isolated from the rest of the detection unit, as well as from the ceiling, it can be assumed that the conductive portion of the heat release rate (Q_{cond}) is also negligible, especially when compared to the convective heat transfer rate. Because the majority of the heat transfer to the detection element is via convection, the following equation can be used to calculate the total heat transfer:

$$Q = Q_{conv} = H_c A(T_g - T_d) \tag{B.9}$$

where:

Q_{conv} = convective heat transfer (kW or Btu/sec)
H_c = convective heat transfer coefficient for the detector (kW/m²·°C or Btu/ft²·sec·°F)
A = surface area of the detector's element (m² or ft²)
T_g = temperature of fire gases at the detector (°C or °F)
T_d = temperature rating, or set point, of the detector (°C or °F)

B.3.3.3.2 Assuming the detection element can be treated as a lumped mass (m) (kg or lbm), its temperature change can be defined as follows:

$$\frac{dT_d}{dt} = \frac{Q}{mc} \tag{B.10}$$

where:

dT_d/dt = change in temperature of detection element (deg/sec)
Q = heat release rate (kW or Btu/sec)
m = detector element's mass (kg or lbm)
c = detector element's specific heat (kJ/kg·°C or Btu/lbm·°F)

B.3.3.3.3 Substituting this into the previous equation, the change in temperature of the detection element over time can be expressed as follows:

$$\frac{dT_d}{dt} = \frac{H_c A(T_g - T_d)}{mc} \tag{B.11}$$

Note that the variables are identified in Section B.7.

B.3.3.3.4 The use of a time constant (τ) was proposed by Heskestad and Smith [8] in order to define the convective heat transfer to a specific detector's heat-sensing element. This time constant is a function of the mass, specific heat, convective heat transfer coefficient, and area of the element and can be expressed as follows:

$$\tau = \frac{mc}{H_c A} \tag{B.12}$$

where:

m = detector element's mass (kg or lbm)

c = detector element's specific heat (kJ/kg·°C or Btu/lbm·°F)

H_c = convective heat transfer coefficient for the detector (kW/m²·°C or Btu/ft²·sec·°F)

A = surface area of the detector's element (m² or ft²)

τ = detector time constant (seconds)

B.3.3.3.5 As seen in the equation B.12, τ is a measure of the detector's sensitivity. By increasing the mass of the detection element, the time constant, and thus the response time, increases.

B.3.3.3.6 Substituting into equation B.11 produces the following:

$$\frac{dT_d}{dt} = \frac{T_g - T_d}{\tau}$$

(B.13)

Note that the variables are identified in Section B.7.

B.3.3.3.7 Research has shown [24] that the convective heat transfer coefficient for sprinklers and heat detection elements is similar to that of spheres, cylinders, and so forth, and is thus approximately proportional to the square root of the velocity of the gases passing the detector. As the mass, thermal capacity, and area of the detection element remain constant, the following relationship can be expressed as the response time index (RTI) for an individual detector:

$$\tau u^{1/2} \sim \tau_0 u_0^{1/2} = \text{RTI}$$

(B.14)

where:

τ = detector time constant (seconds)

u = velocity of fire gases (m/sec or ft/sec)

u_0 = instantaneous velocity of fire gases (m/sec or ft/sec)

RTI = response time index

B.3.3.3.8 If τ_0 is measured at a given reference velocity (u_0), τ can be determined for any other gas velocity (u) for that detector. A plunge test is the easiest way to measure τ_0. It has also been related to the listed spacing of a detector through a calculation. Table B.3.2.5 presents results from these calculations [10]. The RTI value can then be obtained by multiplying τ_0 values by $u_0^{1/2}$.

B.3.3.3.9 It has become customary to refer to the time constant using a reference velocity of $u_0 = 1.5$ m/sec (5 ft/sec). For example, where $u_0 = 1.5$ m/sec (5 ft/sec), a τ_0 of 30 seconds corresponds to an RTI of 36 sec$^{1/2}$/m$^{1/2}$ (or 67 sec$^{1/2}$/ft$^{1/2}$). On the other hand, a detector that has an RTI of 36 sec$^{1/2}$/m$^{1/2}$ (or 67 sec$^{1/2}$/ft$^{1/2}$) would have a τ_0 of 23.7 seconds, if measured in an air velocity of 2.4 m/sec (8 ft/sec).

Research performed by FM Global on the response of heat detectors shows that the use of the reference velocity of 1.5 m/sec (5 ft/sec) is suitable for electronic heat detectors used in fire alarm systems. Comparison experiments were run in which response predictions were computed based upon RTI values derived in accordance with FM Approval Standard 3210. Then full-scale fire tests were conducted to see how close the computed predictions came to predicting actual heat detector. In almost all cases, the predicted detection times and actual detection times were within a few seconds. All tests were sufficiently close to validate the test method.

B.3.3.3.10 The following equation can therefore be used to calculate the heat transfer to the detection element and thus determine its temperature from its local fire-induced environment:

$$\frac{dT_d}{dt} = \frac{u^{1/2}(T_g - T_d)}{\text{RTI}}$$ (B.15)

Note that the variables are identified in Section B.7.

B.3.3.4 Temperature and Velocity Correlations. [26, 28] In order to predict the operation of any detector, it is necessary to characterize the local environment created by the fire at the location of the detector. For a heat detector, the important variables are the temperature and velocity of the gases at the detector. Through a program of full-scale tests and the use of mathematical modeling techniques, general expressions for temperature and velocity at a detector location have been developed by Heskestad and Delichatsios *(refer to references 4, 9, 10, and 16 in H.1.2.15)*. These expressions are valid for fires that grow according to the following power law relationship:

$$Q = \alpha t^p$$ (B.16)

where:

Q = theoretical convective fire heat release rate (kW or Btu/sec)

α = fire growth rate (kW/sec^2 or Btu/sec^3)

t = time (seconds)

p = positive exponent

Several other ceiling jet correlations [41] have been developed over the years that the designer should also review as to their applicability to the particular design case. Sensitivity analyses should also be conducted with the analysis.

The *t*-squared fire growth curve is a specific case of equation B.16 where $p = 2$. Few situations exist where p will take on a value other than 2. Nitrated and perchlorated propellants might be better described as *t*-cubed fires. It is conceivable that fuels might be stored in a manner in which the rate of fire extension is offset by the rate of fuel consumption to give a total fire growth rate that could be described as having an exponent of 1.5, but such cases are rare.

Other fire growth correlations exist. For more information, see the references in B.6.5. Some correlations have been published in the *SFPE Handbook of Fire Protection Engineering*. NIST has also published correlations that can be used for prediction of detector response.

B.3.3.4.1 Relationships have been developed by Heskestad and Delichatsios [9] for temperature and velocity of fire gases in a ceiling jet. These have been expressed as follows [26]:

$$U_p^* = \frac{u}{A^{1/(3+p)}u^{1/(3+p)}H^{(p-1)/(3+p)}} = f\left(t_p^*, \frac{r}{H}\right)$$ (B.17)

$$\Delta T_p^* = g\left(t_p^*, \frac{r}{H}\right) = \frac{\Delta T}{A^{2/(3+p)}\left(\dfrac{T_a}{g}\right)\alpha^{2/(3+p)}H^{-(5-p)/(3+p)}}$$ (B.18)

where:

$$t_p^* = \frac{t}{A^{-1/(3+p)}\alpha^{-1/(3+p)}H^{4/(3+p)}}$$ (B.19)

and

$$A = \frac{g}{C_p T_a \rho_0}$$ (B.20)

Note that the variables are identified in Section B.7.

B.3.3.4.2 Using the preceding correlations, Heskestad and Delichatsios [9], and with later updates from another paper by Heskestad [11], the following correlations were presented for fires that had heat release rates that grew according to the power law equation, with $p = 2$. As previously discussed [10, 18], the $p = 2$ power law fire growth model can be used to model the heat release rate of a wide range of fuels. These fires are therefore referred to as *t-squared* fires.

$$t_{2f}^* = 0.861\left(1 + \frac{r}{H}\right) \tag{B.21}$$

$$\Delta T_2^* = 0 \qquad \text{for } t_2^* < t_{2f}^* \tag{B.22}$$

$$\Delta T_2^* = \left(\frac{t_2^* - t_{2f}^*}{0.146 + 0.242r/H}\right)^{4/3} \qquad \text{for } t_2^* \geq t_{2f}^* \tag{B.23}$$

$$\frac{u_2^*}{(\Delta T_2^*)^{1/2}} = 0.59\left(\frac{r}{H}\right)^{-0.63} \tag{B.24}$$

Note that the variables are identified in Section B.7.

B.3.3.4.3 Work by Beyler [4] determined that the preceding temperature and velocity correlations could be substituted into the heat transfer equation for the detector and integrated. His analytical solution is as follows:

$$T_d(t) - T_d(0) = \left(\frac{\Delta T}{\Delta T_2^*}\right)\Delta T_2^*\left[\frac{1 - (1 - e^{-Y})}{Y}\right] \tag{B.25}$$

$$\frac{dT_d(t)}{dt} = \frac{\left(\frac{4}{3}\right)\left(\frac{\Delta T}{\Delta T_2^*}\right)(\Delta T_2^*)^{1/4}(1 - e^{-Y})}{\left(\frac{t}{t_2^*}\right)D} \tag{B.26}$$

where:

$$Y = \left(\frac{3}{4}\right)\left(\frac{u}{u_2^*}\right)^{1/2}\left(\frac{u_2^*}{\Delta T_2^{*1/2}}\right)^{1/2}\left(\frac{\Delta T_2^*}{\text{RTI}}\right)\left(\frac{t}{t_2^*}\right)D \tag{B.27}$$

and

$$D = 0.146 + 0.242r/H \tag{B.28}$$

Note that the variables are identified in Section B.7.

B.3.3.4.4 The steps involved in solving these equations for either a design or analysis situation are presented in Figure B.3.3.4.4 [28].

Designers and engineers who expect to do performance estimates on a regular basis are advised to set up an application using a popular spreadsheet program to run the calculations outlined on the worksheet.

B.3.3.5 Limitations. [26]

It is extremely important that users of this computational method keep in mind the limitations in B.3.3.5.

B.3.3.5.1 [26] If velocity and temperature of the fire gases flowing past a detector cannot be accurately determined, errors will be introduced when calculating the response of a detector. The graphs presented by Heskestad and Delichatsios indicate the errors in the calculated fire–gas temperatures and velocities [10]. A detailed analysis of these errors is beyond the scope of this annex; however, some discussion is warranted. In using the method as previously described, the user should be aware of the limitations of these correlations, as outlined in Reference 26. The designer should also refer back to the original reports.

Fire Detection Design and Analysis Worksheet [28]
Design Example

1.	Determine ambient temperature (T_a) ceiling height or height above fuel (H).	$T_a =$ _____ °C + 273 = _____ K $H =$ _____ m
2.	Determine the fire growth characteristic (α or t_g) for the expected design fire.	$\alpha =$ _____ kW/sec^2 $t_g =$ _____ sec
3a.	Define the characteristics of the detectors.	$T_s =$ _____ °C + 273 = _____ K RTI = _____ m$^{1/2}$sec$^{1/2}$ $\dfrac{dT_d}{dt} =$ _____ °C/min $\tau_0 =$ _____ sec
3b. or	*Design* — Establish system goals (t_{CR} or Q_{CR}) and make a first estimate of the distance (r) from the fire to the detector.	$t_{CR} =$ _____ sec $r =$ _____ m $Q_{CR} =$ _____ kW
3b.	*Analysis* — Determine spacing of existing detectors and make a first estimate of the response time or the fire size at detector response ($Q = \alpha t^2$).	$r =$ _____ *1.41 = _____ = S (m) $Q =$ _____ kW $t_d =$ _____ sec
4.	Using equation B.21, calculate the nondimensional time (t^*_{2f}) at which the initial heat front reaches the detector.	$t^*_{2f} = 0.861\left(1 + \dfrac{r}{H}\right)$ $t^*_{2f} =$
5.	Calculate the factor A defined by the relationship for A in equation B.20.	$A = \dfrac{g}{C_p T_a \rho_0}$ $A =$
6.	Use the required response time (t_{CR}) along with the relationship for t^*_p in equation B.19 and $p = 2$ to calculate the corresponding value of t^*_2.	$t^*_2 = \dfrac{t_{CR}}{A^{-1/(3+p)}\,\alpha^{-1/(3+p)}\,H^{4/(3+p)}}$ $t^*_2 =$
7.	If $t^*_2 > t^*_{2f}$, continue to step 8. If not, try a new detector position (r) and return to step 4.	
8.	Calculate the ratio $\dfrac{u}{u^*_2}$ using the relationship for U^*_p in equation B.17.	$\dfrac{u}{u^*_2} = A^{1/(3+p)}\,\alpha^{1/(3+p)}\,H^{(p-1)/(3+p)}$ $\dfrac{u}{u^*_2} =$
9.	Calculate the ratio $\dfrac{\Delta T}{\Delta T^*_2}$ using the relationship for ΔT^*_p in equation B.18.	$\dfrac{\Delta T}{\Delta T^*_2} = A^{2/(3+p)}(T_a/g)\,\alpha^{2/(3+p)}\,H^{-(5-p)/(3+p)}$ $\dfrac{\Delta T}{\Delta T^*_2} =$
10.	Use the relationship for ΔT^*_2 in equation B.23 to calculate ΔT^*_2.	$\Delta T^*_2 = \left[\dfrac{t^*_2 - t^*_{2f}}{(0.146 + 0.242r/H)}\right]^{4/3}$ $\Delta T^*_2 =$
11.	Use the relationship for $\dfrac{u^*_2}{(\Delta T^*_2)^{1/2}}$ in equation B.24 to calculate the ratio $\dfrac{u^*_2}{(\Delta T^*_2)^{1/2}}$.	$\dfrac{u^*_2}{(\Delta T^*_2)^{1/2}} = 0.59\left(\dfrac{r}{H}\right)^{-0.63}$ $\dfrac{u^*_2}{(\Delta T^*_2)^{1/2}} =$
12.	Use the relationships for Y and D in equations B.27 and B.28 to calculate Y.	$Y = \left(\dfrac{3}{4}\right)\left(\dfrac{u}{u^*_2}\right)^{1/2}\left[\dfrac{u^*_2}{(\Delta T^*_2)^{1/2}}\right]^{1/2}\left(\dfrac{\Delta T^*_2}{\text{RTI}}\right)\left(\dfrac{t}{t^*_2}\right)D$ $Y =$
13.	*Fixed Temperature HD* — Use the relationship for $T_d(t) - T_d(0)$ in equation B.25 to calculate the resulting temperature of the detector $T_d(t)$.	$T_d(t) = \left(\dfrac{\Delta T}{\Delta T^*_2}\right)\Delta T^*_2\left[1 - \dfrac{(1-e^{-Y})}{Y}\right] + T_d(0)$ $T_d(t) =$
14.	*Rate of Rise HD* — Use the relationship for $\dfrac{dT_d(t)}{dt}$ in equation B.26.	$dT_d = \left[\left(\dfrac{4}{3}\right)\left(\dfrac{\Delta T}{\Delta T^*_2}\right)(\Delta T^*_2)^{1/4}\dfrac{(1-e^{-Y})}{[(t/t^*_2)D]}\right]dt$ $dT_d =$
15.	If: 1. $T_d > T_s$ 2. $T_d < T_s$ 3. $T_d = T$	Repeat Procedure Using Design Analysis 1. a larger r 1. a larger t_r 2. a smaller r 2. a smaller t_r 3. $s = 1.41 \times r =$ ___ m 3. $t_r =$ ___ sec

FIGURE B.3.3.4.4 *Fire Detection Design and Analysis Worksheet.* [28]

Graphs of actual and calculated data show that errors in $T_2{}^*$ can be as high as 50 percent, although generally there appears to be much better agreement. The maximum errors occur at r/H values of about 0.37. All other plots of actual and calculated data, for various r/H, show much smaller errors. In terms of the actual change in temperature over ambient, the maximum errors are on the order of 5°C to 10°C (9°F to 18°F). The larger errors occur with faster fires and lower ceilings.

At $r/H = 0.37$, the errors are conservative when the equations are used in a design problem. That is, the equations predicted lower temperatures. Plots of data for other values of r/H indicate that the equations predict slightly higher temperatures.

Errors in fire–gas velocities are related to errors in temperatures. The equations show that the velocity of the fire gases is proportional to the square root of the change in temperatures of the fire gases. In terms of heat transfer to a detector, the detector's change in temperature is proportional to the change in gas temperature and the square root of the fire–gas velocity. Hence, the expected errors bear the same relationships.

Based on the preceding discussion, errors in predicted temperatures and velocities of fire gases will be greatest for fast fires and low ceilings. Sample calculations simulating these conditions show errors in calculated detector spacings on the order of plus or minus one meter, or less.

B.3.3.5.2 The procedures presented in this annex are based on an analysis of test data for ceiling heights up to 9.1 m (30 ft). No data were analyzed for ceilings greater than 9.1 m (30 ft). The reader should refer to Reference 40 for additional insight.

B.3.3.6 Design Examples.

B.3.3.6.1 Define Project Scope. A fire detection system is to be designed for installation in an unsprinklered warehouse building. The building has a large, flat ceiling that is approximately 4 m (13.1 ft) high. The ambient temperature inside is normally 10°C (50°F). The municipal fire service has indicated that it can begin putting water on the fire within 5.25 minutes of receiving the alarm.

B.3.3.6.2 Identify Goals. Provide protection of property.

B.3.3.6.3 Define Stakeholder's Objective. No fire spread from initial fuel package.

B.3.3.6.4 Define Design Objective. Prevent radiant ignition of adjacent fuel package.

B.3.3.6.5 Develop Performance Criteria. After discussions with the plant fire brigade with regard to their capability and analyzing the radiant energy levels necessary to ignite adjacent fuel packages, it was determined that the fire should be detected and suppression activities started prior to its reaching 10,000 kW (9478 Btu/sec).

B.3.3.6.6 Develop Fire Scenarios and the Design Fire. Evaluation of the potential contents to be warehoused identified the areas where wood pallets are stored to be one of the highest fire hazards.

The designer cannot come to the conclusion in B.3.3.6.6 without reviewing all the combustibles, their heat release rates, and their orientation. With this analysis, the designer can then determine if the stack of wood pallets indeed presents the worst case. The designer must analyze other scenarios using fire loads in other areas to verify that this represents the worst-case scenario. Furthermore, if stakeholders desire future flexibility in the use of the space, the designer must use additional factors of safety.

B.3.3.6.6.1 The fire scenario involving the ignition of a stack of wood pallets will therefore be evaluated. The pallets are stored 0.5 m (1.5 ft) high. Fire test data *[see Table B.2.3.2.6.2(a)]* indicate that this type of fire follows the t^2 power law equation with a t_g equal to approximately 150 to 310 seconds. To be conservative, the faster fire growth rate will be used. Thus, using equation B.16,

$$Q = \alpha t^p$$
$$1055 \text{ kW} = (\alpha \text{ kW/sec}^2)(150 \text{ sec})^2$$
$$\alpha = 0.047 \text{ kW/sec}^2$$

or

$$Q = \alpha t^p$$
$$1000 \text{ Btu/sec} = (\alpha \text{ Btu/sec}^3)(150 \text{ sec})^2$$
$$\alpha = 0.044 \text{ Btu/sec}^3$$

Note that the variables are identified in Section B.7.

B.3.3.6.6.2 Using the power law growth equation with $p = 2$, the time after open flaming until the fire grows to 10,000 kW (9478 Btu/sec) can be calculated as follows:

$$Q = \left(\frac{1055}{t_c^2}\right)t_{DO}^2 = \alpha t^2 \text{ (for SI units)} \qquad \text{(B.29a)}$$

or

$$Q = \left(\frac{1000}{t_c^2}\right)t_{DO}^2 = \alpha t^2 \text{ (for inch-pound units)} \qquad \text{(B.29b)}$$

$$t_{DO} = 461 \text{ seconds}$$

Note that the variables are identified in Section B.7.

As part of this analysis, the designer should verify that sufficient fuel exists in the initial fuel package to allow the fire to sustain the continued growth rate over this length of time. Insufficient fuel or a change in fire growth rate will affect the detector response.

B.3.3.6.6.3 The critical heat release rate and time to detection can therefore be calculated as follows, assuming $t_{respond}$ equals the 5.25 minutes necessary for the fire brigade to respond to the alarm and begin discharging water:

$$t_{CR} = t_{DO} - t_{respond} \qquad \text{(B.30)}$$
$$t_{CR} = 461 - 315 = 146 \text{ seconds}$$

and thus

$$Q_{CR} = \alpha t_{CR}^2 \qquad \text{(B.31)}$$
$$Q_{CR} = 1000 \text{ kW (948 Btu/sec)}$$

Note that the variables are identified in Section B.7.

B.3.3.7 Develop Candidate Designs.

B.3.3.7.1 Fixed-temperature heat detectors have been selected for installation in the warehouse with a 57°C (135°F) operating temperature and a UL-listed spacing of 9.1 m (30 ft). From Table B.3.2.5, the time constant is determined to be 80 seconds when referenced to a gas velocity of 1.5 m/sec (5 ft/sec). When used with equation B.14, the detector's RTI can be calculated as follows:

$$\text{RTI} = \tau_0 u_0^{1/2} \qquad \text{(B.32)}$$
$$\text{RTI} = 98 \text{ m}^{1/2}\text{sec}^{1/2}$$

or

$$\text{RTI} = 179 \text{ ft}^{1/2}\text{sec}^{1/2}$$

B.3.3.7.2 To begin calculations, it will be necessary to make a first guess at the required detector spacing. For this example, a first estimate of 4.7 m (15.3 ft) is used. This correlates to a radial distance of 3.3 m (10.8 ft).

B.3.3.8 Evaluate Candidate Designs. These values can then be entered into the design and analysis worksheet shown in Figure B.3.3.8 in order to evaluate the candidate design.

Fire Detection Design and Analysis Worksheet [28]
Design Example

1.	Determine ambient temperature (T_a) ceiling height or height above fuel (H).	$T_a = \underline{\quad 10 \quad}$ °C + 273 = $\underline{\quad 283 \quad}$ K $H = \underline{\quad 4 \quad}$ m
2.	Determine the fire growth characteristic (α or t_g) for the expected design fire.	$\alpha = \underline{\quad 0.047 \quad}$ kW/sec^2 $t_g = \underline{\quad 150 \quad}$ sec
3a.	Define the characteristics of the detectors.	$T_s = \underline{\quad 57 \quad}$ °C + 273 = $\underline{330}$ K RTI = $\underline{98}$ m$^{1/2}$sec$^{1/2}$ $\dfrac{dT_d}{dt} = \underline{\qquad\qquad}$ °C/min $\tau_0 = \underline{\qquad\qquad}$ sec
3b. or	*Design* — Establish system goals (t_{CR} or Q_{CR}) and make a first estimate of the distance (r) from the fire to the detector.	$t_{CR} = \underline{\quad 146 \quad}$ sec $r = \underline{\quad 3.3 \quad}$ m $Q_{CR} = \underline{\quad 1000 \quad}$ kW
3b.	*Analysis* — Determine spacing of existing detectors and make a first estimate of the response time or the fire size at detector response ($Q = \alpha t^2$).	$r = \underline{\qquad\qquad}$ *1.41 = $\underline{\qquad\qquad}$ = S (m) $Q = \underline{\qquad\qquad}$ kW $t_d = \underline{\qquad\qquad}$ sec
4.	Using equation B.21, calculate the nondimensional time $\left(t^*_{2f}\right)$ at which the initial heat front reaches the detector.	$t^*_{2f} = 0.861\left(1 + \dfrac{r}{H}\right)$ $t^*_{2f} = 1.57$
5.	Calculate the factor A defined by the relationship for A in equation B.20.	$A = \dfrac{g}{C_p T_a \rho_0}$ $A = 0.030$
6.	Use the required response time (t_{CR}) along with the relationship for t^*_p in equation B.19 and $p = 2$ to calculate the corresponding value of t^*_2.	$t^*_2 = \dfrac{t_{CR}}{A^{-1/(3+p)}\,\alpha^{-1/(3+p)}\,H^{4/(3+p)}}$ $t^*_2 = 12.98$
7.	If $t^*_2 > t^*_{2f}$, continue to step 8. If not, try a new detector position (r) and return to step 4.	
8.	Calculate the ratio $\dfrac{u}{u^*_2}$ using the relationship for U^*_p in equation B.17.	$\dfrac{u}{u^*_2} = A^{1/(3+p)}\,\alpha^{1/(3+p)}\,H^{(p-1)/(3+p)}$ $\qquad \dfrac{u}{u^*_2} = 0.356$
9.	Calculate the ratio $\dfrac{\Delta T}{\Delta T^*_2}$ using the relationship for ΔT^*_p in equation B.18.	$\dfrac{\Delta T}{\Delta T^*_2} = A^{2/(3+p)}(T_a/g)\,\alpha^{2/(3+p)}\,H^{-(5-p)/(3+p)}$ $\qquad \dfrac{\Delta T}{\Delta T^*_2} = 0.913$
10.	Use the relationship for ΔT^*_2 in equation B.23 to calculate ΔT^*_2.	$\Delta T^*_2 = \left[\dfrac{t^*_2 - t^*_{2f}}{(0.146 + 0.242r/H)}\right]^{4/3}$ $\qquad \Delta T^*_2 = 105.89$
11.	Use the relationship for $\dfrac{u^*_2}{(\Delta T^*_2)^{1/2}}$ in equation B.24 to calculate the ratio $\dfrac{u^*_2}{(\Delta T^*_2)^{1/2}}$.	$\dfrac{u^*_2}{(\Delta T^*_2)^{1/2}} = 0.59\left(\dfrac{r}{H}\right)^{-0.63}$ $\qquad \dfrac{u^*_2}{(\Delta T^*_2)^{1/2}} = 0.66$
12.	Use the relationships for Y and D in equations B.27 and B.28 to calculate Y.	$Y = \left(\dfrac{3}{4}\right)\left(\dfrac{u}{u^*_2}\right)^{1/2}\left[\dfrac{u^*_2}{(\Delta T^*_2)^{1/2}}\right]^{1/2}\left(\dfrac{\Delta T^*_2}{\text{RTI}}\right)\left(\dfrac{t}{t^*_2}\right)D$ $\quad Y = 1.533$
13.	*Fixed Temperature HD* — Use the relationship for $T_d(t) - T_d(0)$ in equation B.25 to calculate the resulting temperature of the detector $T_d(t)$.	$T_d(t) = \left(\dfrac{\Delta T}{\Delta T^*_2}\right)\Delta T^*_2\left[1 - \dfrac{(1-e^{-Y})}{Y}\right] + T_d(0)$ $\quad T_d(t) = 57.25$
14.	*Rate of Rise HD* — Use the relationship for $\dfrac{dT_d(t)}{dt}$ in equation B.26.	$dT_d = \left[\left(\dfrac{4}{3}\right)\left(\dfrac{\Delta T}{\Delta T^*_2}\right)(\Delta T^*_2)^{1/4}\dfrac{(1-e^{-Y})}{[(t/t^*_2)D]}\right]dt$ $\quad dT_d =$

15.			
If:		**Repeat Procedure Using**	
		Design	Analysis
1. $T_d > T_s$		1. a larger r	1. a larger t_r
2. $T_d < T_s$		2. a smaller r	2. a smaller t_r
3. $T_d = T$		3. $s = 1.41 \times r = \underline{\quad 4.7 \quad}$ m	3. $t_r = \underline{\qquad}$ sec

FIGURE B.3.3.8 *Fire Detection Design and Analysis Worksheet [28] — Design Example.*

B.3.3.8.1 After 146 seconds, when the fire has grown to 1000 kW (948 Btu/sec) and at a radial distance of 3.3 m (10.8 ft) from the center of the fire, the detector temperature is calculated to be 57°C (135°F). This is the detector actuation temperature. If the calculated temperature of the detector were higher than the actuation temperature, the radial distance could be increased. The calculation would then be repeated until the calculated detector temperature is approximately equal to the actuation temperature.

If for some reason the detector spacing cannot be changed, the designer can select another type of heat detector with a different listed spacing and, hence, a different RTI. The designer can then repeat the design calculation to determine if a system using the second type of detector meets the performance criteria.

B.3.3.8.2 The last step is to use the final calculated value of r with the equation relating spacing to radial distance. This will determine the maximum installed detector spacing that will result in detector response within the established goals.

$$S = 2^{1/2}r \tag{B.33}$$
$$S = 4.7 \text{ m (15.3 ft)}$$

where:

S = spacing of detectors

r = radial distance from fire plume axis (m or ft)

B.3.3.8.3 The following example of analysis is provided.

B.3.3.8.3.1 The following example shows how an existing heat detection system or a proposed design can be analyzed to determine the response time or fire size at response. The scenario that was analyzed in the previous example will be used again, with the exception that the warehouse building has existing heat detectors. The fire, building, and detectors have the same characteristics as the previous example with the exception of spacing. The detectors are spaced evenly on the ceiling at 9.1 m (30 ft) intervals.

B.3.3.8.3.2 The following equation is used to determine the maximum radial distance from the fire axis to a detector:

$$S = 1.414r \tag{B.34}$$

    or

$$r = \frac{S}{1.414}$$
$$r = 6.5 \text{ m (21.2 ft)}$$

where:

S = spacing of detectors

r = radial distance from fire plume axis (m or ft)

At this point, the designer should perform a sensitivity analysis for each of the variables to determine if the design inordinately relies on an assumed value for one or more parameters.

B.3.3.8.3.3 Next, the response time of the detector or the fire size at response is estimated. In the preceding design, the fire grew to 1000 kW (948 Btu/sec) in 146 seconds when the detector located at a distance of 3.3 m (10.8 ft) responded. As the radial distance in this example is larger, a slower response time and thus a larger fire size at response is expected. A first approximation at the response time is made at 3 minutes. The corresponding fire size is found using the power law fire growth equation B.16 with $p = 2$ and α from B.3.3.6.6.1:

$$Q = \alpha t^p$$
$$Q = (0.047 \text{ kW/sec}^2)(180 \text{ sec})^2$$
$$Q = 1523 \text{ kW}$$

or

$$Q = (0.044 \text{ Btu/sec}^3)(180 \text{ sec})^2$$
$$Q = 1426 \text{ Btu/sec}$$

B.3.3.8.3.4 These data can be incorporated into the fire detection design and analysis worksheet shown in Figure B.3.3.8.3.4 in order to carry out the remainder of the calculations.

B.3.3.8.3.5 Using a radial distance of 6.5 m (21 ft) from the axis of this fire, the temperature of the detector is calculated to be 41°C (106°F) after 3 minutes of exposure. The detector actuation temperature is 57°C (135°F). Thus, the detector response time is more than the estimated 3 minutes. If the calculated temperature were more than the actuation temperature, then a smaller t would be used. As in the previous example, calculations should be repeated varying the time to response until the calculated detector temperature is approximately equal to the actuation temperature. For this example, the response time is estimated to be 213 seconds. This corresponds to a fire size at response of 2132 kW (2022 Btu/sec).

B.3.3.8.4 The preceding examples assume that the fire continues to follow the t-squared fire growth relationship up to detector activation. These calculations do not check whether this will happen, nor do they show how the detector temperature varies once the fire stops following the power law relationship. The user should therefore determine that there will be sufficient fuel, since the preceding correlations do not perform this analysis. If there is not a sufficient amount of fuel, then there is the possibility that the heat release rate curve will flatten out or decline before the heat release rate needed for actuation is reached.

The use of the t-squared model presumes sufficient fuel to permit the fire to grow according to the t-squared model. The designer should verify that the hazard provides sufficient fuel. Because $Q = mH_c$, the designer can determine the required fuel load by integrating this relation over the time period in question and then dividing by H_c.

B.3.3.8.5 Table B.3.3.8.5(a) through Table B.3.3.8.5(k) provide a comparison of heat release rates, response times, and spacings when variables characteristic of the fires, detectors, and room are changed from the analysis example.

B.3.3.9 Rate-of-Rise Heat Detector Spacing.

B.3.3.9.1 The preceding procedure can be used to estimate the response of rate-of-rise heat detectors for either design or analysis purposes. In this case, it is necessary to assume that the heat detector response can be modeled using a lumped mass heat transfer model.

TABLE B.3.3.8.5(a) *Operating Temperature Versus Heat Transfer Rate [S = 9.1 m (30 ft)]*

Operating Temperature		Heat Release Rate/ Response Time	
°C	°F	kW/sec	Btu/sec/sec
57	135	2132/213	2022/213
74	165	2798/244	2654/244
93	200	3554/275	3371/275

TABLE B.3.3.8.5(b) *Operating Temperature Versus Spacing [Q_d = 1000 kW (948 Btu/sec)]*

Operating Temperature		Spacing	
°C	°F	m	ft
57	135	4.7	15.4
74	165	3.5	11.5
93	200	2.5	8.2

Fire Detection Design and Analysis Worksheet [28]
Design Analysis 2

1.	Determine ambient temperature (T_a) ceiling height or height above fuel (H).	$T_a =$ _____10_____ °C + 273 = _____283_____ K $H =$ _____4_____ m
2.	Determine the fire growth characteristic (α or t_g) for the expected design fire.	$\alpha =$ _____0.047_____ kW/sec² $t_g =$ _____150_____ sec
3a.	Define the characteristics of the detectors.	$T_s =$ _____57_____ °C + 273 = __330__ K RTI = __98__ m$^{1/2}$sec$^{1/2}$ $\dfrac{dT_d}{dt} =$ _____ °C/min $\tau_0 =$ _____ sec
3b. or	*Design* — Establish system goals (t_{CR} or Q_{CR}) and make a first estimate of the distance (r) from the fire to the detector.	$t_{CR} =$ _____ sec $r =$ _____ m $Q_{CR} =$ _____ kW
3b.	*Analysis* — Determine spacing of existing detectors and make a first estimate of the response time or the fire size at detector response ($Q = \alpha t^2$).	$r =$ _____6.5_____ *1.41 = _____9.2_____ = S (m) $Q =$ _____1,523_____ kW $t_d =$ _____180_____ sec
4.	Using equation B.21, calculate the nondimensional time (t^*_{2f}) at which the initial heat front reaches the detector.	$t^*_{2f} = 0.861 \left(1 + \dfrac{r}{H}\right)$ $t^*_{2f} =$ **2.26**
5.	Calculate the factor A defined by the relationship for A in equation B.20.	$A = \dfrac{g}{C_p T_a \rho_0}$ $A =$ **0.030**
6.	Use the required response time (t_{CR}) along with the relationship for t^*_p in equation B.19 and $p = 2$ to calculate the corresponding value of t^*_2.	$t^*_2 = \dfrac{t_{CR}}{A^{-1/(3+p)} \alpha^{-1/(3+p)} H^{4/(3+p)}}$ $t^*_2 =$ **16**
7.	If $t^*_2 > t^*_{2f}$, continue to step 8. If not, try a new detector position (r) and return to step 4.	
8.	Calculate the ratio $\dfrac{u}{u^*_2}$ using the relationship for U^*_p in equation B.18.	$\dfrac{u}{u^*_2} = A^{1/(3+p)} \alpha^{1/(3+p)} H^{(p-1)/(3+p)}$ $\dfrac{u}{u^*_2} =$ **0.356**
9.	Calculate the ratio $\dfrac{\Delta T}{\Delta T^*_2}$ using the relationship for ΔT^*_p in equation B.18.	$\dfrac{\Delta T}{\Delta T^*_2} = A^{2/(3+p)} (T_a/g)\, \alpha^{2/(3+p)} H^{-(5-p)/(3+p)}$ $\dfrac{\Delta T}{\Delta T^*_2} =$ **0.913**
10.	Use the relationship for ΔT^*_2 in equation B.23 to calculate ΔT^*_2.	$\Delta T^*_2 = \left[\dfrac{t^*_2 - t^*_{2f}}{(0.146 + 0.242 r/H)}\right]^{4/3}$ $\Delta T^*_2 =$ **75.01**
11.	Use the relationship for $\dfrac{u^*_2}{(\Delta T^*_2)^{1/2}}$ in equation B.24 to calculate the ratio $\dfrac{u^*_2}{(\Delta T^*_2)^{1/2}}$.	$\dfrac{u^*_2}{(\Delta T^*_2)^{1/2}} = 0.59 \left(\dfrac{r}{H}\right)^{-0.63}$ $\dfrac{u^*_2}{(\Delta T^*_2)^{1/2}} =$ **0.435**
12.	Use the relationships for Y and D in equations B.27 and B.28 to calculate Y.	$Y = \left(\dfrac{3}{4}\right)\left(\dfrac{u}{u^*_2}\right)^{1/2} \left[\dfrac{u^*_2}{(\Delta T^*_2)^{1/2}}\right]^{1/2} \left(\dfrac{\Delta T^*_2}{RTI}\right)\left(\dfrac{t}{t^*_2}\right) D$ $Y =$ **1.37**
13.	*Fixed Temperature HD* — Use the relationship for $T_d(t) - T_d(0)$ in equation B.25 to calculate the resulting temperature of the detector $T_d(t)$.	$T_d(t) = \left(\dfrac{\Delta T}{\Delta T^*_2}\right)\Delta T^*_2 \left[1 - \dfrac{(1-e^{-Y})}{Y}\right] + T_d(0)$ $T_d(t) =$ **41**
14.	*Rate of Rise HD* — Use the relationship for $\dfrac{dT_d(t)}{dt}$ in equation B.26.	$dT_d = \left[\left(\dfrac{4}{3}\right)\left(\dfrac{\Delta T}{\Delta T^*_2}\right)(\Delta T^*_2)^{1/4} \dfrac{(1-e^{-Y})}{[(t/t^*_2)D]}\right] dt$ $dT_d =$
15.	If: 1. $T_d > T_s$ 2. $T_d < T_s$ 3. $T_d = T$	**Repeat Procedure Using** Design / Analysis Design: 1. a larger r Analysis: 1. a larger t_r 2. a smaller r 2. a smaller t_r 3. $s = 1.41 \times r =$ _____ m 3. $t_r =$ _____ sec

FIGURE B.3.3.8.3.4 *Fire Detection Design and Analysis Worksheet [28] — Analysis Example 2.*

TABLE B.3.3.8.5(c) *RTI Versus Heat Release Rate [S = 9.1 m (30 ft)]*

RTI		Heat Release Rate/ Response Time	
$m^{1/2} \, sec^{1/2}$	$ft^{1/2} \, sec^{1/2}$	kW/sec	Btu/sec/sec
50	93	1609/185	1526/185
150	280	2640/237	2504/237
300	560	3898/288	3697/288

TABLE B.3.3.8.5(d) *RTI Versus Spacing [Q_d = 1000 kW (948 Btu/sec)]*

RTI		Spacing	
$m^{1/2} \, sec^{1/2}$	$ft^{1/2} \, sec^{1/2}$	m	ft
50	93	6.1	20.0
150	280	3.7	12.1
300	560	2.3	7.6

TABLE B.3.3.8.5(e) *Ambient Temperature Versus Heat Release Rate [S = 9.1 m (30 ft)]*

Ambient Temperature		Heat Release Rate/ Response Time	
°C	°F	kW/sec	Btu/sec/sec
0	32	2552/233	2420/233
20	68	1751/193	1661/193
38	100	1058/150	1004/150

TABLE B.3.3.8.5(f) *Ambient Temperature Versus Spacing [Q_d = 1000 kW (948 Btu/sec)]*

Ambient Temperature		Spacing	
°C	°F	m	ft
0	32	3.8	12.5
20	68	5.7	18.7
38	100	8.8	28.9

TABLE B.3.3.8.5(g) *Ceiling Height Versus Heat Release Rate [S = 9.1 m (30 ft)]*

Ceiling Height		Heat Release Rate/ Response Time	
m	ft	kW/sec	Btu/sec/sec
2.4	8	1787/195	1695/195
4.9	16	2358/224	2237/224
7.3	24	3056/255	2899/255

TABLE B.3.3.8.5(h) *Ceiling Height Versus Spacing [Q_d = 1000 kW (948 Btu/sec)]*

Ceiling Height		Spacing	
m	ft	m	ft
2.4	8	5.8	19.0
4.9	16	4.0	13.1
7.3	24	2.1	6.9

TABLE B.3.3.8.5(i) *Detector Spacing Versus Heat Release Rate [S = 9.1 m (30 ft)]*

Detector Spacing		Heat Release Rate/ Response Time	
m	ft	kW/sec	Btu/sec/sec
4.6	15	1000/146	949/146
9.1	30	2132/213	2022/213
15.2	50	4146/297	3932/297

TABLE B.3.3.8.5(j) *Fire Growth Rate Versus Heat Release Rate [S = 9.1 m (30 ft)]*

Fire Growth Rate	Heat Release Rate/ Response Time	
	kW/sec	Btu/sec/sec
Slow t_g = 400 sec	1250/435	1186/435
Medium t_g = 250 sec	1582/306	1499/306
Fast t_g = 100 sec	2769/162	2626/162

TABLE B.3.3.8.5(k) *Fire Growth Rate Versus Spacing* *[Q_d = 1000 kW (948 Btu/sec)]*

	Spacing	
Fire Growth Rate	*m*	*ft*
Slow, t_g = 400 sec	8.2	26.9
Medium, t_g = 250 sec	6.5	21.3
Fast, t_g = 100 sec	3.7	12.1

B.3.3.9.2 In step 3 of Figure B.3.3.4.4, Figure B.3.3.8, and Figure B.3.3.8.3.4, the user must determine the rate of temperature rise (dT_d/dt) at which the detector will respond from the manufacturer's data. [Note that listed rate-of-rise heat detectors are designed to activate at a nominal rate of temperature rise of 8°C (15°F) per minute.] The user must use the relationship for $dT_d(t)/dt$ in equation B.26 instead of the relationship for $T_d(t) - T_d(0)$ in equation B.25 in order to calculate the rate of change of the detector temperature. This value is then compared to the rate of change at which the chosen detector is designed to respond.

NOTE: The assumption that heat transfer to a detector can be modeled as a lumped mass might not hold for rate-of-rise heat detectors. This is due to the operating principle of this type of detector, in that most rate-of-rise detectors operate when the expansion of air in a chamber expands at a rate faster than it can vent through an opening. To accurately model the response of a rate-of-rise detector would require modeling the heat transfer from the detector body to the air in the chamber, as well as the air venting through the hole.

B.3.3.10 Rate Compensation–Type Heat Detectors. Rate-compensated detectors are not specifically covered by Annex B. However, a conservative approach to predicting their performance is to use the fixed-temperature heat detector guidance contained herein.

B.4 Smoke Detector Spacing for Flaming Fires

With the issuance of the 2002 edition of the Code, performance-based designs were formally recognized as an alternative to designs developed using the prescriptive rules of the Code. Calculations, such as those outlined in Section B.4, represent an integral part of the performance-based design. However, performance-based design is a process, and the computational tools outlined in this section are intended to be used in the context of that process. The user should review Section 17.3 carefully before undertaking a design based on these computational methods.

When undertaking a performance-based design, designers assume the responsibility for the propriety of the design assumptions being offered to the other stakeholders as well as the assessment of the implications of adopting such assumptions or criteria. This approach puts a greater burden of responsibility on the designers than when they are implementing the requirements of a prescriptive code.

B.4.1 Introduction.

B.4.1.1 The listing investigation for smoke detectors does not yield a "listed spacing" as it does for heat detectors. Instead, the manufacturers recommend a spacing. Because the largest spacing that can be evaluated in the full-scale fire test room is 7.6 m (25 ft), it has become common practice to recommend 9.1 m (30 ft) spacing for smoke detectors when they are installed on flat, smooth ceilings. Reductions in smoke detector spacing are made empirically to address factors that can affect response, including ceiling height, beamed or joisted ceilings, and areas that have high rates of air movement.

Chapter 17 addresses the effects of exposed joists and beams and provides prescriptive design rules that are valid over the limitations stipulated in the text. The chapter also provides design rules to address the effect of ceiling slope on a qualitative basis. Thus far, the requisite research to develop quantitative design calculations for smoke detector spacings exceeding 9.1 m (30 ft) have not yet been performed.

B.4.1.2 The placement of smoke detectors, however, should be based on an understanding of fire plume and ceiling jet flows, smoke production rates, particulate changes due to aging, and the operating characteristics of the particular detector being used. The heat detector spacing information presented in Section B.3 is based on knowledge of plume and jet flows. An understanding of smoke production and aging lags considerably behind an understanding of heat production. In addition, the operating characteristics of smoke detectors in specific fire environments are not often measured or made generally available for other than a very few number of combustible materials. Therefore, the existing knowledge base precludes the development of complete engineering design information for smoke detector location and spacing.

Designers should proceed with caution when designing or analyzing the response of smoke detection systems. Currently available analytical methods do not account for variations in the composition of smoke, the effects of smoke aging, or the detection mechanism appropriate to different detection technologies.

B.4.1.3 In design applications where predicting the response of smoke detectors is not critical, the spacing criteria presented in Chapter 17 should provide sufficient information to design a very basic smoke detection system. However, if the goals and objectives established for the detection system require detector response within a certain amount of time, optical density, heat release rate, or temperature rise, then additional analysis might be needed. For these situations, information regarding the expected fire characteristics (fuel and its fire growth rate), transport characteristics, detector characteristics, and compartment characteristics is required. The following information regarding smoke detector response and various performance-based approaches to evaluating smoke detector response is therefore provided.

B.4.2 Response Characteristics of Smoke Detectors. To determine whether a smoke detector will respond to a given Q_{CR}, a number of factors need to be evaluated. These factors include smoke characteristics, smoke transport, and detector characteristics.

B.4.3 Smoke Characteristics.

B.4.3.1 Smoke characteristics are a function of the fuel composition, the mode of combustion (smoldering or flaming), and the amount of mixing with the ambient air (dilution). These factors are important for determining the characteristics of the products of combustion, such as particle size, distribution, composition, concentration, refractive index, and so on. The significance of these features with regard to smoke detector response is well documented. [29, 30]

B.4.3.2 Whether smoke detectors detect by sensing scattered light, loss of light transmission (light extinction), or reduction of ion current, they are particle detectors. Thus, particle concentration, size, color, size distribution, and so forth, affect each sensing technology differently. It is generally accepted that a flaming, well-ventilated, energetic fire produces smoke having a larger proportion of the sub-micron diameter particulates as opposed to a smoldering fire that produces smoke with a predominance of large, super-micron particulates. It is also known that as the smoke cools, the smaller particles agglomerate, forming larger ones as they age, and are carried away from the fire source. More research is necessary to provide sufficient data to allow the prediction of smoke characteristics at the source, as well as during transport. Furthermore, response models must be developed that can predict the response of a particular detector to different kinds of smoke as well as smoke that has aged during the flow from the fire to the detector location.

B.4.4 Transport Considerations.

B.4.4.1 All smoke detection relies on the plume and ceiling jet flows to transport the smoke from the locus of the fire to the detector. Various considerations must be addressed during this transport time, including changes to the characteristics of the smoke that occur with time and distance from the source, and transport time of smoke from the source to the detector.

B.4.4.2 The smoke characteristic changes that occur during transport relate mainly to the particle size distribution. Particle size changes during transport occur mainly as a result of sedimentation and agglomeration.

B.4.4.3 Transport time is a function of the characteristics of the travel path from the source to the detector. Important characteristics that should be considered include ceiling height and configuration (e.g., sloped, beamed), intervening barriers such as doors and beams, as well as dilution and buoyancy effects such as stratification that might delay or prevent smoke in being transported to the detector.

B.4.4.4 In smoldering fires, thermal energy provides a force for transporting smoke particles to the smoke sensor. However, usually in the context of smoke detection, the rate of energy (heat) release is small and the rate of growth of the fire is slow. Consequently, other factors such as ambient airflow from HVAC systems, differential solar heating of the structure, and wind cooling of the structure can have a dominant influence on the transport of smoke particles to the smoke sensor when low-output fires are considered.

B.4.4.5 In the early stages of development of a growing fire, the same interior environmental effects, including ambient airflow from HVAC systems, differential solar heating of the structure, and wind cooling of the structure, can have a dominant influence on the transport of smoke. This is particularly important in spaces having high ceilings. Greater thermal energy release from the fire is necessary to overcome these interior environmental effects. Because the fire must attain a sufficiently high level of heat release before it can overcome the interior environmental airflows and drive the smoke to the ceiling-mounted detectors, the use of closer spacing of smoke detectors on the ceiling might not significantly improve the response of the detectors to the fire. Therefore, when considering ceiling height alone, smoke detector spacing closer than 9.1 m (30 ft) might not be warranted, except in instances where an engineering analysis indicates additional benefit will result. Other construction characteristics also should be considered. (*Refer to the appropriate sections of Chapter 17 dealing with smoke detectors and their use for the control of smoke spread.*)

B.4.5 Smoke Dilution. Smoke dilution causes a reduction in the quantity of smoke per unit of air volume of smoke reaching the detector. Dilution typically occurs either by entrainment of air in the plume or the ceiling jet or by effects of HVAC systems. Forced ventilation systems with high air change rates typically cause the most concern, particularly in the early stages of fire development, when smoke production rate and plume velocity are both low. Airflows from supply as well as return vents can create defined air movement patterns within a compartment, which can either keep smoke away from detectors that are located outside of these paths or can inhibit smoke from entering a detector that is located directly in the airflow path. [26]

There currently are no quantitative methods for estimating either smoke dilution or airflow effects on locating smoke detectors. These factors should therefore be considered qualitatively. The designer should understand that the effects of airflow become larger as the fire size at detection (Q_{CR}) gets smaller. Depending on the application, the designer might find it useful to obtain airflow and velocity profiles within the room or to even conduct small-scale smoke tests under various conditions to assist in the design of the system.

NIST first investigated the issues addressed in B.4.5 using the Harwell Flow 3D CFD model as part of the International Fire Detection Research Project. NIST conducted this research under the auspices of the Fire Protection Research Foundation with technical advice and support from the Fire Detection Institute.

B.4.6 Stratification.

B.4.6.1 The potential for the stratification of smoke is another concern in designing and analyzing the response of detectors. This is of particular concern with the detection of low-energy fires and fires in compartments with high ceilings.

B.4.6.2 The upward movement of smoke in the plume depends on the smoke being buoyant relative to the surrounding air. Stratification occurs when the smoke or hot gases flowing from the fire fail to ascend to the smoke detectors mounted at a particular level (usually on the ceiling) above the fire due to the loss of buoyancy. This phenomenon occurs due to the continuous entrainment of cooler air into the fire plume as it rises, resulting in cooling of the smoke and fire plume gases. The cooling of the plume results in a reduction in buoyancy. Eventually the plume cools to a point where its temperature equals that of the surrounding air and its buoyancy diminishes to zero. Once this point of equilibrium is reached, the smoke will cease its upward flow and form a layer, maintaining its height above the fire, regardless of the ceiling height, unless and until sufficient additional thermal energy is provided from the fire to raise the layer due to its increased buoyancy. The maximum height to which plume fluid (smoke) will ascend, especially early in the development of a fire, depends on the convective heat release rate of the fire and the ambient temperature in the compartment.

B.4.6.3 Because warm air rises, there will usually be a temperature gradient in the compartment. Of particular interest are those cases where the temperature of the air in the upper portion of the compartment is greater than at the lower level before the ignition. This can occur as a result of solar load where ceilings contain glazing materials. Computational methods are available to assess the potential for intermediate stratification for the following two cases, depicted in Figure B.4.6.3(a).

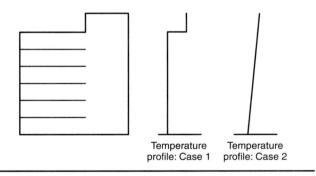

Temperature profile: Case 1   Temperature profile: Case 2

FIGURE B.4.6.3(a) *Pre-Fire Temperature Profiles.*

Case 1. The temperature of the ambient is relatively constant up to a height above which there is a layer of warm air at uniform temperature. This situation can occur if the upper portion of a mall, atrium, or other large space is unoccupied and the air is left unconditioned.

Case 2. The ambient interior air of the compartment has a constant and uniform temperature gradient (temperature change per unit height) from floor to ceiling. This case is generally encountered in industrial and storage facilities that are normally unoccupied.

The analysis of intermediate stratification is presented in Figure B.4.6.3(b). Plume centerline temperatures from two fires, 1000 kW (948 Btu/sec) and 2000 kW (1896 Btu/sec), are graphed based on estimates from correlations presented in this section. In Case 1, a step function is assumed to indicate a 30°C/m (16.5°F/ft) change in temperature 15 m (49.2 ft) above the floor due to the upper portion of the atrium being unconditioned. For Case 2, a temperature gradient of 1.5°C/m (0.82°F/ft) is arbitrarily assumed in an atrium that has a ceiling height of 20 m (65.6 ft).

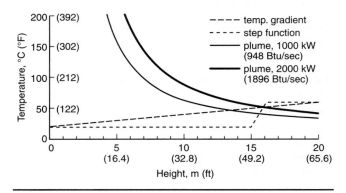

FIGURE B.4.6.3(b) *Indoor Air and Plume Temperature Profiles with Potential for Intermediate Stratification.*

B.4.6.3.1 Step Function Temperature Gradient Spaces. If the interior air temperature exhibits a discrete change at some elevation above the floor, the potential for stratification can be assessed by applying the plume centerline temperature correlation. If the plume centerline temperature is equal to the ambient temperature, the plume is no longer buoyant, loses its upward momentum, and stratifies at that height. The plume centerline temperature can be calculated by using the following equation:

$$T_c = 25\ Q_c^{2/3} z^{-5/3} + 20 \quad \text{(for SI units)} \tag{B.35a}$$

$$T_c = 316 Q_c^{2/3} z^{-5/3} + 70 \quad \text{(for inch-pound units)} \tag{B.35b}$$

where:

T_c = plume centerline temperature (°C or °F)

Q_c = convective portion of fire heat release rate (kW or Btu/sec)

z = height above the top of the fuel package involved (m or ft)

B.4.6.3.2 Linear Temperature Gradient Spaces. To determine whether or not the rising smoke or heat from an axisymmetric fire plume will stratify below detectors, the following equation can be applied where the ambient temperature increases linearly with increasing elevation:

$$Z_m = 5.54 Q_c^{1/4} \left(\frac{\Delta T_0}{dZ}\right)^{-3/8} \quad \text{(for SI units)} \tag{B.36a}$$

or

$$Z_m = 14.7 Q_c^{1/4} \left(\frac{\Delta T_0}{dZ}\right)^{-3/8} \quad \text{(for inch-pound units)} \tag{B.36b}$$

where:

Z_m = maximum height of smoke rise above the fire surface (m or ft)

ΔT_0 = difference between the ambient temperature at the location of detectors and the ambient temperature at the level of the fire surface (°C or °F)

Q_c = convective portion of the heat release rate (kW or Btu/sec)

B.4.6.3.2.1 The convective portion of the heat release rate (Q_c) can be estimated as 70 percent of the heat release rate.

B.4.6.3.2.2 As an alternative to using the noted expression to directly calculate the maximum height to which the smoke or heat will rise, Figure B.4.6.3.2.2 can be used to determine Z_m for given fires. Where Z_m, as calculated or determined graphically, is greater than the installed height of detectors, smoke or heat from a rising fire plume is predicted to reach the detectors. Where the compared values of Z_m and the installed height of detectors are comparable heights, the prediction that smoke or heat will reach the detectors might not be a reliable expectation.

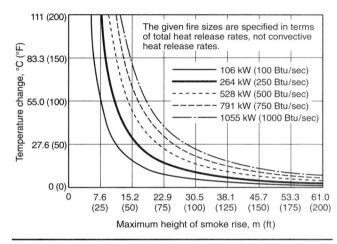

FIGURE B.4.6.3.2.2 *Temperature Change and Maximum Height of Smoke Rise for Given Fire Sizes.*

B.4.6.3.2.3 Assuming the ambient temperature varies linearly with the height, the minimum Q_c required to overcome the ambient temperature difference and drive the smoke to the ceiling ($Z_m = H$) can be determined from the following equation:

$$Q_c = 0.0018 H^{5/2} \Delta T_0^{3/2} \text{ (for SI units)} \qquad \text{(B.37a)}$$

or

$$Q_c = 2.39 \times 10^{-5} H^{5/2} \Delta T_0^{3/2} \text{ (for inch-pound units)} \qquad \text{(B.37b)}$$

Note that the variables are identified in Section B.7.

B.4.6.3.2.4 The theoretical basis for the stratification calculation is based on the works of Morton, Taylor, and Turner [15] and Heskestad [9]. For further information regarding the derivation of the expression defining Z_m, the user is referred to the work of Klote and Milke [13] and NFPA 92B, *Standard for Smoke Management Systems in Malls, Atria, and Large Spaces*.

B.4.7 Detector Characteristics.

The following discussion applies primarily to spot-type smoke detectors. Although some of the comments might also apply to projected beam–type or air sampling–type smoke detectors, B.4.7 does not include a detailed discussion of those types of detectors. The original Fire Detection Institute research project conducted by Factory Mutual Research Corporation from 1976 to 1978 did not include projected beam–type and air sampling–type smoke detectors.

B.4.7.1 General. Once smoke is transported to the detector, additional factors become important in determining whether response will occur. These include the aerodynamic characteristics of the detector and the type of sensor within the detector. The aerodynamics of the detector relate to how easily smoke can pass through the detector housing and enter the sensor portion of the unit. Additionally, the location of the entry portion to the sensor with respect to the velocity profile of the ceiling jet is also an important factor. Finally, different sensing methods (e.g., ionization or photoelectric) will respond differently, depending on the smoke characteristics (smoke color, particle size, optical density, and so forth). Within the family of photoelectric devices, there will be variations depending on the wavelengths of light and the scattering angles employed. The following paragraphs discuss some of these issues and various calculation methods.

B.4.7.2 Resistance to Smoke Entry.

B.4.7.2.1 All spot-type smoke detectors require smoke to enter the detection chamber in order to be sensed. This requires additional factors to be taken into consideration when attempting to estimate smoke detector response, as smoke entry into the detection chamber can be affected in several ways, for example, insect screens, sensing chamber configuration, and location of the detector with respect to the ceiling.

Refer to 17.7.3.6.1 relating spot-type detectors and sampling ports. The International Fire Detection Research Project considered an issue directly related to air sampling–type detectors when it evaluated the flow velocity field in the immediate vicinity of the sampling port. This research showed that the sampling port does *not* produce the effect of drawing the smoke up to the sampling port from lower in the compartment. Consequently, air sampling–type detectors rely either on ambient air currents or on the fire plume and ceiling jet as much as spot-type smoke detectors do.

B.4.7.2.2 In trying to quantify this, Heskestad [32] developed the idea of smoke detector lag to explain the difference in optical density outside (D_{ur}) versus inside (D_{uo}) of a detector when the detector activates. It was demonstrated that this difference could be explained by the use of a correction factor D_{uc} using the following relationship:

$$D_{uc} = \frac{L\frac{d(D_u)}{dt}}{V} \tag{B.38}$$

where:

L = characteristic length for a given detector design, represents the ease of smoke entry into the sensing chamber

$d(D_u)/dt$ = rate of increase of optical density outside the detector

V = velocity of the smoke at the detector

B.4.7.2.3 Various studies regarding this correlation have provided additional insight regarding smoke entry and associated lags [33, 34, 34a, 34b, 34c, 34d, 34e]; however, the difficulty in quantifying L for different detectors and relating it to spacing requirements can have limited usefulness, and the concept of critical velocity (u_c) could be more applicable. [21]

B.4.7.3 Critical Velocity. A smoke detector's critical velocity refers to the minimum velocity of the smoke necessary to enter the sensing chamber to cause an alarm without significant delays due to smoke entry lag. Alarms can occur at velocities less than the critical velocity value, but their response can be delayed or require greater smoke concentrations than would normally be necessary. Flow across a detector causes a pressure differential between the upstream and downstream sides of the detector. This pressure differential is the principal driving force for the smoke entering the unit.

Experimental work has indicated that the critical velocity is approximately 0.15 m/sec (0.49 ft/sec) for the ionization detectors tested in one particular study. [21] Once velocities were reduced below this level, the smoke concentration level outside the detector before an alarm condition increased dramatically when compared to smoke concentration levels when the velocity was above the critical value. Another study found that measured velocities at the time of alarm for ionization and photoelectric detectors in full-scale flaming fire tests generally supported this velocity value, with a mean value of 0.13 m/sec (0.43 ft/sec) and a standard deviation of 0.07 m/sec (0.23 ft/sec) [46]. Estimating the critical velocity can therefore be useful for design and analysis.

It is interesting to note that this critical velocity value (0.15 m/sec or 0.49 ft/sec) is close to that at which a smoke detector must respond in the UL smoke detector sensitivity chamber in order to become listed. [35] The location in the ceiling jet where this velocity occurs for a given fire and ceiling height might therefore be considered as a first approximation for locating detectors. This again assumes a horizontal, smooth ceiling. Care should also be taken when using this correlation, such that consideration is given to potential effects of coagulation and agglomeration, and settling of the smoke within the ceiling jet as it moves away from the fire source and loses its buoyancy. The velocity for smoke entry might be present, but the concentration of smoke might not be sufficient to activate the detector.

Note that the use of the critical velocity method essentially establishes an outer boundary to the distance at which one can expect timely response from a smoke detector. Once the ceiling jet velocity has decreased below 0.15 m/sec (30 ft/min), the possibility exists that the detector will respond. However, response becomes problematic and inconsistent at such low ceiling jet velocities. The method does not account for smoke concentration or the loss of concentration due to entrainment nor the change in the content of the smoke due to agglomeration, condensation, and adsorption by compartment surfaces.

B.4.7.4 Response to Smoke Color. Smoke detectors that use an optical means to detect smoke respond differently to smokes of different colors.

B.4.7.4.1 Manufacturers currently provide limited information regarding the response of smoke detectors in their specifications as well as in the information contained on the labels on the backs of the detectors. This response information indicates only their nominal response values with respect to gray smoke, not to black, and is often provided with a response range instead of an exact response value. This range is in accordance with ANSI/UL 268, *Standard for Smoke Detectors for Fire Alarm Systems.*

The sensitivity marked on the smoke detector label is part of the manufacturing quality monitoring protocols. The marking is not intended to be nor can it be used as a basis of design. The tests conducted in the course of a listing investigation include a sensitivity measurement in a "smoke box." The manufacturer marks the detector with its sensitivity, based upon the response obtained in the "smoke box" test as outlined in the listing investigation standard that was used. However, the sensitivity measurements obtained from this test are relevant only in the context of the smoke box and smoke used. The measurements are not intended to predict performance in any other context. Consequently, a marking of a nominal smoke obscuration of 1 percent to 4 percent obscuration per foot does not necessarily mean that an installed detector will respond to a real fire at that level of optical obscuration. Therefore, a designer must not base a design on this marked sensitivity.

Full-scale room fire tests are also conducted by the listing agencies during the listing evaluation of a smoke detector. The detectors are required to render an alarm when subjected to fires that ultimately produce smoke obscurations of 37 percent per foot for a paper fire, 17 percent per foot for a wood fire, 21 percent per foot for a heptane/toluene fire, and 10 percent per foot for a smoldering wood fire. These pass/fail tests do not provide a meaningful basis for predicting smoke detector performance either.

B.4.7.4.2 The response ranges allowable by UL for gray smoke are shown in Table B.4.7.4.2. Older editions of ANSI/UL 268 contained response ranges for black smoke and are also shown for comparison.

Review of the most recent edition of ANSI/UL 268, *Standard for Smoke Detectors for Fire Alarm Systems,* reveals that UL is no longer conducting the black smoke test during the listing

TABLE B.4.7.4.2 *ANSI/UL 268 Smoke Detector Test Acceptance Criteria for Different Colored Smoke [35]*

Color of Smoke	Acceptable Response Range	
	%/m	*%/ft*
Gray	1.6–12.5	0.5–4.0
Black	5.0–29.2	1.5–10.0

investigation. The values for black smoke shown in Table B.4.7.4.2 reflect the criteria in older editions. Consequently, designers using current products do not know how much the detector's sensitivity is affected by the differences in smoke color. The technical committee has been unable to find any basis to assume that black smoke performance has improved over what is presented in Table B.4.7.4.2.

B.4.7.4.3 Detectors respond at different optical density levels to different fuels and different types of smoke. Examples of this are shown in Table B.4.7.4.3, which contains values of optical density at response recommended by Heskestad and Delichatsios [10] based on their test.

Note the large variations in response not only to materials producing relatively the same color of smoke but also to smoke of different color, which is much more pronounced. Also note that there was variation in the optical density at response values for a given material in the test conducted by Heskestad and Delichatsios, which is not shown in Table B.4.7.4.3. The values cited in Table B.4.7.4.3 are provided as an example of the variation in optical density at response, but these values are not necessarily appropriate for all analyses. For example, the results presented for polyurethane and PVC involved relatively large, rapidly developing fires, and fires with smaller growth rates could result in smaller values of optical density at response [10]. More information on the variation of optical density at response is available from Geiman and Gottuk [48] and Geiman [46].

B.4.7.5 Optical Density and Temperature. During a flaming fire, smoke detector response is affected by ceiling height and the size and rate of fire growth in much the same way as heat detector response. The thermal energy of the flaming fire transports smoke particles to the sensing chamber just as it does heat to a heat sensor. While the relationship between the amount of smoke and the amount of heat produced by a fire is highly dependent on the fuel and the way it is burning, research has shown that the relationship between temperature and the optical density of smoke remains somewhat constant within the fire plume and on the ceiling in the proximity of the plume.

TABLE B.4.7.4.3 *Values of Optical Density at Response for Flaming Fires [18]*

Material	Optical Density at Response				Relative Smoke Color
	$D_{ur}(m^{-1})$		$D_{ur}(ft^{-1})$		
	Ionization	*Photoelectric*	*Ionization*	*Photoelectric*	
Wood crib	0.016	0.049	0.005	0.015	Light
Cotton fabric	0.002	0.026	0.0005	0.008	Light
Polyurethane foam	0.164	0.164	0.05	0.05	Dark
PVC	0.328	0.328	0.1	0.1	Dark
Variation			200:1	12.5:1	

TABLE B.4.7.5.1 *Ratio of Optical Density to Temperature Rise*

Material	$D_u/\Delta T[(m°C)^{-1}]$ Representative Value	$D_u/\Delta T[(m°C)^{-1}]$ Value Range	$D_u/\Delta T[(ft°F)^{-1}]$ Representative Value	$D_u/\Delta T[(ft°F)^{-1}]$ Value Range	Maximum: Minimum
Wood (sugar pine, 5% moist)	1.20E-03	8.9E-4–3.2E-3	2.00E-04	1.5E–5.5E-4	3.7:1
Cotton (unbleached muslin fabric)	5.9E-4/1.2E-3	3.0E-4–1.8E-3	1.0E-04/2.0–4	5.0E-5–3.0E-4	6:1
Paper (in trash can)	1.80E-03	Data not available	3.00E-04	Data not available	—
Polyurethane foam	2.40E-03	1.2E-2–3.2E-2	4.00E-04	2.0E-3–5.5E-3	2.8:1
Polyester fiber (bed pillow)	1.80E-02	Data not available	5.0E-3/1.0E-2	Data not available	—
PVC (wire insulation)	3.0E-2/5.9E-2	5.9E-3–5.9E-2	3.00E-03	1.0E-3–1.0E-2	10:1
Foam rubber PU (sofa cushion)	7.70E-02	Data not available	1.30E-02	Data not available	—
Average	2.10E-02	3.0E-4–7.7E-2	3.60E-03	5.0E-05–1.3E-2	260:1

B.4.7.5.1 These results were based on the work by Heskestad and Delichatsios [10] and are indicated in Table B.4.7.5.1. Note that for a given fuel, the optical density to temperature rise ratio between the maximum and minimum levels is 10 or less.

B.4.7.5.2 In situations where the optical density at detector response is known and is independent of particle size distribution, the detector response can be approximated as a function of the heat release rate of the burning fuel, the fire growth rate, and the ceiling height, assuming that the preceding correlation exists.

B.4.7.5.3 When Appendix C of NFPA 72E (no longer in print) was first published in 1984, a 13°C (20°F) temperature rise was used to indicate detector response. Schifiliti and Pucci [18] have combined some of the data from Heskestad and Delichatsios [10] to produce Table B.4.7.5.3 showing the temperature rise at detector response. Note that the temperature rise associated with detector response varies significantly depending on the detector type and fuel.

Also note that the values in Table B.4.7.5.3 are not based on temperature measurements taken at the detector response times, but were calculated by Heskestad and Delichatsios [10] from their recommended values of optical density at response (Table B.4.7.4.3) and their recommended ratios of optical density to temperature rise (Table B.4.7.5.1).

TABLE B.4.7.5.3 *Temperature Rise for Detector Response [18]*

Material	Ionization Temperature Rise °C	Ionization Temperature Rise °F	Scattering Temperature Rise °C	Scattering Temperature Rise °F
Wood	13.9	25	41.7	75
Cotton	1.7	3	27.8	50
Polyurethane	7.2	13	7.2	13
PVC	7.2	13	7.2	13
Average	7.8	14	21.1	38

Several experimental studies have cited temperature rises at detection as low as 1°C to 3°C (1.8°F to 5.4°F). Of particular note, Geiman [46] found that for flaming fires, 80 percent of the ionization detectors examined in full-scale smoke detection tests alarmed at measured temperature rises less than or equal to 3°C (5.4°F).

A careful review of the original report by Heskestad and Delachatsios shows that they never really advanced the idea of a fixed correlation between temperature increase and optical density. Other researchers, referencing the 1978 FM research by Heskestad and Delachatsios, have concluded that one must exist, and 20°F (13°C) became the default value for a number of fire modeling programs. Much more realistic predictions are obtained by using values closer to 3.6°F to 9°F (2°C to 5°C). However, these are response estimates and are subject to wide margins of error based upon temperature conditions within the compartment, fuel, fuel moisture content, ventilation, and a host of detector-related variables.

B.4.8 Methods for Estimating Smoke Detector Response.

B.4.8.1 General. There are various methods to estimate smoke detector response. Research is still needed in this area to reflect smoke production, transport to the detector, response of the detector, and performance metrics of the smoke detector. Designers should be aware of the advantages and disadvantages, as well as limitations, of these methods and undertake sensitivity analyses and use of multiple methods where applicable.

B.4.8.1.1 Method 1 — Optical Density Versus Temperature.

B.4.8.1.2 It is intended to determine whether an existing fire detection system can detect a fire in part of a warehouse used to store wardrobes in sufficient time to prevent radiant ignition of adjacent wardrobes. The area under review has a large, flat ceiling, 5 m (16.5 ft) high. The ambient temperature within the compartment is 20°C (68°F). The compartment is not sprinklered. The wardrobes are constructed mainly of particleboard. The detectors are ionization-type smoke detectors spaced 6.1 m (20 ft) on center. The design objective is to keep the maximum heat release rate (Q_{DO}) below 2 MW (1897 Btu/sec) in order to ensure that radiant ignition of the wardrobes in the adjacent aisle will not occur. There is an on-site fire brigade that can respond to and begin discharging water on the fire within 90 seconds of receiving the alarm. It can be assumed that there are no other delays between the time the detector reaches its operating threshold and the time to notification of the fire brigade. Given this information, would the existing system be sufficient?

B.4.8.1.3 The following assumptions are made for this example:

$$\alpha = 0.047 \text{ kW/sec}^2 \ (0.044 \text{ Btu/sec}^3)$$
$$\text{RTI} = 25 \text{ m}^{1/2}\text{sec}^{1/2} \ (45 \text{ ft}^{1/2}\text{sec}^{1/2})$$

Temperature rise for response = 14°C (25°F)

Refer to Table B.4.7.5.3 for temperature rise to response of an ionization smoke detector for a wood fire.

B.4.8.1.4 Using the power law equation, the design objective response time is calculated as follows:

$$Q_{DO} = \alpha t_{DO}^2 \tag{B.39}$$
$$2000 \text{ kW} = 0.047 \text{ kW/sec}^2 (t_{DO}^2)$$
$$t_{DO} = 210 \text{ sec}$$

or

$$1897 \text{ Btu/sec} = 0.044 \text{ Btu/sec}^3 \ (t_{DO}^2)$$
$$t_{DO} = 210 \text{ sec}$$

B.4.8.1.5 Next, subtract the time for the fire brigade to respond to determine what time after ignition that detection should occur. Note that a 30-second safety factor has been added to the fire brigade's response time.

$$t_{CR} = 210 \text{ sec} - 120 \text{ sec} = 90 \text{ sec} \tag{B.40}$$

B.4.8.1.6 Then calculate the critical heat release rate at which detection should occur as follows:

$$Q_{CR} = \alpha t_{CR}^2 \qquad\qquad\qquad (B.41)$$

$$Q_{CR} = 0.047 \text{ kW/sec}^2 (90 \text{ sec})^2 = 380 \text{ kW}$$

or

$$Q_{CR} = 0.044 \text{ Btu/sec}^3 (90 \text{ sec})^2 = 360 \text{ Btu/sec}$$

Although the assumptions in B.4.8.1.3 use a 14°C (25°F) temperature rise correlation, this is not intended to suggest that 14°C (25°F) should be used. Many designers use values between 2°C and 5°C (3.6°F and 9°F) for smoke detector response estimates. Once again, the designer should perform a sensitivity analysis on pertinent variables used in this analysis to determine if the results inordinately rely on specific parameter values. For example, considerable variation exists in the response range of the detectors. The value range column in Table B.4.7.5.1 illustrates this variation.

B.4.8.1.7 Using the numbers in the fire detection design and analysis worksheet at 90 seconds into the fire when the heat release rate is 380 kW (360 Btu/sec), the temperature rise at the detector is calculated to be approximately 17°C (30.6°F). This, therefore, might be a reasonable approximation to show that the detector might respond.

B.4.8.2 Method 2 — Mass Optical Density.

B.4.8.2.1 Data regarding smoke characteristics for given fuels can be used as another method to evaluate detector response.

B.4.8.2.2 The following example is provided.

The design objective established for this scenario is to detect the smoke from a flaming 400 g (1.0 lb) polyurethane chair cushion in less than 2 minutes. The chair is placed in a compartment that is 40 m² (431 ft²). The ceiling height is 3.0 m (10 ft). It has been determined that the burning rate of the cushion is a steady rate of 50 g/min (0.09 lb/min). Determine whether the design objective will be met.

B.4.8.2.3 The total mass loss of the cushion due to combustion at 2 minutes is 100 g (0.22 lb). Therefore, the optical density in the room produced by the burning cushion can be calculated from the following equation: [5]

$$D = \frac{D_m M}{V_c} \qquad\qquad\qquad (B.42)$$

where:

D_m = mass optical density (m²/g) [26]

M = mass (g)

V_c = volume of the compartment

D = [(0.22 m²/g)(100 g)]/(40 m²)(3 m) = 0.183 m⁻¹

or

where:

D_m = mass optical density (ft²/lb) [26]

M = mass (lb)

V_c = volume of the compartment

D = [(1075 ft²/lb)(0.22 lb)]/(431 ft²)(9.8 ft) = 0.056 ft⁻¹

B.4.8.2.4 If it is assumed that the detector responds at an optical density of 0.15 m⁻¹ (0.046 ft⁻¹), the maximum black smoke optical density allowed in a previous edition of the ANSI/UL 268 sensitivity test [35], it can be assumed that the detector will respond within 2 minutes.

The conversion from percent obscuration (O), measured in percent per foot, to obscuration, measured in m^{-1}, is not a simple one. The obscuration of 0.15 m^{-1} is the UL upper limit for black smoke, 10 percent per foot. Note that percent obscuration measured in percent per meter is not a common practice.

Percent obscuration, O, is obtained from

$$O = 100 \, (1 - I/I_0)$$

where:

I = light intensity received by the photocell in the presence of smoke

I_0 = intensity received by the photocell in clear air

Percent obscuration per unit of distance, O_u, is obtained from:

$$O_u = 100 \, [1 - (I/I_0)^{1/L}]$$

where L = distance over which the obscuration was measured.

Optical density, D, is a different measurement and is obtained from

$$D = \log_{10}(I_0/I) = -\log_{10}(I/I_0)$$

Optical density per unit of distance, D_u, also called *obscuration,* is obtained from

$$D_u = D/L = (1/L) \cdot \log_{10}(I_0/I) = -(1/L) \cdot \log_{10}(I/I_0)$$

Thus, D_u has units of m^{-1}.

B.4.8.2.5 It should be noted that this method presents a very simplified approach, and that various assumptions would need to be made including that the smoke is confined to the room, is well mixed, can reach the ceiling, and can enter the detector.

B.4.8.2.6 The preceding estimation assumes that the smoke is evenly distributed throughout the entire compartment volume. This is rarely the case but establishes a very conservative limit. For design purposes, one can model the smoke layer as a cylindrical volume centered about the fire plume having a depth equivalent to the ceiling jet thickness or some multiple of it. Refer to Figure B.4.8.2.6.

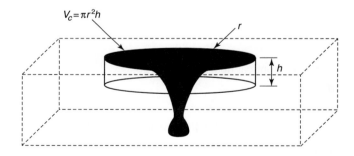

FIGURE B.4.8.2.6 *Smoke Layer Volume Model.*

The volume of the cylinder can now be used as the solution volume:

$$D = \frac{D_m M}{V_c} \tag{B.43}$$

is used with the substitution of

$$V_c = \pi r^2 h \tag{B.44}$$

To obtain the maximum radius from the fire plume center-line at which detector response is expected, the nominal 0.14 m^{-1} optical density criterion is substituted into the relation and an explicit relation for r is obtained,

$$r = \left(\frac{D_m M}{0.14\pi h}\right)^{1/2}$$ (B.45)

Note that the results of this calculation are highly dependent upon the assumed layer thickness, h. The designer must carefully document the value used for the ceiling jet thickness for this reason. This method does not assume any minimum velocity across the detector, nor does it provide for any delay due to smoke entry. Finally, it assumes uniform smoke concentration throughout the solution volume. Failure to use prudently selected values for ceiling jet thickness and use of this relation outside the limitations imposed by the assumptions can lead to invalid designs.

The use of a cylindrical volume solution, noted in B.4.8.2.6, is valid only for cases where response is expected before the ceiling jet impinges upon a compartment wall. Once the ceiling jet impinges upon a wall, the ceiling jet begins to deepen. Under these circumstances, the user should modify the equation to use a rectilinear volume rather than a cylindrical volume for the solution volume, V_c.

Also, although it is customary to deem that the ceiling jet occupies a depth of approximately 10 percent of the floor-to-ceiling thickness, use of that thickness in this response estimation leads to very optimistic results. More realistic results are obtained when a ceiling jet thickness of 20 to 25 percent of the floor-to-ceiling height is assumed.

B.4.8.2.7 The mass optical density method also enables the designer to analyze existing systems. When we accept the assumption that smoke detectors listed by UL will respond at an optical density of 0.14 m^{-1}, we can write the relation:

$$D_A = 0.14 = \frac{D_m M}{V_c}$$ (B.46)

and thus

$$M = D_A \pi r^2 h / D_m$$ (B.47)

for a cylindrical solution volume.

Since $H(t) = M\Delta H_c$ and $H(t) = (\alpha t^3)/3$, we can write the relation

$$M = \frac{(\alpha t^3)}{3\Delta H_c}$$ (B.48)

Substituting, this leads to the relation

$$\frac{(\alpha t^3)}{3\Delta H_c} = \frac{D_A \pi r^2 h}{D_m}$$ (B.49)

This relation is reorganized to be explicit in t,

$$t = \left(\frac{3D_A \pi r^2 h \Delta H_c}{\alpha D_m}\right)^{1/3}$$ (B.50)

This time estimate must be corrected for the lag time produced by the resistance to smoke entry of the detector. Currently, this time delay, which is a function of detector design and ceiling jet velocity, is not quantified in the listing process. Consequently, the designer must make an estimate of the time delay due to smoke entry, t_e. Thus, the response time estimate becomes:

$$t = \left(\frac{3D_A \pi r^2 h \Delta H_c}{\alpha D_m}\right)^{1/3} + t_e$$ (B.51)

This relation predicts the time at which the mass optical density attains the detector alarm threshold in the solution volume derived from the detector spacing and an assumed ceiling jet thickness. Again, the results of this calculation are highly dependent upon the assumed ceiling jet layer thickness. However, once time, t, is known, if the fire can be characterized as a t-square fire, the fire size can be calculated from the relation

$$Q = \alpha t^2 \tag{B.52}$$

Consequently, substitution of this relation into the preceding relation yields the final analytical relation for the heat release rate at alarm, Q_a:

$$Q_a = \alpha \left[\left(\frac{3D_A \pi r^2 h \Delta H_c}{\alpha D_m} \right)^{1/3} + t_e \right]^2 \tag{B.53}$$

This relation provides an estimate of detector response subject to the assumptions and values selected or the relevant parameters. The estimate can be no better than the data used to generate it.

When using this method for system analysis, as when using the method noted in B.4.8.2.6 for design, the use of a cylindrical volume solution is valid only for cases where response is expected before the ceiling jet impinges upon a compartment wall. Once the ceiling jet impinges upon a wall, the ceiling jet begins to deepen. Under these circumstances the user should modify the equation to use a rectilinear volume rather than a cylindrical volume for the solution volume, V_c.

Also, although it is customary to deem that the ceiling jet occupies a depth of approximately 10 percent of the floor-to-ceiling thickness, use of that thickness in this response estimation leads to very optimistic results. More realistic results are obtained when a ceiling jet thickness of 20 to 25 percent of the floor-to-ceiling height is assumed.

B.4.8.3 Critical Velocity Method. Research shows that a minimum critical velocity is necessary before smoke can enter the sensing chamber of the smoke detector. *(See B.4.7.3.)* This method assumes that, if this critical velocity has been attained, sufficient smoke concentration is in the ceiling jet gas flow to produce an alarm signal. Ceiling jet velocity correlations exist for steady-state fires, not t-square fires. However, a t-square fire can be modeled as a succession of steady-state fires for slow and medium growth rate fires. In the UL smoke box test, the minimum flow velocity at the detector is 0.152 m/sec (30 ft/minute). The correlation

$$\frac{0.195(Q^{1/3} H^{1/2})}{r^{5/6}} \quad \text{for } r/h \geq 0.15 \tag{B.54}$$

is used. U_r is set to equal 0.152 m/sec. With this substitution the relation becomes:

$$r \leq (1.28 Q_c^{1/3} H^{1/2})^{6/5} \tag{B.55}$$

This relation is solved to obtain the maximum distance between the fire plume centerline and the detector at which the critical jet velocity is expected to be obtained for the given convective heat release rate and ceiling height.

The critical velocity method noted in B.4.8.3 is derived from correlations that were developed for steady-state fires. Consequently, response estimates based on this critical velocity relation tend to overestimate response when used for t-squared fires. The error becomes very large as the fire growth rate increases. Furthermore, this method does not take into account the changes in smoke concentration and content as the smoke ages during flow from the plume toward the detector. The smoke is cooling due to expansion and cool air entrainment. This cooling causes the condensation of gas constituents into liquid droplets and the coagulation of solid particles into aggregates. These changes in the constitution of the smoke can reduce the effective concentration and affect the ability of the detector to detect the smoke particulate that eventually arrives at the detector. The critical velocity method is therefore the least credible of the three response estimations available for smoke detectors.

B.4.9 Projected Beam Smoke Detection.

B.4.9.1 Projected beam smoke detection is often used in large open spaces with high ceilings where the use of spot-type detectors is impractical due to the problems of smoke stratification. In these spaces, there is questionable basis for the use of the prescriptive spacings presented in Section 17.7. However, beams can be installed such that, regardless of the fire origin, the plume will intersect at least one beam. To employ this strategy, the plume divergence is calculated as a function of the altitude at which the projected beam detectors are installed. The region of relatively uniform temperature and smoke density in a buoyant plume diverges at an angle of approximately 22 degrees, as shown in Figure B.4.9.1.

Another method involves assessing the smoke obstruction through the plume to determine the reduction in light from the receiver to the transmitter of the beam-type smoke detector to determine whether the detector might respond. [47]

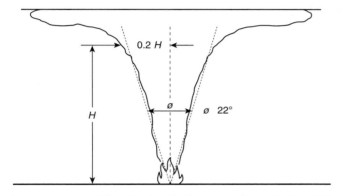

FIGURE B.4.9.1 *The Plume Divergence of an Unconstrained Fire.*

B.5 Radiant Energy Detection

The Technical Committee on Initiating Devices for Fire Alarm Systems introduced performance-based design criteria in the section on radiant energy–sensing fire detectors in the 1990 edition of NFPA 72E, *Automatic Fire Detectors.* Because a performance-based design method is the only permissible means to design a detection system using radiant energy–sensing fire detectors, the authors have added this commentary in Section B.5 to provide the designer with more specific guidance on how to design consistently with the performance criteria in the Code. Section B.5 does *not* provide an alternative method to that required by the body of the Code. Instead, Section B.5 outlines how to meet the current requirements of the Code.

B.5.1 General.

B.5.1.1 Electromagnetic Radiation. Electromagnetic radiation is emitted over a broad range of the spectrum during the combustion process. The portion of the spectrum in which radiant energy–sensing detectors operate has been divided into three bands: ultraviolet (UV), visible, or infrared (IR). These wavelengths are defined with the following wavelength ranges: [3]

(1) Ultraviolet 0.1–0.35 microns
(2) Visible 0.35–0.75 microns
(3) Infrared 0.75–220 microns

B.5.1.2 Wavelength. These wavelength ranges correspond to the quantum-mechanical interaction between matter and energy. Photonic interactions with matter can be characterized by wavelength as shown in Table B.5.1.2.

TABLE B.5.1.2 *Wavelength Ranges*

Wavelength	Photonic Interaction
$\lambda < 50$ micron	Gross molecular translations
$50 \ \mu m < \lambda < 1.0 \ \mu m$	Molecular vibrations and rotations
$1.0 \ \mu m < \lambda < 0.05 \ \mu m$	Valence electron bond vibrations
$0.3 \ \mu m < \lambda < 0.05 \ \mu m$	Electron stripping and recombinations

B.5.1.3 Photon Transfer. When a fuel molecule is oxidized in the combustion process, the combustion intermediate molecule must lose energy to become a stable molecular species. This energy is emitted as a photon with a unique wavelength determined by the following equation:

$$e = \frac{hc}{\lambda} \tag{B.56}$$

where:

e = energy (joules)

h = Planck's constant (6.63E-23 joule-sec)

c = speed of light (m/sec)

λ = wavelength (microns)

[1.0 joule = 5.0345E+18(λ), where λ is measured in microns.]

B.5.1.4 Type of Detector. The choice of the type of radiant energy–sensing detector to use is determined by the type of emissions that are expected from the fire radiator.

B.5.1.4.1 Fuels that produce a flame, a stream of combustible or flammable gases involved in the combustion reaction with a gaseous oxidizer, radiate quantum emissions. These fuels include flammable gases, flammable liquids, combustible liquids, and solids that are burning with a flame.

B.5.1.4.2 Fuels that are oxidized in the solid phase or radiators that are emitting due to their internal temperature (sparks and embers) radiate Planckian emissions. These fuels include carbonaceous fuels such as coal, charcoal, wood, and cellulosic fibers that are burning without an established flame, as well as metals that have been heated due to mechanical impacts and friction.

B.5.1.4.3 Almost all combustion events produce Planckian emissions, emissions that are the result of the thermal energy in the fuel mass. Therefore, spark/ember detectors that are designed to detect these emissions are not fuel specific. Flame detectors detect quantum emissions that are the result of changes in molecular structure and energy state in the gas phase. These emissions are uniquely associated with particular molecular structures. This can result in a flame detector that is very fuel specific.

If a photon could be held in the hand, it could not be determined whether it was a Planckian photon or a quantum photon. The distinction between the two merely alludes to the theory of physics that explains the mechanism of their formation. Designers should note this distinction because it helps in the detector selection process. Designers must understand what emits photons and why — only then can they select the appropriate type of detection device.

B.5.1.5 Effects of Ambient. The choice of radiant energy–sensing detector is also limited by the effect of ambient conditions. The design must take into account the radiant energy absorption of the atmosphere, presence of non-fire-related radiation sources that might cause nuisance alarms, the electromagnetic energy of the spark, ember, or fire to be detected, the distance from the fire source to the sensor, and characteristics of the sensor.

The assumption that the fire can be modeled as a point-source radiator is rarely unjustified. When conditions are such that the fire to be detected is too close to the detector for the point-source radiator assumption to be valid, there is also no doubt that the fire will be detected.

The response model is derived from first principles of physics. Since conventional flame detectors merely measure radiant intensity as a function of time to infer the presence of a flame, this simple response model is sufficient. Video image flame detectors use not only intensity but also image recognition. At this juncture the technical committee does not have sufficient information about the performance limitations on the video image flame detectors to develop an analogous model for that technology.

B.5.1.5.1 Ambient Non-Fire Radiators. Most ambients contain non-fire radiators that can emit at wavelengths used by radiant energy–sensing detectors for fire detection. The designer should make a thorough evaluation of the ambient to identify radiators that have the potential for producing unwarranted alarm response from radiant energy–sensing detectors. Since radiant energy–sensing detectors use electronic components that can act as antennas, the evaluation should include radio band, microwave, infrared, visible, and ultraviolet sources.

B.5.1.5.2 Ambient Radiant Absorbance. The medium through which radiant energy passes from fire source to detector has a finite transmittance. Transmittance is usually quantified by its reciprocal, absorbance. Absorbance by atmospheric species varies with wavelength. Gaseous species absorb at the same wavelengths that they emit. Particulate species can transmit, reflect, or absorb radiant emission, and the proportion that is absorbed is expressed as the reciprocal of its emissivity, ε.

B.5.1.5.3 Contamination of Optical Surfaces. Radiant energy can be absorbed or reflected by materials contaminating the optical surfaces of radiant energy–sensing detectors. The designer should evaluate the potential for surface contamination and implement provisions for keeping these surfaces clean. Extreme caution must be employed when considering the use of surrogate windows. Common glass, acrylic, and other glazing materials are opaque at the wavelengths used by most flame detectors and some spark/ember detectors. Placing a window between the detector and the hazard area that has not been listed by a nationally recognized testing laboratory (NRTL) for use with the detector in question is a violation of the detector listing and will usually result in a system that is incapable of detecting a fire in the hazard area.

B.5.1.5.4 Design Factors. These factors are important for several reasons. First, a radiation sensor is primarily a line-of-sight device, and must "see" the fire source. If there are other radiation sources in the area, or if atmospheric conditions are such that a large fraction of the radiation could be absorbed in the atmosphere, the type, location, and spacing of the sensors could be affected. In addition, the sensors react to specific wavelengths, and the fuel must emit radiation in the sensor's bandwidth. For example, an infrared detection device with a single sensor tuned to 4.3 microns (the CO_2 emission peak) cannot be expected to detect a non-carbon-based fire. Furthermore, the sensor needs to be able to respond reliably within the required time, especially when activating an explosion suppression system or similar fast-response extinguishing or control system.

B.5.1.6 Detector Response Model. The response of radiant energy–sensing detectors is modeled with a modified inverse square relationship as shown in the following equation [5]:

$$S = \frac{kPe^{-\zeta d}}{d^2} \tag{B.57}$$

where:

S = radiant power reaching the detector (W or Btu/sec) sufficient to produce alarm response

k = proportionality constant for the detector

P = radiant power emitted by the fire (W or Btu/sec)

ζ = extinction coefficient of air at detector operating wavelengths

d = distance between the fire and the detector (m or ft)

This relationship models the fire as a point source radiator, of uniform radiant output per steradian, some distance (d) from the detector. This relationship also models the effect of absorbance by the air between the fire and the detector as being a uniform extinction function. The designer must verify that these modeling assumptions are valid for the application in question.

B.5.2 Design of Flame Detection Systems.

B.5.2.1 Detector Sensitivity. Flame detector sensitivity is traditionally quantified as the distance at which the unit can detect a fire of given size. The fire most commonly used by the NRTLs in North America is a 0.9 m² (1.0 ft²) fire fueled with regular grade, unleaded gasoline. Some special-purpose detectors are evaluated using 150 mm (6 in.) diameter fires fueled with isopropanol.

B.5.2.1.1 This means of sensitivity determination does not take into account that flames can best be modeled as an optically dense radiator in which radiant emissions radiated from the far side of the flame toward the detector are re-absorbed by the flame. Consequently, the radiated power from a flame is not proportional to the area of the fire but to the flame silhouette, and hence to the height and width of the fire.

The radiant power emitted by a flaming fire is a function of the radiant power per unit of flame area multiplied by the flame area (the height times the width of the flame silhouette). This method of computing flame radiant power is predicated upon the assumption that a flame is an optically dense radiator. This assumption, which has been shown to be valid, means that the flame itself absorbs radiation emitted by the back side of the flame and then re-emits it. The optically dense flame model greatly simplifies response prediction calculations. The optically dense flame assumption means that in the calculation of flame detector response, the emitted radiant power is not directly proportional to the surface area of a pool fire or the surface area of the flame volume. In a comparison of two combustible liquid fires with the identical pool surface areas shown in Exhibit B.1, the fire from pool (b) will appear twice as large to the flame detector as the fire from pool (a), as shown in Exhibit B.2.

For calculation of radiated power toward the detector, the radiating profile is used, that is, the flame modeled as a triangular flat radiator having a height equal to the flame height and a width equal to the pool width.

B.5.2.1.2 Because flame detectors detect the radiant emissions produced during the formation of flame intermediates and products, the radiant intensity produced by a flame at a given wavelength is proportional to the relative concentration of the specific intermediate or product in the flame and that portion of the total heat release rate of the fire resulting from the formation of that specific intermediate or product. This means that the response of a detector can vary widely as different fuels are used to produce a fire of the same surface area and flame width.

Designers must verify that the fuels present in the hazard area match those used in the listing evaluation of the flame detector. Relatively small variations in chemical composition can have profound effects on the response of the detector. For instance, a detector might detect a gasoline fire at 24 m (80 ft) but detect the same size fire fueled with #2 fuel oil at 12 m (40 ft).

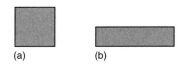

(a)   (b)

EXHIBIT B.1 *Combustible Liquid Fire Pool Surfaces.*

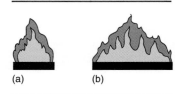

(a)   (b)

EXHIBIT B.2 *Pool Appearance.*

This variation represents a fourfold difference in sensitivity. Unfortunately, the range of fuels used by the listing agencies is limited. Designers must be extremely careful in verifying detector sensitivity whenever oxygenated, aromatic, or silicone-containing fuels are present.

B.5.2.1.3 Many flame detectors are designed to detect specific products such as water (2.5 microns) and CO_2 (4.35 microns). These detectors cannot be used for fires that do not produce these products as a result of the combustion process.

The designer could expect a flame detector that uses 2.5-micron (water emission) photocells to promptly detect a methane fire. Detection occurs because the hydrogen of the methane molecule combines with oxygen to produce two water molecules. However, the designer could not expect such a detector to detect burning sulfur or metals. Likewise, the designer cannot expect a detector using the 4.35-micron (CO_2 emission) photocell to respond to sulfur, combustible metal, or hydrogen fires, because none of those fuels contains a carbon atom that can be oxidized to form carbon dioxide and emit the 4.35-micron emission the detector depends upon for recognition of a flame.

B.5.2.1.4 Many flame detectors use time variance of the radiant emissions of a flame to distinguish between non-fire radiators and a flame. Where a deflagration hazard exists, the designer must determine the sample time period for such flame detectors and how such detectors will operate in the event of a deflagration of fuel vapor or fuel gases.

The organization and design of the electronics in a flame detector can have unanticipated effects on its performance as a fire detection device. Many flame detectors require a time-variant, repetitive radiant signal before the radiation is interpreted as a flame emission. This type of circuit is ideal for detecting a growing hydrocarbon pool fire. However, this type of circuitry might not detect a deflagration of a fuel vapor–air mixture. The deflagration produces a single immense flash of radiant energy that can "saturate" photocells, rendering them incapable of detection for short periods of time. With an accidental fuel spill, immediate ignition is not guaranteed. A significant passage of time might elapse during which fuel vapors are released into the air, creating a condition that will produce a deflagration rather than an expanding spill fire. The designer should verify that the listing agency has tested the detector for the fire scenarios appropriate to the hazard area, including partial volume deflagration.

B.5.2.2 Design Fire. Using the process outlined in Section B.2, determine the fire size (kW or Btu/sec) at which detection must be achieved.

Paragraphs B.5.2.2 through B.5.2.6 provide a step-wise method for designing and analyzing a flame detection system.

B.5.2.2.1 Compute the surface area the design fire is expected to occupy from the correlations in Table B.2.3.2.6.2(a) or other sources. Use the flame height correlation to determine the height of the flame plume:

$$h_f = 0.182(kQ)^{2/5} \quad \text{(for SI units)} \tag{B.58b}$$

or

$$h_f = 0.584(kQ)^{2/5} \quad \text{(for inch-pound units)} \tag{B.58a}$$

where:

h_f = flame height (m or ft)

Q = heat release rate (kW or Btu/sec)

k = wall effect factor

Where there are no nearby walls, use $k = 1$.
Where the fuel package is near a wall, use $k = 2$.
Where the fuel package is in a corner, use $k = 4$.

Determine the minimum anticipated flame area width (w_f). Where flammable or combustible liquids are the fuel load and are unconfined, model the fuel as a circular pool. Compute the radiating area (A_r) using the following equation:

$$A_r = \frac{1}{2h_f w_f} \qquad \text{(B.59)}$$

where:

A_r = radiating area (m² or ft²)

h_f = flame height (m or ft)

w_f = flame width (m or ft)

This design fire computation models the fire as an optically dense radiator of uniform radiant intensity per unit area having a silhouette of an isosceles triangle. The altitude of the triangle is derived from the flame height correlations. Once the height is determined, the designer selects the base width and calculates the radiation area.

Note that this method does not employ the commonly used ratio of 35 percent radiant heat release and 65 percent convective heat release. This method cannot use those ratios because the test methods employed by the listing agencies do not quantify the test fires in terms of radiant heat release rate. The fires are quantified by pool surface area only. The method in Annex B uses a consistent approach to estimate the radiating area of the design fire and the test fire. The method then compares the design fire to the test fire on the basis of radiating area and power per unit area.

B.5.2.2.2 The radiant power output of the fire to the detector can be approximated as being proportional to the radiating area (A_r) of the flame:

$$P = cA_r \qquad \text{(B.60)}$$

where:

A_r = radiating area (m² or ft²)

c = power per unit area proportionality constant

P = radiated power (W or Btu/sec)

Users will see that the actual sensitivity of the detector is never explicitly calculated when this method is used. The detector performance relation (equation B.57) is used to compare performance in the listing agency's fire tests (equation B.61) to the performance of the design fire (equation B.62). The parameters c and P drop out of the final equation (equation B.64).

B.5.2.3 Calculate Detector Sensitivity. Using equation B.58a or B.58b compute the radiating area of the test fire used by the NRTL in the listing process (A_t). The radiant power output of the test fire to the detector in the listing process is proportional to the radiating area (A_t) of the listing test flame.

The same relations and process that were used to calculate the design fire radiating area are used to calculate the listing agency's test fire radiating area.

B.5.2.4 Calculate Detector Response to Design Fire. Because the sensitivity of a flame detector is fixed during the manufacturing process, the following is the relationship that determines the radiant power reaching the detector sufficient to produce an alarm response:

$$S = \frac{kcA_t e^{-\zeta d}}{d^2} \qquad \text{(B.61)}$$

where:

S = radiant power reaching the detector (W or Btu/sec) sufficient to produce alarm response

k = proportionality constant for the detector

A_t = radiant area of the listing test fire (m² or ft²)

ζ = extinction coefficient of air at detector operating wavelengths

d = distance between the fire and the detector during the listing fire test (m or ft)

c = emitted power per unit flame radiating area correlation

Because the sensitivity of the detector is constant over the range of ambients for which it is listed:

$$S = \frac{kcA_r e^{-\zeta d'}}{d'^2} \tag{B.62}$$

where:

S = radiant power reaching the detector (W or Btu/sec) sufficient to produce alarm response

k = proportionality constant for the detector

c = emitted power per unit flame radiating area correlation

A_r = radiant area of the design fire (m² or ft²)

ζ = extinction coefficient of air at detector operating wavelengths

d' = distance between the design fire and the detector (m or ft)

Therefore, use the following equation to determine the following:

$$\frac{kcA_t e^{-\zeta d}}{d^2} = \frac{kcA_r e^{-\zeta d'}}{d'^2} \tag{B.63}$$

To solve for d' use the following equation:

$$\left(\frac{d^2 A_r e^{-\zeta d'}}{A_t e^{-\zeta d}} \right)^{1/2} = d' \tag{B.64}$$

This relation is solved iteratively for d', the distance at which the detector can detect the design fire.

The method in B.5.2.4 relies on several important assumptions. First, the design fire is assumed to have the same fuel as the fire in the listing evaluation. This assumed scenario allows the emitted power per unit of flame silhouette area correlation parameter (c) to cancel out in the final equation. Second, this method assumes that the fire can be modeled as a point source radiator. This assumption becomes invalid when the flame area occupies a substantial fraction of the total field of view of the detector. Finally, this method demands that the data generated in the listing evaluation must include a numerical value for the atmospheric extinction coefficient (ζ).

A value for ζ can be calculated by testing the flame detector to two different sizes of test fires at two different distances, determining the maximum distance at which the detector can detect the two different fires. With those data in hand, the design equation is simply reorganized to be explicit in ζ and the fire radiating areas and distances from the two different tests are inserted. The value of ζ is a constant for the make and model of detector.

B.5.2.5 Correction for Angular Displacement.

B.5.2.5.1 Most flame detectors exhibit a loss of sensitivity as the fire is displaced from the optical axis of the detector. This correction to the detector sensitivity is shown as a polar graph in Figure A.17.8.3.2.3.

B.5.2.5.2 When the correction for angular displacement is expressed as a reduction of normalized detection distance, the correction is made to detection distance (d').

B.5.2.5.3 When the correction for angular displacement is expressed as a normalized sensitivity (fire size increment), the correction must be made to A_r, prior to calculating response distance (d').

B.5.2.6 Corrections for Fuel. Most flame detectors exhibit some level of fuel specificity. Some manufacturers provide "fuel factors" that relate detector response performance to a fire of one fuel to the response performance of a benchmark fuel. Other manufacturers provide performance criteria for a list of specific fuels. Unless the manufacturer's published instructions, bearing the listing mark, contain explicit instructions for the application of the detector for fuels other than those used in the listing process, the unit cannot be deemed listed for use in hazard areas containing fuels different from those employed in the listing process.

B.5.2.6.1 When the fuel factor correction is expressed as a detection distance reduction, the correction should be applied after the detection distance has been computed.

B.5.2.6.2 When the fuel factor correction is expressed as a function of normalized fire size, the correction must be made prior to calculating detection distance.

B.5.2.7 Atmospheric Extinction Factors.

B.5.2.7.1 Because the atmosphere is not infinitely transmittent at any wavelength, all flame detectors are affected by atmospheric absorption to some degree. The effect of atmospheric extinction on the performance of flame detectors is determined to some degree by the wavelengths used for sensing and the detector electronic architecture. Values for the atmospheric extinction coefficient (ζ) should be obtained from the detector manufacturer's published instructions.

B.5.2.7.2 The numerical value of ζ can be determined experimentally for any flame detector. The detector must be tested with two different sized test fires to determine the distance at which each of the fires can be detected by the detector in question. The larger the difference between the sizes of the flaming fires, the more precise the determination of ζ. Ideally, one test fire would be approximately 4 times the heat release rate (surface area) of the other. The data are then used in the relation:

$$\zeta = \frac{\ln[d_1^2 A_2)/(d_2^2 A_1)]}{d_2 - d_1} \tag{B.65}$$

where:

"1" = subscripts referring to the first test fire

"2" = subscripts referring to the second test fire

d = maximum distance between the flame detector and the fire at which the fire is detected

A = the radiating area of the test fire as determined per B.5.2.2.1

This relation allows the designer to determine the value of ζ for detectors that are already installed or for those that were evaluated for listing before the inclusion of the requirement for the publishing of ζ appeared in ANSI/FM-3260.

The relation for calculating ζ is derived from the response relation, equation B.61. The relation is particularly useful in the analysis of existing systems where the manufacturer's published documentation does not include the design value.

B.5.3 Design of Spark/Ember Detection Systems.

The similarity between the methods for the design of flame detection systems in B.5.2 and for spark/ember detection systems in B.5.3 is not accidental. Each method employs the same physics but different chemistry. Because spark/ember detectors are designed to detect the

Planckian emissions emanating from an ember due to its temperature, designers do not have to deal with fuel specificity as they do when designing with flame detectors. An important note is that all flames emit radiation over the range of wavelengths normally used for spark/ember detectors. However, normal ambient light as well as light from artificial light sources is also rich in near infrared radiation. This fact prevents the use of most spark/ember detectors in normally lit ambient environments.

B.5.3.1 Design Fire. Using the process outlined in Section B.2, determine the fire size (kW or Btu/sec) at which detection must be achieved.

B.5.3.1.1 The quantification of the fire is generally derived from the energy investment per unit time sufficient to propagate combustion of the combustible particulate solids in the fuel stream. Because energy per unit time is power, expressed in watts, the fire size criterion is generally expressed in watts or milliwatts.

B.5.3.1.2 The radiant emissions, integrated over all wavelengths, from a non-ideal Planckian radiator is expressed with the following form of the Stefan–Boltzmann equation:

$$P = \varepsilon A \sigma T^4 \tag{B.66}$$

where:

P = radiant power (W or Btu/sec)

ε = emissivity, a material property expressed as a fraction between 0 and 1.0

A = area of radiator (m^2 or ft^2)

σ = Stefan–Boltzmann constant 5.67E-8 W/m^{2}K^4

T = temperature (K or R)

B.5.3.1.3 This models the spark or ember as a point source radiator.

With regard to B.5.3.1.2, U.S. customary units of measure (inch-pound system) has never been accepted as a practical measurement system in the field of quantum mechanics, and the authors have never seen a reference relating to these physics that employed inch-pound units of measure. Consequently, no conversions have been derived.

B.5.3.2 Fire Environment. Spark/ember detectors are usually used on pneumatic conveyance system ducts to monitor combustible particulate solids as they flow past the detector(s). This environment puts large concentrations of combustible particulate solids between the fire and the detector. A value for ζ must be computed for the monitored environment. The simplifying assumption that absorbance at visible levels is equal to or greater than that at infrared wavelengths yields conservative designs and is used.

B.5.3.3 Calculate Detector Response to Design Fire. Because the sensitivity of a spark/ember detector is fixed during the manufacturing process,

$$S = \frac{kPe^{-\zeta d}}{d^2} \tag{B.67}$$

where:

S = radiant power reaching the detector (W or Btu/sec) sufficient to produce alarm response

k = proportionality constant for the detector

P = radiant power emitted by test spark (W or Btu/sec)

ζ = extinction coefficient of air at detector operating wavelengths

d = distance between the fire and the detector during the listing fire test (m^2 or ft^2)

Because the sensitivity of the detector is constant over the range of ambients for which it is listed,

$$S = \frac{kP'e^{-\zeta d'}}{d'^2} \tag{B.68}$$

where:

S = radiant power reaching the detector (W or Btu/sec) sufficient to produce alarm response

k = proportionality constant for the detector

P' = radiant power from the design fire (W or Btu/sec)

ζ = the extinction coefficient of air at detector operating wavelengths

d' = the distance between the design fire and the detector (m² or ft²)

Therefore, use the following equation to solve for

$$\frac{kPe^{-\zeta d}}{d^2} = \frac{kP'e^{-\zeta d'}}{d'^2} \tag{B.69}$$

To solve for d',

$$d' = \left(\frac{d^2 P' e^{-\zeta d'}}{Pe^{-\zeta d}}\right)^{1/2} \tag{B.70}$$

This relation is solved iteratively for d', the distance at which the detector can detect the design fire.

Because the spark is essentially a point source radiator of measurable radiant power, the designer does not need to perform a flame area calculation for spark/ember detectors. However, the designer should keep in mind that spark/ember detectors generally respond only to a step-function increase in radiant power. Consequently, these detectors cannot be used to detect slowly developing smoldering conditions or for looking down the length of a conveyance duct.

The numerical value used for ζ is the optical obscuration of the air within the duct. This value is derived from the mass per unit of air volume for the particulate transported through the duct.

B.5.3.4 Correction for Angular Displacement.

B.5.3.4.1 Most spark/ember detectors exhibit a loss of sensitivity as the fire is displaced from the optical axis of the detector. This correction to the detector sensitivity is shown as a polar graph in Figure A.17.8.3.2.3.

B.5.3.4.2 When the correction for angular displacement is expressed as a reduction of normalized detection distance, the correction is made to detection distance (d').

B.5.3.4.3 When the correction for angular displacement is expressed as a normalized sensitivity (fire size increment), the correction must be made to P' prior to calculating response distance (d').

B.5.3.5 Corrections for Fuel. Because spark/ember detectors respond to Planckian emission in the near infrared portion of the spectrum, corrections for fuels are rarely necessary.

B.6 Computer Fire Models

Several special application computer models are available to assist in the design and analysis of both heat detectors (e.g., fixed-temperature, rate-of-rise, sprinklers, fusible links) and smoke detectors. These computer models typically run on personal computers and are available from NIST website http:\\fire.nist.gov.

B.6.1 DETACT — T².

DETACT — T² (DETector ACTuation — time squared) calculates the actuation time of heat detectors (fixed-temperature and rate-of-rise) and sprinklers to user-specified fires that grow with the square of time. DETACT — T² assumes the detector is located in a large compartment with an unconfined ceiling, where there is no accumulation of hot gases at the ceiling. Thus, heating of the detector is only from the flow of hot gases along the ceiling. Input data include H, τ_0, RTI, T_s, S, and α. The program calculates the heat release rate at detector activation, as well as the time to activation.

B.6.2 DETACT — QS.

DETACT — QS (DETector ACTuation — quasi-steady) calculates the actuation time of heat detectors and sprinklers in response to fires that grow according to a user-defined fire. DETACT — QS assumes the detector is located in a large compartment with unconfined ceilings, where there is no accumulation of hot gases at the ceiling. Thus, heating of the detector is only from the flow of hot gases along the ceiling. Input data include H, τ_0, RTI, T_s, the distance of the detector from the fire's axis, and heat release rates at user-specified times. The program calculates the heat release rate at detector activation, the time to activation, and the ceiling jet temperature.

DETACT — QS can also be found in HAZARD I, FIREFORM, FPETOOL. A comprehensive evaluation of DETACT QS can be found in the *SFPE Engineering Guide: Evaluation of the Computer Fire Model DETACT QS*. This guide provides information on the theoretical basis, mathematical robustness, sensitivity of output to input, and an evaluation of the predictive ability of the model.

B.6.3 LAVENT.

LAVENT (Link Actuated VENT) calculates the actuation time of sprinklers and fusible link-actuated ceiling vents in compartment fires with draft curtains. Inputs include the ambient temperature, compartment size, thermophysical properties of the ceiling, fire location, size and growth rate, ceiling vent area and location, RTI, and temperature rating of the fusible links. Outputs of the model include the temperatures and release times of the links, the areas of the vents that have opened, the radial temperature distribution at the ceiling, and the temperature and height of the upper layer.

B.6.4

JET is a single-compartment, two-zone computer model. It has been designed to calculate the centerline temperature of the plume, the ceiling jet temperature, and the ceiling jet velocity. JET can model ceiling-mounted fusible links, as well as link-actuated ceiling vents. JET evolved from the model platform used for LAVENT and contains many of the same features. Some of the major differences between them include the ceiling jet temperature and velocity algorithms, the fusible link algorithm, and the use of a variable radiative fraction. [57]

JET is the computer model that is likely to be used.

B.6.5 References.

(1) Alpert, R. "Ceiling Jets," *Fire Technology*, Aug. 1972.

(2) "Evaluating Unsprinklered Fire Hazards," *SFPE Technology Report* 83-2.

(3) Babrauskas, V., Lawson, J. R., Walton, W. D., and Twilley, W. H. "Upholstered Furniture Heat Release Rates Measured with a Furniture Calorimeter," (NBSIR 82-2604) (Dec. 1982). National Institute of Standards and Technology (formerly National Bureau of Standards), Center for Fire Research, Gaithersburg, MD 20889.

(4) Beyler, C. "A Design Method for Flaming Fire Detection," *Fire Technology*, Vol. 20, No. 4, Nov. 1984.

(5) DiNenno, P., ed. Chapter 31, *SFPE Handbook of Fire Protection Engineering*, by R. Schifiliti, Sept. 1988.

(6) Evans, D. D. and Stroup, D. W. "Methods to Calculate Response Time of Heat and Smoke Detectors Installed Below Large Unobstructed Ceilings," (NBSIR 85-3167) (Feb. 1985, issued Jul. 1986). National Institute of Standards and Technology (formerly National Bureau of Standards), Center for Fire Research, Gaithersburg, MD 20889.

(7) Heskestad, G. "Characterization of Smoke Entry and Response for Products-of-Combustion Detectors" Proceedings, 7th International Conference on Problems of Automatic Fire Detection, Rheinish-Westfalischen Technischen Hochschule Aachen (Mar. 1975).

(8) Heskestad, G. "Investigation of a New Sprinkler Sensitivity Approval Test: The Plunge Test," FMRC Tech. Report 22485, Factory Mutual Research Corporation, 1151 Providence Turnpike, Norwood, MA 02062.

(9) Heskestad, G. and Delichatsios, M. A. "The Initial Convective Flow in Fire: Seventeenth Symposium on Combustion," The Combustion Institute, Pittsburgh, PA (1979).

(10) Heskestad, G. and Delichatsios, M. A. "Environments of Fire Detectors — Phase 1: Effect of Fire Size, Ceiling Height and Material," Measurements Vol. I (NBS-GCR-77-86), Analysis Vol. II (NBS-GCR-77-95). National Technical Information Service (NTIS), Springfield, VA 22151.

(11) Heskestad, G. and Delichatsios, M. A. "Update: The Initial Convective Flow in Fire," *Fire Safety Journal*, Vol. 15, No. 5, 1989.

(12) International Organization for Standardization, *Audible Emergency Evacuation Signal*, ISO 8201, 1987.

(13) Klote, J. and Milke, J. "Principles of Smoke Management," American Society of Heating, Refrigerating and Air Conditioning Engineers, Atlanta, GA, 2002.

(14) Lawson, J. R., Walton, W. D., and Twilley, W. H. "Fire Performance of Furnishings as Measured in the NBS Furniture Calorimeter, Part 1," (NBSIR 83-2787) (Aug. 1983). National Institute of Standards and Technology (formerly National Bureau of Standards), Center for Fire Research, Gaithersburg, MD 20889.

(15) Morton, B. R., Taylor, Sir Geoffrey, and Turner, J. S. "Turbulent Gravitational Convection from Maintained and Instantaneous Sources," Proc. Royal Society A, 234, 1–23, 1956.

(16) Schifiliti, R. "Use of Fire Plume Theory in the Design and Analysis of Fire Detector and Sprinkler Response," Master's Thesis, Worcester Polytechnic Institute, Center for Firesafety Studies, Worcester, MA, 1986.

(17) Title 47, Code of Federal Regulations, Communications Act of 1934 Amended.

(18) Schifiliti, R. and Pucci, W. "Fire Detection Modelling, State of the Art," 6 May, 1996 sponsored by the Fire Detection Institute, Bloomfield, CT.

(19) Forney, G., Bukowski, R., Davis, W. "Field Modelling: Effects of Flat Beamed Ceilings on Detector and Sprinkler Response," Technical Report, Year 1. International Fire Detection Research Project, Fire Protection Research Foundation, Quincy, MA. October, 1993.

(20) Davis, W., Forney, G., Bukowski, R. "Field Modelling: Simulating the Effect of Sloped Beamed Ceilings on Detector and Sprinkler Response," Year 1. International Fire Detection Research Project Technical Report, Fire Protection Research Foundation, Quincy, MA. October, 1994.

(21) Brozovski, E. "A Preliminary Approach to Siting Smoke Detectors Based on Design Fire Size and Detector Aerosol Entry Lag Time," Master's Thesis, Worcester Polytechnic, Worcester, MA, 1989.

(22) Cote, A. *NFPA Fire Protection Handbook*, 19th Edition, National Fire Protection Association, Quincy, MA, 2003.

(23) Tewarson, A., "Generation of Heat and Chemical Compounds in Fires," *SFPE Handbook of Fire Protection Engineering*, Second Edition, NFPA and SFPE, 1995.

(24) Hollman, J. P. *Heat Transfer*, McGraw-Hill, New York, 1976.

(25) Custer, R. L. P., and Meacham, B. "Introduction to Performance Based Fire Safety," SFPE, 1997.

(26) Schifiliti, R. P., Meacham B., Custer, R. L. P. "Design of Detection Systems," *SFPE Handbook of Fire Protection Engineering*.

(27) Marrion, C. "Correction Factors for the Heat of Combustion in NFPA 72," Appendix B, Fire Protection Engineering, SFPE, 1998.

(28) Marrion, C. "Designing and Analyzing the Response of Detection Systems: An Update to Previous Correlations," 1988.

(29) Custer, R. and Bright, R. "Fire Detection: The State-of-the-Art," NBS Tech. Note 839, National Bureau of Standards, Washington, 1974.

(30) Meacham, Brian J. "Characterization of Smoke from Burning Materials for the Evaluation of Light Scattering-Type Smoke Detector Response," MS Thesis, WPI Center for Firesafety Studies, Worcester, MA, 1991.

(31) Delichatsios, M. A. "Categorization of Cable Flammability, Detection of Smoldering, and Flaming Cable Fires," Interim Report, Factory Mutual Research Corporation, Norwood, MA, NP-1630, Nov. 1980.

(32) Heskestad, G. FMRC Serial Number 21017, Factory Mutual Research Corp., Norwood, MA, 1974.

(33) Marrion, C. E. "Lag Time Modeling and Effects of Ceiling Jet Velocity on the Placement of Optical Smoke Detectors," MS Thesis, WPI Center for Firesafety Studies, Worcester, MA, 1989.

(34) Kokkala, M. et al. "Measurements of the Characteristic Lengths of Smoke Detectors," *Fire Technology*, Vol. 28, No. 2, National Fire Protection Association, Quincy, MA, 1992.

(34a) Yamauchi et al. "A Calculation Method for Predicting Heat and Smoke Detector's Response."

(34b) Cleary et al. "Particulate Entry Lag in Spot Type Smoke Detectors," IAFSS Proceedings, Boston, MA 2000.

(34c) Keski-Rahkonen, "Revisiting Modeling of Fluid Penetration into Smoke Detectors," AUBE 2001.

(34d) Bjoerkman et al. "Determination of Dynamic Model Parameters of Smoke Detectors," *Fire Safety Journal*, No 37, pp. 395 — 407, 2002.

(34e) Keski-Rahkonen, "A New Model for Time Lag of Smoke Detectors," International Collaborative Project to Evaluate Fire Models for Nuclear Power Plant Application, Gaithersburg, MD May 2002.

(35) UL 268, *Standard for Smoke Detectors for Fire Alarm Signaling Systems*, Underwriters Laboratories, Inc., Northbrook, IL, 2006.

(36) Deal, Scott. "Technical Reference Guide for FPEtool Version 3.2," NISTIR 5486, National Institute for Standards and Technology, U.S. Department of Commerce, Gaithersburg, MD, Aug. 1994.

(37) Mowrer, F. W. "Lag Times Associated with Detection and Suppression," *Fire Technology*, Vol. 26, No. 3, pp. 244–265, 1990.

(38) Newman, J. S. "Principles for Fire Detection," *Fire Technology*, Vol. 24, No. 2, pp. 116–127, 1988.

(39) Custer, R., Meacham, B., Wood, C. "Performance Based Design Techniques for Detection and Special Suppression Applications," Proceedings of the SFPE Engineering Seminars on Advances in Detection and Suppression Technology, 1994.

(40) SFPE *Engineering Guide to Performance Based Fire Protection Analysis and Design*, 2007, SFPE, Bethesda, MD.

(41) SFPE Handbook of Fire Protection Engineering, Third Edition, SFPE, Bethesda, MD, 2002.

(42) Drysdale, Dougal, *An Introduction to Fire Dynamics*, John Wiley & Sons, New York, NY, 1998, ISBN 0 471 90613 1, Second Edition.

(43) Nam S., Donovan L.P. and Kim S.G.; Establishing Heat Detectors Thermal Sensitivity Through Bench Scale Tests; *Fire Safety Journal*, Volume 39, Number 3, 191–215; April 2004.

(44) Nam S.; Thermal Response Coefficient TRC of Heat Detectors and Its Field Applications; Fire Detection and Research Applications Symposium; NFPA Research Foundation; January 2003.

(45) Nam S.; Performance-Based Heat Detector Spacing; Interflam 2004; pages 883–892.

(46) Geiman, J.A., "Evaluation of Smoke Detector Response Estimation Methods," Master of Science Thesis, University of Maryland, College Park, MD, December 2003.

(47) Projected Beam Smoke Detectors — More Than Just a Substitute for Spot Detectors; Fire Protection Engineering; Summer 2004; SFPE

(48) Geiman, J.A., and Gottuck, D.T., "Alarm Thresholds for Smoke Detector Modeling," *Fire Safety Science — Proceeding of the Seventh International Symposium*, 2003, pp. 197–208.

(49) *The SFPE Code Official's Guide to Performance-based Design Review and Analysis of Buildings*, Society of Fire Protection Engineers, Bethesda, MD, 2004.

(50) NFPA *101*, *Life Safety Code*, National Fire Protection Association, Quincy, MA, 2006.

(51) NFPA 909, *Code for the Protection of Cultural Resource Properties — Museums, Libraries, and Places of Worship*, National Fire Protection Association, Quincy, MA, 2005.

(52) NFPA 914, *Code for Fire Protection of Historic Structures*, National Fire Protection Association, Quincy, MA, 2007.

(53) Performance-based Building Design Concepts, International Code Council, Washington DC, 2004.

(54) *Extreme Event Mitigation In Buildings — Analysis and Design*, Meacham, National Fire Protection Association, Quincy MA, 2006.

(55) Geiman, Gottuk and Milke "Evaluation of Smoke Detector Response Estimation Methods: Optical Density, Temperature Rise and Velocity at Alarm" by *Journal of Fire Protection Engineering*, 2006.

(56) Su et al. "Kemano Fire Studies — Part 1: Response of Residential Smoke Alarms," Research Report 108, NRCC, April 2003.

(57) Davis, W, The Zone Model Jet, "A Model for the Prediction of Detector Activation and Gas Temperature in the Presence of a Smoke Layer," NISTIR 6324, NIST, May 1999.

B.7 Nomenclature

The nomenclature used in Annex B is defined in Table B.7.

TABLE B.7 Nomenclature

α	= fire intensity coefficient (kW/sec² or Btu/sec³)
A	= area (m² or ft²)
A_0	= $g/(C_p T_a \rho)$ [m⁴/(sec²kJ) or ft⁴/(sec²Btu)]
A_r	= radiating area (m² or ft²)
A_t	= radiating area of test fire
C	= specific heat of detector element (kJ/kg·°C or Btu/lbm·°F)
c	= speed of light (m/sec or ft/sec)
C_p	= specific heat of air [kJ/(kg K) or Btu/lbm R (1.040 kJ/kg K)]
D_m	= mass optical density (m²/g or ft²/lb)
d	= distance between fire and radiant energy–sensing detector
d'	= distance between fire and detector
$d(Du)/dt$	= rate of increase of optical density outside the detector
D	= $0.146 + 0.242 r/H$

TABLE B.7 *Continued*

Δt	=	change in time (seconds)
ΔT	=	increase above ambient in temperature of gas surrounding a detector (°C or °F)
Δt_d	=	increase above ambient in temperature of a detector (°C or °F)
Δt_p^*	=	change in reduced gas temperature
e	=	energy (joules or Btu)
f	=	functional relationship
g	=	gravitational constant (9.81 m/sec^2 or 32 ft/sec^2)
h	=	Planck's constant (6.63E-23 joule-sec)
H	=	ceiling height or height above fire (m or ft)
H_c	=	convective heat transfer coefficient (kW/m^2·°C or Btu/ft^2·sec·°F)
ΔH_c	=	heat of combustion (kJ/mol)
h_f	=	flame height (m or ft)
H_f	=	heat of formation (kJ/mol)
L	=	characteristic length for a given detector design
k	=	detector constant, dimensionless
m	=	mass (kg or lbm)
p	=	positive exponent
P	=	radiant power (watts or Btu/sec)
q	=	heat release rate density per unit floor area (watts/m^2 or Btu/sec·ft^2)
Q	=	heat release rate (kW or Btu/sec)
Q_c	=	convection portion of fire heat release rate (kW or Btu/sec)
Q_{cond}	=	heat transferred by conduction (kW or Btu/sec)
Q_{conv}	=	heat transferred by convection (kW or Btu/sec)
Q_d	=	threshold fire size at which response must occur
Q_{rad}	=	heat transferred by radiation (kW or Btu/sec)
Q_{total}	=	total heat transfer (kW or Btu/sec)
Q_{CR}	=	critical heat release rate (kW or Btu/sec)
Q_{DO}	=	design heat release rate (kW or Btu/sec)
Q_m	=	maximum heat release rate (kW or Btu/sec)
Q_p	=	predicted heat release rate (kW or Btu/sec)
Q_T	=	threshold heat release rate at response (kW or Btu/sec)
r	=	radial distance from fire plume axis (m or ft)
ρ_0	=	density of ambient air [kg/m^3 or lb/ft^3 (1.1 kg/m^3)]
RTI	=	response time index (m$^{1/2}$sec$^{1/2}$ or ft$^{1/2}$ sec$^{1/2}$)
S	=	spacing of detectors or sprinkler heads (m or ft)
S	=	radiant energy
t_{DO}	=	time at which the design objective heat release rate (Q_{DO}) is reached (seconds)
t_{CR}	=	time at which the critical heat release rate (Q_{CR}) is reached (seconds)
t	=	time (seconds)
t_c	=	critical time — time at which fire would reach a heat release rate of 1055 kW (1000 Btu/sec) (seconds)
t_d	=	time to detector response
t_g	=	fire growth time to reach 1055 kW (1000 Btu/sec) (seconds)
t_r	=	response time (seconds)
$t_{respond}$	=	time available, or needed, for response to an alarm condition (seconds)
t_v	=	virtual time of origin (seconds)
t_{2f}	=	arrival time of heat front (for $p = 2$ power law fire) at a point r/H (seconds)
t_{2f}^*	=	reduced arrival time of heat front (for $p = 2$ power law fire) at a point r/H (seconds)
t_p^*	=	reduced time
T	=	temperature (°C or °F)
T_a	=	ambient temperature (°C or °F)
T_c	=	plume centerline temperature (°C or °F)

(continues)

TABLE B.7 *Continued*

T_d	=	detector temperature (°C or °F)
T_g	=	temperature of fire gases (°C or °F)
T_s	=	rated operating temperature of a detector or sprinkler (°C or °F)
u_0	=	instantaneous velocity of fire gases (m/sec or ft/sec)
u	=	velocity (m/sec or ft/sec)
u_c	=	critical velocity
U_p^*	=	reduced gas velocity
V	=	velocity of smoke at detector
w_f	=	flame width (m or ft)
Y	=	defined in equation B.27
z	=	height above top of fuel package involved (m or ft)
λ	=	wavelength (microns)
Z_m	=	maximum height of smoke rise above fire surface (m or ft)
τ	=	detector time constant mc/H_cA (seconds)
τ_0	=	detector time constant measured at reference velocity u_0 (seconds)
ε	=	emissivity, a material property expressed as a fraction between 0 and 1.0

REFERENCES CITED IN COMMENTARY

ANSI/UL 268, *Standard for Smoke Detectors for Fire Alarm Systems*, 2006, American National Standards Institute, Inc., New York, NY.

Custer, R. L. P., and Meacham, B. J., *Introduction to Performance-Based Fire Safety,* National Fire Protection Association, Quincy, MA, 1997.

FM Approval Standard 3210, *Heat Detectors for Automatic Fire Alarm Signaling*, 2006 edition, FM Global, Norwood, MA.

Meacham, B. J., and Custer, R. L. P., "Performance-Based Fire Safety Engineering: An Introduction of Basic Concepts," *Journal of Fire Protection Engineering,* 1995; 7(2).

NFPA 72E, *Automatic Fire Detectors*, 1990 edition, National Fire Protection Association, Quincy, MA.

SFPE Handbook of Fire Protection Engineering, 4th edition, National Fire Protection Association, Quincy, MA, and Society of Fire Protection Engineers, Bethesda, MD, 2008.

System Performance and Design Guide

This annex is not a part of the requirements of this NFPA document but is included for informational purposes only.

This annex is new to the 2010 edition of the Code. Chapter 23, Protected Premises Fire Alarm Systems, provides the minimum requirements for a protected premises fire alarm system. While compliance with minimum code requirements is important, seldom do those minimum requirements address the site-specific needs and conditions that exist at a particular facility. The requirements of the Code are intended to provide the minimum level of protection for all facilities regardless of their occupancy, operations, mission importance, or a myriad of other factors. For a particular application, in addition to the minimum requirements of the Code, the system designer should also consider the site-specific fire protection objectives of the building owner. Those objectives are generally expressed as some level of life safety, property protection, and mission continuity that are generally above and beyond the minimum requirements of the Code.

This annex is intended as a guide for system designers to determine the characteristics, features, and functions that may be needed for a fire alarm system in a particular application. The annex material provides a framework within which a system designer can develop a fire alarm system design that is integrated with the other fire protection features of the facility, such as the capabilities of the emergency responders, desired features of the fire alarm system, the size and use of the buildings, and other factors that should be considered in the design decision process.

C.1 Scope

The requirements of the protected premises Chapter 23 provide for minimum levels of protection for fire alarm systems to protect life and property, regardless of the building characteristics, contents, or use. This System Performance and Design Guide provides additional considerations for users of the NFAC when planning, designing, and installing protected premises fire alarm systems for buildings that might be unusual in scale, mission, use, symbolism, or other critical or high-profile characteristics.

This guidance suggests potential system characteristics to enhanced system performance for protection of life, mission, and property in high-profile and other critical buildings, including signaling path integrity, redundancies, survivability, backup fire control stations, non-erasable logs, multiple information stations, and the benefits of networked and peer-to-peer configurations.

C.2 Building Scale

The size of a building to be protected influences fire alarm system operating characteristics, control functions, circuit integrity, annunciation, and other factors for protection of life, property, or the mission of the building.

C.2.1 Fire Service Response Location(s).

C.2.1.1 Location(s). Determine the fire service response location(s) by inquiry to the responding fire department (and building operating personnel, if appropriate).

C.2.1.2 Quantity. The fire service might desire more than one response location. Building operators might desire redundancies for security or operations under emergency conditions.

C.2.1.3 Functions. The primary response location is the normally expected location of the fire command center (FCC). In general, the fire command center provides information and control functions for the entire building. One or more redundant or abbreviated fire command centers might be desired for security or operations under emergency conditions.

C.2.1.3.1 Information. Nonprimary response locations might be intended to provide annunciation equipment to provide information for the entire building, or for a portion of the building associated with the response location.

C.2.1.3.2 Control. Nonprimary response locations might be intended to provide a partial or complete fire command center to provide control functions for the entire building, or for a portion of the building associated with the response location.

C.2.2 System Operational Characteristics.

C.2.2.1 On-Premises Response. Determine an alarm response plan considering the requirements of NFAC, local codes and regulations, the availability and responsibility of building operating personnel, and the mobility of occupants.

C.2.2.1.1 Investigation. Building security or operating personnel should investigate every alarm signal, and the alarm response plan might include investigation of initial alarm signals prior to activating a general alarm or the evacuation or relocation of occupants.

C.2.2.1.2 Communication. Determine appropriate methods to provide alarm information, and instructions when required, to building security and operating personnel, supervisory and management personnel, and building occupants. Consider the need for predetermined messages, single- or multiple-channel communications systems, and coordination of communications system coverage and zoning with building subdivisions, including smoke compartments and automatic suppression system coverage and zoning. Consider the need for multiple languages in emergency communications.

C.2.2.1.3 Evacuation/Relocation. Determine the extent to which the emergency egress plan is based on total evacuation, relocation and partial evacuation, areas of rescue assistance and/or defending in place.

C.2.2.1.4 Survivability. Consider means to harden the fire notification circuits/paths to attack by fire for a period of time necessary to notify building operating personnel and occupants of a fire emergency and/or provide instructions if appropriate.

C.2.2.1.5 Control. Fire alarm system control units can be arranged to activate other building systems and to condition passive fire barriers to enhance fire safety in the building.

C.2.2.1.6 Building Systems. Consider activation or release of building systems and elements including, but not limited to, closing fire/smoke doors and dampers, recall of elevators, unlocking stairway doors, activating smoke control systems and or shut-down fans to prevent recirculation of smoke.

C.2.2.1.7 Fire Scene Operations. Compartmentation, water supply, fire fighter access, and communication links are important for manual fire-fighting operations. Fire alarm system monitoring, reporting, display, and control functions that enhance the maintenance and operation of these elements that enhance fire scene operations should be considered in the design, installation, and maintenance of protected premises fire alarm systems. An example would be a flashing light over the fire department connection.

C.2.2.2 External Response.

C.2.2.2.1 Resources Available. Determine the availability and responsibility of fire service resources. An example of the use of this information might be determining how to stage evacuation.

C.2.2.2.2 Time Required. Consider the time required for fire service response to the building. Consider travel time at various times of day and seasons of year.

C.2.2.2.3 Notification. Determine one or more acceptable means of automatic and manual notification of the fire service to initiate response to the building. Consider the extent of information that might be transmitted to the responding fire service to enhance response to the building and to provide incident information prior to its arrival.

C.2.2.2.4 Evacuation/Relocation. Consider system operational characteristics that might enhance coordination of control and direction to building operating personnel and occupants. Consider means of control and shift in control of evacuation or relocation direction from building operating personnel to fire service command.

C.2.2.2.5 Knowledge of Premises. Harmonize system operating characteristics to pre-incident planning with fire service and building operating and security personnel.

C.2.2.2.6 Communications and Control. Provide for fire-fighter communications through dedicated two-way fire-fighter communication systems, or consider a means to provide enhanced operation of fire service radio communications in the protected premises.

C.3 Premises Mission/Use/Property Protection

The loss of use or mission of a facility to the effects of accidental fire can have a very significant impact on the community or organization served by the facility. In such a case, it is appropriate to enhance functional characteristics of the protected premises system. Considerations include the following:

(1) Criticality/Mission Continuity

    (a) Community — Loss of operations of the facility might affect the community beyond the facility. Consider the sensitivity of fire detection and the effectiveness of alarm processing, emergency response, and fire suppression to minimize effects on the community served due to facility impairment by fire.

    (b) Operations

        i. On-premises — Fire might result in business interruption or reduced effectiveness.

        ii. Elsewhere — Services provided by the facility to remote locations might cease or be reduced.

(2) Life Safety

    (a) Evacuation/Relocation — Size, distribution, and mobility of the occupant population should be considered with knowledge of facility emergency planning and availability of emergency response resources to determine the extent to which people movement might be managed during a fire incident.

    (b) Defend In Place — A protected premises system might be used to activate facility fire safety elements necessary to defend occupants in place or to enhance rescue assistance.

(3) Property

 (a) Value — Cost, availability, and time required to reestablish facility contents should be considered when determining the sensitivity of fire detection and the effectiveness of alarm processing, emergency response, and fire suppression.

 (b) Replacement — Availability and time required to replace damaged facility contents should be considered when determining the sensitivity of fire detection and the effectiveness of alarm processing emergency response and fire suppression.

 (c) Redundancy — Duplication of facility contents in separate locations might reduce the need for sensitivity of fire detection or other property protection system capabilities.

C.4 Protected Premises Signaling System Features

C.4.1 Event Logs. Computer processor–based systems are capable of assembling logs of system events by date and time, including alarm history. Such logs are an important resource in assessing system performance or malfunctions and in understanding or reconstructing a fire event after the fact. It is imperative that such logs are preserved and protected against deletion until it is affirmed that no further need for a log exists. Caution is recommended to secure system history logs when system software changes are made.

C.4.2 Network Configuration. Systems that use digital means to transfer signal information might provide benefits in economy of installation and distribution of information to multiple locations to enable rigorous alarm processing and response. Transmission of digital alarm information to remote locations might assist responding personnel by providing incident information prior to arrival at the location of the fire.

C.4.3 Peer to Peer Data Communication. Systems that duplicate the operating and history data bases in multiple network control units provide redundant monitoring and control points on a system that can enhance the reliability of the system and the operation of the system during emergency or degraded conditions.

Speech Intelligibility

This annex is not a part of the requirements of this NFPA document but is included for informational purposes only.

Users of Annex D should refer back to the text of NFPA 72 to familiarize themselves with the specific requirements for the planning, design, installation, and testing of voice communication systems.

D.1 Introduction

D.1.1 This annex is intended to provide guidance on the planning, design, installation, and testing of voice communication systems. The majority of this annex contains recommendations for testing of the intelligibility of voice systems.

D.1.2 As with most systems, proper system performance is related to good planning, design, installation, and maintenance. Similarly, test results are a valuable feedback mechanism for persons planning, designing, and installing systems.

D.1.3 This annex describes when, where, and how to test for speech intelligibility. It is also not the intent of this test protocol to describe how to interpret results or how to correct systems or environments that contribute to poor speech intelligibility.

D.1.4 For occupancies that do not yet exist, the designer should have an understanding of the acoustic characteristics of the architectural design, as well as the acoustic performance properties of available loudspeakers. Architecturally, this includes the physical size and shape of the space, as well as the acoustic properties of the walls, floors, ceilings, and interior furnishings. A proper design analysis can sometimes reveal that an intelligible system is not achievable unless some features of the architectural design are changed. The designer should be prepared to defend such conclusions and, if necessary, refuse to certify the installation of such a system. While "hand calculations" and experience work well for simpler installations, more complex designs are frequently better and more cost-effectively analyzed using one of a number of readily available computer-based design programs.

D.1.5 The designer and the authority having jurisdiction should both be aware that the acoustic performance parameters of the chosen loudspeakers, as well as their placement in the structure, play a major role in determining how many appliances are necessary for adequate intelligibility. The numerical count of appliances for a given design and protected space cannot, by itself, be used to determine the adequacy of the design. Sometimes, the acoustic problems of certain placement constraints can be satisfactorily overcome through the careful selection of loudspeakers with the requisite performance characteristics, rather than by increasing their number.

D.2 Fundamentals of Test Protocol

D.2.1 Measurement Method.

D.2.1.1 STI/STIPA.

D.2.1.1.1 Where the method for measuring speech intelligibility is the Speech Transmission Index (STI), this test protocol should be followed.

D.2.1.1.2 There are several methods that measure the Speech Transmission Index (STI). One method common to the emergency communications system industry uses a test signal referred to as STIPA — STI-Public Address.

D.2.1.2 Other Methods. Where the method for measuring speech intelligibility is the Phonetically Balanced Word test (PB), Modified Rhyme Test (MRT), or Speech Intelligibility Index (SII) method, the same methods for determining measurement locations should be used.

D.2.2 References.

D.2.2.1 IEC 60268-16, *"Sound system equipment — Part 16: Objective rating of speech intelligibility by speech transmission index"*, International Electrotechnical Commission, Geneva, Switz., 22 May 2003.

D.2.2.2 ISO 7240-19, *"Fire Detection and Alarm Systems — Part 19: Design, Installation, Commissioning and Service of Sound Systems for Emergency Purposes"*, International Organization for Standardization, Geneva, Switz., 1st edition, 15 Aug 2007.

D.2.2.3 NEMA Standards Publication SB 50-2008, *"Emergency Communications Audio Intelligibility Applications Guide"*, National Electrical Manufacturers Association, Rosslyn VA, 2008.

D.2.3 Terminology.

D.2.3.1 Acoustically Distinguishable Space *(ADS).*

D.2.3.1.1 An acoustically distinguishable space *(ADS)* can be an emergency communication system notification zone, or subdivision thereof, that can be an enclosed or otherwise physically defined space, or that can be distinguished from other spaces because of different acoustical, environmental, or use characteristics such as reverberation time and ambient sound pressure level. The *ADS* might have acoustical design features that are conducive for voice intelligibility, or it might be a space where voice intelligibility could be difficult or impossible to achieve.

D.2.3.1.2 All parts of a building or area intended to have occupant notification are subdivided into *ADS*s as defined. Some *ADS*s might be designated to have voice communication capability and require that those communications be intelligible. Other spaces might not require voice intelligibility or might not be capable of reliable voice intelligibility. Each is still referred to as an *ADS*.

D.2.3.1.3 In smaller areas, such as those under 400 ft² (40 m²), walls alone will define the *ADS*. In larger areas, other factors might have to be considered. In spaces that might be subdivided by temporary or movable partitions, such as ballrooms and meeting rooms, each individual configuration should be considered a separate *ADS*. Physical characteristics such as a change in ceiling height of more than 20 percent or change in acoustical finish, such as carpet in one area and tile in another, would require those areas to be treated as separate *ADS*s. In larger areas there might be noise sources that require a section to be treated as a separate

ADS. Any significant change in ambient sound pressure level or frequency might necessitate an area be considered a separate *ADS.*

D.2.3.1.4 In areas of 85 dBA or greater ambient sound pressure level, meeting the pass/fail criteria for intelligibility might not be possible and other means of communication might be necessary. So, for example, the space immediately surrounding a printing press or other high noise machine might be designated as a separate *ADS* and the design might call for some form of effective notification but not necessarily require the ability to have intelligible voice communication. The aisles or operator's control stations might be separate *ADS*s where intelligible voice communication might be desired.

D.2.3.1.5 Significant differences in furnishings, for example, an area with tables, desks, or low dividers adjacent to an area with high shelving, would require separate consideration. The entire desk area could be a single acoustic zone whereas each area between shelving could be a unique zone. Essentially, any noteworthy change in the acoustical environment within an area will mandate consideration of that portion of the area to be treated as an acoustic zone. Hallways and stairwells will typically be considered as individual acoustic zones.

D.2.3.1.6 Spaces confined by walls with carpeting and acoustical ceilings can be deemed to be one *ADS.* An *ADS* should be an area of consistent size and material. A change of materials from carpet to hard tile, the existence of sound sources such as decorative waterfalls, large expanses of glass, and changes in ceiling height are all factors that might separate one *ADS* from another.

D.2.3.1.7 Each *ADS* might require different components and design features to achieve intelligible voice communication. For example, two *ADS*s with similar acoustical treatments and noise levels might have different ceiling heights. The *ADS* with the lower ceiling height might require more ceiling-mounted speakers to ensure that all listeners are in a direct sound field. See Figure D.2.3.1.7. Other *ADS*s might benefit from the use of alternate speaker technologies such as line arrays to achieve intelligibility.

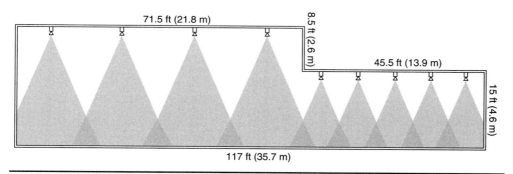

FIGURE D.2.3.1.7 *Illustration Demonstrating the Effect of Ceiling Height. (Source: R. P. Schifiliti Associates, Inc.)*

D.2.3.1.8 An *ADS* that differs from another because of the frequency and level of ambient sound pressure level might require the use of speakers and system components that have a wider frequency bandwidth than conventional emergency communications equipment. However, designers should not use higher bandwidth speakers in all locations unless needed to overcome certain acoustic and ambient conditions. This is because the higher bandwidth appliance will require more energy to perform properly. This increases amplifier and wire size and power supply requirements.

D.2.3.1.9 In some spaces it might be impractical to achieve intelligibility, and in such a case alternatives to voice evacuation might be required within such areas.

D.2.3.1.10 There might be some areas of a facility where there are several spaces of the same approximate size and with the same acoustic properties. For example, there might be an office space with multiple individual offices, each with one speaker. If one or two are satisfactorily tested, there is no need to test all of them for speech intelligibility.

D.2.3.2 Audibility Test. Measurement of the sound pressure level of a tone signal in accordance with the requirements of NFPA 72.

D.2.3.3 Intelligibility Test. A test method used to predict how well speech is understood by a listener.

D.2.3.4 Occupied Ambient Sound Pressure Level. The period of time when the building involved in the test is occupied and is reasonably close to having maximum background noise. For example, this might involve the operation of HVAC equipment, an industrial process, or a maximum number of occupants such as might occur in a place of public assembly.

D.2.3.5 STI or STIPA Test Signal.

D.2.3.5.1 A special audio signal that is played over the emergency communications system being tested.

D.2.3.5.2 Instruments that measure STI using a STIPA signal use a special signal that consists of signals in seven octave bands. The sound in each octave band is modulated using two (separate) modulation frequencies. The STI and STIPA have been standardized in IEC 60268. However, at the present time, the implementation of the measurement software and correlations with the test signal can differ between instrument manufacturers. Therefore, until there is further standardization, only the test signal recommended by the instrument manufacturer should be used with their instrument. Although the STIPA test signals can sound similar, there might be speed or other differences that affect results if one manufacturer's test signal is used with another manufacturer's instrument.

D.2.3.6 Talkbox. An instrument usually consisting of a high quality audio speaker and a CD player or other method used to play an STI or STIPA test signal.

D.2.3.7 Unoccupied Ambient Sound Pressure Level. The period of time when the primary occupants of the facility are not present, or when ambient sound pressure level is not at its highest level.

D.2.4 Acceptability Criteria.

D.2.4.1 The intelligibility of an emergency communication system is considered acceptable if at least 90 percent of the measurement locations within each *ADS* have a measured STI of not less than 0.45 (0.65 CIS) and an average STI of not less than 0.50 STI (0.70 CIS).

D.2.4.2 Speech intelligibility is not a physical quantity like meters, feet, amperes, volts, or even decibels. It is a benchmark of the degree to which we understand spoken language, and as such is a complex phenomenon affected by many variables (Ref: Jacob, K. & Tyson, T., "Computer-Based Prediction of Speech Intelligibility for Mass Notification Systems", SUPDET 2008, Fire Protection Research Foundation, Mar 2008). There are two basic categories of intelligibility testing: (1) subject (human) based testing and (2) instrument based test methods. Test methods that use human subjects are only statistical predictions of how well speech might be understood at any other time for any other group of listeners. Several subject based test methods have been extensively researched, tested for reliability, and standardized. Examples include the Phonetically Balanced (PB) word scores (256 words or 1000 words) and Modified Rhyme Test (MRT). (Ref: ANSI S3.2-1989, "Method for Measuring the Intelligibility of Speech over Communication Systems". Ref: ISO/TR 4870, "Acoustics – The Construction and Calibration of Speech Intelligibility Tests").

D.2.4.3 Subject based test methods can gauge how much of the spoken information is correctly understood by a person or group of persons for that particular test. When properly done, that resulting value is a prediction of how much of the spoken word will be correctly understood by others at some other time. Therefore, the results of speech intelligibility testing are usually described as predictions, not measurements. However, most users of the instruments refer to the results as measurements, not as predictions. Since the use of portable instruments is the more common method in the alarm and emergency communications industries, in this document the results will be referred to as measurements to avoid confusion. However, in scientific and general acoustic literature, readers can see the measured values correctly referred to as predictions.

D.2.4.4 Several instrument based methods for predicting speech intelligibility have been extensively researched and tested for accuracy and repeatability, and the methods have been standardized, most notably the Speech Intelligibility Index (SII) (formerly the Articulation Index, AI), Speech Transmission Index (STI), and Speech Transmission Index for Public Address (STIPA) (Ref: IEC 60268-16, "Sound system equipment — Part 16: Objective rating of speech intelligibility by speech transmission index", 2003. Ref: ANSI/ASA S3.5, "American National Standard Methods for Calculation of the Speech Intelligibility Index", 1997). Accuracy is how close the meter corresponds to actual human test results. Thus, even though an instrument is used, the results are subjective in that they correlate with how humans perceive the quality of speech.

D.2.4.5 Each of the established methods for measuring speech intelligibility has its own scale. The Common Intelligibility Scale (CIS) was developed in 1995 to show the relationship between the different methods and to permit codes and standards to require a certain level of performance while permitting any of the accepted measurement methods to be employed (Ref: Barnett, P.W. & Knight, A.D., "The Common Intelligibility Scale", Proceedings of the Institute of Acoustics, Vol. 17, Part 7, 1995). The Speech Transmission Index (STI) is widely used and has been implemented in portable equipment using a modified method called STIPA (STI Public Address). For this reason, the performance metrics cited in this document use units of STI with units of CIS in parentheses. The relationship between the two is: CIS = 1-log10 (STI). Relationships between other methods can be found in the literature (Ref: IEC 60849, Annex B, Sound Systems for Emergency Purposes, Feb 1998).

D.2.4.6 If an *ADS* is small enough to only require one measurement location (see the requirements for measurement point spacing), the result should be 0.50 STI (0.70 CIS) or more for the *ADS* to pass the requirement for speech intelligibility. This is based on the requirement for an average of 0.50 STI (0.70 CIS) or more in that *ADS*. Therefore, a single measurement of 0.45 STI (0.65 CIS) would not be considered acceptable, because that one measurement would be below the minimum required average of 0.50 STI (0.70 CIS) in that *ADS*.

D.2.4.7 If the value at that one measurement location were less than 0.50 STI (0.70 CIS), additional measurements could be taken at that same single measurement location. As with simple sound pressure level measurements, intelligibility measurements at any point will vary. If the average of all the measurements at that location were 0.50 STI (0.70 CIS) or more, the *ADS* would pass the requirement for speech intelligibility.

D.2.4.8 Some *ADS*s might require multiple measurement points due to their larger size. (See the requirements for measurement point spacing.) However, even in a small *ADS* where one measurement point would be permitted, a designer might intend that multiple measurements be made because of conditions that might result in specific points having intelligibility scores below the minimum. Where an *ADS* has multiple measurement locations, the requirement is that at least 90 percent of the measurement locations have values not less than 0.45 STI, (0.65 CIS) and that all measurement points average to 0.50 STI (0.70 CIS) or greater.

D.2.4.9 The use of an average intelligibility score as a part of the requirement permits a wider range of measured values within an *ADS* than would a simple minimum requirement. A range of permitted values is not appropriate since there is no need for an upper limit for intelligibility — prefect intelligibility is certainly acceptable.

D.2.4.10 The requirement that only 90 percent of the measured points in the ADS meet the minimum and that the average for the entire *ADS* be 0.50 STI (0.70 CIS) or greater recognizes that in any space, with any system and any set of acoustic conditions, there can be points where the intelligibility score might be below the minimum. See also the discussion on the definition of an *ADS* and how some *ADS*s might be designated to not require speech intelligibility at all. For example, in a room that is otherwise similar from an acoustics standpoint, the space around a loud machine might be one *ADS* while the rest of the room is a separate *ADS*. The *ADS* surrounding the machine might be designed to have some form of occupant notification, but not to have intelligible voice communications. This type of *ADS* designation permits the remainder of the room to be scored without being penalized by the fact that intelligible communication near some loud sound sources might not be possible.

D.2.4.11 The intelligibility performance requirement cited herein intentionally uses two decimal points. Portable instruments that use the STIPA method for measuring the Speech Transmission Index (STI) generally have a precision on the order of 0.02 to 0.03 (Ref: Sander J. van Wijngaarden and Jan A. Verhave, Past Present and Future of the Speech Transmission Index, Chapter 9, Measurement and Prediction of Speech Intelligibility in Traffic Tunnels Using the STI, p113, TNO Human Factors, The Netherlands, 2002.). Other methods that measure STI can have a greater measurement precision. Other measurement methods, such as Modified Rhyme Test (MRT), Phonetically Balanced Word (PB) lists, and Speech Intelligibility Index (SII), also have levels of precision in the hundredths when properly conducted and scored. However, there might be slight variations in measured values between any two meters or between any two persons taking measurements with the same instrument, or between any two listener panels when using subject based test methods. This is true for any measurement method or instrument, including simple scales for measuring length or mass.

D.2.4.12 Measurements should be made and recorded using two decimal places. Averages can be calculated to three decimal points and rounded. The calculated average value should be rounded to the nearest five-hundredths (0.05) to reflect possible measurement errors and the intent of the requirement (Ref: Mapp, P., "Systematic & Common Errors in Sound System STI and Intelligibility Measurements", Convention Paper 6271, Audio Engineering Society, 117th Convention, San Fran, CA, 28-31 Oct 2004. Ref: Peter Mapp, Past Present and Future of the Speech Transmission Index, Chapter 8, Practical Application of STI to Assessing Public Address and Emergency Sound Systems, TNO Human Factors, The Netherlands, 2002.). For example, averages of 0.47–0.525 STI would all be rounded to report an average of 0.50 STI (0.70 CIS). The minimum value permitted for all but 10 percent of the measurement locations in an *ADS* should be 0.45 STI (0.65 CIS) or greater. For example, values of 0.44 STI are below the minimum; they are not rounded up to 0.45 STI.

D.2.5 Limitations of Test Method.

D.2.5.1 Equipment designed in accordance with UL 864 and fire alarm speakers designed in accordance with UL 1480 are only tested for and only required to produce frequencies of 400 to 4000 Hz. Speech, however, includes a wider range of frequencies. Speech intelligibility measurements using STI and STIPA include octave band measurements that range from 125 Hz to 8000 Hz. STI results are most dependent on the 2000, 1000, 500, and 4000 Hz octave bands (in order of weighting) and to a lesser extent the 8000 and 250 Hz octave bands and to an even lesser extent, the 125 Hz band (again, in order of weighting).

D.2.5.2 While the lower and higher octave bands in STI calculations are weighted much less than the others, under certain acoustic conditions, systems that do not produce the highs and the lows can produce speech intelligibility that is less than desired. This does not imply that all systems should use equipment capable of greater bandwidth sound reproduction. While the larger frequency response will probably sound better and be more intelligible to a listener, it might not be necessary for the minimum desired performance. The use of equipment with higher bandwidth will require an increase in power supplies, amplifiers, and wire sizes to drive the speaker appliances.

D.2.5.3 Areas of high ambient sound pressure levels ("noise") might be incapable of meeting the acceptability criteria in D.2.4.

D.2.5.4 In areas where the ambient sound pressure level exceeds 90 dBA, speech satisfactory speech intelligibility is difficult to achieve with conventional communications equipment and design practice. A better system design might include alternate communications methods, such as signs and displays, or might involve providing occupant notification but not communication at that location.

D.2.5.5 Impulse sounds made during measurements can impact measurement accuracy or cause instrument error.

D.2.5.6 Impulse sounds such as accidentally tapping the meter microphone, or a nearby door slamming can cause a measurement error. Some meters will display an error message. If an impulse sound occurs during the measurement, consider taking another measurement to check the results. This process is analogous to ignoring temporary sound sources, as permitted by NFPA 72 when taking sound pressure level measurements.

D.2.5.7 Natural variation in ambient sound pressure level levels can affect the results.

D.2.6 General Requirements.

D.2.6.1 The qualified staff should be identified on the system design documents. Acceptable evidence of qualifications or certification should be provided when requested by the authority having jurisdiction. Qualified personnel should include, but not be limited to, one or more of the following:

(1) Personnel who are factory trained and certified for fire alarm system design of the specific type and brand of system addressed by this test protocol
(2) Personnel who are certified by a nationally recognized certification organization acceptable to the authority having jurisdiction
(3) Personnel who are registered, licensed, or certified by a state or local authority

D.2.6.2 All necessary precautions should be taken with the facility owner to work with appropriately qualified staff when handling or performing any function with the emergency communications system control unit.

D.2.6.3 Testing impairment and record keeping requirements of NFPA 72, Chapter 14 should apply.

D.2.6.4 Test measurements and other documentation should be maintained as required by the authority having jurisdiction.

D.2.6.5 Impairment management procedures of NFPA 72, Section 10.19 should be followed.

D.2.6.6 Test Participants. The test participants should include representatives of and/or coordination with the following: building owners; the organizations responsible for the fire alarm or emergency communications system design and installation; system equipment supplier and/or manufacturer; and the authority having jurisdiction.

D.3 Pre-Planning

D.3.1 Facility Occupancy and Use.

D.3.1.1 Occupancy/Use Types. Prior to testing, the pre-planning effort should identify the occupancy or use type to better minimize disruption to the facility occupants during the test.

D.3.1.2 Normal Operational Time Periods. Prior to testing, pre-planning efforts should identify the operational time periods when the Occupied Ambient Sound Pressure Level and the Unoccupied Ambient Sound Pressure Level are most likely to occur.

D.3.1.3 Testing Before Building Furnishing Completion. It might be necessary to perform testing to permit partial use before the building is in its final acoustic configuration. The results of intelligibility testing at this stage can differ from the final performance of the system. It might be necessary to work with the AHJ to develop a testing plan. For example, until acoustical treatments such as carpeting, ceiling tiles, and other furnishings are in place, the system can be partially tested to meet audibility requirements but not necessarily intelligibility requirements. Other test plans or mitigating procedures might be permitted.

D.3.1.4 Facility Construction and Condition. Construction in the facility to be tested should be completed for areas that will be subject to intelligibility testing. This specifically requires that the command center and all locations of system microphones to be tested should be completed. Any location of remote system microphones not tested during this time should be noted, and said locations should be fully tested with positive results within 90 days of area occupancy or as required by the authority having jurisdiction. Also, all building systems such as environmental conditioning systems should be completed and operational, as they both produce noise and provide acoustic noise travel paths. In addition, all floor treatments and any acoustical wall or ceiling treatments should be in place.

D.3.1.5 System Under Test Status. The System Under Test should be completed for all areas where intelligibility testing will be done.

D.3.1.6 System Under Test Power. System Under Test should be on permanent primary power source as defined in NFPA 72.

D.3.1.7 System Under Test Secondary Power. Secondary power, where required and/or provided for the System Under Test, should be fully functional. If batteries are used for this purpose, batteries should be fully charged for a minimum of 48 hours prior to the commencement of any testing.

D.3.2 Emergency Communication Equipment.

D.3.2.1 As discussed in D.2.3.1, not all *ADS*s will require or be capable of intelligible voice communications. It is the designer's job to define areas that will have voice communication versus those that might have tone-only signaling, as well as which spaces will have strobes, textual signage, or other forms of notification and/or communication. This document intends that "notification" mean any form of notification, not just voice communication, whether audible, visual, or using some other human sense.

D.3.2.2 There might be applications where not all spaces will require intelligible voice signaling (Ref: NFPA 72, *National Fire Alarm Code*, 2007, Section A.7.4.1.4). For example, in a residential occupancy such as an apartment, the authority having jurisdiction and the designer might agree to a system that achieves the required audibility throughout but does not result in intelligible voice signaling in the bedrooms. The system would be sufficient to awaken and alert. However, intelligibility might not be achieved in the bedrooms with the doors closed and the sounder in the adjacent hallway or room. In some cases this can require that messages repeat a sufficient number of times to ensure that occupants can reach a location where the system is sufficiently intelligible to be understood. Systems that use tone signaling in some areas and voice signaling in other areas would not require voice intelligibility in those areas only covered by the tone.

D.3.2.3 Emergency Communications System Control Panel. The System Under Test for the emergency communications system should be located and identified prior to testing, and its operation features necessary for the testing clarified. Personnel who are authorized to access and service the control panel are necessary for the testing and should be included within the team performing the tests. If necessary, notification to locations beyond the facility that is being tested (e.g., fire department or a supervising station) should be notified of the tests, and if appropriate, their automatic notification feature disabled. Upon completion of the tests the emergency communications system should be returned to its normal operating condition.

D.3.2.4 Test Set-up. The function and operation of the emergency communication system control unit should be reviewed with personnel authorized to access and operate this equipment. Information should be acquired on the functioning of the voice notification portion of the system, and whether it has zone capabilities that will allow minimal disruption to building occupants by testing each zone individually. The test plan should also specify whether other functions of the system, such as elevator recall and air handler control, will be disabled during the testing of the emergency communications system.

D.3.2.5 System Under Test Calibration. The complete System Under Test audio path should be fully calibrated in accordance with manufacturer's instructions. On systems with adjustable technology, if manufacturer's instructions are not provided, the alternate calibration procedure offered below can be employed to calibrate the System Under Test.

D.3.2.5.1 Alternate Calibration Procedure.

D.3.2.5.1.1 This calibration is to be performed with the System Under Test on normal AC power, then checked with the system on secondary power (if so equipped).

D.3.2.5.1.2 The System Under Test amplifier output or the circuit being calibrated should have a minimum of a 1-watt load during the calibration process.

D.3.2.5.1.3 Perform pre-test occupant and remote monitoring station notification requirements specified in NFPA 72-2010, Chapter 14.

D.3.2.5.1.4 Introduce a 1 kHz sine-wave tone (± 100 Hz) at 90 dBA-fast 4″ (4 in.) to the system microphone on-axis, perpendicular to the face of the microphone.

D.3.2.5.1.5 Place the System Under Test into manual paging mode (microphone "live" and connected to amplifier circuitry with notification appliance circuits active).

D.3.2.5.1.6 Using a 4-digit accuracy RMS meter, set on AC scale, set the output of the System Under Test audio notification appliance circuits to between 24 and 26 Vrms for 25.2 volt systems or between 69 and 71 Vrms for 70.7 volt systems.

D.3.2.5.1.7 Once System Under Test manual paging mode has been calibrated, pre-recorded tone (if so equipped) should then be tested by playing it through the System Under Test to ensure that there is no more than a 3 dBA difference between manual paging using the system microphone and the pre-recorded message. The dBA measurement should be made using an integrating/averaging meter and averaged over approximately 10 seconds of voice announcement to compensate for voice amplitude modulation.

D.3.2.5.1.8 On a System Under Test with more than one emergency paging microphone and/or pre-recorded message units, the primary units should be calibrated, then secondary units tested to ensure that they produce signals throughout the System Under Test at the same amplitude as the primary units.

D.3.3 Plans and Specifications.

D.3.3.1 The approved plans and specifications for the system should be used to plan and document the tests.

D.3.3.2 Testing is best accomplished using large scale plans showing all notification appliances.

D.3.3.3 The plans should show the different system notification zones.

D.3.3.4 The type and location of the notification appliances used in the emergency communication system should be identified prior to testing.

D.3.3.5 Notification appliance symbols should differentiate the type of appliance where more than one type is used.

D.3.3.6 Notification appliance symbols should include the design wattage for each speaker appliance.

D.3.3.7 The plans should show the ambient sound pressure levels used as a basis for the system design.

D.3.4 Assignment of Acoustically Distinguishable Spaces.

D.3.4.1 *ADS*s should be assigned prior to the test, and be subject to review by all test participants.

D.3.4.2 *ADS* assignments should be a part of the original design process. See the discussion in D.2.3.1.

D.3.4.3 The design drawings should be used to plan and show the limits of each *ADS* where there is more than one.

D.3.4.4 All areas that are intended to have audible occupant notification, whether by tone only or by voice are to be designated as one or more *ADS*s. See D.2.3.1.

D.3.4.5 The drawings or a table listing all *ADS*s should be used to indicate which *ADS*s will require intelligible voice communications and which will not. The same drawings or table could be used to list audibility requirements where tones are used and to list any forms of visual or other notification or communications methods being employed in the *ADS*.

D.3.4.6 *ADS* layouts that differ from the original, approved design documents should be approved by the AHJ.

D.3.5 Spaces Not Requiring Testing.

D.3.5.1 Buildings and areas of buildings that are not acoustically challenging such as traditional office environments, hotel guest rooms, dwelling units, and spaces with carpeting and furnishings generally meet intelligibility levels if the audibility levels are consistent with the requirements of *NFPA 72, National Fire Alarm and Signaling Code.* Performing intelligibility testing might not be necessary in these areas. Areas of a typical building that can be acoustically challenging could include vehicle parking levels and large lobby areas with hard floors and wall surfaces, stairs, and other spaces with high reverberation. Intelligibility meeting the requirements in this document can be difficult to achieve throughout these spaces. Specialized sound system design procedures, principles, and equipment might be necessary to achieve speech intelligibility in high noise areas or areas with challenging acoustics. Alternatively, intelligibility could be provided near exits and within specific areas (elevator lobby of a parking level) where occupants can obtain clear instructions after being alerted. This is done, in part, by the proper planning and designation of *ADS*s.

D.3.5.2 Factors that influence the decision to measure speech intelligibility include:

D.3.5.2.1 Possible reasons not to test speech intelligibility include the following:

(1) Distance listener to speaker less than 30 ft (9.1 m) in the room (assuming proper audibility and low reverberation)
(2) Ambient sound level is less than 50 dBA and the average SPL of the voice message is 10–15 dBA fast greater
(3) No appreciable hard surfaces (e.g., glass, marble, tile, metal, etc.)
(4) No appreciable high ceilings (i.e., ceiling height equals speaker spacing at a ratio of 1:1 optimal or 1:2 max)

D.3.5.2.2 Possible reasons not to test intelligibility, except possibly for spot sample testing include the following:

(1) Space has been acoustically designed by individuals having skills sufficient to properly design a voice/alarm system for the occupancy to be protected (e.g., space has been designed using commercially available computer modeling software acceptable to AHJ)

D.3.5.2.3 Possible reasons to test include the following:

(1) Appreciable hard surfaces (e.g., glass, marble, tile, metal, etc.)
(2) Appreciable high ceilings (e.g., atriums, multiple ceiling heights)

D.3.5.3 In situations where there are several *ADS*s that have the exact same physical and system configuration, it might be possible to test only a representative sample and then just check the others to confirm system and appliance operation — for example, hotel rooms with similar layouts or offices of similar size and furnishings where each has a speaker appliance. In these cases there would be no expected difference in system intelligibility. The only possible problem would be one where an appliance was not operational or tapped at the incorrect wattage. These problems would be apparent by a basic "listening" test.

D.3.5.4 Not all *ADS*s will require speech intelligibility testing. Some areas might be designed for notification, but not for voice communication. Notification can be accomplished by tone-only signaling or by a pre-alert tone preceding a voice message. See D.3.4.5.

D.3.5.5 By definition, an *ADS* is relatively uniform in acoustic characteristics. However, speech intelligibility will vary at different points within an *ADS* depending primarily on distance to noise sources and distance to speaker appliances. Generally, in smaller spaces up to about 40 ft × 40 ft (12.2 m × 12.2 m), one measurement location will be sufficient. The location should not be directly in front of a wall mounted speaker or directly under a ceiling mounted speaker. Neither should it be in the far corner right next to walls or windows. Generally, try to stay about 5 to 10 ft (1.5 to 3.0 m) away from vertical surfaces that reflect sound. In larger spaces, a grid of about 40 ft × 40 ft (12.2 m × 12.2 m) can be used as a starting guide, then adjusted for the locations of machines and other obstructions and for speaker appliance locations. See D.2.4 for additional discussion on measuring points and the averaging of results in an *ADS*.

D.3.5.6 Of the *ADS*s that do require intelligible voice communications, some will require speech intelligibility testing and others might only require audibility testing.

D.3.5.7 Testing of intelligibility might not be required in buildings and areas of buildings that are not acoustically challenging and that meet the audibility requirements of NFPA 72. Spaces that are not considered to be acoustically challenging include traditional office environments, hotel guest rooms, spaces with carpeting and furnishings that reduce reverberation, and other, smaller spaces where a speaker appliance is installed in the space.

D.3.6 Measurement Points Within an *ADS*.

D.3.6.1 Measurements should be taken at an elevation of 5 ft (1.5 m) or at any other elevation deemed appropriate if the area is subject to normal occupant access (e.g., elevated walkways).

D.3.6.2 The number and location of measurement points in each *ADS* should be planned and based on the area and volume of the space and the speaker appliance location within the space. The location of noise sources, egress paths, and the locations of personnel in the space should also be considered.

D.3.6.3 Testing when the area is occupied and when the ambient sound level is at or near its expected maximum is preferred because it is easier. However, it does involve playing of a test signal through the emergency communications system for the duration of the test. When testing using the STIPA signal, the signal is a continuous noise signal. Other methods that measure STI use a swept tone that should be repeated for each measurement location. The alternate procedure is to test and save the STI measurement data during unoccupied times, measure and save the unoccupied sound level, and then take and save sound level measurements during occupied times. The three data sets are combined by software to calculate the corrected STI for the area. Testing using this method requires three measurements at each measurement location, but does not subject occupants to constant test signals. The choice of testing occupied versus unoccupied for intelligibility is the same as for audibility testing of tone signaling systems and is based on convenience versus disruption of normal use of the space. However, unlike audibility testing, intelligibility testing is less likely to contribute to the Cry Wolf Syndrome because the test signal is not the same as the evacuation tone, which would be sounded throughout testing of a tone signaling system. [REF: Schifiliti, Robert P., "Fire Alarm Testing Strategies Can Improve Occupant Response and Reduce the "Cry Wolf" Syndrome," NEMA Supplement in Fire Protection Engineering, Society of Fire Protection Engineers, Bethesda, MD 20814, Fall 2003.] and [REF: Brezntiz, S., "Cry Wolf: The Psychology of False Alarms", Lawrence Erlbaum Associates, Hillsdale, NJ, February 1984.]

D.3.6.4 If multiple measurement points are required within an *ADS*, they should be separated by about 40 ft (12.2 m).

D.3.6.5 No more than one third of the measurement points within an *ADS* should be on the axis of a speaker.

D.3.6.6 See D.2.4 for the requirements for averaging the results at different measurement points within an *ADS*.

D.3.6.7 Measurement points should be shown on plans or otherwise described in a way that permits future testing at the same locations.

D.3.7 Test Method — Occupied versus Unoccupied.

D.3.7.1 It is possible to conduct STI measurements when the area is occupied or when it is not occupied. In this document "occupied" versus "unoccupied" is intended to be consistent with the definitions in Section D.2.3 for Occupied Ambient Sound Pressure Level and for Unoccupied Ambient Sound Pressure Level.

D.3.7.2 The preferred procedure is to conduct the STI/STIPA test in the presence of the Occupied Ambient Sound Pressure Level. See Section D.6.4.

D.3.7.3 Where the test method is measuring the STI using the STIPA test signal, the STIPA test signal can be played through the system and the STI can be measured and the data saved by the test instrument when the area is either not occupied or when the background ambient conditions are not the Occupied Ambient Sound Pressure Level. It is also necessary to measure and save the unoccupied ambient sound level at each measurement location. Then, during occupied times, take and save ambient sound level measurements. The three data sets are combined by software to calculate the corrected STI for the area. See Section D.6.5.6.

D.4 Test Equipment Calibration for Testing using the STIPA Test Signal

D.4.1 General.

D.4.1.1 The calibration of the STI test instrument is done in accordance with this section using a Talkbox or in accordance with manufacturer's instructions.

D.4.1.2 The Intelligibility Test System consists of a Talkbox and STIPA test meter (analyzer) all from one manufacturer. Units from other manufacturers should not be interchanged unless said units have been tested by a recognized testing laboratory for compatibility (see D.2.3.6).

D.4.1.3 Prior to performing any intelligibility testing or intelligibility system calibration, verify that the test meter's microphone, Talkbox, and analyzer are within calibration date as listed on the unit's calibration tag.

D.4.1.4 All audio test equipment, including ANSI Type 2 sound pressure level meters required by NFPA 72 for audibility testing, require regular calibration to known, traceable standards. The portable meters used to measure STI using the STIPA test signal should meet or exceed ANSI Type 2 meter requirements. In addition, the STIPA test signal and the meter algorithm for measuring the received signal and calculating the modulation transfer function to arrive at the STI should be tested by a certifying laboratory for accuracy to the IEC standard for STI.

D.4.2 Calibration Procedure.

D.4.2.1 The following procedures should be performed at the commencement and conclusion of intelligibility testing. If the following procedure differs from that recommended by the manufacturer of the test equipment, follow their calibration test procedure.

D.4.2.2 Perform these calibration procedures in a quiet room (45 dBA or less) without any extraneous sounds or any talking, music, etc.

D.4.2.3 Start STIPA test tone as instructed by the manufacturer.

D.4.2.4 Apply power to the Talkbox and then activate the STIPA test signal.

D.4.2.5 Turn on the analyzer and set it to SPL A Fast measurement mode.

D.4.2.6 Place the analyzer's microphone approximately one inch, on axis, from the Talkbox. Do not place the analyzer microphone against any hard surface — this can lead to induced noise and affect the calibration.

D.4.2.7 Adjust the Talkbox volume so that the STI Analyzer's reading is approximately 92 dBA.

D.4.2.8 Keeping the analyzer in approximately the same position, measure the STI. Note that some meters display STI measurements using the CIS scale while some can display results in either STI or CIS units. See D.2.4 for an explanation of the CIS scale.

D.4.2.9 The equipment is working properly if the reading is greater than 0.91 STI or 0.96 CIS. Up to three tests can be performed. If the system does not pass after three tests, it should be returned to the manufacturer for repair or recalibration.

D.5 Talkbox Set-up

D.5.1 Input Test Signal.

D.5.1.1 The input test signal should be configured to produce the proper level by utilizing either the Microphone Input Method or the Direct Input Injection Method.

D.5.1.2 Most emergency communications systems have microphones for manual voice communication and should be tested using the microphone test method. Systems that do not have microphones and that only play pre-recorded voice announcements can be tested using the direct input injection method.

D.5.1.3 By putting the STI or STIPA test signal into the system via the system microphone, the ECS system is being tested from end to end. If an ECS system has the test signal pre-recorded in its hardware, playback of that test signal would not be testing the microphone and the part that feeds the microphone signal into the system.

D.5.1.4 Direct Input Injection Method for Test Signals.

D.5.1.4.1 With this method the STI or STIPA test signals are pre-recorded in the emergency communications system hardware in the same way as the pre-recorded voice messages and at the same input levels. Alternately, the test signal can input to the system via input jacks or terminals.

D.5.1.4.2 The input level of the test signal should be tested by the ECS listing agency as being the same as the pre-recorded voice levels or should be calibrated using the ECS equipment manufacturer's instructions.

D.5.1.4.3 For ECS systems that permit voice messages to be custom recorded, the equivalent sound level (see A.18.4.3.1) L_{eq} of the recorded voice over a period of 10 seconds or the length of the voice message should be measured and should be within 3 dB of the prerecorded STI or STIPA test signal to ensure that it is at the correct level.

D.5.1.4.4 Field measurements of the STI are made using the procedure in Section D.5.

D.5.1.5 Microphone Input Method for Test Signals.

D.5.1.5.1 With this method a recording of the STI or STIPA test signals are played into the system microphone using a Talkbox.

D.5.1.5.2 The Talkbox is set up and calibrated per D.5.2, and field measurements of the STI are made using the procedure in Section D.6.

D.5.2 Calibrating the Input Test Signal for the Microphone Input Method.

D.5.2.1 Of the two methods for setting the test signal input to the system microphone, the method that sets the level to match that of a person speaking into the microphone is the one required by IEC 60268-16, Sound system equipment — Part 16: *Objective rating of speech intelligibility by speech transmission index,* the standard that defines STI and STIPA.

D.5.2.2 In theory, the two methods for setting up the Talkbox should result in the Talkbox being set at approximately the same sound level. The ECS should be designed and configured so that input to the microphone results in the same output level that any pre-recorded announcements would produce.

D.5.2.3 General.

D.5.2.3.1 There are two methods for setting the level of the STI or STIPA test signal at the input microphone.

D.5.2.3.2 Method 1 sets the volume of the input test signal so that the dBA output in the area under test is the same as that for a pre-recorded message.

D.5.2.3.3 Method 2 sets the volume of the input test signal to match that of speech level under normal conditions.

D.5.2.3.4 The room where the Talkbox and system under test microphone are located should be quiet.

D.5.2.3.5 An emergency command center will not be free of noise during an actual emergency. However, for testing purposes, the room should be relatively free of extraneous noises that could affect the results. The purpose of the tests is to establish the baseline capability of the system and acoustic environment to support intelligible communications. Good design practice for an emergency command center is to isolate the space so that only emergency command personnel have access. In addition, the location of the microphone for manual input should be such that background discussions and noise are minimized.

D.5.2.3.6 Set up the Talkbox in accordance with the manufacturer's instructions.

D.5.2.4 Method 1 — Matching Recorded Message Level.

D.5.2.4.1 The intent of this method is to set the Talkbox or audio source input level into the emergency communications system microphone so that the output at a location in the area under test is the same as the level of prerecorded messages played by the system.

D.5.2.4.2 The sound pressure level produced by the Talkbox while playing the STI or STIPA test signal should be matched with the sound pressure level of the pre-recorded voice message.

D.5.2.4.3 Two people will be needed to perform the calibration procedure. One person needs to be present at the Talkbox while the other person needs to operate the analyzer at a typical location in the facility.

D.5.2.4.4 At a typical location in the facility, position the analyzer it so its microphone is approximately 5 ft (1.5 m) above the finished floor.

D.5.2.4.5 Set the analyzer (meter) to measure sound pressure level, A-weighted, Fast.

D.5.2.4.6 Activate the pre-recorded voice message from the ECS.

D.5.2.4.7 The decibel reading at the analyzer will be somewhat erratic due to the nature of speech signals.

D.5.2.4.8 Record the highest dB reading the system produces.

D.5.2.4.9 Do not move the analyzer from the test location.

D.5.2.4.10 Turn off the pre-recorded voice message.

D.5.2.4.11 Place the microphone of the emergency communications system at a distance from the Talkbox as recommended by the microphone or ECS manufacturer.

D.5.2.4.12 Start the Talkbox STI or STIPA test signal.

D.5.2.4.13 Adjust the Talkbox sound level until the field measurement of the test signal is ± 3 dB of the level generated when the pre-recorded voice message was played and measured. This setting should not change for the remainder of the testing.

D.5.2.4.14 Begin field testing in accordance with Section D.6.

D.5.2.5 Method 2 — Matching Speech Level.

D.5.2.5.1 The intent of this method is to set the Talkbox or audio source input level to the emergency communications system microphone to match that of an average person speaking into the microphone.

D.5.2.5.2 Set the analyzer (meter) to measure sound pressure level, A-weighted, Fast.

D.5.2.5.3 Start the STI or STIPA test signal and hold the meter at a distance of 39.4 in. (1.0 m) on-axis from the Talkbox or audio source.

D.5.2.5.4 Set the Talkbox volume (level) so that the meter registers 65 dBA at a distance of 39.4 in. (1.0 m). This setting should not change for the remainder of the testing.

D.5.2.5.5 The distance from the microphone to the Talkbox should be documented so that future tests can be set up consistently. Most microphone manufacturers or ECS equipment manufacturers will state a recommended distance for a person to hold the microphone when talking. Some microphone use chin guards or some physical means to help users know when they are holding the microphone at the correct distance. If the manufacturer has not recommended a talking distance, 4 in. (100 mm) is recommended as a guide.

D.5.2.5.6 Place the microphone of the emergency communications system at a distance from the Talkbox as recommended by the microphone or ECS manufacturer.

D.5.2.5.7 A level of 60 dBA at one meter is required by IEC 60268-16, *Sound system equipment — Part 16: Objective rating of speech intelligibility by speech transmission index*, the standard that defines STI and STIPA and is considered a normal speech level. While 60 dBA at 1 m is documented as "normal" speech, in areas where there is background noise, the Lombard effect causes a person to talk at an elevated volume. For this document, the committee chose to use 65 dBA as more representative of speech levels during emergency situations. It is recommended that at least one field STI measurement be made at both 60 dBA and 70 dBA at one meter talking level to test the effects of elevated voice level.

D.5.2.5.8 Sound pressure level increases 6 dB whenever the distance is halved. So, the test could be set up so that the Talkbox level achieves $65 + 6 = 71$ dBA at a distance of 19.7 in. (0.50 m). Table D.5.2.5.8 shows different dB levels at distances that would be equivalent to 65 dBA at 39.4 in. (1.0 m).

TABLE D.5.2.5.8 *Audibility Equivalent to 65 dBA at a Distance of One Meter*

r (in.)	r (m)	L_p (dB)	r (in.)	r (m)	L_p (dB)	r (in.)	r (m)	L_p (dB)
0.1	0	117	4	0.10	85	11	0.28	76
0.2	0.01	111	5	0.13	83	12	0.30	75
0.5	0.01	103	6	0.15	81	20	0.50	71
1.0	0.03	97	7	0.18	80	24	0.61	69
1.5	0.04	93	8	0.20	79	39.37	1.00	65
2.0	0.05	91	9	0.23	78	78.8	2.00	59
3.0	0.08	87	10	0.25	77			

D.5.2.5.9 Begin field testing in accordance with Section D.6.

D.6 STI/STIPA Test Procedure

D.6.1 General. This test procedure permits testing during either occupied conditions or during unoccupied conditions. See D.3.7.

D.6.2 Power. The system under test should be tested on secondary power for a minimum of 15 minutes and then on primary power for the remainder of the testing.

D.6.3 System Operation. Where two *ADSs* are adjacent to each other and not separated by physically barriers that significantly prevent noise penetration from one *ADS* to another, the notification appliances in both *ADSs* should be operating during the testing. It is acceptable for intelligibility testing to silence or disable other notification zones that would not potentially interfere with each other. However, regular testing per NFPA 72 would require that all circuits be operated simultaneously at one point to ensure proper operation and to verify power requirements.

D.6.4 Occupied Testing.

D.6.4.1 Testing should be done during a period of time when the area is occupied and is reasonably close to having maximum background noise.

D.6.4.2 Set up the Talkbox in accordance with Section D.4 and start the STI or STIPA test signal.

D.6.4.3 At each measurement point in each *ADS* measure the STI.

D.6.4.4 Document the results on plans or forms in a way that accurately describes the measurement point and that permits future testing at the same locations.

D.6.5 Unoccupied Testing.

D.6.5.1 General. Testing of speech intelligibility in the presence of the occupied ambient sound pressure level is the preferred method. However, for various reasons, including disruption of normal work, it might be desirable to only do "silent" testing during occupied periods and to do testing with the STI or STIPA test signal during unoccupied or less occupied conditions.

D.6.5.2 Number of Tests. This test method requires three different measurements at each measurement point, typically made during two site visits. The data for each measurement is saved in a format in accordance with the instrument manufacturer's requirements. The three data files are then post-processed to arrive at the final corrected STI.

D.6.5.3 Occupied Ambient Sound Pressure Level Measurement.

D.6.5.3.1 At each measurement point in each *ADS* measure the occupied ambient sound pressure level.

D.6.5.3.2 Save the measurement data in accordance with the instrument manufacturer's requirements to permit post-processing of the data.

D.6.5.3.3 Document the results in writing on plans or forms in a way that accurately describes the measurement point and that permits future testing at the same locations.

D.6.5.4 Unoccupied Ambient Sound Pressure Level Measurement.

D.6.5.4.1 At each measurement point in each *ADS* measure the unoccupied ambient sound pressure level.

D.6.5.4.2 Save the measurement data in accordance with the instrument manufacturer's requirements to permit post-processing of the data.

D.6.5.4.3 Document the results in writing on plans or forms in a way that accurately describes the measurement point and that permits future testing at the same locations.

D.6.5.5 Unoccupied STI Measurement.

D.6.5.5.1 Set up the Talkbox in accordance with Section D.4 and start the STI or STIPA test signal.

D.6.5.5.2 At each measurement point in each ADS measure the uncorrected STI.

D.6.5.5.3 Save the measurement data in accordance with the instrument manufacturer's requirements to permit post-processing of the data.

D.6.5.5.4 Document the results in writing on plans or forms in a way that accurately describes the measurement point and that permits future testing at the same locations.

D.6.5.6 Post Processing.

D.6.5.6.1 The corrected STI is arrived at by post-processing of the occupied ambient sound pressure level measurement, the unoccupied ambient sound pressure level measurement, and the unoccupied STI measurement. In effect, the measured STI (uncorrected) is being corrected by adding in the effects the actual expected (occupied) ambient sound pressure level.

D.6.5.6.2 The post processing procedure or software provided by the instrument manufacturer should be used to calculate the final corrected STI for each measurement point.

D.6.5.6.3 Document the results in writing on plans or forms in a way that accurately describes the measurement point and that permits future testing at the same locations.

D.6.5.6.4 Documentation of the final results for each point should include the results of all three measurements and the final corrected STI value. The manufacturer's software revision should also be included in the results documentation.

D.7 Post Test Procedures

D.7.1 Test Closure. Upon completion of all testing, the emergency communications system should be returned to its normal operating condition.

D.7.2 Results.

D.7.2.1 It is also not the intent of this test protocol to describe how to interpret results or how to correct systems or environments that contribute to poor speech intelligibility. However, depending on the instrument used, it might be possible to have data retained by the instrument to determine possible causes and their effects on STI results. Consult with the instrument manufacturer to determine if the instrument has the capability to display or save the intermediate STI modulation indices and octave band measurement results and for instructions on how to interpret those data.

D.7.2.2 For each *ADS*, summarize the results in accordance with the performance requirements of D.2.4.

D.7.2.3 For an *ADS* that had multiple measurement points or that had multiple measurements at only one measurement point, calculate the average per D.2.4 and list the average and the minimum measurement per D.2.4 in the results summary.

D.7.3 Documentation.

D.7.3.1 The test results should be fully documented and provided to the building owner, the emergency communications system contractor, the system designer, the authority having jurisdiction, and any other individual or organization deemed appropriate.

D.7.3.2 In addition to the requirements for test documentation contained in NFPA 72 Chapter 10, the test results should include:

(1) Building location and related descriptive facility information
(2) Names, titles, and contact information for individuals involved in test
(3) Dates and times of tests

(4) A list of testing instruments, including manufacturer's name, model, serial number, and date of most recent calibration
(5) Technical description of emergency communications system
(6) Identification of *ADSs*
(7) Locations of specific measurement points (in a list or on a set of drawings)
(8) Site definition of ambient sound pressure levels
(9) STI/STIPA measurements at each measurement point
(10) Final corrected STI/STIPA values where the post-processing procedure is used
(11) Indication of whether or not the test met the pass/fail criteria
(12) Record of system restoration
(13) Any additional information to assist with future evaluation of system performance

D.7.3.3 If appropriate, the Plans and Specifications addressed in D.3.3 should be updated based on the results of the test.

NEMA SB 30, *Fire Service Annunciator and Interface*

ANNEX E

E.1 General

This standard was developed jointly by the National Institute of Standards and Technology, Building and Fire Research Laboratory, NEMA, and the U.S. Fire Alarm industry to guide the development of uniform equipment for use by the fire service to display information of use during fires or other emergencies.

E.1.1 Scope. This standard covers the design, operation, and arrangement of equipment intended to display data and status of building systems, and to provide certain control functions. This standard addresses displays installed in buildings or other locations specified by the fire service for their use in responding to fires and other emergencies.

The document scope presents information for fire fighters in the roles of "First Responder" (the first fire command at the scene) and "Incident Commander" (the ongoing fire command at the scene.)

E.1.2 Intent. The intent of this standard is to provide a uniform set of requirements that result in equipment sufficiently similar across different manufacturers' systems that fire service personnel trained in the general arrangement and use of these systems be able to operate and extract information from the equipment in various buildings with a fair degree of familiarity and confidence without the need for specialized training on each individual system.

It is anticipated that firefighter interface training will become a part of all new firefighter training programs. It is also the intent that the training required be minimal and the interactions of the fire service with the systems be as intuitive as possible. Finally, it is the intent that the equipment, displays and interactions be based, as much as is sensible for quick understanding, on common fire fighter knowledge.

E.1.3 Purpose. The purpose of this equipment is to provide real-time information of value in making tactical decisions and monitoring the safety of firefighters. These goals are met through interaction with the equipment by both First Responders and Incident Commanders.

The information of value to the First Responder arriving on the scene must be readily available for quick processing, planning and response.

The Incident Commander, also, must have information readily available for quick processing, planning and response. The Incident Commander may continue to process information, plan and direct the incident through out the emergency. They may spend more time with the system using it as an ongoing tactical tool after the initial response has commenced.

Both the user interactions required for the First Responder's quick assessment and the Incident Commander's ongoing analysis should be supported in uniform, consistent and intuitive ways. The design of the system interactions shall not change based on the user role.

E.2 Standards and Codes

The following standards and codes are referenced explicitly or implicitly regarding the design, installation, testing, maintenance, and use of these systems and their components. These were used when developing this standard, but are not necessarily required practice for manufacturers.

E.2.1 Building Codes.

IBC-ICC, *International Building Code* (IBC-ICC)
NFPA 5000, Building Construction and Safety Code

E.2.2 Underwriters Laboratories (UL) Standards.

UL 864, *Control Units for Fire Protective Signaling Systems*
UL 268, *Smoke Detectors for Fire Protective Signaling Systems*
UL 521, *Heat Detectors for Fire Protective Signaling Systems*

E.2.3 National Fire Protection Association (NFPA) Standards.

NFPA 72, *National Fire Alarm and Signaling Code®*
NFPA 70, *National Electrical Code®*
NFPA 13, *Standard for the Installation of Sprinkler Systems*
NFPA 25, *Standard for the Inspection, Testing, and Maintenance of Water-Based Fire Protection Systems*
NFPA 90A, *Standard for the Installation of Air-Conditioning and Ventilating Systems*
NFPA 92A, *Standard for Smoke-Control Systems Utilizing Barriers and Pressure Differences*
NFPA 92B, *Standard for Smoke Management Systems in Malls, Atria, and Large Spaces*
NFPA 101, *Life Safety Code®*

E.2.4 American Society of Mechanical Engineers (ASME) Standards.

ASME A17.1, *Safety Code for Elevators and Escalators*
ASME A17.4, *Guide for Emergency Personnel*

E.2.5 Standards Related to People with Disabilities.

ICC/ANSI A117.1, *Standard on Accessible and Useable Buildings and Facilities*
ADAAG, *U.S. Department of Justice, Americans with Disabilities Act Accessibility Guidelines*

E.2.6 American Society of Heating, Refrigerating and Air-Conditioning Engineers (ASHRAE) Standards.

ASHRAE 135, *BACnet, A Data Communication Protocol for Building Automation and Control Networks*

E.2.7 Arcnet Trade Association (ATA) Standards.

ANSI/ATA 878.1-1999, *ARCNET Local Area Network*

E.2.8 Electronic Industries Alliance (EIA) Standards.

ANSI/EIA 709.1, *LonWorks Control Networking Standard*

E.3 Equipment

Whether facilities are very small, mid-size, large, or monumental (very large), the same basic rules for display and interface must apply. Fire alarm systems can range from being small, non-addressable panels having very basic and limited functionality to the most sophisticated computerized multiplex systems. The system type, size, design, and specified functionality are factors in determining the presentation methods for the annunciation and control interface. However, keeping the goals of ease-of-use and interoperability in mind, user interactions regardless of the equipment and display systems must focus on common guidelines wherever feasible.

This section focuses on system power, location, and security.

E.3.1 Power and Communications Redundancy. To achieve the goal of providing real-time information of value in making tactical decisions to the fire service, the system should be powered up at all times. In order to be fault tolerant and reliable during emergencies, the system must be powered from at least two independent sources and be able to maintain communications during any single fault.

E.3.1.1 Duration of standby power shall be at least equal to that of the fire alarm system to which it is connected.

E.3.1.2 Communication shall be by at least two independent paths (routed separately through protected construction) or one trunk and one wireless link, or any combination so arranged that any single failure of one trunk or wireless link shall not result in loss of function.

E.3.2 Fixed Location(s). The equipment shall be installed in the location designated by the responsible fire department. The primary display location would most likely be in a fire command station, building lobby, or other location from which the responding fire service would expect to establish incident command.

E.3.3 Wireless Applications. It should be recognized that the specific conditions of an incident may require that incident command be moved to another location for the safety or efficiency of operations. Additionally, some departments may wish to be able to access information from dispatch, headquarters, mobile command centers, or even from vehicles in route to an incident. Thus it is advantageous for these systems to incorporate wireless technologies and multi-platform software capable of such use.

E.3.4 Remote Access. Remote access is a feature desired by the fire service. Browser interfaces are becoming ubiquitous and can use existing standards such as DHTML (Dynamic Hypertext Markup Language) with CSS (Cascading Style Sheets) or XML (eXtensible Markup Language) with XSL (eXtensible Stylesheet Language). Systems that utilize these, or other, existing browser display standards may have the flexibility to provide remote information access via many common devices that implement common browser protocols. These common devices include, but are not limited to, touch screen panels, PDAs, and cellular phones.

E.3.5 Security Considerations. The systems addressed by this standard display information that could be invaluable to terrorists, burglars, or other parties. Information about a building's structure, organization, and alarm systems can be used to prepare attacks. As such, unauthorized access to these must be inhibited.

While it may not be possible to provide perfect security, this must not be used as an excuse for providing no security. Systems that conform to this standard cannot be required to solve every security need listed below. The list is provided as a guideline for minimum set of security aspects to be considered. The underlying principle is that every interface presents a potential security problem. Anytime another system, file, or hardware is connected, a security hole could be created. Security considerations:

(1) Physical access to systems.
(2) How access to systems is authorized, and how these authorization systems could be fooled or bypassed.
(3) Access to building information (including floor plans, access routes, water supplies, hazardous materials).
(4) Access to alarm and emergency response system information (including locations of detectors, fire-suppression systems, emergency response plans).
(5) Ability to read or change files used by the system, thereby ensuring that only authorized personnel can modify these files.

(6) If data is transmitted between systems (especially over public networks), ensurance that it cannot be intercepted and read, or intercepted and changed.

E.4 User Interaction

This section's primary purpose is to provide guidelines that result in interfaces that are consistent in their operation and use. The primary characteristics of this guideline address the need for uniformity, consistency, and intuitiveness of user interactions. In cases where the user interface incorporates switches and lights the recommendations of this section should be used wherever applicable.

The guidelines in this section are based on the firefighters' capabilities and limitations as described in E.4.1.

In order for the firefighter to be able to understand the situation well enough to act safely and effectively, the fire service interfaces must adhere to the following guidelines.

(1) Information shall be presented uniformly. For example, labels and colors should be consistent throughout the interface.
(2) Information that the firefighters frequently need shall be always displayed.
(3) Information that the firefighters do not need or need infrequently shall not be displayed. If this information may be important, it should still be available (perhaps with a single button press).
(4) Physical input devices (touch screen, keyboard, mouse) shall have minimal, intuitive actions.

    (a) Touch screen input shall be limited to single touch only. It shall not require dragging, holding down of the finger or stylus, nor double tapping of the screen.
    (b) Mouse input shall be limited to moving the cursor and clicking a single button. If the mouse has multiple buttons, they shall all have the same function.
    (c) Mouse input shall not require holding down a button while moving nor double-clicking.
    (d) Keyboard input shall not be used unless no simpler mechanism is available.
    (e) Keyboard input shall not require the use of any shortcuts (such as holding down the control key while pressing the 'S' key).

(5) The interface shall display the recommended information in a size and with a contrast ratio that makes it easily readable by the operator under any expected lighting condition in the location where it is installed.

E.4.1 Firefighter Capabilities and Limitations.

When firefighters arrive on the scene of a building fire emergency, their first need is to gather information in order to accurately assess the situation. Speed of assessment is of the essence. The quicker the seat of the fire and its progression is identified, the quicker an attack on the fire can be planned and launched. With speed and accuracy of response comes a reduction in loss of property and life.

In order to meet the goals of speed and accuracy, firefighter displays must be designed in a way that considers the capabilities and limitations of firefighters and the constraints under which they operate. Specific capabilities of concern include:

(1) Computer skills. Many firefighters will have little familiarity with computers and related technology. Displays and user interfaces need to be extremely simple and easy to use and not make any assumptions about the firefighter's familiarity with standard user interface paradigms.
(2) Training. Designs for firefighter displays should not assume that interface complexity will be overcome by training. There may be little or no training. Also, training on the display may be forgotten under the stress of real tactical conditions.

(3) Vision. Some firefighters may have impaired and uncorrected reading vision. Display design must consider this limitation in scaling drawings, symbols and text.

E.4.2 Presentation Guidelines. All fire service interfaces shall follow these guidelines whenever the system's equipment has capabilities to support them. The resulting consistency of presentation will reduce training and ensure efficient comprehension of information.

E.4.2.1 Icons. One of the ways to achieve consistency in the fire service interface is by means of a standard set of icons. These icons must be capable of clean rendering on a range of display technologies from color to monochrome, and varying in display size and resolution. Most importantly, these standard icons must be intuitive to the firefighter.

A good icon has the following properties:

(1) Mimics both the physical appearance and the function or action of the object it represents
(2) Clearly represents the state of the object if it is an object that can assume more than one state
(3) Uses only widely recognized conventions for color and shape
(4) Is not directional and can be used without rotation
(5) Is not culture-bound

    (a) No embedded text characters
    (b) No culture-specific metaphors

(6) Is recognizable by a high percentage of firefighters

The icons in Figure E.4.2.1 resulted from user feedback obtained during a series of fire service display usability tests conducted with fire service incident commanders and a series of subsequent usability tests that compared alternative representations of the same icon. The icons shown in Figure E.4.2.1 are those that performed the best during the latter tests.

For further information refer to Figure E.4.2.1.

E.4.2.2 Text. Text shall be presented in a large font with no serifs or other decoration. The size of the font will vary depending on the physical display device and expected viewing conditions. Text should not be presented in all capital letters, unless a standard acronym such as 'NFPA', since this slows reading.

E.4.2.3 Abbreviations. Abbreviations shall be avoided wherever possible. If abbreviations are used, they shall be made as clear as possible. In general, truncated abbreviations (e.g., temperature = temp) are more recognizable than concatenated abbreviations (e.g., temperature = tmp).

E.4.2.4 Colors. The use of color shall be minimized. Extraneous use of color reduces the usability of the display by inappropriately highlighting items of lesser importance and making it more difficult to notice the items of greater importance.

Where possible, color shall be a redundant visual coding of information. Color should be used in conjunction with another coding dimension, such as shape, texture, or text.

E.4.2.5 Modes. The displays shall not make use of modes. Modes cause the display to function differently in response to the same inputs, which increases the users' confusion. All interactions shall remain consistent regardless of the state of the system. For instance, a system that uses a pair of up and down arrows to scroll through pages of information should not have a separate state of operation where those two arrow keys are used to change the contrast of the screen. Changing the behavior of controls this way is especially confusing to users if the screens in the separate modes are similar in appearance.

E.4.2.6 Display Units. Quantitative display of values shall be in the units specified by the fire department expected to use the system. It is important that the system not overwhelm the operator with quantitative data. Therefore, access to quantitative values shall require manual action by the operator.

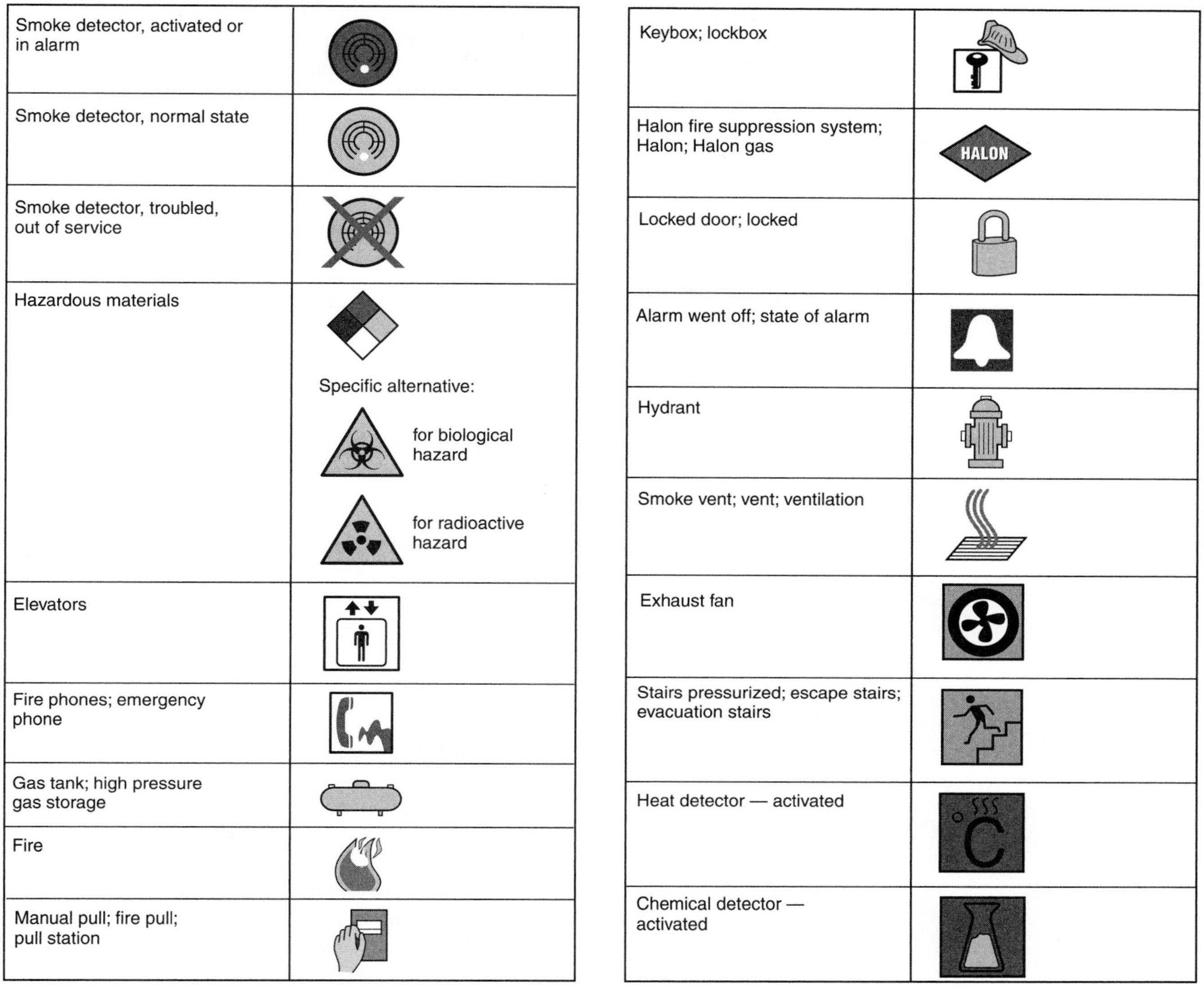

Smoke detector, activated or in alarm	
Smoke detector, normal state	
Smoke detector, troubled, out of service	
Hazardous materials	Specific alternative: for biological hazard for radioactive hazard
Elevators	
Fire phones; emergency phone	
Gas tank; high pressure gas storage	
Fire	
Manual pull; fire pull; pull station	

Keybox; lockbox	
Halon fire suppression system; Halon; Halon gas	
Locked door; locked	
Alarm went off; state of alarm	
Hydrant	
Smoke vent; vent; ventilation	
Exhaust fan	
Stairs pressurized; escape stairs; evacuation stairs	
Heat detector — activated	
Chemical detector — activated	

NFPA Editor's Note: The color versions of these display icons contained in NEMA SB 30-2005 are reproduced here in gray scale.

FIGURE E.4.2.1 *Recommended Fire Service Display Icons.*

E.4.2.7 Query for Information. Selecting an icon or button shall result in the display of further information. Usually this is done by touching or clicking or by pressing an associated switch.

E.5 Fire Service Interface for Small Systems

Smaller and less complex buildings may not require a full Incident Commander Display, such as that described in Section E.6 to support effective fire service situation assessment and decision-making. This section describes a fire service interface for such small systems.

E.5.1 Required Information Elements and Functions. The following is the minimum set of information elements and functions that must be supported by the Fire Service Small System Interface. This list of required functions includes only those that are widely deployable today.

The minimum set of required information elements and functions includes:

(1) Display of information describing detected fire events including: time; date; floor number and room number or zone; type of detector (smoke-ion, heat, etc.); detector identification number; indication of alarm acknowledgement.
(2) Display of information describing supervisory and trouble events.
(3) An interactive control mechanism for navigating through the above events.
(4) A display indicating that the panel is powered up, no alarms exist and system condition is normal.
(5) A display indicating that a fire condition exists.
(6) A display indicating that a trouble/supervisory condition exists.
(7) A control for acknowledging events.
(8) A control for silencing evacuation devices in the building.
(9) A control for resetting the building fire alarm system to its normal state.

E.5.2 Layout. General layout. The fire service interface should be enclosed within a red border of approximately 6.4 mm (0.25 in.) width. The words "FIRE SERVICE INTERFACE" should be located at the top center of the border in bold capital letters approximately 6.4 mm (0.25 in.) high. All controls and indicators within this border should be located and labeled as described herein. Additional controls and indicators for the system can be provided but should be located outside of the red border.

The display consists of the following windows and fields:

(1) *Event Display Window.* This window shall be located in the upper center area of the interface, as shown in Figure E.5.2. The display is intended to show the minimum information associated with each detected fire, supervisory or trouble condition.
(2) *Navigation and Acknowledge Area.* The area adjacent to the left-hand side of the display shall be dedicated to controls for navigating the event display and a prominent button for acknowledging individual events. Between the navigation area and the button assigned to acknowledge the individual alarms selected in the display to the right is a slightly less prominent button for acknowledging all events. This button would acknowledge all currently unacknowledged alarms, troubles and supervisory indications in the events list. A pair of Acknowledgement indicators shall be located immediately above the Acknowledge Selected Event button.
(3) *System Control and Status Indicator Area.* The area on the far right-hand side of the display shall be dedicated to controls and indicators for the functions Reset System and Silence Evacuation Devices.
(4) *Optional Function Keys.* Any additional function keys required to interact with the information in the Event Display Window shall be located below the Event Display Window.

E.5.3 Interaction.

E.5.3.1 Logical Grouping of Features. Principles of logical spatial grouping shall be applied to the display layout. First, the most important or most frequently used features are placed in the most central location. In the Small System Fire Service Interface, this is the event display window, its navigation controls, and the Acknowledge button. Features of less importance or less frequently used, such as the System Reset and Silence Evac. controls, are relegated to the periphery. Second, buttons, indicators, and displays that are closely coupled in their use are grouped closely together. Thus, the navigation controls for the Event Display

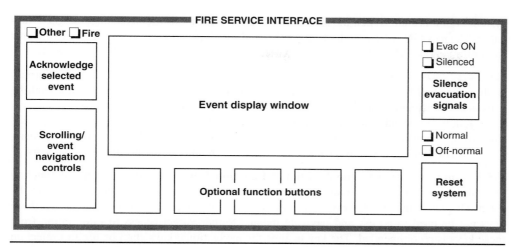

FIGURE E.5.2 *Alarm Event Display.*

Window, the Acknowledge button and the Acknowledge indicators are all grouped together in a manner that facilitates the behavior of navigating through events and acknowledging them.

E.5.3.2 Button Size and Layout. Whether implemented as soft keys on a touch screen or as hard keys on a panel, buttons shall be at least 0.75 in. square and separated from one another by a minimum of 0.25 in. of space. The Acknowledge button shall be larger than other buttons to reflect its importance and frequency of use.

E.5.3.3 Event Display Interaction. The sequential display presents alarm and other alerting events in the form of a list of alphanumeric messages. Each event message shall consist of an icon indicating the type of event (fire, supervisory or trouble event) followed by the description of the event. For all event messages, the icons shall flash until acknowledged. If the display supports color, the icons indicating fire shall be red and flash until acknowledged and the icons for supervisory and trouble event messages shall be yellow. Events shall be grouped by type with fire events shown first in the list followed by supervisory and trouble events. Within each grouping, events shall be listed in order of time of occurrence, with the most recent listed first.

The list of events shall be scrolled by operating the navigation controls to the left of the display. A message is acknowledged by scrolling to it and then pressing the Acknowledge button to the left of the display. The up-down arrow buttons shown in Figure E.5.3.3 are a good example of an intuitive control for this purpose.

Indicator lights above the Acknowledge Selected Event button flash until all events are acknowledged. These indicators show that there are unacknowledged events remaining somewhere in the list including some that might have scrolled off the screen and are out of view. In that case, the indicators would alert the user that even though all the events in view have been acknowledged, there are still some that have not been acknowledged. The Fire indicator shall flash red if there are unacknowledged fire event messages remaining in the Event Display Window. The Other indicator shall flash yellow if there are still unacknowledged supervisory or trouble messages in the Event Display Window. When all alarms and alerts are acknowledged, the lights shall go steady. If the Acknowledge All button is pressed, all alarms and alerts are considered acknowledged and thus, the lights shall go steady. When the system returns to normal the lights shall extinguish.

E.5.3.4 Interaction with the System Control and Status Indicator Area.

E.5.3.4.1 Silence Evacuation Devices. The Silence Evacuation Devices feature has two states: Evacuation Devices ON and Evacuation Devices Silenced. Both states shall be shown explicitly by indicator lights. The Evacuation Devices ON indicator shall turn red when the

FIGURE E.5.3.3 *Sequential Display.*

system is in this state. When the state is switched to Evacuation Devices Silenced, the Evacuation Devices ON indicator shall extinguish and the Evacuation Devices Silenced indicator shall turn yellow. When the system is returned to a normal state, both lights shall be off.

E.5.3.4.2 Reset System. The Reset System feature has two states: Normal and Off-Normal. Both states shall be shown explicitly by indicator lights. The Off-Normal indicator shall be activated and illuminate steady yellow when the first off-normal condition appears. It shall remain yellow and steady until the system is reset to normal at which time it shall extinguish. The Normal indicator shall be activated after the system is reset and returns to normal state. Then it shall illuminate steady green. It shall remain on until an off-normal event appears.

E.5.3.5 Interactions with the Additional Function Keys. The row of optional function keys at the bottom of the display provides the possibility of additional interactions with the Event Display Window. However, for firefighter use, it is strongly recommended that these keys not be used to access and navigate menus. Rather, direct access to information from these keys is recommended. The key nearest the navigational keys shall be used to select an event from the list (sequential display) or the array (simultaneous display). Selecting an event would open a window with additional information about that event. The window shall be placed in the display area in a way that minimally interferes with the users' view of the event list or array. The other function keys shall be used in a similar manner to directly access additional information without the requirement to traverse a menu or change interaction modes. An intuitive and obvious control for closing these information pop-up windows shall be provided.

E.6 Incident Commander Display

The purpose of the Incident Commander Display is to support the fire incident commander's situation assessment task by providing easy access to critical elements of fire incident and building information in a graphical and spatial format that is accessible at the scene of the fire.

E.6.1 Required Functions. The following is the minimum set of information elements and functions that must be supported by the Incident Commander Display. This list of required functions includes only those that are widely deployable today. Functions for which technology is still developing and is not yet widely deployed are included under Optional Functions in E.6.2.

The minimum set of required information elements and functions is:

(1) Display of the location of the fire on a graphical (for example, floor plan) view of the building.
(2) An interactive control to navigate between floors of the building shown on the graphical display and to select the floor of interest for display.
(3) An interactive control to navigate around a single floor of a large or wide building on the graphical display.
(4) Display of the location of building features critical for firefighting on the graphical view of the building. These include:

    (a) Standpipes
    (b) Hydrants
    (c) Firewalls
    (d) Hazardous materials
    (e) Gas shutoffs
    (f) Power shutoffs
    (g) HVAC shutoffs
    (h) Master sprinkler shutoff

(i) Own location (location of the Incident Commander's Display)

(j) Elevators and elevator machine rooms (if possible)

(k) Stairs

(l) Exits

(m) Locked exit doors and confirmation that locks have been released

(n) Points of access to the roof

(o) Fire phones

(p) Fire keybox (knox box)

(q) Pre-positioned firefighting gear

(r) Airpack refilling stations

(s) Halon fire suppression systems

(t) Fuel and compressed gas tanks

(u) Heavy objects located on the roof such as air handlers and generators

(v) Annotation to indicate if the roof has steel bar joist or tensioned concrete construction

(w) The direction NORTH labeled clearly

(5) On the graphical display of the roof-level of the building, display the following information:

(a) Roof access doors and their condition, locked or not locked

(b) Any hazardous construction features such as steel bar joists or tensioned concrete. A sample annotation might be "HAZARD: TENSIONED CONCRETE"

(c) Any large heavy objects such as cooling towers, generators, or air handlers

(d) Air/smoke evacuation vents or ducts

(6) Graphical display of a building site plan that shows the immediate area surrounding the building and includes the following features: access streets/roads, driveways, parking lots, emergency access pathways such as sidewalks, grassy areas, sufficiently wide and firm to accommodate firefighting vehicles, building entrances, standpipes and primary and secondary hydrants. Large volume hydrants shall be distinguished from standard hydrants.

(7) In a prominent position on the screen, the name and address of the building shall be displayed.

(8) In a prominent position on the screen, a short summary description of the first alarm shall be displayed and shall include: time of initial activation; floor and room or zone in which initial activation occurred; type of detector (smoke, heat, chemical, duct-smoke). For example: 12:01AM Floor 11 Room 11437 Duct-smoke Water flowing

E.6.2 Optional Functions. Beyond the minimum set of information elements and functions discussed above, the Incident Commander Display may provide other information and functions of benefit to the fire service. Some of these optional functions are already supported by the necessary sensor and software technology and are feasible to deploy at the present time. Others are limited by the current availability of the underlying technology and will become options only in the future. In either case, these optional functions pose the problem of potentially overloading the firefighter/user with information and functionality. Therefore, caution must be exercised in adding any of these functions to the already substantial amount of basic information and functionality described in E.6.1.

Optional information elements and functions include:

(1) An alarm list display showing an alphanumeric table of alarm data similar to what is typically shown on fire panels.

(2) A display of building contact information (name and phone numbers) including: building owner; facility manager; HVAC maintenance technician; power company emergency contact; gas company emergency contact; water department emergency contact; State Hazardous Materials Duty Officer.

(3) A display of building information including: commissioning date; primary use; number of occupants — daytime; number of occupants — nighttime; hazardous structures (steel bar joist construction; tensioned concrete in walls or roof).

(4) A display of the location of firefighters inside the building.

(5) Display of individual firefighter identification, physiological condition and qualifications.

(6) A display of gas shutoff information: location of the gas shutoff; current state (ON or OFF); building engineer phone number; local gas company emergency phone number.

(7) A display of electrical power shutoff information: location of the power shutoff; current state (ON or OFF); building engineer phone number; local electrical power company emergency phone number.

(8) A display of master sprinkler shutoff information: location of the master sprinkler shutoff; current state (ON or OFF); building engineer phone number.

(9) Display of elevator information including:

(a) Layout of the elevators and their identification number (1-N).

(b) Operating status of each elevator — Operational, Disabled, In Use By Fire Command

(c) The floors which are served by each elevator

(d) The current location of each elevator and direction of movement.

(10) Display of information on building occupants. In its simplest form, the total number of occupants remaining in the building. In more complex form, the locations and identity of occupants remaining in the building.

(11) Display of detailed information about hazardous materials housed in the building, including cautions and warnings for firefighting similar to those in NFPA 704 or in MSDS.

(12) A display of water flow in the sprinkler system branch lines or in specific sprinkler heads.

(13) Estimates of heat release rate of the fire and the potential for flashover.

(14) Temperature and visibility distance ($V=1.4D^{0.767}$ where visibility distance V is in meters and D is the optical density per meter) information in the fire zone and other locations in the building such as elevator machine rooms, elevator lobbies, hoistways, and cars.

(15) Status of any smoke control system in the building.

(16) Display of pressure difference in a stairway, hoistway, or zone/floor produced by a smoke control system.

(17) Display of locations of video cameras, and the ability to display the video feed from selected cameras.

E.6.3 Control Functions. Beyond the minimum set of control functions necessary to interact with the display as discussed above in E.6.1 the Incident Commander Display could provide other control functions of benefit to the fire service. These are optional and include:

(1) A control to silence alarms.

(2) Controls that would allow the incident commander to manually control specific HVAC equipment.

(3) Elevator controls that would allow the incident commander to initiate Phase 1 recall (protected) elevator systems.

(4) Controls that would allow the incident commander to manually control gas and power shutoffs.

(5) Controls that would allow the incident commander to manually control the master sprinkler shutoffs.

(6) Controls that would allow the incident commander to select individual paging zones, groups, or all call to receive messages.

E.6.4 Layout. Figure E.6.4 shows the screen layout. The display consists of the following windows and text fields:

(1) *Fire Situation Window.* In this window a graphical view of the building is shown overlaid with graphical icons to show the locations of active alarms and other fire-relevant building objects.

(2) *Building Navigation Controls.* Immediately to the left of the Fire Situation Window is an area containing an interactive control for navigating between floors in the building and selecting a floor to be shown graphically in the Fire Situation Window.

(3) *Function Buttons.* Above the Fire Situation Window is an area reserved for touch-activated function buttons that would provide direct access to various functions and information. For example, building information, contact information, the site plan, and alarm list might be accessed by means of these buttons. Also, if any of the optional control functions described in E.6.3 are implemented, they would be accessed by means of touch-activated function buttons in this area of the display.

(4) *Address Text Field.* At the very top of the display is a text field in which the address is displayed for the subject building.

(5) *Initial Alarm Text Field.* Immediately above the Fire Situation Window is a text field in which the details of the initial alarm are displayed.

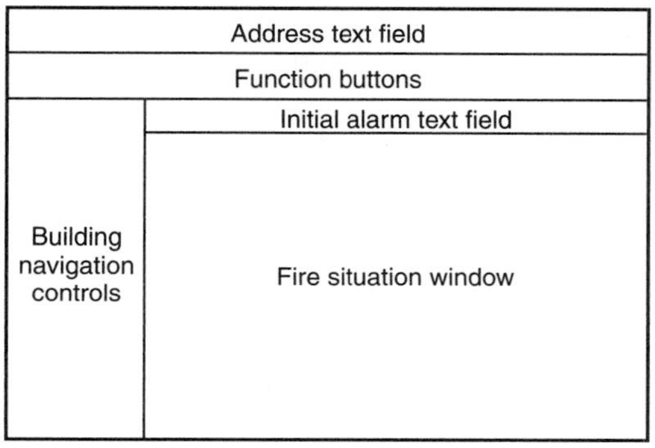

Address text field	
Function buttons	
	Initial alarm text field
Building navigation controls	Fire situation window

FIGURE E.6.4 *Incident Commander Display Layout.*

E.6.5 Interaction.

E.6.5.1 Point and Touch Interaction. There shall be no keyboard or mouse. All user interaction with the display shall be by means of other interaction methods such as touch screen interaction or function keys/buttons.

E.6.5.2 Minimal User Interaction. User interactions with the display shall be minimized as much as possible. There shall be no menus. The user shall be able to directly access all information and functions with a single touch control action.

E.6.5.3 Navigation.

E.6.5.3.1 Fire Situation Window Priority. The Fire Situation Window shall be displayed at all times. The incident commander shall have no control with which to close it.

E.6.5.3.2 Other Information. Menus shall *not* be used for accessing information or functions. The information and functions described in E.6.1 through E.6.3 shall be displayed in pop-up windows. These windows shall be placed on the screen in a way that minimally interferes with the view of the Fire Situation Window.

E.6.5.3.3 Closing Windows. An intuitive and obvious control for closing an information pop-up window shall be provided. The exception is the Fire Situation Window which shall have no close control.

E.6.5.3.4 Navigating Building Graphics — Vertical Navigation. An interactive control shall be required for the user to navigate, vertically, between floors of the building shown in the Fire Situation Window graphics. This control also shall allow the user to select the floor of interest for display.

E.6.5.3.5 Navigating Building Graphics — Horizontal Navigation. In the case of a building with a very large footprint, it may not be possible to graphically display an entire floor of the building at a sufficient level of resolution for fire command use. In these cases, a second interactive control shall be needed to navigate horizontally within a single floor to the area of interest so that the area of interest may be displayed at a sufficient level of resolution. This navigational control must be designed in a way that helps the incident commander remain well-oriented to the overall building layout while simultaneously showing details in one portion of the building.

E.6.5.3.6 Exiting the Display. The incident commander shall not be permitted to exit or otherwise turn off the Incident Commander Display.

Sample Ordinance Adopting
NFPA 72

This annex is not a part of the requirements of this NFPA document but is included for informational purposes only.

F.1

The following sample ordinance is provided to assist a jurisdiction in the adoption of this Code and is not part of this Code.

ORDINANCE NO. _____

An ordinance of the *[jurisdiction]* adopting the 2010 edition of *NFPA 72®*, *National Fire Alarm and Signaling Code*, and documents listed in Chapter 2 of that Code; prescribing regulations governing conditions hazardous to life and property from fire or explosion; providing for the issuance of permits and collection of fees; repealing Ordinance No. _____ of the *[jurisdiction]* and all other ordinances and parts of ordinances in conflict therewith; providing a penalty; providing a severability clause; and providing for publication; and providing an effective date.

BE IT ORDAINED BY THE *[governing body]* OF THE *[jurisdiction]*:

SECTION 1 That the *NFPA 72, National Fire Alarm and Signaling Code*, and documents adopted by Chapter 2, three (3) copies of which are on file and are open to inspection by the public in the office of the *[jurisdiction's keeper of records]* of the *[jurisdiction]*, are hereby adopted and incorporated into this ordinance as fully as if set out at length herein, and from the date on which this ordinance shall take effect, the provisions thereof shall be controlling within the limits of the *[jurisdiction]*. The same are hereby adopted as the Code of the *[jurisdiction]* for the purpose of prescribing regulations governing conditions hazardous to life and property from fire or explosion and providing for issuance of permits and collection of fees.

SECTION 2 Any person who shall violate any provision of this code or standard hereby adopted or fail to comply therewith; or who shall violate or fail to comply with any order made thereunder; or who shall build in violation of any detailed statement of specifications or plans submitted and approved thereunder; or fail to operate in accordance with any certificate or permit issued thereunder; and from which no appeal has been taken; or who shall fail to comply with such an order as affirmed or modified by a court of competent jurisdiction, within the time fixed herein, shall severally for each and every such violation and noncompliance, respectively, be guilty of a misdemeanor, punishable by a fine of not less than $ _____ nor more than $_____ or by imprisonment for not less than _____ days nor more than _____ days or by both such fine and imprisonment. The imposition of one penalty for any violation shall not excuse the violation or permit it to continue; and all such persons shall be required to correct or remedy such violations or defects within a reasonable time; and when not otherwise specified the application of the above penalty shall not be held to prevent the enforced removal of prohibited conditions. Each day that prohibited conditions are maintained shall constitute a separate offense.

SECTION 3 Additions, insertions, and changes — that the 2010 edition of *NFPA 72, National Fire Alarm and Signaling Code* is amended and changed in the following respects:

List Amendments

SECTION 4 That ordinance No. _____ of *[jurisdiction]* entitled *[fill in the title of the ordinance or ordinances in effect at the present time]* and all other ordinances or parts of ordinances in conflict herewith are hereby repealed.

SECTION 5 That if any section, subsection, sentence, clause, or phrase of this ordinance is, for any reason, held to be invalid or unconstitutional, such decision shall not affect the validity or constitutionality of the remaining portions of this ordinance. The *[governing body]* hereby declares that it would have passed this ordinance, and each section, subsection, clause, or phrase hereof, irrespective of the fact that any one or more sections, subsections, sentences, clauses, and phrases be declared unconstitutional.

SECTION 6 That the *[jurisdiction's keeper of records]* is hereby ordered and directed to cause this ordinance to be published.

[NOTE: An additional provision may be required to direct the number of times the ordinance is to be published and to specify that it is to be in a newspaper in general circulation. Posting may also be required.]

SECTION 7 That this ordinance and the rules, regulations, provisions, requirements, orders, and matters established and adopted hereby shall take effect and be in full force and effect *[time period]* from and after the date of its final passage and adoption.

Wiring Diagrams and Guide for Testing Fire Alarm Circuits

This annex is not a part of the requirements of this NFPA document but is included for informational purposes only.

This annex was originally based on the performance requirements for circuit styles and classes specified in Tables 6.5, 6.6.1, and 6.7 of the 2002 and earlier editions of the Code. These tables were substantially revised for the 2007 edition of the Code and are now shown as Tables A.12.3(a), A.12.3(b), and A.12.3(c), respectively. The tables from the 2002 edition are shown as Commentary Tables G.1, G.2, and G.3 to provide the user a more direct reference in applying the guidance of this annex.

Annex G provides guidance for testing of the various circuit styles and classes identified in Table A.12.3(a), Table A.12.3(b), and Table A.12.3(c). These tables correspond to Table 6.5, Table 6.6.1, and Table 6.7 of the 2007 edition of the Code, respectively, which had been substantially revised from previous editions, but these revisions have not been reflected in Annex G. The changes made to these tables for the 2007 edition are summarized below:

Table 6.5 Performance of Initiating Device Circuits:

(1) Circuit Styles A, C, and E were completely eliminated.

(2) Performance information for circuit Styles B and D were retained, but these circuits were designated simply Class B and Class A, respectively, without any style designation.

Table 6.6.1 Performance of Signaling Line Circuit:

(1) Circuit Styles 0.5, 1, 2, 3, 3.5, 4.5, and 5 were completely eliminated.

(2) Circuit Styles 4, 6, and 7 were retained.

COMMENTARY TABLE G.1 *Performance of Initiating Device Circuits (IDC)*
[Table 6.5 from NFPA 72, 2002 edition]

Class	B			B			B			A			A		
Style	A			B			C			D			E_α		
Abnormal Condition	Alm	Trbl	ARC	Alm	Trbl	ARC	Alm	Trbl	ARC	Alm	Trbl	ARC	Alm	Trbl	ARC
	1	2	3	4	5	6	7	8	9	10	11	12	13	14	15
Single open	—	X	—	—	X	—	—	X	—	—	X	R	—	X	R
Single ground	—	X	—	—	X	R	—	X	R	—	X	R	—	X	R
Wire-to-wire short	X	—	—	X	—	—	—	X	—	X	—	—	—	X	—
Loss of carrier (if used)/ channel interface	—	—	—	—	—	—	—	X	—	—	—	—	—	X	—

Alm = Alarm.

Trbl = Trouble.

ARC = Alarm receipt capability during abnormal condition.

R = Required capacity.

X = Indication required at protected premises and as required by Chapter 26.

α = Style exceeds minimum requirements of Class A.

COMMENTARY TABLE G.2 *Performance of Signaling Line Circuits (SLC)*
[Table 6.6.1 from NFPA 72, 2002 edition]

Class	B			B			A			B			B		
Style	0.5			1			2_α			3			3.5		
Abnormal Condition	Alm	Trbl	ARC	Alm	Trbl	ARC	Alm	Trbl	ARC	Alm	Trbl	ARC	Alm	Trbl	ARC
	1	2	3	4	5	6	7	8	9	10	11	12	13	14	15
Single open	—	X	—	—	X	—	—	X	R	—	X	—	—	X	—
Single ground	—	X	—	—	X	R	—	X	R	—	X	R	—	X	—
Wire-to-wire short	—	—	—	—	—	—	—	—	M	—	X	—	—	X	—
Wire-to-wire short & open	—	—	—	—	—	—	—	—	M	—	X	—	—	X	—
Wire-to-wire short & ground	—	—	—	—	—	—	—	X	M	—	X	—	—	X	—
Open and ground	—	—	—	—	—	—	—	X	R	—	X	—	—	X	—
Loss of carrier (if used)/ channel interface	—	—	—	—	—	—	—	—	—	—	—	—	—	X	—

Class	B			B			A			A			A		
Style	4			4.5			5_α			6_α			7_α		
Abnormal Condition	Alm	Trbl	ARC	Alm	Trbl	ARC	Alm	Trbl	ARC	Alm	Trbl	ARC	Alm	Trbl	ARC
	16	17	18	19	20	21	22	23	24	25	26	27	28	29	30
Single open	—	X	—	—	X	R	—	X	R	—	X	R	—	X	R
Single ground	—	X	R	—	X	—	—	X	R	—	X	R	—	X	R
Wire-to-wire short	—	X	—	—	X	—	—	X	—	—	X	—	—	X	R
Wire-to-wire short & open	—	X	—	—	X	—	—	X	—	—	X	—	—	X	—
Wire-to-wire short & ground	—	X	—	—	X	—	—	X	—	—	X	—	—	X	—
Open and ground	—	X	—	—	X	—	—	X	—	—	X	R	—	X	R
Loss of carrier (if used)/ channel interface	—	X	—	—	X	—	—	X	—	—	X	—	—	X	—

Alm = Alarm.

Trbl = Trouble.

ARC = Alarm receipt capability during abnormal condition.

M = May be capable of alarm with wire-to-wire short.

R = Required capability.

X = Indication required at protected premises and as required by Chapter 8.

α = Style exceeds minimum requirements of Class A.

Table 6.7 Notification Appliance Circuit:
(1) Circuit Styles W and X were completely eliminated.
(2) Performance information for circuit Styles Y and Z were retained, but these circuits were designated simply Class B and Class A, respectively, without any style designation.
Since Annex G has not changed, it still provides useful guidance for applications that use the older style designations. However, for these older styles, users of this annex will need to consult 2002 and earlier editions of the Code to obtain related circuit performance information.

G.1

The wiring diagrams depicted in Figure G.2.1 through Figure G.2.17 are representative of typical circuits encountered in the field and are not intended to be all-inclusive.

COMMENTARY TABLE G.3 *Notification Appliance Circuits (NAC)*
[Table 6.7 from NFPA 72, 2002 edition]

Class	B		B		B		A	
Style	W		X		Y		Z	
	Trouble indication at protected premises	Alarm capability during abnormal conditions	Trouble indication at protected premises	Alarm capability during abnormal conditions	Trouble indication at protected premises	Alarm capability during abnormal conditions	Trouble indication at protected premises	Alarm capability during abnormal conditions
Abnormal Condition	1	2	3	4	5	6	7	8
Single open	X	—	X	R	X	—	X	R
Single ground	X	—	X	—	X	R	X	R
Wire-to-wire short	X	—	X	—	X	—	X	—

X = Indication required at protected premises.
R = Required capability.

The noted styles are as indicated in Table 6.5, Table 6.6.1, Table 6.7, and Table 8.5.3.2.2.2 (reference 2002 edition).

The noted symbols are as indicated in NFPA 170, *Standard for Fire Safety and Emergency Symbols*.

Because ground-fault detection is not required for all circuits, tests for ground-fault detection should be limited to those circuits equipped with ground-fault detection.

An individual point-identifying (addressable) initiating device operates on a signaling line circuit and not on a Style A, B, C, D, or E (Class B and Class A) initiating device circuit.

All of the following initiating device circuits are illustrative of either alarm or supervisory signaling. Alarm-initiating devices and supervisory initiating devices are not permitted on the same initiating device circuit.

In addition to losing its ability to receive an alarm from an initiating device located beyond an open fault, a Style A (Class B) initiating device circuit also loses its ability to receive an alarm when a single ground fault is present.

Style C and Style E (Class B and Class A) initiating device circuits can discriminate between an alarm condition and a wire-to-wire short. In these circuits, a wire-to-wire short provides a trouble indication. However, a wire-to-wire short prevents alarm operation. Shorting-type initiating devices cannot be used without an additional current or voltage limiting element.

Directly connected system smoke detectors, commonly referred to as two-wire detectors, should be listed as being electrically and functionally compatible with the fire alarm control unit and the specific subunit or module to which they are connected. If the detectors and the units or modules are not compatible, it is possible that, during an alarm condition, the detector's visible indicator will illuminate, but no change of state to the alarm condition will occur at the fire alarm control unit. Incompatibility can also prevent proper system operation at extremes of operating voltage, temperature, and other environmental conditions.

Where two or more two-wire detectors with integral relays are connected to a single initiating device circuit and their relay contacts are used to control essential building functions (e.g., fan shutdown, elevator recall), it should be clearly noted that the circuit might be capable of supplying only enough energy to support one detector/relay combination in an alarm mode. If control of more than one building function is required, each detector/relay combination used to control separate functions should be connected to separate initiating device circuits, or they should be connected to an initiating device circuit that provides adequate power to allow all the detectors connected to the circuit to be in the alarm mode simultaneously. During acceptance and reacceptance testing, this feature should always be tested and verified.

A speaker is an alarm notification appliance, and, if used as shown in the diagrams in G.2, the principle of operation and supervision is the same as for other audible alarm notification appliances (e.g., bells and horns).

The testing of supervised remote relays is to be conducted in the same manner as for notification appliances.

G.2 Wiring Diagrams

When testing circuits, the correct wiring size, insulation type, and conductor fill should be verified in accordance with the requirements of *NFPA 70, National Electrical Code.*

G.2.1 Nonpowered Alarm-Initiating or Supervisory-Initiating Devices (e.g., Manual Station or Valve Supervisory Switch) Connected to Style A, B, or C Initiating Device Circuits. Disconnect conductor at device or control unit, then reconnect. Temporarily connect a ground to either leg of conductors, then remove ground. Both operations should indicate audible and visual trouble with subsequent restoration at control unit. Conductor-to-conductor short should initiate alarm. Style A and Style B (Class B) indicate trouble Style C (Class B). Style A (Class B) does not initiate alarm while in trouble condition. See Figure G.2.1.

G.2.2 Nonpowered Alarm-Initiating or Supervisory-Initiating Devices Connected to Style D or E Initiating Device Circuits. Disconnect a conductor at a device at midpoint in the circuit. Operate a device on either side of the device with the disconnected conductor. Reset fire alarm control unit and reconnect conductor. Repeat test with a ground applied to either conductor in place of the disconnected conductor. Both operations should indicate audible and visual trouble, then alarm or supervisory indication with subsequent restoration. See Figure G.2.2.

G.2.3 Circuit-Powered (Two-Wire) Smoke Detectors for Style A, B, or C Initiating Device Circuits. Remove smoke detector where installed with plug-in base or disconnect conductor from fire alarm control unit beyond first device. Activate smoke detector per manufacturer's published instructions between fire alarm control unit and circuit break. Restore detector or circuit, or both. Fire alarm control unit should indicate trouble where fault occurs and alarm where detectors are activated between the break and the fire alarm control unit. See Figure G.2.3.

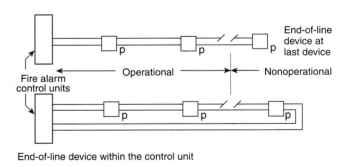

FIGURE G.2.1 Nonpowered Alarm-Initiating or Supervisory-Initiating Devices Connected to Style A, B, or C Initiating Device Circuits.

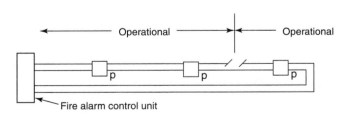

FIGURE G.2.2 Nonpowered Alarm-Initiating or Supervisory-Initiating Devices Connected to Style D or E Initiating Device Circuits.

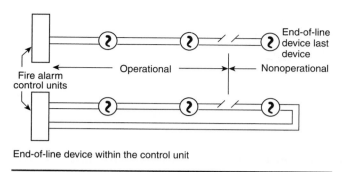

End-of-line device within the control unit

FIGURE G.2.3 *Circuit-Powered (Two-Wire) Smoke Detectors for Style A, B, or C Initiating Device Circuits.*

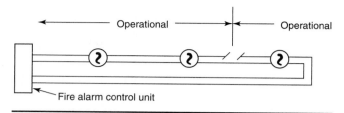

FIGURE G.2.4 *Circuit-Powered (Two-Wire) Smoke Detectors for Style D or E Initiating Device Circuits.*

G.2.4 Circuit-Powered (Two-Wire) Smoke Detectors for Style D or E Initiating Device Circuits. Disconnect conductor at a smoke detector or remove where installed with a plug-in base at midpoint in the circuit. Operate a device on either side of the device with the fault. Reset control unit and reconnect conductor or detector. Repeat test with a ground applied to either conductor in place of the disconnected conductor or removed device. Both operations should indicate audible and visual trouble, then alarm indication with subsequent restoration. See Figure G.2.4.

G.2.5 Combination Alarm-Initiating Device and Notification Appliance Circuits. Disconnect a conductor either at indicating or initiating device. Activate initiating device between the fault and the fire alarm control unit. Activate additional smoke detectors between the device first activated and the fire alarm control unit. Restore circuit, initiating devices, and fire alarm control unit. Confirm that all notification appliances on the circuit operate from the fire alarm control unit up to the fault and that all smoke detectors tested and their associated ancillary functions, if any, operate. See Figure G.2.5.

G.2.6 Combination Alarm-Initiating Device and Notification Appliance Circuits Arranged for Operation with a Single Open or Ground Fault. Testing of the circuit is similar to that described in G.2.5. Confirm that all notification appliances operate on either side of fault. See Figure G.2.6.

G.2.7 Style A, B, or C Circuits with Four-Wire Smoke Detectors and an End-of-Line Power Supervision Relay. Testing of the circuit is similar to that described in G.2.3 and G.2.4. Disconnect a leg of the power supply circuit beyond the first device on the circuit. Activate initiating device between the fault and the fire alarm control unit. Restore circuits,

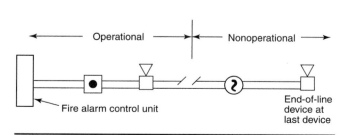

FIGURE G.2.5 *Combination Alarm-Initiating Device and Notification Appliance Circuits.*

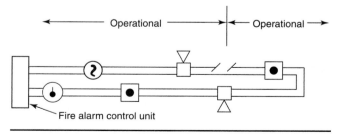

FIGURE G.2.6 *Combination Alarm-Initiating Device and Notification Appliance Circuits Arranged for Operation with a Single Open or Ground Fault.*

initiating devices, and fire alarm control unit. Audible and visual trouble should indicate at the fire alarm control unit where either the initiating or power circuit is faulted. All initiating devices between the circuit fault and the fire alarm control unit should activate. In addition, removal of a smoke detector from a plug-in-type base can also break the power supply circuit. Where circuits contain various powered and nonpowered devices on the same initiating circuit, verify that the nonpowered devices beyond the power circuit fault can still initiate an alarm. A return loop should be brought back to the last powered device and the power supervisory relay to incorporate into the end-of-line device. See Figure G.2.7.

G.2.8 Style A, B, or C Initiating Device Circuits with Four-Wire Smoke Detectors That Include Integral Individual Supervision Relays. Testing of the circuit is similar to that described in G.2.3 with the addition of a power circuit. See Figure G.2.8.

G.2.9 Alarm Notification Appliances Connected to Style W and Y (Two-Wire) Circuits. Testing of the notification appliances connected to Style W and Style Y (Class B) is similar to that described in G.2.3. See Figure G.2.9.

G.2.10 Alarm Notification Appliances Connected to Style X and Z (Four-Wire) Circuits. Testing of the notification appliances connected to Style X and Style Z (Class B and Class A) is similar to that described in G.2.4. See Figure G.2.10.

G.2.11 System with a Supervised Audible Notification Appliance Circuit and an Unsupervised Visible Notification Appliance Circuit. Testing of the notification appliances connected to Style X and Style Z (Class B and Class A) is similar to that described in G.2.4. See Figure G.2.11.

G.2.12 System with Supervised Audible and Visible Notification Appliance Circuits. Testing of the notification appliances connected to Style X and Style Z (Class B and Class A) is similar to that described in G.2.4. See Figure G.2.12.

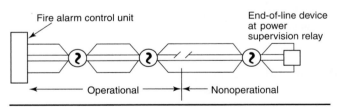

FIGURE G.2.7 *Style A, B, or C Circuits with Four-Wire Smoke Detectors and an End-of-Line Power Supervision Relay.*

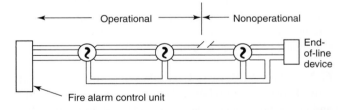

FIGURE G.2.8 *Style A, B, or C Initiating Device Circuits with Four-Wire Smoke Detectors That Include Integral Individual Supervision Relays.*

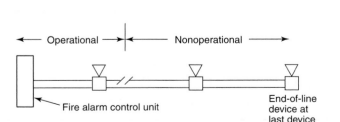

FIGURE G.2.9 *Alarm Notification Appliances Connected to Styles W and Y (Two-Wire) Circuits.*

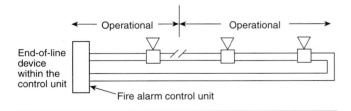

FIGURE G.2.10 *Alarm Notification Appliances Connected to Style X and Z (Four-Wire) Circuits.*

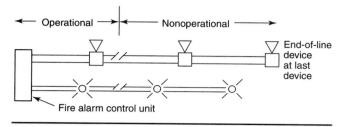

FIGURE G.2.11 *Supervised Audible Notification Appliance Circuit and an Unsupervised Visible Notification Appliance Circuit.*

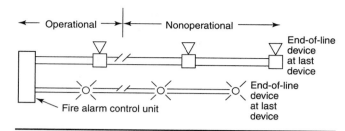

FIGURE G.2.12 *Supervised Audible and Visible Notification Appliance Circuits.*

G.2.13 Series Notification Appliance Circuit, Which No Longer Meets the Requirements of *NFPA 72.* An open fault in the circuit wiring should cause a trouble condition. See Figure G.2.13.

G.2.14 Supervised Series Supervisory-Initiating Circuit with Sprinkler Supervisory Valve Switches Connected, Which No Longer Meets the Requirements of *NFPA 72.* An open fault in the circuit wiring of operation of the valve switch (or any supervisory signal device) should cause a trouble condition. See Figure G.2.14.

G.2.15 Initiating Device Circuit with Parallel Waterflow Alarm Switches and a Series Supervisory Valve Switch, Which No Longer Meets the Requirements of *NFPA 72.* An open fault in the circuit wiring or operation of the valve switch should cause a trouble signal. See Figure G.2.15.

G.2.16 System Connected to a Municipal Fire Alarm Master Box Circuit. Disconnect a leg of municipal circuit at master box. Verify alarm sent to public communications center. Disconnect leg of auxiliary circuit. Verify trouble condition on control unit. Restore circuits. Activate control unit and send alarm signal to communications center. Verify control unit in trouble condition until master box reset. See Figure G.2.16.

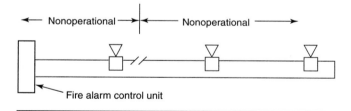

FIGURE G.2.13 *Series Notification Appliance Circuit.*

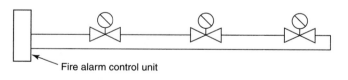

FIGURE G.2.14 *Supervised Series Supervisory-Initiating Circuit with Sprinkler Supervisory Valve Switches Connected.*

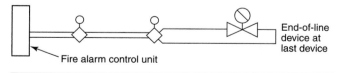

FIGURE G.2.15 *Initiating Device Circuit with Parallel Waterflow Alarm Switches and a Series Supervisory Valve Switch.*

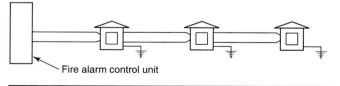

FIGURE G.2.16 *System Connected to a Municipal Fire Alarm Master Box Circuit.*

G.2.17 Auxiliary Circuit Connected to a Municipal Fire Alarm Master Box. For operation with a master box, an open or ground fault (where ground detection is provided) on the circuit should result in a trouble condition at the fire alarm control unit. A trouble signal at the fire alarm control unit should persist until the master box is reset. For operation with a shunt trip master box, an open fault in the auxiliary circuit should cause an alarm on the municipal system. See Figure G.2.17.

FIGURE G.2.17 *Auxiliary Circuit Connected to a Municipal Fire Alarm Master Box.*

G.3 Circuit Styles

Some testing laboratories and authorities having jurisdiction permit systems to be classified as a Style 7 (Class A) by the application of two circuits of the same style operating in parallel. An example of this is to take two series circuits, either Style 0.5 or Style 1.0 (Class B), and operate them in parallel. The logic is that if a condition occurs on one of the circuits, the other parallel circuit remains operative.

To understand the principles of the circuit, alarm receipt capability should be performed on a single circuit, and the style type, based on the performance, should be indicated on the record of completion.

G.3.1 Style 0.5. This signaling circuit operates as a series circuit in performance. This is identical to the historical series audible signaling circuits. Any type of break or ground in one of the conductors, or the internal of the multiple interface device, and the total circuit is rendered inoperative.

To test and verify this type of circuit, either a conductor should be lifted or an earth ground should be placed on a conductor or a terminal point where the signaling circuit attaches to the multiplex interface device.

G.3.2 Style 0.5(a) (Class B) Series. Style 0.5(a) functions so that, when a box is operated, the supervisory contacts open, making the succeeding devices nonoperative while the operating box sends a coded signal. Any alarms occurring in any successive devices will not be received at the receiving station during this period. See Figure G.3.2.

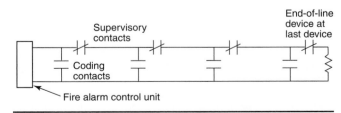

FIGURE G.3.2 *Style 0.5(a) (Class B) Series.*

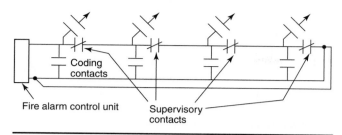

FIGURE G.3.3 *Style 0.5(b) (Class B) Shunt.*

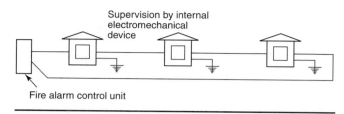

FIGURE G.3.4 *Style 0.5(c) (Class B) Positive Supervised Successive.*

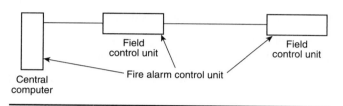

FIGURE G.3.5(a) *Style 1.0 (Class B).*

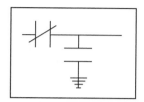

FIGURE G.3.5(b) *Typical Transmitter Layout.*

G.3.3 Style 0.5(b) (Class B) Shunt. The contact closes when the device is operated and remains closed to shunt out the remainder of the system until the code is complete. See Figure G.3.3.

G.3.4 Style 0.5(c) (Class B) Positive Supervised Successive. An open or ground fault on the circuit should cause a trouble condition at the control unit. See Figure G.3.4.

G.3.5 Style 1.0 (Class B). This is a series circuit identical to the diagram for Style 0.5, except that the fire alarm system hardware has enhanced performance. [See Figure G.3.5(a) and Figure G.3.5(b).] A single earth ground can be placed on a conductor or multiplex interface device, and the circuit and hardware will still have alarm operability.

If a conductor break or an internal fault occurs in the pathway of the circuit conductors, the entire circuit becomes inoperative.

To verify alarm receipt capability and the resulting trouble signal, place an earth ground on one of the conductors or at the point where the signaling circuit attaches to the multiplex interface device. One of the transmitters or an initiating device should then be placed into alarm.

G.3.6 Typical McCulloh Loop. This is the central station McCulloh redundant-type circuit and has alarm receipt capability on either side of a single break. See Figure G.3.6.

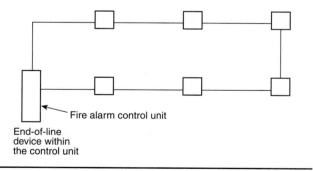

FIGURE G.3.6 *Typical McCulloh Loop.*

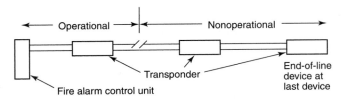

FIGURE G.3.7 *Style 3.0 (Class B).*

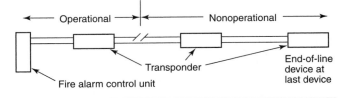

FIGURE G.3.8 *Style 3.5 (Class B).*

G.3.6.1 To test, lift one of the conductors and operate a transmitter or initiating device on each side of the break. This activity should be repeated for each conductor.

G.3.6.2 Place an earth ground on a conductor and operate a single transmitter or initiating device to verify alarm receipt capability and trouble condition for each conductor.

G.3.6.3 Repeat the instructions of G.3.6.1 and G.3.6.2 at the same time, verify alarm receipt capability, and verify that a trouble condition results.

G.3.7 Style 3.0 (Class B). This is a parallel circuit in which multiplex interface devices transmit signal and operating power over the same conductors. (See Figure G.3.7.) The multiplex interface devices might be operable up to the point of a single break. Verify by lifting a conductor and causing an alarm condition on one of the units between the central alarm unit and the break. Either lift a conductor to verify the trouble condition or place an earth ground on the conductors. Test for all the valuations shown on the signaling table.

On ground-fault testing, verify alarm receipt capability by actuating a multiplex interface initiating device or a transmitter.

G.3.8 Style 3.5 (Class B). Repeat the instructions for Style 3.0 (Class B) and verify the trouble conditions by either lifting a conductor or placing a ground on the conductor. See Figure G.3.8.

G.3.9 Style 4.0 (Class B). Repeat the instructions for Style 3.0 (Class B) and include a loss of carrier where the signal is being used. See Figure G.3.9.

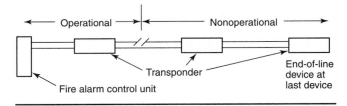

FIGURE G.3.9 *Style 4.0 (Class B).*

G.3.10 Style 4.5 (Class B). Repeat the instructions for Style 3.5 (Class B). Verify alarm receipt capability while lifting a conductor by actuating a multiple interface device or transmitter on each side of the break. See Figure G.3.10.

G.3.11 Style 5.0 (Class A). Verify the alarm receipt capability and trouble annunciation by lifting a conductor and actuating a multiplex interfacing device or a transmitter on each side of the break. For the earth ground verification, place an earth ground and certify alarm receipt capability and trouble annunciation by actuating a single multiplex interfacing device or a transmitter. See Figure G.3.11.

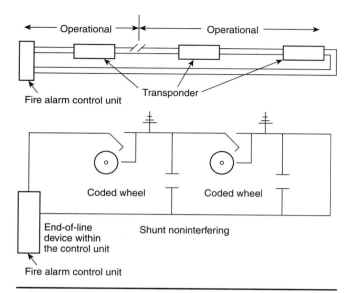

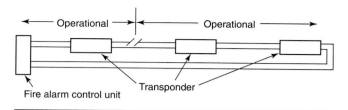

FIGURE G.3.11 *Style 5.0 (Class A).*

FIGURE G.3.10 *Style 4.5 (Class B).*

G.3.12 Style 6.0 (Class A). Repeat the instructions for Style 2.0 [Class A (a) through (c)]. Verify the remaining steps for trouble annunciation for the various combinations. See Figure G.3.12.

G.3.13 Style 6.0 (with Circuit Isolators) (Class A). For the portions of the circuits electrically located between the monitoring points of circuit isolators, follow the instructions for a Style 7.0 (Class A) circuit. It should be clearly noted that the alarm receipt capability for remaining portions of the circuit protection isolators is not the capability of the circuit but is permitted with enhanced system capabilities. See Figure G.3.13.

G.3.14 Style 7.0 (Class A). Repeat the instructions for testing of Style 6.0 (Class A) for alarm receipt capability and trouble annunciation. See Figure G.3.14(a) through Figure G.3.14(k).

NOTE: A portion of the circuit between the alarm processor or central supervising station and the first circuit isolator does not have alarm receipt capability in the presence of a wire-to-wire short. The same is true for the portion of the circuit from the last isolator to the alarm processor or the central supervising station.

NOTE: Some manufacturers of this type of equipment have isolators as part of the base assembly. Therefore, in the field, this component might not be readily observable without the assistance of the manufacturer's representative.

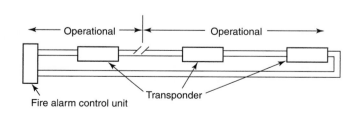

FIGURE G.3.12 *Style 6.0 (Class A).*

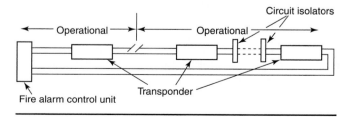

FIGURE G.3.13 *Style 6.0 (with Circuit Isolators) (Class A).*

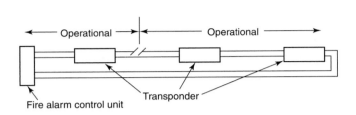

FIGURE G.3.14(a) Style 7.0 (Class A).

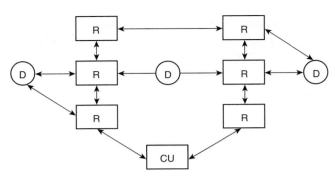

CU = Wireless control unit
(with power supply and standby power)
R = Wireless repeater
(with power supply and standby power)
D = Wireless initiating, indicating, and control device
(either primary battery or primary standby battery)

FIGURE G.3.14(b) Low-Power Radio (Wireless) Fire Alarm System.

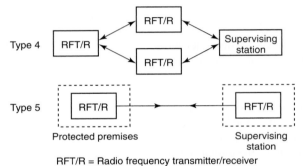

RFT/R = Radio frequency transmitter/receiver

FIGURE G.3.14(c) Two-Way RF Multiplex Systems.

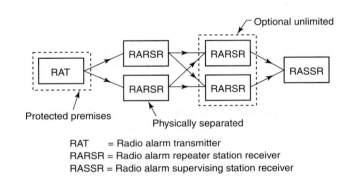

RAT = Radio alarm transmitter
RARSR = Radio alarm repeater station receiver
RASSR = Radio alarm supervising station receiver

FIGURE G.3.14(d) One-Way Radio Alarm System.

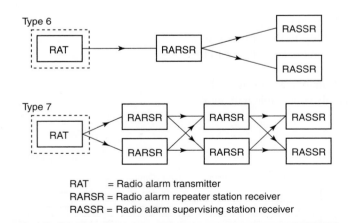

RAT = Radio alarm transmitter
RARSR = Radio alarm repeater station receiver
RASSR = Radio alarm supervising station receiver

FIGURE G.3.14(e) One-Way Radio Alarm System (Type 6 and Type 7).

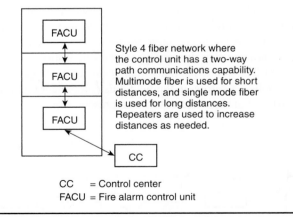

Style 4 fiber network where the control unit has a two-way path communications capability. Multimode fiber is used for short distances, and single mode fiber is used for long distances. Repeaters are used to increase distances as needed.

CC = Control center
FACU = Fire alarm control unit

FIGURE G.3.14(f) Style 4 Fiber Network.

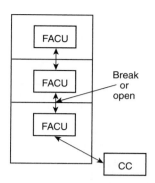

Style 4 fiber network where the control unit has a two-way path communications capability. A single break separates the system into two LANs, both with Style 4 capabilities.

CC = Control center
FACU = Fire alarm control unit

FIGURE G.3.14(g) *Style 4 Fiber Network (Single Break).*

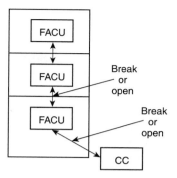

Style 4 fiber network where the control unit has a two-way path communications capability. A double break isolates the control units and the control center in this case. There is one LAN and one isolated control unit operating on its own. Control center is isolated completely with no communications with the network.

CC = Control center
FACU = Fire alarm control unit

FIGURE G.3.14(h) *Style 4 Fiber Network (Double Break).*

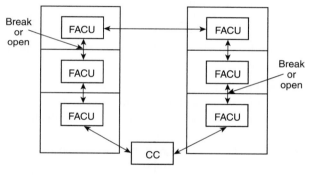

Style 7 fiber network where the control unit has a two-way path communications capability with the two breaks now breaking into two LANs, both functioning as independent networks with the same Style 7 capabilities.

CC = Control center
FACU = Fire alarm control unit

FIGURE G.3.14(i) *Style 7 Fiber Network (Two LANs).*

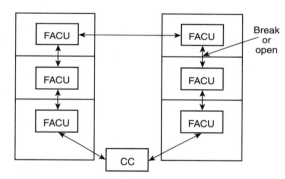

Style 7 fiber network where the control unit has a two-way path communications capability, with one break. System remains as one LAN and meets Style 7.

CC = Control center
FACU = Fire alarm control unit

FIGURE G.3.14(j) *Style 7 Fiber Network (One LAN).*

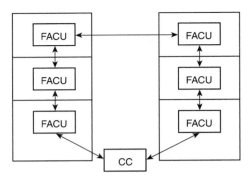

Style 7 fiber network where the control unit has a two-way path communications capability.

CC   = Control center
FACU = Fire alarm control unit

FIGURE G.3.14(k) *Style 7 Fiber Network.*

G.4 Batteries

To maximize battery life, nickel-cadmium batteries should be charged as in Table G.4(a).

To maximize battery life, the battery voltage for lead-acid cells should be maintained within the limits shown in Table G.4(b).

The following procedure is recommended for checking the state of charge for nickel-cadmium batteries:

(1) The battery charger should be switched from float to high-rate mode.
(2) The current, as indicated on the charger ammeter, will immediately rise to the maximum output of the charger, and the battery voltage, as shown on the charger voltmeter, will start to rise at the same time.
(3) The actual value of the voltage rise is unimportant, because it depends on many variables. The length of time it takes for the voltage to rise is the important factor.
(4) If, for example, the voltage rises rapidly in a few minutes, then holds steady at the new value, the battery is fully charged. At the same time, the current will drop to slightly above its original value.
(5) In contrast, if the voltage rises slowly and the output current remains high, the high-rate charge should be continued until the voltage remains constant. Such a condition is an indication that the battery is not fully charged, and the float voltage should be increased slightly.

TABLE G.4(a) *Voltage for Nickel-Cadmium Batteries*

| Float voltage | 1.42 volts/cell + 0.01 volt |
| High-rate voltage | 1.58 volts/cell + 0.07 volt − 0.00 volt |

Note: High- and low-gravity voltages are (+) 0.07 volt and (−) 0.03 volt, respectively.

TABLE G.4(b) *Voltage for Lead-Acid Batteries*

Float Voltage	*High-Gravity Battery (Lead Calcium)*	*Low-Gravity Battery (Lead Antimony)*
Maximum	2.25 volts/cell	2.17 volts/cell
Minimum	2.20 volts/cell	2.13 volts/cell
High-rate voltage	—	2.33 volts/cell

Informational References

H.1 Referenced Publications

The documents or portions thereof listed in this annex are referenced within the informational sections of this Code and are not part of the requirements of this document unless also listed in Chapter 2 for other reasons.

H.1.1 NFPA Publications. National Fire Protection Association, 1 Batterymarch Park, Quincy, MA 02169-7471.

NFPA 10, *Standard for Portable Fire Extinguishers*, 2007 edition.

NFPA 11, *Standard for Low-, Medium-, and High-Expansion Foam*, 2005 edition.

NFPA 12, *Standard on Carbon Dioxide Extinguishing Systems*, 2008 edition.

NFPA 12A, *Standard on Halon 1301 Fire Extinguishing Systems*, 2009 edition.

NFPA 13, *Standard for the Installation of Sprinkler Systems*, 2010 edition.

NFPA 14, *Standard for the Installation of Standpipe and Hose Systems*, 2007 edition.

NFPA 15, *Standard for Water Spray Fixed Systems for Fire Protection*, 2007 edition.

NFPA 17, *Standard for Dry Chemical Extinguishing Systems*, 2009 edition.

NFPA 17A, *Standard for Wet Chemical Extinguishing Systems*, 2009 edition.

NFPA 25, *Standard for the Inspection, Testing, and Maintenance of Water-Based Fire Protection Systems*, 2008 edition.

NFPA 70®, *National Electrical Code*®, 2008 edition.

NFPA 80, *Standard for Fire Doors and Other Opening Protectives*, 2010 edition.

NFPA 90A, *Standard for the Installation of Air-Conditioning and Ventilating Systems*, 2009 edition.

NFPA 90B, *Standard for the Installation of Warm Air Heating and Air-Conditioning Systems*, 2009 edition.

NFPA 92A, *Standard for Smoke-Control Systems Utilizing Barriers and Pressure Differences*, 2009 edition.

NFPA 92B, *Standard for Smoke Management Systems in Malls, Atria, and Large Spaces*, 2009 edition.

NFPA *101*®, *Life Safety Code*®, 2009 edition.

NFPA 170, *Standard for Fire Safety and Emergency Symbols*, 2009 edition.

NFPA 551, *Guide for the Evaluation of Fire Risk Assessments*, 2007 edition.

NFPA 704, *Standard System for the Identification of the Hazards of Materials for Emergency Response*, 2007 edition.

NFPA 720, *Standard for the Installation of Carbon Monoxide (CO) Detection and Warning Equipment*, 2009 edition.

NFPA 1221, *Standard for the Installation, Maintenance, and Use of Emergency Services Communications Systems*, 2010 edition.

NFPA *5000*®, *Building Construction and Safety Code*®, 2009 edition.

NFPA *Emergency Evacuation Planning Guide for People with Disabilities*, June 2007. (www.nfpa.org/assets/files/PDF/forms/EvacuationGuide.pdf).

H.1.2 Other Publications.

H.1.2.1 ANSI Publications. American National Standards Institute, Inc., 25 West 43rd Street, 4th floor, New York, NY 10036.

ANSI/ASME A17.1a/CSA B44a, *Safety Code for Elevators and Escalators*, 2008.

ANSI/ATA 878.1, *ARCNET Local Area Network*, 1999.

ANSI/EIA 709.1, *LonWorks Control Networking Standard*, 1999.

ANSI/FM 3260, *American National Standard for Energy-Sensing Fire Detectors for Automatic Fire Alarm Signaling*, 2004.

ANSI S3.2, *Method for Measuring the Intelligibility of Speech Over Communications Systems*, 1989, revised 1999.

ANSI S3.41, *American National Standard Audible Emergency Evacuation Signal*, 1990, reaffirmed 2008.

ANSI/UL 268, *Standard for Smoke Detectors for Fire Alarm Systems*, 2006.

ANSI/UL 464, *Standard for Audible Signaling Appliances*, 2003, revised 2008.

ANSI/UL 521, *Standard for Heat Detectors for Fire Protective Signaling Systems*, 1999, revised 2004.

ANSI/UL 864, *Standard for Control Units and Accessories for Fire Alarm Systems*, 2003, revised 2006.

ANSI/UL 1638, *Standard for Visual Signaling Appliances — Private Mode Emergency and General Utility Signaling*, 2001, revised 2008.

ANSI/UL 1971, *Standard for Signaling Devices for the Hearing Impaired*, 2002, revised 2008.

H.1.2.2 ASME Publication. American Society of Mechanical Engineers, Three Park Avenue, New York, NY 10016-5990.

ASME A17.4, *Guide for Emergency Personnel*, 1999.

H.1.2.3 ASHRAE Publication. American Society of Heating, Refrigerating and Air Conditioning Engineers, Inc., 1791 Tullie Circle, N.E., Atlanta, GA 30329-2305.

ASHRAE 135, *BACnet, A Data Communication Protocol for Building Automation and Control Networks*, 1995.

H.1.2.4 FM Publications. FM Global, 1301 Atwood Avenue, P.O. Box 7500, Johnston, RI 02919.

FM 3210, *Heat Detectors for Automatic Fire Alarm Signaling*, 2007.

H.1.2.5 ICC Publications. International Code Council, 5203 Leesburg Pike, Suite 600, Falls Church, VA 22041.

ICC/ANSI A117.1, *Standard on Accessible and Useable Buildings and Facilities*, 2003.

IBC-ICC, *International Building Code*, 2006.

H.1.2.6 IEC Publications. International Electrotechnical Commission, 3 rue de Varembé, P.O. Box 131, CH-1211 Geneva 20, Switzerland. IEC documents are available through ANSI.

IEC 60268, Sound System Equipment Part 16, *Objective rating of speech intelligibility by speech transmission index,* Second Edition: 1998.

H.1.2.7 IES Publication. Illuminating Engineering Society of North America, 120 Wall Street, 17th floor, New York, NY 10005.

Lighting Handbook Reference and Application, 2008.

H.1.2.8 IMSA Publication. International Municipal Signal Association, P.O. Box 539, 165 E. Union Street, Newark, NY 14513.

"IMSA Official Wire and Cable Specifications," 1998.

H.1.2.9 ISO Publications. Standards Secretariat, Acoustical Society of America, 335 East 45th Street, New York, NY 10017-3483.

ISO/TR 4870, *Acoustics — The Construction and Calibration of Speech Intelligibility Tests*, 1991.

ISO 7240-19, *Fire Detection and Alarm Systems — Part 19: Design, Installation, Commissioning, and Service of Sound Systems for Emergency Purposes*, 2007.

ISO 8201, *Audible Emergency Evacuation Signal*, 1990, revised 2008.

H.1.2.10 NEMA Publication. 1300 North 17th Street, Suite 1752, Rosslyn, VA 22209.

NEMA SB-30, *Fire Service Annunciator and Interface*, 2005.

NEMA SB-40, *Communications Systems For Life Safety in Schools*, 2008.

NEMA SB-50, *Emergency Communications Audio Intelligibility Applications Guide*, 2008.

H.1.2.11 NTIA Publication. National Telecommunications and Information Administration (NTIA), Herbert C. Hoover Building, U.S. Department of Commerce/NTIA, 1401 Constitution Avenue, N.W., Washington, DC 20230.

Manual of Regulations and Procedures for Federal Radio Frequency Management.

H.1.2.12 SFPE Publications. Society of Fire Protection Engineers, 7315 Wisconsin Avenue, #620E, Bethesda, MD 20814.

Guide to Performance Based Design.

SFPE Engineering Guide: Evaluation of the Computer Fire Model DETACT QS, 2002.

SFPE Engineering Guide to Human Behavior in Fire, 2003.

SFPE Engineering Guide to Performance Based Fire Protection Analysis and Design of Buildings, 2000.

SFPE Handbook of Fire Protection Engineering, 3rd Edition, 2002.

H.1.2.13 U.S. Government Publications. U.S. Government Printing Office, Washington, DC 20402.

ADAAG, *Americans with Disabilities Act Accessibility Guidelines for Building and Facility,* U.S. Department of Justice.

Title 29, Code of Federal Regulations, Part 1910.5.

Title 47, Code of Federal Regulations, Part 15.

H.1.2.14 References Associated with Annex A.

H.1.2.14.1 References to A.24.4.1.8.

(1) Schifiliti, R.P., "To Leave or Not to Leave — That is the Question!", National Fire Protection Association, World Fire Safety Congress & Exposition, May 16, 2000, Denver, CO.

(2) Ramachandran, G., "Informative Fire Warning Systems," *Fire Technology,* Volume 47, Number 1, February 1991, National Fire Protection Association, 66-81.

(3) J. Bryan, "Psychological Variables That May Affect Fire Alarm Design," *Fire Protection Engineering,* Society of Fire Protection Engineers, Issue No. 11, Fall 2001.

(4) Proulx, G., "Cool Under Fire," *Fire Protection Engineering,* Society of Fire Protection Engineers, Issue No. 16, Fall 2002.

(5) General Services Administration, Proceedings of the Reconvened International Conference on Fire Safety in High Rise Buildings, Washington, D.C., October 1971.

(6) Proulx, G., "Strategies for Ensuring Appropriate Occupant Response to Fire Alarm Signals," National Research Council of Canada, Ottawa, Ontario, *Construction Technology Update,* No. 43, 1–6, December 2000.

H.1.2.14.2 Reference to A.18.4.7.2. http://www.aip.org/pt/nov99/locsound.html.

H.1.2.15 References Associated with Annex B.

(1) Alpert, R. "Ceiling Jets," *Fire Technology*, Aug. 1972.

(2) "Evaluating Unsprinklered Fire Hazards," *SFPE Technology Report* 83-2.

(3) Babrauskas, V., Lawson, J. R., Walton, W. D., and Twilley, W. H. "Upholstered Furniture Heat Release Rates Measured with a Furniture Calorimeter," (NBSIR 82-2604) (Dec. 1982). National Institute of Standards and Technology (formerly National Bureau of Standards), Center for Fire Research, Gaithersburg, MD 20889.

(4) Beyler, C. "A Design Method for Flaming Fire Detection," *Fire Technology*, Vol. 20, No. 4, Nov. 1984.

(5) DiNenno, P., ed. Chapter 31, *SFPE Handbook of Fire Protection Engineering*, by R. Schifiliti, Sept. 1988.

(6) Evans, D. D. and Stroup, D. W. "Methods to Calculate Response Time of Heat and Smoke Detectors Installed Below Large Unobstructed Ceilings," (NBSIR 85-3167) (Feb. 1985, issued Jul. 1986). National Institute of Standards and Technology (formerly National Bureau of Standards), Center for Fire Research, Gaithersburg, MD 20889.

(7) Heskestad, G. "Characterization of Smoke Entry and Response for Products-of-Combustion Detectors" Proceedings, 7th International Conference on Problems of Automatic Fire Detection, Rheinish-Westfalischen Technischen Hochschule Aachen (Mar. 1975).

(8) Heskestad, G. "Investigation of a New Sprinkler Sensitivity Approval Test: The Plunge Test," FMRC Tech. Report 22485, Factory Mutual Research Corporation, 1151 Providence Turnpike, Norwood, MA 02062.

(9) Heskestad, G. and Delichatsios, M. A. "The Initial Convective Flow in Fire: Seventeenth Symposium on Combustion," The Combustion Institute, Pittsburgh, PA (1979).

(10) Heskestad, G. and Delichatsios, M. A. "Environments of Fire Detectors — Phase 1: Effect of Fire Size, Ceiling Height and Material," Measurements Vol. I (NBS-GCR-77-86), Analysis Vol. II (NBS-GCR-77-95). National Technical Information Service (NTIS), Springfield, VA 22151.

(11) Heskestad, G. and Delichatsios, M. A. "Update: The Initial Convective Flow in Fire," *Fire Safety Journal*, Vol. 15, No. 5, 1989.

(12) International Organization for Standardization, *Audible Emergency Evacuation Signal*, ISO 8201, 1987.

(13) Klote, J. and Milke, J. "Principles of Smoke Management," American Society of Heating, Refrigerating and Air Conditioning Engineers, Atlanta, GA, 2002.

(14) Lawson, J. R., Walton, W. D., and Twilley, W. H. "Fire Performance of Furnishings as Measured in the NBS Furniture Calorimeter, Part 1," (NBSIR 83-2787) (Aug. 1983). National Institute of Standards and Technology (formerly National Bureau of Standards), Center for Fire Research, Gaithersburg, MD 20889.

(15) Morton, B. R., Taylor, Sir Geoffrey, and Turner, J. S. "Turbulent Gravitational Convection from Maintained and Instantaneous Sources," Proc. Royal Society A, 234, 1–23, 1956.

(16) Schifiliti, R. "Use of Fire Plume Theory in the Design and Analysis of Fire Detector and Sprinkler Response," Master's Thesis, Worcester Polytechnic Institute, Center for Firesafety Studies, Worcester, MA, 1986.

(17) Title 47, Code of Federal Regulations, Communications Act of 1934 Amended.

(18) Schifiliti, R. and Pucci, W. "Fire Detection Modelling, State of the Art," 6 May, 1996 sponsored by the Fire Detection Institute, Bloomfield, CT.

(19) Forney, G., Bukowski, R., Davis, W. "Field Modelling: Effects of Flat Beamed Ceilings on Detector and Sprinkler Response," Technical Report, Year 1. International Fire Detection Research Project, National Fire Protection Research Foundation, Quincy, MA. October, 1993.

(20) Davis, W., Forney, G., Bukowski, R. "Field Modelling: Simulating the Effect of Sloped Beamed Ceilings on Detector and Sprinkler Response," Year 1. International Fire Detection Research Project Technical Report, National Fire Protection Research Foundation, Quincy, MA. October, 1994.

(21) Brozovski, E. "A Preliminary Approach to Siting Smoke Detectors Based on Design Fire Size and Detector Aerosol Entry Lag Time," Master's Thesis, Worcester Polytechnic, Worcester, MA, 1989.

(22) Cote, A. *NFPA Fire Protection Handbook*, 17th Edition, National Fire Protection Association, Quincy, MA, 1992.

(23) Tewarson, A., "Generation of Heat and Chemical Compounds in Fires," *SFPE Handbook of Fire Protection Engineering*, Second Edition, NFPA and SFPE, 1995.

(24) Hollman, J. P. *Heat Transfer*, McGraw-Hill, New York, 1976.

(25) Custer, R. L. P., and Meacham, B. "Introduction to Performance Based Fire Safety," SFPE, 1997.

(26) Schifiliti, R. P., Meacham B., Custer, R. L. P. "Design of Detection Systems," *SFPE Handbook of Fire Protection Engineering*.

(27) Marrion, C. "Correction Factors for the Heat of Combustion in NFPA 72," Appendix B, Fire Protection Engineering, SFPE, 1998.

(28) Marrion, C. "Designing and Analyzing the Response of Detection Systems: An Update to Previous Correlations," 1988.

(29) Custer, R. and Bright, R. "Fire Detection: The State-of-the-Art," NBS Tech. Note 839, National Bureau of Standards, Washington, 1974.

(30) Meacham, Brian J. "Characterization of Smoke from Burning Materials for the Evaluation of Light Scattering-Type Smoke Detector Response," MS Thesis, WPI Center for Firesafety Studies, Worcester, MA, 1991.

(31) Delichatsios, M. A. "Categorization of Cable Flammability, Detection of Smoldering, and Flaming Cable Fires," Interim Report, Factory Mutual Research Corporation, Norwood, MA, NP-1630, Nov. 1980.

(32) Heskestad, G. FMRC Serial Number 21017, Factory Mutual Research Corp., Norwood, MA, 1974.

(33) Marrion, C. E. "Lag Time Modeling and Effects of Ceiling Jet Velocity on the Placement of Optical Smoke Detectors," MS Thesis, WPI Center for Firesafety Studies, Worcester, MA, 1989.

(34) Kokkala, M. et al. "Measurements of the Characteristic Lengths of Smoke Detectors," *Fire Technology*, Vol. 28, No. 2, National Fire Protection Association, Quincy, MA, 1992.

(34a) Yamauchi et al. "A Calculation Method for Predicting Heat and Smoke Detector's Response."

(34b) Cleary et al. "Particulate Entry Lag in Spot Type Smoke Detectors," IAFSS Proceedings, Boston, MA 2000.

(34c) Keski-Rahkonen, "Revisiting Modeling of Fluid Penetration into Smoke Detectors," AUBE 2001.

(34d) Bjoerkman et al. "Determination of Dynamic Model Parameters of Smoke Detectors," *Fire Safety Journal*, No 37, pp. 395–407, 2002.

(34e) Keski-Rahkonen, "A New Model for Time Lag of Smoke Detectors," International Collaborative Project to Evaluate Fire Models for Nuclear Power Plant Application, Gaithersburg, MD May 2002.

(35) UL 268, *Standard for Smoke Detectors for Fire Alarm Systems*, Underwriters Laboratories, Inc., Northbrook, IL, 2006.

(36) Deal, Scott."Technical Reference Guide for FPEtool Version 3.2," NISTIR 5486, National Institute for Standards and Technology, U.S. Department of Commerce, Gaithersburg, MD, Aug. 1994.

(37) Mowrer, F. W. "Lag Times Associated with Detection and Suppression," *Fire Technology*, Vol. 26, No. 3, pp. 244–265, 1990.

(38) Newman, J. S. "Principles for Fire Detection," *Fire Technology*, Vol. 24, No. 2, pp. 116–127, 1988.

(39) Custer, R., Meacham, B., Wood, C. "Performance Based Design Techniques for Detection and Special Suppression Applications," Proceedings of the SFPE Engineering Seminars on Advances in Detection and Suppression Technology, 1994.

(40) SFPE *Engineering Guide to Performance Based Fire Protection Analysis and Design*, 2007, SFPE, Bethesda, MD.

(41) SFPE Handbook of Fire Protection Engineering, Third Edition, SFPE, Bethesda, MD, 2002.

(42) Drysdale, Dougal, *An Introduction to Fire Dynamics*, John Wiley & Sons, New York, NY, 1998, ISBN 0 471 90613 1, Second Edition.

(43) Nam S., Donovan L.P. and Kim S.G.; Establishing Heat Detectors Thermal Sensitivity Through Bench Scale Tests; *Fire Safety Journal*, Volume 39, Number 3, 191–215; April 2004.

(44) Nam S.; Thermal Response Coefficient TRC of Heat Detectors and Its Field Applications; Fire Detection and Research Applications Symposium; NFP Research Foundation; January 2003.

(45) Nam S.; Performance-Based Heat Detector Spacing; Interflam 2004; pages 883–892.

(46) Geiman, J.A., "Evaluation of Smoke Detector Response Estimation Methods," Master of Science Thesis, University of Maryland, College Park, MD, December 2003.

(47) Projected Beam Smoke Detectors - More Than Just a Substitute for Spot Detectors; Fire Protection Engineering; Summer 2004; SFPE

(48) Geiman, J.A., and Gottuck, D.T., "Alarm Thresholds for Smoke Detector Modeling," *Fire Safety Science — Proceeding of the Seventh International Symposium*, 2003, pp. 197–208.

(49) *The SFPE Code Official's Guide to Performance-based Design Review and Analysis of Buildings*, Society of Fire Protection Engineers, Bethesda, MD, 2004.

(50) NFPA *101, Life Safety Code*, National Fire Protection Association, Quincy, MA, 2006.

(51) NFPA 909, *Code for the Protection of Cultural Resource Properties — Museums, Libraries, and Places of Worship*, National Fire Protection Association, Quincy, MA, 2005.

(52) NFPA 914, *Code for Fire Protection of Historic Structures*, National Fire Protection Association, Quincy, MA, 2007.

(53) Performance-based Building Design Concepts, International Code Council, Washington DC, 2004.

(54) *Extreme Event Mitigation In Buildings — Analysis and Design*, Meacham, National Fire Protection Association, Quincy MA, 2006.

(55) Geiman, Gottuk and Milke "Evaluation of Smoke Detector Response Estimation Methods: Optical Density, Temperature Rise and Velocity at Alarm" by *Journal of Fire Protection Engineering*, 2006.

(56) Su et al. "Kemano Fire Studies — Part 1: Response of Residential Smoke Alarms," Research Report 108, NRCC, April 2003.

(57) Davis, W, The Zone Model Jet, "A Model for the Prediction of Detector Activation and Gas Temperature in the Presence of a Smoke Layer," NISTIR 6324, NIST, May 1999.

H.2 Informational References

The documents or portions thereof listed in this annex are referenced within the informational sections of this Code and are not part of the requirements of this document unless also listed in Chapter 2 for other reasons.

H.2.1 ANSI/UL 2074, *Gas and Vapor Detectors and Sensors*, 2004.

H.3 References for Extracts in Informational Sections

NFPA 70®, *National Electrical Code*®, 2008 edition.

NFPA 92B, *Standard for Smoke Management Systems in Malls, Atria, and Large Spaces*, 2009 edition.

NFPA 92B, *Standard for Smoke Management Systems in Malls, Atria, and Large Spaces*, 1995 edition.

NFPA *101*®, *Life Safety Code*®, 2009 edition.

Cross-Reference Table

I.1

This cross-reference table has been compiled to assist users familiar with the 2007 edition of the *National Fire Alarm Code®* to locate material in the 2010 edition. It is provided for information only and should not be relied upon as the only means of determining the disposition of requirements.

2007	2010	2007	2010	2007	2010	2007	2010
1.1	1.1	1.7	1.7	3.3.6	3.3.9	3.3.24.1	3.3.33.1
1.1.1	1.1.1	2.1	2.1	3.3.7	3.3.10	3.3.24.2	3.3.33.2
1.1.2	1.1.2	2.2	2.2	—	3.3.11 (new)	3.3.24.3	3.3.33.3
1.2	1.2	2.3	2.3	3.3.8	3.3.12	3.3.24.4	3.3.33.4
1.2.1	1.2.1	2.3.1	2.3.1	3.3.9	3.3.13	—	3.3.34 (new)
1.2.2	1.2.2	2.3.2	2.3.2	3.3.10	3.3.14	3.3.25	3.3.35
1.2.3	1.2.3	2.3.3	2.3.3	—	3.3.15 (new)	3.3.26	3.3.36
1.2.4	1.2.4	—	2.3.4 (new)	3.3.11	3.3.16	3.3.27	3.3.37
1.3	1.3	2.3.4	2.3.5	3.3.12	3.3.17	3.3.28	3.3.39
1.3.1	1.3.1	2.4	2.4	3.3.13	3.3.18	3.3.29	(deleted)
–	1.3.2 (new)	3.1	3.1	3.3.14	3.3.19	3.3.30	3.3.40
1.3.2	1.3.3	3.2	3.2	3.3.15	3.3.20	3.3.30.1	3.3.40.1
1.3.3	1.3.4	3.2.1	3.2.1	—	3.3.22 (new)	3.3.30.2	3.3.40.2
1.4	1.4	3.2.2	3.2.2	3.3.16	3.3.24	3.3.30.3	3.3.40.3
1.4.1	1.4.1	3.2.3	3.2.3	3.3.17	3.3.23	3.3.30.4	3.3.40.4
1.4.2	1.4.2	3.2.4	3.2.4	3.3.18	3.3.25	3.3.31	3.3.127.1
1.5	1.5	3.2.5	3.2.5	3.3.19	3.3.26	3.3.32	3.3.42
1.5.1	1.5.1	3.2.6	3.2.6	—	3.3.28 (new)	3.3.33	3.3.43
1.5.2	1.5.2	3.2.7	3.2.7	3.3.20	3.3.29	3.3.34	3.3.44
1.5.3	1.5.3	3.3	3.3	3.3.21	3.3.30	—	3.3.45 (new)
1.6	1.6	3.3.1	3.3.1	3.3.22	3.3.31	3.3.35	3.3.46
1.6.1	1.6.1	—	3.3.2 (new)	3.3.22.1	3.3.31.1	3.3.36	3.3.47
1.6.1	1.6.2	3.3.2	3.3.3	3.3.22.2	3.3.31.2	3.3.37	(deleted)
1.6.2	1.6.3	3.3.3	3.3.4	3.3.22.3	3.3.31.3	—	3.3.48 (new)
1.6.3	1.6.4	3.3.4	3.3.5	3.3.22.4	3.3.31.4	—	3.3.49 (new)
1.6.4	1.6.5	3.3.5	3.3.7	3.3.23	3.3.32	—	3.3.51 (new)
1.6.5	1.6.6	3.3.5.1	(deleted)	3.3.24	3.3.33	3.3.38	3.3.52

2007	2010	2007	2010	2007	2010	2007	2010
3.3.39	3.3.53	—	3.3.72 (new)	3.3.67.3	3.3.95.2	3.3.88	3.3.119
—	3.3.53.1 (new)	3.3.53	3.3.73	3.3.67.4	3.3.95.3	—	3.3.120 (new)
—	3.3.53.2 (new)	3.3.54	3.3.74	3.3.67.5	3.3.95.4	—	3.3.121 (new)
3.3.39.1	3.3.53.4	3.3.54.1	3.3.74.1	3.3.67.5.1	3.3.95.4.1	3.3.89	3.3.122
3.3.40	3.3.54	3.3.54.2	3.3.74.2	3.3.67.5.2	3.3.95.4.2	3.3.89.1	3.3.122.1
3.3.41	3.3.57	3.3.55	3.3.75	3.3.67.5.3	3.3.95.4.3	3.3.89.2	3.3.122.2
3.3.42	3.3.58	3.3.56	3.3.77	3.3.67.6	3.3.199	3.3.89.3	3.3.122.3
3.3.43	3.3.59	—	3.3.78 (new)	3.3.67.6.1	3.3.199.2	3.3.89.4	3.3.122.4
3.3.43.1	3.3.59.1	—	3.3.79 (new)	3.3.67.6.2	3.3.199.3	3.3.89.5	3.3.122.5
3.3.43.2	3.3.59.2	—	3.3.79.1 (new)	3.3.67.7	3.3.267	3.3.90	3.3.123
3.3.43.3	3.3.59.3	—	3.3.79.1.1 (new)	3.3.67.7.1	3.3.267.1	—	3.3.124 (new)
3.3.43.4	3.3.59.4	3.3.57	3.3.79.1.2	3.3.67.7.2	3.3.267.2	—	3.3.125 (new)
3.3.43.5	3.3.59.5	—	3.3.79.1.3 (new)	3.3.67.7.3	3.3.267.3	—	3.3.126 (new)
3.3.43.6	3.3.59.6	—	3.3.79.1.4 (new)	3.3.68	3.3.96	3.3.91	3.3.128
3.3.43.7	3.3.59.7	—	3.3.79.2 (new)	3.3.69	3.3.97	3.3.92	3.3.129
3.3.43.8	3.3.59.8	—	3.3.80 (new)	3.3.70	(deleted)	3.3.93	3.3.130
3.3.43.9	3.3.59.9	—	3.3.81 (new)	3.3.71	3.3.82	3.3.94	3.3.131
3.3.43.10	3.3.59.10	—	3.3.84 (new)	3.3.72	3.3.83	3.3.95	3.3.133
3.3.43.11	3.3.59.11	3.3.58	3.3.85	3.3.73	3.3.99	3.3.96	3.3.134
3.3.43.12	3.3.59.12	3.3.59	3.3.86	3.3.74	3.3.100	—	3.3.136 (new)
3.3.43.13	3.3.59.13	3.3.60	3.3.87	3.3.75	3.3.102	3.3.97	3.3.137
3.3.43.14	3.3.59.14	3.3.61	(deleted)	3.3.76	3.3.103	3.3.98	3.3.138
3.3.43.15	3.3.59.15	3.3.62	3.3.90	3.3.77	3.3.104	3.3.99	3.3.139
3.3.43.16	3.3.59.16	3.3.63	3.3.8	3.3.78	3.3.105	3.3.100	3.3.140
3.3.43.17	3.3.59.17	3.3.63.1	3.3.8.1	—	3.3.106 (new)	—	3.3.141 (new)
3.3.43.18	3.3.59.18	3.3.63.2	3.3.8.2	—	3.3.106.1 (new)	3.3.101	3.3.142
3.3.43.19	3.3.59.19	3.3.63.3	3.3.8.3	—	3.3.106.2 (new)	—	3.3.143 (new)
3.3.43.20	3.3.59.20	3.3.63.4	3.3.8.4	—	3.3.106.3 (new)	3.3.102	3.3.144
3.3.43.21	3.3.59.21	3.3.63.5	3.3.8.5	—	3.3.106.4 (new)	3.3.103	3.3.145
3.3.44	3.3.60	3.3.64	3.3.92	—	3.3.106.5 (new)	3.3.104	3.3.146
3.3.45	3.3.61	3.3.64.1	3.3.92.1	3.3.79	3.3.107	3.3.105	3.3.149
3.3.46	3.3.62	3.3.64.2	3.3.92.2	3.3.80	3.3.109	3.3.106	3.3.150
3.3.47	3.3.63	3.3.64.2.1	3.3.92.2.1	3.3.81	3.3.110	3.3.107	3.3.151
3.3.48	3.3.64	3.3.64.2.2	3.3.92.2.2	3.3.82	3.3.111	3.3.108	3.3.153
3.3.49	3.3.65	3.3.65	3.3.93	3.3.83	3.3.112	3.3.109	3.3.154
3.3.50	3.3.66	3.3.66	3.3.94	—	3.3.113 (new)	—	3.3.155 (new)
—	3.3.67 (new)	3.3.67	3.3.95	3.3.84	3.3.114	—	3.3.156 (new)
—	3.3.68 (new)	3.3.67.1	3.3.199.1	3.3.85	3.3.115	3.3.110	3.3.157
—	3.3.69 (new)	3.3.67.1.1	3.3.199.1.1	—	3.3.116 (new)	3.3.111	3.3.158
3.3.51	3.3.70	3.3.67.1.2	3.3.199.1.2	3.3.86	3.3.117	3.3.112	3.3.159
3.3.52	3.3.71	3.3.67.2	3.3.95.1	3.3.87	3.3.118	3.3.113	3.3.160

2007	2010	2007	2010	2007	2010	2007	2010
3.3.113.1	3.3.160.1	3.3.138.1	3.3.191.1	3.3.170	3.3.235	3.3.194	3.3.266
3.3.113.1.1	3.3.160.1.1	3.3.138.2	3.3.191.2	—	3.3.236 (new)	3.3.194.1	3.3.266.1
3.3.113.1.2	3.3.160.1.2	3.3.139	3.3.192	3.3.171	3.3.237	3.3.194.2	3.3.266.2
3.3.113.2	3.3.160.2	3.3.140	3.3.193	—	3.3.238 (new)	3.3.194.3	3.3.266.3
3.3.113.3	3.3.160.3	3.3.141	3.3.194	3.3.172	3.3.240	3.3.195	3.3.267
3.3.113.3.1	3.3.160.3.1	3.3.142	3.3.195	3.3.172.1	3.3.240.1	3.3.195.1	3.3.267.1
3.3.114	3.3.161	3.3.143	3.3.196	3.3.172.2	3.3.240.2	3.3.195.2	3.3.267.2
3.3.115	3.3.162	3.3.144	3.3.197	3.3.172.3	3.3.240.3	3.3.195.3	3.3.267.3
3.3.116	(deleted)	—	3.3.198 (new)	3.3.172.4	3.3.240.4	—	3.3.268 (new)
3.3.117	3.3.163	3.3.145	3.3.199	3.3.172.5	3.3.240.5	—	3.3.268.1 (new)
3.3.117.1	3.3.163.1	3.3.146	(deleted)	3.3.172.6	3.3.240.6	—	3.3.268.2 (new)
3.3.118	3.3.164	3.3.147	3.3.200	3.3.172.7	3.3.240.7	—	3.3.268.3 (new)
—	3.3.166	—	3.3.201 (new)	3.3.173	3.3.242	3.3.196	3.3.269
3.3.119	3.3.167	—	3.3.202 (new)	3.3.174	3.3.127.1.1	3.3.197	3.3.270
3.3.120	3.3.168	—	3.3.203 (new)	3.3.175	3.3.241	3.3.198	3.3.271
3.3.121	3.3.169	—	3.3.206 (new)	3.3.176	3.3.245	3.3.199	3.3.272
3.3.121.1	3.3.169.1	3.3.148	3.3.208	3.3.177	3.3.246	3.3.200	3.3.273
3.3.121.2	3.3.169.2	3.3.149	3.3.209	3.3.178	3.3.247	3.3.200.1	3.3.273.1
3.3.122	(deleted)	3.3.150	3.3.210	3.3.179	3.3.248	—	3.3.274 (new)
3.3.123	3.3.171	3.3.151	3.3.211	3.3.180	3.3.251	3.3.201	3.3.275
3.3.124	3.3.172	3.3.152	3.3.212	3.3.181	3.3.252	3.3.202	3.3.276
3.3.125	3.3.173	3.3.153	3.3.213	3.3.181.1	3.3.252.1	—	3.3.277 (new)
3.3.126	3.3.174	3.3.154	3.3.214	3.3.181.2	3.3.252.2	—	3.3.277.1 (new)
—	3.3.175 (new)	3.3.155	3.3.215	3.3.181.3	3.3.252.3	—	3.3.277.2 (new)
3.3.127	3.3.176	3.3.156	3.3.216	3.3.181.4	3.3.252.4	—	3.3.278 (new)
—	3.3.177 (new)	—	3.3.217 (new)	3.3.181.5	3.3.252.5	3.3.203	3.3.279
—	3.3.177.1 (new)	3.3.157	3.3.220	3.3.182	3.3.253	3.3.204	3.3.280
—	3.3.177.2 (new)	3.3.158	3.3.221	3.3.183	3.3.254	3.3.205	3.3.281
—	3.3.177.3 (new)	3.3.159	3.3.222	—	3.3.255 (new)	3.3.206	3.3.282
3.3.128	3.3.178	3.3.160	3.3.223	—	3.3.255.1 (new)	3.3.207	3.3.283
3.3.129	3.3.179	3.3.161	3.3.224	3.3.184	3.3.256	3.3.208	3.3.284
3.3.130	3.3.180	3.3.162	3.3.225	3.3.185	3.3.257	—	3.3.285 (new)
3.3.131	3.3.182	3.3.163	3.3.226	3.3.186	3.3.258	—	3.3.286 (new)
3.3.132	3.3.183	3.3.164	3.3.227	3.3.187	3.3.259	—	3.3.287 (new)
3.3.133	3.3.184	3.3.165	3.3.228	3.3.188	3.3.260	—	3.3.288 (new)
3.3.134	3.3.185	—	3.3.229 (new)	3.3.189	3.3.261	3.3.209	3.3.289
3.3.135	3.3.186	3.3.166	3.3.230	—	3.3.262 (new)	3.3.210	3.3.291
3.3.136	3.3.187	3.3.167	3.3.231	3.3.190	(deleted)	3.3.211	(deleted)
3.3.137	3.3.188	3.3.168	3.3.232	3.3.191	3.3.263	—	3.3.292 (new)
—	3.3.189 (new)	3.3.169	3.3.233	3.3.192	3.3.264	3.3.212	3.3.293
3.3.138	3.3.191	—	3.3.234 (new)	3.3.193	3.3.265	3.3.213	3.3.294

2007	2010	2007	2010	2007	2010	2007	2010
—	3.3.295	—	10.5.4.3 (new)	4.4.1.8.3.1	10.5.9.3.1	4.4.3.2.4	10.11.4-10.11.4.2
3.3.214	3.3.296	4.4.1.4	10.5.5	4.4.1.8.3.2	10.5.9.3.2		
3.3.215	3.3.297	4.4.1.4.1	10.5.5.1	4.4.1.8.3.3	10.5.9.3.3	4.4.3.3	10.7.1
3.3.216	3.3.298	—	10.5.5.2 (new)	4.4.1.8.3.4	10.5.9.3.4	4.4.3.4	10.13
3.3.217	3.3.299	4.4.1.4.2	10.5.5.3	4.4.1.8.3.5	10.5.9.3.5	4.4.3.4.1	10.13.1
3.3.218	3.3.300	4.4.1.4.2.1	10.5.5.3	4.4.1.8.4	10.5.9.4	4.4.3.4.2	10.13.2
3.3.218.1	3.3.300.1	4.4.1.4.2.2	10.5.5.2.2-10.5.5.2.4	4.4.1.8.4.1	10.5.9.4.1	4.4.3.5	10.12
3.3.218.2	3.3.300.2			4.4.1.8.4.2	10.5.9.4.2	4.4.3.5.1	10.12.1, 10.12.2
4.1	10.1	4.4.1.4.2.3	10.5.5.2.1	4.4.1.8.5	10.5.9.5	4.4.3.5.2	10.7.5
4.1.1	10.1.1	4.4.1.4.3	10.5.5.4	4.4.1.8.6	10.5.9.6-10.5.9.6.2	4.4.3.5.3	10.12.3
4.1.2	10.1.2	4.4.1.4.4	(deleted)			4.4.3.5.4	10.12.4
4.2	10.2	4.4.1.5	10.5.6	4.4.1.9	10.5.10	4.4.3.5.5	10.12.5
4.3	10.3	4.4.1.5.1	10.5.6.1, 10.5.6.1.1	4.4.1.9.1	10.5.10.1	4.4.3.5.6	10.12.6
4.3.1	10.3.1, 10.3.2			4.4.1.9.2	10.5.10.2, 10.5.10.2.1, 10.5.10.2.2	4.4.3.5.7	10.12.7
—	10.4 (new)	—	10.5.6.1.2 (new)			4.4.3.5.8	10.12.8
4.3.2	10.4.1	4.4.1.5.2	10.5.6.2			4.4.3.5.8.1	10.12.8.1
4.3.2.1	10.4.1.1	4.4.1.5.2.1	10.5.6.2.1	4.4.1.9.3	10.5.10.3	4.4.3.5.8.2	10.12.8.2
4.3.2.2	10.4.1.2-10.4.1.4	4.4.1.5.2.2	10.5.6.2.2	4.4.1.9.3.1	10.5.10.3.1	4.4.3.5.8.3	10.12.8.3
		4.4.1.5.3	10.5.6.3	4.4.1.9.3.2	10.5.10.3.2	4.4.3.5.8.4	10.12.8.4
4.3.3	10.4.2-10.4.2.3	4.4.1.5.3.1	10.5.6.3.1	4.4.1.9.4	10.5.10.4	4.4.3.6	10.7
		4.4.1.5.3.2	10.5.6.3.2	4.4.1.9.5	10.5.10.5	4.4.3.6.1	10.7.2
—	10.4.3 (new from Ch 10)	4.4.1.5.4	10.5.6.4-10.5.6.4.3	4.4.1.9.6	10.5.10.6	4.4.3.6.2	10.7.3-10.7.6
—	10.4.3.1 (new from Ch 10)			4.4.1.9.6.1	10.5.10.6.1	—	10.8 (new)
		4.4.1.6	10.5.7	4.4.1.9.6.2	10.5.10.6.2	—	10.9 (new)
—	10.4.3.2 (new from Ch 10)	4.4.1.6.1	10.5.7.1	4.4.1.9.6.3	10.5.10.6.3	—	10.9.1 (new)
		4.4.1.6.2	10.5.7.2	4.4.1.9.7	10.5.10.7	—	10.9.2 (new)
—	10.4.4 (new)	4.4.1.6.3	10.5.7.3	—	10.6 (new)	4.4.3.7	10.10
—	10.4.4.1 (new)	4.4.1.6.3.1	10.5.7.3.1	—	10.6.1 (new)	4.4.3.7.1	10.10.1
—	10.4.4.1.1 (new)	4.4.1.6.3.2	10.5.7.3.2	—	10.6.2 (new)	4.4.3.7.2	10.10.2
—	10.4.4.1.2 (new)	4.4.1.7	10.5.8	—	10.6.3 (new)	4.4.3.7.3	10.10.3
—	10.4.4.1.3 (new)	4.4.1.7.1	10.5.8.1	—	10.6.4 (new)	4.4.3.7.4	10.10.4
4.4	(deleted)	4.4.1.7.2	10.5.8.2-10.5.8.4	—	10.6.5 (new)	4.4.3.7.5	10.10.5
4.4.1	10.5			—	10.6.6 (new)	4.4.3.7.6	10.10.6
4.4.1.1	10.5.1	4.4.1.8	10.5.9	—	10.6.7 (new)	—	10.10.7 (new)
4.4.1.2	10.5.2	4.4.1.8.1	10.5.9.1, 10.5.9.1.1	4.4.2	10.3.3	4.4.3.8	10.11.5, 10.11.5.1
4.4.1.3	10.5.3			4.4.3	(deleted)		
4.4.1.3.1	10.5.3.1-10.5.3.3	—	10.5.9.1.2 (new)	4.4.3.1	10.9.3, 10.9.4	4.4.3.8.1	10.11.5.2
		4.4.1.8.2	10.5.9.2	4.4.3.2	10.11	4.4.3.8.2	10.11.5.3
4.4.1.3.2	10.5.3.4	4.4.1.8.2.1	10.5.9.2.1-10.5.9.2.3	4.4.3.2.1	10.11.1-10.11.1.2	4.4.3.8.3	10.11.5.4, 10.11.5.5
—	10.5.4 (new)						
—	10.5.4.1 (new)	4.4.1.8.2.2	10.5.9.2.4	4.4.3.2.2	10.11.2	4.4.4	10.14
—	10.5.4.2 (new)	4.4.1.8.2.3	10.5.9.2.5	4.4.3.2.3	10.11.3	4.4.4.1	10.14.1
		4.4.1.8.3	10.5.9.3				

2007	2010	2007	2010	2007	2010	2007	2010
4.4.4.2	10.14.2	4.4.7.1.16	10.17.1.17	—	10.18.2.1.2.8 (new)	5.5.2.1	17.5.3.1
4.4.4.2.1	10.14.2.1	—	10.17.1.17.1 (new)			5.5.2.1.1	17.5.3.1.1
4.4.4.2.2	10.14.2.2			4.5.2.2	10.18.2.2-10.18.2.2.2	5.5.2.1.2	17.5.3.1.2
4.4.4.2.3	10.14.2.3	—	10.17.1.17.2 (new)			5.5.2.1.3	17.5.3.1.3
4.4.4.2.4	10.14.2.4	4.4.7.1.17	10.17.1.18	4.5.2.3	10.18.2.3	5.5.2.1.4	17.5.3.1.4
4.4.4.3	12.2.4.2			4.5.2.4	10.18.2.4	5.5.2.1.5	17.5.3.1.5
4.4.4.4	12.2.4.3	—	10.17.1.19 (new)	4.5.2.4.1	10.18.2.4.1, 10.18.2.4.2	5.5.2.2	17.5.3.2
4.4.4.5	12.2.4.4	4.4.7.2	10.17.2			5.5.2.3	17.5.3.3
4.4.4.6	10.14.3	4.4.7.2.1	10.17.2.1	4.5.2.4.2	10.18.2.4.3	5.5.2.3.1	17.5.3.3.1
4.4.4.6.1	10.14.3.1	4.4.7.2.1.1	10.17.2.1.1	4.5.3	10.18.3	5.5.2.3.2	17.5.3.3.2
4.4.4.6.2	10.14.3.2	4.4.7.2.1.2	10.17.2.1.2	4.5.3.1	10.18.3.1	5.6	17.6
4.4.5	10.15	4.4.7.2.1.3	10.17.2.1.3	4.5.3.2	10.18.3.2	5.6.1	17.6.1
4.4.6	10.16	4.4.7.2.2	10.17.2.2-10.17.2.2.3	4.5.3.3	10.18.3.3	5.6.1.1	17.6.1.1
4.4.6.2	10.16.2-10.16.2.1.2			4.6	10.19	5.6.1.2	17.6.1.2
		4.4.7.3	10.17.3	4.6.1	10.19.1	5.6.1.3	17.6.1.3
4.4.6.3	10.16.3-10.16.3.2	4.4.7.3.1	10.17.3.1-10.17.3.1.2	4.6.2	10.19.2	5.6.1.4	17.6.1.4
				4.6.3	10.19.3	5.6.2	17.6.2
4.4.6.4	10.16.4-10.16.4.2	4.4.7.3.1.1	10.17.3.1.3	4.6.4	10.19.4	5.6.2.1	17.6.2.2.1
4.4.6.5	10.16.5	4.4.7.3.1.2	10.17.3.1.4	4.7	(deleted)	5.6.2.1.1	17.6.2.1, 17.6.2.1.1
4.4.6.6	10.16.6	4.4.7.3.1.3	10.17.3.1.5	5.1	17.1		
4.4.6.6.1	10.16.6.1, 10.16.6.2	4.4.7.3.1.4	10.17.3.1.6	5.1.1	17.1.1	5.6.2.1.2	17.6.2.2.1.2
		4.4.7.3.2	10.17.3.2	5.1.2	17.1.2	5.6.2.2	17.6.3.6
4.4.6.6.2	10.16.6.3	4.4.7.3.3	10.17.3.3	5.1.3	17.1.3	—	17.6.2.2.2 (new)
4.4.7	10.17	4.4.7.3.4	10.17.3.4	5.1.4	17.1.4	5.6.2.3	17.6.2.2.2.1, 17.6.2.2.2.3
4.4.7.1	10.17.1-10.17.1.2	4.5	10.18	5.1.5	17.1.5		
		4.5.1	10.18.1	5.1.6	17.1.6	—	17.6.2.2.2.2 (new)
4.4.7.1.1	(deleted)	4.5.1.1	10.18.1.1, 10.18.1.2	5.2	17.2		
4.4.7.1.2	10.17.1.3			5.3	17.3	5.6.3	17.6.3.1.3
4.4.7.1.3	10.17.1.4	4.5.1.2	10.18.1.3	5.3.1	17.3.1	5.6.3.1	17.6.3.1.3.1
4.4.7.1.4	10.17.1.5	4.5.1.3	10.18.1.4	5.3.2	17.3.2	5.6.3.1.1	17.6.3.2.2
4.4.7.1.5	10.17.1.6	4.5.1.4	10.18.1.5	5.3.3	17.3.3	5.6.3.1.2	17.6.3.3.2
4.4.7.1.6	10.17.1.7	4.5.2	10.18.2	5.4	17.4	5.6.3.2	17.6.3.1.3.2
4.4.7.1.7	10.17.1.8	4.5.2.1	10.18.2.1-10.18.2.1.2	5.4.1	17.4.1	5.6.3.2.1	17.6.3.2.2
4.4.7.1.8	10.17.1.9			5.4.2	17.4.2	5.6.3.2.2	17.6.3.3.2
4.4.7.1.9	10.17.1.10	4.5.2.1.1 10.18.2.1.2.2	10.18.2.1.2.1,	5.4.3	17.4.3	5.6.3.2.3	17.6.3.7
4.4.7.1.10	10.17.1.11			5.4.4	17.4.4	5.6.4	17.6.2.3
4.4.7.1.11	10.17.1.12	4.5.2.1.2 10.18.2.1.2.4	10.18.2.1.2.3,	5.4.5	17.4.5	5.6.5	17.6.3
4.4.7.1.12	10.17.1.13			5.4.6	17.4.6	5.6.5.1	17.6.3.1
4.4.7.1.13	10.17.1.14	4.5.2.1.3 10.18.2.1.2.6	10.18.2.1.2.5,	5.4.7	17.4.7	5.6.5.1.1	17.6.3.1.1
4.4.7.1.14	10.17.1.15			5.5	17.5	5.6.5.1.2	17.6.3.1.2
		—	10.18.2.1.2.7 (new)	5.5.1	17.5.1	5.6.5.2	17.6.3.2
4.4.7.1.15	10.17.1.16			5.5.2	17.5.3	5.6.5.3	17.6.3.3

2007	2010	2007	2010	2007	2010	2007	2010
—	17.6.3.3.1 (new)	5.7.3.1	17.7.3.1	5.7.3.7	17.7.3.5	5.8.3.2.4	17.8.3.2.4
5.6.5.3.1	17.6.3.3.1.1	5.7.3.1.1	17.7.3.1.1	5.7.3.7.1	17.7.3.5.1	5.8.3.2.5	17.8.3.2.5
5.6.5.3.2	17.6.3.3.1.2	5.7.3.1.2	17.7.3.1.2	5.7.3.7.2	17.7.3.5.2	5.8.3.2.6	17.8.3.2.6
5.6.5.3.3	17.6.3.3.1.3	5.7.3.1.3	17.7.3.1.3	5.7.3.8	17.5.2	5.8.3.3	17.8.3.3
5.6.5.4	17.6.3.4	—	17.7.3.1.4 (new)	5.7.4	17.7.4	5.8.3.3.1	17.8.3.3.1
—	17.6.3.4.1 (new)	5.7.3.2	17.7.3.2	5.7.4.1	17.7.4.1	5.8.3.3.2	17.8.3.3.2
—	17.6.3.4.2 (new)	5.7.3.2.1	17.7.3.2.1	5.7.4.2	17.7.4.2	5.8.3.3.3	17.8.3.3.3
5.6.5.4.1	17.6.3.4.2.1, 17.6.3.4.2.2, 17.6.3.4.1.3	5.7.3.2.2	17.7.3.2.2	5.7.4.2.1	17.7.4.2.1	5.8.3.3.4	17.8.3.3.4
		5.7.3.2.3	17.7.3.2.3	5.7.4.2.2	17.7.4.2.2	5.8.3.3.5	17.8.3.3.5
5.6.5.4.2	17.6.3.4.2.1, 17.6.3.4.2.2, 17.6.3.4.1.3	5.7.3.2.3.1	17.7.3.2.3.1	5.7.5	17.7.6	5.8.3.3.6	17.8.3.3.6
		5.7.3.2.3.2	17.7.3.2.3.2	5.7.5.1	17.7.6.1	5.8.4	17.8.4
		5.7.3.2.3.3	17.7.3.2.3.3	5.7.5.1.1	17.7.6.1.1	5.8.4.1	17.8.4.1
5.6.5.4.3	17.6.3.4.1.1, 17.6.3.4.1.2	5.7.3.2.3.4	17.7.3.2.3.4	5.7.5.1.2	17.7.6.1.2	5.8.4.2	17.8.4.2
		5.7.3.2.3.5	17.7.3.2.3.5	5.7.5.2	17.7.6.2	5.8.4.3	17.8.4.3
5.6.5.5	17.6.3.5	5.7.3.2.4	17.7.3.2.4	5.7.5.3	17.7.6.3	5.8.4.4	17.8.4.4
5.6.5.5.1	17.6.3.5.1	5.7.3.2.4.1	17.7.3.2.4.1	5.7.5.3.1	17.7.6.3.1	5.8.5	17.8.5
5.6.5.5.2	17.6.3.5.2	5.7.3.2.4.2	17.7.3.2.4.2	5.7.5.3.2	17.7.6.3.2	5.8.5.1	17.8.5.1
5.6.5.6	17.6.3.8	5.7.3.2.4.3	17.7.3.2.4.3	5.7.5.3.3	17.7.6.3.3-17.7.6.3.3.2	5.8.5.2	17.8.5.2
5.7	17.7	5.7.3.2.4.4	17.7.3.2.4.4			5.8.5.3	17.8.5.3
5.7.1	17.7.1	—	17.7.3.2.4.5 (new)	5.7.5.3.4	17.7.6.3.4	5.8.5.4	17.8.5.4
5.7.1.1	17.7.1.1			5.7.6	17.7.7	5.9	17.9
5.7.1.2	17.7.1.2	5.7.3.2.4.5	17.7.3.2.4.6	5.7.6.1	17.7.7.1	5.9.1	17.9.1
5.7.1.3	17.7.1.3	5.7.3.3	17.7.3.6	5.7.6.2	17.7.7.2	5.9.2	17.9.2
5.7.1.4	17.7.1.4	5.7.3.3.1	17.7.3.6.1	5.7.6.2.1	17.7.7.2.1	5.9.2.1	17.9.2.1
5.7.1.5	17.7.1.5	5.7.3.3.2	17.7.3.6.2	5.7.6.2.2	17.7.7.2.2	5.9.2.2	17.9.2.2
5.7.1.6	17.7.1.6	5.7.3.3.3	17.7.3.6.3	5.7.6.3	17.7.7.3	5.9.3	17.9.3
5.7.1.7	17.7.1.7	5.7.3.3.4	17.7.3.6.4	5.7.6.4	17.7.7.4	5.9.3.1	17.9.3.1
5.7.1.8	17.7.1.8	5.7.3.3.5	17.7.3.6.5	5.8	17.8	5.9.3.2	17.9.3.2
5.7.1.9	17.7.1.9	5.7.3.3.6	17.7.3.6.6	5.8.1	17.8.1	5.9.4	17.9.4
5.7.1.10	17.7.1.10	5.7.3.3.7	17.7.3.6.7	5.8.1.1	17.8.1.1	5.9.4.1	17.9.4.1
5.7.1.11	17.7.1.11	5.7.3.3.8	17.7.3.6.8	5.8.1.2	17.8.1.2	5.9.4.2	17.9.4.2
—	17.7.1.11.1 (new)	5.7.3.4	17.7.3.7	5.8.2	17.8.2	—	17.10 (new)
		5.7.3.4.1	17.7.3.7.1	5.8.2.1	17.8.2.1	—	17.10.1 (new)
—	17.7.1.11.2 (new)	5.7.3.4.2	17.7.3.7.2	5.8.2.2	17.8.2.2	—	17.10.2 (new)
		5.7.3.4.3	17.7.3.7.3	5.8.3	17.8.3	—	17.10.2.1 (new)
—	17.7.1.11.3	5.7.3.4.4	17.7.3.7.4	5.8.3.1	17.8.3.1	—	17.10.2.2 (new)
5.7.2	17.7.2	5.7.3.4.5	17.7.3.7.5	5.8.3.1.1	17.8.3.1.1	—	17.10.2.3 (new)
5.7.2.1	17.7.2.1	5.7.3.4.6	17.7.3.7.6	5.8.3.1.2	17.8.3.1.2	—	17.10.2.4 (new)
5.7.2.2	17.7.2.2	5.7.3.4.7	17.7.3.7.7	5.8.3.2	17.8.3.2	5.10	17.11
5.7.2.3	17.7.2.3	5.7.3.4.8	17.7.3.7.8	5.8.3.2.1	17.8.3.2.1	5.10.1	17.11.1, 17.11.1.1
5.7.2.4	17.7.2.4	5.7.3.5	17.7.3.3	5.8.3.2.2	17.8.3.2.2		
5.7.3	17.7.3	5.7.3.6	17.7.3.4	5.8.3.2.3	17.8.3.2.3	5.10.2	17.11.2

2007	2010	2007	2010	2007	2010	2007	2010
5.10.3	17.11.3	5.15.5	17.16.5	5.16.6.5.3.1	17.7.5.6.5.3(A)	6.4.2.2.2	23.4.2.2
5.10.4	17.11.4	5.16	17.7.5	5.16.6.5.3.2	17.7.5.6.5.3(B)	6.4.2.2.3	23.4.2.3
5.10.5	17.11.5	5.16.1	17.7.5.1	5.16.6.5.3.3	17.7.5.6.5.3(C)	6.4.3	23.4.3
5.10.5.1	17.11.5.1	5.16.2	17.7.5.2	5.16.6.5.4	17.7.5.6.5.4	6.4.3.1	23.4.3.1
5.10.5.2	17.11.5.2, 17.11.5.2.1	5.16.2.1	17.7.5.2.1	5.16.6.6	17.7.5.6.6	6.4.3.2	23.4.3.2
		6.16.2.2	17.7.5.2.2	5.16.6.6.1	17.7.5.6.6.1	6.4.3.3	23.4.3.3
5.10.5.3	17.11.5.3	5.16.3	17.7.5.3	5.16.6.6.2	17.7.5.6.6.2	6.5	23.5, 23.5.1
5.11	17.12	5.16.3.1	17.7.5.3.1	5.17	(deleted)	—	23.5.2 (new)
5.11.1	17.12.1	5.16.3.2	17.7.5.3.2	6.1	23.1	—	23.5.3 (new)
5.11.2	17.12.2	5.16.3.3	17.7.5.3.3	6.1.1	23.1.1	6.6	23.6
5.11.3	17.12.3	5.16.3.4	17.7.5.3.4	6.1.2	23.1.2	6.6.1	23.6.1
5.12	17.13	5.16.4	17.7.5.4	6.1.3	23.1.3	—	23.6.2 (new)
5.13	17.14	5.16.4.1	17.7.5.4.1	6.1.4	23.1.4	—	23.6.3 (new)
5.13.1	17.14.1	5.16.4.2	17.7.5.4.2	—	23.1.5 (new)	—	23.6.4 (new)
—	17.14.1.1 (new)	5.16.4.2.1	17.7.5.4.2.1	6.2	23.2	6.6.2	23.6.5
—	17.14.1.2 (new)	5.16.4.2.2	17.7.5.4.2.2	6.2.1	23.2.1	6.7	23.7, 23.7.1
—	17.14.1.3 (new)	5.16.4.2.2.1	17.7.5.4.2.2(A)	6.2.2	23.2.2	—	23.7.2 (new)
5.13.2	17.14.2	5.16.4.2.2.2	17.7.5.4.2.2(B)	6.2.2.1	23.2.2.1	—	23.7.3 (new)
5.13.3	17.14.3	5.16.5	17.7.5.5	—	23.2.2.1.1 (new)	6.8	23.8
5.13.4	17.14.4	5.16.5.1	17.7.5.5.1	—	23.2.2.1.2 (new)	6.8.1	23.8.1
5.13.5	17.14.5	5.16.5.2	17.7.5.5.2	6.2.2.2	23.2.2.2	6.8.1.1	23.8.1.1
5.13.6	17.14.6	5.16.5.3	17.7.5.5.3	6.2.2.3	23.2.2.3	6.8.1.2	23.8.1.2- 23.8.1.2.2
5.13.7	17.14.7	5.16.5.4	17.7.5.5.4	6.2.3	23.2.3		
5.13.8	17.14.8	5.16.5.5	17.7.5.5.5	6.2.3.1	23.2.3.1	6.8.1.3	23.8.1.3
5.14	17.15	5.16.5.6	17.7.5.5.6	6.2.3.2	23.2.3.2	6.8.1.3.1	23.8.1.3.1
5.15	17.16	5.16.5.7	17.7.5.5.7	6.3	23.3	6.8.1.3.1.1	23.8.1.3.1.1
5.15.1	17.16.1	5.16.5.8	17.4.8	6.3.1	23.3.1	6.8.1.3.1.2	23.8.1.3.1.1
5.15.1.1	17.16.1.1	5.16.5.9	17.4.9	6.3.2	23.3.2	6.8.1.3.2	23.8.1.3.1.1
5.15.1.2	17.16.1.2	5.16.6	17.7.5.6	6.3.3	23.3.3	6.8.1.3.3	23.8.1.3.1.1
5.15.1.3	17.16.1.3	5.16.6.1	17.7.5.6.1	6.3.3.1	23.3.3.1	6.8.1.3.4	23.8.1.3.1.1
5.15.1.4	17.16.1.4	5.16.6.2	17.7.5.6.2	6.3.3.2	23.3.3.2	6.8.2	23.8.2
5.15.2	17.16.2	5.16.6.3	17.7.5.6.3	6.3.3.2.1	23.3.3.2.1	6.8.2.1	23.8.2.1, 23.8.2.2, 23.8.2.3
5.15.2.1	17.16.2.1	5.16.6.4	17.7.5.6.4	6.3.3.2.2	23.3.3.2.2		
5.15.2.2	17.16.2.2- 17.16.2.2.4	5.16.6.5	17.7.5.6.5	6.4	23.4		
		5.16.6.5.1	17.7.5.6.5.1	6.4.1	23.4.1	6.8.2.2	23.8.2.4
5.15.3	17.16.3	5.16.6.5.1.1	17.7.5.6.5.1(A)	6.4.2	23.4.2	6.8.2.3	23.8.2.5
5.15.3.1	17.16.3.1	5.16.6.5.1.2	17.7.5.6.5.1(B)	6.4.2.1	(deleted)	6.8.2.4	23.8.2.6
5.15.3.2	17.16.3.2, 17.16.3.2.1	5.16.6.5.1.3	17.7.5.6.5.1(C)	6.4.2.1.1	(deleted)	6.8.2.4.1	23.8.2.6.1
		5.16.6.5.1.4	17.7.5.6.5.1(D)	6.4.2.1.2	23.4.2.1	6.8.2.4.2	23.8.2.6.2
5.15.3.3	17.16.3.3	5.16.6.5.2	17.7.5.6.5.2	6.4.2.2	(deleted)	6.8.2.5	23.8.2.7
5.15.4	17.16.4- 17.16.4.2	5.16.6.5.3	17.7.5.6.5.3	6.4.2.2.1	(deleted)	6.8.2.6	23.8.2.8
						6.8.2.7	23.8.2.9

2007	2010	2007	2010	2007	2010	2007	2010
6.8.2.8	23.8.2.10	6.8.5.7	23.8.5.7	6.9.2.2	24.4.1.1.2	6.10.1.6	24.5.1.6
6.8.3	23.8.3	6.8.5.7.1	23.8.5.7.1	6.9.3	24.4.1.2	6.10.1.7	24.5.1.7
6.8.3.1	23.8.3.1	6.8.5.7.2	23.8.5.7.2	6.9.3.1	(deleted)	6.10.1.8	24.5.1.8
6.8.3.2	23.8.3.2	6.8.5.8	23.8.5.8	6.9.3.2	24.4.1.2.2	6.10.1.9	24.5.1.9
6.8.3.3	23.8.3.3	6.8.5.8.1	23.8.5.8.1	6.9.4	24.4.1.3	6.10.1.10	24.5.1.10
6.8.3.4	23.8.3.4	6.8.5.8.2	23.8.5.8.2	6.9.5	24.4.1.4	6.10.1.11	24.5.1.11
6.8.3.5	23.8.3.5	6.8.5.9	23.8.5.9	6.9.6	24.4.1.5	6.10.1.12	24.5.1.12
6.8.4	23.8.4	6.8.5.9.1	23.8.5.9.1	6.9.6.1	24.4.1.5.1	6.10.1.13	24.5.1.13
6.8.4.1	23.8.4.1	6.8.5.9.2	23.8.5.9.2	6.9.6.2	24.4.1.5.2	6.10.1.14	24.5.1.14
6.8.4.2	23.8.4.2	6.8.5.10	23.8.5.10	6.9.6.3	24.4.1.5.3	6.10.1.15	24.5.1.15
6.8.4.3	23.8.4.3.2.1	6.8.5.10.1	23.8.5.10.1	6.9.6.4	24.4.1.5.4	6.10.1.16	24.5.1.16
6.8.4.4	23.8.4.3	6.8.5.10.2	23.8.5.10.2	6.9.6.5	24.4.1.5.5	6.10.2	24.5.2
6.8.4.5	24.3.4.2	6.8.5.10.3	23.8.5.10.3	6.9.6.6	24.4.1.5.6	6.10.2.1	(deleted)
6.8.4.6	23.8.4.4	6.8.5.10.4	23.8.5.10.4	6.9.6.7	24.4.1.5.7	6.10.2.2	(deleted)
6.8.4.7	23.8.4.5	6.8.5.10.5	23.8.5.10.5	6.9.7	24.4.1.6	6.11	23.12
6.8.4.8	23.8.4.6	6.8.5.11	23.8.5.11	6.9.8	(deleted)	6.11.1	23.12.1
6.8.4.9	(deleted)	6.8.5.11.1	23.8.5.11.1	6.9.9	(deleted)	6.11.2	23.12.2
6.8.4.10	23.8.4.7	6.8.5.11.2	23.8.5.11.2	6.9.10	24.4.1.8	6.12	23.13
6.8.4.11	23.8.4.8	6.8.6	23.8.6	6.9.10.1	24.4.1.8.1	6.12.1	23.13.1
6.8.5	23.8.5	6.8.6.1	23.8.6.1	6.9.10.2	24.4.1.8.2	6.12.2	23.13.2
6.8.5.1	23.8.5.1	6.8.6.2	23.8.6.2	6.9.10.3	24.4.1.8.3	6.12.3	23.13.3
6.8.5.1.1	23.8.5.1.1	6.8.6.2.1	23.8.6.2.1	6.9.10.4	23.10.1, 24.4.1.8.4	6.12.4	23.13.4
6.8.5.1.2	23.8.5.1.2	6.8.6.2.2	6.8.6.2.2			6.12.5	23.13.5
6.8.5.2	23.8.5.2	6.8.6.2.3	23.8.6.2.3	6.9.10.4.1	23.10.2, 24.4.1.8.4.1, 24.4.1.8.4.2	6.12.5.1	23.13.5.1
6.8.5.2.1	23.8.5.2.1	6.8.6.3	23.8.6.3			6.12.5.2	23.13.5.2
6.8.5.2.2	23.8.5.2.2	6.8.6.3.1	23.8.6.3.1	—	23.10.3 (new)	6.12.6	23.13.6
6.8.5.3	23.8.5.3	6.8.6.3.2	23.8.6.3.2	6.9.10.4.2	12.4, 24.4.1.8.4.3	6.12.7	23.13.7
6.8.5.3.1	23.8.5.3.1	6.8.6.4	23.8.6.4	6.9.10.4.3	12.4, 24.4.1.8.4.4	6.12.8	23.13.8- 23.13.10
6.8.5.3.2	23.8.5.3.2	6.8.6.4.1	23.8.6.4.1	6.9.10.4.4	24.4.1.8.4.5	6.12.9	23.13.11
6.8.5.4	23.8.5.4	6.8.6.4.2	23.8.6.4.2	6.9.11	24.4.1.9	6.13	23.14
6.8.5.4.1	23.8.5.4.1	6.8.6.4.3	23.8.6.4.3	6.9.11.1	24.4.1.9.1	6.13.1	23.14.1
6.8.5.4.2	23.8.5.4.2	6.8.6.5	18.4.2	6.9.11.2	24.4.1.9.2, 24.4.1.9.3	6.13.2	23.14.2
6.8.5.4.3	23.8.5.4.3	6.8.6.5.1	18.4.2.1			6.13.3	23.14.3
6.8.5.4.4	23.8.5.4.4	—	18.4.2.2 (new)	6.10	23.11, 24.5	—	23.14.4 (new)
6.8.5.4.5	23.8.5.4.5	—	18.4.2.3 (new)	6.10.1	24.5.1	—	23.14.4.1 (new)
6.8.5.5	23.8.5.5	6.8.6.5.2	18.4.2.4	6.10.1.1	24.5.1.1	—	23.14.4.2 (new)
6.8.5.5.1	23.8.5.5.1	6.8.6.5.3	18.4.2.5	6.10.1.2	24.5.1.2	6.14	23.15
6.8.5.5.2	23.8.5.5.2	6.9	23.9	6.10.1.3	24.5.1.3	6.14.1	23.15.1
6.8.5.6	23.8.5.6	6.9.1	23.9.1, 24.4.1	6.10.1.4	24.5.1.4	6.14.2	23.15.2
6.8.5.6.1	23.8.5.6.1	6.9.2	24.4.1.1	6.10.1.5	24.5.1.5	6.14.3	23.15.3
6.8.5.6.2	23.8.5.6.2	6.9.2.1	24.4.1.1.1			6.14.4	23.15.4, 23.15.5

2007	2010	2007	2010	2007	2010	2007	2010
6.14.5	23.15.6	6.16.4.1	21.4.1	6.17	23.18	7.3.5.2	18.3.5.2
6.15	23.16	6.16.4.2	21.4.2	6.17.1	23.18.1	7.3.6	18.3.6
6.15.1	23.16.1	6.16.4.3	21.4.3	6.17.2	23.18.2	7.4	18.4
6.15.2	23.16.2, 23.16.3	6.16.4.4	21.4.4	6.17.3	23.18.3	7.4.1	18.4.1
6.15.3	23.16.4	6.16.4.5	21.4.5	6.17.3.1	23.18.3.1	7.4.1.1	18.4.1.1
6.15.4	23.16.5	—	21.5 (new)	6.17.3.2	23.18.3.2	7.4.1.2	18.4.1.2
6.15.5	23.16.6	—	21.5.1 (new)	6.17.3.3	23.18.3.3	7.4.1.3	18.4.1.3
6.15.6	23.16.7	—	21.5.2 (new)	6.17.3.4	23.18.3.4	7.4.1.4	18.4.10
6.16	23.17	—	21.6 (new)	6.17.3.5	23.18.3.5	—	18.4.10.1 (new)
—	23.17.1 (new)	—	21.6.1 (new)	6.17.4	23.18.4	—	18.4.10.2 (new)
—	23.17.2 (new)	—	21.6.2 (new)	6.17.4.1	23.18.4.1	—	18.4.10.3 (new)
—	23.17.3 (new)	—	21.6.2.1 (new)	6.17.4.2	23.18.4.2	7.4.1.5	18.4.1.4
—	23.17.4 (new)	—	21.6.2.2 (new)	6.17.4.3	23.18.4.3	7.4.1.6	18.4.1.5
—	23.17.5 (new)	6.16.5	21.7	6.17.4.4	23.18.4.4	7.4.1.7	18.4.1.6
6.16.1	21.1	6.16.5.1	21.7.1	6.17.4.5	23.18.4.5	—	18.4.2 (new from Ch 6)
6.16.2	21.2	6.16.5.2	21.7.2	6.17.4.6	23.18.4.6	—	18.4.2.1
6.16.2.1	21.2.1-21.2.3	6.16.5.3	21.7.3, 21.7.4	6.17.5	23.18.5	—	18.4.2.2
6.16.2.2	21.2.4	6.16.5.4	21.7.5	6.18	(deleted)	—	18.4.2.3
6.16.2.3	21.2.5	6.16.5.5	21.7.6	7.1	18.1	—	18.4.2.4
6.16.2.4	21.2.6	6.16.5.6	21.7.7	7.1.1	18.1.1	—	18.4.2.5
6.16.2.5	21.2.7	6.16.6	21.8	7.1.2	18.1.2	7.4.2	18.4.3
6.16.2.6	21.2.8-21.2.10	6.16.6.1	21.8.1	7.1.3	18.1.3	7.4.2.1	18.4.3.1
6.16.2.7	21.2.11	6.16.6.2	21.8.2	7.1.4	18.1.4	7.4.2.2	18.4.3.2
6.16.2.8	21.2.12	6.16.6.3	21.8.3	7.1.6	18.1.6	7.4.2.3	18.4.3.3
6.16.3	21.3	6.16.6.4	21.8.4	7.1.7	18.1.7	7.4.2.4	18.4.3.4
6.16.3.1	21.3.1	6.16.7	21.9	7.2	18.2	7.4.2.5	18.4.3.5
6.16.3.2	21.3.2	6.16.7.1	21.9.1	7.3	18.3	7.4.2.5.1	18.4.3.5.1
6.16.3.3	21.3.3	6.16.7.2	21.9.2	7.3.1	18.3.1	7.4.2.5.2	18.4.3.5.2
6.16.3.4	21.3.4	6.16.7.3	21.9.3	7.3.2	18.3.2	7.4.2.5.3	18.4.3.5.3
6.16.3.5	21.3.5	6.16.7.4	21.9.4	7.3.2.1	18.3.2.1	7.4.3	18.4.4
6.16.3.6	21.3.6	6.16.7.5	21.9.5	7.3.2.2	18.3.2.2	7.4.3.1	18.4.4.1
6.16.3.7	21.3.7	6.16.7.6	21.9.6	7.3.2.3	18.3.2.3	7.4.3.2	18.4.4.2
6.16.3.8	21.3.8	6.16.8	21.10	7.3.3	18.3.3	7.4.3.3	18.4.4.3
6.16.3.9	21.3.9	6.16.8.1	21.10.1	7.3.3.1	18.3.3.1	7.4.3.3.1	18.4.4.3.1
6.16.3.10	21.3.10	6.16.8.2	21.10.2	7.3.3.2	18.3.3.2	7.4.3.3.2	18.4.4.3.2
6.16.3.11	21.3.11	—	23.17 (new)	7.3.4	18.3.4	7.4.3.3.3	18.4.4.3.3
6.16.3.12	21.3.12	—	23.17.1 (new)	7.3.4.1	18.3.4.1	7.4.4	18.4.5
6.16.3.12.1	21.3.12.1	—	23.17.2 (new)	7.3.4.2	18.3.4.2	7.4.4.1	18.4.5.1
6.16.3.12.2	21.3.12.2	—	23.17.3 (new)	7.3.4.3	18.3.4.3	7.4.4.2	18.4.5.2
6.16.3.12.3	21.3.12.3	—	23.17.4 (new)	7.3.5	18.3.5	—	18.4.5.3 (new)
6.16.4	21.4	—	23.17.5 (new)	7.3.5.1	18.3.5.1	7.4.5	18.4.6

2007	2010	2007	2010	2007	2010	2007	2010
7.4.5.1	18.4.6.1	7.5.4.4	18.5.4.4	8.1.1	26.1.1	8.3.6.1	26.3.6.1
7.4.5.2	18.4.6.2	7.5.4.4.1	18.5.4.4.1	8.1.2	26.1.2	8.3.6.1.1	26.3.6.1.1
7.4.5.3	18.4.6.3	7.5.4.4.2	18.5.4.4.2	8.1.3	26.1.3	8.3.6.1.2	26.3.6.1.2
7.4.5.4	18.4.6.4	7.5.4.4.3	18.5.4.4.3	8.2	26.2	8.3.6.1.3	26.3.6.1.3
7.4.5.5	18.4.6.5	7.5.4.4.4	18.5.4.4.4	8.2.1	26.2.1	8.3.6.1.4	26.3.6.1.4
7.4.5.5.1	18.4.6.5.1	7.5.4.4.5	18.5.4.4.5	8.2.2	26.2.2	8.3.6.1.5	26.3.6.1.5
7.4.5.5.2	18.4.6.5.2	7.5.4.4.6	18.5.4.4.6	8.2.3	26.2.3	8.3.6.1.6	26.3.6.1.6
7.4.6	18.4.7	7.5.4.4.7	18.5.4.4.7	8.2.3.1	26.2.3.1	8.3.6.1.6.1	26.3.6.1.6.1
7.4.6.1	18.4.7.1	7.5.4.4.8	18.5.4.4.8	8.2.3.2	26.2.3.2	8.3.6.1.6.2	26.3.6.1.6.2
7.4.6.2	18.4.7.2	7.5.4.5	18.5.4.5	8.2.3.3	26.2.3.3	8.3.6.1.6.3	26.3.6.1.6.3
7.4.6.3	18.4.7.3	7.5.4.5.1	18.5.4.5.1	—	26.2.4 (new)	8.3.6.1.6.4	26.3.6.1.6.4
7.4.6.4	18.4.7.4	7.5.4.5.2	18.5.4.5.2	—	10.4.4.1.1 (new)	8.3.6.2	26.3.6.2
7.4.6.5	18.4.7.5	7.5.4.6	18.5.4.6	—	10.4.4.1.2 (new)	8.3.6.2.1	26.3.6.2.1
7.4.7	18.4.8	7.5.4.6.1	18.5.4.6.1	—	10.4.4.1.3 (new)	8.3.6.2.2	26.3.6.2.2
7.4.7.1	18.4.8.1	7.5.4.6.2	18.5.4.6.2	8.3	26.3	8.3.7	26.3.7
7.4.7.2	18.4.8.2	7.5.4.6.3	18.5.4.6.3	8.3.1	26.3.1	8.3.7.1	26.3.7.1
7.4.7.3	18.4.8.3	7.5.5	18.5.5	8.3.2	26.3.2	8.3.7.1.1	26.3.7.1.1
7.4.7.4	18.4.8.4	7.6	18.6	8.3.3	26.3.3	8.3.7.1.2	26.3.7.1.2
7.4.7.5	18.4.8.5	7.7	18.7	8.3.4	26.3.4	8.3.7.2	26.3.7.2
7.4.8	18.4.9	7.7.1	18.7.1	8.3.4.1	26.3.4.1	8.3.7.2.1	26.3.7.2.1
7.5	18.5	7.7.2	18.7.2	8.3.4.2	26.3.4.2	8.3.7.2.2	26.3.7.2.2
7.5.1	18.5.1	7.8	18.8	8.3.4.3	26.3.4.3	8.3.7.3	26.3.7.3
7.5.2	18.5.2	7.8.1	18.8.1	8.3.4.4	26.3.4.4	8.3.7.4	26.3.7.4
7.5.2.1	18.5.2.1	7.8.1.1	18.8.1.1	8.3.4.5	26.3.4.5	8.3.7.5	26.3.7.5
7.5.2.2	18.5.2.2	7.8.1.2	18.8.1.2	8.3.4.6	26.3.4.6	8.3.7.5.1	26.3.7.5.1
7.5.2.3	18.5.2.3	7.8.2	18.8.2	8.3.4.7	26.3.4.7	8.3.7.5.2	26.3.7.5.2
7.5.2.4	18.5.2.4	7.8.2.1	18.8.2.1	8.3.4.8	26.3.4.8	8.3.7.5.3	26.3.7.5.3
7.5.2.5	18.5.2.5	7.8.2.2	18.8.2.2	8.3.5	26.3.5	8.3.7.5.4	26.3.7.5.4
7.5.2.6	18.5.2.6	7.8.2.3	18.8.2.3	8.3.5.1	26.3.5.1	8.3.7.5.5	26.3.7.5.5
7.5.3	18.5.3	7.9	18.9	8.3.5.2	26.3.5.2	8.3.7.5.6	26.3.7.5.6
7.5.4	18.5.4	7.9.1	18.9.1	8.3.5.2.1	26.3.5.2.1	8.3.8	26.3.8
7.5.4.1	18.5.4.1	7.9.2	18.9.2	8.3.5.2.2	26.3.5.2.2	8.3.8.1	26.3.8.1
7.5.4.2	18.5.4.2	7.9.3	18.9.3	8.3.5.2.3	26.3.5.2.3	8.3.8.2	26.3.8.2
7.5.4.3	18.5.4.3	7.9.3.1	18.9.3.1	8.3.5.2.4	26.3.5.2.4	8.3.8.3	26.3.8.3
7.5.4.3.1	18.5.4.3.1	7.9.3.2	18.9.3.2	8.3.5.2.5	26.3.5.2.5	8.3.9	26.3.9
7.5.4.3.2	18.5.4.3.2	7.10	18.10	8.3.5.2.6	26.3.5.2.6	8.4	26.4
7.5.4.3.3	18.5.4.3.3	7.10.1	18.10.1	8.3.5.2.7	26.3.5.2.7	8.4.1	26.4.1
7.5.4.3.4	18.5.4.3.4	7.10.2	18.10.2	8.3.5.2.8	26.3.5.2.8	8.4.2	26.4.2
7.5.4.3.5	18.5.4.3.5	7.11	18.11	8.3.5.2.8.1	26.3.5.2.8.1	8.4.2.1	26.4.2.1
7.5.4.3.6	18.5.4.3.6	7.12	(deleted)	8.3.5.2.8.2	26.3.5.2.8.2	8.4.2.2	26.4.2.2
7.5.4.3.7	18.5.4.3.7	8.1	26.1	8.3.6	26.3.6	8.4.2.3	26.4.2.3

2007	2010	2007	2010	2007	2010	2007	2010
8.4.2.4	26.4.2.4	8.4.5.1.1	26.4.5.1.1	8.5.3.3	26.5.4.3	8.6.3.1.1.2	(deleted)
8.4.3	26.4.3	8.4.5.1.2	26.4.5.1.2	8.5.3.4	26.5.4.4	8.6.3.1.2	(deleted)
8.4.3.1	26.4.3.1	8.4.5.2	26.4.5.2	8.5.3.5	26.5.4.5	8.6.3.1.2.1	(deleted)
8.4.3.2	26.4.3.2	8.4.5.2.1	26.4.5.2.1	8.5.3.5.1	26.5.4.5.1	8.6.3.1.2.2	(deleted)
8.4.3.3	26.4.3.3	8.4.5.2.2	26.4.5.2.2	8.5.3.5.2	26.5.4.5.2	8.6.3.1.3	(deleted)
8.4.3.4	26.4.3.4	8.4.5.3	26.4.5.3	8.5.4	26.5.5	8.6.3.1.4	(deleted)
8.4.3.4.1	26.4.3.4.1	8.4.5.4	26.4.5.4	8.5.4.1	26.5.5.1	8.6.3.1.5	(deleted)
8.4.3.4.2	26.4.3.4.2	8.4.5.5	26.4.5.5	8.5.4.2	26.5.5.2	8.6.3.1.6	(deleted)
8.4.3.4.3	26.4.3.4.3	8.4.5.6	26.4.5.6	8.5.4.3	26.5.5.3	8.6.3.1.6.1	(deleted)
8.4.3.5	26.4.3.5	8.4.5.6.1	26.4.5.6.1	8.5.5	26.5.6	8.6.3.1.6.2	(deleted)
8.4.4	26.4.4	8.4.5.6.2	26.4.5.6.2	8.5.5.1	26.5.6.1	8.6.3.1.6.3	(deleted)
8.4.4.1	26.4.4.1	8.4.5.6.3	26.4.5.6.3	8.5.5.2	26.5.6.2	8.6.3.1.7	(deleted)
8.4.4.1.1	26.4.4.1.1	8.4.5.6.4	26.4.5.6.4	8.5.5.3	26.5.6.3	8.6.3.1.8	(deleted)
8.4.4.1.2	26.4.4.1.2	8.4.6	26.4.6	8.5.6	26.5.7	8.6.3.2	26.6.3.2
8.4.4.1.3	26.4.4.1.3	8.4.6.1	26.4.6.1	8.5.6.1	26.5.7.1	8.6.3.2.1	26.6.3.2.1
8.4.4.1.4	26.4.4.1.4	8.4.6.2	26.4.6.2	8.6	26.6	8.6.3.2.1.1	26.6.3.2.1.1
8.4.4.2	26.4.4.2	8.4.6.3	26.4.6.3	8.6.1	26.6.1	8.6.3.2.1.2	26.6.3.2.1.2
8.4.4.2.1	26.4.4.2.1	8.4.7	26.4.7	8.6.2	26.6.2	8.6.3.2.1.3	26.6.3.2.1.3
8.4.4.2.1.1	26.4.4.2.1.1	8.5	26.5	8.6.2.1	26.6.2.1	8.6.3.2.1.4	26.6.3.2.1.4
8.4.4.2.1.2	26.4.4.2.1.2	8.5.1	26.5.1	8.6.2.2	26.6.2.2	8.6.3.2.1.5	26.6.3.2.1.5
8.4.4.2.1.3	26.4.4.2.1.3	8.5.1.1	26.5.1.1	8.6.2.3	26.6.2.3	8.6.3.2.2	26.6.3.2.2
8.4.4.2.1.4	26.4.4.2.1.4	8.5.1.2	26.5.1.2	8.6.2.4	26.6.2.4	8.6.3.2.2.1	26.6.3.2.2.1
8.4.4.2.2	26.4.4.2.2	8.5.1.3	26.5.1.3	8.6.2.4.1	26.6.2.4.1	8.6.3.2.2.2	26.6.3.2.2.2
8.4.4.2.2.1	26.4.4.2.2.1	8.5.1.4	26.5.1.4	8.6.2.4.2	26.6.2.4.2	8.6.3.2.3	26.6.3.2.3
8.4.4.2.2.2	26.4.4.2.2.2	8.5.1.5	26.5.1.5	8.6.2.4.3	26.6.2.4.3	8.6.3.2.3.1	26.6.3.2.3.1
8.4.4.2.2.3	26.4.4.2.2.3	8.5.1.6	26.5.1.6	8.6.2.5	26.6.2.5	8.6.3.2.3.2	26.6.3.2.3.2
8.4.4.2.2.4	26.4.4.2.2.4	—	26.5.2 (new)	8.6.2.5.1	26.6.2.5.1	8.6.3.2.3.3	26.6.3.2.3.3
8.4.4.3	26.4.4.3	8.5.2	26.5.3	8.6.2.5.2	26.6.2.5.2	8.6.3.3	(deleted)
8.4.4.3.1	26.4.4.3.1	8.5.2.1	26.5.3.1	8.6.2.5.2.1	26.6.2.5.2.1	8.6.3.3.1	(deleted)
8.4.4.3.2	26.4.4.3.2	8.5.2.1.1	26.5.3.1.1, 26.5.3.1.2	8.6.2.5.2.2	26.6.2.5.2.2	8.6.3.3.1.1	(deleted)
8.4.4.4	26.4.4.4	8.5.2.1.2	26.5.3.1.3	8.6.2.5.2.3	26.6.2.5.2.3	8.6.3.3.1.2	(deleted)
8.4.4.5	26.4.4.5	8.5.2.2	26.5.3.2	8.6.2.5.3	26.6.2.5.3	8.6.3.3.1.3	(deleted)
8.4.4.5.1	26.4.4.5.1	8.5.2.3	26.5.3.3	8.6.2.6	26.6.2.6	8.6.3.3.1.4	(deleted)
8.4.4.5.2	26.4.4.5.2	8.5.3	26.5.4	8.6.2.6.1	26.6.2.6.1	8.6.3.3.2	(deleted)
8.4.4.6	26.4.4.6	8.5.3.1	26.5.4.1	8.6.2.6.1.1	26.6.2.6.1.1	8.6.3.3.2.1	(deleted)
8.4.4.6.1	26.4.4.6.1	8.5.3.1.1	26.5.4.1.1	8.6.2.6.1.2	26.6.2.6.1.2	8.6.3.3.2.2	(deleted)
8.4.4.6.2	26.4.4.6.2	8.5.3.1.2	26.5.4.1.2	8.6.2.6.2	26.6.2.6.2	8.6.3.3.2.3	(deleted)
8.4.4.6.3	26.4.4.6.3	8.5.3.1.3	26.5.4.1.3	8.6.3	26.6.3	8.6.3.3.2.4	(deleted)
8.4.4.6.4	26.4.4.6.4	8.5.3.1.4	26.5.4.1.4	8.6.3.1	(deleted)	8.6.3.3.2.5	(deleted)
8.4.5	26.4.5	8.5.3.1.5	26.5.4.1.5	8.6.3.1.1	(deleted)	8.6.3.3.2.6	(deleted)
8.4.5.1	26.4.5.1	8.5.3.2	26.5.4.2	8.6.3.1.1.1	(deleted)	8.6.3.3.2.7	(deleted)

2007	2010	2007	2010	2007	2010	2007	2010
8.6.3.3.2.8	(deleted)	8.6.3.5.4.6	26.6.3.3.2.4(F)	8.6.4.13	(deleted)	—	27.4 (new)
8.6.3.3.3	(deleted)	8.6.3.5.5	26.6.3.3.2.5	8.6.4.14	(deleted)	—	27.4.1 (new)
8.6.3.3.3.1	(deleted)	8.6.3.5.6	26.6.3.3.2.6	8.6.4.15	26.6.3.1.13	—	27.4.1.1 (new)
8.6.3.3.3.2	(deleted)	8.6.3.5.6.1	26.6.3.3.2.6(A)	8.6.5	26.6.4	—	27.4.1.2 (new)
8.6.3.3.3.3	(deleted)	8.6.3.5.6.2	26.6.3.3.2.6(B)	8.6.5.1	26.6.4.1	—	27.4.2 (new)
8.6.3.3.3.4	(deleted)	8.6.3.6	(deleted)	8.6.5.2	26.6.4.2	—	27.4.2.1 (new)
8.6.3.3.3.5	(deleted)	8.6.3.6.1	(deleted)	8.6.5.3	26.6.4.3	—	27.4.2.2 (new)
8.6.3.3.3.6	(deleted)	8.6.3.6.1.1	(deleted)	8.6.6	26.6.5	—	27.4.2.3 (new)
8.6.3.3.3.7	(deleted)	8.6.3.6.1.2	(deleted)	8.7	(deleted)	—	27.4.2.4 (new)
8.6.3.3.3.8	(deleted)	8.6.3.6.2	(deleted)	9.1	27.1	—	27.4.3 (new)
8.6.3.3.3.9	(deleted)	8.6.3.6.2.1	(deleted)	—	27.1.1 (new)	—	27.4.3.1 (new)
8.6.3.3.3.10	(deleted)	8.6.3.6.2.2	(deleted)	9.1.1	27.1.2	—	27.4.3.4 (new)
8.6.3.3.4	(deleted)	8.6.3.6.2.3	(deleted)	9.1.2	27.1.3	—	27.4.3.5 (new)
—	26.6.3.3 (new)	8.6.3.7	(deleted)	9.1.3	27.1.4	—	27.4.3.6 (new)
8.6.3.4	26.6.3.3.1	8.6.3.7.1	(deleted)	9.1.4	27.1.5	—	27.5 (new)
8.6.3.4.1	26.6.3.3.1.1	8.6.3.7.2	(deleted)	9.1.5	27.1.6	9.4	27.6
8.6.3.4.2	26.6.3.3.1.2	8.6.3.7.3	(deleted)	—	27.1.7 (new)	9.4.1	27.6.1
8.6.3.4.3	26.6.3.3.1.3	8.6.3.7.3.1	(deleted)	9.2	27.2	9.4.1.1	27.6.1.1
8.6.3.4.3.1	26.6.3.3.1.3(A)	8.6.3.7.3.2	(deleted)	9.2.1	27.2.1	9.4.1.2	27.6.1.2
8.6.3.4.3.2	26.6.3.3.1.3(B)	8.6.4	(deleted)	9.2.2	27.2.2	9.4.1.3	27.6.1.3
8.6.3.4.4	26.6.3.3.1.4	8.6.4.1	26.6.3.1.1	9.2.3	27.4.2.1.1	9.4.1.4	27.6.1.4
8.6.3.4.4.1	26.6.3.3.1.4(A)	8.6.4.2	26.6.3.1.2	9.2.4	27.2.3	—	27.6.1.5 (new)
8.6.3.4.4.2	26.6.3.3.1.4(B)	8.6.4.3	26.6.3.1.3	—	27.2.3.1 (new)	9.4.1.5	27.6.1.6
8.6.3.4.5	26.6.3.3.1.5	8.6.4.4	26.6.3.1.4	9.3	27.3	9.4.2	27.6.2
8.6.3.4.5.1	26.6.3.3.1.5(A)	—	26.6.3.1.4.1 (new)	9.3.1	27.3.1	9.4.2.1	27.6.2.1
8.6.3.4.5.2	26.6.3.3.1.5(B)			9.3.2	27.3.2	9.4.2.1.1	27.6.2.1.1
8.6.3.4.5.3	26.6.3.3.1.5(C)	—	26.6.3.1.4.2 (new)	9.3.3	27.3.3	9.4.2.1.2	27.6.2.1.2
8.6.3.5	26.6.3.3.2			9.3.4	27.3.4	9.4.2.1.3	27.6.2.1.3
8.6.3.5.1	26.6.3.3.2.1	8.6.4.5	26.6.3.1.5	9.3.5	27.3.5	9.4.2.1.4	27.6.2.1.4
8.6.3.5.2	26.6.3.3.2.2	8.6.4.6	26.6.3.1.6	9.3.6	27.3.6	9.4.2.1.5	27.6.2.1.5
8.6.3.5.3	26.6.3.3.2.3	8.6.4.6.1	26.6.3.1.6.1	9.3.6.1	27.3.6.1	9.4.2.1.6	27.6.2.1.6
8.6.3.5.3.1	26.6.3.3.2.3(A)	8.6.4.6.2	26.6.3.1.6.2	9.3.6.2	27.3.6.2	9.4.2.1.7	27.6.2.1.7
8.6.3.5.3.2	26.6.3.3.2.3(B)	8.6.4.7	26.6.3.1.7	9.3.7	27.3.7	9.4.2.1.8	27.6.2.1.8
8.6.3.5.3.3	26.6.3.3.2.3(C)	8.6.4.8	26.6.3.1.8	9.3.7.1	27.3.7.1	9.4.2.1.9	27.6.2.1.9
8.6.3.5.3.4	26.6.3.3.2.3(D)	8.6.4.9	26.6.3.1.9	9.3.7.1.1	27.3.7.1.1	9.4.2.1.10	27.6.2.1.10
8.6.3.5.4	26.6.3.3.2.4	8.6.4.10	26.6.3.1.10	9.3.7.1.2	27.3.7.1.2	9.4.2.1.11	27.6.2.1.11
8.6.3.5.4.1	26.6.3.3.2.4(A)	8.6.4.10.1	26.6.3.1.10.1	9.3.7.2	27.3.7.2	9.4.2.1.11.1	27.6.2.1.11.1
8.6.3.5.4.2	26.6.3.3.2.4(B)	8.6.4.10.2	26.6.3.1.10.2	9.3.7.3	27.3.7.3	9.4.2.1.11.2	27.6.2.1.11.2
8.6.3.5.4.3	26.6.3.3.2.4(C)	8.6.4.11	(deleted)	9.3.7.4	27.3.7.4	9.4.2.2	27.6.5
8.6.3.5.4.4	26.6.3.3.2.4(D)	8.6.4.12	26.6.3.1.11	9.3.7.4.1	27.3.7.4.1	9.4.2.3	27.6.6
8.6.3.5.4.5	26.6.3.3.2.4(E)	—	26.6.3.1.12 (new)	9.3.7.4.2	27.3.7.4.2	9.4.2.3.1	27.4.3.2, 27.6.6.1

2007	2010	2007	2010	2007	2010	2007	2010
9.4.2.3.2	27.6.6.2	9.4.3.2.2.1	27.6.3.2.2.1	9.5.1.4.3	27.5.2.4.3	9.5.2.2.2	27.5.4.2.2
9.4.2.3.3	27.6.6.3	9.4.3.2.2.2	27.6.3.2.2.2	9.5.1.4.4	27.5.2.4.4	9.5.2.2.3	27.5.4.2.3
9.4.2.3.4	27.6.6.4	9.4.3.2.2.3	27.6.3.2.2.3	9.5.1.4.5	27.5.2.4.5	9.5.2.2.4	27.5.4.2.4
9.4.2.3.5	27.6.6.5	9.4.3.2.3	27.6.3.2.3	9.5.1.5	27.5.2.5	9.5.2.2.5	27.5.4.2.5
9.4.2.3.6	27.6.6.6	9.4.3.2.3.1	27.6.3.2.3.1	9.5.1.5.1	27.5.2.5.1	9.5.2.2.6	27.5.4.2.6
9.4.2.3.7	27.6.6.7	9.4.3.2.3.2	27.6.3.2.3.2	9.5.1.5.2	27.5.2.5.2	9.5.2.3	27.5.4.3
9.4.2.3.8	27.6.6.8	9.4.3.2.3.3	27.6.3.2.3.3	9.5.1.5.3	27.5.2.5.3	9.5.2.3.1	27.5.4.3.1
9.4.2.3.9	27.6.6.9	9.4.3.2.3.4	27.6.3.2.3.4	9.5.1.5.4	27.5.2.5.4	9.5.2.3.2	27.5.4.3.2
9.4.2.3.9.1	27.6.6.9.1	9.4.3.2.3.5	27.6.3.2.3.5	9.5.1.5.5	27.5.2.5.5	9.5.3	27.5.5
9.4.2.3.9.2	27.6.6.9.2	9.4.3.2.3.6	27.6.3.2.3.6	9.5.1.5.6	27.5.2.5.6	9.5.3.1	27.5.5.1
9.4.2.3.9.3	27.6.6.9.3	9.4.3.2.3.7	27.6.3.2.3.7	9.5.1.5.6.1	27.5.2.5.6.1	9.5.3.1.1	27.5.5.1.1
9.4.2.3.9.4	27.6.6.9.4	9.4.3.2.3.8	27.6.3.2.3.8	9.5.1.5.6.2	27.5.2.5.6.2	9.5.3.1.1.1	27.5.5.1.1.1
9.4.2.3.9.5	27.6.6.9.5	9.4.3.2.3.9	27.6.3.2.3.9	9.5.1.5.7	27.5.2.5.7	9.5.3.1.1.2	27.5.5.1.1.2
9.4.2.3.9.6	27.6.6.9.6	9.4.3.2.3.10	27.6.3.2.3.10	9.5.1.5.8	27.5.2.5.8	9.5.3.1.1.3	27.5.5.1.1.3
9.4.2.3.10	27.6.6.10	9.4.3.2.3.11	27.6.3.2.3.11	9.5.1.6	27.5.2.6	9.5.3.1.1.4	27.5.5.1.1.4
9.4.2.3.10.1	27.6.6.10.1	9.4.3.2.3.12	27.6.3.2.3.12	9.5.1.6.1	27.5.2.6.1	9.5.3.1.1.5	27.5.5.1.1.5
9.4.2.3.10.2	27.6.6.10.2	9.4.3.2.3.13	27.6.3.2.3.13	—	27.5.2.6.1.1	9.5.3.1.1.6	27.5.5.1.1.6
9.4.2.3.10.3	27.6.6.10.3	9.4.3.2.3.14	27.6.3.2.3.14	9.5.1.6.2	27.5.2.6.2	9.5.3.1.2	27.5.5.1.2
9.4.2.3.10.4	27.6.6.10.4	9.4.4	27.6.4	9.5.1.6.3	27.5.2.6.3	9.5.3.1.2.1	27.5.5.1.2.1
9.4.2.3.10.5	27.6.6.10.5	9.5	27.5.2	9.5.1.6.4	27.5.2.6.4	9.5.3.1.2.2	27.5.5.1.2.2
9.4.2.3.11	27.6.6.11	9.5.1	27.5.1	9.5.1.7	27.5.2.7	9.5.3.1.3	27.5.5.1.3
9.4.2.3.12	27.6.6.12	9.5.1.1	27.5.2.1	9.5.1.8	27.5.2.8	9.5.3.1.4	27.5.5.1.4
9.4.2.3.12.1	27.6.6.12.1	9.5.1.1.1	27.5.2.1.1	9.5.1.8.1	27.5.2.8.1	9.5.3.2	27.4.3.3
9.4.2.3.12.2	27.6.6.12.2	9.5.1.1.2	27.5.2.1.2	9.5.1.8.2	27.5.2.8.2, 27.5.2.8.3, 27.5.2.8.4	9.5.3.3	27.5.5.2
9.4.2.3.12.3	27.6.6.12.3	9.5.1.1.3	27.5.2.1.3			9.5.3.4	27.5.5.3
9.4.2.4	27.6.5.1	9.5.1.2	27.5.2.2	—	27.5.2.8.5 (new)	9.5.3.4.1	27.5.5.3.1
9.4.2.4.1	27.6.5.1.1	9.5.1.2.1	27.5.2.2.1	9.5.1.8.3	27.5.2.8.6	9.5.3.4.2	27.5.5.3.2
9.4.2.4.2	27.6.5.1.2	9.5.1.2.2	27.5.2.2.2	9.5.1.8.4	27.5.2.8.7	9.5.3.4.3	27.5.5.3.3
9.4.3	27.6.3	9.5.1.2.3	27.5.2.2.3	9.5.1.9	27.5.2.9	9.5.3.4.4	27.5.5.3.4
9.4.3.1	27.6.3.1	9.5.1.2.3.1	27.5.2.2.3.1	9.5.2	27.5.4	9.5.3.4.5	27.5.5.3.5
9.4.3.1.1	27.6.3.1.1	9.5.1.2.3.2	27.5.2.2.3.2	9.5.2.1	27.5.4.1	9.5.3.4.6	27.5.5.3.6
9.4.3.1.2	27.6.3.1.2	9.5.1.2.4	27.5.2.2.4	9.5.2.1.1	27.5.4.1.1	9.5.3.4.7	27.5.5.3.7
9.4.3.1.3	27.6.3.1.3	9.5.1.2.5	27.5.2.2.5	9.5.2.1.2	27.5.4.1.2	9.5.3.4.7.1	27.5.5.3.7.1
9.4.3.1.4	27.6.3.1.4	9.5.1.2.6	27.5.2.2.6	9.5.2.1.3	27.5.4.1.3	9.5.3.4.7.2	27.5.5.3.7.2
9.4.3.1.5	27.6.3.1.5	9.5.1.2.7	27.5.2.2.7	9.5.2.1.4	27.5.4.1.4	9.5.3.4.8	27.5.5.3.8
9.4.3.2	27.6.3.2	9.5.1.3	27.5.2.3	9.5.2.1.5	27.5.4.1.5	9.5.3.5	27.5.5.4
9.4.3.2.1	27.6.3.2.1	9.5.1.3.1	27.5.2.3.1	9.5.2.1.6	27.5.4.1.6	9.5.4	27.5.4.4
9.4.3.2.1.1	27.6.3.2.1.1	9.5.1.3.2	27.5.2.3.2	9.5.2.1.6.1	27.5.4.1.6.1	9.5.4.1	27.5.4.4.1
9.4.3.2.1.2	27.6.3.2.1.2	9.5.1.4	27.5.2.4	9.5.2.1.6.2	27.5.4.1.6.2	9.5.4.1.1	27.5.4.4.1.1
9.4.3.2.1.3	27.6.3.2.1.3	9.5.1.4.1	27.5.2.4.1	9.5.2.2	27.5.4.2	9.5.4.1.2	27.5.4.4.1.2
9.4.3.2.2	27.6.3.2.2	9.5.1.4.2	27.5.2.4.2	9.5.2.2.1	27.5.4.2.1	9.5.4.2	27.5.4.4.2

2007	2010	2007	2010	2007	2010	2007	2010
9.5.4.3	27.5.4.4.3	9.7.1.3.5	27.7.1.3.5	9.7.3.4	27.7.3.4	10.2.5	14.2.5
9.5.4.4	27.5.4.4.4	9.7.1.3.6	27.7.1.3.6	9.7.3.5	27.7.3.5	10.2.5.1	14.2.5.1
9.5.4.5	27.5.4.4.5	9.7.1.3.6.1	27.7.1.3.6.1	9.7.3.6	27.7.3.6	10.2.5.2	14.2.5.2
9.5.4.6	27.5.4.4.6	9.7.1.3.6.2	27.7.1.3.6.2	9.7.3.7	27.7.3.7	10.2.5.3	14.2.5.3
9.5.4.7	27.5.4.4.7	9.7.1.3.7	27.7.1.3.7	9.7.3.8	27.7.3.8	10.2.5.4	14.2.5.4
9.5.4.8	27.5.4.4.8	9.7.1.3.7.1	27.7.1.3.7.1	9.7.3.9	27.7.3.9	10.2.5.5	14.2.5.5
9.6	27.5.3	9.7.1.3.7.2	27.7.1.3.7.2	9.7.3.10	27.7.3.10	10.2.5.6	14.2.5.6
9.6.1	27.5.3.1	9.7.1.4	27.7.1.4	9.7.3.11	27.7.3.11	10.2.6	14.2.6
9.6.2	27.5.3.2	9.7.1.4.1	27.7.1.4.1	9.7.3.12	27.7.3.12	10.2.6.1	14.2.6.1
9.6.3	27.5.3.3	9.7.1.4.1.1	27.7.1.4.1.1	9.8	(deleted)	10.2.6.2	14.2.6.2
9.6.4	27.5.3.4	9.7.1.4.1.2	27.7.1.4.1.2	—	27.8 (new)	—	14.2.7 (new)
9.6.5	27.5.3.5	9.7.1.4.2	27.7.1.4.2	—	27.8.1 (new)	—	14.2.7.1 (new)
9.6.6	27.5.3.6	9.7.1.4.3	27.7.1.4.3	—	27.8.2 (new)	—	14.2.7.2 (new)
9.6.7	27.5.3.7	9.7.1.4.4	27.7.1.4.4	10.1	14.1	—	14.2.8 (new)
9.6.8	27.5.3.8	9.7.1.5	27.7.1.5	10.1.1	14.1.1	10.3	14.3
9.6.8.1	27.5.3.8.1	9.7.1.5.1	27.7.1.5.1	10.1.2	14.1.2	10.3.1	14.3.1, 14.3.2, 14.3.3
9.6.8.2	27.5.3.8.2	9.7.1.5.2	27.7.1.5.2	10.1.3	14.1.3		
9.6.8.3	27.5.3.8.3	9.7.1.6	27.7.1.6	10.1.4	14.1.4	10.3.2	14.3.4
9.7	27.7	9.7.1.6.1	27.7.1.6.1	10.2	14.2	10.4	14.4
9.7.1	27.7.1	9.7.1.6.2	27.7.1.6.2	10.2.1	14.2.1	10.4.1	14.4.1
9.7.1.1	27.7.1.1	9.7.1.6.3	27.7.1.6.3	10.2.1.1	14.2.1.1, 14.2.1.1.1, 14.2.1.1.2	10.4.1.1	14.4.1.1, 14.4.1.1.1, 14.4.1.1.1.1, 14.4.1.1.1.2
9.7.1.1.1	27.7.1.1.1	9.7.1.6.4	27.7.1.6.4				
9.7.1.1.2	27.7.1.1.2	9.7.1.6.4.1	27.7.1.6.4.1				
9.7.1.1.3	27.7.1.1.3	9.7.1.6.4.2	27.7.1.6.4.2	10.2.1.2	14.2.1.2	10.4.1.2	14.4.1.2
9.7.1.1.4	27.7.1.1.4	9.7.1.6.5	27.7.1.6.5	10.2.1.2.1	14.2.1.2.1	10.4.1.2.1	14.4.1.2.1
9.7.1.2	27.7.1.2	9.7.1.6.6	27.7.1.6.6	10.2.1.2.2	14.2.1.2.2	10.4.1.2.1.1	14.4.1.2.1.1
9.7.1.2.1	27.7.1.2.1	9.7.1.6.7	27.7.1.6.7	10.2.1.2.3	14.2.1.2.3	10.4.1.2.1.2	14.4.1.2.1.2
9.7.1.2.2	27.7.1.2.2	9.7.2	27.7.2	10.2.2	14.2.2	10.4.1.2.1.3	14.4.1.2.1.3
9.7.1.2.3	27.7.1.2.3	9.7.2.1	27.7.2.1	10.2.2.1	14.2.2.1	10.4.1.2.1.4	14.4.1.2.1.4
9.7.1.2.4	27.7.1.2.4	9.7.2.1.1	27.7.2.1.1	10.2.2.2	14.2.2.2	10.4.1.2.2	14.4.1.2.2
9.7.1.2.4.1	27.7.1.2.4.1	9.7.2.1.2	27.7.2.1.2	10.2.2.3	14.2.2.3	10.4.2	14.4.2
9.7.1.2.4.2	27.7.1.2.4.2	9.7.2.1.3	27.7.2.1.3	10.2.2.4	14.2.2.4	10.4.2.1	14.4.2.1
9.7.1.2.5	27.7.1.2.5	9.7.2.1.4	27.7.2.1.4	10.2.2.5	14.2.2.5, 10.4.3	10.4.2.2	14.4.2.2
9.7.1.2.5.1	27.7.1.2.5.1	9.7.2.1.5	27.7.2.1.5	10.2.2.5.1	10.4.3.1	10.4.3	14.4.3
9.7.1.2.5.2	27.7.1.2.5.2	9.7.2.2	27.7.2.2	10.2.2.5.2	10.4.3.2	—	14.4.4 (new)
9.7.1.2.6	27.7.1.2.6	9.7.2.2.1	27.7.2.2.1	10.2.3	14.2.3	10.4.4	14.4.5, 14.4.5.1
9.7.1.3	27.7.1.3	9.7.2.2.2	27.7.2.2.2	10.2.3.1	14.2.3.1	10.4.4.1	14.4.5.2
9.7.1.3.1	27.7.1.3.1, 27.7.1.3.1.1	9.7.3	27.7.3	10.2.3.2	14.2.3.2	10.4.4.2	14.4.5.3
		9.7.3.1	27.7.3.1	10.2.3.3	14.2.3.3	10.4.4.2.1	14.4.5.3.1
9.7.1.3.2	27.7.1.3.2	9.7.3.2	27.7.3.2	10.2.4	14.2.4	10.4.4.2.2	14.4.5.3.2
9.7.1.3.3	27.7.1.3.3	9.7.3.3	27.7.3.3	—	14.2.4.1 (new)	10.4.4.2.3	14.4.5.3.3
9.7.1.3.4	27.7.1.3.4			—	14.2.4.2 (new)		

2007	2010	2007	2010	2007	2010	2007	2010
10.4.4.2.3.1	14.4.5.3.3.1	10.5.2	14.5.2	11.4	29.4	11.7.5.6	29.7.5.6
10.4.4.2.3.2	14.4.5.3.3.2	10.5.3	14.5.3	11.4.1	29.4.1	11.7.5.7	29.7.5.7
10.4.4.2.4	14.4.5.3.4	10.5.4	14.5.4	11.4.2	29.4.2	11.7.6	29.7.6
10.4.4.2.5	14.4.5.3.5, 14.4.5.3.6	10.5.5	14.5.5, 14.5.6	11.4.2.1	29.4.2.1	11.7.6.1	29.7.6.1
		10.5.6	14.5.7	11.4.2.2	29.4.2.2	11.7.6.2	29.7.6.2
10.4.4.2.6	14.4.5.3.7	10.6	14.6	—	29.4.2.3 (new)	11.7.6.3	29.7.6.3
10.4.4.3	14.4.5.4	10.6.1	14.6.1	11.4.3	29.4.3	11.7.6.4	29.7.6.4
10.4.4.4	14.4.5.5	10.6.1.1	14.6.1.1	11.5	29.5	11.7.6.5	29.7.6.5
10.4.4.4.1	14.4.5.5.1	—	14.6.1.2 (new)	11.5.1	29.5.1	11.7.6.6	29.7.6.6
10.4.4.4.2	14.4.5.5.2, 14.4.5.5.3	10.6.1.2	14.6.1.2.1, 14.6.1.2.2	11.5.1.1	29.5.1.1	11.7.6.7	29.7.6.7
				11.5.1.2	29.5.1.2	—	29.7.7 (new)
10.4.4.4.3	14.4.5.5.4	10.6.1.3	14.6.1.3	11.5.1.3	29.5.1.3	11.7.7	29.7.7.1
10.4.4.5	(deleted)	10.6.2	14.6.2	11.5.1.3.1	29.5.1.3.1	—	29.7.7.2 (new)
—	14.4.5.6 (new)	10.6.2.1	14.6.2.1	11.5.1.3.2	29.5.1.3.2	—	29.7.7.2.1 (new)
10.4.5	14.4.6	—	14.6.2.2 (new)	11.5.2	29.5.2	—	29.7.7.2.2 (new)
10.4.6	14.4.7	10.6.2.2	14.6.2.3	11.5.2.1	29.5.2.1	—	29.7.7.2.3 (new)
10.4.6.1	14.4.7.1	10.6.2.3	14.6.2.4	11.5.2.1.1	29.5.2.1.1	—	29.7.7.2.4 (new)
10.4.6.2	14.4.7.2	10.6.3	14.6.3, 14.6.3.1, 14.6.3.2	11.5.2.1.2	29.5.2.1.2	—	29.7.7.2.5 (new)
10.4.7	14.4.8, 14.4.8.1			11.5.2.2	29.5.2.2	11.7.8	29.7.8
—	14.4.8.2 (new)	10.6.4	14.6.4	11.6	29.6	11.7.8.1	29.7.8.1
10.4.8	14.4.9	10.7	(deleted)	11.6.1	29.6.1	11.7.8.1.1	29.7.8.1.1
10.4.9	14.4.10	11.1	29.1	11.6.2	29.6.2	11.7.8.1.2	29.7.8.1.2
10.4.10	14.4.11	11.1.1	29.1.1	11.6.3	29.6.3	11.7.8.1.3	29.7.8.1.3
10.4.10.1	14.4.11.1–14.4.11.1.2	11.1.2	29.1.2	11.6.4	29.6.4	—	29.7.8.1.4 (new)
		11.1.3	29.1.3	11.6.5	29.6.5	—	29.7.8.1.5 (new)
10.4.10.2	14.4.11.2, 14.4.11.3	11.1.4	29.1.4	11.6.6	29.6.6	11.7.8.2	29.7.8.2
10.4.11	14.4.12	11.1.5	29.1.5	11.6.7	29.6.7	—	29.7.8.3 (new)
—	14.4.12.1 (new)	11.2	29.2	11.6.8	29.6.8	11.8	29.8
—	14.4.12.1.1 (new)	11.3	29.3	11.7	29.7	11.8.1	29.8.1
		11.3.1	29.3.1	11.7.1	29.7.1	11.8.1.1	29.8.1.1
—	14.4.12.1.2 (new)	11.3.2	29.3.2	11.7.2	29.7.2	11.8.1.2	29.8.1.2
		11.3.3	29.3.3	11.7.3	29.7.3	11.8.1.3	29.8.1.3
—	14.4.12.1.3 (new)	11.3.4	29.3.4	11.7.3.1	29.7.3.1	11.8.1.4	29.8.1.4
		11.3.5	29.3.5	11.7.3.2	29.7.3.2	11.8.2	29.8.2
—	14.4.12.1.4 (new)	11.3.5.1	29.3.5.1	11.7.4	29.7.4	11.8.2.1	29.8.2.1
—	14.4.12.1.5 (new)	11.3.5.2	29.3.5.2	11.7.5	29.7.5	11.8.2.2	29.8.2.2
		11.3.6	29.3.6	11.7.5.1	29.7.5.1	11.8.2.3	29.8.2.3
—	14.4.12.1.6 (new)	11.3.7	29.3.7	11.7.5.2	29.7.5.2	11.8.2.4	29.8.2.4
		—	29.3.8 (new)	11.7.5.3	29.7.5.3	11.8.3	29.8.3
—	14.4.13 (new)	—	29.3.8.1 (new)	11.7.5.4	29.7.5.4	11.8.3.1	(deleted)
10.5	14.5	—	29.3.8.2 (new)	11.7.5.5	29.7.5.5	11.8.3.2	29.8.3.1
10.5.1	14.5.1	11.3.8	29.3.9				

2007	2010	2007	2010	2007	2010	2007	2010
11.8.3.3	29.8.3.2	11.8.4.1	29.8.4.1	11.8.4.5	29.8.4.5	11.11	29.11
11.8.3.4	29.8.3.3	11.8.4.2	29.8.4.2	11.8.5	29.8.5	11.11.1	29.11.1
11.8.3.5	29.8.3.4	11.8.4.3	29.8.4.3	11.9	29.9	11.11.2	29.11.2
11.8.4	29.8.4	11.8.4.4	29.8.4.4	11.10	29.10	11.12	(deleted)

PART TWO

Supplements

In addition to the code text and commentary presented in Part One, the *National Fire Alarm and Signaling Code Handbook* includes supplements. They are not part of the Code but are included as additional information for handbook users. In the following four supplements, Part Two explores the background of four selected topics related to *NFPA 72* in more detail than the commentary. For additional supplemental material, visit *www.nfpa.org/72handbook*.

1. Performance-Based Design and Fire Alarm Systems
2. Emergency Communications Systems Design and Application Challenges
3. Voice Intelligibility for Emergency Voice/Alarm Communications Systems
4. *Life Safety Code®* Enabling References

Performance-Based Design and Fire Alarm Systems

John M. Cholin, P.E., FSFPE
J. M. Cholin Consultants, Inc.

Editor's Note: Chapter 17 of the 2010 edition of the National Fire Alarm and Signaling Code includes a performance-based option in the design of the fire detection portion of fire alarm systems. Long-time users of the Code will also see the expansion and refinement of the performance-based design methods outlined in Annex B. This supplement provides an overview of the underlying concepts of performance-based design as they can be applied to fire alarm systems.

INTRODUCTION

Over the past decade, fire protection engineers have introduced the term *performance-based design* into the language of the fire protection community. To many, performance-based design seems like a new concept. However, since the birth of engineering as a profession most engineering has been executed in an essentially performance-based design environment. The application of this design philosophy to the design of fire protection systems is a recent development, although arguably long overdue.

Performance-based design can be thought of as a design process where calculations and computer modeling are used to predict the capability of a contemplated design and to show that the design will meet specific performance criteria, indicating that a specific design objective or set of objectives has been met. This environment is very different from the prescriptive design environment with which most fire protection practitioners are familiar. The National Fire Protection Association (NFPA) has assumed a leadership role in formulating the concepts that make the development of performance-based codes and standards possible. As part of that larger effort, this supplement to the *National Fire Alarm and Signaling Code Handbook* provides a review of the performance-based design concepts for the fire alarm system designer and technician.

Prescriptive Design

In the current environment of prescriptive building and fire codes, the process of design is largely a process of complying with a set of prescribed design features implemented according to a design standard. That design standard stipulates exactly how the building feature is to be designed.

Generally, a jurisdiction such as a state passes a law adopting one of the model building codes, often with local amendments as the enforceable building code. The legal basis for the law is usually the protection of the citizens of that particular state. Rarely does a state or other governmental entity have a legal authority to force building owners to protect their own property. But building owners can be required to ensure that citizens, including emergency responders, are protected *from* the building in the event of a fire or other type of calamity. This is an important, but often overlooked, aspect of the law. The building is essentially expendable, as long as no citizens are injured as a consequence of the loss of the building. Thus the general goal of the building code is the protection of the building's occupants, emergency responders who might enter the building, and adjacent property owners. The property interests of the building owner are not intentionally addressed by the building code.

Usually, the building code explicitly prescribes the design features a building must possess, based on its size and contemplated use. These prescribed building features have usually been derived from the analysis of past fire experience and building failures. The locally adopted construction codes reflect a consensus among the building community on how to prevent specific adverse impacts upon the citizenry resulting from a set of recognized fire scenarios. The building community has a collective understanding of the outcome it wishes to prevent and adopts a prescribed means to prevent that outcome.

Before the owner is permitted to occupy a building, the owner must demonstrate to the local building code enforcement authorities that the building is safe. The prescriptive requirements in the building code effectively define what features the building must possess in order for it to be deemed acceptably "safe" for occupation by the residents of the municipality or other governmental subdivision. If the building does not include all of the construction provisions required by the relevant building code, it is presumed to be "unsafe." In this case the building code authorizes the building official to withhold the Certificate of Occupancy, denying the owner the use of the building.

The design process in the current prescriptive environment generally begins by defining the use group or occupancy type of the contemplated structure. When an architect categorizes a building or space as a particular use group, he or she is accepting a set of assumptions regarding the anticipated type and quantity of combustibles, the probable sources of ignition, the number of occupants, and the capabilities of the occupants for that building or space. None of these assumptions are explicitly stated, nor are the expectations regarding the performance of the structure under fire conditions. Instead, the assumptions are implicit in the prescriptive requirements.

When using prescriptive codes, the design process is reduced to identifying the type of intended use (occupancy classification) for the structure and then applying the prescribed design features. The designer does not determine whether those features are necessary or sufficient to attain the intended level of fire safety for the particular structure. It is assumed that compliance with the prescriptive criteria will yield a "safe" building. There is over one hundred years of experience to substantiate the assumption.

Codes and standards that are written in prescriptive terms are often referred to as "cookbook codes." As the user follows the design rules outlined in the code, she or he has little opportunity or incentive to consider the design basis for the fire alarm system.

The designer who designs a facility in accordance to a prescriptive code and standard must remain mindful that the objectives of the code writers are not necessarily the same as those of the building owner or operator. Indeed, they usually are not. The sole objective of the writers of the building code is to prevent the building from injuring citizens or from a failure of the subject building adversely impacting the property value of its neighbors. The building owner has an interest in preserving the value of the building. The building occupant has an interest in maintaining the utilization of the building. Insurers for both the owner and occupant (if different) have an interest in minimizing insured losses including property, business continuity, and possibly environmental impacts. These different objectives often result in the addition of capabilities and features to a fire protection system that exceed the minimums established by the relevant building code. This is often seen in the context of fire alarm system design.

Furthermore, most assume that if the fire alarm system complies with the building code or NFPA *101*®, *Life Safety Code*®, and if the installation complies with *NFPA 72*®, it will provide sufficiently early warning of a fire regardless of the nature of the fire, where it originates, and the objectives for the system. The purpose in 1.2.3 of *NFPA 72* states: "This Code establishes minimum required levels of performance, extent of redundancy, and quality of installation but does not establish the only methods by which these requirements are to be achieved." As indicated, the required levels are minimums. There are many design issues that are not addressed in the regional building codes or *National Fire Alarm and Signaling Code* because they are relevant only for a subset of facilities and are not appropriate for inclusion into a minimum compliance consensus standard. Designing to a minimum prescriptive code does not guarantee early warning of a fire. If the fire is remote from the detection devices, notification will be delayed until the fire grows sufficiently large to produce effects that finally cause a detector to transition to the alarm state. Owners who accept the minimums prescribed by these codes do not have the benefit of the increased performance that can be attained from a fire alarm system designed to meet their goals and objectives.

Thus, while the construction code requirements do reflect a set of objectives, those objectives are not explicitly stated. Furthermore, the prescribed building features do not necessarily represent the only means by which the implicit objective can be achieved. For any given objective there are quite possibly a number of means by which it can be achieved. Consequently, occasions do arise where prescriptive codes and standards preclude a solution that makes perfectly good sense for a given application.

PERFORMANCE-BASED DESIGN

The performance-based design method is radically different from the prescriptive design method. Performance-based design is a design process in which the ability of the design to achieve a certain objective is demonstrated by means of calculations and/or computational modeling rather than compliance with an empirically developed recipe of prescribed features that has evolved from years of experience. As a design method, performance-based design relies on principles of mathematics, physics, and engineering, whether it is used to produce a building, fire protection system, or bridge. Rather than relying upon a set of prescribed design rules that have been derived from past experience, the designer develops and evaluates the design in terms of its ability to achieve the performance objective through engineering calculations.

As a design method, this method is not a new approach. In other engineering disciplines, this method is the norm rather than an exception. For example, an engineer designs a bridge to support a design load under the range of conditions expected at the contemplated location. There is no code that spells out the size of the beams, footings, or suspension cables. The engineer performs calculations to determine whether each element in the structure is capable of supporting the load anticipated under the conditions of use. Engineers use a similar design process for automobiles, computers, and aircraft. In the case of an aircraft, the design process begins when someone defines the payload, range, and cost of the contemplated airplane. The objectives for the finished product then lead to specific design and performance criteria. These criteria relate to the engine thrust, wing dimensions, cruising altitude, required runway, and so forth. The designer benchmarks each of these criteria against the overall objectives of the contemplated aircraft. Where unavoidable, the designer makes concessions. Eventually a design emerges. If the designer has done his or her job properly, the prototype airplane flies as well as fulfills the various operational objectives of the purchaser.

In a performance-based design environment, the design of a fire alarm system begins with an objective — perhaps to provide alarm sufficiently early to permit the occupants to leave before the loss of tenability. Specific, quantitative criteria are then developed regarding what smoke concentrations and temperatures establish the limits of tenability. Various fire scenarios are considered. Generally, a *t*-square fire is assumed. See Exhibit S1.1 for a *t*-square fire growth curve. Fire models are used to determine how long after the emergence of a stable flame tenability persists in the occupied compartments and the routes to means of egress. Usually the same fire model can be used to predict how long it will take for the fire alarm system to detect that fire. The time point of detection starts the notification time – the period of time needed for the occupants to conclude that there is a fire and that they must

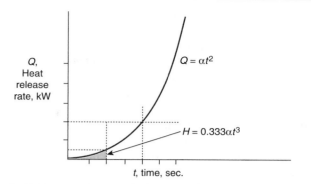

EXHIBIT S1.1 *The t-Square Fire. (J. M. Cholin Consultants, Inc., Oakland, NJ)*

leave the building. Egress models are used to determine how long it will take for the occupants to completely vacate the building. The loss of tenability time is compared to the sum of the notification and egress times to determine if all of the occupants are able to vacate the building before tenability has been lost. This process is repeated for an array of "worst-case" fire scenarios to develop a level of confidence that the system will achieve the objective over the entire range of fire and occupancy scenarios possible for the building.

In most facilities the fire alarm system is only one part of the larger fire protection strategy for the building, facility, or process. Yet it often plays a crucial role in initiating a tactical response to the occurrence of a fire. When a fire alarm system is designed and installed in compliance with a prescriptive building code requirement, that role has been defined, tacitly if not explicitly, by virtue of the existence of the requirement. The fire alarm technologist and technician should be made aware of how the fire alarm system fits into the overall fire protection strategy for a given building. In a performance-based design environment there is a fire protection strategy that establishes a defined role for the fire alarm system. When performance-based design methods are used, an understanding of the interdependency of all the fire protection features is critical.

In most states, the design of fire alarm systems is required to be performed by state licensed professional engineers. Performance-based designs must always be performed by an engineer knowledgeable in the principles of fire protection engineering. When undertaking the design of a fire alarm system in either the prescriptive or performance-based design environments, he or she must apply these principles judiciously.

The fire protection engineer uses the building design, type of construction, water supplies, fixed suppression systems, fire alarm systems, fixed extinguishing systems, off-site reporting, and fire service capabilities as essential elements in the fire safety strategy for the building. Each of these elements interacts with, and often relies upon, one or more other elements to achieve the final objective of a fire-safe building. When a change is made to one of those elements, changes must often be made to one or more of the other elements in order to maintain an equivalent level of fire safety. The interrelation and interdependency between the various elements of the facility fire safety features become far more apparent when an engineer considers performance-based design. When a system is designed using performance-based methods, the design remains valid only as long as all of the building features and other fire protection systems remain. If other building features and systems are modified, the design of those systems where performance-based design was used must be re-evaluated to verify that the modifications did not make a material impact on the design. Even changes as simple as the replacement of furniture can invalidate a performance-based design. Changing the furniture can change the fuel load and fire growth parameter of the probable fires, changing the requisite response time of the fire detection and fire suppression or extinguishment to control the fire to the assumed maximum heat release rate. Consequently, when an owner opts to rely on a performance-based design approach there will be a going-forward need to reevaluate any use changes as they affect design decisions, often on a regular basis, to ensure that the objectives are still achieved in spite of changes that have occurred or are expected to occur.

THE PERFORMANCE-BASED DESIGN PROCESS

Performance-based design is a *process,* and there are two very important things to remember about that process. The first is that the design methods normally associated with performance-based design can lead to erroneous conclusions and fundamentally flawed designs when the design method is used outside the context of the performance-based design *process.* The computational methods for predicting the response of a fire detection device only provide a number. That number is *not* a design. The number is one of many that are then used to support a design. For example, a response calculation predicts the response of a smoke detector to a 100 kilowatt growing fire in 60 seconds. Is that soon enough to meet the design objectives? We can't say until we know a lot more about the scenario. But we can see that this single calculation does not produce a design. The design is derived from the results of numerous calculations.

Second, performance-based design is not generally used for a whole building. The designer doesn't look at an architectural site plan and decide to use performance-based design on the project. Instead, performance-based design is most often used where the prescriptive design cannot be rationally used. For example, a fire alarm system is to be designed for a large, multi-story office building with a central, multi-story atrium space used as a cafeteria and general assembly area. The designer will probably use a prescriptive design method for determining the type of initiating devices and their spacings in the offices and the corridors serving those offices. However, a performance-based design method would be used for the atrium because the prescriptive spacing design rules for smoke detectors were never intended to be applied to a multi-story atrium space.

The *SFPE Engineering Guide to Performance-Based Fire Protection* (2007) defines *performance-based design* as a process that includes: "an engineering approach to fire protection design based on (1) agreed upon fire safety goals and objectives, (2) deterministic and/or probabilistic analysis of fire scenarios, and (3) quantitative assessment of design alternatives against the fire safety goals and objectives using accepted engineering tools, methodologies, and performance criteria." We will discuss the methods of performance-based design later, but we must keep in mind that *performance-based design* is a process and that the methods should only be used in the context of the whole process.

The process of developing a performance-based design begins with the identification of all the *stakeholders* in the finished building. The *Guide* also defines *stakeholder* as "one who has a share or an interest, as in an enterprise." In the context of the fire alarm system, the stakeholder is an individual (or a representative of a group of people) having an interest in the successful completion of the project or the operation of the facility in which it is to be installed. The reason for having an interest in the successful completion of a project may be related to legal, operational, financial, or safety concerns. When designing in accordance with the performance-based design process, it is critical to identify all of the stakeholders at the beginning of the project. The stakeholders each contribute to the identification of the goals and, subsequently, objectives for the project. They each also approve the methods that are used to achieve these goals and objectives.

The *Guide* identifies the following individuals as possible stakeholders:

- Building owner
- Building manager
- Authorities having jurisdiction (AHJs)
  - Fire
  - Building

- Insurance
- Accreditation agencies
- Construction team
  - Construction manager
  - General contractor
  - Subcontractors
- Tenants
- Building operations and maintenance staff
- Emergency responders
- Peer reviewer

Each of these individuals brings to the project her/his own viewpoint and performance goals. On occasion some of the stakeholders will find that their goals are the same. In other cases they will have widely divergent goals. Each has a role to play and something to contribute during the design process. The final design must be acceptable to all of the stakeholders. Consequently, the design must adequately address the goals of each stakeholder. Again, to quote the *Guide*, "It is imperative for the engineer to identify the stakeholders in order to obtain acceptance of the performance-based strategies used in the [design] process." The most demanding goals must be allowed to prevail over those that are less demanding. A stakeholder cannot reduce or rescind a goal of some other stakeholder, but it is always permissible to exceed a stakeholder's goal.

Once the stakeholders have articulated their goals, the fire protection engineer helps them translate those goals into specific design objectives. While a goal is expressed in general terms, objectives are specific and can ultimately be measured quantitatively. For example, perhaps the owner's goal is to get all of the employees out of the building unharmed in the event of a fire. In this case the objective can be stated as "completing all occupant egress before the loss of tenability." We can measure whether all of the occupants have left at any particular moment in time. We can quantify tenability in terms of carbon monoxide concentration, smoke obscuration, temperature, radiant flux, and so on, at various points in time during a hypothetical fire using compartment fire models run on a computer. So the process of translating goals into carefully worded objectives leads the stakeholders towards explicit performance criteria. This process is foreign to many people who have traditionally been involved in the design of fire protection systems, and so it is not an easy transition. But it is a critical part of the design process.

Once the stakeholders agree on the design objectives, the fire protection engineer must then reduce those objectives to specific performance criteria. Performance criteria are quantitative and can be measured to an appropriate level of precision. As mentioned above, tenability criteria are expressed as a concentration in parts per million of carbon monoxide, radiant flux in watts per square centimeter, air temperature in degrees Kelvin, visibility in optical density, and so on. Occupant egress rates can be quantified, leading to predictions of the number of people still within the facility at any point in time during a hypothetical fire. These performance criteria become the benchmarks against which candidate designs are measured. If a design does not achieve a level of performance equal to or better than the benchmark performance criteria, it cannot achieve the performance established by the stakeholders' goals and objectives.

For example, one objective of the fire alarm system in a particular facility might be to warn the occupants of a fire in sufficient time to allow them to extinguish the fire with hand-portable fire extinguishers before the fire suppression sprinkler system operates. This objective can be evaluated quantitatively for a given set of hypothetical circumstances. Let's assume that the fire suppression sprinkler system will respond to a 1.0 megawatt (MW) fire. This assumption can be checked for validity with a number of computational methods. If an employee will need 1.0 minute to react to a fire alarm signal, find a fire extinguisher, take the extinguisher to the fire, and deploy the extinguishing agent, then the fire alarm systems must be capable of detecting the fire at least 1.0 minute sooner than the fire suppression sprinkler system. (We are using 1.0 minute as an example and the use of this example should not be construed to suggest that this is a realistic time interval for any particular situation.) Using a *t*-square fire growth model, we can calculate how large the fire will be 1.0 minute before it attains a heat release rate of 1.0 MW. A suitable numerical value for α is obtained from fire protection engineering references and plugged into the equation in Exhibit S1.1 to obtain a heat release rate. This calculated fire size then becomes the response criterion for the fire alarm system. The fire detection system must respond to a fire of $1.0\ \text{MW} - X$, where X is the magnitude of the fire growth during the 1.0 minute response time of the personnel to the fire alarm signal. In this manner, performance criteria that have been derived from the stakeholder goals and objectives become the minimum compliance criteria in the performance-based design environment, rather than the specific design features in the prescriptive code.

When using the performance-based design process, the designer then develops candidate designs. The designer then can use the fire size criterion and fire detector response models to establish the appropriate spacing for detectors. The performance of each candidate design is modeled using any of a number of computational methods, tools, or modeling programs. These models produce a prediction of the performance of the system to a set of fire scenarios. Once the fire protection engineer has developed a design that achieves the performance criteria derived from the stakeholder objectives, the fire protection engineer presents the design to the stakeholders for review and acceptance. It is only after all of the stakeholders have accepted the design that the fire protection engineer can begin writing specifications and the production of drawings.

The performance-based design process derives the design features directly from the explicitly stated goals and objectives the stakeholders have for the facility. Goals are established. Those goals lead to concrete objectives. Those objectives lead to explicit, measurable performance criteria. Computational methods are then used to demonstrate that the system achieves the objectives by meeting the performance criteria that were derived from those objectives. The goals and objectives established by the stakeholders become the minimum compliance requirements for the design rather than a set of prescribed design features, as is found in our current codes. The designer proves the system design meets the performance criteria obtained from the design objectives through calculations and computational modeling. The methods used for each step in the process should only be used in the context of the performance-based design process and be well documented.

REASONS FOR A PERFORMANCE-BASED DESIGN METHOD

The current system of prescriptive codes and standards provides a level of fire safety in the new built environment that is acceptable to the public at large. Most newly constructed buildings provide greater fire safety than those built even a decade ago. Despite this positive trend, the ever-increasing need to use resources more wisely dictates change.

In an increasingly competitive world environment, the need to use resources wisely has become the fundamental driving force behind the transition toward a performance-based design environment. The inherent flexibility in the performance-based design method permits the selection of fire protection features based on actual need rather than legislated conformity. Where the design of fire protection systems through the use of performance-based design is allowed by locally adopted codes and the jurisdictional enforcement authorities, the design flexibility allowed by performance-based design results in a greater efficiency in the use of fire protection resources. In some instances, the routine application of the requirements of our current prescriptive codes results in a design that commits fire protection resources to systems that are not likely to make significant contributions to the fire safety of the structure.

For example, general purpose sprinkler heads are often installed in an atrium space at ordinary hazard spacing, 70 ft or 80 ft (21 m or 24 m) above the floor. In the past engineers have specified spot-type smoke detectors in that same location because these are usually classified as assembly spaces and a code requires smoke detectors in all places of assembly.

A quick calculation shows that a fire would probably have to reach a heat release rate of approximately 14,200 Btu/sec (15 MW) (approximately equivalent to an 80 ft² [7.5 m²] pool of gasoline in free burn) before the first sprinkler head would actuate. Yet, under these conditions the water discharging from those sprinkler heads would probably fail to penetrate the fire plume to the flame surface where it could contribute to controlling the fire. Relying on experience rather than calculation, it would be expected that a smoke detector installed at such a height would need a similar size fire before an alarm response would be attained. The smoke detectors at those heights would certainly not meet the implied goal of early warning. Finally, it is possible that the available fuel load in the space could not produce the needed 14,200 Btu/sec (15 MW) fire. The relevant construction codes severely limit the quantity of combustible materials in assembly spaces. So, neither the sprinkler system nor the smoke detection system can be expected to achieve the implied design objectives in the event of a fire in this example. The fire safety objectives for such a space remain the same as they are for the remainder of the building, but the prescribed means by which those objectives are presumably met are ineffective. This is a classic case of designing a building space by including the design features prescribed by the relevant building code and fire code, rather than designing fire protective features that provide for a given level of fire safety. A design is needed that is appropriate to the space.

Numerous historical fire incidents have shown that sprinklers prove extremely effective in controlling fire, by holding the fire to the compartment of origin, protecting the compartmentation, and maintaining structural integrity until the fire is extinguished. Accordingly, the model building codes have adopted a requirement for most occupancies to equip all such compartments with sprinkler systems. Undeniably, smoke detectors provide early warning in most fires, so the model building codes have adopted requirements for smoke detection for many occupancies. Numerous other historical fire incidents have shown that limiting the quantity and type of combustibles available in compartments enhances the survival prospects of the occupants and the protection of the structure. Therefore, requirements relating to the flame spread rating of wall coverings and interior furnishings for public places have become incorporated into the model building codes.

Lastly, the model building codes also might require 2-hour rated compartment construction under some circumstances. Required construction provides a passive compartmentation of the fire, limiting the probability of fire spread to adjacent areas.

Separately, each of these building code requirements offers valid strategies for limiting the hazard of a fire in the particular compartment. To a significant degree in the preceding example, the requirements for sprinklers, smoke detectors, and fuel load limitations address the same general goal: to limit the size of a fire. Considering the fire resistance rating required of the compartment in the atrium example, at least four required fire protection strategies address the same fundamental objective: to contain the fire to the compartment of ignition. Is it necessary to provide all of these required features for the same compartment? The current prescriptive building and fire codes do not explicitly address this question, nor do they provide a means to quantify the contribution each feature makes to the overall fire safety of the facility. The result is required redundancies.

There is nothing wrong with redundancies as long as they are intentional and based on a rational analysis. The logic usually used to justify redundancy is: if strategy A doesn't work, then strategy B is there to fall back on. It is essentially a "belt and suspenders" argument. A fire protection strategy that uses redundant features is more reliable than a strategy that relies on a single feature, assuming that all of the fire protection features have equivalent reliability. If the fire compromises one feature, then the other still maintains the safety of the structure.

If the redundancies were intentional, wouldn't it indicate that there was a tacit concern for the fundamental reliability of the "required" building features? How can the reliability of these required fire safety features be quantified? How many redundancies are enough? By the sixth or seventh set of "suspenders," isn't it fair to ask how much incremental benefit is accrued from the last set?

If this same atrium space were addressed in a performance-based design environment, the fire safety objective would remain the same: to limit the spread of a fire to the compartment of fire origin. In the performance-based design environment, where allowed by locally adopted codes or jurisdictional authorities, the engineer is not limited to the choice of means adopted by a building code. He or she is free to develop any means that can be shown to accomplish the fundamental performance objective. Appropriate construction of the walls and doors can contain a fire involving the worst-case fire load. The fire load can be limited. The fire can be suppressed. The fire can be detected early in its development and manually extinguished before it breaches the compartment. Any of these approaches can achieve the basic objective of confining the fire to the compartment of origin. In the performance-based environment, the engineer responsible for designing the fire protective features is free to select one or more means as part of an integrated fire protection strategy that best fulfills the objective at an acceptable level of reliability.

The use of a performance-based design method does not necessarily mean that the engineer will not employ intentional redundancies to ensure that he or she meets the objective in the event of a failure of one of the fire protection features. However, the engineer will base the selection of fire protection features on a rational analysis of the possible fire scenarios for a particular compartment and the computed mission effectiveness of the fire protection features. Then, he or she will select the most efficient means to accomplish the objectives in the event of that fire. Thus, performance-based design provides the engineer with the flexibility to address unique structures and sets of performance objectives that might not have been contemplated during the drafting of a model building or fire code. Performance-based design also provides a means of achieving society's fire safety objectives in unusual and unique environments. For example, an eighteenth century house that has been restored to its original eighteenth century condition is now used as a site for education and lectures on the local history. Conflicting goals immediately surface. The social value of the structure relies on its being preserved exactly as it existed in the eighteenth century. This preservation connects us to our history. Yet one of the means to preserve this heritage will change the structure by adding to it modern fire detection and suppression. These additions will limit the damage to the building if a fire occurs. Furthermore, because the public assembles in this structure, there is a social value in providing for a level of occupant life safety consistent with the expectations of the community in general. This life safety objective also might necessitate changes to the structure. For example, it might be necessary to widen or add doors to provide sufficient egress capacity.

Certainly, the historical value will erode the least when the changes to the building are minimized. With a purely prescriptive code, the designer of the fire protection systems has only a few alternatives. The authority having jurisdiction may or may not allow noncompliance with the prescriptive requirements of the code because he/she does not want to assume the inherent responsibility. With a performance-based environment, the solution becomes a "reasonable engineering approach" to finding acceptable methods to meet the fire safety goals. The inherent flexibility of the performance-based design environment also enables the designer to satisfy conflicting social values through the use of creative design. The inherent flexibility of performance-based design permits the selection of fire protection features based on the design goals and objectives, allowing the engineer to tailor the fire protection features to the specific structure and circumstances.

Obviously, only qualified designers working with the building design team should undertake the design of engineered fire protection systems in the performance-based context. Because many of the fire protection features of the structure are interdependent, a thorough understanding of each of those features and their interdependencies is critical. In the case of fire alarm systems, the designer should possess substantial design experience not only with fire alarm systems, but also with the other interdependent fire protection systems including the passive fire resistance and compartmentation, structures, HVAC systems, sprinkler fire suppression systems, fire service response capabilities, special extinguishing systems, and the principles of fire protection engineering, before undertaking a performance-based design project.

The designer should be included in the building design team as early as possible, ideally beginning with the feasibility stage. The designer of the fire alarm system addresses a wide range of fire protection issues that impact the fire alarm system design. As the owner and the authority having jurisdiction establish their fire safety goals and objectives, the fire alarm system designer must be able to advise them of the feasibility and prerequisite conditions for attaining those goals. Clearly, this design environment places far greater demands upon the designer. This increased demand is the price paid for the design freedom, improved cost efficiency, and design flexibility that performance-based design provides.

The locally adopted construction codes generally do not explicitly state what level of functional performance the prescribed design attains. Lacking clear performance objectives, how can a designer develop a performance-equivalent alternative design? Fortunately the fire scenario evaluation methods employed in the process of performance-based design can be applied to the prescribed features in a prescriptive code to deduce the apparent performance objective underlying a prescriptive feature. How can the designer determine the types and extents of necessary and sufficient changes to the structure in order to achieve the objectives of society? Answers to these questions emerge through the use of performance-based codes.

THE PERFORMANCE-BASED DESIGN PROCESS: EXPLICIT STATEMENT OF FIRE PROTECTION GOALS

The performance-based design process begins with explicitly stated fire safety goals. The stakeholders must answer the question: "What level of fire safety does society expect from the building?" The goals generally reflect a consensus of social values. The basic goals relating to life safety, protection of adjacent properties, environmental impact, and fire fighter safety will eventually be part of a locally adopted performance-based code. Until such codes are in place, the fire protection engineer must lead the stakeholders in developing their own goals.

Other fire safety goals relating to mission continuity might be established by the owner and insurance authorities. For example, a building should maintain its structural integrity during certain situations such as a fire. This goal could include maintaining the structural integrity even after all of the combustible material within it has burned. The goal may also require that a structure maintain its integrity during, and in spite of, fire-fighting activities. Another fire safety goal might be to warn the occupants of a fire in sufficient time to allow them to escape from imminent danger without harm. Some will complain that these goals seem so general that they add nothing to the design process. However, they are important to ensure that all of the relevant social values are reflected in the design of the building and its fire protection systems.

Fire protection goals generally address a range of issues relating to occupant life safety, fire fighter life safety, citizen life safety, citizen property rights, property loss limitation, the continuity of the facility mission, the preservation of heritage, and the environmental impact from the fire. Society puts these issues in a hierarchy, reflecting consensus social values. Avoiding a long-term environmental impact might be considered more important than limiting property damage. Therefore, the use of a very effective extinguishing agent for the protection of property that also produces a long-term environmental degradation would not be permitted. However, society will permit an airline to use the same extinguishing agent to extinguish engine fires on their commercial aircraft. In this case, society values the obvious life safety goal for the occupants of an airplane at a higher level than the environmental goal.

Further examples of fire safety goals are listed in the *SFPE Engineering Guide to Performance-Based Fire Protection*, including efforts to

- Minimize fire-related injuries and prevent undue loss of life
- Minimize fire-related damage to the building, its contents, and its historical features and attributes
- Minimize undue loss of operations and business-related revenue due to fire-related damage
- Limit the environmental impact of the fire and fire protection measures

THE PERFORMANCE-BASED DESIGN PROCESS: EXPLICIT STATEMENT OF FIRE PROTECTION OBJECTIVES

Once the stakeholders have agreed upon the fire safety goals, they must derive specific objectives that reflect how and to what degree the system must fulfill those goals. (See NFPA *Primer #1: Performance-Based Goals, Objectives and Criteria* [1997].) Although the objectives are derived from the goals, they are more specific and quantifiable. If the goal is to ensure that there is no loss of life due to fire in the building, then one objective derived from this goal is that the building should provide sufficient warning to all occupants in sufficient time to permit them to escape or relocate without loss of life or injury. As the fire protection engineer leads the stakeholders through the process of refining goals into objectives, the fire protection engineer is beginning the process of developing potential strategies. The use of occupant warning as the means to attain the goal implies the use of a fire alarm system as part of the occupant protection strategy. This objective also presumes that the design of the building provides a means of egress to the building exterior or to an area of refuge. Both of these fire protective features must be in place in order to attain the life safety objective. Because performance-based design permits flexibility, the designer can freely consider alternatives to the customary approach as long as the alternatives provide equivalent or superior performance.

THE PERFORMANCE-BASED DESIGN PROCESS: QUANTITATIVELY EXPRESSED PERFORMANCE CRITERIA

Once the stakeholders have established explicit objectives, the fire protection engineer develops *quantitative* performance criteria that provide the yardstick for measuring performance and attainment of the design objective. In the earlier example we used the objective of "providing warning in sufficient time to permit the occupants to escape without injury." A fire protection engineer will measure this objective using performance criteria that relate specifically to the process of notifying occupants and their response to the signal. These include the following:

- Sound pressure level needed to warn the occupants
- Number of occupants
- Condition of the occupants
- Egress speed of the occupants along the egress path
- Length of the egress path
- Size of the fire at the moment of detection
- Rate of fire growth

- Rate of deterioration of the tenability in each of the compartments, as well as along the egress route

The designer must quantify each of these criteria before the process of outlining possible designs can begin.

For example, a quantitative criterion for the warning of the occupants must exist. Research has shown that audible notification with sound pressure levels of 15 dB above average ambient or 5 dB above momentary ambient peaks lasting more than 60 seconds effectively warns occupants with normal hearing. For conscious, hearing-impaired occupants, visible notification intensities of 0.0375 lm/ft^2 (0.4037 lm/m^2) have been shown to be sufficient to warn such occupants. Consequently, the designer could formulate the performance criteria for occupant notification to read as follows:

Occupant notification shall be deemed to have been provided when the following conditions occur:

1. Attainment in all occupiable portions of the compartment, the Temporal Code-3 audible notification having a sound pressure of at least 15 dB above average ambient or 5 dB above momentary maximum (greater than 60 seconds duration) ambient and
2. Attainment in all occupiable portions of the compartment, visible notification producing an effective luminance of 0.0375 lm/ft^2 (0.4037 lm/m^2) with an integrated flash rate no greater than 2 Hz and no less than 1 Hz.

One way of achieving these performance criteria is to install audible and visible notification appliances according to the prescriptive criteria in the current edition of *National Fire Alarm and Signaling Code*.

However, in very large spaces the 0.0375 lm/ft^2 (0.4037 lm/m^2) effective luminance might be impossible to attain with currently available notification appliances. The effective luminance criterion was established assuming indirect viewing — the occupant is *not* looking in the direction of the notification appliance but is instead responding to the reflected light off walls, ceiling, and floors. In the case of large atria, auditoria, and other similar spaces, the designer might rely, instead, on direct view and use calculations to show that the radiant intensity of the notification appliances in direct view mode is sufficient to achieve notification. (Additional insight on these types of applications can be found in A.18.5.3 of *NFPA 72*.)

The Technical Committee on Notification Appliances for Fire Alarm Systems has included performance criteria in the body of the Code along with the prescriptive criteria for visible notification. However, the prescriptive requirements of other chapters in the *National Fire Alarm and*

Signaling Code are not as easily restated as performance-based criteria. In this case, a validated performance demonstration method must be used to determine the implied performance criteria of a design using the prescriptive criteria. Then the designer must use that same method to demonstrate that an alternative design meets or exceeds the performance implied by the prescriptive design.

Once again, the *SFPE Engineering Guide to Performance-Based Fire Protection* designates areas in which performance criteria may be needed:

- *Life safety criteria.* These criteria address the survivability of persons exposed to fire and fire products
- *Thermal effects.* These effects include both the effects on the occupants and on materials and equipment
- *Toxicity effects.* These effects, primarily on humans, consist of reduced decision-making capability and impaired motor activity leading to incapacity or death
- *Visibility.* This criterion affects the ability of occupants to safely exit from a fire
- *Non-life safety criteria.* These criteria address issues relating to acceptable damage levels to property
- *Ignition of objects.* These effects include the source of energy and what can be expected to ignite
- *Flame spread.* These effects assess the propagation of flame once ignition has occurred
- *Smoke damage.* This criterion includes smoke aerosols and particulates as well as corrosive combustion products
- *Fire barrier damage and structural integrity.* This criterion addresses the loss of fire barriers resulting in fire extension, increased damage, and structural collapse
- *Damage to exposed properties.* The engineer may need to develop this criterion in order to measure the potential for fire spread or damage to exposed properties

The *SFPE Guide* provides references to assist the designer in determining how to account for the list of performance criteria given.

THE PERFORMANCE-BASED DESIGN PROCESS: DEVELOPING THE VERIFICATION METHODS FOR DEMONSTRATING PERFORMANCE

Once the stakeholders have agreed upon fire protection goals, objectives, and performance criteria, the fire protection engineer must develop a method for demonstrating performance. The method usually employs a means of modeling how a fire of given characteristics will impact the facility. There is a wide range of conceivable fire sce-narios for any contemplated structure, but usually there are but a few that represent the credible worst case. These scenarios might include a rapidly developing fire of maximum credible fuel load and a slowly developing fire that produces extensive non-thermal smoke damage. These fire scenarios are then modeled using computer modeling programs.

Computer modeling programs exist that iteratively solve the equations that describe fire plume dynamics, fluid flow, heat transfer, and other physical phenomena involved in a fire and their impact on the building compartment. These programs require detailed input data about the particular compartment, fire, and ambient conditions. The programs account for all of the heat and mass evolved from the fire in order to predict the impact the fire has on the compartment and fire protection equipment.

Even though computer fire modeling is often a fundamental part of the process of demonstrating performance, engineers often address many issues in a performance-based design with algebraic formulas. Annex B, Engineering Guide for Automatic Fire Detector Spacing, of *NFPA 72* provides numerous algebraic formulas for solving specific aspects of the performance prediction of a fire alarm system. *The SFPE Handbook of Fire Protection Engineering* (2008) provides additional formulas.

It is critical that the method used to demonstrate the performance of the fire alarm system be validated to the greatest extent possible using documented research. First principles of physics or the reduction of experimental data to engineering correlations generally form the basis for performance prediction methods used by the designer. The performance-based design documentation must identify the source of the correlations or physical relation used to demonstrate performance for review by the authority having jurisdiction.

The sources, methodologies, and data used in performance-based designs must be based on technical references that are widely accepted and used by the fire protection community. As advised by the *SFPE Guide,* "The engineer and other stakeholders should determine the acceptability of the sources and methodologies for the particular applications in which they are used." The *Guide* provides guidance as to what constitutes a valid technical reference.

THE PERFORMANCE-BASED DESIGN PROCESS: COMPARISON OF PREDICTED PERFORMANCE WITH PERFORMANCE CRITERIA

Once the stakeholders have agreed on the goals, objectives, performance criteria, and the tools to be used to demonstrate performance, the designer can research potential design approaches. Usually, the process of deriving performance objectives from stakeholder goals and reducing those objectives to quantitative criteria will lead the designer to design approaches. This is where the designer often draws on the experience the designer has accrued over the years dealing with similar structures.

Usually, the designer outlines each candidate design in a narrative form, and the critical performance criteria for the design are identified. The candidate designs are essentially hypotheses that must now be tested using the verification methods the stakeholders have agreed are a valid measure of performance.

The performance demonstration starts with describing the fire scenarios. The choice of fire scenarios establishes the severity of the fire challenge the facility is expected to handle. Therefore, the choice implies value judgments on relative probabilities of occurrence and acceptable losses. Usually, an analysis of the range of types of combustibles, the extremes of combustible quantity, extremes of ambient conditions, extremes of asset vulnerability, and other circumstances lead to a limited number of worst-case scenarios. The engineer presumes that if the proposed system can achieve the design objectives under worst-case conditions, it will achieve the objectives under less arduous conditions. Profound errors can occur during this phase when the engineer defines "reasonable" worst-case conditions, so caution must be used. Furthermore, the designer should obtain input from the stakeholders as each has a contribution to make in this part of the process.

Once the engineer defines the scenarios, she or he usually uses a fire model to predict the impact of the fire on the compartment. The rate of heat release and rate of fire growth are used in a computer fire model to predict the development of the ceiling jet, its velocity, and its temperature. The model uses the ceiling jet dynamics to predict the rate of formation of a ceiling layer and, hence, the rate of interface descent. The computer fire model provides estimates of smoke and heat detector response time as well as a determination of the response time for the first sprinkler head. The engineer uses the predicted time for the upper layer to descend to a level that impedes egress to infer the time available for escape.

The response of the occupants is also modeled. Occupant reaction time and egress velocity are used as input parameters in egress models to determine how rapidly the occupants can vacate the facility under the fire scenario conditions. Other issues such as the rate of heat transfer through a fire barrier are addressed with other models or algebraic relations.

Eventually, the designer has a body of data that she or he can use to compare the performance of the proposed de-

sign to the performance criteria derived from the objectives established for the building. This comparison determines whether the proposed design passes or fails. See Exhibit S1.2. If the design passes the evaluation of the first scenario, the designer moves to the next scenario and repeats the process. If the design fails to meet these conditions, the engineer must develop a modified design and put that design to the same test. The designer repeats this evaluation process until a design emerges that achieves the design objectives for all contemplated fire scenarios.

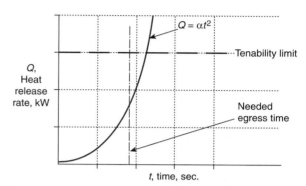

EXHIBIT S1.2 *Comparison of Predicted Egress — Time versus Tenability Limit. (J. M. Cholin Consultants, Inc., Oakland, NJ)*

Once a design has been shown to achieve all of the performance objectives for all of the fire scenarios, the designer is then ready to complete the design documentation and commence developing specifications and drawings for the systems to be used. Clearly, the performance-based design process is more involved than the prescriptive design process. Consequently, performance-based design is usually reserved for those situations where the prescriptive approach is clearly inadequate or not applicable.

CAUTIONS AND CAVEATS FOR THE DESIGNER

The analysis of fire alarm systems and the development of a system design predicated upon performance objectives and criteria are one step in the process of developing a fire protection strategy for the building as a whole. Although there are some very compelling advantages of performance-based design, there are also some very important disadvantages.

Performance-based design does provide a method that enables the designer to tackle difficult and unique hazards either where consensus standards do not outline an accepted protection method or where no consensus standard exists. However, performance-based design relies entirely on the designer's understanding of the hazard area, as well as an understanding of the process and progress of the potential fires in that hazard area. Failure to consider material aspects of the hazard area and how a fire will develop in that area can lead to fire protection systems that are doomed to failure. Consequently, the performance-based design of fire alarm systems requires a licensed professional engineer to perform the design. The designer should be knowledgeable in the principles of fire protection engineering and apply these principles judiciously.

The process of performance-based design often relies on the use of computer fire models. Some of these models are no longer actively supported and have been released to the public domain by the developer. In some cases, the validation of the computational routines nested within the software is tenuous or entirely lacking. In other cases, the software has minimal documentation. Consequently, the designer must take care that he or she only uses the model within the range of parametric variation over which the developer has validated the model.

The level of precision of the available performance measurements for fire alarm initiating devices is not equivalent to the level of precision generally implied by the results of the computer modeling techniques. Clearly, the most critical issue in evaluating the performance of a fire alarm system in a performance-based environment is the prediction of the time at which the system responds to the design fire. How big, or small, a fire will be detected by the detection portion of the fire alarm system? Sound validated performance metrics for heat detectors are now available. Engineers can predict the response of sprinkler heads when the temperature rating, response time index (RTI) for the particular model of sprinkler head, ceiling height, ambient temperature, and fire heat release rate are known.

Similar information is now available for heat detectors. In the past, Annex B has relied upon a rough correlation between listed spacing and the calculated RTI to predict the response time of heat detectors in a given environment and to a given fire. That correlation is still included in Annex B. However, with the adoption of the 2007 edition of the Code, manufacturers of heat detectors have been required to mark heat detectors with their RTI values or publish the RTI values in the detector bulletin. Since it takes time for the testing laboratories to test and determine the RTI of all of the models of heat detectors available, the effective date of the requirement was established for July 1, 2008.

Unfortunately, no credible predictive tool for smoke detector performance has yet been developed for use in the performance-based environment. Until sound validated performance metrics are available, the design engineer has little alternative to making estimates for smoke detector response. Small errors in these estimates often produce large differences in the predicted performance of the system.

The prescriptive spacing for smoke detectors cannot be used for performance-based design. There is little technical basis for it; it has been derived historically. Nor can the sensitivity marked on the detector be used as a performance metric for smoke detectors. This sensitivity value is only valid in the UL 268 laboratory smoke box. The detector sensitivity measured in the UL 268 laboratory smoke box is intended to serve only for manufacturer quality control and is not applicable outside the context of that test. There is no basis for a designer to presume that a detector will respond at that obscuration level in actual installation and fire conditions. Consequently, the only performance metrics available for smoke detectors are the smoke levels attained during the full-scale room fire tests conducted during the listing evaluation. These tests produce maximum optical obscurations that range between 10 percent per foot and 37 percent per foot at the detector locations, depending on the fuel and the individual test run. These are pass/fail tests, and commercially available detectors respond long before these levels are achieved. Unfortunately, the smoke level at the time of detector response is not recorded. (Refer to Sections 39 and 40 in UL 268, *Standard for Safety for Smoke Detectors for Fire Protective Signaling Systems*, 5th edition, 2006.)

Because a credible performance metric for smoke detectors is lacking, one way of predicting the response of a smoke detector is to adopt the simplifying assumption that in a flaming fire the plume's buoyancy serves as the driving force that conveys the smoke to the detector. This assumption allows a designer to model the smoke detector as a very sensitive heat detector, using the iterative method outlined in Annex B of *NFPA 72*. A second method incorporated into Annex B is a mass density approximation method. Both of these methods are reliant upon performance criteria selected by the user. Consequently, these methods can be used to produce wildly unrealistic response predictions if used by the uninformed. The inaccuracy and lack of precision in these methods can lead to *predictions* of failure to achieve design objectives when, in reality, the system will meet the performance objectives. The converse is also true. Consequently, these methods must be subjected to rigorous sensitivity analyses to ensure that a design based upon these methods will achieve the design objectives.

Very little credible data exist regarding the relative reliability of various fire protection strategies. Clearly, unless the engineer can compare the mission effectiveness of a proposed fire protection strategy with the alternatives, he or she cannot make a legitimate decision between them.

Fire alarm systems equipment, being assembled from electronic components with documented failure rates, can be assessed for equipment reliability using the methods outlined in the *Military Handbook for Reliability Prediction of Electronic Equipment*, MIL HDBK 217X ("X" stands for the revision letter). However, contributions to the mission effectiveness of the fire alarm system are also made by the design, installation, and maintenance elements of the system. These elements are more difficult to assess.

When comparing a design reliant upon a fire alarm system to some other strategy, the designer must compute the mission effectiveness of that other strategy using the same method he or she uses for the fire alarm system. In general, little information exists regarding the failure rates of system components. Consequently, estimates of the reliability of these systems must be used. In addition, the quality of the fire alarm system installation, testing, and maintenance has a great impact on the mission effectiveness of all active fire protection systems. The performance-based design environment both permits and demands that the designer evaluate these factors and incorporate them into the overall design of the building protection scheme.

Lastly, the performance-based design is far more reliant on a complete documentary trail of the entire decision-making process. There are no prescriptive requirements that can be used as a reference years after the project has been completed. Because any change in the facility can trigger the need for a reassessment of the design, the design must be thoroughly documented and the documentation must be maintained for the life of the structure. The documentation of the entire basis for developing the performance-based alternatives must include the following items in order to be considered complete:

1. *Project scope.* The project scope establishes the extent of the fire alarm system design and issues such as occupant characteristics, building characteristics, location of the property, fire service capabilities, utilities, environmental considerations, heritage preservation, building management, security, economic and social value of the building, the project delivery process, and the applicable regulations.
2. *Goals and objectives.* Goals and objectives include the general goals and specific objectives developed and accepted by all of the stakeholders.
3. *Performance criteria.* The performance criteria are quantitative measures that indicate attainment of the objectives. They must include how the engineer developed the criteria and what safety factors are used.
4. *Evaluation methods.* Evaluation methods discuss how trial designs will be evaluated.

5. *Fire scenarios and design fires.* Fire scenarios and design fires establish the range of variation of conditions under which the design will be valid, including the following:
   - Form of ignition source
   - Different items first ignited
   - Ignition in different rooms of a building
   - Effects of compartment geometry
   - Whether doors and windows are open or closed, and at what time in the fire scenario they are open or closed
   - Ventilation, whether natural (doors and windows) or mechanical (HVAC, etc.)
   - Form of intervention (occupants, automatic sprinklers, fire department, etc.)
6. *Final design.* The final design discusses how the design meets the performance criteria.
7. *Evaluation.* The evaluation discusses how to evaluate the design. What are the uncertainty factors? What are the safety factors?
8. *Critical design assumptions.* Critical design assumptions establish the limits of conditions and maintenance within which the system will achieve the design objectives and performance criteria.
9. *Critical design features.* Critical design features discuss what must stay in place from a building design scenario to ensure the fire alarm system will continue to operate.
10. *References.* References are the sources of information used to develop the design.

It is important to keep in mind that where there is a prescriptive code or design standard, the prescriptive approach to code compliance continues to serve as one of the acceptable methods to meet the performance objectives. When use of the prescriptive approach is chosen, the resulting system can be expected to achieve the minimum performance criteria established by the prescriptive code or design standard.

CONCLUSION

As the fire protection community moves toward a performance-based code, an engineer could encounter performance requirements something like the following: "Fire detection systems shall be designed to activate before a fire reaches a size that represents an unreasonable hazard to the building occupants or to the building itself." How an engineer approaches that requirement will depend on his or her understanding of basic fire protection engineering principles and the accepted procedure for developing a performance-based design.

The recommended steps in the process of developing performance-based approaches to a design problem can be summarized as follows:

1. Define the project scope.
2. Identify goals.
3. Define objectives.
4. Develop performance criteria.
5. Develop an evaluation method.
6. Develop trial designs.
7. Evaluate trial designs with fire scenarios.
8. Select the final design.
9. Develop a design brief.
10. Document the design.

This supplement to the *National Fire Alarm and Signaling Code Handbook* has discussed the concept of performance-based design and what it is, and it has described the design process. Even after performance-based design has become adopted into code, most fire protection features for most facilities will be designed using the prescriptive criteria that exist in the current codes and standards. However, as the need for greater design flexibility and efficiency increases, the trend toward the greater use of performance-based design methods will continue.

REFERENCES

References Cited

DiNenno, P.J. et al., eds., *The SFPE Handbook of Fire Protection Engineering*, 4th edition, National Fire Protection Association, Quincy, MA, and Society of Fire Protection Engineers, Bethesda, MD, 2008.

Hurley, M., ed., *SFPE Engineering Guide to Performance-Based Fire Protection*, 2nd edition, National Fire Protection Association, Quincy, MA, and Society of Fire Protection Engineers, Bethesda, MD, 2007.

National Fire Protection Association, *#1: Performance-Based Goals, Objectives and Criteria,* Revision 1.1, National Fire Protection Association, Quincy, MA, 1997.

NFPA 72®, National Fire Alarm and Signaling Code, 2010 edition, National Fire Protection Association, Quincy, MA.

NFPA *101®, Life Safety Code®*, 2009 edition, National Fire Protection Association, Quincy, MA.

UL 268, *Standard for Smoke Detectors for Fire Alarm Systems,* 5th edition, Underwriters Laboratories Inc., Northbrook, IL, 2006.

U.S. Dept. of Defense, *Military Handbook for Reliability Prediction of Electronic Equipment,* MIL HDBK 217, U.S. Government Printing Office, Washington, DC.

Bibliography

Custer, R.L.P. and Meacham, B. J., *Introduction to Performance-Based Fire Safety*, National Fire Protection Association Quincy, MA, 1997.

National Fire Protection Association, *NFPA's Future in Performance-Based Codes and Standards,* Report of the NFPA In-House Task Group, July 1995, National Fire Protection Association, Quincy, MA.

National Fire Protection Association, *Primer #3: Performance-Based Fire Scenarios,* Revision 1.1, National Fire Protection Association, Quincy, MA, 1998.

National Fire Protection Association, *Primer #4: Performance-Based Verification Methods,* Draft 9, National Fire Protection Association, Quincy, MA, 1999.

SUPPLEMENT 2

Emergency Communications Systems Design and Application Challenges

Wayne D. Moore, P.E., FSFPE

Editor's Note: Chapter 24 of the 2010 edition of the National Fire Alarm and Signaling Code is a new chapter that covers the requirements for the installation and performance of emergency communications systems for in-building fire emergency voice/alarm communications systems and other communications systems. This supplement focuses on those systems where the design includes the use of speakers. These systems often present the most design challenges and include in-building fire EVACS, in-building MNS, wide-area MNS, distributed recipient MNS, two-way emergency services ECS, area of refuge ECS, and elevator ECS.

Almost 30 years ago, NFPA began work on NFPA 72F, the first installation *Standard for the Installation, Maintenance and Use of Emergency Voice/Alarm Communication Systems.*[1] Finally published in 1985, the document contained approximately two pages of requirements, including additional pages of Appendix (Annex) material for "Voice/Alarm Signaling Service" and "Two-Way Telephone Communication Service."

In contrast, the 2010 edition of the *National Fire Alarm and Signaling Code,* Chapter 24, provides the requirements for *Emergency Communications Systems* with a total of 23 pages, including the Annex material. The major difference: the fact that this chapter of the *National Fire Alarm and Signaling Code* now covers more than just in-building fire emergency voice/alarm communications systems (EVACS). It also requires much more in terms of system arrangement and performance.

Chapter 24 is structured to include many types of emergency communications systems (ECSs). These have been divided into two basic categories, one-way and two-way. The one-way emergency communications systems include in-building systems as well as wide-area and distributed recipient mass notification systems. The two-way emergency communications systems provide requirements for both wired and radio emergency services systems, area of refuge systems, and elevator communication systems.

Chapter 24 includes a section that pertains to information, command, and control. This is for the communications methods and equipment used to receive and transmit information between premises sources or premises systems and the central control station(s). These may include wired or wireless networks for one- or two-way communications and/or control between a building or area and a central control station and could include an emergency services organization or public alarm reporting system. In a very basic configuration, a system and the receiving facility could be a supervising station system. However, there can be more complex systems that allow control of building systems and communication to building occupants from a remote location, including a municipal or other public alarm reporting command center or possibly even from a mobile command vehicle using secure communications.

Although prescriptive-based, mass notification systems will be required to serve very specific yet very varied needs. As such, mass notification systems design will require significant reliance on the risk analysis. Section 24.7 provides a performance-based design approach.

Each of these sections addresses requirements for pathway survivability. The arrangement of the sections containing the requirements for the different emergency communications systems presented is shown in *NFPA 72®* Figure A.24.3.6, which is reproduced here as Exhibit S2.1.

In recent years, the use of communications systems, both inside buildings and outside, has become more common for many different reasons. With the advent of terrorist activities, shootings on college campuses and high schools, and extreme weather issues, the public increasingly demands actionable information in real time. As a result of that demand, mass notification systems (MNSs) have become the norm in all Department of Defense buildings and sites. These systems have begun to make their way into other government and commercial buildings, college campuses, and outside environments. Many, if not most of the MNS designs, have combined or integrated these systems with the in-building fire EVACS.

During the 25-year history of EVACS, the Code did not allow for the sharing of the fire alarm textual audible notification appliances (speakers) or control equipment by any other system. The Code did not allow the use of the EVACS for anything other than fire alarm signaling, except under very strict control and approval by the authority having jurisdiction. However, for the first time in the history of the Code, the requirements permit the combining or integrating in-building fire emergency voice/alarm communications systems with other communications systems, such as mass notification systems, public address, and paging systems. In addition, again for the first time in the history of the Code, certain mass notification messages may take precedence over a fire alarm signal.

The technology has become available to ensure that fire alarm or priority mass notification messages — as determined by a careful and thorough risk analysis — can take precedence over any other announcements from non-emergency systems, including paging from a telephone system or other public address system. Speaker system designs have become available that incorporate volume controls and components that allow occupants to lower or turn off the speakers in their area or office, but switch the speakers back on to operate at their required power output when the fire alarm system or MNS actuates. This is one of the safeguards now available to meet the requirements of the Code and allow integration of in-building fire emergency voice/alarm communications systems with other communications systems.

No one would question that using one speaker system to serve multiple functions offers financial benefits to the owner of the facility. Using one system reduces the costs of design, installation, and maintenance throughout the life cycle of the system. In addition, regular use of the system for normal paging functions provides an end-to-end test of the audible notification components and circuits. As occupants become familiar with use of the system for normal paging, they will also more likely become comfortable and proficient with use of the system during an emergency.

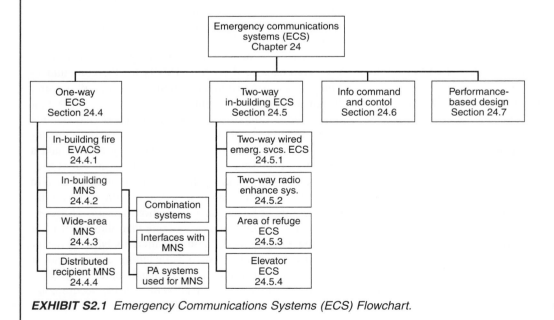

EXHIBIT S2.1 *Emergency Communications Systems (ECS) Flowchart.*

Since 1999, additions to the Code have required both audibility and intelligibility of voice communications. Prior to the introduction of intelligibility requirements, EVACS might have met the audibility requirements, but nothing ensured that occupants could comprehend and then react properly to the voice message. Typically, fire alarm system designers, installers, and authorities having jurisdiction had a limited background in the science of sound and communications. In previous editions, the Code offered only limited guidance on how to provide intelligible voice messages.

Users of the 2010 edition of the Code will find much improved design guidance for the layout of effective, audible, and intelligible communications systems. Of course, neither the Code itself nor this Supplement intends to serve as a complete design guide. See the References and bibliography at the end of this Supplement for additional design information.

Table S2.1 provides a list of emergency communications systems with their specific requirements. Integration of each of these systems can provide emergency information to the building occupants and meet the communications needs required by the owner.

TABLE S2.1 *Emergency Communications Systems*

One-Way ECS	Two-Way In-Building ECS
In-building fire EVACS ECS	Two-way wired emergency services (ECS)
In-building MNS ECS	Two-way radio emergency services (ECS)
Wide-area MNS	Area of refuge ECS
Distributed recipient MNS	Elevator ECS

According to Wikipedia, communication is the process to impart information from a sender to a receiver with the use of a medium. The first step in any design process is to determine what ECS the owner or occupants of a building or area require or desire. In most situations, a voice communication system will need to include a combination system providing in-building fire EVACS, in-building MNS, and paging to meet the operational goals and cost savings objectives of the owner.

The next step is to evaluate the expected or measured ambient noise conditions of the building. Exhibit S2.2 shows typical levels of ambient noise.

As stated previously, one of the major operational goals is to ensure the messages distributed by the ECS are intelligible. The 2010 Code defines intelligible as "capable of being understood; comprehensible; clear" and defines intelligibility as "the quality or condition of being intelli-

dB SPL Operating Levels						
Listening level		Ear level range	Comments	High level music	Med. level music	Low level music
dB SPL	dB SPLPk					
133	145					
130	142		Pain threshold			
127	139					
124	136					
121	133		Non-linear region			
118	130					
115	127					
112	124					
109	121		High level music			
106	118					
103	115			X		
100	112			N		
97	109		Medium level music	O		
94	106			M		
91	103			I	X	
88	100			N	N	
85	97		Low level music	A	O	
82	94			L	M	
79	91				I	X
76	88				N	N
73	85				A	O
70	82		Speech @ 0.5 meter		L	M
67	79					I
64	76					N
61	73		Speech @1 meter			A
58	70		Noisy HVAC			L
55	67		Speech @2 meters			
52	64					
49	61		Typical HVAC			
46	58					
43	55					
40	52		Quiet room			
37	49					
34	46		VERY quiet room	N		
31	43			O		
28	40			I		
25	37			S	N	
22	34		Recording Studio	E	O	
19	31				I	
16	28				S	N
13	25		Dream on!		E	O
10	22					I
7	19					S
4	16		Brownian motion			E
1	13		Noise floor of air and ear			
−2	10					
−5	7	N				
−8	4	O				
−11	1	I				
		S				
		E				

EXHIBIT S2.2 *Typical Operational Level Over the Dynamic Range of the Ear. (Source: Bob McCarthy, Sound Systems: Design and Optimization, Elsevier, Ltd., 2008, Figure 1.14, page 15)*[2]

gible." Although the Code does not yet require a system to meet a specific level of intelligibility, it does provide a new Annex D, entitled Speech Intelligibility, that treats the subject of measuring intelligibility levels in detail. In most designs of typical sound and communications systems, stakeholders measure intelligibility by whether or not the designers, installers, authorities having jurisdiction, and occupants can understand the messages. The stakeholders do not expect anyone to actually quantify intelligibility through measurements or tests.

The issue in design becomes how to ensure that the system "delivers" intelligible messages through an installation of cabling and equipment consisting of amplifiers and speakers. See Exhibit S2.3.

The "source" shown in Exhibit S2.3 could consist of a person orally giving emergency instructions via the microphone. Or, the source could consist of a prerecorded message. Once either of these signal sources are present, the next step occurs in the signal processing and amplifier equipment.

The NEMA *Emergency Communications Audio Intelligibility Applications Guide*[3] provides a description of factors that affect intelligibility:

> There are many factors that affect the intelligibility of messages presented over public address systems in public and private spaces. Some major intelligibility factors include:
>
> - Background noise.
> - The configuration of the space being addressed.
> - The acoustical properties of the materials on the walls, floors, and ceilings.
> - The distortion and bandwidth of the sound equipment.
> - The characteristics of the person speaking (male/female, accent, microphone technique, etc.)

The ECS system designer cannot control all of these factors, but he or she must design the system to compensate for those factors not under his or her control. The designer must address background noise or "ambient noise levels" as part of the design. In order for the system to meet the intelligibility goals, the system must have an adequate signal-to-noise ratio. If the system provides a speech signal at least 15 dB higher than the ambient noise level, this will minimize the intelligibility loss from the ambient noise levels.

However, if the ambient noise levels reach exceedingly high levels — greater than 90 dB — then attempting to present a signal with sufficient level to overcome the ambient noise level will likely decrease the intelligibility of the message. Using the example of an ambient noise level of 90 dB, such as in a noisy manufacturing area, the speaker must deliver 105 dB at the listener to overcome the noise. Such a level from the speaker could exceed 120 dB nearer the speaker, depending on the location of the listener in relationship to the placement of the speaker. The Code permits a maximum sound pressure level (SPL) of 110 dB. The SPL of 120 dB could result in hearing damage. The Code requires the use of visible notification appliances (strobes) in locations with such high ambient noise levels; see 18.4.1.2. In addition, the occupants of areas with such a high ambient noise level would need training to respond to the visible notification appliances and relocate to an area where they could hear the message from the speakers.

The Code also recognizes that some ambient noise signals are made up of different frequencies and states "in areas where the background noise is generated by machinery and is fairly constant, a frequency analysis can be warranted." See A.18.4.3.1.

One must understand that proper microphone technique presents one of the uncontrollable factors in any design. The installer of an ECS system must provide the operators of the system with proper training in the use of a microphone, as well as for the other operation use of the system. In many cases, designers may prefer to use prerecorded messages or digitally compiled phrases rather than let untrained users operate the microphone. Recorded messages provide a consistent sound level output and a controlled speech pattern generally performed by recording professionals. Such output will provide a more intelligible message than a nonprofessional who makes an unpracticed announcement using a microphone.

Designers must consider other intelligibility issues, including possible distortion introduced by the amplifier and signal processing equipment. It should come as no surprise that equipment quality plays an important part in the delivery of an intelligible message to the listener. Although the Code requires the use of products listed by an organization acceptable to the authority having jurisdiction, such listings do not guarantee the equipment's quality to reproduce clear, understandable messages. Assuming that the control and amplifier equipment meets the quality goal and

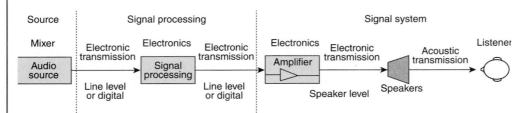

EXHIBIT S2.3 *Transition Flow from the Signal Source to the Listener. (Source: Bob McCarthy, Sound Systems: Design and Optimization, Elsevier, Ltd., 2008, Figure 1.1, page 3)*[2]

operational needs of the design, the next important consideration must include an analysis of the effect of the environment on the speakers and the speaker placement throughout the facility.

The designer must understand the acoustics of the space. In addition, the designer must understand and address the acoustic performance properties of the proposed speakers. These considerations help ensure that he or she chooses the right speaker, its output, and placement. The analysis may disclose that the only way to achieve a proper design for the ECS is to include the modification of some architectural design features of the space.

As stated in Annex D of the 2010 edition of the Code, D.1.5, "The designer and the authority having jurisdiction should both be aware that the acoustic performance parameters of the chosen loudspeakers, as well as their placement in the structure, play a major role in determining how many appliances are necessary for adequate intelligibility. The numerical count of appliances for a given design and protected space cannot, by itself, be used to determine the adequacy of the design. Sometimes, the acoustic problems of certain placement constraints can be satisfactorily overcome through the careful selection of loudspeakers with the requisite performance characteristics, rather than by increasing their number."

Chapter 18 of the Code requires designers to specify "acoustically distinguishable spaces" (ADSs) when designing an ECS. Annex D states that an ADS may be a physically defined notification zone or part of a notification zone. An ADS is a space "distinguished from other spaces because of different acoustical, environmental or use characteristics such as reverberation time and ambient sound pressure level." The Code allows the designer to define an ADS as a space that "might have acoustical design features that are conducive for voice intelligibility, or it might be a space where voice intelligibility could be difficult or impossible to achieve." In essence all parts of a building are a part of an ADS. There can be many different ADSs in a building. Some ADSs might require intelligible voice and others may be designated by the designer as requiring only tone signaling, or no occupant notification at all. See Exhibit 18.13, which is a decision tree that can be used for determining the requirements or needs for each ADS. Annex D encourages designers to review all of the information it provides regarding acoustically distinguishable spaces.

Reverberation time — also known as RT60 time — is defined as the amount of time it takes for a sound to diminish 60 dB below the original level. Sound reflecting off hard surfaces such as wood or tiled floors, concrete walls, ceilings, or other hard surfaces produces reverberation. Reverberation can seriously contribute to reduced intelligibility. When a speaker broadcasts a message, the listener hears direct sound from the speaker and somewhat delayed sound from reverberation. The degree of intelligibility of the sound will depend on the listener's physical location in relation to the location of the speaker.

Reverberation in a room or space depends on the nature of that space: dimension of the space, construction materials used in the space, whether or not the space includes occupants, and furnishings in the space. The amount of reverberation in a room diminishes when the room or space includes construction features, people, or furnishings that absorb sound. The amount of reverberation varies from space to space, depending on the absorption characteristics of the materials in a particular space. Hard surfaces reflect sound rather than absorb it. Soft surfaces, such as drapes and carpeting, tend to absorb sound. The more reflection in a space, the greater the reverberation that space will have. The more absorbency in a space, the less reverberation that space will have. To help reduce reverberation in a room, designers should locate speakers away from hard surfaces, such as walls, and point the speakers towards soft, absorbent surfaces.

Increasing the power (wattage) of the speaker often distorts the message content from a speaker. Generally, a more efficient design locates the speakers in occupied areas of the space and uses more speakers at reduced power for each speaker. Both of these design considerations help reduce the effects of reverberation, provide a better direct signal to the listener, and increase the intelligibility of the messages. This guidance applies best where the ceiling heights do not exceed 10 to 12 ft (3.0 to 3.7 m). In rooms or spaces with high ceilings, the designer should use a more "focused" or directional speaker than a standard ceiling- or wall-mounted speaker.

UL Standard 1480, *Standard for Speakers for Fire Alarm, Emergency, and Commercial and Professional Use*[4], requires a reverberant chamber test and an anechoic rating as defined by CAN/ULC-S541-07, *Speakers for Fire Alarm Systems, Including Accessories*[5]. The reverberant chamber test measures the total sound power output of a speaker in a chamber specifically designed to reflect a certain amount of the sound. Yet, it has proven difficult to correlate a speaker's reverberant chamber sensitivity rating with real-world acoustics. Typically, the anechoic rating at 1 kHz is more representative of real world performance.[3] A designer should consult a manufacturer's product information sheets to determine the speaker characteristics available. Because speakers are "point source" appliances, ideally the sound radiates outward in a near spherical pattern. As the sound moves away from the speaker, the inverse square law relates a drop of 6 dB of sound pressure level every time the distance is doubled from the speaker.

The sensitivity of a speaker is defined as the amount of sound a speaker can produce with a known signal frequency, power level, and distance from the speaker. For fire alarm speakers listed under UL Standard 1480, the sensitivity is rated at 1 Watt of power measured 10 ft (3.0 m) from the speaker.

Speaker sensitivity may prove useful for comparing different models and manufacturers of speakers. However, a designer may find a polar distribution plot for a speaker more useful when choosing a speaker for a particular design. This is because speakers in the direct line of the listener actually produce the loudest sound. As the listener moves away from that centerline, speakers produce less loud sounds. This directionality information is useful when determining the coverage area of a speaker. The "coverage angle" is defined as the angle where the SPL drops 6 dB from the on-axis SPL. As stated in the NEMA *Guide*,[3]

> Speakers used for emergency voice/alarm communication system are wired as 'Constant Voltage' systems, where the maximum power output of the amplifier is obtained at a certain speaker voltage, such as 25 V or 70.7 V. The power output of a speaker, and thus the resulting SPL is controlled by wattage taps on the speakers themselves. The minimum wattage tap for a UL Standard 1480 listed speaker is $\frac{1}{4}$ W. Typical 4-inch speakers have wattage taps in 3 dB increments: $\frac{1}{4}$ W, $\frac{1}{2}$ W, 1 W, and 2 W. Each wattage tap doubles the power delivered by the speaker, and so increases the SPL output by 3 dB for each increasing tap. An increase of 3 dB is considered a just noticeable increase in SPL, changing the wattage tap from $\frac{1}{4}$ W to 2 W increases the perceived loudness by slightly less than double.

A designer may choose one of many speaker layout options. The layout will obviously depend on the room or space geometry. See Tables S2.2 and S2.3 and Exhibit S2.4 for some recommendations for ceiling-mounted speakers. As stated in the NEMA *Guide*, in general low ceilings require more ceiling-mounted speakers per square foot of area than high ceilings.

Designers have also used wall-mounted speakers in many applications, especially in corridors and other narrow spaces. The NEMA *Guide* lists some of the advantages and disadvantages of wall-mounted speakers, which are extracted below:

Advantages

- For narrow areas such as hallways, fewer speakers and less amplifier power may be needed to cover the same size area. This is because all of the speaker's sound contributes to useable audibility.
- Mounting can be on more than one wall. This further improves the distribution of direct sound to the listener.

TABLE S2.2 *Examples of Typical 4-in. Speaker Coverage for Varying Ceiling Heights*

| | Listener Height = 5 ft | |
Ceiling Height	Coverage Diameter	Coverage Area
8 ft	7.7 ft	46 ft²
10 ft	12.8 ft	129 ft²
12 ft	17.9 ft	252 ft²
14 ft	23.0 ft	417 ft²
16 ft	28.2 ft	623 ft²
18 ft	33.3 ft	870 ft²
20 ft	38.4 ft	1158 ft²
	Listener Height = 1.5 m	
2.5 m	2.6 m	5.1 m²
3 m	3.8 m	11.6 m²
3.5 m	5.1 m	20.6 m²
4 m	6.4 m	32.2 m²
4.5 m	7.7 m	46.3 m²
5 m	9.0 m	63.0 m²
5.5 m	10.2 m	82.3 m²
6 m	11.5 m	104.2 m²

Source: NEMA Standards Publication SB 50-2008, *Emergency Communications Audio Intelligibility Applications Guide*, Table 2-1.[3]

TABLE S2.3 *Layout Pattern Selection Guide*

Layout	Description
2× Edge-to-edge	Not recommended except for tone only signaling or small rooms with low noise or low reverberation.
1.4× Edge-to-edge	Uses fewer speakers than edge-to-edge pattern. Only appropriate for rooms with low noise and low reverberation.
Edge-to-edge	Preferred layout pattern for most areas.
Minimum overlap	Use with areas of high reverberation and/or high ceilings.
Full overlap	For the worst areas, generally provides excellent intelligibility for even difficult areas. Use with caution. This type of pattern can result in lower than expected intelligibility due to multiple speaker interaction. Modeling is recommended for areas that would need this layout pattern.

Source: NEMA Standards Publication SB 50-2008, *Emergency Communications Audio Intelligibility Applications Guide*, Table 2-2.[3]

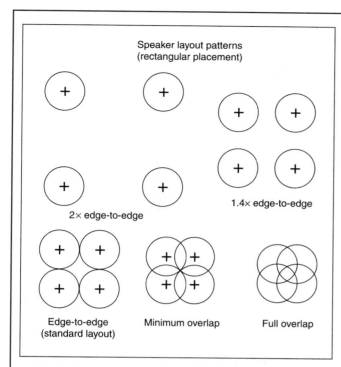

Speaker layout patterns
(rectangular placement)

2× edge-to-edge

1.4× edge-to-edge

Edge-to-edge
(standard layout)

Minimum overlap

Full overlap

EXHIBIT S2.4 *Speaker Layout Patterns. (Source: NEMA Standards Publication SB 50-2008, Emergency Communications Audio Intelligibility Applications Guide, Figure 2-7)*[3]

- Wall mounted speakers put sound directly into the listener area. This can reduce the excitation of the reverberant field.
- Combination speaker strobe units permit voice and visual notification in a single appliance.

Disadvantages

- The sound field from wall mount speakers is more likely to encounter obstructions from furnishings such as cubicle walls in office environments or movable partitions in conference rooms. If the furnishings in a room are likely to change, a distributed overhead system or a combination wall mount and overhead design should be considered. This minimizes the variation of audibility and intelligibility.
- In rooms with low, hard ceilings the sound emitting from the top hemisphere of the coverage pattern is reflected off the ceiling and down to the listener. This can increase the reverberant field sound level and result in delayed arrival of sound. These factors both contribute to a reduction in intelligibility.

The principal difference between a wall-mounted speaker system and a ceiling-mounted speaker system is the influence speaker location has on the distance from the speaker to the listener's location in the room.

The Code requires installers to locate wall-mounted speakers at heights not less than 90 in. (2.29 m) above the floor. When provided with a visible notification appliance, the unit is required to be installed such that the entire lens is not less than 80 in. (2.03 m) and not greater than 96 in. (2.44 m) above finished floor. With wall-mounted speakers, designers must determine coverage for each speaker using the diameter of coverage rather than the coverage area used for ceiling-mounted speakers. The speaker spacing is then determined using the width of the wall coverage defined by the diameter of coverage. See Table S2.4.

TABLE S2.4 *Wall-Mounted Speaker Coverage Width vs. Room Depth*

Wall-Mounted Speakers (in Feet)	
Room Width	Coverage Width 3 ft (1 m) from Wall Opposite Speaker
10 ft	18 ft
12 ft	23 ft
14 ft	28 ft
16 ft	33 ft
18 ft	38 ft
20 ft	44 ft

Wall-Mounted Speakers (in Meters)	
2.5 m	3.8 m
3.0 m	5.1 m
3.5 m	6.4 m
4.0 m	7.7 m
4.5 m	9.0 m
5.0 m	10.2 m
5.5 m	11.5 m
6.0 m	12.8 m

Source: NEMA Standards Publication SB 50-2008, *Emergency Communications Audio Intelligibility Applications Guide,* Table 2-4.[3]

Wall-mounted speakers generally consist of a single row on one side of a space. However, a designer must take care to not overextend the expected sound penetration into a room larger than 20 ft (6.1 m) wide. When the opposite wall is greater than 15 ft (4.6 m) away from the wall where the speakers are installed, a second group of speakers should be installed on the facing wall with full overlap of the speaker coverage. See Exhibits S2.5 and S2.6 for a typical wall-mount coverage layout.

For both ECS and MNS systems, intelligibility of the voice message is one of the most important aspects of a well-designed system. But equally important is the development of the messages to be used during an emergency. Additional information on planning, design, and testing for speech intelligibility can be found in Chapter 18, Annex D, and Supplement 3.

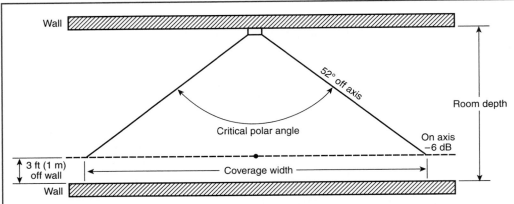

EXHIBIT S2.5 *Wall-Mount Speaker Coverage Pattern (Viewed from Ceiling). (Source: NEMA Standards Publication SB 50-2008, Emergency Communications Audio Intelligibility Applications Guide, Figure 2-8)*[3]

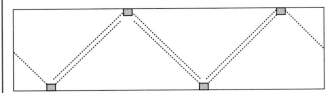

EXHIBIT S2.6 *Typical Wall-Mount Speaker Coverage Layouts (Source: NEMA Standards Publication SB 50-2008, Emergency Communications Audio Intelligibility Applications Guide, Figure 2-9)*[3]

Research shows that the message is one of the most important factors in determining the effectiveness of a warning system[6]. The warning style is also crucial and should be specific, consistent, certain, clear, and accurate. All emergency communications systems used to communicate emergency directions or messages should ensure the information provided meets the following general criteria:

- Must be real time — should not rely solely on prerecorded messages, although they might provide limited value in some scenarios.
- Must be rich in content — actionable information. An informed population will respond more efficiently. The message must provide the following content:
  - Information on the hazard and danger
  - Guidance on what people should do
  - Description of the location of the risk or hazard
  - An idea of when they need to act
  - The name of the source of the warning (who is giving it, i.e., the identity of the authority)
- Must be intelligible — audibility is not the same as intelligibility; the message must not just be loud, it must be understood.

- Must be zonable — able to allow addressing only those population groups affected by the situation.
- Must be intrusive — must gain and retain the population's attention. Warning style is also crucial; it must be specific, consistent, certain, clear, and accurate.

The design of an ECS should also allow informed emergency managers to provide live and correct information to the population as a situation develops. For example, consider an incident where a vehicle strikes the wing of a fueled aircraft resulting in a significant fuel spill at a terminal gate. Just sounding the fire alarm with no instructions would result in passengers exiting to the tarmac. In this example, live messages to the occupants near the incident could instruct them to move away from the gate waiting area to a safe location.

Another example to consider would occur when the MNS initiates amber strobes (labeled ALERT) in an airport terminal and all monitors in the terminal change to display information on the nature of the emergency and the action needed by passengers. Will the passengers and staff know what the amber strobes mean? Will they know to look at the monitors for instructions? Will all the passengers read English?

In addition to the information about message use and content stated above, it becomes very important to repeat the messages and provide timely updates to avoid incorrect actions by the building occupants. Empirical research of natural disasters, technological events, terrorism, and more has developed some general guidance. This information will provide direction on the following generic issues:

- Deciding to warn (how, when, who, where)
- Writing the warning message(s) — content matters

- Disseminating the message (channels, frequency)
- Monitoring real-time response and updating
- Testing the warning systems

Once stakeholders have made decisions on the basic information needed in a message, they should refine the message to accommodate specific needs. Such needs include addressing unique community demographics — elderly, disabled, non-English speaking — and any unique geographical feature of the location where the message will be delivered. In addition, the stakeholders must consider how sudden or protracted events, large or even concurrent disasters, will change the message.

In order to ensure the maximum effectiveness of the messages, the recipients of the messages must receive training and education. In the case of a mass notification system, the training and education of the public becomes critically important. They must understand the nature of the messages they may receive and how the technology will deliver those messages in an emergency.

The system and its components must remain secure. The design of speakers and control equipment — hardware and software — must render them tamper-proof and hacker-proof. The ECS must include interoperability, so that it can complement other local and regional emergency response systems. And finally, the system must be survivable. Chapters 12 and 24 of the Code have specific levels of survivability for various emergency communications systems. The system must be able to withstand attack based on the planned ECS use. Also, the stakeholders must determine the use of the system by a rigorous risk analysis, following guidance provided by the Code and other applicable codes and standards.

Emergency communications systems — whether they consist of stand-alone in-building EVACS or MNS or include some other form of integrated ECS — provide a critical emergency capability that can save lives and property. Designers must keep in mind that for any design of an ECS, intelligibility, security, survivability, and the proper use of messaging all represent important aspects of a complete design.

REFERENCES

References Cited

1. NFPA 72F, *Standard for the Installation, Maintenance and Use of Emergency Voice/Alarm Communication Systems,* 1985 edition, NFPA, Quincy, MA.
2. McCarthy, B., *Sound Systems: Design and Optimization*, Elsevier, Ltd., London, 2008.
3. NEMA Standards Publication SB 50, *Emergency Communications Audio Intelligibility Applications Guide*, National Electrical Manufacturers Association, Rosslyn, VA, 2008.
4. UL 1480, *Standard for Speakers for Fire Alarm, Emergency, and Commercial and Professional Use*, Underwriters Laboratories Inc., Northbrook, IL, 2003.
5. CAN/ULC-S541, *Speakers for Fire Alarm Systems, Including Accessories*, Underwriters Laboratories of Canada, Toronto, ON, 2007.
6. Gray, R., "Taking it From the Experts When Crafting Your Messages," *Campus Safety Magazine*, May/June 2008.

Selected Technical Bibliography

Beranek, L. L., *Music, Acoustics & Architecture,* Wiley, New York, 1962.

Beranek, L. L., *Concert Halls and Opera Houses: Music, Acoustics, and Architecture,* 2nd ed., Springer, New York, 2004.

Cantu, L., "Monaural Hearing and Sound Localization," Austin State University, Nacogdoches, TX, 1999.

Cavanaugh, W. J., and Wilkes, J. A., *Architectural Acoustics Principles and Practice,* Wiley, New York, 1999.

Davis, D., and Davis, C., *Sound System Engineering,* 2nd ed., H. W. Sams, Indianapolis, IN, 1987.

Duda, R. O., Sound Localization Research, San Jose State University, San Jose, CA, 1998.

Eargle, J., *Electroacoustical Reference Data*, Van Nostrand Reinhold, New York, 1994.

Everest, F. A., *The Master Handbook of Acoustics,* 3rd ed., TAB Books, Blue Ridge Summit, PA, 1994.

Giddings, P., *Audio System: Design and Installation,* H. W. Sams, Indianapolis, IN, 1990.

Herlufsen, H., *Dual Channel FFT Analysis (Part 1),* Technical Review, Advanced Techniques in Acoustical, Electrical and Mechanical Measurement, No. 1, Bruel & Kjaer, 1984.

Martin, K. D., "A Computational Model of Spatial Hearing," Massachusetts Institute of Technology, Cambridge, MA, 1994. McCarthy, B., *Meyer Sound Design Reference for Sound Reinforcement,* Meyer Sound Laboratories, 1998.

"Message Mapping: How to Communicate During the Six Stages of a Crisis," White Paper, 3n Global, 2008.

NEMA Standards Publication SB 40-2008, *Communications Systems for Life Safety in Schools*, National Electrical Manufacturers Association, Rosslyn, VA, 2008.

Sound System Design Reference Manual, JBL Professional, 1999.

Tremaine, H., *Audio Cyclopedia*, H. W. Sams, Indianapolis, IN, 1979.

Various, *Sound Reinforcement*, an anthology of articles on sound reinforcement from the *Journal of the Audio Engineering Society*, volumes 1 through 26. (Available from the AES)

Papers

Boner, C. P., and Boner, R. E., "The Gain of a Sound System," *J. Audio Engineering Society*, 1969;17(2).

Haas, H., "The Influence of a Single Echo on the Audibility of Speech," *J. Audio Engineering Society*, 1972; 20(2).

Hopkins, H. F., and Stryker, N. R., "A Proposed Loudness-Efficiency Rating for Loudspeakers and the Determination of System Power Requirements for Enclosures," *Proceedings of the IRE*, March 1948.

Molloy, C. T., "Calculation of the Directivity Index for Various Types of Radiators," *J. Acoustical Society of America*, 1948;20:387–405.

Peutz, V. M. A., "Articulation Loss of Consonants as a Criterion for Speech Transmission in a Room," *J. Audio Engineering Society*, 1971;19(11).

Peutz, V. M. A., "Quasi-steady-state and Decaying Sound Fields," *Ingenieursblad*, 1973;42(18) (in Dutch).

Various, "Loudspeaker Arrays — Design and Performance," *J. Audio Engineering Society*, 1990;38(4).

SUPPLEMENT 3

Voice Intelligibility for Emergency Voice/Alarm Communications Systems

Robert P. Schifiliti
R. P. Schifiliti Associates, Inc.

Editor's Note: Chapter 24 of the 2010 edition includes requirements in 24.3.1 that emergency communications systems be capable of the reproduction of prerecorded, synthesized, or live messages with voice intelligibility. Chapter 18 also addresses speech intelligibility in 18.4.1.5 and 18.4.10. This supplement explores the broad concept of voice intelligibility and provides insights into the methods of assessing and designing intelligible voice systems. New Annex D, Speech Intelligibility, has a great deal of information about testing for speech intelligibility and some information that addresses planning and design.

BACKGROUND

Language requiring voice alarm systems to be "intelligible" was first introduced to the *National Fire Alarm Code* in 1999. In the 2010 edition of the Code, this requirement can be found in 24.3.1.[1] Annex D, new in the 2010 edition, offers guidelines on how the intelligibility performance of systems and their environments might be assessed. This supplement provides more discussion of the subject and includes an extensive bibliography.

Much of the research on speech intelligibility metrics was born out of the widespread acceptance of the telephone and the use of telephones and radios for military communications in the early part of the 20th century. It is not surprising that an industry other than the fire alarm industry studied and solved the question of how to best measure or model speech intelligibility — it was necessary for the survival of those fledgling industries. With the telephone, the needs of the consumer drove the level of quality necessary for product success. The industry found that

it became necessary to develop objective methods to evaluate products and services to ensure baseline quality. Military communications via radio and telephone also drove the development of ways to measure or predict speech intelligibility.

INTRODUCTION

Most fire alarm systems use a combination of simple audible and visible appliances to make noise and flash lights, signaling the need to evacuate a building or an area. However, in situations where egress is complex or difficult, such as in high-rise buildings or large factories, or for emergency communications systems (ECSs) used for a variety of threats other than fire, human voice is often used to provide *information*. If an audible signal is not loud enough to alert occupants, it has failed its mission. If a voice signal is not understood, it too will have failed. Listening to an unintelligible voice announcement is like trying to read in the dark — depending on a number of conditions, it might or might not be possible to get useful and accurate information.

Failure to understand a voice message can be the result of several factors. A message that is not *intelligent* may not be understood in the way the talker intended. For example, the sentence, "Go to stair B if there is no smoke," can be interpreted at least two ways ("no smoke where I am" or "no smoke in the stair") and therefore may not be understood by some listeners. Similarly, if told to "follow the building emergency evacuation plan," you need to know what that plan is to fully understand the command. Those messages were not crafted intelligently. If a message is spoken in Spanish, and the listener only understands Cantonese, the message is not understood. Also, a person talking too fast or someone with a speech impediment can cause a message to not be understood. Finally, even a well-spoken, intelligent message in the listener's native language can be misunderstood if it is not audible to the listener or if its delivery to the listener is distorted by either the delivery system or the acoustic environment. See Exhibit S3.1. It is this last factor that forms the basis for the performance specification, modeling, and measurement of speech intelligibility. Intelligible voice communications reduces the chances of "Stair B" being misinterpreted as "Stair D," "Stair C," or "Stair E."

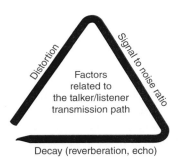

EXHIBIT S3.1 *Causes of Unintelligible Communications. (Source: R. P. Schifiliti Associates, Inc., Reading, MA)*

THE PROBLEM

Is there a problem with the intelligibility of installed and operational in-building fire emergency voice/alarm communication systems (EVACs) and other voice systems? Like audibility of tone systems, there are installations that perform well and others that fail. Fires such as the Kings Cross fire in London in 1987 and an apartment fire in York, Ontario, have been cited as situations where intelligibility of voice communication to occupants was a contributing factor in the losses.[2,3] However, more numerous are the many systems that have not (yet) been called to action dur-

ing a fire that have been judged subjectively to be of low intelligibility for one reason or another.

Intelligibility is often an issue between designers, contractors, owners, and authorities having jurisdiction who disagree as to whether a system is adequate or not. In this respect, intelligibility is similar to audibility. For many years, codes required systems to be "audible throughout the protected area" without any definition of what *audible* meant. Nor was there any description of what *throughout the protected area* meant. The result was many systems with corridor-based sounders and ineffective audibility in apartments, classrooms, and offices. Sometimes the opposite occurs, with audibility being required in small closets. Disagreements regarding audibility led the industry to adopt well-established audio definitions and measurement systems that had already been researched, tested, and developed by audio professionals. This moved the fire alarm industry from using *subjective* evaluations of audibility to *objective* methods.

In 1997, the Technical Committee on Notification Appliances for Fire Alarm Systems began working with the audio industry to learn more about speech intelligibility and how to establish objective performance requirements for voice systems.

SPEECH INTELLIGIBILITY DEFINED

Exhibit S3.2 shows the path of a voice signal from a talker to a listener and is useful in understanding and categorizing the places where the signal can be affected in its delivery.

The exhibit shows each part of the communications chain and the types of error that can be introduced into the message. Each segment of the message path shown in Exhibit S3.2 affects whether the listener understands the information content. Failure of any one of the six stages shown in the figure results in a failure to understand the information. Also, problems or faults in each of the stages are cumulative. For example, a person might speak with an accent but still be understood by a listener who is face-to-face with the talker. The communications system might add some distortion that results in the message not being understood. Or, perhaps even with an accent and some distortion by the system electronics, it is understood when there is little or no background noise, but not understood when there is background noise. Or, perhaps the system is too loud — a good signal-to-noise ratio — resulting in excessive reverberation that causes degradation of the speech intelligibility.

Others have begun to address and attempt to understand the two ends of the communications chain shown in Exhibit S3.2 — the talker and the listener.[5,6] In 1997, the

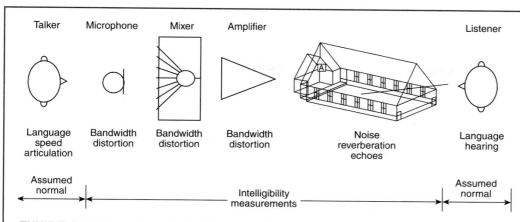

EXHIBIT S3.2 *Voice Signal Path. (Courtesy of K. Jacob, Bose® Professional Systems)[4]*

Technical Committee on Notification Appliances for Fire Alarm Systems researched and began to address the performance requirements for the communications system and listening environment. For the purposes of this supplement, speed of talking, language, and talker articulation are not directly addressed. They are indirectly addressed because a system that can reliably deliver a message, with a good signal-to-noise ratio and a limited amount of distortion, reverberation, and echo, has a higher likelihood of being understood even when a talker introduces problems or when a listener has degraded hearing. The cellular telephone industry has no control over the talker and the listener. Nevertheless, the industry uses intelligibility measurement and prediction methods to understand and improve the parts of the communications chain (Exhibit S3.2) that it can control and increase the likelihood of successful communication between the talker and the listener.

Speech intelligibility is a measure of the effectiveness of speech. The measurement can be expressed as a percentage of a message that is understood correctly.[7] Any measure of speech intelligibility is actually a prediction of how well the system will perform at other times. Speech intelligibility does not imply speech *quality*. A synthesized voice message may be completely understood by the listener, but may be judged to be harsh, unnatural, and of low quality. A message that lacks quality or fidelity may still be intelligible.

FACTORS AFFECTING SPEECH INTELLIGIBILITY

Satisfactory speech intelligibility requires adequate *audibility* and adequate *clarity* of the voice message. Audibility is relative to the background noise — the signal-to-noise ratio. The audibility of a voice message cannot be directly compared to the audibility of a tone signal because of the

modulation of voice signals. A tone and a voice message that are both perceived as equally loud may have considerably different readings on a dB or dBA meter using fast or even slow time constants. That is one reason that audibility measurements are not required by the *National Fire Alarm and Signaling Code* for voice signals. However, the integrated average sound pressure level, L_{eq}, of a voice message taken over some time period can be measured and used to compare to background noise. While a positive signal-to-noise ratio of about 10 dB is usually a design goal for voice, a 0 dB ratio or even a negative ratio can still result in some or all of a voice message being understood. This is due, in part, to differences between the noise and speech patterns and to the complexity of the human brain. This phenomenon is often referred to as the "cocktail party effect" and has been extensively researched. So, while background noise or the signal-to-noise ratio is important, there are other factors, as shown in Exhibit S3.1.

Clarity is the property of sound that allows its information-bearing components to be distinguished by a listener.[8] Phonemes are the smallest phonetic unit capable of conveying a distinction in meaning in a particular language and are instrumental in accurate word recognition.[9] Examples are the *m* of *mat* and the *b* of *bat* in English. Clarity is the freedom of these sound units from distortion introduced by any part of the sound system or environment shown in Exhibit S3.2.

The reduction of clarity by distortion can be caused by: (1) amplitude distortion caused by the electronics/hardware; (2) frequency distortion caused by either the electronics/hardware or the acoustic environment; and (3) time domain distortion due to reflection and reverberation in the acoustic environment. Research done by Richard Heyser[10] of the Jet Propulsion Laboratories of the California Institute of Technology regarding these three effects led to the development of time delay spectrometry (TDS), one of the most significant scientific advancements in the measurement and evaluation of audio system and acoustic environments.

SPEECH INTELLIGIBILITY MEASUREMENT (SUBJECTIVE OR OBJECTIVE?)

Is the measurement of speech intelligibility subjective or objective? It can be argued that intelligibility and audibility are both subjective and objective evaluations. The definitions and the measurements that we use for audibility are based on many years of testing with real people. The decibel (dB) is actually a ratio of the actual fluctuating sound pressure to the threshold pressure variation of human hearing. Certainly, the threshold of human hearing is subjective. The threshold of hearing is peculiar to a particular individual, and is modified or affected by personal views, experience, or background.[11]

However, when a large data set is analyzed and used to scientifically and statistically establish a threshold, and when used as a baseline or standard for relative comparison, it becomes an objective quantity. It is objective because the chosen standard is used as a reference to remove statistical variation and distortion by personal feelings, prejudices, or interpretations for subsequent measurements, reducing subjective factors to a minimum.[11] So, although the threshold of hearing varies from individual to individual, a representative standard quantification (0 dB) has been established for comparison of other sound level measurements.

Similarly, the human ear hears some frequencies better than others. Of course, no two human hearing systems (ears and brain) are the same. Nevertheless, after considerable research the scientific community has accepted the Fletcher-Munson curves as "typical" of human hearing. Going further, the audio and psychoacoustics communities have adopted a smoothed inverse of one of the Fletcher-Munson curves to define the A-weighting curve. The A-weighting curve is used to adjust dB measurements for the way a human ear will perceive the sound. Thus, dBA measurements are objective evaluations of sound even though they are based on numerous subjective tests.

Speech intelligibility evaluations can also be either subjective or objective. Reading an article from a newspaper and asking a listener to write down what they understand the message to be is a subjective evaluation. One reader/talker might better enunciate certain words or slur other word parts. The news article used for a test one day may differ from one used another day and may be composed of short simple words, or the word and phoneme order may be less susceptible to distortion caused by reverberation and echo. At the other end of the communication chain, the listener used in the evaluation might have hearing deficiencies or learning disabilities, including auditory dyslexia. The content and context of the article may cause the listener to guess at words and content that are actually not intelligibly received. For subject-based testing to be *objective*, it must use a scientific and statistically valid methodology.

An Internet discussion among persons interested in fire alarm systems started with the idea that a simple test of intelligibility could be performed using the "newspaper test." Comments went back and forth, and it was suggested that professionally developed word lists designed to test all components of human speech should be used. It was then suggested that a protocol be established to document the conditions and variables. The ad hoc protocol evolved to suggesting multiple listeners and statistical analysis of the results. Interestingly, the discussion began to resemble established international standards that had been developed by researchers in the audio field over 50 years ago and that have been used by acoustic professionals and audiologists for decades to objectively evaluate personal hearing ability, sound systems, and acoustic environments.[12]

One should not confuse subjective with subject-based testing. It is possible for tests using talkers and listeners (subject-based tests) to be objective. The key is to use established protocols that reduce the impact of personal conditions and produce results that are repeatable. Similarly, an instrument-based test that is repeatable for a given set of conditions may not be objective if it does not have an established basis in reality. Both subject-based testing and instrument-based testing require peer-reviewed research, testing, and established standards to become accepted objective measurement methods.

MEASURING SPEECH INTELLIGIBILITY

The performance of a voice system depends on the system hardware and the acoustic environment. They cannot be separated when evaluating speech intelligibility. A fire alarm horn can be specified for a space and required to produce 80 dBA at 10 ft (3 m). However, the power supply and wiring will affect the output of the horn. The mounting location will affect the distribution of the sound. The acoustic environment will affect the energy dissipation in the space and the loudness. Finally, the background noise will affect whether the horn is heard reliably. The fire alarm industry has recognized that there are situations where the installed field performance of an audible signaling system must be measured in order to evaluate its performance with respect to the system's design objectives. Similarly, speech intelligibility is affected by all of these systems, environmental factors, and more. (See section on Factors Affecting Speech Intelligibility.) Thus, the performance metric for speech intelligibility must also assess all of the requisite parameters.

Other international standards organizations — namely, the IEC (International Electrotechnical Commission) and ISO (International Standards Organization) — have already reviewed and evaluated objective methods for evaluating speech intelligibility. Some of the methods recognized and accepted in international standards and by the acoustics and professional sound industries are subject-based and others use instrumentation. For each of the rec-

ognized methods, there already exists an internationally accepted standard for the test method/protocol. Four of the recognized methods use test instruments. Three subject-based methods are also recognized. One method has both a subject-based solution and an instrument-based solution. These methods are summarized in Table S3.1.

By comparing evaluations between different test methods, a common intelligibility scale (CIS) was developed.[18] The CIS permits comparison of test results using the different methods. It also permits a designer, code, or authority having jurisdiction to specify a requirement that can be evaluated using any one of the test methods listed

TABLE S3.1 *Speech Intelligibility Test Methods*

Method	Standard References	Comments
STI (Speech Transmission Index)	IEC 60268-16, *The Objective Rating of Speech Intelligibility by Speech Transmission Index*, 1998.[13]	This is an objective, instrument-based method. Requires hardware and software for measurement and solution. Available in a computer based solution, as a feature of some multi-function audio analysis equipment, and as a handheld meter.
STIPA (Speech Transmission Index – Public Address)	IEC 60268-16, *The Objective Rating of Speech Intelligibility by Speech Transmission Index*, 1998.[13]	This is an objective, instrument-based method. Measures STI using a test signal and a hand-held meter. Test protocol described in *NFPA 72*, Annex D.
RASTI (Rapid or Room Acoustics Speech Transmission Index)	IEC 60268-16, *The Objective Rating of Speech Intelligibility by Speech Transmission Index*, 1998.[13]	This is an objective, instrument-based method. Reduced STI method. Available in a handheld format. Many limitations. Effectively replaced by STIPA.
PB (Phonetically Balanced Word Scores)	ISO/TR 4870, *Acoustics –The Construction and Calibration of Speech Intelligibility Tests*, 1991.[12]	This is an objective, subject-based method. ANSI S3.2, *Method for Measuring the Intelligibility of Speech Over Communication Systems*, 1989,[17] is a better reference for evaluations using the English language.
MRT (Modified Rhyme Test)	No reference given.	This is an objective, subject-based method. No standard listed. ANSI S3.5[15] notes that the method has the same limits as given in ISO/TR 4870.[12] Good reference is ANSI S3.2, *Method for Measuring the Intelligibility of Speech Over Communication Systems*, 1989.[17]
AI (Articulation Index)	ANSI S3.5, *Methods for the Calculation of the Articulation Index*, 1969.[14] ANSI S3.5, *Methods for the Calculation of the Speech Intelligibility Index (SII)*, 1997.[15]	This is an objective, instrument-based method. The 1969 version of ANSI S3.5 is referenced. This has been updated to the 1997 edition. Requires hardware and software for measurement and solution.
%AL$_{cons}$ (Articulation Loss of Consonants)	Peutz, V.M.A., 1971. "Articulation Loss of Consonants as a Criterion for Speech Transmission in a Room," *J. Aud. Eng. Soc.* 19(11).[16]	This is an objective, instrument-based method *or* an objective, subject-based method. Available in a computer based solution.

in the table. Consult the references for more detail on each of the test methods.

Annex D recommends specific acceptability criteria in the form of a minimum and an average speech transmission index (STI) — with the equivalent CIS score also listed. See Section D.2.4, which also has extensive discussion on the variability of measurements, precision, and rounding of results.

PLANNING, DESIGNING, INSTALLING, TESTING, AND USING INTELLIGIBLE SYSTEMS

How does measuring speech intelligibility solve the problem of unintelligible systems? Measuring the audibility of a system does not make it louder or softer. Similarly, measuring speech intelligibility will not directly result in better system performance.

A system that reliably communicates a message to a listener must be properly planned, designed, and installed. Testing not only uncovers faults and allows corrections to be made, but also shows successful techniques for future reference. Finally, even the perfect system design can be improperly adjusted, unbalanced, or not properly installed and result in degradation of the signal to a point where it is not understood by the user.

The scope of *NFPA 72* is not to plan or design systems, but to provide minimum prescriptive and performance requirements for systems and components. The *National Fire Alarm and Signaling Code* does not tell you when you must have smoke detectors nor when you must have voice systems. Those concerns are the jurisdiction of other codes, laws, standards, and authorities. One issue that designers and authorities must face when planning a system is the question of where intelligible voice communication is needed. For this reason, in part, Chapter 18 now requires system designers to plan and designate acoustically distinguishable spaces (ADSs). See 18.4.10, A.18.4.10, and D.2.3.1 for the requirements and for additional commentary and examples.

In a large space used for public meetings, conventions, and trade shows, an ECS needs to be reliably intelligible because it is intended to give information to the general public that is not familiar with the space. However, in a high-rise apartment building, is voice intelligibility required in all spaces? The ECS is used to give information to occupants when the fire is not in their apartment. If the fire is in their particular apartment, their own local smoke alarms are used to provide an audible signal. If the fire is not in their apartment, the fire alarm system is used to give them information about whether to evacuate, relocate, or remain in place. It may not be necessary that the EVAC or MNS be intelligible in all parts of the apartment. It certainly must be audible in all parts of the apartment, as is currently required by the codes. However, it may be sufficient to provide a speaker in a common space and to provide an adequate audible tone signal in other spaces to awaken and alert the occupants.

The voice message produced by a living room speaker appliance may not be intelligible behind closed bedroom and bathroom doors. However, the occupants, having been alerted, and not being endangered in their own apartments, can move to a location where a repeating message can be intelligibly heard. The same signaling plan may work for office complexes: a person may have to open his or her office door to reliably understand the message. In large public spaces, a person should not have to move any great distance to find a place where he or she can understand the message. Thus, for these spaces, intelligibility is important and the statistical performance recommended by Annex D becomes useful. The performance requirement recommended in Annex D allows up to 10 percent of the measurement locations in an ADS to fail. See D.2.4.1, D.2.4.8, and D.2.4.10. The remaining measurements must have a certain minimum (0.45 STI or 0.65 CIS) and a certain average (0.50 STI or 0.70 CIS). If an ADS is small enough to only require one measurement location (see the requirements for measurement point spacing in Annex D), the result should be 0.50 STI (0.70 CIS) or more for the ADS to pass the recommendation for speech intelligibility.

Once a person plans to have some type of system, and determines that the system must be intelligible in certain spaces or areas, the Code recommendations become the basis for *design objectives* or goals. For complex issues, such as visible signaling, the Code often starts with empirically based prescriptive requirements. These are menus of solutions that designers choose from.

Unlike visible notification, voice signaling does not lend itself well to prescriptive design. There are prescriptive rules that sound system designers often start with, such as one watt per 750 to 1000 ft^2 (70 to 93 m^2). However, these guidelines must be adjusted to the acoustic environment, and they assume certain equipment performance characteristics. Don't the environment and equipment also affect the performance of visible signaling systems? Yes, but to a lesser, more controllable degree. The prescriptive requirements for visible notification appliances are based on possible equipment degradation (power supply voltage and current) and on conservative assumptions about ambient lighting conditions and surface colors. The effects of varying acoustic environments on speech intelligibility have a much wider range and impact. Prescriptive solutions for voice systems would result in severe overdesign and would not necessarily guarantee

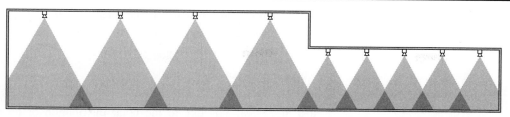

EXHIBIT S3.3 *Distribution of Speakers Showing the Need for Reduced Spacing in Smaller Spaces. (Source: R. P. Schifiliti Associates, Inc., Reading, MA)*

intelligibility of the message. For example, evaluation of an installation in an open plan office showed that the signal-to-noise ratio was the main problem with failure to meet the intelligibility performance requirement. However, simply specifying a louder system would result in degradation of the intelligibility in parts of the open office that did not have as many cubicles or where tile was used in lieu of carpet.

As another example, consider a large space with two ceiling heights (low and high) and a sound system. One of the basic concepts in the design of intelligible sound systems is to have all listeners in the direct field of a single speaker. If a person is in the direct field of two speakers, the sound from the farther one arrives some time after the sound from the closer speaker. The degree of impact on intelligibility depends on the time difference. Distributing the speakers to reduce or eliminate the overlap of the direct field sound is the best design practice. Though at first counterintuitive to many fire alarm system designers, the smaller space (lower ceiling height) requires a smaller spacing between the speakers. See Exhibit S3.3.

Sound does not come out of a speaker in a perfect cone, as shown in Exhibit S3.3. A good design for speech intelligibility is to have a fairly uniform distribution of energy. Exhibit S3.4 shows the relative sound a person might experience as he or she walks through a space with two loudspeakers driven at fairly high levels. Directly under a speaker, the sound level is very high. Between two speakers, it is lowest. Exhibit S3.5 shows the same space with more speakers, closer together, but driven at a lower level.

A system designed for intelligible voice communication typically aims for a difference of no more than about 6 dB between the high and the low sound pressure level presented to the listener. That sound level is predominantly a function of the output of the speakers and the distance to the listener. The number of speakers being heard also can affect the sound level. If a person is directly between two sound sources of equal volume, the net sound level will be +3 dB compared to that from either speaker by itself. Reverberation and echoes can also contribute, though a good design attempts to minimize these factors.

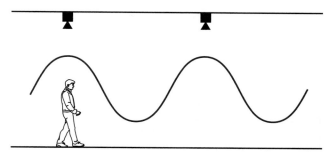

EXHIBIT S3.4 *Relative Sound Level Distribution (1). (Source: R. P. Schifiliti Associates, Inc., Reading, MA)*

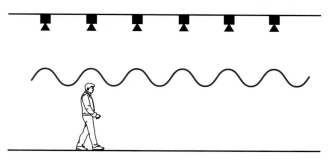

EXHIBIT S3.5 *Relative Sound Level Distribution (2). (Source: R. P. Schifiliti Associates, Inc., Reading, MA)*

The output of a speaker can be represented by a polar plot of sound level in dB as a function of angle from the main axis, as shown in Exhibit S3.6. The plot shows a particular ceiling mounted speaker with an output that is reduced about −6 db at an angle of 75° off-axis — a 150° cone. However, the designer cannot just aim to have 150° cones meet at or slightly above ear level. That scheme accounts for the fact that at the 75° off-axis point, the speaker is putting out 6 dB less, but it does not account for the fact that the sound must also travel a greater distance from the speaker than if the person were directly under the speaker. It can be mathematically shown that as a person walks from under a speaker to a point 75° off-axis, he or she will actually experience a loss of 11.7 dB just due to the increased distance from the speaker. This phenomenon is

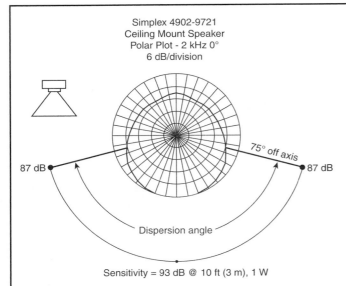

EXHIBIT S3.6 *Polar Plot for a Ceiling Mounted Speaker. (Source: NEMA Standards Publication SB 50-2008, National Electrical Manufacturers Association, Rosslyn, VA)[19]*

independent of the particular model speaker. In this example, the distance loss is given by:

$$\Delta db = 20\log_{10} (cos\ \theta)$$

where θ is the angle off-axis.

For the speaker in this example, an additional 6 dB is lost at 75° off-axis due to the polar distribution of the sound for a net loss of 11.7 + 6 = 17.7 dB. At what angle does the combination of polar output data and distance attenuation result in a net difference of only 6 dB or less (our design goal)? Exhibit S3.7 shows more precise polar loss data, the distance loss calculations, and the net loss for several angles.

For that particular speaker, a design must use cones having a 104° angle (52° off-axis) to ensure no more than a 6 dB difference between the loudest and lowest sound levels. However, for a design where the cones of two speakers meet at the −6 dB point, each speaker is contributing the same sound level to the listener. Therefore, the net sound level would be +3 dB. For this speaker the contribution from one speaker at an angle of 60° would be −9 dB relative to the on-axis value. Therefore, with two

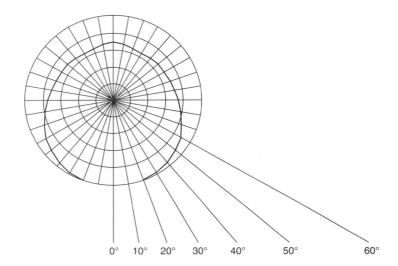

Angle off-axis (θ)	0°	10°	20°	30°	40°	50°	60°
Polar Loss (1)	0.0 dB	0.0 dB	−0.1 dB	−0.5 dB	−1.3 dB	−1.8 dB	−3.0 dB
+ Distance Loss (2)	0.0 dB	−0.1 dB	−0.5 dB	−1.2 dB	−2.3 dB	−3.8 dB	−6.0 dB
= Total Loss	0.0 dB	−0.1 dB	−0.6 dB	−1.7 dB	−3.6 dB	−5.6 dB	−9.0 dB

−6 dB Point	52°
Critical Polar Angle	104°

Notes:
(1) Polar Loss interpreted from polar plot
(2) Distance Loss calculated as 20*log(cos(θ))

EXHIBIT S3.7 *Coverage Angle Calculation for a Ceiling Mounted Speaker. (Source: NEMA Standards Publication SB 50-2008, National Electrical Manufacturers Association, Rosslyn, VA)[19]*

speakers the relative loss would be −6 dB. Thus, the speakers could be spaced so that 120° degree cones meet at or slightly above ear level. The cones depicted in Exhibit S3.3 overlap at a plane chosen by the designer, such as 6 ft (1.8 m) above the floor. Knowing the ceiling height and the calculated cone angle for a maximum 6 dB loss, the spacing of the speakers can be calculated.

Note that the entire discussion and the calculations discussed above have not yet addressed what dB level is needed. The calculations for speaker spacing have all been made to ensure no more than a 6 dB variation in sound level in the space using the on-axis level as the starting point. What that on-axis value needs to be depends on the noise level in the space. The speaker is selected so that the on-axis value and the off-axis value meet the system goals for signal-to-noise ratio. A common goal for voice systems is a 10 dB signal-to-noise ratio. However, Exhibit S3.1 shows that intelligibility is a balance of different factors. In some spaces, a system that produces 10 dB over the ambient might produce sufficient reverberation to actually reduce intelligibility. It is possible to reduce the signal-to-noise ratio and actually increase intelligibility in some situations because of a net reduction in reverberation. An example would be in a space with very low ambient noise and with surfaces that reflect most of the acoustic energy — stone floors, a marble wall on one side, and a glass exterior wall on the other side might be one example.

In a high noise situation a signal-to-noise ratio of +10 dB might require the speakers to be driven at very high levels. Are the electronics of the system and the frequency response of the speaker sufficient to operate at these levels without adding distortion and reducing intelligibility — the third leg of the triangle in Exhibit S3.1?

The design process can require several iterations, because speakers can be tapped at different wattages and because each speaker will have a different polar plot and frequency response at different levels. There are generic acoustic software programs that can be used to model spaces and systems. Some manufacturers also have their own tools that designers can use. Just as fires can be modeled, acoustic and audio engineers can model speech intelligibility before a building is built and before a system is installed. Fortunately, acoustic and electronic properties are better documented and more accurately modeled than fire properties, resulting in reliable evaluations of proposed designs. However, modeling can be time-consuming and complex and therefore generally is done only for larger, more costly systems requiring a high degree of performance.

The Code permits designers to use any and all reasonable means to achieve the objectives. Designers and installers who are new to the subject or who want to learn more about proper system design and installation need to consult other resources. In addition to the references cited at the end of this supplement, a bibliography has also been provided. As with fire alarms, there is a National Institute for Certification in Engineering Technologies (NICET) program for Audio Systems[20] and a trade organization, National Systems Contractors Association, that provide training and support.[21]

Testing speech intelligibility can be simple or complex, low cost or high cost. The least expensive dB meters meeting the requirements of Chapter 14 of the *National Fire Alarm and Signaling Code* (ANSI Type 2 meters are required) cost several hundred dollars. When amortized over several years of use on many jobs, the cost, including periodic calibration, is low. However, these meters do not diagnose why a system is not audible, nor prescribe how to fix it. For diagnostics, more expensive meters and systems are required. Fortunately, most audibility problems have solutions that are intuitive to most designers and installers.

Similarly, instrument-based intelligibility measuring systems vary in price range, as does the cost of subject-based testing. More complex measurement systems require considerable expertise, training, and set-up, but provide diagnostics at the same time. Handheld meters, on the order of a couple thousand dollars, require only a little more training and care than a dB meter. In fact, the only difference in using an intelligibility meter compared to a simple sound level meter is that you must push a button to start a measurement and wait about 15 seconds for the results. See Annex D for a complete description of a recommended test protocol. Relative to the cost of voice systems, handheld solutions for measuring speech intelligibility amortize to unit life-cycle costs similar to the costs of dB meters.

Exhibits S3.8 and S3.9 show handheld meters that can be used for both audibility measurements and for

EXHIBIT S3.8 *Combination Sound Pressure Level Meter/Analyzer and Speech Intelligibility Meter. (Source: Gold Line, West Redding, CT)*

EXHIBIT S3.9 *NTI AL1 Displaying Basic STIPA Result. (Source: NTI Americas, Tigard, OR)*

EXHIBIT S3.10 *STIPA NTI Talkbox. (Source: NTI Americas, Tigard, OR)*

intelligibility measurements of the speech transmission index (STI). See Table S3.1, Speech Intelligibility Test Methods. Handheld meters such as those shown in the two exhibits measure the STI using the STIPA method. The STIPA method requires that a special test signal be sent through the communications system. The STIPA test signal contains a sample of modulated voice frequencies (see D.2.3.5). The meter measures how that test signal is changed as it goes through the communications path shown in Exhibit S3.2. Annex D describes how to conduct a STI test using the STIPA method. The test signal can be programmed into the system and played back. However, that method would not measure the impact of any distortion caused by the system microphone, if one is used. A more complete system test is made by using an artificial talker or "talkbox" to play the STIPA test signal into the system microphone. These "talking heads" are commonly used in audio research. Exhibit S3.10 is an example of a talkbox for STIPA testing (see D.2.3.6 and D.5).

Annex D discusses the fact that even where intelligible speech is desired, measurement of speech intelligibility might not be necessary. However, where measurements are desired or recommended, how many tests should be made in a particular space? There is no guidance for audibility measurements regarding the number and locations of test points. For intelligibility measurements Annex D, Section D.2.4, discusses the number and location of measurements and how the data should be compiled and averaged. The Fire Protection Research Foundation report that led to

the development of Annex D has more discussion and sample forms as well.[22]

With audibility, the designer has an intuitive sense of where a system might fail and tends to concentrate the testing plan in those areas. How many designers, technicians, and authorities have such intuition regarding intelligibility? This is not an argument not to test for intelligibility. Rather, it means that testing needs to be performed and that a designer is likely to test a larger number of points initially as he or she gathers experience.

As with audibility, there are methods to test when a space is not occupied and then "add in" the expected or measured noise level at a later time during analysis. This permits less invasive testing. For audibility, the background noise is measured. Then, at another time, the alarm signal is measured to determine the signal-to-noise ratio. For speech intelligibility, the instrument is used to measure and save the noise profile. Then, at another time, the speech test signal is measured and saved. Software provided by the meter manufacturer is used to combine the two data sets and get the resulting prediction of speech intelligibility. The protocol listed in Annex D addresses this type of testing.

After acceptance testing, should systems be periodically tested? Yes, but measurements might not be required. Table 14.4.2.2, item 15(b), for textual audible notification appliances (speakers) requires measurements of "signals" to be performed only when there are changes in occupancy, the building, or the system — all factors that can affect intelligibility. However, by reference to the requirements of Chapter 18, the intent is that measurements, whether at acceptance or during periodic testing, be made of the alert tone or evacuation tone, not measurements of voice levels or of speech intelligibility. Note that the wording of Table 14.4.2.2, item 27(f), for textual audible notification appliances (speakers) that are part of a mass notification system differs and does not address periodic testing. The intent would be for the requirement to mirror the entry in 14.4.2.2, item 15(b).

Regardless of whether the testing is at acceptance or is part of the annual requirement for periodic testing of notification appliances, voice content must be verified to be distinguishable and understandable and must comply with 18.4.10, which in turn references Chapter 18 and also points to Annex D on Speech Intelligibility. Although Annex D has a recommended protocol for testing speech intelligibility, the body of the code only requires a "listen" test. Designers, owners, and authorities having jurisdiction will have to decide when and where testing is desirable, if at all.

Although the sound pressure level of voice signals cannot be measured for comparison to tone signaling requirements, the sound pressure level of voice signals can be measured and recorded as a baseline to determine if a system or the building environment has changed significantly from initial testing. Changes in the sound pressure level of the voice message could point to possible changes in speech intelligibility. If baseline sound level measurements of voice messages are made, they should be made with an integrating, averaging meter — a capability that many sound level meters have and a capability that is required to measure average ambient sound pressure levels as required by Chapter 18. The equivalent sound level over some time period, L_{eq}, should be measured using the same text passage each time in order to make a valid comparison. Combined with already required inspections of a space for changing conditions, measuring and documenting the L_{eq} may be adequate for periodic review of voice systems in some spaces.

In some situations, the best test plan is to use a combination system that is used for routine purposes on a daily basis, such as the sound system in an airport. Those systems are constantly being "tested" through their regular use. See Annex D, Reference 4, and the Bibliography for more information on testing guidelines.

CONCLUSION

The *National Fire Alarm and Signaling Code* — and common sense and fairness — requires voice signals to be intelligible in many spaces. Modeling and measurement methods and standards for speech intelligibility are well researched and documented. Some in the fire alarm community, being new to the concepts involved, have a steep learning curve to improve their planning, design, installation, and testing of intelligible voice communication systems. The new requirements in Chapter 18 for the designation of ADSs will help the planning and education process.

Researchers are investigating *what* should be said and *how* it should be said, when giving information using a voice system. See Supplement 2 on emergency communications systems for more information. The Code is not intended to be a design guide, textbook, and handbook. Those who plan, design, install, test, and approve voice systems for emergency communications systems must seek information from established disciplines, groups, and literature — and by testing systems — to learn what works and what does not work.

REFERENCES

References Cited

1. *NFPA 72®, National Fire Alarm and Signaling Code*, 2010 edition, National Fire Protection Association, Quincy, MA.
2. Proulx, G., "Is it Wise to Evacuate During a High Rise Fire?" National Fire Protection Association World Safety Congress, Denver, CO, May, 2000.
3. Proulx, G., "Highrise Evacuation: A Questionable Concept," 2nd International Symposium on Human Behavior in Fire – Conference Proceedings. London: Interscience Communications, 2001.
4. Jacob, K., "Understanding Speech Intelligibility and the Fire Alarm Code," Framingham, MA: Bose® Professional Systems. Presented at the National Fire Protection Association World Safety Congress, Anaheim, May 14, 2001. Available at *www.rpsa-fire.com*.
5. Proulx, G., and J.D. Sime, "To Prevent 'Panic' in an Underground Emergency: Why Not Tell People the Truth?" *Proceedings of the Third International Symposium on Fire Safety Science,* London: Elsevier, 1991.
6. Pauls, J.L., and B.K. Jones, "Building Evacuation: Research Methods and Case Studies," *Fires and Human Behaviour*, New York: John Wiley and Sons, 1980.
7. ISO 9921-1, *Ergonomics-Assessment of Speech Communication,* International Standards Organization, Geneva, Switzerland, 2003.
8. IEC 60849, *Sound Systems for Emergency Purposes*, International Electrotechnical Commission, Geneva, Switzerland, 1998.
9. Mannell, R.H., "Natural and Synthetic Speech Intelligibility and Quality Testing," Speech, Hearing and Language Research Centre (SHLRC), Macquarie University, Sydney, Australia, 1984.
10. Heyser, R.C., "Acoustical Measurements by Time Delay Spectrometry," *Journal of the Audio Engineering Society*, 1967.
11. Merriam-Webster, Inc., *Merriam-Webster's Collegiate Dictionary,* Springfield, MA, 2003, http://www.merriam-webster.com. [definitions for *subjective* and *objective*]
12. ISO/TR 4870, *Acoustics – The Construction and Calibration of Speech Intelligibility Tests*, International Standards Organization, Geneva, Switzerland, 1991.

13. IEC 60268-16, *The Objective Rating of Speech Intelligibility by Speech Transmission Index*, 1998.

14. ANSI S 3.5, *Methods for the Calculation of the Articulation Index*, American National Standards Institute, New York, NY, 1969.

15. ANSI S 3.5, *Methods for the Calculation of the Speech Intelligibility Index (SII)*. American National Standards Institute, New York, NY, 1997.

16. Peutz, V. M.A., "Articulation Loss of Consonants as a Criterion for Speech Transmission in a Room," *Journal of the Audio Engineering Society*, 1971; 19(11): 915–919.

17. ANSI S 3.2, *Method for Measuring the Intelligibility of Speech Over Communication Systems,* American National Standards Institute, New York, NY, 1989.

18. Barnett, P. W., and Knight, A. D., "The Common Intelligibility Scale," *Proceedings of the Institute of Acoustics,* AMS Acoustics, 43 Chase Side, Southgate, London, N14 5BP, 1995; 17(7).

19. NEMA Standards Publication SB 50-2008, *Emergency Communications Audio Intelligibility Applications Guide*, National Electrical Manufacturers Association, Rosslyn, VA 22209.

20. National Institute for Certification in Engineering Technologies (NICET), 1420 King Street, Alexandria, VA 22314-2794.

21. National Systems Contractors Association, 625 First Street SE, Suite 420, Cedar Rapids, IA 52401.

22. Grant, C., *Intelligibility of Fire Alarm & Emergency Communication Systems*, the Fire Protection Research Foundation, Quincy, MA, 2008.

Selected Technical Bibliography

(A more complete bibliography can be found at *www.rpsa-fire.com*.)

Ballou, G., ed., *Handbook for Sound Engineers*, The New Audio Cyclopedia, 2nd ed., Howard W. Sams, Indianapolis, IN: pp. 1277–1298.

Bell, T., "A New Measure of Word Recognition," *Sound & Video Contractor (S&VC)* 1996; 14(11):28–33.

Chéenne, D. J., "Getting Testy about Intelligibility," *Sound & Video Contractor (S&VC)*, 1996; 14(11):22–26.

Davis, C. and D. Davis, "Speech Intelligibility Workshop," *Syn-Aud-Con Tech Topic*, 1986, 1987; 14(1):14(8).

Davis, C. P., "Measurement of %ALcons," *Journal of the Audio Engineering Society*, 1986; 34(11):905–909.

Davis, D. and C. Davis, "Sound System Engineering," 2nd ed., Cannel, IN: SAMS, a Division of Macmillan Computer Publishing, 1986.

Davis, D. and C. Davis, "Application of Speech Intelligibility to Sound Reinforcement," *Journal of the Audio Engineering Society*, 1989; 37(12).

Houtgast, T. and H.J.M. Steeneken, "A Multi-Lingual Evaluation of the RASTI-Method for Estimating Speech Intelligibility in Auditoria," *Acustica* 1984; 54:185–199.

Houtgast, T. and H.J.M. Steeneken, "The Modulation Transfer Function in Room Acoustics as a Predictor of Speech Intelligibility," *Acustica* 1973; 28:66–73.

Houtgast, T., H. J. M. Steeneken, and R. Plomp, "Predicting Speech Intelligibility in Rooms from the Modulation Transfer Function," *Acustica*, 1980; 46.

Howes, D., "On the Relation Between the Intelligibility and Frequency of Occurrence of English Words," *Journal of the Acoustical Society of America*, 1957; 29:296–305.

Hudgins, C. V., T. E. Hawkins, J. E. Karlin, and S. S. Stevens, "The Development of Recorded Auditory Tests for Measuring Hearing Loss for Speech," *Laryngoscope* 1947; 57:57–89.

Klein, W., "Articulation Loss of Consonants as a Basis for Design and Judgment of Sound Reinforcement Systems," *Journal of the Audio Engineering Society*, 1971; 19(11):920–922.

Latham, H. G., "The Signal-to-Noise Ratio for Speech Intelligibility — an Auditorium Design Index," *Applied Acoustics*, 1979; 12.

Licklider, J. C. R., D. Bindra, and I. Pollack, "The Intelligibility of Rectangular Speech Waves." *American Journal of Psychology* 1948; 61:1–20.

Lochner, J. P. A., and J. F. Burger, "The Intelligibility of Reinforced Speech," *Acustica*, 1959; 9.

Mapp, P., and P. Doany, "Speech Intelligibility Analysis and Measurement for a Distributed Sound System in a Reverberant Environment," Audio Engineering Society 87th Convention, NY, 1989.

Mapp, P., "An Issue of Safety," *Sound & Video Contractor (S&VC)*, 1996; 14(11):34–48.

Mapp, P., "Installation Profile — The National Ice Centre," *Sound & Video Contractor (S&VC)* 1999; 18(14):77–84.

Mapp, P., *Reaching the Audience*, "Proven Techniques for Evaluating, Maintaining and Optimizing Systems Design for Speech Intelligibility," *Sound & Video Contractor (S&VC)*, 1999; 17(11):17–32.

Mapp, P., "Speaking of Speaking," *Sound & Video Contractor (S&VC)*, 2001; 19(10):36–48.

Marshall, A. H., "Acoustical Determinants for the Architectural Design of Concert Halls," *Architectural Science Review*, 1968; 11:81–87.

Peutz, V. M. A., and B. M. Kok, "Speech Intelligibility," Audio Engineering Society 75th Convention, 1984.

Peutz, V. M. A., "Articulation Loss of Consonants as a Criterion for Speech Transmission in a Room," *Journal of* the *Audio Engineering Society*, 1971; 19(11):915–919.

Peutz, V. M. A., "Speech Information and Speech Intelligibility," Audio Engineering Society 85th Convention, 1988.

Pratt, P., "Intelligibility and International Standards," *Sound & Video Contractor (S&VC)* 1996; 14(11):49–54.

Rosenzweig, M. R., and L. Postman, "Intelligibility as a Function of Frequency of Usage." *Journal of Experimental Psychology*, 1957; 54:412–422.

Spieth, W., J. F. Curtis, and J. C. Lebster, "Responding to One of Two Simultaneous Messages." *Journal of the Acoustical Society of America*, 1954; 26:391–396.

Steeneken, H.J.M., "The Measurement of Speech Intelligibility," 2002.

Steeneken, H.J.M. and T. Houtgast, 1980. "A Physical Method for Measuring Speech Transmission Quality."

J. Acoustical Society of America, 1980; 67(31):318–326.

Steeneken, H.J.M. and T. Houtgast, "On the Mutual Dependence of Octave Band Contributions to Speech Intelligibility." Proc. Eurospeech 91, Genoa, 1991; 1133–1136.

Steeneken, H.J.M. and T. Houtgast, "Some Applications of the Speech Transmission Index (STI) in Auditoria." *Acustica* 1982; 51:229–234.

Steeneken, H. J. M., and J. Houtgast, "RASTI. A Tool for Evaluating Auditorium," *B&K Technical Review*, 1989; 3.

Stiernberg, J, "The Science of Perception and Reception," *Sound & Video Contractor (S&VC)* 1996; 14(11):14–20, 92.

Treisman, A. M., "Verbal Cues, Language, and Meaning in Relative Attention," *American Journal of Psychology*, 1964; 77:206–219.

SUPPLEMENT 4

Life Safety Code® Enabling References

Editor's Note: *Supplement 4 provides users of NFPA 72*®, *National Fire Alarm and Signaling Code, with a summary of requirements from NFPA 101*®, *Life Safety Code*®, *2009 edition, that relate to fire alarm systems and fire alarm system features.*

Users of *NFPA 72*®, *National Fire Alarm and Signaling Code*, often ask when a fire alarm system is required or when certain fire alarm system features are needed. Generally speaking, *NFPA 72* does not provide the answers to these questions. For "required" fire alarm systems, these requirements are found in occupancy, fire or building codes, or in local statutes. (For "nonrequired" fire alarm systems they must be determined by the system designer based on the goals and objectives of the building owner.) This supplement is intended to assist the user of *NFPA 72* in understanding how to determine when a fire alarm system is required and what features and attributes it must have.

Within NFPA's set of codes and standards, NFPA *101*®, *Life Safety Code*®, 2009 edition, is the primary document used to establish these "enabling" requirements. This supplement provides a summary compilation of references and requirements from NFPA *101*, grouped by occupancy and organized by related fire alarm system feature. This summary is only intended to provide a starting point for users, and the organization and presentation of the requirements contained in this summary have been subject to interpretation by the preparers of this supplement.

It is not intended that this supplement be used without consulting the complete requirements of NFPA *101*, and it should not be assumed that this supplement includes a complete and total set of fire alarm requirements from NFPA *101*. It is also important to note that many jurisdictions amend national codes at the local level. The reader is highly encouraged to review the *Life Safety Code* or local

codes and all local amendments before beginning any work, and if needed to consult with the authority having jurisdiction on matters of interpretation.

The use of NFPA *101*, *Life Safety Code*, is fairly straightforward. The reader is directed first to the occupancy chapter that encompasses the building in question. This chapter will contain all requirements for the fire alarm system in sections entitled "Detection, Alarm, and Communications Systems." The individual sections in each occupancy chapter will contain requirements that reference the requirements of Section 9.6. The requirements in Section 9.6 in turn reference *NFPA 72, National Fire Alarm Code*, for the remaining installation requirements. Refer to the following section for an excerpt of Section 9.6.

The occupancies that are included in this supplement are as follows:

- Assembly Occupancies, New and Existing — NFPA *101*, Chapters 12 and 13
- Educational Occupancies, New and Existing — NFPA *101*, Chapters 14 and 15
- Day-Care Occupancies, New and Existing — NFPA *101*, Chapters 16 and 17
- Health Care Occupancies, New and Existing — NFPA *101*, Chapters 18 and 19
- Ambulatory Health Care Occupancies, New and Existing — NFPA *101*, Chapters 20 and 21
- Detention and Correctional Occupancies, New and Existing — NFPA *101*, Chapters 22 and 23
- One- and Two-Family Dwellings — NFPA *101*, Chapter 24

- Lodging or Rooming Houses — NFPA *101,* Chapter 26
- Hotels and Dormitories, New and Existing — NFPA *101,* Chapters 28 and 29
- Apartment Buildings, New and Existing — NFPA *101,* Chapters 30 and 31
- Residential Board and Care Occupancies, New and Existing — NFPA *101,* Chapters 32 and 33
- Mercantile Occupancies, New and Existing — NFPA *101,* Chapters 36 and 37
- Business Occupancies, New and Existing — NFPA *101,* Chapters 38 and 39
- Industrial Occupancies — NFPA *101,* Chapter 40
- Storage Occupancies — NFPA *101,* Chapter 42

High-rise buildings and special structures are addressed by the requirements of Chapter 11 in addition to the requirements of the applicable occupancy chapter, and related fire alarm system requirements are summarized in the next-to-last table of this supplement.

Additionally, the requirements of Chapters 1, 4, and 6 and the definitions in Chapter 3 of NFPA *101* apply generally. (The performance-based design requirements of Chapter 5 are not addressed in this summary.) The requirements of Chapters 7 and 8 also apply in addition to the requirements of the applicable occupancy chapter, and related fire alarm system requirements are summarized in the last table of this supplement.

Users of this supplement should note that excerpts from NFPA *101* and *NFPA 72* in the summary tables are shown only once, are extracted without modification, and are shown in black text. References to the excerpted text and to other references in NFPA *101* are shown in red print to distinguish them from the extracted text.

EXTRACTED SECTION 9.6 FROM THE *LIFE SAFETY CODE*

9.6 Fire Detection, Alarm, and Communications Systems.

9.6.1* General.

A.9.6.1 The provisions of Section 9.6 cover the basic functions of a complete fire alarm system, including fire detection, alarm, and communications. These systems are primarily intended to provide the indication and warning of abnormal conditions, the summoning of appropriate aid, and the control of occupancy facilities to enhance protection of life.

Some of the provisions of Section 9.6 originated with *NFPA 72, National Fire Alarm Code.* For purposes of this *Code,* some provisions of Section 9.6 are more stringent than those of *NFPA 72,* which should be consulted for additional details.

9.6.1.1 The provisions of Section 9.6 shall apply only where specifically required by another section of this *Code.*

9.6.1.2 Fire detection, alarm, and communications systems installed to make use of an alternative permitted by this *Code* shall be considered required systems and shall meet the provisions of this *Code* applicable to required systems.

9.6.1.3 A fire alarm system required for life safety shall be installed, tested, and maintained in accordance with the applicable requirements of NFPA 70, *National Electrical Code,* and *NFPA 72, National Fire Alarm Code,* unless it is an approved existing installation, which shall be permitted to be continued in use.

9.6.1.4 All systems and components shall be approved for the purpose for which they are installed.

9.6.1.5* To ensure operational integrity, the fire alarm system shall have an approved maintenance and testing program complying with the applicable requirements of *NFPA 70, National Electrical Code,* and *NFPA 72, National Fire Alarm Code.*

A.9.6.1.5 Records of conducted maintenance and testing and a copy of the certificate of compliance should be maintained.

9.6.1.6* Where a required fire alarm system is out of service for more than 4 hours in a 24-hour period, the authority having jurisdiction shall be notified, and the building shall be evacuated or an approved fire watch shall be provided for all parties left unprotected by the shutdown until the fire alarm system has been returned to service.

A.9.6.1.6 A fire watch should at least involve some special action beyond normal staffing, such as assigning an additional security guard(s) to walk the areas affected. Such individuals should be specially trained in fire prevention and in occupant and fire department notification techniques, and they should understand the particular fire safety situation for public education purposes. *(Also see NFPA 601, Standard for Security Services in Fire Loss Prevention.)*

The term *out of service* in 9.6.1.6 is intended to imply that a significant portion of the fire alarm system is not in operation, such as an entire initiating device, signaling line, or notification appliance circuit. It is not the intent of the *Code* to require notification of the authority having jurisdiction, or evacuation of the portion of the building affected, for a single device or appliance.

9.6.1.7 For the purposes of this *Code*, a complete fire alarm system shall provide functions for initiation, notification, and control, which shall perform as follows:

(1) The initiation function provides the input signal to the system.
(2) The notification function is the means by which the system advises that human action is required in response to a particular condition.
(3) The control function provides outputs to control building equipment to enhance protection of life.

9.6.1.8 Protection of Fire Alarm System.

9.6.1.8.1* In areas that are not continuously occupied, and unless otherwise permitted by 9.6.1.8.1.1, 9.6.1.8.1.2, or 9.6.1.8.1.3, automatic smoke detection shall be installed to provide notification of fire at the following locations:

(1) Each fire alarm control unit
(2) Notification appliance circuit power extenders
(3) Supervising station transmitting equipment

A.9.6.1.8.1 The *Code* intends that only one smoke detector is required to be installed at the fire alarm control unit, the notification circuit power extenders, and the supervising station transmitting equipment, even when the area of the room would require more than one smoke detector if installed according to the spacing rules in *NFPA 72, National Fire Alarm Code*, Chapter 5.

9.6.1.8.1.1 The provisions of 9.6.1.8.1(2) and 9.6.1.8.1(3) shall not apply to existing alarm systems.

9.6.1.8.1.2 Where ambient conditions prohibit installation of a smoke detector, a heat detector shall be used.

9.6.1.8.1.3 Automatic smoke detection shall not be required where buildings are protected throughout by an approved, supervised automatic sprinkler system in accordance with Section 9.7 and the area containing the fire alarm control unit is sprinklered

9.6.2 Signal Initiation.

9.6.2.1 Where required by other sections of this *Code*, actuation of the complete fire alarm system shall be initiated by, but shall not be limited to, any or all of the following means:

(1) Manual fire alarm initiation
(2) Automatic detection
(3) Extinguishing system operation

9.6.2.2 Manual fire alarm boxes shall be used only for fire-protective signaling purposes. Combination fire alarm and guard's tour stations shall be acceptable.

9.6.2.3 A manual fire alarm box shall be provided as follows, unless modified by another section of this *Code*.

(1) For new alarm system installations, the manual fire alarm box shall be located within 5 ft (1.5 m) of exit doorways.
(2) For existing alarm system installations, the manual fire alarm box either shall be provided in the natural exit access path near each required exit or within 5 ft (1.5 m) of exit doorways.

9.6.2.4 Manual fire alarm boxes shall be mounted on both sides of grouped openings over 40 ft (12.2 m) in width, and within 5 ft (1.5 m) of each side of the opening.

9.6.2.5* Additional manual fire alarm boxes shall be located so that, on any given floor in any part of the building, no horizontal distance on that floor exceeding 200 ft (60 m) shall need to be traversed to reach a manual fire alarm box.

A.9.6.2.5 It is not the intent of 9.6.2.4 to require manual fire alarm boxes to be attached to movable partitions or to equipment, nor is it the intent to require the installation of permanent structures for mounting purposes only.

9.6.2.6* For fire alarm systems using automatic fire detection or waterflow detection devices to initiate the fire alarm system in accordance with Chapters 11 through 43, not less than one manual fire alarm box shall be provided to initiate a fire alarm signal. The manual fire alarm box shall be located where required by the authority having jurisdiction.

A.9.6.2.6 The manual fire alarm box required by 9.6.2.6 is intended to provide a means to manually activate the fire alarm system when the automatic fire detection system or waterflow devices are out of service due to maintenance or testing, or where human discovery of the fire precedes automatic sprinkler system or automatic detection system activation. Where the fire alarm system is connected to a monitoring facility, the manual fire alarm box required by 9.6.2.6 should be connected to a separate circuit that is not placed "on test" when the detection or sprinkler system is placed "on test." The manual fire alarm box should be located in an area that is accessible to occupants of the building and should not be locked.

9.6.2.7* Each manual fire alarm box on a system shall be accessible, unobstructed, and visible.

A.9.6.2.7 Manual fire alarm boxes can include those with key-operated locks for detention areas or psychiatric hospitals, manual fire alarm boxes in areas where explosive vapors or dusts might be a hazard, or manual fire alarm boxes in areas with corrosive atmospheres. The appearance of manual fire alarm boxes for special uses often differs from those used in areas of normal occupancy. Manual fire alarm boxes, such as those with locks, that are located in areas where the general public has limited access might need to have signage advising persons to seek assistance from staff in the event a fire is noted.

9.6.2.8 Where a sprinkler system provides automatic detection and alarm system initiation, it shall be provided with an approved alarm initiation device that operates when the flow of water is equal to or greater than that from a single automatic sprinkler.

9.6.2.9 Where a total (complete) coverage smoke detection system is required by another section of this *Code*, automatic detection of smoke in accordance with *NFPA 72, National Fire Alarm Code*, shall be provided in all occupiable areas, common areas, and work spaces in environments that are suitable for proper smoke detector operation.

9.6.2.10 Smoke Alarms.

9.6.2.10.1 General.

9.6.2.10.1.1 Where required by another section of this *Code*, single-station and multiple-station smoke alarms shall be in accordance with *NFPA 72, National Fire Alarm Code*, unless otherwise provided in 9.6.2.10.1.2, 9.6.2.10.1.3, or 9.6.2.10.1.4.

9.6.2.10.1.2 The installation of smoke alarms in sleeping rooms shall be required where required by Chapters 11 through 43.

9.6.2.10.1.3* The interconnection of smoke alarms shall apply only to new construction as provided in 9.6.2.10.3.

A.9.6.2.10.1.3 *NFPA 72, National Fire Alarm Code*, mandates smoke alarms in all sleeping rooms, and interconnection of smoke alarms is required for both new and existing installations. Per 9.6.2.10.1.2, the residential occupancy chapters determine whether smoke alarms are needed within sleeping rooms. Paragraph 9.6.2.10.1.3 limits the requirement for interconnection of smoke alarms to those in new construction. This *Code* does not intend to require compliant, existing smoke alarm installations to be interconnected. This *Code* is periodically revised to add retrospective requirements only where the need is clearly substantiated.

9.6.2.10.1.4 System smoke detectors in accordance with *NFPA 72, National Fire Alarm Code*, and arranged to function in the same manner as single-station or multiple-station smoke alarms shall be permitted in lieu of smoke alarms.

9.6.2.10.2 Smoke alarms, other than existing battery-operated smoke alarms as permitted by other sections of this *Code*, shall be powered in accordance with the requirements of *NFPA 72, National Fire Alarm Code*.

9.6.2.10.3* In new construction, where two or more smoke alarms are required within a dwelling unit, suite of rooms, or similar area, they shall be arranged so that operation of any smoke alarm shall cause the alarm in all smoke alarms within the dwelling unit, suite of rooms, or similar area to sound, unless otherwise permitted by the following:

(1) The requirement of 9.6.2.10.3 shall not apply where permitted by another section of this *Code*.
(2) The requirement of 9.6.2.10.3 shall not apply to configurations that provide equivalent distribution of the alarm signal.

A.9.6.2.10.3 A dwelling unit is that structure, area, room, or combination of rooms, including hotel rooms/suites, in which a family or individual lives. A dwelling unit includes living areas only and not common usage areas in multifamily buildings, such as corridors, lobbies, and basements.

9.6.2.10.4 The alarms shall sound only within an individual dwelling unit, suite of rooms, or similar area and shall not actuate the building fire alarm system, unless otherwise permitted by the authority having jurisdiction. Remote annunciation shall be permitted.

9.6.2.11 Where required by Chapter 11 through Chapter 43, an automatic fire detection system shall be provided in hazardous areas for initiation of the signaling system.

9.6.3 Occupant Notification.

9.6.3.1 Occupant notification shall be provided to alert occupants of a fire or other emergency where required by other sections of this *Code*.

9.6.3.2 Occupant notification shall be in accordance with 9.6.3.3 through 9.6.3.10.2, unless otherwise provided in 9.6.3.2.1 through 9.6.3.2.4.

9.6.3.2.1* Elevator lobby, hoistway, and associated machine room smoke detectors used solely for elevator recall, and heat detectors used solely for elevator power shutdown, shall not be required to activate the building evacuation alarm if the power supply and installation wiring to such detectors are monitored by the building fire alarm system, and if the activation of such detectors initiates a supervisory signal at a constantly attended location.

A.9.6.3.2.1 Elevator lobbies have been considered areas subject to unwanted alarms due to factors such as low ceilings and smoking. In the past several years, new features have become available to reduce this problem. These features are, however, not necessarily included in any specific installation.

9.6.3.2.2* Smoke detectors used solely for closing dampers or heating, ventilating, and air-conditioning system shutdown shall not be required to activate the building evacuation alarm, provided that the power supply and installation wiring to the detectors are monitored by the building fire alarm system, and the activation of the detectors initiates a supervisory signal at a constantly attended location.

A.9.6.3.2.2 The concept addressed is that detectors used for releasing service, such as door or damper closing and fan shutdown, are not required to sound the building alarm.

9.6.3.2.3* Smoke detectors located at doors for the exclusive operation of automatic door release shall not be required to activate the building evacuation alarm, provided that the power supply and installation wiring to the detectors are monitored by the building fire alarm system, and the activation of the detectors initiates a supervisory signal at a constantly attended location.

A.9.6.3.2.3 The concept addressed is that detectors used for releasing service, such as door or damper closing and fan shutdown, are not required to sound the building alarm.

9.6.3.2.4 Detectors in accordance with 22.3.4.3.1(2) and 23.3.4.3.1(2) shall not be required to activate the building evacuation alarm.

9.6.3.3 Where permitted by Chapter 11 through Chapter 43, a presignal system shall be permitted where the initial fire alarm signal is automatically transmitted without delay to a municipal fire department, to a fire brigade (if provided), and to an on-site staff person trained to respond to a fire emergency.

9.6.3.4 Where permitted by Chapter 11 through Chapter 43, a positive alarm sequence shall be permitted, provided that it is in accordance with *NFPA 72, National Fire Alarm Code*.

9.6.3.5 Unless otherwise provided in 9.6.3.5.1 through 9.6.3.5.8, notification signals for occupants to evacuate shall be audible and visible signals in accordance with *NFPA 72, National Fire Alarm Code*, and ICC/ANSI A117.1, *American National Standard for Accessible and Usable Buildings and Facilities*, or other means of notification acceptable to the authority having jurisdiction shall be provided.

9.6.3.5.1 Areas not subject to occupancy by persons who are hearing impaired shall not be required to comply with the provisions for visible signals.

9.6.3.5.2 Visible-only signals shall be provided where specifically permitted in health care occupancies in accordance with the provisions of Chapter 18 and Chapter 19.

9.6.3.5.3 Existing alarm systems shall not be required to comply with the provision for visible signals.

9.6.3.5.4 Visible signals shall not be required in lodging or rooming houses in accordance with the provisions of Chapter 26.

9.6.3.5.5 Visible signals shall not be required in exit stair enclosures.

9.6.3.5.6 Visible signals shall not be required in elevator cars.

9.6.3.5.7* Public mode visual notification appliances in accordance with *NFPA 72* shall not be required in designated areas as permitted by Chapters 11 through 43, provided that they are replaced with approved alternative visible means.

A.9.6.3.5.7 Visual notification appliances installed in large volume spaces, such as arenas, stadiums, malls and atriums, can be alternative devices which are not listed as visible notification appliances for fire alarm systems provided that the notification objective of the visual signal is reasonably achieved. Examples of alternative devices include, but are not limited to, scoreboards, message boards, and other electronic devices that meet the performance objectives of visible fire alarm appliances in large volume spaces.

It is the intent to permit the omission of visible notification appliances as identified in 9.6.3.5.7 provided that the adjacent areas that have not been specifically designated as exempt are provided with visible notification as required by 9.6.3.5.

9.6.3.5.8* Where visible signals are not required, as permitted by 9.6.3.5.7, documentation of such omission shall be maintained in accordance with 9.7.7.

A.9.6.3.5.8 Documentation should be maintained with the as-built drawings so that inspection and testing personnel understand that the visible appliances have been exempted from certain areas and, therefore, can note the deviation on the acceptance test documentation and ongoing inspection reports. This will provide inspection and testing personnel with necessary details regarding the omission of visible notification appliances.

9.6.3.6 The general evacuation alarm signal shall operate in accordance with one of the methods prescribed by 9.6.3.6.1 through 9.6.3.6.3.

9.6.3.6.1 The general evacuation alarm signal shall operate throughout the entire building.

9.6.3.6.2* Where total evacuation of occupants is impractical due to building configuration, only the occupants in the affected zones shall be notified initially. Provisions shall be made to selectively notify occupants in other zones to afford orderly evacuation of the entire building.

A.9.6.3.6.2 To approve an evacuation plan to selectively notify building occupants, the authority having jurisdiction should consider several building parameters, including building compartmentation, detection and suppression system zones, occupant loads, and the number and arrangement of the means of egress.

In high-rise buildings, it is typical to evacuate the fire floor, the floor(s) above, and the floor immediately below. Other areas are then evacuated as the fire develops.

9.6.3.6.3 Where occupants are incapable of evacuating themselves because of age, physical or mental disabilities, or physical restraint, the private operating mode as described in *NFPA 72, National Fire Alarm Code*, shall be permitted to be used. Only the attendants and other personnel required to evacuate occupants from a zone, area, floor, or building shall be required to be notified. The notification shall include means to readily identify the zone, area, floor, or building in need of evacuation.

9.6.3.6.4 The general evacuation signal shall not be required to operate in exit stair enclosures.

9.6.3.6.5 The general evacuation signal shall not be required to operate in elevator cars.

9.6.3.7 Audible alarm notification appliances shall be of such character and so distributed as to be effectively heard above the average ambient sound level that exists under normal conditions of occupancy.

9.6.3.8 Audible alarm notification appliances shall produce signals that are distinctive from audible signals used for other purposes in a given building.

9.6.3.9 Automatically transmitted or live voice evacuation or relocation instructions shall be permitted to be used to notify occupants and shall comply with either 9.6.3.9.1 or 9.6.3.9.2.

9.6.3.9.1 Automatically transmitted or live voice evacuation or relocation instructions shall be in accordance with *NFPA 72, National Fire Alarm Code*.

9.6.3.9.2* Where permitted by Chapters 11 through 43, automatically transmitted or live voice announcements shall be permitted to be made via a voice communication or public address system that complies with the following:

(1) Occupant notification, either live or recorded, shall be initiated at a constantly attended receiving station by personnel trained to respond to an emergency.
(2) An approved secondary power supply shall be provided for other than existing, previously approved systems.
(3) The system shall be audible above the expected ambient noise level.
(4) Emergency announcements shall take precedence over any other use.

A.9.6.3.9.2 The provisions of 9.6.3.9.2 offer an alternative to the emergency voice alarm and communications system provisions (live voice or recorded voice announcements) of *NFPA 72, National Fire Alarm Code*. Occupancies, such as large-venue assembly occupancies and mercantile mall buildings, are occupancies in which the physical configuration (e.g., large-volume spaces), function, and human behavior (including elevated levels of occupant-generated noise) present challenges with respect to effective occupant notification by standard means in accordance with *NFPA 72*. Because the routine operation of these occupancies demands highly reliant, acoustically capable, and sufficiently audible public address systems, properly trained staff can be relied on to use these public address systems to effect occupant evacuation, relocation, or both.

As 9.6.3.9.2 specifically permits an alternative means of notification to that prescribed by *NFPA 72*, it does not mandate that the secondary power supply and the intelligibility and audibility facets of the public address system comply with *NFPA 72* or suggest that equivalency with the related provisions of *NFPA 72* is required. However, it is anticipated that, when approving the secondary power and audibility capabilities of public address systems, authorities having jurisdiction will ensure that these systems are conceptually comparable to the emergency voice alarm and communications system provisions of *NFPA 72*, such that a reliable and effective occupant notification system is provided.

9.6.3.10 Unless otherwise permitted by another section of this *Code*, audible and visible fire alarm notification appliances shall comply with either 9.6.3.10.1 or 9.6.3.10.2.

9.6.3.10.1 Audible and visible fire alarm notification appliances shall be used only for fire alarm system or other emergency purposes.

9.6.3.10.2 Emergency voice/alarm communication systems shall be permitted to be used for other purposes, subject to the approval of the authority having jurisdiction, if the fire alarm system takes precedence over all other signals, with the exception of mass notification inputs.

9.6.4 Emergency Forces Notification.

9.6.4.1 Where required by another section of this *Code*, emergency forces notification shall be provided to alert the municipal fire department and fire brigade (if provided) of fire or other emergency.

9.6.4.2 Where fire department notification is required by another section of this *Code*, the fire alarm system shall be arranged to transmit the alarm automatically via any of the following means acceptable to the authority having jurisdiction and shall be in accordance with *NFPA 72, National Fire Alarm Code*:

(1) Auxiliary fire alarm system
(2) Central station fire alarm system
(3) Proprietary supervising station fire alarm system
(4) Remote supervising station fire alarm system

9.6.4.3 For existing installations where none of the means of notification specified in 9.6.4.2(1) through (4) are available, an approved plan for notification of the municipal fire department shall be permitted.

9.6.5 Fire Safety Functions.

9.6.5.1 Fire safety functions shall be installed in accordance with the requirements of *NFPA 72, National Fire Alarm Code*.

9.6.5.2 Where required by another section of this *Code*, the following functions shall be actuated:

(1) Release of hold-open devices for doors or other opening protectives
(2) Stairwell or elevator shaft pressurization
(3) Smoke management or smoke control systems
(4) Unlocking of doors
(5) Elevator recall and shutdown

9.6.6 Location of Controls. Operator controls, alarm indicators, and manual communications capability shall be installed at a convenient location acceptable to the authority having jurisdiction.

9.6.7 Annunciation.

9.6.7.1 Where alarm annunciation is required by another section of this *Code*, it shall comply with 9.6.7.2 through 9.6.7.7.

9.6.7.2 Alarm annunciation at the control center shall be by means of audible and visible indicators.

9.6.7.3 For the purposes of alarm annunciation, each floor of the building, other than floors of existing buildings, shall be considered as not less than one zone, unless otherwise permitted by 9.6.7.4.3, 9.6.7.4.4, 9.6.7.4.5 or as another section of this *Code*.

9.6.7.4 If a floor area exceeds 22,500 ft^2 (2090 m^2), additional fire alarm zoning shall be provided, and the length of any single fire alarm zone shall not exceed 300 ft (91 m) in any direction, except as provided in 9.6.7.4.1 through 9.6.7.4.5 or otherwise modified by another section of this *Code*.

9.6.7.4.1 Where permitted by another section of this *Code*, fire alarm zones shall be permitted to exceed 22,500 ft^2 (2090 m^2), and the length of a zone shall be permitted to exceed 300 ft (91 m) in any direction.

9.6.7.4.2 Where the building is protected by an automatic sprinkler system in accordance with 9.7.1.1(1), the area of the fire alarm zone shall be permitted to coincide with the allowable area of the sprinkler system.

9.6.7.4.3 Unless otherwise prohibited elsewhere in this *Code*, where a building not exceeding four stories in height is protected by an automatic sprinkler system in accordance with 9.7.1.1(1), the sprinkler system shall be permitted to be annunciated on the fire alarm system as a single zone.

9.6.7.4.4 Where the building is protected by an automatic sprinkler system in accordance with 9.7.1.1(2), the sprinkler system shall be permitted to be annunciated on the fire alarm system as a single zone.

9.6.7.4.5 Where the building is protected by an automatic sprinkler system in accordance with 9.7.1.1(3), the sprinkler system shall be permitted to be annunciated on the fire alarm system as a single zone.

9.6.7.6 A system supervisory signal shall be annunciated at the control center by means of audible and visible indicators.

9.6.7.7 Where the system serves more than one building, each building shall be annunciated separately.

LIFE SAFETY CODE OCCUPANCY TABLES

Assembly Occupancies

The following excerpts from NFPA *101*, 2009 edition, are provided for reference:

12.1.1 Application. The requirements of this chapter shall apply to new buildings or portions thereof used as an assembly occupancy (*see 1.3.1*).

13.1.1 Application.

13.1.1.1 The requirements of this chapter shall apply to existing buildings or portions thereof currently occupied as assembly occupancies, unless otherwise specified by 13.1.1.2. (*See 3.3.178.2 for definition of assembly occupancy.*)

3.3.178.2* Assembly Occupancy. An occupancy (1) used for a gathering of 50 or more persons for deliberation, worship, entertainment, eating, drinking, amusement, awaiting transportation, or similar uses; or (2) used as a special amusement building, regardless of occupant load.

Assembly Occupancies

	New Assembly		Existing Assembly	
	101 Ref.	Requirement	101 Ref.	Requirement
Fire alarm system	12.3.4.1.1	Assembly occupancies with occupant loads of more than 300 and all theaters with more than one audience-viewing room shall be provided with an approved fire alarm system in accordance with 9.6.1 and 12.3.4, unless otherwise permitted by 12.3.4.1.2	13.3.4.1.1	Assembly occupancies with occupant loads of more than 300 and all theaters with more than one audience-viewing room shall be provided with an approved fire alarm system in accordance with 9.6.1 and 13.3.4, unless otherwise permitted by the: 13.3.4.1.2, 13.3.4.1.3, or 13.3.4.1.4
	12.3.4.1.2	Assembly occupancies that are a part of a multiple occupancy protected as a mixed occupancy (*see 6.1.14*) shall be permitted to be served by a common fire alarm system, provided that the individual requirements of each occupancy are met.	13.3.4.1.2	Assembly occupancies that are a part of a multiple occupancy protected as a mixed occupancy (*see 6.1.14*) shall be permitted to be served by a common fire alarm system, provided that the individual requirements of each occupancy are met.
			13.3.4.1.3	Voice communication or public address systems complying with 13.3.4.3.6 shall not be required to comply with 9.6.1.
			13.3.4.1.4	This requirement of 13.3.4.1.1 shall not apply to assembly occupancies where, in the judgment of the authority having jurisdiction, adequate alternative provisions exist or are provided for the discovery of a fire and for alerting the occupants promptly.

Fire alarm signal initiation				

Manual initiation	12.3.4.2.1	Initiation of the required fire alarm system shall be by both of the following means:
		
		(1) Manual means in accordance with 9.6.2.1(1), unless otherwise permitted by the following:
		
		  (a) The requirement of 12.3.4.2.1(1) shall not apply where initiation is by means of an approved automatic fire detection system in accordance with 9.6.2.1(2) that provides fire detection throughout the building.
		
		  (b) The requirement of 12.3.4.2.1(1) shall not apply where initiation is by means of an approved automatic sprinkler system in accordance with 9.6.2.1(3) that provides fire detection and protection throughout the building.
		
		(2) Where automatic sprinklers are provided, sprinkler system waterflow shall initiate the fire alarm system, even where manual fire alarm boxes are provided in accordance with 12.3.4.2.1(1).
		
		Also see 12.3.4.2.2 below.
			13.3.4.2.1	Initiation of the required fire alarm system shall be by both of the following means, and the system shall be provided with an emergency power source:
				
				(1) Manual means in accordance with 9.6.2.1(1), unless otherwise permitted by the following:
				
				  (a) The requirement of 13.3.4.2.1(1) shall not apply where initiation is by means of an approved automatic fire detection system in accordance with 9.6.2.1(2) that provides fire detection throughout the building.
				
				  (b) The requirement of 13.3.4.2.1(1) shall not apply where initiation is by means of an approved automatic sprinkler system in accordance with 9.6.2.1(3) that provides fire detection and protection throughout the building.
				
				(2) Where automatic sprinklers are provided, sprinkler system waterflow shall initiate the fire alarm system, even where manual fire alarm boxes are provided in accordance with 13.3.4.2.1(1).
				
				Also see 13.3.4.2.2 below.

Automatic detection	12.3.4.2.3	In assembly occupancies with occupant loads of more than 300, automatic detection shall be provided in all hazardous areas that are not normally occupied, unless such areas are protected throughout by an approved, supervised automatic sprinkler system in accordance with Section 9.7. Also see 12.3.4.2.1(1) above and 12.3.4.2.2 below. Also see 12.3.6, 12.4.3.3.4, 12.4.5.5.1.2, 12.4.5.7.1, 12.4.7.6, 12.7.5.3.7.1, and 12.7.12 in NFPA *101*.	13.3.4.2.3	In assembly occupancies with occupant loads of more than 300, automatic detection shall be provided in all hazardous areas that are not normally occupied, unless such areas are protected throughout by an approved automatic sprinkler system in accordance with Section 9.7. Also see 13.3.4.2.1(1) above and 13.3.4.2.2 below. Also see 13.4.5.5.1.2, 13.4.7.6, 13.7.5.3.7.1, and 13.7.12 in NFPA *101*.

(continues)

Assembly Occupancies Continued

		New Assembly		Existing Assembly	
		101 Ref.	Requirement	101 Ref.	Requirement
Fire alarm signal initiation (continued)	Automatic detection (continued)	12.4.7.4	**Special Amusement Buildings** Where the nature of the special amusement building is such that it operates in reduced lighting levels, the building shall be protected throughout by an approved automatic smoke detection system in accordance with Section 9.6.	13.4.7.4	**Special Amusement Buildings** Where the nature of the special amusement building is such that it operates in reduced lighting levels, the building shall be protected throughout by an approved automatic smoke detection system in accordance with Section 9.6.
		12.4.7.5	Actuation of any smoke detection system device shall sound an alarm at a constantly attended location on the premises.	13.4.7.5	Actuation of any smoke detection system device shall sound an alarm at a constantly attended location on the premises.
	Extinguishing system operation		See 9.7.2.2 below. Also see 12.3.4.2.1(2) and 12.3.4.2.3 above. Also see 12.3.5 and 12.4.7.2 in NFPA *101* for extinguishing system requirements.		See 9.7.2.2 below. See 13.3.4.2.1(2) and 13.3.4.2.3 above. Also see 13.3.5 and 13.4.7.2 in NFPA *101* for extinguishing system requirements.
FAS supervisory signal initiation	Extinguishing system supervision	9.7.2.1	Where supervised automatic sprinkler systems are required by another section of this *Code*, supervisory attachments shall be installed and monitored for integrity in accordance with *NFPA 72, National Fire Alarm Code*, and a distinctive supervisory signal shall be provided to indicate a condition that would impair the satisfactory operation of the sprinkler system. System components and parameters that are required to be monitored shall include, but shall not be limited to, control valves, fire pump power supplies and running conditions, water tank levels and temperatures, tank pressure, and air pressure on dry-pipe valves. Supervisory signals shall sound and shall be displayed either at a location within the protected building that is constantly attended by qualified personnel or at an approved, remotely located receiving facility. Also see 12.3.4.2.1(2) and 12.3.4.2.3 above. Also see 12.3.5 and 12.4.7.2 in NFPA *101* for extinguishing system requirements.	9.7.2.1	Where supervised automatic sprinkler systems are required by another section of this *Code*, supervisory attachments shall be installed and monitored for integrity in accordance with *NFPA 72, National Fire Alarm Code*, and a distinctive supervisory signal shall be provided to indicate a condition that would impair the satisfactory operation of the sprinkler system. System components and parameters that are required to be monitored shall include, but shall not be limited to, control valves, fire pump power supplies and running conditions, water tank levels and temperatures, tank pressure, and air pressure on dry-pipe valves. Supervisory signals shall sound and shall be displayed either at a location within the protected building that is constantly attended by qualified personnel or at an approved, remotely located receiving facility. Also see 13.3.4.2.1(2) and 13.3.4.2.3 above. Also see 13.3.5 and 13.4.7.2 in NFPA *101* for extinguishing system requirements.

Occupant notification		12.3.4.3		13.3.4.3	
	Audible/visible	12.3.4.3	The required fire alarm system shall activate an audible and visible alarm in a constantly attended receiving station within the building when occupied for purposes of initiating emergency action.	13.3.4.3	The required fire alarm system shall activate an audible alarm in a constantly attended receiving station within the building when occupied for purposes of initiating emergency action.
	Positive alarm sequence	12.3.4.3.1	Positive alarm sequence in accordance with 9.6.3.4 shall be permitted.	13.3.4.3.1	Positive alarm sequence in accordance with 9.6.3.4 shall be permitted.
	Presignal system		Not addressed.	13.3.4.3.2	A presignal system in accordance with 9.6.3.3 shall be permitted.
	Voice announcements	12.3.4.3.3	Occupant notification shall be by means of voice announcements, in accordance with 9.6.3.9, initiated by the person in the constantly attended receiving station.	13.3.4.3.3	Occupant notification shall be by means of voice announcements in accordance with 9.6.3.9 initiated by the person in the constantly attended receiving station.
		12.3.4.3.4	Occupant notification shall be by means of visible signals in accordance with 9.6.3.5, initiated by the person in the constantly attended receiving station, unless otherwise permitted by 12.3.4.3.5.		
		12.3.4.3.5	Visible signals shall not be required in the assembly seating area, or the floor area used for the contest, performance, or entertainment, where the occupant load exceeds 1000 and an approved, alternative visible means of occupant notification is provided. (See 9.6.3.5.7.)		
		12.3.4.3.6	The announcement shall be permitted to be made via a voice communication or public address system in accordance with 9.6.3.9.2.	13.3.4.3.6	The announcement shall be permitted to be made via a voice communication or public address system in accordance with 9.6.3.9.2.
		12.3.4.3.7	Where the authority having jurisdiction determines that a constantly attended receiving station is impractical, both of the following shall be provided: (1) Automatically transmitted evacuation or relocation instructions shall be provided in accordance with *NFPA 72, National Fire Alarm Code.* (2) The system shall be monitored by a supervising station in accordance with *NFPA 72, National Fire Alarm Code.*	13.3.4.3.7	Where the authority having jurisdiction determines that a constantly attended receiving station is impractical, automatically transmitted evacuation or relocation instructions shall be provided in accordance with *NFPA 72, National Fire Alarm Code.* Also see 13.3.4.1.3 above.

(continues)

Assembly Occupancies Continued

		New Assembly		Existing Assembly	
		101 Ref.	Requirement	101 Ref.	Requirement
Occupant notification *(continued)*	Other provisions	12.3.4.2.2	The initiating device shall be capable of transmitting an alarm to a receiving station, located within the building, that is constantly attended when the assembly occupancy is occupied.	13.3.4.2.2	The initiating device shall be capable of transmitting an alarm to a receiving station, located within the building, that is constantly attended when the assembly occupancy is occupied.
Emergency forces notification		9.7.2.2	Where supervision of automatic sprinkler systems is provided in accordance with another provision of this *Code*, waterflow alarms shall be transmitted to an approved, proprietary alarm-receiving facility, a remote station, a central station, or the fire department. Such connection shall be in accordance with 9.6.1.3. Also see 12.3.4.2.1(2) and 12.3.4.2.3 above. Also see 12.3.5 and 12.4.7.2 in NFPA *101* for extinguishing system requirements.	9.7.2.2	Where supervision of automatic sprinkler systems is provided in accordance with another provision of this *Code*, waterflow alarms shall be transmitted to an approved, proprietary alarm-receiving facility, a remote station, a central station, or the fire department. Such connection shall be in accordance with 9.6.1.3. Also see 13.3.4.2.1(2) and 13.3.4.2.3 above. Also see 13.3.5 and 13.4.7.2 in NFPA *101* for extinguishing system requirements.
Annunciator			Not addressed.		Not addressed.
Emergency control (fire safety) functions			See separate summary table for emergency control (fire safety) functions, where applicable.		See separate summary table for emergency control (fire safety) functions, where applicable.

Educational Occupancies

The following excerpts from NFPA *101*, 2009 edition, are provided for reference:

14.1.1 Application.

14.1.1.1 The requirements of this chapter shall apply to new buildings or portions thereof used as educational occupancies (*see 1.3.1*).

15.1.1 Application.

15.1.1.1 The requirements of this chapter shall apply to existing buildings or portions thereof currently occupied as educational occupancies.

3.3.178.6 Educational Occupancy. An occupancy used for educational purposes through the twelfth grade by six or more persons for 4 or more hours per day or more than 12 hours per week.

Educational Occupancies

		New Educational		Existing Educational	
		101 Ref.	Requirement	101 Ref.	Requirement
Fire alarm system		14.3.4.1.1	Educational occupancies shall be provided with a fire alarm system in accordance with Section 9.6.	15.3.4.1.1	Educational occupancies shall be provided with a fire alarm system in accordance with Section 9.6.
		14.3.4.1.2	The requirement of 14.3.4.1.1 shall not apply to buildings meeting all of the following criteria: (1) Buildings having an area not exceeding 1000 ft² (93 m²) (2) Buildings containing a single classroom (3) Buildings located not less than 30 ft (9.2 m) from another building	15.3.4.1.2	The requirement of 15.3.4.1.1 shall not apply to buildings meeting all of the following criteria: (1) Buildings having an area not exceeding 1000 ft² (93 m²) (2) Buildings containing a single classroom (3) Buildings located not less than 30 ft (9.2 m) from another building
Fire alarm signal initiation	Manual initiation	14.3.4.2.1	Initiation of the required fire alarm system, other than as permitted by 14.3.4.2.3, shall be by manual means in accordance with 9.6.2.1(1).	15.3.4.2.1	Initiation of the required fire alarm system shall be by manual means in accordance with 9.6.2.1(1), unless otherwise permitted by the following:
		14.3.4.2.3	Manual fire alarm boxes shall be permitted to be eliminated in accordance with 14.3.4.2.3.1 or 14.3.4.2.3.2.		(1) Manual fire alarm boxes shall not be required where permitted by 15.3.4.2.3. (2) In buildings where all normally occupied spaces are provided with a two-way communication system between such spaces and a constantly attended receiving station from where a general evacuation alarm can be sounded, the manual fire alarm boxes shall not be required, except in locations specifically designated by the authority having jurisdiction.
		14.3.4.2.3.1	Manual fire alarm boxes shall be permitted to be eliminated where all of the following conditions apply: (1) Interior corridors are protected by smoke detectors using an alarm verification system as described in *NFPA 72, National Fire Alarm Code.*		

(continues)

Educational Occupancies Continued

		New Educational		Existing Educational	
		101 Ref.	**Requirement**	**101 Ref.**	**Requirement**
Fire alarm signal initiation *(continued)*	Manual initiation *(continued)*		(2) Auditoriums, cafeterias, and gymnasiums are protected by heat-detection devices or other approved detection devices. (3) Shops and laboratories involving dusts or vapors are protected by heat-detection devices or other approved detection devices. (4) Provision is made at a central point to manually activate the evacuation signal or to evacuate only affected areas.	15.3.4.2.3	Manual fire alarm boxes shall be permitted to be eliminated in accordance with 15.3.4.2.3.1 or 15.3.4.2.3.2.
				15.3.4.2.3.1	Manual fire alarm boxes shall be permitted to be eliminated where all of the following conditions apply: (1) Interior corridors are protected by smoke detectors using an alarm verification system as described in *NFPA 72, National Fire Alarm Code*. (2) Auditoriums, cafeterias, and gymnasiums are protected by heat-detection devices or other approved detection devices. (3) Shops and laboratories involving dusts or vapors are protected by heat-detection devices or other approved detection devices. (4) Provision is made at a central point to manually activate the evacuation signal or to evacuate only affected areas.
		14.3.4.2.3.2	Manual fire alarm boxes shall be permitted to be eliminated where all of the following conditions apply: (1) The building is protected throughout by an approved, supervised automatic sprinkler system in accordance with Section 9.7. (2) Provision is made at a central point to manually activate the evacuation signal or to evacuate only affected areas.	15.3.4.2.3.2	Manual fire alarm boxes shall be permitted to be eliminated where all of the following conditions apply: (1) The building is protected throughout by an approved, supervised automatic sprinkler system in accordance with Section 9.7. (2) Provision is made at a central point to manually activate the evacuation signal or to evacuate only affected areas.
	Automatic detection		See 14.3.4.2.3.1 above. Also see 14.7.4.2(2) in NFPA *101*.		See 15.3.4.2.3.1 above. Also see 15.7.4.2(2) in NFPA *101*.
	Extinguishing system operation	14.3.4.2.2	In buildings provided with automatic sprinkler protection, the operation of the sprinkler system shall automatically activate the fire alarm system in addition to the initiation means required in 14.3.4.2.1. Also see 9.7.2.2 below.	15.3.4.2.2	In buildings provided with automatic sprinkler protection, the operation of the sprinkler system shall automatically activate the fire alarm system in addition to the initiation means required in 15.3.4.2.1. Also see 9.7.2.2 below.

			(NFPA 101 Chapter 14)		(NFPA 101 Chapter 15)
			Also see 14.3.4.2.3.2 above. Also see 14.3.5 in NFPA *101* for extinguishing system requirements and 14.3.6, 14.3.7, and 14.7.4 for additional extinguishing system provisions.		Also see 15.3.4.2.3.2 above. Also see 15.3.5 in NFPA *101* for extinguishing system requirements and 15.3.6, 15.3.7, and 15.7.4 for additional extinguishing system provisions.
FAS supervisory signal initiation	Extinguishing system supervision	9.7.2.1	Where supervised automatic sprinkler systems are required by another section of this *Code*, supervisory attachments shall be installed and monitored for integrity in accordance with *NFPA 72, National Fire Alarm Code*, and a distinctive supervisory signal shall be provided to indicate a condition that would impair the satisfactory operation of the sprinkler system. System components and parameters that are required to be monitored shall include, but shall not be limited to, control valves, fire pump power supplies and running conditions, water tank levels and temperatures, tank pressure, and air pressure on dry-pipe valves. Supervisory signals shall sound and shall be displayed either at a location within the protected building that is constantly attended by qualified personnel or at an approved, remotely located receiving facility. Also see 14.3.4.2.3.2 above. Also see 14.3.5 in NFPA *101* for extinguishing system requirements and 14.3.6, 14.3.7, and 14.7.4 for additional extinguishing system provisions.	9.7.2.1	Where supervised automatic sprinkler systems are required by another section of this *Code*, supervisory attachments shall be installed and monitored for integrity in accordance with *NFPA 72, National Fire Alarm Code*, and a distinctive supervisory signal shall be provided to indicate a condition that would impair the satisfactory operation of the sprinkler system. System components and parameters that are required to be monitored shall include, but shall not be limited to, control valves, fire pump power supplies and running conditions, water tank levels and temperatures, tank pressure, and air pressure on dry-pipe valves. Supervisory signals shall sound and shall be displayed either at a location within the protected building that is constantly attended by qualified personnel or at an approved, remotely located receiving facility. Also see 15.3.4.2.3.2 above. Also see 15.3.5 in NFPA *101* for extinguishing system requirements and 15.3.6, 15.3.7, and 15.7.4 for additional extinguishing system provisions.
Occupant notification	Audible/visible	14.3.4.3.1.1	Occupant notification shall be accomplished automatically in accordance with 9.6.3.	15.3.4.3.1.1	Occupant notification shall be accomplished automatically in accordance with 9.6.3.
	Positive alarm sequence	14.3.4.3.1.2	Positive alarm sequence shall be permitted in accordance with 9.6.3.4.	15.3.4.3.1.2	Positive alarm sequence shall be permitted in accordance with 9.6.3.4.
	Presignal system		Not addressed.		Not addressed.
	Voice announcements		Not specifically addressed; however, see 9.6.3.9.		Not specifically addressed; however, see 9.6.3.9.
	Other provisions	14.3.4.3.1.3	Where installed and operated per *NFPA 72, National Fire Alarm Code*, the fire alarm system shall be permitted to be used for other emergency signaling or for class changes.	15.3.4.3.1.3	Where acceptable to the authority having jurisdiction, the fire alarm system shall be permitted to be used for other emergency signaling or for class changes, provided that the fire alarm is distinctive in signal and overrides all other use.

(continues)

Educational Occupancies Continued

		New Educational		Existing Educational	
		101 Ref.	Requirement	101 Ref.	Requirement
Occupant notification *(continued)*	Other provisions *(continued)*	14.3.4.3.1.4	To prevent students from being returned to a building that is burning, the recall signal shall be separate and distinct from any other signals, and such signal shall be permitted to be given by use of distinctively colored flags or banners.	15.3.4.3.1.4	To prevent students from being returned to a building that is burning, the recall signal shall be separate and distinct from any other signals, and such signal shall be permitted to be given by use of distinctively colored flags or banners.
		14.3.4.3.1.5	If the recall signal required by 14.3.4.3.1.4 is electric, the push buttons or other controls shall be kept under lock, the key for which shall be in the possession of the principal or another designated person in order to prevent a recall at a time when there is an actual fire.	15.3.4.3.1.5	If the recall signal required by 15.3.4.3.1.4 is electric, the push buttons or other controls shall be kept under lock, the key for which shall be in the possession of the principal or another designated person in order to prevent a recall at a time when there is an actual fire.
		14.3.4.3.1.6	Regardless of the method of recall signal, the means of giving the recall signal shall be kept under lock.	15.3.4.3.1.6	Regardless of the method of recall signal, the means of giving the recall signal shall be kept under lock.
Emergency forces notification		14.3.4.3.2	Fire department notification shall be accomplished in accordance with 9.6.4.	15.3.4.3.2	Wherever any of the school authorities determine that an actual fire exists, they shall immediately call the local fire department using the public fire alarm system or other available facilities.
		9.7.2.2	Where supervision of automatic sprinkler systems is provided in accordance with another provision of this *Code*, waterflow alarms shall be transmitted to an approved, proprietary alarm-receiving facility, a remote station, a central station, or the fire department. Such connection shall be in accordance with 9.6.1.3. Also see 14.3.4.2.2 and 14.3.4.2.3.2 above. Also see 14.3.5 in NFPA *101* for extinguishing system requirements and 14.3.6, 14.3.7, and 14.7.4 for additional extinguishing system provisions.	9.7.2.2	Where supervision of automatic sprinkler systems is provided in accordance with another provision of this *Code*, waterflow alarms shall be transmitted to an approved, proprietary alarm-receiving facility, a remote station, a central station, or the fire department. Such connection shall be in accordance with 9.6.1.3. Also see 15.3.4.2.2 and 15.3.4.2.3.2 above. Also see 15.3.5 in NFPA *101* for extinguishing system requirements and 15.3.6, 15.3.7, and 15.7.4 for additional extinguishing system provisions.
Annunciator			Not addressed.		Not addressed.
Emergency control (fire safety) functions			See separate summary table for emergency control (fire safety) functions, where applicable.		See separate summary table for emergency control (fire safety) functions, where applicable.

Day Care Occupancies

The following excerpts from NFPA *101*, 2009 edition, are provided for reference:

16.1.1* Application.

16.1.1.1 The requirements of this chapter shall apply to new buildings or portions thereof used as day-care occupancies *(see 1.3.1).*

17.1.1* Application.

17.1.1.1 The requirements of this chapter shall apply to existing buildings or portions thereof currently occupied as day-care occupancies.

3.3.178.4 Day-Care Occupancy. An occupancy in which four or more clients receive care, maintenance, and supervision, by other than their relatives or legal guardians, for less than 24 hours per day.

3.3.131.1* Day-Care Home. A building or portion of a building in which more than 3 but not more than 12 clients receive care, maintenance, and supervision, by other than their relative(s) or legal guardians(s), for less than 24 hours per day.

The following excerpts from *NFPA 72,* 2010 edition, are provided for reference:

3.3.100 Fire Warning Equipment. Any detector, alarm, device, or material related to single- and multiple-station alarms or household fire alarm systems.

3.3.149 Multiple Station Alarm. A single station alarm capable of being interconnected to one or more additional alarms so that the actuation of one causes the appropriate alarm signal to operate in all interconnected alarms.

3.3.245 Single Station Alarm. A detector comprising an assembly that incorporates a sensor, control components, and an alarm notification appliance in one unit operated from a power source either located in the unit or obtained at the point of installation.

3.3.251 Smoke Alarm. A single or multiple station alarm responsive to smoke.

Day Care Occupancies

	New Day Care		Existing Day Care	
	101 Ref.	Requirement	101 Ref.	Requirement
Fire alarm system/fire warning equipment	16.3.4.1	Day-care occupancies, other than day-care occupancies housed in one room, having at least one door opening directly to the outside at grade plane or to an exterior exit access balcony in accordance with 7.5.3, shall be provided with a fire alarm system in accordance with Section 9.6.	17.3.4.1	Day-care occupancies, other than day-care occupancies housed in one room, shall be provided with a fire alarm system in accordance with Section 9.6.
Fire alarm signal initiation	Manual initiation	16.3.4.2	Initiation of the required fire alarm system shall be by manual means and by operation of any required smoke detectors and required sprinkler systems. *(See 16.3.4.5.)*	17.3.4.2	Initiation of the required fire alarm system shall be by manual means and by operation of any required smoke detectors and required sprinkler systems. *(See 17.3.4.5.)*

(continues)

Day Care Occupancies Continued

		New Day Care		Existing Day Care	
		101 Ref.	Requirement	101 Ref.	Requirement
Fire alarm signal initiation (continued)	Automatic detection	16.3.4.5	A smoke detection system in accordance with Section 9.6 shall be installed in day-care occupancies, other than those housed in one room, having at least one door opening directly to the outside at grade plane or to an exterior exit access balcony in accordance with 7.5.3, and such system shall comply with both of the following: (1) Detectors shall be installed on each story in front of the doors to the stairways and in the corridors of all floors occupied by the day-care occupancy. (2) Detectors also shall be installed in lounges, recreation areas, and sleeping rooms in the day-care occupancy.	17.3.4.5	A smoke detection system in accordance with Section 9.6 shall be installed in day-care occupancies, other than those housed in one room or those housing clients capable of self-preservation where no sleeping facilities are provided, and such system shall comply with both of the following: (1) Detectors shall be installed on each story in front of the doors to the stairways and in the corridors of all floors occupied by the day-care occupancy. (2) Detectors shall be installed in lounges, recreation areas, and sleeping rooms in the day-care occupancy.
		Day-Care Homes		**Day-Care Homes**	
		16.6.3.4.1	Smoke alarms shall be installed within day-care homes in accordance with 9.6.2.10.	17.6.3.4.1	Smoke alarms shall be installed within day-care homes in accordance with 9.6.2.10.
		16.6.3.4.2	Where a day-care home is located within a building of another occupancy, such as in an apartment building or office building, any corridors serving the day-care home shall be provided with a smoke detection system in accordance with Section 9.6.	17.6.3.4.2	Where a day-care home is located within a building of another occupancy, such as in an apartment building or office building, any corridors serving the day-care home shall be provided with a smoke detection system in accordance with Section 9.6.
		16.6.3.4.3	Single-station or multiple-station smoke alarms or smoke detectors shall be provided in all rooms used for sleeping in accordance with 9.6.2.10.	17.6.3.4.3	Single-station or multiple-station smoke alarms or smoke detectors shall be provided in all rooms used for sleeping in accordance with 9.6.2.10, other than as permitted by 17.6.3.4.4.
				17.6.3.4.4	Approved existing battery-powered smoke alarms, rather than house electrical service-powered smoke alarms required by 17.6.3.4.3, shall be permitted where the facility has testing, maintenance, and battery replacement programs that ensure reliability of power to the smoke alarms.

FAS supervisory signal initiation	Extinguishing system operation		See 16.3.4.2 above. Also see 9.7.2.2 below. Also see 16.3.5 in NFPA *101* for extinguishing system requirements and 16.3.6 for additional extinguishing system provisions.		See 17.3.4.2 above. Also see 9.7.2.2 below. Also see 17.3.5 in NFPA *101* for extinguishing system requirements and 17.3.6 for additional extinguishing system provisions.
	Extinguishing system supervision	9.7.2.1	Where supervised automatic sprinkler systems are required by another section of this *Code*, supervisory attachments shall be installed and monitored for integrity in accordance with *NFPA 72, National Fire Alarm Code*, and a distinctive supervisory signal shall be provided to indicate a condition that would impair the satisfactory operation of the sprinkler system. System components and parameters that are required to be monitored shall include, but shall not be limited to, control valves, fire pump power supplies and running conditions, water tank levels and temperatures, tank pressure, and air pressure on dry-pipe valves. Supervisory signals shall sound and shall be displayed either at a location within the protected building that is constantly attended by qualified personnel or at an approved, remotely located receiving facility. Also see 16.3.5 in NFPA *101* for extinguishing system requirements and 16.3.6 for additional extinguishing system provisions.	9.7.2.1	Where supervised automatic sprinkler systems are required by another section of this *Code*, supervisory attachments shall be installed and monitored for integrity in accordance with *NFPA 72, National Fire Alarm Code*, and a distinctive supervisory signal shall be provided to indicate a condition that would impair the satisfactory operation of the sprinkler system. System components and parameters that are required to be monitored shall include, but shall not be limited to, control valves, fire pump power supplies and running conditions, water tank levels and temperatures, tank pressure, and air pressure on dry-pipe valves. Supervisory signals shall sound and shall be displayed either at a location within the protected building that is constantly attended by qualified personnel or at an approved, remotely located receiving facility. Also see 17.3.5 in NFPA *101* for extinguishing system requirements and 17.3.6 for additional extinguishing system provisions.
Occupant notification	Audible/visible	16.3.4.3.1	Occupant notification shall be in accordance with 9.6.3.	17.3.4.3.1	Occupant notification shall be in accordance with 9.6.3.
	Positive alarm sequence	16.3.4.3.2	Positive alarm sequence shall be permitted in accordance with 9.6.3.4.	17.3.4.3.2	Positive alarm sequence shall be permitted in accordance with 9.6.3.4.
	Presignal system		Not addressed.		Not addressed.
	Voice announcements		Not specifically addressed; however, see 9.6.3.9.		Not specifically addressed; however, see 9.6.3.9.
	Other provisions	16.3.4.3.3	Where occupant notification appliances are provided in all occupied rooms and corridors, the private operating mode as described in *NFPA 72, National Fire Alarm Code*, shall be permitted to be used in either or both of the following locations:	17.3.4.3.3	Where occupant notification appliances are provided in all occupied rooms and corridors, the private operating mode as described in *NFPA 72, National Fire Alarm Code*, shall be permitted to be used in either or both of the following locations:

(continues)

Day Care Occupancies Continued

		New Day Care		Existing Day Care	
		101 Ref.	Requirement	101 Ref.	Requirement
Occupant notification (*continued*)	Other provisions (*continued*)		(1) Occupied rooms (2) Corridors		(1) Occupied rooms (2) Corridors
Emergency forces notification		16.3.4.4	Fire department notification shall be accomplished in accordance with 9.6.4.	17.3.4.4	Fire department notification, other than for day-care occupancies with not more than 100 clients, shall be accomplished in accordance with 9.6.4.
		9.7.2.2	Where supervision of automatic sprinkler systems is provided in accordance with another provision of this *Code*, waterflow alarms shall be transmitted to an approved, proprietary alarm-receiving facility, a remote station, a central station, or the fire department. Such connection shall be in accordance with 9.6.1.3. Also see 16.3.5 in NFPA *101* for extinguishing system requirements and 16.3.6 for additional extinguishing system provisions.	9.7.2.2	Where supervision of automatic sprinkler systems is provided in accordance with another provision of this *Code*, waterflow alarms shall be transmitted to an approved, proprietary alarm-receiving facility, a remote station, a central station, or the fire department. Such connection shall be in accordance with 9.6.1.3. Also see 17.3.5 in NFPA *101* for extinguishing system requirements and 17.3.6 for additional extinguishing system provisions.
Annunciator			Not addressed.		Not addressed.
Emergency control (fire safety) functions			See separate summary table for emergency control (fire safety) functions, where applicable.		See separate summary table for emergency control (fire safety) functions, where applicable.

Health Care Occupancies

The following excerpts from NFPA *101*, 2009 edition, are provided for reference:

18.1.1.1* The requirements of this chapter shall apply to new buildings or portions thereof used as health care occupancies *(see 1.3.1)*.

19.1.1.1* The requirements of this chapter shall apply to existing buildings or portions thereof currently occupied as health care occupancies, unless the authority having jurisdiction has determined equivalent safety has been provided in accordance with Section 1.4.

3.3.178.7* Health Care Occupancy. An occupancy used to provide medical or other treatment or care simultaneously to four or more patients on an inpatient basis, where such patients are mostly incapable of self-preservation due to age, physical or mental disability, or because of security measures not under the occupants' control.

3.3.131.2 Nursing Home. A building or portion of a building used on a 24-hour basis for the housing and nursing care of four or more persons who, because of mental or physical incapacity, might be unable to provide for their own needs and safety without the assistance of another person.

3.3.82.2* Limited Care Facility. A building or portion of a building used on a 24-hour basis for the housing of four or more persons who are incapable of self-preservation because of age; physical limitations due to accident or illness; or limitations such as mental retardation/developmental disability, mental illness, or chemical dependency.

Health Care Occupancies

		New Health Care		Existing Health Care	
		101 Ref.	Requirement	101 Ref.	Requirement
Fire alarm system		18.3.4.1	Health care occupancies shall be provided with a fire alarm system in accordance with Section 9.6.	19.3.4.1	Health care occupancies shall be provided with a fire alarm system in accordance with Section 9.6.
Fire alarm signal initiation	Manual initiation	18.3.4.2.1	Initiation of the required fire alarm systems shall be by manual means in accordance with 9.6.2 and by means of any required sprinkler system waterflow alarms, detection devices, or detection systems, unless otherwise permitted by 18.3.4.2.2.	19.3.4.2.1	Initiation of the required fire alarm systems shall be by manual means in accordance with 9.6.2 and by means of any required sprinkler system waterflow alarms, detection devices, or detection systems, unless otherwise permitted by 19.3.4.2.2 through 19.3.4.2.4.
		18.3.4.2.2	Manual fire alarm boxes in patient sleeping areas shall not be required at exits if located at all nurses' control stations or other continuously attended staff location, provided that both of the following criteria are met: (1) Such manual fire alarm boxes are visible and continuously accessible. (2) Travel distances required by 9.6.2.5 are not exceeded.	19.3.4.2.2	Manual fire alarm boxes in patient sleeping areas shall not be required at exits if located at all nurses' control stations or other continuously attended staff location, provided that both of the following criteria are met: (1) Such manual fire alarm boxes are visible and continuously accessible. (2) Travel distances required by 9.6.2.54 are not exceeded.

(continues)

Health Care Occupancies Continued

		New Health Care		Existing Health Care	
		101 Ref.	Requirement	101 Ref.	Requirement
Fire alarm signal initiation *(continued)*	Manual initiation *(continued)*			19.3.4.2.3	Fixed extinguishing systems protecting commercial cooking equipment in kitchens that are protected by a complete automatic sprinkler system shall not be required to initiate the fire alarm system.
				19.3.4.2.4	Detectors required by 19.7.5.3 and 19.7.5.5 shall not be required to initiate the fire alarm system.
	Automatic detection	18.3.4.5.1	Detection systems, where required, shall be in accordance with Section 9.6.	19.3.4.5.2	See 19.3.6.1 in NFPA *101* for detection in spaces open to corridors.
		18.3.4.5.2	See 18.3.6.1 in NFPA *101* for detection in spaces open to corridors. Also see 18.3.4.2.1 above.		Also see 19.3.4.2.1 and 19.3.4.2.4 above. Also see 19.7.5.3 and 19.7.5.5 in NFPA *101* for nursing home provisions.
			Nursing Homes	19.3.4.5.1	**Limited Care Facility**
		18.3.4.5.3	An approved automatic smoke detection system shall be installed in corridors throughout smoke compartments containing patient sleeping rooms and in spaces open to corridors as permitted in nursing homes by 18.3.6.1, unless otherwise permitted by the following: (1) Corridor systems shall not be required where each patient sleeping room is protected by an approved smoke detection system. (2) Corridor systems shall not be required where patient room doors are equipped with automatic door-closing devices with integral smoke detectors on the room side installed in accordance with their listing, provided that the integral detectors provide occupant notification.		An approved automatic smoke detection system in accordance with Section 9.6 shall be installed in all corridors of limited care facilities, unless otherwise permitted by the following: (1) Where each patient sleeping room is protected by an approved smoke detection system, and a smoke detector is provided at smoke barriers and horizontal exits in accordance with Section 9.6, the corridor smoke detection system shall not be required on the patient sleeping room floors. (2) Smoke compartments protected throughout by an approved, supervised automatic sprinkler system in accordance with 19.3.5.76 shall be permitted.
	Extinguishing system operation		See 18.3.4.2.1 above. Also see 9.7.2.2 below. Also see 18.3.5 in NFPA *101* for extinguishing system requirements and 18.3.6 for additional extinguishing system provisions.		See 19.3.4.2.3 above. Also see 19.3.4.2.1 above. Also see 9.7.2.2 below. Also see 19.3.5 in NFPA *101* for extinguishing system requirements and 19.3.6 for additional extinguishing system provisions.

FAS supervisory signal initiation	Extinguishing system supervision	9.7.2.1	Where supervised automatic sprinkler systems are required by another section of this *Code*, supervisory attachments shall be installed and monitored for integrity in accordance with *NFPA 72, National Fire Alarm Code*, and a distinctive supervisory signal shall be provided to indicate a condition that would impair the satisfactory operation of the sprinkler system. System components and parameters that are required to be monitored shall include, but shall not be limited to, control valves, fire pump power supplies and running conditions, water tank levels and temperatures, tank pressure, and air pressure on dry-pipe valves. Supervisory signals shall sound and shall be displayed either at a location within the protected building that is constantly attended by qualified personnel or at an approved, remotely located receiving facility. Also see 18.3.5 in NFPA 101 for extinguishing system requirements and 18.3.6 for additional extinguishing system provisions.	9.7.2.1	Where supervised automatic sprinkler systems are required by another section of this *Code*, supervisory attachments shall be installed and monitored for integrity in accordance with *NFPA 72, National Fire Alarm Code*, and a distinctive supervisory signal shall be provided to indicate a condition that would impair the satisfactory operation of the sprinkler system. System components and parameters that are required to be monitored shall include, but shall not be limited to, control valves, fire pump power supplies and running conditions, water tank levels and temperatures, tank pressure, and air pressure on dry-pipe valves. Supervisory signals shall sound and shall be displayed either at a location within the protected building that is constantly attended by qualified personnel or at an approved, remotely located receiving facility. Also see 19.3.5 in NFPA 101 for extinguishing system requirements and 19.3.6 for additional extinguishing system provisions.
Occupant notification	Audible/visible	18.3.4.3.1	Occupant notification shall be accomplished automatically in accordance with 9.6.3, unless otherwise modified by the following: (1) Paragraph 9.6.3.2.3 shall not be permitted to be used. (2)* In lieu of audible alarm signals, visible alarm-indicating appliances shall be permitted to be used in critical care areas.	19.3.4.3.1	Occupant notification shall be accomplished automatically in accordance with 9.6.3, unless otherwise modified by the following: (1)* In lieu of audible alarm signals, visible alarm-indicating appliances shall be permitted to be used in critical care areas. (2) Where visual devices have been installed in patient sleeping areas in place of an audible alarm, they shall be permitted where approved by the authority having jurisdiction.
	Positive alarm sequence	18.3.4.3	Positive alarm sequence in accordance with 9.6.3.4 shall be permitted.	19.3.4.3	Positive alarm sequence in accordance with 9.6.3.4 shall be permitted in health care occupancies protected throughout by an approved, supervised automatic sprinkler system in accordance with 9.7.1.1(1).
	Presignal system		Not addressed.		Not addressed.
	Voice announcements		Not specifically addressed; however, see 9.6.3.9.		Not specifically addressed; however, see 9.6.3.9.
	Other provisions				

(continues)

Health Care Occupancies Continued

	New Health Care		Existing Health Care	
	101 Ref.	Requirement	101 Ref.	Requirement
Emergency forces notification	18.3.4.3.2.1	Fire department notification shall be accomplished in accordance with 9.6.4.	19.3.4.3.2.1	Fire department notification shall be accomplished in accordance with 9.6.4.
	9.7.2.2	Where supervision of automatic sprinkler systems is provided in accordance with another provision of this *Code*, waterflow alarms shall be transmitted to an approved, proprietary alarm-receiving facility, a remote station, a central station, or the fire department. Such connection shall be in accordance with 9.6.1.3.	19.3.4.3.2.2	Smoke detection devices or smoke detection systems equipped with reconfirmation features shall not be required to automatically notify the fire department, unless the alarm condition is reconfirmed after a period not exceeding 120 seconds.
		Also see 18.3.5 in NFPA *101* for extinguishing system requirements and in 18.3.6 for additional extinguishing system provisions.	9.7.2.2	Where supervision of automatic sprinkler systems is provided in accordance with another provision of this *Code*, waterflow alarms shall be transmitted to an approved, proprietary alarm-receiving facility, a remote station, a central station, or the fire department. Such connection shall be in accordance with 9.6.1.3.
				Also see 19.3.5 in NFPA *101* for extinguishing system requirements and in 19.3.6 for additional extinguishing system provisions.
Annunciator	18.3.4.3.3.1	Annunciation and annunciation zoning shall be provided in accordance with 9.6.7, unless otherwise permitted by 18.3.4.3.3.2 or 18.3.4.3.3.3.		Not addressed.
	18.3.4.3.3.2	The alarm zone shall be permitted to coincide with the permitted area for smoke compartments.		
	18.3.4.3.3.3	The provision of 9.6.7.4.3, which permits sprinkler system waterflow to be annunciated as a single building zone, shall be prohibited.		
Emergency control (fire safety) functions	18.3.4.4	Operation of any activating device in the required fire alarm system shall be arranged to accomplish automatically any control functions to be performed by that device. (*See 9.6.5.*)	19.3.4.4	Operation of any activating device in the required fire alarm system shall be arranged to accomplish automatically any control functions to be performed by that device. (*See 9.6.5.*)
		Also see separate summary table for emergency control (fire safety) functions, where applicable.		Also see separate summary table for emergency control (fire safety) functions, where applicable.

Ambulatory Health Care Occupancies

The following excerpts from NFPA *101*, 2009 edition, are provided for reference:

20.1.1.1 The requirements of this chapter shall apply to new buildings or portions thereof used as ambulatory health care occupancies (see 1.3.1).

21.1.1.1 The requirements of this chapter shall apply to existing buildings or portions thereof currently occupied as an ambulatory health care occupancy.

3.3.178.1* Ambulatory Health Care Occupancy. An occupancy used to provide services or treatment simultaneously to four or more patients that provides, on an outpatient basis, one or more of the following: (1) treatment for patients that renders the patients incapable of taking action for self-preservation under emergency conditions without the assistance of others; (2) anesthesia that renders the patients incapable of taking action for self-preservation under emergency conditions without the assistance of others; (3) emergency or urgent care for patients who, due to the nature of their injury or illness, are incapable of taking action for self-preservation under emergency conditions without the assistance of others.

Ambulatory Health Care Occupancies

	New Ambulatory Health Care		Existing Ambulatory Health Care	
	101 Ref.	Requirement	101 Ref.	Requirement
Fire alarm system	20.3.4.1	Ambulatory health care facilities shall be provided with fire alarm systems in accordance with Section 9.6, except as modified by 20.3.4.2 through 20.3.4.4.	21.3.4.1	Ambulatory health care facilities shall be provided with fire alarm systems in accordance with Section 9.6, except as modified by 21.3.4.2 through 21.3.4.4.
Fire alarm signal initiation — Manual initiation	20.3.4.2	Initiation of the required fire alarm systems shall be by manual means in accordance with 9.6.2 and by means of any detection devices or detection systems required.	21.3.4.2	Initiation of the required fire alarm systems shall be by manual means in accordance with 9.6.2 and by means of any detection devices or detection systems required.
Automatic detection		See 20.3.4.2 above. Also see 20.3.7.2(1) in NFPA *101*.		See 21.3.4.2 above. Also see 21.3.7.2(1) in NFPA *101*.
Extinguishing system operation		See 20.3.4.2 above. Also see 9.7.2.2 below. Also see 20.3.5 in NFPA *101* for extinguishing system requirements and 20.3.6 and 20.3.7 for additional extinguishing system provisions.		See 21.3.4.2 above. Also see 9.7.2.2 below. Also see 21.3.5 in NFPA *101* for extinguishing system requirements and 21.3.7 for additional extinguishing system provisions.
FAS supervisory signal initiation — Extinguishing system supervision	9.7.2.1	Where supervised automatic sprinkler systems are required by another section of this *Code*, supervisory attachments shall be installed and monitored for integrity in accordance with *NFPA 72, National Fire Alarm Code,* and a distinctive supervisory signal shall be provided to indicate a condition that would impair the	9.7.2.1	Where supervised automatic sprinkler systems are required by another section of this *Code*, supervisory attachments shall be installed and monitored for integrity in accordance with *NFPA 72, National Fire Alarm Code,* and a distinctive supervisory signal shall be provided to indicate a

(continues)

Ambulatory Health Care Occupancies Continued

		New Ambulatory Health Care		Existing Ambulatory Health Care	
		101 Ref.	Requirement	101 Ref.	Requirement
FAS supervisory signal initiation (continued)	Extinguishing system supervision (continued)		satisfactory operation of the sprinkler system. System components and parameters that are required to be monitored shall include, but shall not be limited to, control valves, fire pump power supplies and running conditions, water tank levels and temperatures, tank pressure, and air pressure on dry-pipe valves. Supervisory signals shall sound and shall be displayed either at a location within the protected building that is constantly attended by qualified personnel or at an approved, remotely located receiving facility. Also see 20.3.5 in NFPA 101 for extinguishing system requirements and 20.3.6 and 20.3.7 for additional extinguishing system provisions.		condition that would impair the satisfactory operation of the sprinkler system. System components and parameters that are required to be monitored shall include, but shall not be limited to, control valves, fire pump power supplies and running conditions, water tank levels and temperatures, tank pressure, and air pressure on dry-pipe valves. Supervisory signals shall sound and shall be displayed either at a location within the protected building that is constantly attended by qualified personnel or at an approved, remotely located receiving facility. Also see 21.3.5 in NFPA 101 for extinguishing system requirements and 21.3.7 for additional extinguishing system provisions.
Occupant notification	Audible/visible	20.3.4.3.1	Occupant notification shall be accomplished automatically, without delay, in accordance with 9.6.3 upon operation of any fire alarm activating device.	21.3.4.3.1	Occupant notification shall be accomplished automatically, without delay, in accordance with 9.6.3 upon operation of any fire alarm activating device.
	Positive alarm sequence	20.3.4.3	Positive alarm sequence in accordance with 9.6.3.4 shall be permitted.	21.3.4.3	Positive alarm sequence in accordance with 9.6.3.4 shall be permitted.
	Presignal system		Not addressed		Not addressed.
	Voice announcements		Not specifically addressed; however, see 9.6.3.9.		Not specifically addressed; however, see 9.6.3.9.
	Other provisions				
Emergency forces notification		20.3.4.3.2.1	Fire department notification shall be accomplished in accordance with 9.6.4.	21.3.4.3.2.1	Fire department notification shall be accomplished in accordance with 9.6.4.
		9.7.2.2	Where supervision of automatic sprinkler systems is provided in accordance with another provision of this *Code*, waterflow alarms shall be transmitted to an approved, proprietary alarm-receiving facility, a remote station, a central station, or the fire department. Such connection shall be in accordance with 9.6.1.3.	21.3.4.3.2.2	Smoke detection devices or smoke detection systems equipped with reconfirmation features shall not be required to automatically notify the fire department unless the alarm condition is reconfirmed after a period not exceeding 120 seconds.

		9.7.2.2	Where supervision of automatic sprinkler systems is provided in accordance with another provision of this *Code*, waterflow alarms shall be transmitted to an approved, proprietary alarm-receiving facility, a remote station, a central station, or the fire department. Such connection shall be in accordance with 9.6.1.3. Also see 21.3.5 in NFPA *101* for extinguishing system requirements and 21.3.7 for additional extinguishing system provisions.
			Also see 20.3.5 in NFPA *101* for extinguishing system requirements and 20.3.6 and 20.3.7 for additional extinguishing system provisions.
Annunciator			Not addressed.
Emergency control (fire safety) functions	20.3.4.4	21.3.4.4	Operation of any activating device in the required fire alarm system shall be arranged to accomplish automatically, without delay, any control functions required to be performed by that device. (*See 9.6.5.*) Also see separate summary table for emergency control (fire safety) functions, where applicable.

Detention and Correctional Occupancies

The following excerpts from NFPA *101*, 2009 edition, are provided for reference:

22.1.1.1 The requirements of this chapter shall apply to new buildings or portions thereof used as detention or correctional occupancies (*see 1.3.1*).

23.1.1.1 The requirements of this chapter shall apply to existing buildings or portions thereof currently occupied as detention or correctional occupancies.

3.3.178.5* **Detention and Correctional Occupancy.** An occupancy used to house one or more persons under varied degrees of restraint or security where such occupants are mostly incapable of self-preservation because of security measures not under the occupants' control.

The following occupancy classifications are common to 22.1.4 and 23.1.4:

Use Condition I — Free Egress. Use Condition I shall be defined as a condition under which free movement is allowed from sleeping areas and other spaces where access or occupancy is permitted to the exterior via means of egress that meet the requirements of the *Code*.

Use Condition II — Zoned Egress. Use Condition II shall be defined as a condition under which free movement is allowed from sleeping areas and any other occupied smoke compartment to one or more other smoke compartments.

Use Condition III — Zoned Impeded Egress. Use Condition III shall be defined as a condition under which free movement is allowed within individual smoke compartments, such as within a residential unit comprised of individual sleeping rooms and a group activity space, with egress impeded by remote-controlled release of means of egress from such a smoke compartment to another smoke compartment.

Use Condition IV — Impeded Egress. Use Condition IV shall be defined as a condition under which free movement is restricted from an occupied space, and remote-controlled release is provided to allow movement from all sleeping rooms, activity spaces, and other occupied areas within the smoke compartment to another smoke compartment.

Use Condition V — Contained. Use Condition V shall be defined as a condition under which free movement is restricted from an occupied space, and staff-controlled manual release at each door is provided to allow movement from all sleeping rooms, activity spaces, and other occupied areas within the smoke compartment to another smoke compartment.

Detention and Correctional Occupancies

	New Detention and Correctional		Existing Detention and Correctional	
	101 Ref.	Requirement	101 Ref.	Requirement
Fire alarm system	22.3.4.1.	Detention and correctional occupancies shall be provided with a fire alarm system in accordance with Section 9.6, except as modified by 22.3.4.2 through 22.3.4.4.3.	23.3.4.1	Detention and correctional occupancies shall be provided with a fire alarm system in accordance with Section 9.6, except as modified by 23.3.4.2 through 23.3.4.4.4.
Fire alarm signal initiation				
Manual initiation	22.3.4.2.1	Initiation of the required fire alarm system shall be by manual means in accordance with 9.6.2, by means of any required detection devices or detection systems, and by means of waterflow alarm in the sprinkler system required by 22.3.5.2, unless otherwise permitted by the following: (1) Manual fire alarm boxes shall be permitted to be locked, provided that staff is present	23.3.4.2.1	Initiation of the required fire alarm system shall be by manual means in accordance with 9.6.2 and by means of any required detection devices or detection systems, unless otherwise permitted by the following: (1) Manual fire alarm boxes shall be permitted to be locked, provided that staff is present within the area when it is

Feature	Section	Requirement	Section	Requirement
	22.4.9.1	within the area when it is occupied and staff has keys readily available to unlock the boxes. (2) Manual fire alarm boxes shall be permitted to be located in a staff location, provided that both of the following criteria are met: (a) The staff location is attended when the building is occupied. (b) The staff attendant has direct supervision of the sleeping area. **Nonsprinklered Existing Building Renovations** Initiation of the fire alarm system required by 22.3.4.1 shall be by manual means in accordance with 9.6.2 and by means of any required detection devices or detection systems, unless otherwise permitted by the following: (1) Manual fire alarm boxes shall be permitted to be locked, provided that staff is present within the area when it is occupied and staff has keys readily available to unlock the boxes. (2) Manual fire alarm boxes shall be permitted to be located in a staff location, provided that both of the following criteria are met: (a) The staff location is attended when the building is occupied. (b) The staff attendant has direct supervision of the sleeping area.		occupied and staff has keys readily available to unlock the boxes. (2) Manual fire alarm boxes shall be permitted to be located in a staff location, provided that both of the following criteria are met: (a) The staff location is attended when the building is occupied. (b) The staff attendant has direct supervision of the sleeping area.
	22.3.4.2.2	Use of the provision of 9.6.1.8.1.3 shall be permitted only as an exemption to 9.6.1.8.1(2) and (3).	23.3.4.2.2	Use of the provision of 9.6.1.8.1.3 shall be permitted only as an exemption to 9.6.1.8.1(2) and (3)
Automatic detection	22.3.4.4	An approved automatic smoke detection system shall be in accordance with Section 9.6, as modified by 22.3.4.4.1 through 22.3.4.4.3, throughout all resident sleeping areas and adjacent day rooms, activity rooms, or contiguous common spaces.	23.3.4.4	An approved automatic smoke detection system shall be in accordance with Section 9.6, as modified by 23.3.4.4.1 through 23.3.4.4.4, throughout all resident housing areas.
	22.3.4.4.1	Smoke detectors shall not be required in sleeping rooms with four or fewer occupants.	23.3.4.4.1	Smoke detectors shall not be required in sleeping rooms with four or fewer occupants in Use Condition II or Use Condition III.

(continues)

Detention and Correctional Occupancies Continued

		New Detention and Correctional		Existing Detention and Correctional	
		101 Ref.	Requirement	101 Ref.	Requirement
Fire alarm signal initiation *(continued)*	Automatic detection *(continued)*	22.3.4.4.2	Other arrangements and positioning of smoke detectors shall be permitted to prevent damage or tampering, or for other purposes.		Other arrangements and positioning of smoke detectors shall be permitted to prevent damage or tampering, or for other purposes.
		22.3.4.4.2.1	Other arrangements, as specified in 22.3.4.4.2, shall be capable of detecting any fire, and the placement of detectors shall be such that the speed of detection is equivalent to that provided by the spacing and arrangements required by the installation standards referenced in Section 9.6.	23.3.4.4.2 23.3.4.4.2.1	Other arrangements, as specified in 23.3.4.4.2, shall be capable of detecting any fire, and the placement of detectors shall be such that the speed of detection is equivalent to that provided by the spacing and arrangements required by the installation standards referenced in Section 9.6.
		22.3.4.4.2.2	Detectors shall be permitted to be located in exhaust ducts from cells, behind grilles, or in other locations.	23.3.4.4.2.2	Detectors shall be permitted to be located in exhaust ducts from cells, behind grilles, or in other locations.
		22.3.4.4.2.3	The equivalent performance of the design permitted by 22.3.4.4.2.2 shall be acceptable to the authority having jurisdiction in accordance with the equivalency concepts specified in Section 1.4.	23.3.4.4.2.3	The equivalent performance of the design permitted by 23.3.4.4.2.2 shall be acceptable to the authority having jurisdiction in accordance with the equivalency concepts specified in Section 1.4.
		22.3.4.4.3	Smoke detectors shall not be required in Use Condition II open dormitories where staff is present within the dormitory whenever the dormitory is occupied. Also see 22.3.4.2 (above).	23.3.4.4.3	Smoke detectors shall not be required in Use Condition II open dormitories where staff is present within the dormitory whenever the dormitory is occupied, and the building is protected throughout by an approved, supervised automatic sprinkler system in accordance with 23.3.5.3.
				23.3.4.4.4	In smoke compartments protected throughout by an approved automatic sprinkler system in accordance with 23.3.5.3, smoke detectors shall not be required, except in corridors, common spaces, and sleeping rooms with more than four occupants. Also see 23.3.4.2 (above).
	Nonsprinklered Existing Building Renovations	22.4.9.2	An approved automatic smoke detection system shall be in accordance with Section 9.6, as modified by 22.4.9.2.1 and		

Category	Feature	Paragraph	Requirement	Paragraph	Reference
		22.4.4.9.2.1	22.4.4.9.2.2, throughout all resident sleeping areas and adjacent day rooms, activity rooms, or contiguous common spaces. Smoke detectors shall not be required in sleeping rooms with four or fewer occupants in Use Condition II or Use Condition III.		
		22.4.4.9.2.2	Other arrangements and positioning of smoke detectors shall be permitted to prevent damage or tampering, or for other purposes. Such arrangements shall be capable of detecting any fire, and the placement of detectors shall be such that the speed of detection is equivalent to that provided by the spacing and arrangements required by the installation standards referenced in Section 9.6. Detectors shall be permitted to be located in exhaust ducts from cells, behind grilles, or in other locations. The equivalent performance of the design, however, shall be acceptable to the authority having jurisdiction in accordance with the equivalency concepts specified in Section 1.4. Also see 2.2.4.4.9.1 (above).		
	Extinguishing system operation		See 22.3.4.2.1, 22.3.4.2.2, and 22.4.4.9.1 above. Also see 9.7.2.2 below. Also see 22.3.5 NFPA 101 for extinguishing system requirements.		See 9.7.2.2 below. Also see 23.3.5 in NFPA 101 for extinguishing system requirements and 23.3.7.4 and 23.4.1.1 for additional extinguishing system provisions.
FAS supervisory signal initiation	Extinguishing system supervision	9.7.2.1	Where supervised automatic sprinkler systems are required by another section of this Code, supervisory attachments shall be installed and monitored for integrity in accordance with NFPA 72, National Fire Alarm Code, and a distinctive supervisory signal shall be provided to indicate a condition that would impair the satisfactory operation of the sprinkler system. System components and parameters that are required to be monitored shall include, but shall not be limited to, control valves, fire pump power supplies and running conditions, water tank levels and temperatures, tank pressure, and air pressure on dry-pipe valves.	9.7.2.1	Where supervised automatic sprinkler systems are required by another section of this Code, supervisory attachments shall be installed and monitored for integrity in accordance with NFPA 72, National Fire Alarm Code, and a distinctive supervisory signal shall be provided to indicate a condition that would impair the satisfactory operation of the sprinkler system. System components and parameters that are required to be monitored shall include, but shall not be limited to, control valves, fire pump power supplies and running conditions, water tank levels and temperatures, tank pressure, and air pressure

(continues)

Detention and Correctional Occupancies Continued

		New Detention and Correctional		Existing Detention and Correctional	
		101 Ref.	Requirement	101 Ref.	Requirement
FAS supervisory signal initiation (continued)	Extinguishing system supervision (continued)		Supervisory signals shall sound and shall be displayed either at a location within the protected building that is constantly attended by qualified personnel or at an approved, remotely located receiving facility. Also see 22.3.5 in NFPA *101* for extinguishing system requirements.		on dry-pipe valves. Supervisory signals shall sound and shall be displayed either at a location within the protected building that is constantly attended by qualified personnel or at an approved, remotely located receiving facility. Also see 23.3.5 in NFPA *101* for extinguishing system requirements and 23.3.7.4 and 23.4.1.1 for additional extinguishing system provisions.
Occupant notification	Audible/visible	22.3.4.3.1	Occupant notification shall be accomplished automatically in accordance with 9.6.3, and the following also shall apply: (1) A positive alarm sequence shall be permitted in accordance with 9.6.3.4. (2)* Any smoke detectors required by this chapter shall be permitted to be arranged to alarm at a constantly attended location only and shall not be required to accomplish general occupant notification.	23.3.4.3.1	Occupant notification shall be accomplished automatically in accordance with 9.6.3, and the following also shall apply: (1) A positive alarm sequence shall be permitted in accordance with 9.6.3.4. (2)* Any smoke detectors required by this chapter shall be permitted to be arranged to alarm at a constantly attended location only and shall not be required to accomplish general occupant notification.
	Positive alarm sequence		See 22.3.4.3.1(1) above.		See 23.3.4.3.1(1) above.
	Presignal system		Not addressed.		Not addressed.
	Voice announcements		Not specifically addressed; however, see 9.6.3.9.		Not specifically addressed; however, see 9.6.3.9.
	Other provisions				
Emergency forces notification		22.3.4.3.2.1	Fire department notification shall be accomplished in accordance with 9.6.4, unless otherwise permitted by the following: (1) A positive alarm sequence shall be permitted in accordance with 9.6.3.4. (2) Any smoke detectors required by this chapter shall not be required to transmit an alarm to the fire department. (3) This requirement shall not apply where	23.3.4.3.2.1	Fire department notification shall be accomplished in accordance with 9.6.4, unless otherwise permitted by the following: (1) A positive alarm sequence shall be permitted in accordance with 9.6.3.4. (2) Any smoke detectors required by this chapter shall not be required to transmit an alarm to the fire department. (3) This requirement shall not apply where

	22.3.4.3.2.2	staff is provided at a constantly attended location that meets one of the following criteria: (a) It has the capability to promptly notify the fire department. (b) It has direct communication with a control room having direct access to the fire department.	23.3.4.3.2.2	staff is provided at a constantly attended location that meets one of the following criteria: (a) It has the capability to promptly notify the fire department. (b) It has direct communication with a control room having direct access to the fire department.
	22.3.4.3.2.2	Where the provision of 22.3.4.3.2.1(3) is utilized, the fire plan, as required by 22.7.1.3, shall include procedures for logging of alarms and immediate notification of the fire department.	23.3.4.3.2.2	Where the provision of 23.3.4.3.2.1(3) is utilized, the fire plan, as required by 23.7.1.3, shall include procedures for logging of alarms and immediate notification of the fire department.
	9.7.2.2	Where supervision of automatic sprinkler systems is provided in accordance with another provision of this *Code*, waterflow alarms shall be transmitted to an approved, proprietary alarm-receiving facility, a remote station, a central station, or the fire department. Such connection shall be in accordance with 9.6.1.3. Also see 22.3.5 in NFPA *101* for extinguishing system requirements.	9.7.2.2	Where supervision of automatic sprinkler systems is provided in accordance with another provision of this *Code*, waterflow alarms shall be transmitted to an approved, proprietary alarm-receiving facility, a remote station, a central station, or the fire department. Such connection shall be in accordance with 9.6.1.3. Also see 23.3.5 in NFPA *101* for extinguishing system requirements and 23.3.7.4 and 23.4.1.1 for additional extinguishing system provisions.
Annunciator		Not addressed.		Not addressed.
Emergency control (fire safety) functions		See separate summary table for emergency control (fire safety) functions, where applicable.		See separate summary table for emergency control (fire safety) functions, where applicable.

One- and Two-Family Dwellings

The following excerpts from NFPA *101*, 2009 edition, are provided for reference:

24.1.1.1 The requirements of this chapter shall apply to one- and two-family dwellings, which shall include those buildings containing not more than two dwelling units in which each dwelling unit is occupied by members of a single family with not more than three outsiders, if any, accommodated in rented rooms.

24.1.1.2 The requirements of this chapter shall apply to new buildings and to existing or modified buildings according to the provisions of 1.3.1 of this *Code.*

3.3.61 Dwelling Unit. One or more rooms arranged for complete, independent housekeeping purposes with space for eating, living, and sleeping; facilities for cooking; and provisions for sanitation.

3.3.61.1 One- and Two-Family Dwelling Unit. A building that contains not more than two dwelling units with independent cooking and bathroom facilities.

3.3.61.2 One-Family Dwelling Unit. A building that consists solely of one dwelling unit with independent cooking and bathroom facilities.

3.3.61.3 Two-Family Dwelling Unit. A building that consists solely of two dwelling units with independent cooking and bathroom facilities.

The following excerpts from *NFPA 72,* 2010 edition, are provided for reference:

3.3.95.2 Household Fire Alarm System. A system of devices that uses a fire alarm control unit to produce an alarm signal in the household for the purpose of notifying the occupants of the presence of a fire so that they will evacuate the premises.

3.3.100 Fire Warning Equipment. Any detector, alarm, device, or material related to single- and multiple-station alarms or household fire alarm systems.

3.3.149 Multiple Station Alarm. A single station alarm capable of being interconnected to one or more additional alarms so that the actuation of one causes the appropriate alarm signal to operate in all interconnected alarms.

3.3.245 Single Station Alarm. A detector comprising an assembly that incorporates a sensor, control components, and an alarm notification appliance in one unit operated from a power source either located in the unit or obtained at the point of installation.

3.3.251 Smoke Alarm. A single or multiple station alarm responsive to smoke.

New and Existing One- and Two-Family Dwellings

		101 Ref.	Requirement
Fire warning equipment		24.3.4	Smoke alarms or a smoke detection system shall be provided in accordance with either 24.3.4.1 or 24.3.4.2, as modified by 24.3.4.3.
Fire alarm signal initiation	Manual initiation		Not addressed.
	Automatic detection	24.3.4.1	Smoke alarms shall be installed in accordance with 9.6.2.10 in the following locations: (1) All sleeping rooms (2) Outside of each separate sleeping area, in the immediate vicinity of the sleeping rooms (3) On each level of the dwelling unit, including basements
		24.3.4.2	Dwelling units shall be protected by an approved smoke detection system in accordance with Section 9.6 and equipped with an approved means of occupant notification.
		24.3.4.3	In existing one- and two-family dwellings, approved smoke alarms powered by batteries shall be permitted.
	Extinguishing system operation		Not addressed.

New and Existing One- and Two-Family Dwellings Continued

		101 Ref.	*Requirement*
FAS supervisory signal initiation	Extinguishing system supervision		See 24.3.5.1 in NFPA *101* for extinguishing system requirements. (Supervision is not required.)
Occupant notification	Audible/Visible		See 24.3.4.2 above.
	Positive Alarm Sequence		Not addressed.
	Presignal system		Not addressed.
	Voice announcements		Not addressed.
	Other provisions		
Emergency forces notification			Not addressed.
Annunciator			Not addressed.
Emergency control (fire safety) functions			

Lodging and Rooming Houses

The following excerpts from NFPA *101*, 2009 edition, are provided for reference:

26.1.1.1* The requirements of this chapter shall apply to buildings that provide sleeping accommodations for 16 or fewer persons on either a transient or permanent basis, with or without meals, but without separate cooking facilities for individual occupants, except as provided in Chapter 24.

26.1.1.2 The requirements of this chapter shall apply to new buildings and to existing or modified buildings according to the provisions of 1.3.1 of this *Code*.

3.3.156 Lodging or Rooming House. A building or portion thereof that does not qualify as a one- or two-family dwelling, that provides sleeping accommodations for a total of 16 or fewer people on a transient or permanent basis, without personal care services, with or without meals, but without separate cooking facilities for individual occupants.

The following excerpts from *NFPA 72*, 2010 edition, are provided for reference:

3.3.100 Fire Warning Equipment. Any detector, alarm, device, or material related to single- and multiple-station alarms or household fire alarm systems.

3.3.149 Multiple Station Alarm. A single station alarm capable of being interconnected to one or more additional alarms so that the actuation of one causes the appropriate alarm signal to operate in all interconnected alarms.

3.3.245 Single Station Alarm. A detector comprising an assembly that incorporates a sensor, control components, and an alarm notification appliance in one unit operated from a power source either located in the unit or obtained at the point of installation.

3.3.251 Smoke Alarm. A single or multiple station alarm responsive to smoke.

New and Existing Lodging and Rooming Houses

		101 Ref.	Requirement
Fire alarm system/fire warning equipment		26.3.4.1.1	Lodging and rooming houses, other than those meeting 26.3.4.1.2, shall be provided with a fire alarm system in accordance with Section 9.6.
		26.3.4.1.2	A fire alarm system in accordance with Section 9.6 shall not be required in existing lodging and rooming houses that have an existing smoke detection system meeting or exceeding the requirements of 26.3.4.5.1 where that detection system includes not less than one manual fire alarm box per floor arranged to initiate the smoke detection alarm.
Fire alarm signal initiation	Manual initiation	26.3.4.2	Initiation of the required fire alarm system shall be by manual means in accordance with 9.6.2, or by alarm initiation in accordance with 9.6.2.1(3) in buildings protected throughout by an approved automatic sprinkler system in accordance with 26.3.6.
	Automatic detection	26.3.4.5.1	Approved single-station smoke alarms, other than existing smoke alarms meeting 26.3.4.5.3, shall be installed in accordance with 9.6.2.10 in every sleeping room.
		26.3.4.5.2	In other than existing buildings, the smoke alarms required by 26.3.4.5.1 shall be interconnected in accordance with 9.6.2.10.3.
		26.3.4.5.3	Existing battery-powered smoke alarms, rather than house electric-powered smoke alarms, shall be permitted where the facility has demonstrated to the authority having jurisdiction that the testing, maintenance, and battery replacement programs will ensure reliability of power to the smoke alarms.
	Extinguishing system operation		See 26.3.4.2 above. Also see 26.3.6 in NFPA *101* for extinguishing system requirements.

New and Existing Lodging and Rooming Houses Continued

		101 Ref.	*Requirement*
FAS supervisory signal initiation	Extinguishing system supervision		See 26.3.6 in NFPA 101 for extinguishing system requirements. (Supervision is not required.)
Occupant notification	Audible/visible	26.3.4.3	Occupant notification shall be provided automatically in accordance with 9.6.3, as modified by 26.3.4.3.1 and 26.3.4.3.2.
		26.3.4.3.1	Visible signals for the hearing impaired shall not be required where the proprietor resides in the building and there are five or fewer rooms for rent.
		26.3.4.3.2	Positive alarm sequence in accordance with 9.6.3.4 shall be permitted.
	Positive alarm sequence		See 26.3.4.3.2 above.
	Presignal system		Not addressed.
	Voice announcements		Not specifically addressed; however, see 9.6.3.9.
	Other provisions		
Emergency forces notification			Not addressed
Annunciator			Not addressed
Emergency control (fire safety) functions			See separate summary table for emergency control (fire safety) functions, where applicable.

Hotels and Dormitories

The following excerpts from NFPA *101*, 2009 edition, are provided for reference:

28.1.1.1 The requirements of this chapter shall apply to new buildings or portions thereof used as hotel or dormitory occupancies *(see 1.3.1)*.

29.1.1.1 The requirements of this chapter shall apply to existing buildings or portions thereof currently occupied as hotel or dormitory occupancies, unless meeting the requirement of 29.1.1.2.

3.3.134* Hotel. A building or groups of buildings under the same management in which there are sleeping accommodations for more than 16 persons and primarily used by transients for lodging with or without meals.

3.3.59* Dormitory. A building or a space in a building in which group sleeping accommodations are provided for more than 16 persons who are not members of the same family in one room, or a series of closely associated rooms, under joint occupancy and single management, with or without meals, but without individual cooking facilities.

The following excerpts from *NFPA 72*, 2010 edition, are provided for reference:

3.3.100 Fire Warning Equipment. Any detector, alarm, device, or material related to single- and multiple-station alarms or household fire alarm systems.

3.3.149 Multiple Station Alarm. A single station alarm capable of being interconnected to one or more additional alarms so that the actuation of one causes the appropriate alarm signal to operate in all interconnected alarms.

3.3.245 Single Station Alarm. A detector comprising an assembly that incorporates a sensor, control components, and an alarm notification appliance in one unit operated from a power source either located in the unit or obtained at the point of installation.

3.3.251 Smoke Alarm. A single or multiple station alarm responsive to smoke.

Hotels and Dormitories

	New Hotels and Dormitories		Existing Hotels and Dormitories	
	101 Ref.	Requirement	101 Ref.	Requirement
Fire alarm system/fire warning equipment	28.3.4.1	A fire alarm system in accordance with Section 9.6, except as modified by 28.3.4.2 through 28.3.4.6, shall be provided.	29.3.4.1	A fire alarm system in accordance with Section 9.6, except as modified by 29.3.4.2 through 29.3.4.6, shall be provided in buildings other than those where each guest room has exterior exit access in accordance with 7.5.3, and the building does not exceed three stories in height.
Fire alarm signal initiation				
Manual initiation	28.3.4.2	The required fire alarm system shall be initiated by each of the following: (1) Manual means in accordance with 9.6.2 (2) Manual fire alarm box located at the hotel desk or other convenient central control point under continuous supervision by responsible employees (3) Required automatic sprinkler system	29.3.4.2	The required fire alarm system shall be initiated by each of the following: (1) Manual means in accordance with 9.6.2, unless there are other effective means to activate the fire alarm system, such as complete automatic sprinkler or automatic detection systems, with manual fire alarm box in accordance with 29.3.4.2(2) required

			(2) Manual fire alarm box located at the hotel desk or other convenient central control point under continuous supervision by responsible employees (3) Required automatic sprinkler system (4) Required automatic detection system other than sleeping room smoke detectors
	Automatic detection	28.3.4.4	29.3.4.5	A corridor smoke detection system in accordance with Section 9.6 shall be provided in buildings other than those protected throughout by an approved, supervised automatic sprinkler system in accordance with 28.3.5.3.	An approved single-station smoke alarm shall be installed in accordance with 9.6.2.10. in every guest room and every living area and sleeping room within a guest suite.
		28.3.4.5	29.3.4.5.1 29.3.4.5.2	An approved single-station smoke alarm shall be installed in accordance with 9.6.2.10 in every guest room and every living area and sleeping room within a guest suite. Also see 28.3.4.2(4) above.	The smoke alarms shall not be required to be interconnected. Single-station smoke alarms without a secondary (standby) power source shall be permitted. Also see 29.3.4.2(4) above.
	Extinguishing system operation			See 28.3.4.2(3) above. Also see 9.7.2.2 below. Also see 28.3.5 in NFPA *101* for extinguishing system requirements and 28.3.6 and 28.3.7 for additional extinguishing system provisions.	See 29.3.4.2(3) above. Also see 9.7.2.2 below. Also see 29.3.5 in NFPA *101* for extinguishing system requirements and 29.3.6 and 29.3.7 for additional extinguishing system provisions.
FAS supervisory signal initiation	Extinguishing system supervision	9.7.2.1	9.7.2.1	Where supervised automatic sprinkler systems are required by another section of this *Code*, supervisory attachments shall be installed and monitored for integrity in accordance with *NFPA 72, National Fire Alarm Code*, and a distinctive supervisory signal shall be provided to indicate a condition that would impair the satisfactory operation of the sprinkler system. System components and parameters that are required to be monitored shall include, but shall not be limited to, control valves, fire pump power supplies and running conditions, water tank levels and temperatures, tank pressure, and air pressure on dry-pipe valves. Supervisory signals shall sound and shall be displayed either at a location within the protected building that is constantly attended by qualified personnel or	Where supervised automatic sprinkler systems are required by another section of this *Code*, supervisory attachments shall be installed and monitored for integrity in accordance with *NFPA 72, National Fire Alarm Code*, and a distinctive supervisory signal shall be provided to indicate a condition that would impair the satisfactory operation of the sprinkler system. System components and parameters that are required to be monitored shall include, but shall not be limited to, control valves, fire pump power supplies and running conditions, water tank levels and temperatures, tank pressure, and air pressure on dry-pipe valves. Supervisory signals shall sound and shall be displayed either at a location within the protected building that is constantly attended by qualified personnel or

(continues)

Hotels and Dormitories Continued

		New Hotels and Dormitories		Existing Hotels and Dormitories	
		101 Ref.	*Requirement*	*101 Ref.*	*Requirement*
FAS supervisory signal initiation (continued)	Extinguishing system supervision (continued)		at an approved, remotely located receiving facility. Also see 28.3.4.2(3) above. Also see 28.3.5 in NFPA *101* for extinguishing system requirements and 28.3.6 and 28.3.7 for additional extinguishing system provisions.		at an approved, remotely located receiving facility. Also see 29.3.4.2(3) above. Also see 29.3.5 in NFPA *101* for extinguishing system requirements and 29.3.6 and 29.3.7 for additional extinguishing system provisions.
Occupant notification	Audible/visible	28.3.4.3.1	Occupant notification shall be provided automatically in accordance with 9.6.3.	29.3.4.3.1	Occupant notification shall be provided automatically in accordance with 9.6.3.
		28.3.4.3.2	Positive alarm sequence in accordance with 9.6.3.4 shall be permitted.	29.3.4.3.2	Positive alarm sequence in accordance with 9.6.3.4, and a presignal system in accordance with 9.6.3.3, shall be permitted.
		28.3.4.3.3	Guest rooms and guest suites specifically required and equipped to accommodate hearing-impaired individuals shall be provided with a visible notification appliance.		
		28.3.4.3.4	In occupiable areas, other than guest rooms and guest suites, visible notification appliances shall be provided.		
	Positive alarm sequence		See 28.3.4.3.2 above.		See 29.3.4.3.2 above.
	Presignal system		Not addressed.		See 29.3.4.3.2 above.
	Voice announcements		Not specifically addressed; however, see 9.6.3.9.		Not specifically addressed; however, see 9.6.3.9.
	Other provisions				
Emergency forces notification		28.3.4.3.6	Emergency forces notification shall be provided in accordance with 9.6.4.	29.3.4.3.6	Provisions shall be made for the immediate notification of the public fire department by telephone or other means in case of fire, and, where there is no public fire department, notification shall be made to the private fire brigade.
		9.7.2.2	Where supervision of automatic sprinkler systems is provided in accordance with another provision of this *Code*, waterflow alarms shall be transmitted to an approved, proprietary alarm-receiving facility, a remote station, a central station, or the fire	9.7.2.2	Where supervision of automatic sprinkler systems is provided in accordance with another provision of this *Code*, waterflow alarms shall be transmitted to an approved, proprietary alarm-receiving facility, a remote station, a central station, or the fire

		department. Such connection shall be in accordance with 9.6.1.3. Also see 28.3.5 in NFPA *101* for extinguishing system requirements and 28.3.6 and 28.3.7 for additional extinguishing system provisions.	department. Such connection shall be in accordance with 9.6.1.3. Also see 29.3.5 in NFPA *101* for extinguishing system requirements and 29.3.6 and 29.3.7 for additional extinguishing system provisions.
Annunciator	28.3.4.3.5	Annunciation and annunciation zoning in accordance with 9.6.7 shall be provided in buildings three or more stories in height or having more than 50 guest rooms or guest suites. Annunciation shall be provided at a location readily accessible from the primary point of entry for emergency response personnel.	Not addressed.
Emergency control (fire safety) functions		See separate summary table for emergency control (fire safety) functions, where applicable.	See separate summary table for emergency control (fire safety) functions, where applicable.

Apartment Buildings

The following excerpts from NFPA *101*, 2009 edition, are provided for reference:

30.1.1.1 The requirements of this chapter shall apply to new buildings or portions thereof used as apartment occupancies (*see 1.3.1*).

31.1.1.1 The requirements of this chapter shall apply to existing buildings or portions thereof currently occupied as apartment occupancies. In addition, the building shall meet the requirements of one of the following options:

(1) Option 1, buildings without fire suppression or detection systems
(2) Option 2, buildings provided with a complete approved automatic fire detection and notification system in accordance with 31.3.4.4
(3) Option 3, buildings provided with approved automatic sprinkler protection in selected areas, as described in 31.3.5.9
(4) Option 4, buildings protected throughout by an approved automatic sprinkler system

3.3.32.3 Apartment Building. A building or portion thereof containing three or more dwelling units with independent cooking and bathroom facilities.

The following excerpts from *NFPA 72*, 2010 edition, are provided for reference:

3.3.100 Fire Warning Equipment. Any detector, alarm, device, or material related to single- and multiple-station alarms or household fire alarm systems.

3.3.149 Multiple Station Alarm. A single station alarm capable of being interconnected to one or more additional alarms so that the actuation of one causes the appropriate alarm signal to operate in all interconnected alarms.

3.3.245 Single Station Alarm. A detector comprising an assembly that incorporates a sensor, control components, and an alarm notification appliance in one unit operated from a power source either located in the unit or obtained at the point of installation.

3.3.251 Smoke Alarm. A single or multiple station alarm responsive to smoke.

Apartment Buildings

	New Apartment Buildings		Existing Apartment Buildings	
	101 Ref.	Requirement	101 Ref.	Requirement
Fire alarm system/fire warning equipment	30.3.4.1.1	Apartment buildings four or more stories in height or with more than 11 dwelling units, other than those meeting the requirements of 30.3.4.1.2, shall be provided with a fire alarm system in accordance with Section 9.6, except as modified by 30.3.4.2 through 30.3.4.6.	31.3.4.1.1	Apartment buildings four or more stories in height or with more than 11 dwelling units, other than those meeting 31.3.4.1.2, shall be provided with a fire alarm system in accordance with Section 9.6, except as modified by 31.3.4.2 through 31.3.4.6.
	30.3.4.1.2	A fire alarm system shall not be required in buildings where each dwelling unit is separated from other contiguous dwelling units by fire barriers (*see Section 8.3*) having a minimum 1-hour fire resistance rating, and where each dwelling unit has either its own independent exit or its own independent stairway or ramp discharging at the finished ground level.	31.3.4.1.2	A fire alarm system shall not be required where each dwelling unit is separated from other contiguous dwelling units by fire barriers (*see Section 8.3*) having a minimum 1-hour fire resistance rating, and where each dwelling unit has either its own independent exit or its own independent stairway or ramp discharging at the finished ground level.

Fire alarm signal initiation	Manual initiation	30.3.4.2.1	Initiation of the required fire alarm system shall be by manual means in accordance with 9.6.2, unless the building complies with 30.3.4.2.2.	31.3.4.2.1	Initiation of the required fire alarm system shall be by manual means in accordance with 9.6.2, unless the building complies with 31.3.4.2.2.
		30.3.4.2.2	Initiation of the required fire alarm system by manual means shall not be required in buildings four or fewer stories in height, containing not more than 16 dwelling units, and protected throughout by an approved, supervised automatic sprinkler system installed in accordance with 30.3.5.1.	31.3.4.2.2	Initiation of the required fire alarm system by manual means shall not be required in buildings four or fewer stories in height, containing not more than 16 dwelling units, and protected throughout by an approved, supervised automatic sprinkler system installed in accordance with 31.3.5.3.
	Automatic detection			31.3.4.2.3	In buildings using Option 2, the required fire alarm system shall be initiated by the automatic fire detection system in addition to the manual initiation means of 31.3.4.2.1.
				31.3.4.4.1	In buildings using Option 2, a complete automatic fire detection system in accordance with 9.6.1.3 and 31.3.4.4.2 shall be required.
				31.3.4.4.2	Automatic fire detection devices shall be installed as follows: (1) Smoke detectors shall be installed in all common areas and workspaces outside the living unit, such as exit stairs, egress corridors, lobbies, storage rooms, equipment rooms, and other tenantless spaces in environments that are suitable for proper smoke detector operation. (2) Heat detectors shall be located within each room of the living unit.
		30.3.4.5	**Smoke Alarms** Smoke alarms shall be installed in accordance with 9.6.2.10 in every sleeping area, outside every sleeping area in the immediate vicinity of the bedrooms and on all levels of the dwelling unit, including basements.	31.3.4.5.1	**Smoke Alarms** In buildings other than those equipped throughout with an existing, complete automatic smoke detection system, smoke alarms shall be installed in accordance with 9.6.2.10, as modified by 31.3.4.5.2, outside every sleeping area in the immediate vicinity of the bedrooms and on all levels of the dwelling unit, including basements.
				31.3.4.5.2	Smoke alarms required by 31.3.4.5.1 shall not be required to be provided with a secondary (standby) power source.

(continues)

Apartment Buildings Continued

		New Apartment Buildings		Existing Apartment Buildings	
		101 Ref.	Requirement	101 Ref.	Requirement
Fire alarm signal initiation (*continued*)	Automatic detection (*continued*)	31.3.4.5.3	In buildings other than those equipped throughout with an existing, complete automatic smoke detection system or a complete, supervised automatic sprinkler system in accordance with 31.3.5, smoke alarms shall be installed in every sleeping area in accordance with 9.6.2.10, as modified by 31.3.4.5.4.	31.3.4.5.4	Smoke alarms required by 31.3.4.5.3 shall be permitted to be battery powered.
	Extinguishing system operation	30.3.4.2.3	In buildings protected throughout by an approved, supervised automatic sprinkler system in accordance with 30.3.5, required fire alarm systems shall be initiated upon operation of the automatic sprinkler system. Also see 30.3.4.2.2 above. Also see 9.7.2.2 below. Also see 30.3.5 in NFPA *101* for extinguishing system requirements and 30.3.6, and 30.3.7 for additional extinguishing system provisions.	31.3.4.2.4 31.3.4.2.5	In buildings using Option 3, the required fire alarm system shall be initiated upon operation of the automatic sprinkler system in addition to the manual initiation means of 31.3.4.2.1. In buildings using Option 4, the required fire alarm system shall be initiated upon operation of the automatic sprinkler system in addition to the manual initiation means of 31.3.4.2.1. Also see 31.3.4.2.2 above. Also see 9.7.2.2 below. Also see 31.3.5 in NFPA *101* for extinguishing system requirements and 31.3.6 for additional extinguishing system provisions.
FAS supervisory signal initiation	Extinguishing system supervision	9.7.2.1	Where supervised automatic sprinkler systems are required by another section of this *Code*, supervisory attachments shall be installed and monitored for integrity in accordance with *NFPA 72, National Fire Alarm Code,* and a distinctive supervisory signal shall be provided to indicate a condition that would impair the satisfactory operation of the sprinkler system. System components and parameters that are required to be monitored shall include, but shall not be limited to, control valves, fire pump power supplies and running conditions, water tank levels and temperatures, tank pressure, and air pressure on dry-pipe valves. Supervisory signals shall sound and shall be displayed either at a location within the protected building that is constantly attended	9.7.2.1	Where supervised automatic sprinkler systems are required by another section of this *Code*, supervisory attachments shall be installed and monitored for integrity in accordance with *NFPA 72, National Fire Alarm Code,* and a distinctive supervisory signal shall be provided to indicate a condition that would impair the satisfactory operation of the sprinkler system. System components and parameters that are required to be monitored shall include, but shall not be limited to, control valves, fire pump power supplies and running conditions, water tank levels and temperatures, tank pressure, and air pressure on dry-pipe valves. Supervisory signals shall sound and shall be displayed either at a location within the protected

	30.3.4.3.1	by qualified personnel or at an approved, remotely located receiving facility. Also see 30.3.4.2.2 above. Also see 9.7.2.2 below. Also see 30.3.5 in NFPA *101* for extinguishing system requirements and 30.3.6 and 30.3.7 for additional extinguishing system provisions.	31.3.4.3.1	building that is constantly attended by qualified personnel or at an approved, remotely located receiving facility. Also see 31.3.4.2.2 above. Also see 9.7.2.2 below. Also see 31.3.5 in NFPA *101* for extinguishing system requirements and 31.3.6 for additional extinguishing system provisions.
Occupant notification — Audible/visible	30.3.4.3.1	Occupant notification shall be provided automatically in accordance with Section 9.6, and the following shall also apply: (1) Visible signals shall be installed in units designed for the hearing impaired. (2) Positive alarm sequence in accordance with 9.6.3.4 shall be permitted.	31.3.4.3.1	Occupant notification shall be provided automatically in accordance with Section 9.6, and the following shall also apply: (1) Visible signals shall be installed in units designed for the hearing impaired. (2) Positive alarm sequence in accordance with 9.6.3.4 shall be permitted. (3) Existing approved presignal systems shall be permitted in accordance with 9.6.3.3.
Positive alarm sequence		See 30.3.4.3.1(2) above.		See 31.3.4.3.1(2) above.
Presignal system		Not addressed.		See 31.3.4.3.1(3) above.
Voice announcements		Not specifically addressed; however, see 9.6.3.9.		Not specifically addressed; however, see 9.6.3.9.
Other provisions				
Emergency forces notification	30.3.4.3.5	Fire department notification shall be accomplished in accordance with 9.6.4.	31.3.4.3.5	Fire department notification shall be accomplished in accordance with 9.6.4.
	9.7.2.2	Where supervision of automatic sprinkler systems is provided in accordance with another provision of this *Code*, waterflow alarms shall be transmitted to an approved, proprietary alarm-receiving facility, a remote station, a central station, or the fire department. Such connection shall be in accordance with 9.6.1.3. Also see 30.3.5 in NFPA *101* for extinguishing system requirements and in 30.3.6, and 30.3.7 for additional extinguishing system provisions.	9.7.2.2	Where supervision of automatic sprinkler systems is provided in accordance with another provision of this *Code*, waterflow alarms shall be transmitted to an approved, proprietary alarm-receiving facility, a remote station, a central station, or the fire department. Such connection shall be in accordance with 9.6.1.3. Also see 31.3.5 in NFPA *101* for extinguishing system requirements and in 31.3.6 for additional extinguishing system provisions.
Annunciator	30.3.4.3.2	Annunciation, and annunciation zoning, in accordance with 9.6.7 shall be provided, unless the building complies with either	31.3.4.3.2	An annunciator panel, whose location shall be approved by the authority having jurisdiction, connected with the required fire alarm system

(continues)

Apartment Buildings Continued

	New Apartment Buildings		Existing Apartment Buildings	
	101 Ref.	*Requirement*	*101 Ref.*	*Requirement*
Annunciator *(continued)*		30.3.4.3.3 or 30.3.4.3.4. Annunciation shall be provided at a location readily accessible from the primary point of entry for emergency response personnel.		shall be provided, unless the building meets the requirements of 31.3.4.3.3 or 31.3.4.3.4.
	30.3.4.3.3	Annunciation, and annunciation zoning, shall not be required in buildings two or fewer stories in height and having not more than 50 dwelling units.	31.3.4.3.3	Annunciation shall not be required in buildings not exceeding 2 stories in height and having not more than 50 rooms.
	30.3.4.3.4	Annunciation, and annunciation zoning, shall not be required in buildings four or fewer stories in height containing not more than 16 dwelling units and protected throughout by an approved, supervised automatic sprinkler system installed in accordance with 30.3.5.1.	31.3.4.3.4	Annunciation shall not be required in buildings four or fewer stories in height containing not more than 16 dwelling units and protected throughout by an approved, supervised automatic sprinkler system installed in accordance with 31.3.5.3.
Emergency control (fire safety) functions		See separate summary table for emergency control (fire safety) functions, where applicable.		See separate summary table for emergency control (fire safety) functions, where applicable.

Residential Board and Care Occupancies

The following excerpts from NFPA *101*, 2009 edition, are provided for reference:

32.1.1.1 General. The requirements of this chapter shall apply to new buildings or portions thereof used as residential board and care occupancies (see 1.3.1).

33.1.1.1 General. The requirements of this chapter shall apply to existing buildings or portions thereof currently occupied as residential board and care occupancies.

3.3.178.12* Residential Board and Care Occupancy. An occupancy used for lodging and boarding of four or more residents, not related by blood or marriage to the owners or operators, for the purpose of providing personal care services.

Small Facilities. Residential board and care occupancies providing sleeping accommodations for not more than 16 residents. Reference 32.1.1.3(2) and 33.1.1.3(2).

Large Facilities. Residential board and care occupancies providing sleeping accommodations for more than 16 residents. Reference 32.1.1.3(3) and 33.1.1.3(3).

The following excerpts from *NFPA 72*, 2010 edition, are provided for reference:

3.3.100 Fire Warning Equipment. Any detector, alarm, device, or material related to single- and multiple-station alarms or household fire alarm systems.

3.3.149 Multiple Station Alarm. A single station alarm capable of being interconnected to one or more additional alarms so that the actuation of one causes the appropriate alarm signal to operate in all interconnected alarms.

3.3.245 Single Station Alarm. A detector comprising an assembly that incorporates a sensor, control components, and an alarm notification appliance in one unit operated from a power source either located in the unit or obtained at the point of installation.

3.3.251 Smoke Alarm. A single or multiple station alarm responsive to smoke.

Residential Board and Care Occupancies

	New Residential Board and Care		Existing Residential Board and Care	
	101 Ref.	Requirement	101 Ref.	Requirement
		Small Facility		**Small Facility**
Fire alarm system/fire warning equipment	32.2.3.4.1	A manual fire alarm system shall be provided in accordance with Section 9.6.	33.2.3.4.1	A manual fire alarm system shall be provided in accordance with Section 9.6, unless the provisions of 33.2.3.4.1.1 or 33.2.3.4.1.2 are met.
			33.2.3.4.1.1	A fire alarm system shall not be required where interconnected smoke alarms complying with 33.2.3.4.3 and not less than one manual fire alarm box per floor arranged to continuously sound the smoke detector alarms are provided.

(continues)

Residential Board and Care Occupancies Continued

		New Residential Board and Care		Existing Residential Board and Care	
		101 Ref.	Requirement	101 Ref.	Requirement
Fire alarm system/fire warning equipment *(continued)*				33.2.3.4.1.2	Other manually activated continuously sounding alarms acceptable to the authority having jurisdiction shall be permitted in lieu of a fire alarm system.
		32.3.3.4.1	**Large Facility** A fire alarm system shall be provided in accordance with Section 9.6.	33.3.3.4.1	**Large Facility** A fire alarm system in accordance with Section 9.6 shall be provided, unless each sleeping room has exterior exit access in accordance with 7.5.3, and the building is not more than three stories in height.
Fire alarm signal initiation	Manual initiation		**Small Facility** See 32.2.3.4.1 above.		**Small Facility** See 33.2.3.4.1 above.
		32.3.3.4.2	**Large Facility** The required fire alarm system shall be initiated by all of the following: (1) Manual means in accordance with 9.6.2 (2) Manual fire alarm box located at a convenient central control point under continuous supervision of responsible employees (3) Required automatic sprinkler system (4) Required detection system	33.3.3.4.2	**Large Facility** The required fire alarm system shall be initiated by all of the following means: (1) Manual means in accordance with 9.6.2, unless there are other effective means (such as a complete automatic sprinkler or automatic detection system) for notification of fire as required (2) Manual fire alarm box located at a convenient central control point under continuous supervision of responsible employees (3) Automatic sprinkler system, other than those not required by another section of this *Code* (4) Required detection system, other than sleeping room smoke alarms
	Automatic detection	32.2.3.4.3.1	**Small Facility** Approved smoke alarms shall be provided in accordance with 9.6.2.10.	33.2.3.4.3.1	**Small Facility** Approved smoke alarms shall be provided in accordance with 9.6.2.10, unless otherwise indicated in 33.2.3.4.3.6 and 33.2.3.4.3.7.
		32.2.3.4.3.2	Smoke alarms shall be installed on all levels, including basements but excluding crawl spaces and unfinished attics.	33.2.3.4.3.2	Smoke alarms shall be installed on all levels, including basements but excluding crawl spaces and unfinished attics.

Reference	Requirement	Reference	Requirement
32.2.3.4.3.3	Additional smoke alarms shall be installed in all living areas, as defined in 3.3.19.5.	33.2.3.4.3.3	Additional smoke alarms shall be installed for living rooms, dens, day rooms, and similar spaces.
32.2.3.4.3.4	Each sleeping room shall be provided with an approved smoke alarm in accordance with 9.6.2.10.	33.2.3.4.3.5	Smoke alarms shall be powered from the building electrical system and, when activated, shall initiate an alarm that is audible in all sleeping areas.
		33.2.3.4.3.6	Smoke alarms in accordance with 33.2.3.4.3.1 shall not be required where buildings are protected throughout by an approved automatic sprinkler system, in accordance with 33.2.3.5, that uses quick-response or residential sprinklers, and are protected with approved smoke alarms installed in each sleeping room, in accordance with 9.6.2.10, that are powered by the building electrical system.
		33.2.3.4.3.7	Smoke alarms in accordance with 33.2.3.4.3.1 shall not be required where buildings are protected throughout by an approved automatic sprinkler system, in accordance with 33.2.3.5, that uses quick-response or residential sprinklers, with existing battery-powered smoke alarms in each sleeping room, and where, in the opinion of the authority having jurisdiction, the facility has demonstrated that testing, maintenance, and a battery replacement program ensure the reliability of power to the smoke alarms.
Large Facility		**Large Facility**	
32.3.3.4.7	Approved smoke alarms shall be installed in accordance with 9.6.2.10 inside every sleeping room, outside every sleeping area in the immediate vicinity of the bedrooms, and on all levels within a resident unit.	33.3.3.4.7	Smoke alarms shall be provided in accordance with 33.3.3.4.7.1, 33.3.3.4.7.2, or 33.3.3.4.7.3.
32.3.3.4.8.1	Corridors and spaces open to the corridors, other than those meeting the requirement of 32.3.3.4.8.3, shall be provided with smoke detectors that comply with *NFPA 72, National Fire Alarm Code*, and are arranged to initiate an alarm that is audible in all sleeping areas.	33.3.3.4.7.1	Each sleeping room shall be provided with an approved smoke alarm in accordance with 9.6.2.10 that is powered from the building electrical system.

(continues)

Residential Board and Care Occupancies Continued

		New Residential Board and Care		Existing Residential Board and Care	
		101 Ref.	Requirement	101 Ref.	Requirement
Fire alarm signal initiation *(continued)*	Automatic detection *(continued)*	32.3.3.4.8.3	Smoke detection systems shall not be required in unenclosed corridors, passageways, balconies, colonnades, or other arrangements with one or more sides along the long dimension fully or extensively open to the exterior at all times. Also see 32.3.3.4.2(4) above.	33.3.3.4.7.2	Existing battery-powered smoke alarms, rather than building electrical service-powered smoke alarms, shall be accepted where, in the opinion of the authority having jurisdiction, the facility has demonstrated that testing, maintenance, and battery replacement programs ensure the reliability of power to the smoke alarms.
				33.3.3.4.7.3	Sleeping room smoke alarms shall not be required in facilities having an existing corridor smoke detection system that complies with Section 9.6 and is connected to the building fire alarm system.
				33.3.3.4.8.1	All living areas, as defined in 3.3.19.5, and all corridors shall be provided with smoke detectors that comply with *NFPA 72, National Fire Alarm Code*, and are arranged to initiate an alarm that is audible in all sleeping areas, as modified by 33.3.3.4.8.2 and 33.3.3.4.8.3.
				33.3.3.4.8.2	Smoke detection systems shall not be required in living areas in facilities protected throughout by an approved automatic sprinkler system installed in accordance with 33.3.5.
				33.3.3.4.8.3	Smoke detection systems shall not be required in unenclosed corridors, passageways, balconies, colonnades, or other arrangements with one or more sides along the long dimension fully or extensively open to the exterior at all times.
	Extinguishing system operation		**Small Facility** See 9.7.2.2 below. Also see 32.2.3.5 in NFPA *101* for extinguishing system requirements and 32.2.3.6 for additional extinguishing system provisions.		**Small Facility** See 9.7.2.2 below. Also see 33.2.3.5 in NFPA *101* for extinguishing system requirements and 32.2.3.6 for additional extinguishing system provisions.

		Large Facility
	32.3.3.5.1	All buildings shall be protected throughout by an approved automatic sprinkler system installed in accordance with 9.7.1.1(1) and provided with quick-response or residential sprinklers throughout. Also see 32.3.3.4.2(3) above. Also see 9.7.2.2 below.	See 33.3.3.4.2(3) above. Also see 33.3.3.5 in NFPA *101* for extinguishing system requirements and in 33.3.3.6 for additional extinguishing system provisions.

		Small Facility	**Large Facility**
FAS supervisory signal initiation	Extinguishing system supervision	9.7.2.1	Where supervised automatic sprinkler systems are required by another section of this *Code*, supervisory attachments shall be installed and monitored for integrity in accordance with *NFPA 72, National Fire Alarm Code,* and a distinctive supervisory signal shall be provided to indicate a condition that would impair the satisfactory operation of the sprinkler system. System components and parameters that are required to be monitored shall include, but shall not be limited to, control valves, fire pump power supplies and running conditions, water tank levels and temperatures, tank pressure, and air pressure on dry-pipe valves. Supervisory signals shall sound and shall be displayed either at a location within the protected building that is constantly attended by qualified personnel or at an approved, remotely located receiving facility. See 32.2.3.5.4 and 32.2.3.5.5 in NFPA *101*.	9.7.2.1	Where supervised automatic sprinkler systems are required by another section of this *Code*, supervisory attachments shall be installed and monitored for integrity in accordance with *NFPA 72, National Fire Alarm Code,* and a distinctive supervisory signal shall be provided to indicate a condition that would impair the satisfactory operation of the sprinkler system. System components and parameters that are required to be monitored shall include, but shall not be limited to, control valves, fire pump power supplies and running conditions, water tank levels and temperatures, tank pressure, and air pressure on dry-pipe valves. Supervisory signals shall sound and shall be displayed either at a location within the protected building that is constantly attended by qualified personnel or at an approved, remotely located receiving facility. See 33.2.3.5.3 in NFPA *101*.

		Large Facility	**Large Facility**
	32.3.3.5.4	Automatic sprinkler systems shall be provided with electrical supervision in accordance with 9.7.2.	33.3.3.5.4	Automatic sprinkler systems shall be supervised in accordance with Section 9.7; waterflow alarms shall not be required to be transmitted off-site.
	9.7.2.1	Where supervised automatic sprinkler systems are required by another section of this *Code*, supervisory attachments shall be installed and monitored for integrity in accordance with *NFPA 72, National Fire Alarm Code,* and a distinctive supervisory signal shall be provided		

(continues)

Residential Board and Care Occupancies Continued

		New Residential Board and Care		Existing Residential Board and Care	
		101 Ref.	*Requirement*	*101 Ref.*	*Requirement*
FAS supervisory signal initiation *(continued)*	Extinguishing system supervision *(continued)*		to indicate a condition that would impair the satisfactory operation of the sprinkler system. System components and parameters that are required to be monitored shall include, but shall not be limited to, control valves, fire pump power supplies and running conditions, water tank levels and temperatures, tank pressure, and air pressure on dry-pipe valves. Supervisory signals shall sound and shall be displayed either at a location within the protected building that is constantly attended by qualified personnel or at an approved, remotely located receiving facility.		
Occupant notification	Audible/visible	32.2.3.4.2	**Small Facility** Occupant notification shall be provided automatically, without delay, in accordance with 9.6.3.	33.2.3.4.2	**Small Facility** Occupant notification shall be in accordance with 9.6.3.
		32.3.3.4.4	**Large Facility** Occupant notification shall be provided automatically, without delay, in accordance with 9.6.3.	33.3.3.4.4	**Large Facility** Occupant notification shall be provided automatically, without delay, by internal audible alarm in accordance with 9.6.3.
	Positive alarm sequence		**Small Facility** Not addressed.		**Small Facility** Not addressed.
			Large Facility See 32.3.3.4.6(2) below.		**Large Facility** Not addressed.
	Presignal system		Not addressed.		Not addressed.
	Voice announcements		**Small Facility** Not specifically addressed; however, see 9.6.3.9.		**Small Facility** Not specifically addressed; however, see 9.6.3.9.

Emergency forces notification	**Other provisions**			
	32.3.4.5	**Large Facility** High-rise buildings shall be provided with an approved emergency voice communication/alarm system in accordance with 11.8.4.	32.3.4.5	**Large Facility** Not specifically addressed; however, see 9.6.3.9.
	9.7.2.2	**Small Facility** Where supervision of automatic sprinkler systems is provided in accordance with another provision of this *Code*, waterflow alarms shall be transmitted to an approved, proprietary alarm-receiving facility, a remote station, a central station, or the fire department. Such connection shall be in accordance with 9.6.1.3. Also see 32.2.3.5.4 and 32.2.3.5.5 in NFPA *101.*	9.7.2.2	**Small Facility** Where supervision of automatic sprinkler systems is provided in accordance with another provision of this *Code*, waterflow alarms shall be transmitted to an approved, proprietary alarm-receiving facility, a remote station, a central station, or the fire department. Such connection shall be in accordance with 9.6.1.3. Also see 33.2.3.5.3 in NFPA *101.*
	32.3.4.6	**Large Facility** Emergency forces notification shall meet the following requirements: (1) Fire department notification shall be accomplished in accordance with 9.6.4. (2) Smoke detection devices or smoke detection systems shall be permitted to initiate a positive alarm sequence in accordance with 9.6.3.4 for not more than 120 seconds.	33.3.3.4.6	**Large Facility** In case of a fire, provisions shall be made for the immediate notification of the public fire department, by either telephone or other means, or, where there is no public fire department, this notification shall be made to the private fire brigade. Also see 33.3.3.5.4 above.
	9.7.2.2	**Small Facility** Where supervision of automatic sprinkler systems is provided in accordance with another provision of this *Code*, waterflow alarms shall be transmitted to an approved, proprietary alarm-receiving facility, a remote station, a central station, or the fire department. Such connection shall be in accordance with 9.6.1.3. Also see 32.3.3.5.1 and 32.3.3.5.4 above.		
Annunciator		**Small Facility** Not addressed.		**Small Facility** Not addressed.

(continues)

Residential Board and Care Occupancies Continued

| | New Residential Board and Care | | Existing Residential Board and Care | |
	101 Ref.	Requirement	101 Ref.	Requirement
Annunciator *(continued)*	32.3.3.4.3	**Large Facility** An annunciator panel, connected to the fire alarm system, shall be provided at a location readily accessible from the primary point of entry for emergency response personnel.		**Large Facility** Not addressed.
Emergency control (fire safety) functions		See separate summary table for emergency control (fire safety) functions, where applicable.		See separate summary table for emergency control (fire safety) functions, where applicable.

Mercantile Occupancies

The following excerpts from NFPA *101*, 2009 edition, are provided for reference:

36.1.1.1 The requirements of this chapter shall apply to new buildings or portions thereof used as mercantile occupancies (*see 1.3.1*).

37.1.1.1 The requirements of this chapter shall apply to existing buildings or portions thereof currently occupied as mercantile occupancies.

3.3.32.4 Bulk Merchandising Retail Building. A building in which the sales area includes the storage of combustible materials on pallets, in solid piles, or in racks in excess of 12 ft (3660 mm) in storage height.

3.3.178.9* Mercantile Occupancy. An occupancy used for the display and sale of merchandise.

3.3.32.9* Mall Building. A single building enclosing a number of tenants and occupancies wherein two or more tenants have a main entrance into one or more malls. For the purpose of this *Code*, anchor buildings shall not be considered as a part of the mall building.

3.3.158 Mall. A roofed or covered common pedestrian area within a mall building that serves as access for two or more tenants and does not exceed three levels that are open to each other.

36.1.4.2.1 Mercantile occupancies shall be subclassified as follows:

(1) Class A, all mercantile occupancies having an aggregate gross area of more than 30,000 ft² (2800 m²) or occupying more than three stories for sales purposes

(2) Class B as follows:

  (a) Class B, all mercantile occupancies of more than 3000 ft² (280 m²), but not more than 30,000 ft² (2800 m²), aggregate gross area and occupying not more than three stories for sales purposes

  (b) All mercantile occupancies of not more than 3000 ft² (280 m²) gross area and occupying two or three stories for sales purposes

(3) Class C, all mercantile occupancies of not more than 3000 ft² (280 m²) gross area and used for sales purposes occupying one story only

36.4.4 Mall Buildings. The provisions of 36.4.4 shall apply to mall buildings three or fewer stories in height and any number of anchor buildings. (*See 3.3.32.9.*)

37.1.4.2.1 Mercantile occupancies shall be subclassified as follows:

(1) Class A, all mercantile occupancies having an aggregate gross area of more than 30,000 ft² (2800 m²) or occupying more than three stories for sales purposes

(2) Class B, as follows:

  (a) All mercantile occupancies of more than 3000 ft² (280 m²) but not more than 30,000 ft² (2800 m²) aggregate gross area and occupying not more than three stories for sales purposes

  (b) All mercantile occupancies of not more than 3000 ft² (280 m²) gross area and occupying two or three stories for sales purposes

(3) Class C, all mercantile occupancies of not more than 3000 ft² (280 m²) gross area used for sales purposes and occupying one story only, excluding mezzanines

Mercantile Occupancies

	New Mercantile		Existing Mercantile	
	101 Ref.	Requirement	101 Ref.	Requirement
Fire alarm system	36.3.4.1	**Class A Mercantile Occupancies** Class A mercantile occupancies shall be provided with a fire alarm system in accordance with Section 9.6.	37.3.4.1	**Class A Mercantile Occupancies** Class A mercantile occupancies shall be provided with a fire alarm system in accordance with Section 9.6.

(continues)

Mercantile Occupancies Continued

		New Mercantile		Existing Mercantile	
		101 Ref.	Requirement	101 Ref.	Requirement
Fire alarm system *(continued)*		36.4.4.4.1	**Mall Buildings** Malls shall be provided with a fire alarm system in accordance with Section 9.6.	37.4.4.4.1	**Mall Buildings** Malls shall be provided with a fire alarm system in accordance with Section 9.6.
		36.4.5.4.1	**Bulk Merchandising Retail Building** Bulk merchandising retail buildings shall be provided with a fire alarm system in accordance with Section 9.6.	37.4.5.4.1	**Bulk Merchandising Retail Building** Bulk merchandising retail buildings shall be provided with a fire alarm system in accordance with Section 9.6.
Fire alarm signal initiation	Manual initiation	36.3.4.2	**Class A Mercantile Occupancies** Initiation of the required fire alarm system shall be by any one of the following means: (1) Manual means in accordance with 9.6.2.1(1) (2) Approved automatic fire detection system that complies with 9.6.2.1(2) and provides protection throughout the building, plus a minimum of one manual fire alarm box in accordance with 9.6.26 (3) Approved automatic sprinkler system that complies with 9.6.2.1(3) and provides protection throughout the building, plus a minimum of one manual fire alarm box in accordance with 9.6.2.6	37.3.4.2	**Class A Mercantile Occupancies** Initiation of the required fire alarm system shall be by one of the following means: (1) Manual means per 9.6.2.1(1) (2) Approved automatic fire detection system that complies with 9.6.2.1(2) and provides protection throughout the building, plus a minimum of one manual fire alarm box in accordance with 9.6.2.6 (3) Approved automatic sprinkler system that complies with 9.6.2.1(3) and provides protection throughout the building, plus a minimum of one manual fire alarm box in accordance with 9.6.2.6
		36.4.4.4.2	**Mall Buildings** Initiation of the required fire alarm system shall be by means of the required automatic sprinkler system in accordance with 9.6.2.1(3).	37.4.4.4.2	**Mall Buildings** Initiation of the required fire alarm system shall be by means of the required automatic sprinkler system in accordance with 9.6.2.1(3).
		36.4.5.4.2	**Bulk Merchandising Retail Building** Initiation of the required fire alarm system shall be by means of the required approved automatic sprinkler system *(see 36.4.5.5)* in accordance with 9.6.2.1(3).	37.4.5.4.2	**Bulk Merchandising Retail Building** Initiation of the required fire alarm system shall be by means of the required approved automatic sprinkler system *(see 37.4.5.5)* in accordance with 9.6.2.1(3).
Automatic detection			For Class A mercantile occupancies see 36.3.4.2(2) above.		For Class A mercantile occupancies see 37.3.4.2(2) above.

Feature	Ref	Requirement	Ref	Requirement
Extinguishing system operation		See 36.3.4.2(3), 36.4.4.4.2, and 36.4.5.4.2 above. Also see 9.7.2.2 below. Also see 36.3.5, 36.4.4.10, and 36.4.5.5 in NFPA *101* for extinguishing system requirements and 36.3.6 for additional extinguishing system provisions.		See 37.3.4.2(3), 37.4.4.4.2, and 37.4.5.4.2 above. Also see 9.7.2.2 below. Also see 37.3.5 and 37.4.5.5 in NFPA *101* for extinguishing system requirements.
Extinguishing system supervision	9.7.2.1	Where supervised automatic sprinkler systems are required by another section of this *Code*, supervisory attachments shall be installed and monitored for integrity in accordance with *NFPA 72, National Fire Alarm Code*, and a distinctive supervisory signal shall be provided to indicate a condition that would impair the satisfactory operation of the sprinkler system. System components and parameters that are required to be monitored shall include, but shall not be limited to, control valves, fire pump power supplies and running conditions, water tank levels and temperatures, tank pressure, and air pressure on dry-pipe valves. Supervisory signals shall sound and shall be displayed either at a location within the protected building that is constantly attended by qualified personnel or at an approved, remotely located receiving facility. Also see 36.3.5, 36.4.4.10, and 36.4.5.5 in NFPA *101* for extinguishing system requirements and 36.3.6 for additional extinguishing system provisions.	9.7.2.1	Where supervised automatic sprinkler systems are required by another section of this *Code*, supervisory attachments shall be installed and monitored for integrity in accordance with *NFPA 72, National Fire Alarm Code*, and a distinctive supervisory signal shall be provided to indicate a condition that would impair the satisfactory operation of the sprinkler system. System components and parameters that are required to be monitored shall include, but shall not be limited to, control valves, fire pump power supplies and running conditions, water tank levels and temperatures, tank pressure, and air pressure on dry-pipe valves. Supervisory signals shall sound and shall be displayed either at a location within the protected building that is constantly attended by qualified personnel or at an approved, remotely located receiving facility. Also see 37.3.5 and 37.4.5.5 in NFPA *101* for extinguishing system requirements.
FAS supervisory signal initiation				
Occupant notification	36.3.4.3.1	**Class A Mercantile Occupancies** During all times that the mercantile occupancy is occupied, the required fire alarm system, once initiated, shall activate an alarm in accordance with 9.6.3 throughout the mercantile occupancy, and positive alarm sequence in accordance with 9.6.3.4 shall be permitted.	37.3.4.3.1	**Class A Mercantile Occupancies** During all times that the mercantile occupancy is occupied, the required fire alarm system, once initiated, shall perform one of the following functions: (1) It shall activate an alarm in accordance with 9.6.3 throughout the mercantile occupancy, and positive alarm sequence in accordance with 9.6.3.4 or a presignal system in accordance with 9.6.3.3 shall be permitted.

(continues)

Mercantile Occupancies Continued

		New Mercantile		Existing Mercantile	
		101 Ref.	Requirement	101 Ref.	Requirement
Occupant notification (continued)	Audible/visible (continued)				(2) Occupant notification shall be permitted to be made via a voice communication or public address system in accordance with 9.6.3.9.2.
		36.4.4.4.3.1	**Mall Buildings** During all times that the mall is occupied, the required fire alarm system, once initiated, shall perform one of the following functions: (1) It shall activate a general alarm in accordance with 9.6.3 throughout the mall. (2) Positive alarm sequence in accordance with 9.6.3.4 shall be permitted. (3) Occupant notification shall be permitted to be made via a voice communication or public address system in accordance with 9.6.3.9.2.	37.4.4.4.3.1	**Mall Buildings** During all times that the mall is occupied, the required fire alarm system, once initiated, shall perform one of the following functions: (1) It shall activate an alarm in accordance with 9.6.3 throughout the mall. (2) Positive alarm sequence in accordance with 9.6.3.4 shall be permitted. (3) Occupant notification shall be permitted to be made via a voice communication or public address system in accordance with 9.6.3.9.2.
		36.4.4.4.3.2	Visible signals shall not be required in malls. (See 9.6.3.5.7 and 9.6.3.5.8.)		
		36.4.5.4.3	**Bulk Merchandising Retail Building** During all times that the mercantile occupancy is occupied, the required fire alarm system, once initiated, shall activate an alarm in accordance with 9.6.3 throughout the mercantile occupancy, and positive alarm sequence in accordance with 9.6.3.4 shall be permitted.	37.4.5.4.3	**Bulk Merchandising Retail Building** During all times that the mercantile occupancy is occupied, the required fire alarm system, once initiated, shall perform one of the following functions: (1) It shall activate an alarm in accordance with 9.6.3 throughout the mercantile occupancy, and positive alarm sequence in accordance with 9.6.3.4 shall be permitted. (2) Occupant notification shall be permitted to be made via a voice communication or public address system in accordance with 9.6.3.9.2.
Positive alarm sequence			See 36.3.4.3.1, 36.4.4.4.3.1(2), and 36.4.5.4.3 above.		See 37.3.4.3.1(1), 37.4.4.4.3.1(2), and 37.4.5.4.3(1) above.
Presignal system			Not addressed.		For Class A mercantile occupancies see 37.3.4.3.1(1) above.

	Reference	Requirement	Reference	Requirement
Voice announcements		See 36.3.4.3.1, 36.4.4.4.3.1(3), and 36.4.5.4.3 above.		See 37.3.4.3.1(2), 37.4.4.4.3.1(3), and 37.4.5.4.3(2) above.
Other provisions		See 36.3.4.3.1, 36.4.4.4.3.1(3), and 36.4.5.4.3 above.		See 37.3.4.3.1(2), 37.4.4.4.3.1(3), and 37.4.5.4.3(2) above.
Emergency forces notification	36.3.4.3.2 36.4.4.4.3.3 36.4.5.4.4	Emergency forces notification shall be provided and shall include notifying the following: (1) Fire department in accordance with 9.6.4 (2) Local emergency organization, if provided	37.3.4.3.2 37.4.4.4.3.2 37.4.5.4.4	Emergency forces notification shall be provided and shall include notifying the following: (1) Fire department in accordance with 9.6.4 (2) Local emergency organization, if provided
	9.7.2.2	Where supervision of automatic sprinkler systems is provided in accordance with another provision of this *Code*, waterflow alarms shall be transmitted to an approved, proprietary alarm-receiving facility, a remote station, a central station, or the fire department. Such connection shall be in accordance with 9.6.1.3. Also see 36.3.4.2(3), 36.4.4.4.2, and 36.4.5.4.2 above. Also see 36.3.5, 36.4.4.10, and 36.4.5.5 in NFPA *101* for extinguishing system requirements and 36.3.6 for additional extinguishing system provisions.	9.7.2.2	Where supervision of automatic sprinkler systems is provided in accordance with another provision of this *Code*, waterflow alarms shall be transmitted to an approved, proprietary alarm-receiving facility, a remote station, a central station, or the fire department. Such connection shall be in accordance with 9.6.1.3. Also see 37.3.4.2(3), 37.4.4.4.2, and 37.4.5.4.2 above. Also see 37.3.5 and 37.4.5.5 in NFPA *101* for extinguishing system requirements.
Annunciator		Not addressed.		Not addressed.
Emergency control (fire safety) functions	36.4.4.4	**Mall Buildings** The fire alarm system shall be arranged to automatically actuate smoke management or smoke control systems in accordance with 9.6.5.2(3). Also see separate summary table for emergency control (fire safety) functions, where applicable.	37.4.4.4	**Mall Buildings** The fire alarm system shall be arranged to automatically actuate smoke management or smoke control systems in accordance with 9.6.5.2(3). Also see separate summary table for emergency control (fire safety) functions, where applicable.

Business Occupancies

The following excerpts from NFPA *101*, 2009 edition, are provided for reference:

38.1.1.1 The requirements of this chapter shall apply to new buildings or portions thereof used as business occupancies (*see 1.3.1*).

39.1.1.1 The requirements of this chapter shall apply to existing buildings or portions thereof currently occupied as business occupancies.

3.3.178.3* Business Occupancy. An occupancy used for the transaction of business other than mercantile.

Business Occupancies

		New Business		Existing Business	
		101 Ref.	Requirement	101 Ref.	Requirement
Fire alarm system		38.3.4.1	A fire alarm system in accordance with Section 9.6 shall be provided in all business occupancies where any one of the following conditions exists: (1) The building is three or more stories in height. (2) The occupancy is subject to 50 or more occupants above or below the level of exit discharge. (3) The occupancy is subject to 300 or more total occupants.	39.3.4.1	A fire alarm system in accordance with Section 9.6 shall be provided in all business occupancies where any one of the following conditions exists: (1) The building is three or more stories in height. (2) The occupancy is subject to 100 or more occupants above or below the level of exit discharge. (3) The occupancy is subject to 1000 or more total occupants.
Fire alarm signal initiation	Manual initiation	38.3.4.2	Initiation of the required fire alarm system shall be by one of the following means: (1) Manual means in accordance with 9.6.2.1(1) (2) Means of an approved automatic fire detection system that complies with 9.6.2.1(2) and provides protection throughout the building (3) Means of an approved automatic sprinkler system that complies with 9.6.2.1(3) and provides protection throughout the building	39.3.4.2	Initiation of the required fire alarm system shall be by one of the following means: (1) Manual means in accordance with 9.6.2.1(1) (2) Means of an approved automatic fire detection system that complies with 9.6.2.1(2) and provides protection throughout the building (3) Means of an approved automatic sprinkler system that complies with 9.6.2.1(3) and provides protection throughout the building
	Automatic detection		See 38.3.4.2(2) above.		See 39.3.4.2(2) above.
	Extinguishing system operation		See 38.3.4.2(3) above. Also see 9.7.2.2 below. Also see 38.3.6 in NFPA *101* for extinguishing system provisions.		See 39.3.4.2(3) above. Also see 9.7.2.2 below.

FAS supervisory signal initiation	Extinguishing system supervision	9.7.2.1	Where supervised automatic sprinkler systems are required by another section of this *Code*, supervisory attachments shall be installed and monitored for integrity in accordance with *NFPA 72, National Fire Alarm Code*, and a distinctive supervisory signal shall be provided to indicate a condition that would impair the satisfactory operation of the sprinkler system. System components and parameters that are required to be monitored shall include, but shall not be limited to, control valves, fire pump power supplies and running conditions, water tank levels and temperatures, tank pressure, and air pressure on dry-pipe valves. Supervisory signals shall sound and shall be displayed either at a location within the protected building that is constantly attended by qualified personnel or at an approved, remotely located receiving facility. See 38.3.6 in NFPA 101 for extinguishing system provisions.	9.7.2.1	Where supervised automatic sprinkler systems are required by another section of this *Code*, supervisory attachments shall be installed and monitored for integrity in accordance with *NFPA 72, National Fire Alarm Code*, and a distinctive supervisory signal shall be provided to indicate a condition that would impair the satisfactory operation of the sprinkler system. System components and parameters that are required to be monitored shall include, but shall not be limited to, control valves, fire pump power supplies and running conditions, water tank levels and temperatures, tank pressure, and air pressure on dry-pipe valves. Supervisory signals shall sound and shall be displayed either at a location within the protected building that is constantly attended by qualified personnel or at an approved, remotely located receiving facility.
Occupant notification	Audible/visible	38.3.4.3	During all times that the building is occupied, the required fire alarm system, once initiated, shall activate a general alarm in accordance with 9.6.3 throughout the building, and positive alarm sequence in accordance with 9.6.3.4 shall be permitted.	39.3.4.3	During all times that the building is occupied (see 7.2.1.1.3), the required fire alarm system, once initiated, shall perform one of the following functions: (1) It shall activate a general alarm in accordance with 9.6.3 throughout the building, and the following also shall apply: (a) Positive alarm sequence in accordance with 9.6.3.4 shall be permitted. (b) A presignal system in accordance with 9.6.3.3 shall be permitted. (2) Occupant notification shall be permitted to be made via a voice communication or public address system in accordance with 9.6.3.9.2.
	Positive alarm sequence		See 38.3.4.3 above.		See 39.3.4.3(1)(a) above.
	Presignal system		Not addressed.		See 39.3.4.3(1)(b) above.
	Voice announcements		See 38.3.4.3 above.		See 39.3.4.3(2) above.
	Other provisions		See 38.3.4.3 above.		See 39.3.4.3(2) above.

(continues)

Business Occupancies Continued

	New Business		Existing Business	
	101 Ref.	*Requirement*	*101 Ref.*	*Requirement*
Emergency forces notification	38.3.4.4	Emergency forces notification shall be provided and shall include notifying the following: (1) Fire department in accordance with 9.6.4 (2) Local emergency organization, if provided		
	9.7.2.2	Where supervision of automatic sprinkler systems is provided in accordance with another provision of this *Code*, waterflow alarms shall be transmitted to an approved, proprietary alarm-receiving facility, a remote station, a central station, or the fire department. Such connection shall be in accordance with 9.6.1.3. See 38.3.6 in NFPA *101* for extinguishing system provisions.	9.7.2.2	Where supervision of automatic sprinkler systems is provided in accordance with another provision of this *Code*, waterflow alarms shall be transmitted to an approved, proprietary alarm-receiving facility, a remote station, a central station, or the fire department. Such connection shall be in accordance with 9.6.1.3.
Annunciator		Not addressed.		Not addressed.
Emergency control (fire safety) functions		See separate summary table for emergency control (fire safety) functions, where applicable.		See separate summary table for emergency control (fire safety) functions, where applicable.

Industrial Occupancies

The following excerpts from NFPA *101*, 2009 edition, are provided for reference:

40.1.1.1 The requirements of this chapter shall apply to both new and existing industrial occupancies.

40.1.4.1.3* High Hazard Industrial Occupancy. High hazard industrial occupancies shall include the following:

(1) Industrial occupancies that conduct industrial operations that use high hazard materials or processes or house high hazard contents
(2) Industrial occupancies in which incidental high hazard operations in low or ordinary hazard occupancies that

are protected in accordance with Section 8.7 and 40.3.2 are not required to be the basis for overall occupancy classification

3.3.178.8* Industrial Occupancy. An occupancy in which products are manufactured or in which processing, assembling, mixing, packaging, finishing, decorating, or repair operations are conducted.

3.3.178.8.2* High Hazard Industrial Occupancy. An industrial occupancy in which industrial operations that include high hazard materials, processes, or contents are conducted.

New and Existing Industrial

		101 Ref.	Requirement
Fire alarm system		40.3.4.1	A fire alarm system shall be required in accordance with Section 9.6 for industrial occupancies, unless the total occupant load of the building is under 100 persons and unless, of these, fewer than 25 persons are above or below the level of exit discharge.
Fire alarm signal initiation	Manual initiation	40.3.4.2	Initiation of the required fire alarm system shall be by any of the following means: (1) Manual means in accordance with 9.6.2.1(1) (2) Approved automatic fire detection system in accordance with 9.6.2.1(2) throughout the building, plus a minimum of one manual fire alarm box in accordance with 9.6.2.6 (3) Approved, supervised automatic sprinkler system in accordance with 9.6.2.1(3) throughout the building, plus a minimum of one manual fire alarm box in accordance with 9.6.2.6
	Automatic detection		See 40.3.4.2(2) above.
	Extinguishing system operation		See 40.3.4.2(3) above. Also see 9.7.2.2 below.
FAS supervisory signal initiation	Extinguishing system supervision	9.7.2.1	Where supervised automatic sprinkler systems are required by another section of this *Code*, supervisory attachments shall be installed and monitored for integrity in accordance with *NFPA 72, National Fire Alarm Code*, and a distinctive supervisory signal shall be provided to indicate a condition that would impair the satisfactory operation of the sprinkler system. System components and parameters that are required to be monitored shall include, but shall not be limited to, control valves, fire pump power supplies and running conditions, water tank levels and temperatures, tank pressure, and air pressure on dry-pipe valves. Supervisory signals shall sound and shall be displayed either at a location within the protected building that is constantly attended by qualified personnel or at an approved, remotely located receiving facility. Also see 40.3.4.2(3) above.

(continues)

New and Existing Industrial Continued

		101 Ref.	Requirement
Occupant notification	Audible/visible	40.3.4.3.1	The required fire alarm system shall meet one of the following criteria: (1) It shall provide occupant notification in accordance with 9.6.3. (2) It shall sound an audible and visible signal in a constantly attended location for the purposes of initiating emergency action.
		40.3.4.3.4	In high hazard industrial occupancies, as described in 40.1.4.1.3, the required fire alarm system shall automatically initiate an occupant evacuation alarm signal in accordance with 9.6.3.
	Positive alarm sequence	40.3.4.3.2	Positive alarm sequence in accordance with 9.6.3.4 shall be permitted.
	Presignal system	40.3.4.3.3	Existing presignal systems in accordance with 9.6.3.3 shall be permitted.
	Voice announcements		Not addressed.
	Other provisions		Not addressed.
Emergency forces notification		9.7.2.2	Where supervision of automatic sprinkler systems is provided in accordance with another provision of this *Code*, waterflow alarms shall be transmitted to an approved, proprietary alarm-receiving facility, a remote station, a central station, or the fire department. Such connection shall be in accordance with 9.6.1.3. Also see 40.3.4.2(3) above.
Annunciator			Not addressed.
Emergency control (fire safety) functions			See separate summary table for emergency control (fire safety) functions, where applicable.

Storage Occupancies

The following excerpts from NFPA *101*, 2009 edition, are provided for reference:

42.1.1.1 The requirements of this chapter shall apply to both new and existing storage occupancies.

42.1.1.2 Storage occupancies shall include all buildings or structures used primarily for the storage or sheltering of goods, merchandise, products, vehicles, or animals.

3.3.178.15* Storage Occupancy. An occupancy used primarily for the storage or sheltering of goods, merchandise, products, vehicles, or animals.

3.3.254.6 Open Parking Structure. A parking structure that, at each parking level, has wall openings open to the atmosphere, for an area of not less than 1.4 ft² for each linear foot (0.4 m² for each linear meter) of its exterior perimeter. Such openings are distributed over at least 40 percent of the building perimeter or uniformly over two opposing sides. Interior wall lines and column lines are at least 20 percent open, with openings distributed to provide ventilation.

New and Existing Storage

		101 Ref.	Requirement
Fire alarm system		42.3.4.1	A fire alarm system shall be required in accordance with Section 9.6 for storage occupancies, except as modified by 42.3.4.1.1, 42.3.4.1.2, and 42.3.4.1.3.
		42.3.4.1.1	Storage occupancies limited to low hazard contents shall not be required to have a fire alarm system.
		42.3.4.1.2	Storage occupancies with ordinary or high hazard contents not exceeding an aggregate floor area of 100,000 ft² (9300 m²) shall not be required to have a fire alarm system.
		42.3.4.1.3	Storage occupancies protected throughout by an approved automatic sprinkler system in accordance with Section 9.7 shall not be required to have a fire alarm system.
		Parking Structures	
		42.8.3.4.1	A fire alarm system shall be required in accordance with Section 9.6 for parking structures, except as modified by 42.3.4.1.1, 42.3.4.1.2, and 42.3.4.1.3.
		42.8.3.4.1.1	Parking structures not exceeding an aggregate floor area of 100,000 ft² (9300 m²) shall not be required to have a fire alarm system.
		42.8.3.4.1.2	Open parking structures shall not be required to have a fire alarm system.
		42.8.3.4.1.3	Parking structures protected throughout by an approved automatic sprinkler system in accordance with Section 9.7 shall not be required to have a fire alarm system.
Fire alarm signal initiation	Manual initiation	42.3.4.2	Initiation of the required fire alarm system shall be by any of the following means: (1) Manual means in accordance with 9.6.2.1(1) (2) Approved automatic fire detection system in accordance with 9.6.2.1(2) throughout the building, plus a minimum of one manual fire alarm box in accordance with 9.6.2.6 (3) Approved, supervised automatic sprinkler system in accordance with 9.6.2.1(3) throughout the building, plus a minimum of one manual fire alarm box in accordance with 9.6.2.6

(continues)

New and Existing Storage Continued

		101 Ref.	Requirement
Fire alarm signal initiation *(continued)*	Manual initiation *(continued)*	42.8.3.4.2	**Parking Structures** Initiation of the required fire alarm system shall be by one of the following means: (1) Manual means in accordance with 9.6.2.1(1) (2) Approved automatic fire detection system in accordance with 9.6.2.1(2) throughout the building, plus a minimum of one manual fire alarm box in accordance with 9.6.2.6 (3) Approved supervised automatic sprinkler system in accordance with 9.6.2.1(3) throughout the building, plus a minimum of one manual fire alarm box in accordance with 9.6.2.6
	Automatic detection		See 42.3.4.2(2) above.
	Extinguishing system operation		See 42.3.4.2(3) and 42.8.3.4.2(3) above. Also see 9.7.2.2 below.
FAS supervisory signal initiation	Extinguishing system supervision	9.7.2.1	Where supervised automatic sprinkler systems are required by another section of this *Code*, supervisory attachments shall be installed and monitored for integrity in accordance with *NFPA 72, National Fire Alarm Code*, and a distinctive supervisory signal shall be provided to indicate a condition that would impair the satisfactory operation of the sprinkler system. System components and parameters that are required to be monitored shall include, but shall not be limited to, control valves, fire pump power supplies and running conditions, water tank levels and temperatures, tank pressure, and air pressure on dry-pipe valves. Supervisory signals shall sound and shall be displayed either at a location within the protected building that is constantly attended by qualified personnel or at an approved, remotely located receiving facility. Also see 42.3.4.2(3) and 42.8.3.4.2(3) above. Also see 42.8.3.1.1.3 and 42.8.3.1.1.4 in NFPA *101* for additional extinguishing system provisions.
Occupant notification	Audible/visible	42.3.4.3.1	The required fire alarm system shall meet one of the following criteria: (1) It shall provide occupant notification in accordance with 9.6.3. (2) It shall sound an audible and visible signal in a constantly attended location for the purposes of initiating emergency action.
		42.3.4.3.4	In high hazard storage occupancies, the required fire alarm system shall automatically initiate an occupant evacuation alarm signal in accordance with 9.6.3.
		42.8.3.4.3.1	**Parking Structures** The required fire alarm system shall sound an audible alarm in a continuously attended location for purposes of initiating emergency action.
	Positive alarm sequence	42.3.4.3.2 42.8.3.4.3.2	Positive alarm sequence in accordance with 9.6.3.4 shall be permitted.
	Presignal system	42.3.4.3.3 42.8.3.4.3.3	Existing presignal systems in accordance with 9.6.3.3 shall be permitted.
	Voice announcements		Not addressed.
	Other provisions		Not addressed.

New and Existing Storage Continued

		101 Ref.	*Requirement*
Emergency forces notification		9.7.2.2	Where supervision of automatic sprinkler systems is provided in accordance with another provision of this *Code*, waterflow alarms shall be transmitted to an approved, proprietary alarm-receiving facility, a remote station, a central station, or the fire department. Such connection shall be in accordance with 9.6.1.3.
			Also see 42.3.4.2(3) and 42.8.3.4.2(3) above.
			Also see 42.8.3.1.1.3 and 42.8.3.1.1.4 in NFPA *101* for additional extinguishing system provisions.
Annunciator			Not addressed.
Emergency control (fire safety) functions			See separate summary table for emergency control (fire safety) functions, where applicable.

Special Structures and High-Rise Buildings

The following excerpts from NFPA *101*, 2009 edition, are provided for reference:

11.1.1 Application. The requirements of Section 11.1 through Section 11.11 shall apply to occupancies regulated by Chapters 12 through 42 that are in a special structure. The applicable provisions of Chapters 12 through 42 shall apply, except as modified by this chapter. Section 11.8 shall apply to high-rise buildings only where specifically required by Chapters 12 through 42.

3.3.32.7* High-Rise Building. A building where the floor of an occupiable story is greater than 75 ft (23 m) above the lowest level of fire department vehicle access.

3.3.262 Tower. An enclosed independent structure or portion of a building with elevated levels for support of equipment or occupied for observation, control, operation, signaling, or similar limited use.

Special Structures and High-Rise Buildings

		Towers		High-Rise	
		101 Ref.	*Requirement*	*101 Ref.*	*Requirement*
Fire alarm system		11.3.3.4	Towers designed for occupancy by not more than three persons shall be exempt from requirements for detection, alarm, and communications systems. Also see occupancy chapter.	11.8.4.1	A fire alarm system using an approved, emergency voice/alarm communication system shall be installed in accordance with Section 9.6. Also see occupancy chapter.
Fire alarm signal initiation	Manual initiation		See occupancy chapter.		See occupancy chapter.
	Automatic detection		See occupancy chapter		See occupancy chapter.
	Extinguishing system operation		See occupancy chapter.	11.8.3.1	High-rise buildings shall be protected throughout by an approved, supervised automatic sprinkler system in accordance with Section 9.7. A sprinkler control valve and a waterflow device shall be provided for each floor. Also see 9.7.2.2 below. Also see occupancy chapter.
FAS supervisory signal initiation	Extinguishing system supervision		See occupancy chapter.	9.7.2.1	Where supervised automatic sprinkler systems are required by another section of this *Code*, supervisory attachments shall be installed and monitored for integrity in accordance with *NFPA 72, National Fire Alarm Code*, and a distinctive supervisory signal shall be provided to indicate a condition that would impair the satisfactory operation of the sprinkler system. System

				components and parameters that are required to be monitored shall include, but shall not be limited to, control valves, fire pump power supplies and running conditions, water tank levels and temperatures, tank pressure, and air pressure on dry-pipe valves. Supervisory signals shall sound and shall be displayed either at a location within the protected building that is constantly attended by qualified personnel or at an approved, remotely located receiving facility. See 11.8.3.1 above. Also see occupancy chapter.
Occupant notification	Audible/visible	See occupancy chapter.		See 11.8.4.1 above. Also see occupancy chapter.
	Positive alarm sequence	See occupancy chapter.		See occupancy chapter.
	Presignal system	See occupancy chapter.		See occupancy chapter.
	Voice announcements	See occupancy chapter.		See 11.8.4.1 above. Also see occupancy chapter.
	Other provisions	See occupancy chapter.	11.8.4.2.1	Two-way telephone communication service shall be provided for fire department use. This system shall be in accordance with *NFPA 72, National Fire Alarm Code.* The communications system shall operate between the emergency command center and every elevator car, every elevator lobby, and each floor level of exit stairs.
			11.8.4.2.2	The requirement of 11.8.4.2.1 shall not apply where the fire department radio system is approved as an equivalent system. Also see occupancy chapter.
Emergency forces notification		See occupancy chapter.	9.7.2.2	Where supervision of automatic sprinkler systems is provided in accordance with another provision of this *Code*, waterflow alarms shall be transmitted to an approved, proprietary alarm-receiving facility, a remote station, a central station, or the fire department. Such connection shall be in accordance with 9.6.1.3. See 11.8.3.1 above. Also see occupancy chapter.

(continues)

Special Structures and High-Rise Buildings Continued

	Towers		High-Rise	
	101 Ref.	Requirement	101 Ref.	Requirement
Annunciator		See occupancy chapter.	11.8.6.1	An emergency command center shall be provided in a location approved by the fire department.
			11.8.6.2	The emergency command center shall contain the following:
				(1) Voice fire alarm system panels and controls
				(2) Fire department two-way telephone communication service panels and controls where required by another section of this *Code*
				(3) Fire detection and fire alarm system annunciation panels
				(4) Elevator floor location and operation annunciators
				(5) Elevator fire recall switch in accordance with ASME A17.1/CSA B44, *Safety Code for Elevators and Escalators*
				(6) Elevator emergency power selector switch(es) where provided in accordance with ASME A17.1/CSA B44.
				(7) Sprinkler valve and waterflow annunciators
				(8) Emergency generator status indicators
				(9) Controls for any automatic stairway door unlocking system
				(10) Fire pump status indicators
				(11) Telephone for fire department use with controlled access to the public telephone system
				Also see occupancy chapter.
Emergency control (fire safety) functions		See occupancy chapter.		See occupancy chapter.

Emergency Control (Fire Safety) Functions

The following excerpts from NFPA *101*, 2009 edition, are provided for reference:

7.1.1* Application. Means of egress for both new and existing buildings shall comply with this chapter. (See also 5.5.3.)

8.1.1 Application. The features of fire protection set forth in this chapter shall apply to both new construction and existing buildings.

3.3.95 Fire Safety Functions. Building and fire control functions that are intended to increase the level of life safety for occupants or to control the spread of the harmful effects of fire.

Emergency Control (Fire Safety) Function	101 Ref.	Requirement
Door release	7.2.1.8.1	**Doors — Self-Closing Devices** A door leaf normally required to be kept closed shall not be secured in the open position at any time and shall be self-closing or automatic-closing in accordance with 7.2.1.8.2, unless otherwise permitted by 7.2.1.8.3.
	7.2.1.8.2	In any building of low or ordinary hazard contents, as defined in 6.2.2.2 and 6.2.2.3, or where approved by the authority having jurisdiction, doors shall be permitted to be automatic-closing, provided that the following criteria are met: (1) Upon release of the hold-open mechanism, the leaf becomes self-closing. (2) The release device is designed so that the leaf instantly releases manually and, upon release, becomes self-closing, or the leaf can be readily closed. (3) The automatic releasing mechanism or medium is activated by the operation of approved smoke detectors installed in accordance with the requirements for smoke detectors for door leaf release service in *NFPA 72, National Fire Alarm Code.* (4) Upon loss of power to the hold-open device, the hold-open mechanism is released and the door leaf becomes self-closing. (5) The release by means of smoke detection of one door leaf in a stair enclosure results in closing all doors leaves serving that stair.
	7.2.1.8.3	The elevator car doors and the associated hoistway enclosure doors at the floor level designated for recall in accordance with the requirements of 9.4.3 shall be permitted to remain open during Phase I Emergency Recall Operation.
	7.2.1.9.2	**Powered Doors** **Self-Closing or Self-Latching Door Leaf Operations.** Where door leaves are required to be self-closing or self latching and are operated by power upon the approach of a person, or are provided with power-assisted manual operation, they shall be permitted in the means of egress where they meet the following criteria: (1) The door leaves can be opened manually in accordance with 7.2.1.9.1 to allow egress travel in the event of power failure. (2) New door leaves remain in the closed position unless actuated or opened manually. (3) When actuated, new door leaves remain open for not more than 30 seconds. (4) Door leaves held open for any period of time close — and the power-assist mechanism ceases to function — upon operation of approved smoke detectors installed in such a way as to detect smoke on either side of the door opening in accordance with the provisions of *NFPA 72, National Fire Alarm Code.* (5) Door leaves required to be self-latching are either self-latching or become self-latching upon operation of approved smoke detectors per 7.2.1.9.2(4).

(continues)

Emergency Control (Fire Safety) Function	101 Ref.	Requirement
Door release (continued)		(6) New power-assisted swinging door assemblies comply with BHMA/ANSI A156.19, *American National Standard for Power Assist and Low Energy Power Operated Doors.* **Smokeproof Enclosures**
	7.2.3.4	Where a vestibule is provided, the door opening into the vestibule shall be protected with an approved fire door assembly having a minimum 1½-hour fire protection rating, and the fire door assembly from the vestibule to the smokeproof enclosure shall have a minimum 20-minute fire protection rating. Door leaves shall be designed to minimize air leakage and shall be self-closing or shall be automatic-closing by actuation of a smoke detector within 10 ft (3050 mm) of the vestibule door opening. New door assemblies shall be installed in accordance with NFPA 105, *Standard for the Installation of Smoke Door Assemblies and Other Opening Protectives.*
	7.2.3.7	**Natural Ventilation.** Smokeproof enclosures using natural ventilation shall comply with 7.2.3.3 and the following: (1) Where access to the enclosure is by means of an open exterior balcony, the door assembly to the enclosure shall have a minimum 1½-hour fire protection rating and shall be self-closing or shall be automatic-closing by actuation of a smoke detector. (2) Openings adjacent to the exterior balcony specified in 7.2.3.7(1) shall be protected in accordance with 7.2.2.6.4. (3) Every vestibule shall have a net area of not less than 16 ft² (1.5 m²) of opening in an exterior wall facing an exterior court, yard, or public space not less than 20 ft (6100 mm) in width. (4) Every vestibule shall have a minimum dimension of not less than the required width of the corridor leading to it and a dimension of not less than 6 ft (1830 mm) in the direction of travel.
	7.2.13.5	**Elevator Lobby Doors** The elevator lobby door leaves shall close in response to a signal from a smoke detector located directly outside the elevator lobby adjacent to or on each door opening. Elevator lobby door leaves shall be permitted to close in response to a signal from the building fire alarm system. Where one elevator lobby door leaf closes by means of a smoke detector or a signal from the building fire alarm system, all elevator lobby doorleaves serving that elevator evacuation system shall close.
Door unlocking	7.2.1.5.7	**Locks, Latches, and Alarm Device** Every door assembly in a stair enclosure serving more than four stories, unless permitted by 7.2.1.5.7.2, shall meet one of the following conditions: (1) Re-entry from the stair enclosure to the interior of the building shall be provided. (2) An automatic release that is actuated with the initiation of the building fire alarm system shall be provided to unlock all stair enclosure doors assemblies to allow re-entry. (3) Selected re-entry shall be provided in accordance with 7.2.1.5.7.1.

	7.2.1.6.1	**Delayed-Egress Locking Systems**
		
		Approved, listed, delayed-egress locking systems shall be permitted to be installed on door assemblies serving low and ordinary hazard contents in buildings protected throughout by an approved, supervised automatic fire detection system in accordance with Section 9.6 or an approved, supervised automatic sprinkler system in accordance with Section 9.7, and where permitted in Chapters 11 through 43, provided that the following criteria are met:
		
		(1) The provisions of 7.2.1.6.2 for access-controlled egress door assemblies shall not apply to door assemblies with delayed-egress locking systems.
		(2) The door leaves shall unlock upon actuation of one of the following:
		  (a) Approved, supervised automatic sprinkler system in accordance with Section 9.7
		  (b) Not more than one heat detector of an approved, supervised automatic fire detection system in accordance with Section 9.6

Emergency Control (Fire Safety) Function	101 Ref.	Requirement

Door unlocking *(continued)*		(c) Not more than two smoke detectors of an approved, supervised automatic fire detection system in accordance with Section 9.6
		(3) The doors shall unlock upon loss of power controlling the lock or locking mechanism.
		(4) An irreversible process shall release the lock within 15 seconds, or 30 seconds where approved by the authority having jurisdiction, upon application of a force to the release device required in 7.2.1.5.9 under the following conditions:
		  (a) The force shall not be required to exceed 15 lbf (67 N).
		  (b) The force shall not be required to be continuously applied for more than 3 seconds.
		  (c) The initiation of the release process shall activate an audible signal in the vicinity of the door opening.
		  (d) Once the door lock has been released by the application of force to the releasing device, relocking shall be by manual means only.
		(5) A readily visible, durable sign in letters not less than 1 in. (25 mm) high and not less than $\frac{1}{8}$ in. (3.2 mm) in stroke width on a contrasting background that reads as follows shall be located on the door leaf adjacent to the release device:
		PUSH UNTIL ALARM SOUNDS
		DOOR CAN BE OPENED IN 15 SECONDS

	7.2.1.6.2	**Access-Controlled Egress Door Assemblies** Where permitted in Chapters 11 through 43, door assemblies in the means of egress shall be permitted to be equipped with an approved entrance and egress access control system, provided that all the following criteria are met: (1) A sensor shall be provided on the egress side, arranged to detect an occupant approaching door leaves that are arranged to unlock in the direction of egress upon detection of an approaching occupant or loss of power to the sensor. (2) Loss of power to the part of the access control system that locks the door leaves shall automatically unlock the door leaves in the direction of egress. (3) The door leaves shall be arranged to unlock in the direction of egress from a manual release device located 40 in. to 48 in. (1015 mm to 1220 mm) vertically above the floor and within 60 in. (1525 mm) of the secured door openings. (4) The manual release device specified in 7.2.1.6.2(3) shall be readily accessible and clearly identified by a sign that reads as follows: PUSH TO EXIT. (5) When operated, the manual release device shall result in direct interruption of power to the lock — independent of the access control system electronics — and the door leaves shall remain unlocked for not less than 30 seconds. (6) Activation of the building fire-protective signaling system, if provided, shall automatically unlock the door leaves in the direction of egress, and they shall remain unlocked until the fire-protective signaling system has been manually reset. (7) The activation of manual fire alarm boxes that activate the building fire-protective signaling system specified in 7.2.1.6.2(6) shall not be required to unlock the door leaves. (8) Activation of the building automatic sprinkler or fire detection system, if provided, shall automatically unlock the door leaves in the direction of egress, and they shall remain unlocked until the fire-protective signaling system has been manually reset.
Mechanical ventilation and pressurized enclosure systems		**Smokeproof Enclosures**
	7.2.3.10.1	For both mechanical ventilation and pressurized enclosure systems, the activation of the systems shall be initiated by a smoke detector installed in an approved location within 10 ft (3050 mm) of each entrance to the smokeproof enclosure.
	7.2.3.10.2	The required mechanical system shall operate upon the activation of the smoke detectors specified in 7.2.3.10.1 and by manual controls accessible to the fire department. The required system also shall be initiated by the following, if provided:

(continues)

Emergency Control (Fire Safety) Function	101 Ref.	Requirement
Mechanical ventilation and pressurized enclosure systems *(continued)*		(1) Waterflow signal from a complete automatic sprinkler system (2) General evacuation alarm signal *(see 9.6.3.6)*
Elevator recall and shutdown	7.2.13.9	**Elevator Operation** Elevators shall be provided with fire fighters' emergency operations in accordance with ASME A17.1/CSA B44, *Safety Code for Elevators and Escalators.*
Marking of means of egress	7.10.1.7	**Floor Proximity Egress Path Marking** Where floor proximity egress path marking is required in Chapters 11 through 43, an approved floor proximity egress path marking system that is internally illuminated shall be installed within 18 in. (455 mm) of the floor. Floor proximity egress path marking systems shall be listed in accordance with ANSI/UL 1994, *Standard for Luminous Egress Path Marking Systems.* The system shall provide a visible delineation of the path of travel along the designated exit access and shall be essentially continuous, except as interrupted by doorways, hallways, corridors, or other such architectural features. The system shall operate continuously or at any time the building fire alarm system is activated. The activation, duration, and continuity of operation of the system shall be in accordance with 7.9.2. The system shall be maintained in accordance with the product manufacturing listing.
	7.10.5.2.1	**Continuous Illumination** Every sign required to be illuminated by 7.10.6.3, 7.10.7, and 7.10.8.1 shall be continuously illuminated as required under the provisions of Section 7.8, unless otherwise provided in 7.10.5.2.2.
	7.10.5.2.2	Illumination for signs shall be permitted to flash on and off upon activation of the fire alarm system.
Smoke control	8.4.6.4	**Smoke Partitions** Dampers in air-transfer openings shall close upon detection of smoke by approved smoke detectors installed in accordance with *NFPA 72, National Fire Alarm Code.*
	8.5.5.4.1	**Smoke Barriers** Air-conditioning, heating, ventilating ductwork, and related equipment, including smoke dampers and combination fire and smoke dampers, shall be installed in accordance with NFPA 90A, *Standard for the Installation of Air-Conditioning and Ventilating Systems,* and NFPA 105, *Standard for the Installation of Smoke Door Assemblies and Other Opening Protectives.* (See NFPA 90A for smoke detection requirements.)
	8.5.5.4.2	Smoke dampers and combination fire and smoke dampers shall be inspected, tested, and maintained in accordance with NFPA 105.
	8.5.5.7.1	Required smoke dampers in ducts penetrating smoke barriers shall close upon detection of smoke by approved smoke detectors in accordance with *NFPA 72, National Fire Alarm Code,* unless one of the following conditions exists: (1) The ducts penetrate smoke barriers above the smoke barrier doors, and the door release detector actuates the damper. (2) Approved smoke detector installations are located within the ducts in existing installations.
	8.5.5.7.2	Where a duct is provided on one side of the smoke barrier, the smoke detectors on the duct side shall be in accordance with 8.5.5.7.1.
	8.5.5.7.3	Required smoke dampers in air-transfer openings shall close upon detection of smoke by approved smoke detectors in accordance with *NFPA 72, National Fire Alarm Code.*

Index

Wireless network, public fire alarm reporting system, 27.4.1.1
Alarm processing equipment, 27.5.5, A.27.5.5.1.1.1, A.27.5.5.3.3
Alarm receiving equipment, public fire service communications center, 27.5.5, A.27.5.5.1.1.1, A.27.5.5.3.3
Publicly accessible alarm boxes, 27.6.6, A.27.6.6.2
Auxiliary systems, public fire alarm reporting systems, Table 27.6.3.2.2.2
Receipt of messages from, 27.5.5.1.1.3, 27.5.5.1.1.4

Wireless protection system (definition), 3.3.298
Wireless repeater (definition), 3.3.299
Wireless signals, mass notification system, Table 14.4.2.2
Wiring, fire alarm control unit to emergency control function relay or other appliance, 21.2.6; *see also* Circuits

Z

Zones
Definition, 3.3.300, A.3.3.300.1
Evacuation signaling, 23.10.2, 24.4.1.1.2, 24.4.1.5.6, 24.4.1.5.7, 24.4.1.8.1, 24.4.1.8.2.1, 24.4.1.8.3, 24.4.1.8.4.1, 24.4.1.9, A.23.10.2, A.24.4.1.8.4.1, A.24.4.1.9.1
Definition, 3.3.300.1, A.3.3.300.1
Notification, 18.4.2.5, 23.8.6.3, 23.8.6.4.1, 23.8.6.4.2, 24.4.2.4.7, 24.4.2.5.2, 24.4.2.15.7, A.18.4.2.5
Definition, 3.3.300.2
High power speaker array, 24.4.3.4.5
Visible zone indication, 10.16.1, 10.16.2

IMPORTANT NOTICES AND DISCLAIMERS CONCERNING NFPA® DOCUMENTS

NOTICE AND DISCLAIMER OF LIABILITY CONCERNING THE USE OF NFPA DOCUMENTS

NFPA® codes, standards, recommended practices, and guides ("NFPA Documents"), of which the NFPA Document contained herein is one, are developed through a consensus standards development process approved by the American National Standards Institute. This process brings together volunteers representing varied viewpoints and interests to achieve consensus on fire and other safety issues. While the NFPA administers the process and establishes rules to promote fairness in the development of consensus, it does not independently test, evaluate, or verify the accuracy of any information or the soundness of any judgments contained in NFPA Documents.

The NFPA disclaims liability for any personal injury, property or other damages of any nature whatsoever, whether special, indirect, consequential or compensatory, directly or indirectly resulting from the publication, use of, or reliance on NFPA Documents. The NFPA also makes no guaranty or warranty as to the accuracy or completeness of any information published herein.

In issuing and making NFPA Documents available, the NFPA is not undertaking to render professional or other services for or on behalf of any person or entity. Nor is the NFPA undertaking to perform any duty owed by any person or entity to someone else. Anyone using this document should rely on his or her own independent judgment or, as appropriate, seek the advice of a competent professional in determining the exercise of reasonable care in any given circumstances.

The NFPA has no power, nor does it undertake, to police or enforce compliance with the contents of NFPA Documents. Nor does the NFPA list, certify, test, or inspect products, designs, or installations for compliance with this document. Any certification or other statement of compliance with the requirements of this document shall not be attributable to the NFPA and is solely the responsibility of the certifier or maker of the statement.

ADDITIONAL NOTICES AND DISCLAIMERS

Updating of NFPA Documents
Users of NFPA codes, standards, recommended practices, and guides ("NFPA Documents") should be aware that these documents may be superseded at any time by the issuance of new editions or may be amended from time to time through the issuance of Tentative Interim Amendments. An official NFPA Document at any point in time consists of the current edition of the document together with any Tentative Interim Amendments and any Errata then in effect. In order to determine whether a given document is the current edition and whether it has been amended through the issuance of Tentative Interim Amendments or corrected through the issuance of Errata, consult appropriate NFPA publications such as the National Fire Codes® Subscription Service, visit the NFPA website at www.nfpa.org, or contact the NFPA at the address listed below.

Interpretations of NFPA Documents
A statement, written or oral, that is not processed in accordance with Section 6 of the Regulations Governing Committee Projects shall not be considered the official position of NFPA or any of its Committees and shall not be considered to be, nor be relied upon as, a Formal Interpretation.

Patents
The NFPA does not take any position with respect to the validity of any patent rights referenced in, related to, or asserted in connection with an NFPA Document. The users of NFPA Documents bear the sole responsibility for determining the validity of any such patent rights, as well as the risk of infringement of such rights, and the NFPA disclaims liability for the infringement of any patent resulting from the use of or reliance on NFPA Documents.

NFPA adheres to the policy of the American National Standards Institute (ANSI) regarding the inclusion of patents in American National Standards ("the ANSI Patent Policy"), and hereby gives the following notice pursuant to that policy:

NOTICE: The user's attention is called to the possibility that compliance with an NFPA Document may require use of an invention covered by patent rights. NFPA takes no position as to the validity of any such patent rights or as to whether such patent rights constitute or include essential patent claims under the ANSI Patent Policy. If, in connection with the ANSI Patent Policy, a patent holder has filed a statement of willingness to grant licenses under these rights on reasonable and nondiscriminatory terms and conditions to applicants desiring to obtain such a license, copies of such filed statements can be obtained, on request, from NFPA. For further information, contact the NFPA at the address listed below.

Law and Regulations
Users of NFPA Documents should consult applicable federal, state, and local laws and regulations. NFPA does not, by the publication of its codes, standards, recommended practices, and guides, intend to urge action that is not in compliance with applicable laws, and these documents may not be construed as doing so.

Copyrights
NFPA Documents are copyrighted by the NFPA. They are made available for a wide variety of both public and private uses. These include both use, by reference, in laws and regulations, and use in private self-regulation, standardization, and the promotion of safe practices and methods. By making these documents available for use and adoption by public authorities and private users, the NFPA does not waive any rights in copyright to these documents.

Use of NFPA Documents for regulatory purposes should be accomplished through adoption by reference. The term "adoption by reference" means the citing of title, edition, and publishing information only. Any deletions, additions, and changes desired by the adopting authority should be noted separately in the adopting instrument. In order to assist NFPA in following the uses made of its documents, adopting authorities are requested to notify the NFPA (Attention: Secretary, Standards Council) in writing of such use. For technical assistance and questions concerning adoption of NFPA Documents, contact NFPA at the address below.

For Further Information
All questions or other communications relating to NFPA Documents and all requests for information on NFPA procedures governing its codes and standards development process, including information on the procedures for requesting Formal Interpretations, for proposing Tentative Interim Amendments, and for proposing revisions to NFPA documents during regular revision cycles, should be sent to NFPA headquarters, addressed to the attention of the Secretary, Standards Council, NFPA, 1 Batterymarch Park, P.O. Box 9101, Quincy, MA 02269-9101; email: stds_admin

For more information about NFPA, visit the NFPA website at www.nfpa.org.

A Guide to Using the National Fire Alarm and Signaling Code Handbook

This sixth edition of the *National Fire Alarm and Signaling Code Handbook* contains the complete text of the 2010 edition of *NFPA 72®*, *National Fire Alarm and Signaling Code*.

---

duced by the fire. Smoke detectors are typically mounted on the ceiling to take advantage of fire plume dynamics and the ceiling jet. However, because of frictional energy loss between the ceiling jet and the ceiling surface, a very thin layer of air immediately beneath the ceiling surface is flowing more slowly than the layer a little farther down. The force that pushes the smoke into the sensing chamber is a function of the ceiling jet velocity. If the velocity at the detector is low, smoke moves into the detector slowly. If a smoke detector is recessed, this more slowly moving air immediately beneath the ceiling surface is the only flow impinging upon the detector. Because a recessed detector is in a no-flow or low-flow location, relative to the ceiling jet, it will be very slow to respond — if it responds at all — compared with the same detector mounted on the ceiling surface.

17.5.2* Partitions. Where partitions extend to within 15 percent of the ceiling height, the spaces separated by the partitions shall be considered as separate rooms.

Research on fire plumes and ceiling jets indicates that the thickness of the ceiling jet under most conditions is approximately 10 percent of the distance from the floor to the ceiling in the fire compartment. Refer to Exhibit 17.6. Keep in mind that the ceiling jet does not have an abrupt boundary. The ceiling jet velocity varies with the distance from the ceiling, and the 10 percent depth criterion is the depth above which the majority of the flow occurs. Some flow exists below the upper 10 percent of the floor-to-ceiling height. Once the ceiling jet collides with the walls of the compartment, it forms an "upper layer." This layer will increase in thickness as the fire grows. However, during the time period in which a fire alarm system should respond, the 10 percent ceiling jet thickness is generally valid.

 ◄ FAQ
What is the reason for the value of 15 percent when considering the effect of partitions?

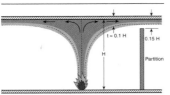

EXHIBIT 17.6 *Partitions Extending Higher Than 85 Percent of the Floor-to-Ceiling Height, Necessitating the Addition of Detectors for Each Partitioned-Off Area. (Source: J. M. Cholin Consultants, Inc., Oakland, NJ)*

The technical committee increased the 10-percent number by 50 percent to provide for a margin of safety and to address the fact that the ceiling jet does not have an abrupt lower boundary. This results in a clearance criterion of 15 percent of the floor-to-ceiling height. Partitions that are more than 85 percent of the floor-to-ceiling height are expected to interfere with the natural flow of the ceiling jet and retard detector response.

In the case of a fire with an established plume, the plume jet is the dominant air mover and produces a ceiling jet. The objective is to ensure that the partition does not interfere with the smoke travel across the ceiling to the detector location.

In the case of a small, low-energy fire, whether the partition affects detection system response depends entirely on the extent to which the partitions impede the flow of smoke entrained in the normal air currents.

The treatment of partitions in the Code is very different from the treatment of partitions in NFPA 13, where the principal concern is the discharge pattern of the sprinkler head and the impact of the partition on that discharge pattern and, thus, on the control of the fire.

The commentary text contains Frequently Asked Questions shown in the margin as FAQs. The FAQs answer the most commonly asked questions throughout the handbook.

FIRE ALARM AND EMERGENCY COMMUNICATION SYSTEM RECORD OF COMPLETION

To be completed by the system installation contractor at the time of system acceptance and approval.
It shall be permitted to modify this form as needed to provide a more complete and/or clear record.
Insert N/A in all unused lines.
Attach additional sheets, data, or calculations as necessary to provide a complete record.

1. PROPERTY INFORMATION
Name of property: _____
Address: _____
Description of property: _____
Occupancy type: _____
Name of property representative: _____
Address: _____
Phone: _____   Fax: _____   E-mail: _____
Authority having jurisdiction over this property: _____
Phone: _____   Fax: _____   E-mail: _____

2. INSTALLATION, SERVICE, AND TESTING CONTRACTOR INFORMATION
Installation contractor for this equipment: _____
Address: _____
License or certification number: _____
Phone: _____   Fax: _____   E-mail: _____
Service organization for this equipment: _____
Address: _____
License or certification number: _____
Phone: _____   Fax: _____   E-mail: _____
A contract for test and inspection in accordance with NFPA standards is in effect as of: _____
Contracted testing company: _____
Address: _____
Phone: _____   Fax: _____   E-mail: _____
Contract expires: _____   Contract number: _____   Frequency of routine inspections: _____

3. DESCRIPTION OF SYSTEM OR SERVICE
❏ Fire alarm system (nonvoice)
❏ Fire alarm with in-building fire emergency voice alarm communication system (EVACS)
❏ Mass notification system (MNS)
❏ Combination system, with the following components:
   ❏ Fire alarm   ❏ EVACS   ❏ MNS   ❏ Two-way, in-building, emergency communication system
❏ Other (specify): _____

NFPA 72 (p. 1 of 12)

FIGURE 10.18.2.1.1 *Record of Completion.*

Interactive forms have been placed on NFPA's website (www.nfpa.org/72forms). Duplication and use of these forms are permitted.